PROSE AND POETRY
OF THE
CONTINENTAL RENAISSANCE
IN TRANSLATION

Prose and Poetry

OF THE

Continental Renaissance

IN TRANSLATION

Selected and Edited by

HAROLD HOOPER BLANCHARD

FLETCHER PROFESSOR OF
ENGLISH LITERATURE
IN TUFTS UNIVERSITY

SECOND EDITION

DAVID McKAY COMPANY, INC.

NEW YORK

PROSE AND POETRY

First Edition 1949
Second Edition 1955
Reprinted June 1959
August 1962

Printed in the United States of America
Vail-Ballou Press, Inc., Binghamton, N. Y.

PREFACE

In an era in which it becomes imperative to understand the minds of other peoples, the impulse to justify the study of foreign literatures in translation becomes perhaps less urgent. There have come into being two general approaches to the study of comparative literature: the one proposes a comprehensive survey of the literature of the world, either by type or in general; the other proceeds from the concept that a great age has an integrated and international culture peculiarly its own, and prefers to concentrate upon each age by itself. As distinguished from anthologies of world literature, this volume presents eleven non-dramatic writers of wide influence who lived in one period of the history of western culture. There are available excellent collections of the literature of the Renaissance in England. This is planned as a companion volume devoted to the foreign writers of that period who contributed so largely to the thought and character of English literature and society.

I have, in preparing this volume, held in mind, first of all, college undergraduates studying the literature of the fourteenth, fifteenth, and sixteenth centuries in Europe as a whole. The book is an outgrowth of my own teaching in this field and the work of my students at Tufts College. I hope it may be of use also to students of the history of the Renaissance. I would wish that it may be of value to all who are interested in the civilization of this most important period. Among the writers here represented, no less than five have long since taken their permanent places among those of world acclaim.

In making these selections, I have tried to take the writings or portions thereof which were best known and had most influence in England and throughout Europe. I have sought also to select material most representative of each writer. The adoption of these two principles together usually resulted in selections of the most human interest. In long works, where possible, I have tried to give parts which leave with the reader a conception of the work as a whole. My efforts to this end in Boccaccio's *Il Filostrato,* in the long poems of Ariosto and Tasso, and in *The Praise of Folly* of Erasmus will be apparent. It was found practicable, however, to restrict selections from Rabelais to the first two books of his works, and in Cervantes' *Don Quixote* to choose chiefly from Part I, giving only the famous fifth chapter of Part II.

For each of the writers in this volume, I have furnished a biographical introduction and a bibliography. The introductions are intended to furnish a point of departure for a well-rounded study of each writer. Obviously they present nothing new, and I have drawn upon many standard works in their preparation — works which appear in the bibliographies that follow. The latter include writings both of popular and scholarly interest. I have considered it worth while to include the standard edition of each writer in the original language, and a few of the most important works, biographical or critical, produced by foreign scholars, although most of the works listed are of course written in English. Apart from these bibliographies devoted to individuals, a selected general bibliography is given at the end of the book. This includes works which deal with national literatures as a whole, or with the entire period of the Renaissance. The table of contents has been considerably elaborated; it is hoped that it will enable the reader to locate readily any separate piece of writing in the volume.

The translations used are mostly standard translations of recognized quality. The text of each translator is reproduced exactly as originally printed, retaining the original spelling, punctuation, and capitalization. In two cases I have reprinted selections from the notes furnished by translator or editor. I regret that I could not include more of the notes of Leonard Eckstein Opdycke for Castiglione's *Book of the Courtier,* as they constitute a part of his work and were planned to accompany his translation. I have necessarily been highly selective also in the valuable notes furnished for Rabelais by Albert Jay Nock and Catherine Rose Wilson. In both cases, where I have printed only a part of a note, I have indicated it by suspension dots. Obviously I have omitted the greater number of their notes entirely.

I am very greatly indebted to translators and publishers for permission to reprint the texts in this volume. Detailed acknowledgment of these obligations is given elsewhere. I wish here especially to express my gratitude to several individuals for their personal graciousness, two of whom have died before this book was completed: Professor Hubertis M. Cummings, who long ago gave me permission to reprint his *Il Filostrato;* the late Curtis Hidden Page, who came and talked with me about the book and placed his skillful translations of Ronsard at my disposal; Professor Leonard Opdycke of Harvard University, who has been most gracious to me concerning his father's distinguished translation of Castiglione; the late Professor Jacob Zeitlin of the University of Illinois, who promptly offered me use of his translation from Petrarch; Professor Allan H. Gilbert of Duke University, who has shown me much courtesy in connection with his translation of Machiavelli; Mrs. Robert S. Peabody of New York, who responded so kindly to my request for her sensitive translation of Petrarch's ode.

I wish here also to express my appreciation to Mr. Robert L. Straker of Longmans, Green and Company, New York, for the care he has given to this volume, and to thank Mrs. Angus McAdam of West Somerville, Mrs. Sidney Hay of Arlington, and Mrs. Stanley Osborn of Medford, Massachusetts, all of whom have given valuable assistance in the preparation of the manuscript.

H.H.B.

Winchester, Massachusetts
February 14, 1948

ACKNOWLEDGMENTS

The editor wishes here to record his indebtedness to the following persons and publishers for permission to reprint selections in this book:

G. Bell & Sons, Ltd., London: for Lady Dacre's translations from Petrarch's sonnets; Ariosto's *Orlando Furioso,* translated by W. S. Rose; Tasso's *Jerusalem Delivered,* translated by J. H. Wiffen; all of which appeared in the Bohn Library.

The Clarendon Press, Oxford: for Erasmus' *Praise of Folly,* translated by John Wilson, 1668, edited by Mrs. P. S. Allen, first published in 1913.

J. M. Dent & Sons, Ltd., London: for J. M. Rigg's translation of Boccaccio's *Decameron,* published in Everyman's Library.

S. N. Draper, Esq., executor of the late W. H. Draper: for W. H. Draper's translation of Petrarch's *Secret,* published by Chatto & Windus, London, in 1911.

E. P. Dutton & Co., Inc., New York: for J. M. Rigg's translation of Boccaccio's *Decameron,* published in Everyman's Library.

Eyre & Spottiswoode, London: for Humbert Wolfe's translation of Ronsard's *Sonnets pour Helene,* published in 1934.

Harcourt, Brace & Co., Inc., New York, and Miss Catherine Rose Wilson: for the Urquhart translation of Rabelais edited with notes by Albert Jay Nock and Catherine Rose Wilson, copyright 1931.

Hendricks House, Packard & Co., and Professor Allan H. Gilbert: for Machiavelli's *The Prince* and *Discourses,* and selections from one letter, taken from *Machiavelli. The Prince and Other Works,* translated by A. H. Gilbert, (University Classics), copyright 1941.

The University of Illinois Press: for Petrarch's *Life of Solitude,* translated by Jacob Zeitlin, copyright by the University of Illinois, 1924.

Alfred A. Knopf, Inc., New York: for Montaigne's *Essays,* translated by Jacob Zeitlin, published in three volumes, with copyright, 1934, 1935, 1936. Also for courtesy concerning John Ormsby's translation of Cervantes' *Don Quixote,* published by Alfred A. Knopf in 1926.

Longmans, Green & Co., Inc., New York, and Joseph Auslander: for Joseph Auslander's translations of Petrarch's sonnets, copyright 1931.

Longmans, Green & Co., Ltd., London, and the representatives of the late Andrew Lang: for five poems by Ronsard, translated by Andrew Lang, first published in *Ballads and Lyrics of Old France,* 1872.

The Macmillan Co., New York: for Humbert Wolfe's translation of Ronsard's *Sonnets pour Helene,* copyright 1934.

Professor Leonard Opdycke: for Castiglione's *Book of the Courtier,* translated with notes by the late Leonard Eckstein Opdycke, and published by Charles Scribner's Sons, copyright 1901, 1903.

The late Curtis Hidden Page: for translations from *Songs and Sonnets of Ronsard,* published by Houghton Mifflin Company, copyright 1903, 1924.

Mrs. Robert S. Peabody: for the translation of Petrarch's "Ode to the Virgin" taken from *Madrigals and Odes from Petrarch,* translated by Helen Lee Peabody, published by Loker Raley, New York, copyright 1940.

G. P. Putnam's Sons: for Petrarch's letters taken from *Petrarch. The First Modern Scholar and Man of Letters,* by James Harvey Robinson and Henry Winchester Rolfe, copyright 1898.

Princeton University Press, and Professor Hubertis M. Cummings: for Boccaccio's *Il Filostrato,* translated by Hubertis Cummings, copyright 1924.

CONTENTS

[The names of the translators appear in brackets.]

PROSE AND POETRY
OF THE
CONTINENTAL RENAISSANCE
IN TRANSLATION

FRANCIS PETRARCH

(1304-1374)

Francis Petrarch was the greatest of early Italian humanists and the most accomplished lyric poet in the vernacular that Italy had produced. By his classical scholarship and the influence of his personality, he initiated most of the phases of the Revival of Learning in Italy. His search for and study of ancient manuscripts, his ardent experience of the spirit and outlook of the Latin writers, provided a knowledge of antiquity which caused him to rise above the decadence of his own age, to live in the association of Cicero and Virgil and Seneca, and to cultivate a Latin style and a way of life consonant with theirs. Furthermore, by his love for Laura of Avignon and the many Italian sonnets written in her honor, he established a literary vogue which echoed through Europe for three centuries.

Our knowledge of the life of Petrarch is richly provided by his many letters. He was born at Arezzo on the 20th of July 1304. His father, Petracco di ser Parenzo, had been a notary in Florence, a friend of Dante, and like him a political exile since 1302. Petrarch's youth was largely lived, however, in or near Avignon, where the Papal Court was then established. He attended school in the nearby town of Carpentras. At the age of twelve, he was sent to the University at Montpellier for four years of study of civil law, to be continued with more years at Bologna. During this time he became devoted to the Latin poets and prose writers, and he came to admire the poetry of the troubadours of Provence and of the *dolce stil nuovo* of Dante's generation in Italy.

Upon the death of his father in 1326, his mother having died before, he abandoned his study of the law and returned to Avignon to a life of youthful pleasures and gayety. According to his note in the margin of his manuscript of Virgil, it was on the morning of the 6th of April 1327, in the Church of Santa Chiara, that the lady Laura first appeared to him, and on the same day of April in the plague year of 1348 that she died. During those twenty-one years he struggled with the "keen but constant and pure attachment" which constituted one of the greatest inspirations of his life and to which he gave expression in the *Canzoniere*. Petrarch's reserve nowhere revealed Laura's identity; and although many attempts have been made to discover who she was, no one has proved satisfactory.

It was during the same years that his genius for friendship brought him into association with the distinguished family of the Colonnesi. He spent with Giacomo Colonna, Bishop of Lombez, "a divine summer among the foot-hills of the Pyrenees, in happy intercourse with my master and the members of our company." Thereafter he lived as chaplain in the house of the Cardinal Giovanni Colonna in the papal city, "not as if he were my lord and master, but rather my father, or better, a most affectionate brother." Impelled by the desire to see new places, however, he traveled to Paris, to the Netherlands, and through the Rhine valley, in 1333; in 1337 he made his first visit to Rome and was profoundly moved by the monuments of antiquity and the sacred relics of the Church.

In the summer of 1337, he turned away from the life of Avignon and established himself and his books in the secluded valley of Vaucluse, at the source of the river Sorgue, fifteen miles east of the city. Captivated by the idyllic charm of the place, he gave himself to a life of study and writing amidst enjoyment of the natural beauty of the country. At this time his major literary works began to appear; he himself wrote that "nearly every work that I have published was either finished, or begun, or conceived there." Although he left for frequent journeys and even long residences in Italy, he continued to return to the Vaucluse he loved for the period lasting until 1353. It was here that he received the invitation from the Senate at Rome to receive the poet's crown of laurel. He was crowned in the Senatorial Palace on the Capitoline on the 8th of April 1341. This honor may be called the climax of Petrarch's career. It gave him early recognition as the greatest poet in Italy then living, as well as the spiritual leader of the movement for national Italian unity and rejuvenation he so ardently promoted.

In 1343, the year in which his only brother Gherardo entered a monastery, Francesco himself seems to have reached a moral and religious crisis in his career. "As I approached the age of forty," he wrote in his "Epistle to Posterity," "while my powers were unimpaired and my passions were still strong, I not only abruptly threw off my bad habits, but even the very recollection of them, as if I had never looked upon a woman." The highly personal confessions or dialogues with St. Augustine which he called his *Secretum* were begun at this time.

From September 1343 until late in 1345, he was again in Italy. He was sent at first as envoy from Cardinal Colonna and the Pope to the court of Naples, but he lived for most of this time in the city of Parma virtually as guest of the reigning house of Correggio. When, in 1347, Cola di Rienzo proclaimed himself ruler of Rome, Petrarch's ardent vision of the restoration of the ancient prestige of the Eternal City drew him again to Italy. Although Cola's power proved to be temporary, Petrarch remained in Italy until 1351, living again at Parma, but with many journeys elsewhere. It was at Parma on the 19th of May 1348 that he received the news of the death of Laura. In the autumn of 1350, he went to Rome on the occasion of the Jubilee: going south, he visited Florence where Boccaccio hastened to meet him for the first time; on his way north, he was publicly welcomed in his native Arezzo. The devastating plague of 1348 had already taken away many of Petrarch's friends, however, so that —"a pilgrim everywhere" as he called himself—he returned to Vaucluse saddened and with a sense of loneliness.

During the years from 1353 to 1361 Petrarch lived in Milan, urged by the hospitality first of Giovanni and then of Bernabò and Galeazzo Visconti. Established as their distinguished guest and furnished with congenial environment for work, he also served at times as secretary, orator, or ambassador. In September 1362 he settled in Venice where the Senate of the Republic granted him a house on the Riva degli Schiavoni with the agreement that he should leave his library to the city. Here Boccaccio joined him in the summer of 1363; later he called his natural daughter, Francesca, and her husband to live with him. In 1368, he settled in Padua, and in 1370 found final retreat at Arquà, twelve miles to the southwest in the Euganean Hills, in the "small and gracious little house surrounded by an olive grove and a vineyard" which lovers of Petrarch have sought ever since. On the morning of the 19th of July 1374, he was found dead with his head bowed upon the book before him in his study. His sarcophagus stands in front of the church in Arquà.

Living in an age of transition, Petrarch reflects the conflicting outlooks of the waning Middle Ages and the approaching Renaissance. Having taken the tonsure, he became the recipient of several church benefices; but his European reputation became such that he was courted by kings, princes, and churchmen alike, and he became the unrivaled leader of the new age of humanism. Deeply imbued with the traditions of both Cicero and St. Augustine, his intellectual development reveals the continuous conflict of their ideals; his ultimate way of life represented a synthesis of both classical culture and Christian doctrine.

Petrarch's literary activity was continuous throughout his life from the time he abandoned the study of the law. He intended his Latin writings, which constitute the greater part of his work, to be the foundation of his fame, but he never ceased to work on his Italian poems. The following may be selected as perhaps his most noted works.

In Latin: the *Africa* (begun c. 1338), a national epic poem, never completed, on the career of Scipio Africanus; *De Viris Illustribus* (begun c. 1338), a series of biographies largely of famous Romans, never completed; the Coronation Oration (delivered in 1341), on the character of poetry and the experience of the poetic task; the *Secretum* (begun c. 1342), Petrarch's most intimate confession of the deepest conflicts of his life, given in a series of imaginary dialogues with St. Augustine; *De Vita Solitaria* (1346), a treatise in praise of the contemplative life, expressive of the emerging ideal of the Renaissance scholar; *Bucolicum Carmen* (begun c. 1346), twelve allegorical eclogues in verse, modeled upon Virgil, dealing with contemporary subjects; *De Remediis Utriusque Fortunae* (begun c. 1354), a treatise on the remedies for good and evil fortune; *De Sui Ipsius et Multorum Ignorantia,* on his own ignorance and that of many others, written while living in Venice, a powerful invective against four Venetian critics, presenting his own philosophical position; the *Epistolae Metricae,* a collection of short Latin poems, written at various times, on the affairs of his personal life and on contemporary matters; Petrarch's letters, grouped especially under three titles—*Familiarum Rerum Liber,* intimate letters of his youth and middle life, *Epistolae*

Seniles, letters of his old age, *Epistolae Sine Nomine,* a minor collection dealing chiefly with the corruption of the papal court.

In Italian: the *Canzoniere,* a collection of 366 poems, including 317 sonnets, 29 *canzoni,* 9 *sestine,* 7 *ballate,* and 4 madrigals, written through much of the poet's life, continuously worked upon, and gradually arranged through the years; and the sequence of *Trionfi* or *Triumphs,* of Love, Chastity, Death, Fame, Time, and Eternity, allegorical visions in *terza rima,* in which the theme of Laura and Petrarch's love is handled with final philosophic perspective and elevation.

SELECTED BIBLIOGRAPHY

EDITIONS

Opera Omnia, Basel, 1554 and 1581: most complete editions yet published, although incomplete. *Edizione Nazionale delle Opere di F. Petrarca,* Florence, Sansoni: I, *L'Africa,* ed. Nicola Festa, 1926; V, *Rerum Memorandarum Libri,* ed. G. Billanovich, 1945; X, *Le Familiari,* libri 1–4, ed. Vittorio Rossi, 1933; XI, *Le Familiari,* libri 5–11, ed. V. Rossi, 1934; XII, *Le Familiari,* libri 12–19, ed. V. Rossi, 1937; XIII, *Le Familiari,* libri 20–24, ed. Umberto Bosco, 1942: to be the first complete edition. *Il Canzoniere,* ed. M. Scherillo, Milan, Hoepli, 1896; *Rime,* ed. G. Carducci and S. Ferrari, Florence, Sansoni, 1899.

TRANSLATIONS

Petrarch's Coronation Oration, trans. E. H. Wilkins, *Pub. Mod. Lang. Assoc.,* LXVIII (1953), 1241–50; *Petrarch's Secret,* trans. William H. Draper, London, Chatto & Windus, 1911; *The Life of Solitude,* trans. Jacob Zeitlin, Univ. of Illinois Press, 1924; *On His Own Ignorance and That of Many Others,* trans. Hans Nachod, in *The Renaissance Philosophy of Man,* ed. E. Cassirer, P. O. Kristeller, J. H. Randall, Jr., 47–133, Univ. of Chicago Press, 1948; Letters. *Petrarch. The First Modern Scholar and Man of Letters.* A selection from his correspondence, by J. H. Robinson and H. W. Rolfe, New York, Putnam, 2nd edit., 1914; *Petrarch's Letters to Classical Authors,* trans. Mario E. Cosenza, Univ. of Chicago Press, 1910; *The Sonnets, Triumphs and Other Poems,* trans. by various hands, Bohn Lib., London, Bell, 1859; *Some Love Songs of Petrarch,* trans. William D. Foulke, London, Oxford Univ. Press, 1915; *Love Rimes of Petrarch,* trans. Morris Bishop, Ithaca, Dragon Press, 1931; *The Sonnets of Petrarch,* trans. Joseph Auslander, New York, Longmans, 1931; *Madrigals and Odes from Petrarch,* trans. Helen Lee Peabody, New York, Loker Raley, 1940; *Petrarch. Sonnets and Songs,* trans. Anna Maria Armi, New York, Pantheon, 1946.

BIOGRAPHY AND CRITICISM

Pierre de Nolhac, *Pétrarque et l'Humanism,* 2nd edit., 2 vols., Paris, Champion, 1907; Luigi Tonelli, *Petrarca,* Milan, Ediz. Corbaccio, 1930; E. Carrara, "F. Petrarca," in *Enciclopedia Italiana,* XXVII, 8–23, 1935; N. Sapegno, "Il Petrarca," in *Il Trecento* (in the *Storia Letteraria d'Italia,* 2nd edit., Milan, Vallardi, 1942, pp. 165–276; Umberto Bosco, *Petrarca,* Turin, 1946.

Ugo Foscolo, *Essays on Petrarch,* Murray, London, 1823; Pierre de Nolhac, *Petrarch and the Ancient World,* Boston, Humanist's Lib., Updike, 1907; H. C. Hollway-Calthrop, *Petrarch, His Life and Times,* New York, Putnam, 1907; Maud F. Jerrold, *F. Petrarca, Poet and Humanist,* New York, Dutton, 1909; M. E. Cosenza, *F. Petrarca and the Revolution of Cola di Rienzo,* Univ. of Chicago Press, 1913; M. A. Potter, *Four Essays,* Harvard Univ. Press, 1917; J. J. Jusserand, "At the Tomb of Petrarch," in *The School for Ambassadors,* 65–101, New York, Putnam, 1925; E. H. R. Tatham, *F. Petrarca. The First Modern Man of Letters,* 2 vols., London, Sheldon Press, 1925–26; W. H. Whitfield, *Petrarch and the Renascence,* Oxford, Blackwell, 1943; E. H. Wilkins, *The Making of the "Canzoniere" and Other Petrarchan Studies,* Ediz. di Storia e Letteratura, Rome, 1951; *ibid., The Prose Letters of Petrarch: A Manual,* Vanni, New York, 1951.

SPECIAL STUDIES

T. E. Mommsen, "Petrarch's Conception of the 'Dark Ages'," *Speculum,* XVII (1942), 226–42; C. C. Bayley, "Petrarch, Charles IV, and the *Renovatio Imperii," Speculum,* XVII (1942), 323–41; R. P. Oliver, "Petrarch's Prestige as a Humanist," in *Class. Studies in Honor of W. A. Oldfather,* 134–53, Univ. of Illinois Press, 1943; E. H. Wilkins, "Petrarchan Byways," *Pub. Mod. Lang. Assoc.,* LXI (1946), 1317–26; D. Phillips, "Petrarch's Ethical Principles," *Italica,* XXIV (1947), 219–32; N. C. Stageberg, "The Aesthetic of the Petrarchan Sonnet," *Jour. Aesthetics and Art Criticism,* VII (1948), 132–7; E. H. Wilkins, "An Introductory Petrarch Bibliography," *Philol. Quar.,* XXVII (1948), 27–36; *ibid.,* "A General Survey of Renaissance Petrarchism," *Compar. Lit.,* II (1950), 327–42; A. S. Bernardo, "The Importance of the Non-Love Poems of Petrarch's *Canzoniere," Italica,* XXVII (1950), 302–12; D. Phillips, "Petrarch's Doctrine of Meditation," *Vanderbilt Stud. in the Humanities,* I (1951), 251–75; D. G. Rees, "Petrarch's *Trionfo della Morte* in English," *Ital. Studies,* VII (1952), 82–96; E. H. Wilkins, "Petrarch's Ecclesiastical Career," *Speculum,* XXVIII (1953), 754–75; A. S. Bernardo, "Dramatic Dialogue and Monologue in Petrarch's Works — II," *Symposium,* VII (1953), 92–119.

CANZONIERE

Translated by Joseph Auslander,
Barbarina, Lady Dacre *and* Helen Lee Peabody

[Taken from: *The Sonnets of Petrarch,* translated by Joseph Auslander, Longmans, Green & Co., New York, 1931; *The Sonnets, Triumphs, and Other Poems of Petrarch,* translated by Various Hands, Bohn Library, G. Bell & Sons, London, 1859; "Ode to the Virgin" from *Madrigals & Odes from Petrarch,* translated by Helen Lee Peabody, Loker Raley, New York, 1940.]

DURING THE LIFE OF LAURA

1. *Voi ch' ascoltate in rime sparse il suono*

Ye, who may listen to each idle strain
Bearing those sighs, on which my heart was fed
In life's first morn, by youthful error led,
(Far other then from what I now remain!)
That thus in varying numbers I complain,
Numbers of sorrow vain and vain hope bred,
If any in love's lore be practisèd,
His pardon, — e'en his pity I may obtain:
But now aware that to mankind my name
Too long has been a bye-word and a scorn,
I blush before my own severer thought;
Of my past wanderings the sole fruit is shame,
And deep repentance, of the knowledge born
That all we value in this world is naught.

[Dacre]

3. *Era il giorno ch' al sol si scoloraro*

It was the morning of that blessèd day
Whereon the Sun in pity veiled his glare
For the Lord's agony, that, unaware,
I fell a captive, Lady, to the sway
Of your swift eyes: that seemed no time to stay
The strokes of Love: I stepped into the snare
Secure, with no suspicion: then and there

I found my cue in man's most tragic play.
Love caught me naked to his shaft, his sheaf,
The entrance for his ambush and surprise
Against the heart wide open through the eyes,
The constant gate and fountain of my grief:
How craven so to strike me stricken so,
Yet from you fully armed conceal his bow!

[Auslander]

13. *Quando fra l' altre donne ad ora ad ora*

When Love his flaming image on her brow
Enthrones in perfect beauty like a star,
As far as she outshines the rest, so far
I feel the blaze of passion surge and grow.
Yet still I bless the place, the hour when so
Supremely high, at light so singular
I dared to look: "O heart, you blessèd are
To gaze upon that pure, that golden glow,"
I murmur. "She inspired the splendid thought
Which points to heaven and teaches honest eyes
All worldly lures and winnings to despise:
Through her that gentle grace of love is taught
Which by the straight path leads to paradise,
And even here hope's holy crown is wrought."

[Auslander]

16. *Movesi il vecchierel canuto e bianco*

The palmer bent, with locks of silver gray,
Quits the sweet spot where he has pass'd his years,
Quits his poor family, whose anxious fears
Paint the loved father fainting on his way;
And trembling, on his aged limbs slow borne,
In these last days that close his earthly course,
He, in his soul's strong purpose, finds new force,
Though weak with age, though by long travel worn:
Thus reaching Rome, led on by pious love,
He seeks the image of that Saviour Lord
Whom soon he hopes to meet in bliss above:
So, oft in other forms I seek to trace
Some charm, that to my heart may yet afford
A faint resemblance of thy matchless grace.

[Dacre]

21. *Mille fiate, o dolce mia guerrera*

A thousand times, O my sweet warrior,
Burning to purchase peace of those proud eyes,
Have I held forth the heart your heart denies,
Which your nobility will not bend for.
And if some other lady love it more,
Vain is her hope and false: what you despise
I must disdain, since what you do not prize
I spurn, and what you hate cannot adore.
Exiled by me, what then if it shall find
With you no word of mercy now or later,
And so, when others call it, stay behind,
Afraid to go, afraid of its dear hater?
Though guilt to both of us must be assigned,
It loves you more, and thus your guilt is greater.

[AUSLANDER]

32. *Quanto più m'avicino al giorno estremo*

The nearer I approach that final day,
Which seems to put an end to human woe,
The more I see how swiftly Time can flow,
And how Time's promise was an empty play.
No more concerning Love: henceforth we may
Dismiss Love's counsel, for like recent snow
The hard and heavy load of Yes and No
Dissolves and yields the peace for which we pray.
And with our hopes, as with our bodies, peace—
Our hopes which here so long beguiled our hearts;
Laughter and tears, terror and pride shall cease:
And we shall see with purged eyes in what parts
Our worldly eyes betrayed us, knowing why
So often and so vainly we would sigh.

[AUSLANDER]

33. *Già fiammeggiava l'amorosa stella*

Already in the east the amorous star
Flamed through the sky, while from the noble north
The cause of Juno's jealousy poured forth
Her wheeling beams, brilliant and singular;
Half-naked and barefoot, the crone of care
Quickens the coals, her spindle at the hearth;

And lovers feel the hour of amorous birth
Which pricks to tears (what burning tears these are!) —
When my dear hope, now at the green last inch
Of candle, reached my heart, not through my eyes
Which sleep had locked and sorrow wet likewise,
Alas! how changed! (O heart, do thou not flinch!):
"Why dost thou lose thy strength?" she seemed to say,
"These eyes from thine are not yet stolen away."

[AUSLANDER]

35. *Solo e pensoso i più deserti campi*

Alone, thought-sick, I pace where none has been,
Roaming the desert with dull steps and slow,
And still glance warily about to know
If the herd follows, if the world has seen:
How else the hoofprint of the Philistine
Escape, but in some cave with grief to go!
I look distraught and haggard: I must show
No one how keen Love's tooth is, O how keen!
Meseems the very mountains and the shores,
Rivers and woods must guess the secret I
So seek to hide from men by desert doors —
O tell me where beneath a savage sky
Is any space the foot of Love ignores,
But with Love's whisper and my soul's rings high!

[AUSLANDER]

49. *Perch' io t' abbia guardato di menzogna*

Although from falsehood I with all my will
Restrained you, and bestowed each honour due,
Ungrateful tongue, no honour came from you
To solace me, but only shame and ill:
When most I need your help, you are most chill,
Winning for me no mercy while I sue;
And those your words are most imperfect too,
You speak as speaks a dreamer strange and still.
And you as well, sad tears, each lonely night
Attend me when I most would be alone;
But, wanted for my peace, you take to flight:
And you, so prompt to give me groan for groan,
O sighs — yours too a slow and broken part —
Only my face does not betray my heart.

[AUSLANDER]

62. *Padre del ciel; dopo i perduti giorni*

Father of heaven! after the days all lost,
After the nights on foolish fancies spent
In that fierce passion's proud imprisonment,
Seeing her beauty to my bitter cost;
Please Thee, with Thy illuminating ghost
Of grace, to new light, worthier intent
Return me, so that Love's snares may be rent
Asunder and my cruel foe be crossed.
Already now, O Lord, the eleventh year
Waxes and wanes, since first his pitiless yoke
Fell on me, that most furious charioteer;
Thy mercy on my meekness I invoke:
To nobler ends my wandering thoughts decree,
Reminding them of Thy Son on His Tree.

[AUSLANDER]

90. *Erano i capei d'oro a l'aura sparsi*

Golden upon the wind her loose hair streaming,
Twisted into a thousand curls was shaken;
And from her eyes, which seldom now awaken
To answer mine, a fiery light was gleaming;
Ah! — was it fancy? — but with wistful seeming,
Her lovely face by pity's tint was taken:
What marvel that my heart, so long Love's beacon,
Should flame out, fueled so by Love's fierce dreaming?
She was no mortal in her stately moving,
But stepped an angel; and her accents glowing
Beyond all human tones passed human heeding,
A spirit of Heaven! — a sun alive was proving
My power of sight. . . What matters that sun's going?
The slackening bow puts no stop to the bleeding.

[AUSLANDER]

97. *Ahi, bella libertà, come tu m' hai*

Ah Liberty, so lovely, so denied!
Alas, how well you teach my bitter heart
To mourn that peace it knew before Love's dart
Smote me the great wound perilous in my side!
Mine eyes are bandaged and bewitched, the pride

And power of reason dully draw apart,
Shun every task, turn blind and deaf to Art,
By my own folly poisoned and defied.
Nothing but what pertains to her, my death,
Attracts my ears; and from my tongue there goes
No sound except her name's beloved breath;
Love to no other quarry my soul spurs,
No other path can pull my feet; nor knows
My hand to write in any praise but hers!

[AUSLANDER]

123. *Quel vago impallidir, che 'l dolce riso*

That touching pallor which, like a soft cloud
Veiled her sweet smile, so delicate, so dear,
So shook my heart that from its stricken sphere
It sought to rise and meet that lovely shroud.
Then felt I how the blessèd lovers crowd
About each other with eyes fixed and near:
For never was a mortal's gaze so clear,
So perfect and so tenderly endowed.
The gentlest glance ever a woman threw
Upon her love were cold and lustreless
Against this look that like celestial dew
She shed upon me with angelic stress
That seemed with mute solicitude to say,
"Who takes from me my faithful friend away?"

[AUSLANDER]

132. *S' amor non è, che dunque è quel ch' io sento?*

If this should not be Love, O God, what shakes me?
If Love it is, what strange, what rich delight!
If Love be kind, why has it fangs to bite?
If cruel, why so sweet the barb that rakes me?
If Love I crave, why this lament that breaks me?
If not, what tears or sighs can mend my plight?
O Death in Life, dear pain, where lies thy might
If I refuse the doom that overtakes me?
If I consent, without a cause I grieve:
So in a tempest do my fortunes heave,
By winds contrary and by waters tost;
So, in a stupor, like a blind man lost
In mischievous error, lured from doubt to doubt,
June freezes, January thaws me out.

[AUSLANDER]

134. *Pace non trovo e non ho da far guerra*

I find no peace, yet from all wars abstain me;
I fear, I hope, I burn — and straightway wizen;
I mount above the wind, yet stay unrisen;
Grasp the world — thus — yet nothing does it gain me.
Love neither lets me go, nor will detain me;
Gives me no leave, nor yet keeps me in prison:
I am not held, and yet the hard chain is on
The heart; he yields no death, yet will he chain me.
Sightless, I see; and without tongue, I sorrow;
I cling to life, and yet would gladly perish;
Detest myself, and yet another cherish;
Feed upon grief; from grief my laughter borrow;
Death is a spear and life a poisoned arrow,
And in delight my fears take root and flourish.

[AUSLANDER]

140. *Amor, che nel penser mio vive e regna*

The long Love that is sovereign to my mind
And in my heart maintains his purple place,
With arrogant stride presses into my face,
Camps, flaunts his flag, parades there proud and blind:
She, that instructs to love and helps us find
Anguish therein, she would our heat abase
By reins of reason, shame and reverent grace,
And in our flesh the spurs of anger grind.
Whereupon Love to the heart's forest flies,
With sharp dismay quitting his enterprise,
And there in tears and panic he must hide.
What can the slave whose lord is terrified
Do more than stand with him in flight or field? —
How dear is death upon Love's battered shield!

[AUSLANDER]

145. *Pommi ove 'l sole occide i fiori e l' erba*

Place me where herb and flower the sun has dried,
Or where numb winter's grasp holds sterner sway:
Place me where Phoebus sheds a temperate ray,
Where first he glows, where rests at eventide.
Place me in lowly state, in power and pride,
Where lour the skies, or where bland zephyrs play:

Place me where blind night rules, or lengthened day,
In age mature, or in youth's boiling tide:
Place me in heaven, or in the abyss profound,
On lofty height, or in low vale obscure,
A spirit freed, or to the body bound;
Rank'd with the great, or all unknown to fame,
I still the same will be! the same endure!
And my trilustral sighs still breathe the same!
[DACRE]

159. *In qual parte del ciel, in quale idea*

In what bright realm, what sphere of radiant thought
Did Nature find the model whence she drew
That delicate dazzling image where we view
Here on this earth what she in heaven wrought?
What fountain-haunting nymph, what dryad, sought
In groves, such golden tresses ever threw
Upon the gust? What heart such virtues knew? —
Though her chief virtue with my death is fraught.
He looks in vain for heavenly beauty, he
Who never looked upon her perfect eyes,
The vivid blue orbs turning brilliantly —
He does not know how Love yields and denies;
He only knows, who knows how sweetly she
Can talk and laugh, the sweetness of her sighs.
[AUSLANDER]

162. *Lieti fiori e felici e ben nate erbe*

O rich and happy flowers forever apart
On which my pensive Lady puts her heel!
O golden acres privileged to feel
Her phrase, her footprint pressed upon your heart!
Trees silver green with April's earliest art;
Pale passionate violets; dark grove that can steal
Only so much of sun as may reveal
Your swarthy steeples in a radiant dart!
O comely landscape! O translucent stream
Mirroring her pure face, her intense eyes
And seizing all alive their bluest beam!
I envy you your crystal burglaries!
No rock, however cold, but with my theme
Shall henceforth kindle and consume in sighs!
[AUSLANDER]

189. *Passa la nave mia colma d' oblio*

My vessel, cargoed with oblivion, cleaves
The boisterous deep, under cold midnight skies,
And mine old enemy, Love, the tiller plies,
While Scylla hisses and Charybdis heaves;
At every oar imagination weaves
Fancies that both the storm and death despise;
A humid and eternal wind of sighs
Wails through my sails and shatters as it grieves.
Torrents of tears and clouds of chilling scorn
Wash and relax the shrouds so overworn,
Of ignorance and error intertwined;
The two dear lights which beaconed me are blind;
Reason and Art the waves to death have torn,
No hope or harbour comforts heart or mind.

[AUSLANDER]

224. *S'una fede amorosa, un cor non finto*

If faith most true, a heart that cannot feign,
If Love's sweet languishment and chasten'd thought,
And wishes pure by nobler feelings taught,
If in a labyrinth wanderings long and vain,
If on the brow each pang pourtray'd to bear,
Or from the heart low broken sounds to draw,
Withheld by shame, or check'd by pious awe,
If on the faded cheek Love's hue to wear,
If than myself to hold one far more dear,
If sighs that cease not, tears that ever flow,
Wrung from the heart by all Love's various woe,
In absence if consumed, and chill'd when near,—
If these be ills in which I waste my prime,
Though I the sufferer be, yours, lady, is the crime.

[DACRE]

245. *Due rose fresche e còlte in paradiso*

Two glowing roses, fresh from Paradise,
That there, on May-Day morning, leaped in light—
Sweet gift sent by a lover wise and white
With age to two young loves in equal wise:
Whereat, so soft the speech, and to the eyes
So excellent his mien (a savage might

Have softened), the same lustre glimmered bright
In both and on their cheeks burned the swift dyes.
"Never had sun looked on a lovelier two,"
Said he, as with a smile and sigh he spoke,
Pressing their ardent palms and turning away.
Of words and roses each shared like and true.
Even now my worn heart breaks, as once it broke,
With bliss, O happy syllables! Holy day!

[AUSLANDER]

AFTER THE DEATH OF LAURA

267. *Oimè il bel viso, oimè il soave sguardo*

Alas! that liquid look, that lovely face!
Alas! the poised grace of that golden head!
Alas! the sweetness of the words she said
That soothed the savage breast, raised up the base!
Alas! the smile — that dart which I embrace,
Whose hope is death now that all hope is dead;
O hadst thou not so late inhabited
This earth, how queenly would have been thy place!
In thee I burn, in thee still draw my breath,
Being all thine. Death now has disciplined
All lesser pain to nothing; no sharp teeth
Can gnaw the constant grief-bright music dinned
By thy last words, snatched up by jealous Death
To vanish with their hope upon the wind.

[AUSLANDER]

269. *Rotta è l'alta colonna e 'l verde lauro*

The lofty Column and the Laurel fall
That gave pavilion to my heart's despair;
I shall not find their equal anywhere,
Though every sea I search and wind and wall.
My double wealth — lost, lost beyond recall
Life's pride and pleasure mated for me there:
Lands cannot buy them back nor kings unsnare,
Nor gold nor gems deliver them at all.
Against this doom what strength to consecrate
Save that of tears that blind these futile eyes,
Save the bowed head, the clenched fists at the Gate!
Ah, life that seems so rich with ecstasies,

Yet can in one swift morning dissipate
What we had gained with years and many sighs!

[AUSLANDER]

272. *La vita fugge e non s' arresta un' ora*

Life ever flies with course that nought may stay,
Death follows after with gigantic stride;
Ills past and present on my spirit prey,
And future evils threat on every side:
Whether I backward look or forward fare,
A thousand ills my bosom's peace molest;
And were it not that pity bids me spare
My nobler part, I from these thoughts would rest.
If ever aught of sweet my heart has known,
Remembrance wakes its charms, while, tempest tost,
I mark the clouds that o'er my course still frown;
E'en in the port I see the storm afar;
Weary my pilot, mast and cable lost,
And set for ever my fair polar star.

[DACRE]

279. *Se lamentar augelli o verdi fronde*

If the lone bird lament or the green leaves
Shiver beneath the summer's soft caresses,
Or rapid streams flash from dark wildernesses
Churning the rock that with my sorrow grieves,
While Love his slow eternal elegy weaves,
Then, then I see her whom this blind earth presses!
Those eyes like wells of stars, those golden tresses,
That voice like tears, that silver breast which heaves:
"Unhappy soul, why weep? Ah why, sad lover,
Thus, thus with anguish and remorse devour
Your splendid manhood in its perfect flower?
Let light and warmth its radiance recover:
Bewail me not: the brightness that seemed over
Has burst into one white perpetual hour!"

[AUSLANDER]

282. *Alma felice che sovente torni*

Soul of my soul, how often you return
Bearing in your small hands the gift of peace

Like perfume; Death has cancelled his dark lease
Upon those eyes, renewed them, bade them burn!
Ah, God be praised that your bliss does not spurn
My blackness, but with radiant increase
Of light illumines grief until it sees
Again your lonely haunts, your lovely urn!
Look you, how here, where so long I had lifted
A joyous voice, I pour laments instead
For you! — Ah no, for my dead dreams thick-drifted
As summer's grave! . . . One solace is not dead:
By many a sign I feel you near and keen —
Your step, voice, look — that robe of cherished green!

[AUSLANDER]

285. *Nè mai pietosa madre al caro figlio*

Ne'er to the son, in whom her age is blest,
The anxious mother — nor to her loved lord
The wedded dame, impending ill to ward,
With careful sighs so faithful counsel press'd,
As she, who, from her high eternal rest,
Bending — as though my exile she deplored —
With all her wonted tenderness restored,
And softer pity on her brow impress'd!
Now with a mother's fears, and now as one
Who loves with chaste affection, in her speech
She points what to pursue and what to shun!
Our years retracing of long, various grief,
Wooing my soul at higher good to reach,
And while she speaks, my bosom finds relief!

[DACRE]

292. *Gli occhi di ch' io parlai sì caldamente*

The eyes, the face, the limbs of heavenly mould,
So long the theme of my impassion'd lay,
Charms which so stole me from myself away,
That strange to other men the course I hold;
The crispèd locks of pure and lucid gold,
The lightning of the angelic smile, whose ray
To earth could all of paradise convey,
A little dust are now! — to feeling cold!
And yet I live! — but that I live bewail,
Sunk the loved light that through the tempest led
My shatter'd bark, bereft of mast and sail:

Hush'd be for aye the song that breathed love's fire!
Lost is the theme on which my fancy fed,
And turn'd to mourning my once tuneful lyre.

[DACRE]

301. *Valle, che de' lamenti miei se' piena*

Valley familiar with my desperate din,
Stream which my tears now feed, have fed before;
Beasts of the brake, bright birds and silver floor
Of Sorga friendly to the jewelled fin;
Air hushed with sighs like some soft medicine;
Delightful path whose sad hints I explore;
Hill that once pleased me — and shall please no more —
Whither Love tugs at me to enter in:
You, you are still unchanged! How changed, alas,
Am I who, from a height so rare, so rich,
Am now of infinite grief the very niche!
Here, here I saw my sweet! Here still I pass
Her farewell footprints and the spot from which,
The flesh discarded, she flamed from the grass!

[AUSLANDER]

302. *Levommi il mio penser in parte ov' era*

An ecstasy of thought upraised me where
She wanders, that shall no more walk with me:
There! — lovelier, humbler — there, ah there I see —
I see her in the third celestial sphere!
She takes my hand and whispers, "With me here
Thou shalt again taste pure felicity:
For I am she that pained thee, even she
That perished in the blossom of her year.
My bliss no mortal hope has ever spanned;
Thee only I await, and that sweet veil
Thou didst so love, my body's golden shell." —
Why did she stop? Ah why release my hand?
Alas! Her tones, her touch beyond control
Had swept me heavenward, snatched my ravished soul!

[AUSLANDER]

310. *Zefiro torna, e 'l bel tempo rimena*

The spring returns, the spring wind softly blowing
Sprinkles the grass with gleam and glitter of showers,

Powdering pearl and diamond, dripping with flowers,
Dropping wet flowers, dancing the winter's going;
The swallow twitters, the groves of midnight are glowing
With nightingale music and madness; the sweet fierce powers
Of Love flame up through the earth; the seed-soul towers
And trembles; Nature is filled to overflowing. . .
The spring returns, but there is no returning
Of spring for me. O heart with anguish burning!
She that unlocked all April in a breath
Returns not. . . And these meadows, blossoms, birds,
These lovely gentle girls — words, empty words,
As bitter as the black estates of death!

[AUSLANDER]

311. *Quel rosigniuol, che sì soave piagne*

That nightingale, who weeps so sweetly, grieves
Perhaps for his lost young or his loved mate,
Drowning the sky with sweetness, and the late
Dark violet valleys and the trembling leaves;
And all night long he in his sorrow cleaves
To me and mine, recalling my harsh fate —
But I have myself to commiserate
Alone, who deemed an angel safe from thieves.
O what an easy dupe the trusting fool!
Who ever would have thought those lamps more bright
Than any sun could go out like a light
Smothered in dust? Now in a bitter school
Fate teaches me the lesson all too sure:
No joy can please and pleasing can endure!

[AUSLANDER]

312. *Nè per sereno ciel ir vaghe stelle*

Not skies serene, with glittering stars inlaid,
Nor gallant ships o'er tranquil ocean dancing,
Nor gay careering knights in arms advancing,
Nor wild herds bounding through the forest glade,
Nor tidings new of happiness delay'd,
Nor poesie, Love's witchery enhancing,
Nor lady's song beside clear fountain glancing,
In beauty's pride, with chastity array'd;
Nor aught of lovely, aught of gay in show,
Shall touch my heart, now cold within her tomb
Who was erewhile my life and light below!

So heavy — tedious — sad — my days unblest,
That I, with strong desire, invoke Death's gloom,
Her to behold, whom ne'er to have seen were best!

[DACRE]

314. *Mente mia, che presàga de' tuoi danni*

My mind! prophetic of my coming fate,
Pensive and gloomy while yet joy was lent,
On the loved lineaments still fix'd, intent
To seek dark bodings, ere thy sorrow's date!
From her sweet acts, her words, her looks, her gait,
From her unwonted pity with sadness blent,
Thou might'st have said, hadst thou been prescient,
"I taste my last of bliss in this low state!"
My wretched soul! the poison, oh, how sweet!
That through my eyes instill'd the burning smart,
Gazing on hers, no more on earth to meet!
To them — my bosom's wealth! condemn'd to part
On a far journey — as to friends discreet,
All my fond thoughts I left, and lingering heart.

[DACRE]

315. *Tutta la mia fiorita e verde etade*

All my green years and golden prime of man
Had pass'd away, and with attemper'd sighs
My bosom heaved — ere yet the days arise
When life declines, contracting its brief span.
Already my loved enemy began
To lull suspicion, and in sportive guise,
With timid confidence, though playful, wise,
In gentle mockery my long pains to scan:
The hour was near when Love, at length, may mate
With Chastity; and, by the dear one's side,
The lover's thoughts and words may freely flow:
Death saw, with envy, my too happy state,
E'en its fair promise — and, with fatal pride,
Strode in the midway forth, an armèd foe!

[DACRE]

341. *Deh qual pietà, qual angel fu sì presto*

What pity-driven angel proved his speed
To swoop through middle Heaven with my appeal?

Instantly, though I hear not, I can feel
My lady's step responsive to my need;
She shines too bright for pride, being rich indeed
With rapt humility whose strength can steal
My life from Death itself, and raise and heal
Till Life goes radiant, having her to lead.
How blessèd are that face, that small strong hand
Stretched out! O Christ! The little phrase! It gnaws!
But only Love and I can understand.
"Lover, your sobs run through me like a spear!
For our own sake I seemed so cruel . . . because . . ."
So sweet the rest, the sun would halt to hear.

[AUSLANDER]

343. *Ripensando a quel ch' oggi il cielo onora*

To that pure look which honours Paradise,
That head bent sideways with its weight of gold,
That face, that voice now warm, now liquid cold,
Which lulled me once, but prompts my present sighs—
Ah, when to these my foolish fancy flies,
I greatly marvel that I am not mold
Long since! But she sustains, her hands uphold
My heart, and with the dawn she decks my eyes.
How tranquil is each attitude, how meek!
With what apparent pity she attends
The telling of my beads . . . until the beak
Of daybreak plunging through my vision ends
The dream, and her familiar haste commends
The bowed head and the thoughts I dare not speak!

[AUSLANDER]

351. *Dolci durezze e placide repulse*

O sweet severity, repulses mild,
With chasten'd love, and tender pity fraught;
Graceful rebukes, that to mad passion taught
Becoming mastery o'er its wishes wild;
Speech dignified, in which, united, smiled
All courtesy, with purity of thought;
Virtue and beauty, that uprooted aught
Of baser temper had my heart defiled;
Eyes, in whose glance man is beatified—
Awful, in pride of virtue, to restrain
Aspiring hopes that justly are denied,

Then prompt the drooping spirit to sustain!
These, beautiful in every change, supplied
Health to my soul, that else were sought in vain.

[DACRE]

353. *Vago augelletto che cantando vai*

Poor solitary bird, that pour'st thy lay,
Or haply mournest the sweet season gone:
As chilly night and winter hurry on,
And day-light fades and summer flies away;
If as the cares that swell thy little throat
Thou knew'st alike the woes that wound my rest,
Ah, thou wouldst house thee in this kindred breast,
And mix with mine thy melancholy note.
Yet little know I ours are kindred ills:
She still may live the object of thy song:
Not so for me stern death or Heaven wills!
But the sad season, and less grateful hour,
And of past joy and sorrow thoughts that throng
Prompt my full heart this idle lay to pour.

[DACRE]

364. *Tennemi Amor anni vent' uno ardendo*

Love kept me one and twenty years a slave;
His flame was bliss, his agony was hope;
When with my heart my Lady reached the Slope
Star-swept, my tears ten summers drenched her grave.
Now, shattered quite, I loathe the life that gave
No comfort to the holy seeds that grope
Toward virtue; now the lost years twist a rope
Around my throat and conscience calls me knave.
Exalted God, in Thee life would have found
Renewed devotion, dark peace out of pain,
Some restitution for the years so vain:
O Father, in this prison Thou hast bound
My soul — O bless me yet, do Thou unchain
The spirit! Let me kneel in holy ground!

[AUSLANDER]

365. *I' vo piangendo i miei passati tempi*

Weeping, I still regret the years that went
In empty sacrifice to mortal things;
No swooping starward, though my soul had wings
Which might have brushed Thy burning element.
O Thou, that know'st so well how I repent,
Sovereign of space, immortal King of Kings,
Succour the soul torn with self-torturings —
To Thee it turns: O prove Thou provident!
To my war-shattered life appoint Thou still
Death as the port of peace; and if my course
Was idle, let it find a quiet hill!
O for the brief remainder, let remorse
Not darken, let Thy hand the end fulfill!
Thou know'st in Thee alone rests my resource!
[AUSLANDER]

366. *Vergine bella, che di sol vestita*

Fair Virgin,
Vestured with the sun!
Bright shining one,
Star-crowned;
Who such sweet ultimate favor found
From all eternity
With the great primal Sun
That from His height
He stooped in thee to hide the light
Of His Divinity:
Now shall my love upraise
New measures in thy praise,
Though to begin without thy aid were vain
And without His,
Who, joined with thee in love, shall ever reign.
Thee I invoke who never turned deaf ear
When ardent faith called to thee without fear.
Virgin, if our poor misery,
Our trafficking with pain,
In thy deep heart stir pity,
Incline to me again;
Once more on thy sure succour now I lean,
Though of base clay am I
And thou be Heaven's queen.

O Virgin wise,
Of prudent virgins blest,

Foremost and best
Beyond compare,
With shining lamp most clear,
Bright shield of the oppressed,
With thee we know
Not mere escape from evil fortune's blow
Or bitter death;
But triumph o'er the foe —
Thou who dost cool this flame
Which, blazing among mortals, love we name.
Virgin, turn thou thine eyes,
Sad eyes that watched beside
The piteous body of thy Son that died,
Unto my dubious state;
Thy counsel now I seek,
Disconsolate.

Pure Virgin, without stain,
God's daughter meet,
And by conception sweet
His mother too,
Thou, a keen brightness to our dark world sent,
Art high Heaven's ornament.
Through thee alone,
O lofty window gleaming with heavenly light,
Came God's Son and thine own,
To save us mortals from our desperate plight.
Among all dusty toilers of the earth,
Virgin most blessed,
Chosen wert thou, pure gold without alloy,
To turn Eve's sorrow into joy.
O make me of God's grace to worthy be,
Thou who art crowned in heaven eternally.

Virgin most holy, filled with every grace,
Who the sure path of true humility did'st trace
To the bright heavens where my prayers ascend,
Thou did'st achieve the much-desired end
That springs from fairest root.
Of Justice and of Piety art thou
The ripened fruit.
Three sweetest names unite
In thee alone,
Mother and spouse and daughter, all in one.
O Virgin glorious,
Sweet spouse of our high King
Who gloriously reigns,
Who freed us from our chains,
By His most sacred wounds — His love's unerring dart,
O soften thou my heart.

Virgin, in all this world unparalleled,
Heaven enamoured is
Of thy pure bliss.
O thou, the living temple of high God,
Who thy virginity did fruitful make,
Most joyful for thy sake,
In spite of inner strife,
Is all my life.
Virgin most pious, sweet,
In whom all graces meet,
My spirit flows to thee,
Praying that thou wilt bend
The twisted fragments of my broken life
Unto a perfect end.

O Virgin, bathed in ever-living light,
Bright star of our tempestuous dark sea,
Thou faithful guide
To mariners that trust in thee,
Behold in what dread tempest I am tossed,
Rudderless and alone,
Fearing myself for lost.
With sinful soul I still in thee confide.
Virgin, I pray
Let not our common enemy deride
My bitter woe.
Remember that for man's sin
God took upon Himself our human flesh,
To thy sweet virgin cloister entering in.

Virgin, how many tears have I not shed,
What prayers have I not offered and in vain!
Sorrow and loss and fear of future pain,
All these have compassed me
Since my first breath I drew by Arno's side;
My searchings far and wide,
My acts, my words and mortal beauty have undone
me quite.
Virgin, sacred of soul,
Do not delay,
For who can say
That I approach not to life's end.
And the long swiftly flowing years,
Swift as an arrow's dart,
Filled to the brim with bitter loss and tears,
Have left no other trace
Than a sure death which looks me in the face.

Virgin, she whom I mourn is now dry dust,
Who, living, caused me full a thousand woes,

But of my bitter throes
She knew not one,
Else had she honor lost, and I had been undone.
But thou, O heavenly Lady fair,
Our Goddess rare,
(If to speak thus of thee is meet)
Virgin of delicate high sentiment,
Thou see'st all.
Others have failed to end my misery;
But now through thy great power can be wrought
Health to my soul, and honor unto thee.

Virgin, with whom my hope is most secure,
In need my refuge sure,
Let not thy gaze
Rest on unworthy me.
But rather see
Him who in likeness to Himself did raise
My fallen nature base,
Enduing it with grace;
Else might my eyes of error take their fill.
Medusa-like,
My heart would turn to stone
And evil humors on the air distill.
O Virgin, thou of pious, saintly tears,
Rid then my soul of cowardly fears,
That my last hours devout may be,
Not mixed as heretofore with earthly mire,
But tinged with heavenly fire.

Virgin, with human heart devoid of pride,
Humanity thou too did'st take
By primal Love's decree.
With contrite heart I pray you pity me.
I that so faithful proved
To mortal lady, greatly, vainly loved,
So gentle art thou, shall I not love thee?
If from my sad and miserable state
By thy sweet hands I rise,
Virgin, I consecrate to thee
All my most treasured enterprise.
My dear imaginings,
My language and my thoughts, my pen, my heart,
My tears and sighs;
Be thou my guide to Heaven, nor fail to weigh
Celestial desires when I pray.

The day approaches now, so swift time flies,
Virgin, uniquely one,
Of my last end.

Pierced is my heart with thought of death;
    Now to thy Son, true Man, true God, commend
My parting soul, that He may give release,
    Receiving my last breath in peace.

[Helen Lee Peabody]

SECRETUM MEUM

Petrarch's Secret or The Soul's Conflict with Passion

Translated by William H. Draper

[Taken from *Petrarch's Secret or The Soul's Conflict with Passion,* translated by William H. Draper, Chatto & Windus, London, 1911.]

AUTHOR'S PREFACE

Often have I wondered with much curiosity as to our coming into this world and what will follow our departure. When I was ruminating lately on this matter, not in any dream as one in sickness and slumber, but wide awake and with all my wits about me, I was greatly astonished to behold a very beautiful Lady, shining with an indescribable light about her. She seemed as one whose beauty is not known, as it might be, to mankind. I could not tell how she came there, but from her raiment and appearance I judged her a fair Virgin, and her eyes, like the sun, seemed to send forth rays of such light that they made me lower my own before her, so that I was afraid to look up. When she saw this she said, "Fear not; and let not the strangeness of my presence affright you in any wise. I saw your steps had gone astray; and I had compassion on you and have come down from above to bring you timely succour. Hitherto your eyes have been darkened and you have looked too much, yes, far too much, upon the things of earth. If these so much delight you, what shall be your rapture when you lift your gaze to things eternal!"

When I heard her thus speak, though my fear still clung about me, with trembling voice I made reply in Virgil's words—

"What name to call thee by, O Virgin fair,
I know not, for thy looks are not of earth
And more than mortal seems thy countenance."

"I am that Lady," she answered, "whom you have depicted in your poem *Africa* with rare art and skill, and for whom, like another Amphion of Thebes, you have with poetic hands built a fair and glorious Palace in the far West on Atlas's lofty peak.

"Be not afraid, then, to listen and to look upon the face of her who, as your finely-wrought allegory proves, has been well known to you from of old."

Scarcely had she uttered these words when, as I pondered all these things in my mind, it occurred to me this could be none other than Truth herself who thus spoke. I remembered how I had described her abode on the heights of Atlas; yet was I ignorant from what region she had come, save only that I felt assured she could have come from none other place than Heaven. Therefore I turned my gaze towards her, eagerly desiring to look upon her face; but lo, the eye of man is unable to gaze on that ethereal Form, wherefore again was I forced to turn them towards the ground. When she took note of this, after a short silence, she spoke once more; and, questioning me many times, she led me to engage with her in long discourse. From this converse I was sensible of gaining a twofold benefit, for I won knowledge, and the very act of talking with her gave me confidence. I found myself by degrees becoming able to look upon the face which at first dismayed me by its splendour, and as soon as I was able to bear it without dread, and gaze fixedly on her wondrous beauty, I looked to see if she were accompanied with any other, or had come upon the retirement of my solitude alone; and as I did so I discerned at her side the figure of an aged man, of aspect venerable and full of majesty. There was no need to inquire his name. His religious bearing, modest brow, his eyes full of dignity, his measured step, his African look, but Roman speech, plainly declared him to be that most illustrious Father, Augustine. Moreover, he had so gracious a mien, and withal so noble, that one could not possibly imagine it to belong to any other than to him. Even so I was on the point of opening my lips to ask, when at that moment I heard the name so dear to me uttered from the lips of Truth herself. Turning herself to him, as if to intervene upon his deep meditation, she addressed him in these words: "Augustine, dear to me above a thousand others, you know how devoted to yourself this man is, and you are aware also with how dangerous and long a malady he is stricken, and that he is so much nearer to Death as he knows not the gravity of his disease. It is needful, then, that one take thought for this man's life forthwith, and who so fit to undertake the pious work as yourself? He has ever been deeply attached to your name and person; and all good doctrine is wont more easily to enter the mind of the disciple when he already starts with loving the Master from whom he is to learn. Unless your present happiness has made you quite forget your former sorrow, you will remember that when you were shut in the prison of the mortal body you also were subject to like temptation as his. And if that were so, most excellent Physician of those passions yourself experienced, even though your silent meditation be full of sweetness to your mind, I beg that your sacred voice, which to me is ever a delight, shall break its silence, and try whether you are able by some means to bring calm to one so deeply distressed."

Augustine answered her: "You are my guide, my Counsellor, my Sovereign, my Ruler; what is it, then, you would have me say in your presence?"

"I would," she replied, "that some human voice speak to the ears of this mortal man. He will better bear to hear truth so. But seeing that whatever you shall say to him he will take as said by me, I also will be present in person during your discourse."

Augustine answered her, "The love I bear to this sick man, as well as the authority of her who speaks, make it my duty to obey." Then, looking kindly at me and pressing me to his heart in fatherly embrace, he led me away to the most retired corner he could find, and Truth herself went on a few steps in front. There we all three sat down. Then while Truth listened as the silent Judge, none other beside her being present, we held long converse on one side and the other; and because of the greatness of the theme, the discourse between us lasted over three days. Though we talked of many things much against the manners of this age, and on faults and failings common to mankind, in such wise that the reproaches of the Master seemed in a sense more directed against men in general than against myself, yet those which to me came closest home I have graven with more especial vividness on the tablet of my memory. That this discourse, so intimate and deep, might not be lost, I have set it down in writing and made this book; not that I wish to class it with my other works, or desire from it any credit. My thoughts aim higher. What I desire is that I may be able by reading to renew as often as I wish the pleasure I felt from the discourse itself. So, little Book, I bid you flee the haunts of men and be content to stay with me, true to the title I have given you of "My Secret": and when I would think upon deep matters, all that you keep in remembrance that was spoken in secret you in secret will tell to me over again.

To avoid the too frequent iteration of the words "said I," "said he," and to bring the personages of the Dialogue, as it were, before one's very eyes, I have acted on Cicero's method and merely placed the name of each interlocutor before each paragraph. My dear Master learned this mode himself from Plato. But to cut short all further digression, this is how Augustine opened the discourse.

DIALOGUE THE THIRD

Petrarch—S. Augustine

S. AUGUSTINE: Supposing that hitherto you have found some good from my words, I beg and implore you in what I have still to say to lend me a ready ear, and to put aside altogether the spirit of dispute and contradiction.

PETRARCH: You may be sure I will so do, for I feel that, owing to your good counsels, I have been set free from a large part of my distress, and am therefore the better disposed to listen to what you may still have to say.

S. AUGUSTINE: I have not at all as yet touched upon the deep-seated wounds which are within, and I rather dread the task when I remember what debate and murmuring were caused by even the lightest allusion to them. But, on the other hand, I am not without hope that when you have rallied your strength, your spirit will more firmly bear without flinching a severer handling of the trouble.

PETRARCH: Have no fear on that score. By this time I am used to hearing the name of my maladies and to bearing the touch of the surgeon's hand.

S. AUGUSTINE: Well, you are still held in bondage, on your right hand and on your left, by two strong chains which will not suffer you to turn your thoughts to meditate on life or on death. I have always dreaded these might bring you to destruction; and I am not yet at all reassured, and I shall only be so when I have seen you break and cast away your bonds and come forth perfectly free. And this I think possible but difficult enough to achieve, and that until it is accomplished I shall only be moving in a futile round. They say that to break a diamond one must use the blood of a goat, and in the same way to soften the hardness of these kinds of passions, this blood is of strange efficacy. No sooner has it touched even the hardest heart but it breaks and penetrates it. But I will tell you what my fear is. In this matter I must have your own full assent as we proceed, and I am haunted by the fear you will not be able, or perhaps I should say will prove unwilling, to give it. I greatly dread lest the glittering brilliance of your chains may dazzle your eyes and hinder you, and make you like the miser bound in prison with fetters of gold, who wished greatly to be set free but was not willing to break his chains.

Now such are the conditions of your own bondage that you can only gain your freedom by breaking your chains.

PETRARCH: Alas, alas, I am more wretched than I thought. Do you mean to tell me my soul is still bound by two chains of which I am unconscious?

S. AUGUSTINE: All the same they are plain enough to see; but, dazzled by their beauty, you think they are not fetters but treasures; and, to keep to the same figure, you are like some one who, with hands and feet fast bound in shackles of gold, should look at them with delight and not see at all that they are shackles. Yes, you yourself with blinded eyes keep looking at your bonds; but, oh strange delusion! you are charmed with the very chains that are dragging you to your death, and, what is most sad of all, you glory in them!

PETRARCH: What may these chains be of which you speak?

S. AUGUSTINE: Love and glory.

PETRARCH: Great Heavens! what is this I hear? You call these things chains? And you would break them from me, if I would let you?

S. AUGUSTINE: Yes, I mean to try, but I doubt if I shall succeed. All the other things that held you back were less strong and also less pleasant to you, so you helped me to break them. These, on the contrary, are pleasant though they injure, and they deceive you by a false show of beauty; so they will demand greater efforts, for you will make resistance as if I were wishing to rob you of some great good. Nevertheless I mean to try.

PETRARCH: Pray what have I done that you should desire to relieve me of the finest passions of my nature, and condemn to everlasting darkness the clearest faculties of my soul?

S. AUGUSTINE: Ah, unhappy man, have you forgotten quite this axiom of philosophy, that the climax of all evils is when a man, rooted in some false opinion, by degrees grows fatally persuaded that such and such a course is right?

PETRARCH: I have by no means forgotten that axiom, but it has nothing to do with the subject, for why in the world should I not think that the course which I indicated is right? No, I never have thought and I never shall think any truth more indisputable than that these two passions, which you cast at me as a reproach, are the very noblest of all.

S. AUGUSTINE: Let us take them separately for the present, while I endeavour to find the remedies, so that I may not blunt the edge of my weapon by striking first at one and then the other indiscriminately. Tell me then, since we have first mentioned love, do you or do you not hold it to be the height of all madness?

PETRARCH: To tell you the whole truth as I conceive it, I judge that love may be either described as the vilest passion or the noblest action of the soul.

S. AUGUSTINE: Do you mind giving me some example to confirm the view you have put forward?

PETRARCH: If my passion is for some low woman of ill fame, my love is the height of folly. But if, fascinated by one who is the image of virtue, I devote myself to love and honour her, what have you to say to that? Do you put no difference between things so entirely opposed? Do you wish to banish all remains of honour from the case? To tell you my real feeling, just as I regard the first kind of love as a heavy and ill-starred burden on the soul, so of the second I think there is hardly any greater blessing to it; if it so happen that you hold an opposite view, let each one follow his own feeling, for, as you are well aware, truth is a large field and every man should have freedom to judge for himself.

S. AUGUSTINE: In matters directly contradictory opinions also may be diverse. But truth itself is one and always the same.

PETRARCH: I admit that is so. But what makes us go wrong is that we bind ourselves obstinately to old opinions, and will not easily part from them.

S. AUGUSTINE: Heaven grant you may think as wisely on the whole matter of love as you do on this point.

PETRARCH: To speak briefly, I think I am so certainly right that those who think the opposite I believe to be quite out of their senses.

S. AUGUSTINE: I should certainly maintain that to take for truth some ancient falsehood, and to take as falsehood some newly-discovered truth, as though all authority for truth were a matter of time, is the very climax of madness.

PETRARCH: You are wasting your labour. Whoever asserts that view of love I shall never believe him. And I will rest on Cicero's saying, "If I err here I err willingly, and I shall never consent to part with this error as long as I live."

S. AUGUSTINE: When Cicero uses those words he is speaking of the immortality of the soul, and referring to it as the noblest of conceptions, and declaring his own belief in it to be so firm that he would not endure to listen to any one who maintained the contrary. You, however, to urge the ignoblest and most false of all opinions, make use of those same terms. Unquestionably, even if the soul were mortal, it would be better to think it immortal. For error though it were, yet would it inspire the love of virtue, and that is a thing to be desired for its own sake alone, even if all hope of future reward were taken away from us; and as to which the desire for it will certainly become weaker, as men come to think the soul a mortal thing; and, on the other hand, the promise of a life to come, even if it were to turn out a delusion, is none the less a powerful incentive to the soul, human nature being what it is.

But you see what will be the consequences of that error in which you stand; it will precipitate your soul into all manner of folly, when shame, and fear, even reason, that now acts as some check on passion, and the knowledge of truth itself shall all have disappeared.

PETRARCH: I have already told you you were wasting your time. My own remembrance tells me that I have never loved anything to be ashamed of, and, on the contrary, have ever loved what is most noble.

S. AUGUSTINE: Even noble things may be loved in a shameful way; it is beyond doubt.

PETRARCH: Neither in the object of love nor in the manner of loving am I guilty. So you may as well give up tormenting me.

S. AUGUSTINE: Well, well! Do you wish, like those with fever on the brain, to die laughing and joking? Or will you rather take some remedy for your mind so pitiable and so far from its true health?

PETRARCH: I will not refuse a remedy if you will prove to me that I am ill, but, when a man is quite well, to begin taking remedies is often fatal.

S. AUGUSTINE: As soon as you have reached the stage of convalescence you will perceive quickly enough, as men generally do, that you have been seriously ill.

PETRARCH: After all, I cannot but show deference to one who often in the past, and especially in these last two days, has given me proof how good were his counsels. So please go on.

S. AUGUSTINE: In the first place I ask you to forgive me if, compelled by the subject, I have to deal severely with what has been so delightful to you. For I cannot but foresee that the truth will sound bitterly in your ears.

PETRARCH: Just one word before you begin. Do you thoroughly know the matter you are to touch upon?

S. AUGUSTINE: I have gone into it all carefully beforehand. It is about a mortal woman, in admiring and celebrating whom you have, alas! spent a large part of your life. That a mind like yours should have felt such an insensate passion and for so long a time does greatly astonish me.

PETRARCH: Spare your reproaches, I pray. Thais and Livia were both mortal women; but you should be aware that she of whom you have set out to speak is a mind that has no care for things of earth, and burns only with the love of what is heavenly. In whose face, unless truth is an empty word, a certain divine loveliness shines out; whose character is the image and picture of perfect honour; whose voice and the living expression of whose eyes has nothing mortal in it; whose very form and motion is not as that of others. Consider this again and again, I entreat you, and I trust you may have understanding in what words to speak.

S. AUGUSTINE: Ah! out of all reason have you grown! Have you then for sixteen long years been feeding with false joys this flame of your heart? Of a truth not longer did Italy once suffer the assaults of her most famous enemy, the great Hannibal; nor did she then endure more frequent onsets of her would-be lover, nor was consumed with more furious fires. You to-day carry within you as hot a flame of passion, you endure as fierce stings. Yet was there found one who forced him to retreat and, though late, to take his leave! But who shall expel this invader from your soul if you yourself forbid him to depart; if you of your own will invite him to stay long with you; if you, unhappy as you are, delight in your own calamity? Far other will be your thoughts when the fatal day shall come that will close for ever those eyes that are now so pleasing to you to look upon; when you shall see that face and those pale limbs changed by death; then you will be filled with shame to have so knit your mortal affections to a perishing body such as this, and what now you so obstinately maintain you will then blush to remember.

PETRARCH: Heaven forbid any such misery. I shall not see your threats fulfilled.

S. AUGUSTINE: They will inevitably come to pass.

PETRARCH: I know it. But the stars in their courses will not so fight against me as to prevent the order of Nature by hastening her death like that. First came I into this world and I shall be first to depart.

S. AUGUSTINE: I think you will not have forgotten that time when you feared the contrary event, and made a song of your beloved as if she were presently to die, a song full of moving sorrow.

PETRARCH: Certainly I remember very well, but the thought that filled me then with grief, and the memory of which makes me shiver, was a jealous indignation at the bare possibility of my outliving her who is the best part of my life and whose presence makes all its sweetness. For that is the motive of that song; I remember it well, and how I was overcome with tears. Its spirit is still with me, if with you perchance are the words.

S. AUGUSTINE: I was not complaining how many tears the fear of her death made you shed, nor of how much grief you felt. I was only concerned that you should realise how this fear of yours in the past may certainly return; and more easily, in that every day is a step nearer to death, and that that fair form, worn by sicknesses and the bearing of many children, has already lost much of its first strength.

PETRARCH: I also am borne down with cares and am worn with age, and in that onward path towards death I have outrun her whom I love.

S. AUGUSTINE: What folly it is to calculate the order of death by that of birth! For what are those sad lamentations of the old but because of the early deaths of their young children? What is it that yonder aged nurse is grieving over but that she sees the loss of her little nursling—

> "Whom some dark day
> Has stripped of his sweet life; and cruel fate
> Snatched from his mother's breast and covered him
> In a too early grave."

In your own case the small number of years by which you have preceded her gives you a very uncertain hope that you will be gone before the fire of your passion shall be extinguished; and yet you indulge the fiction that this order of Nature is unchangeable.

PETRARCH: Not exactly unchangeable, but I pray without ceasing that it may not be changed, and whenever I think of death I remember Ovid's line—

> "Late may her time arrive, and after mine."

S. AUGUSTINE: I can listen to these trifles no more; but since you now admit that she may possibly die before you, I ask what should you say if she really were dead?

PETRARCH: What should I say but that such a calamity would be the climax of all my miseries? Yet I should try and comfort myself with what was past. But may the winds bear away the words from our lips and the hurricane scatter such an omen to the ends of the earth!

S. AUGUSTINE: Ah, blindfold one! you see not yet what foolishness it is so to subject your soul to things of earth, that kindle in it the flames of desire, that have no power to give it rest, that cannot endure; and, while promising to charm you with their sweetness, torment you with perpetual agitations.

PETRARCH: If you have any more effectual remedy, I beg you will point it out. You will never frighten me with talk like this; for I am not, as you suppose, infatuated with any creature that is mortal. You might have known that I have loved her physical charm less than her soul, that what has captivated me has been a life above that of ordinary lives, the witnessing of which has shown me how the blessed live above.

Therefore, since you inquire of me (and the mere question is a torture to listen to) what I should do supposing she were to leave me and be the first to die — well, I should try and console myself in sorrow with Laelius, the wisest of the Romans. With him I should say, "It is her goodness that I loved and that is not dead;" and I would say to myself those other words that he pronounced after the death of him for whom he had conceived an affection surpassing all common affection.

S. AUGUSTINE: You retire to Error's inaccessible fastness, and it will not be easy to dislodge you. But as I notice you are inclined to listen much more patiently to the truth about yourself and her, sing the praises of your darling lady as much as you will, and I will gainsay nothing. Were she a queen, a saint —

"A very goddess, or to Apollo's self
Own sister, or a mother of the nymphs,"

yet all her excellence will in nowise excuse your error.

PETRARCH: Let us see what fresh quarrel you seek with me?

S. AUGUSTINE: It is unquestionably true that oftentimes the loveliest things are loved in a shameful way.

PETRARCH: I have already met that insinuation on a previous occasion. If any one could see the image of the love that reigns in my heart, he would recognise that there is no difference between it and that face that I have praised indeed much, but less by far than it deserves to be praised. I call to witness the spirit of Truth in whose presence we are speaking when I assert that in my love there has never been anything dishonorable, never anything of the flesh, never anything that any man could blame unless it were its mere intensity. And if you add that even so it never passed the line of right, I think a fairer thing could never be conceived.

S. AUGUSTINE: I might reply to you with a word of Cicero and tell you, "You are talking of putting boundary lines in vice itself."

PETRARCH: Not in vice, but in love.

S. AUGUSTINE: But in that very passage he was speaking of love. Do you remember where it occurs?

PETRARCH: Do I remember indeed? Of course I have read it in the *Tusculans*. But he was speaking of men's common love; mine is one by itself.

S. AUGUSTINE: Other people, I fancy, might say the same of theirs; for true it is that in all the passions, and most of all in this, every man interprets his own case favourably, and there is point in the verse though from a common poet —

"To every man his lady,
Then one to me assign;
To every man his love affairs,
And so let me have mine!"

PETRARCH: Would you like, if you have time, to hear me tell you a few of those many charms of hers that would strike you with astonishment and admiration?

S. AUGUSTINE: Do you think I am ignorant of all

"Those pleasant dreams that lovers use to weave"?

Every schoolboy knows the line, but I confess I am ashamed to hear such silliness from the lips of one whose words and thoughts should seek a higher range.

PETRARCH: One thing I will not keep silence on,—call it silliness, call it gratitude, as you please,—namely, that to her I owe whatever I am, and I should never have attained such little renown and glory as I have unless she by the power of this love had quickened into life the feeble germ of virtue that Nature had sown in my heart. It was she who turned my youthful soul away from all that was base, who drew me as it were by a grappling chain, and forced me to look upwards. Why should you not believe it? It is a sure truth that by love we grow like what we love. Now there is no backbiter alive, let his tongue be as sharp as it may, that has ventured to touch her good name, or dared to say he had seen a single fault, I will not say in her conduct, but even in any one of her gestures or words. Moreover, those whisperers who leave no one's reputation untouched if they can help it, have been obliged in her case to utter only reverence and respect.

It is no wonder, then, if such a glory as hers should have fostered in my heart the longing for more conspicuous glory, and should have sweetened those hard toils which I had to endure if I would attain that which I desired. What were all the wishes of my youth but solely to please her who above all others had pleased me? And you are not ignorant that to gain my end I scorned delights a thousand times, I gave myself before my time to labour and to cares without number; and now you bid me forget or diminish somewhat of my love for her who first taught me how to escape the vulgar crowd, who guided all my steps, spurred on my lagging mind, and wakened into life my drowsy spirit.

S. AUGUSTINE: Poor man! you would have done better to be silent than to speak, although even if you had been silent I should have discerned what you are within. But such stout words as these stir my indignation and anger.

PETRARCH: I wonder why?

S. AUGUSTINE: To have a false opinion shows ignorance, but to keep on boldly proclaiming it shows pride as well as ignorance.

PETRARCH: Suppose you try and prove that what I think and say is false.

S. AUGUSTINE: It is all false; and, first, what you say as to owing all you are to her. If you mean that she has made you what you are, there you certainly lie; but if you were to say that it is she who has prevented you being any more than you are, you would speak the truth. O what long contention would you have been spared if by the charm of her beauty she had not held you back. What you are you owe to the bounty of Nature; what you might have been she has quite cut off, or rather let me say you yourself have cut it off, for she indeed is innocent. That beauty which seemed so charming and so sweet, through the burning flame of your desire, through the continual rain of your tears, has done away all that harvest that should have grown from the seeds of virtue in your soul. It is a false boast of yours that she has held you back from base things; from some perhaps she may, but only to plunge you into evils worse still. For if one leads you from some miry path to bring you to a precipice, or in lancing some small abscess cuts your throat, he deserves not the name of deliverer but assassin. Likewise she whom you hold up as your guide, though she drew you away from some base courses, has none the less overwhelmed you in a deep gulf of splendid ruin. As for her having taught you to look upwards and separate yourself from the vulgar crowd, what else is it than to say by sitting at her feet you became so infatuated with the charm of her above as to studiously neglect everything else?

And in the common intercourse of human life what can be more injurious than that? when you say she has involved you in toils without number, there indeed you speak truth. But what great gain is there in that? When there are such varied labours that a man is perforce obliged to engage in, what madness is it of one's own accord to go after fresh ones! As for your boasting that it is she who has made you thirst for glory, I pity your delusion, for I will prove to you that of all the burdens of your soul there is none more fatal than this. But the time for this is not yet come.

PETRARCH: I believe the readiest of warriors first threatens and then strikes. I seem, however, to find threat and wound together. And already I begin to stagger.

S. AUGUSTINE: How much more will you stagger when I deliver my sharpest thrust of all? Forsooth that woman to whom you profess you owe everything, she, even she, has been your ruin.

PETRARCH: Good Heavens! How do you think you will persuade me of that?

S. AUGUSTINE: She has detached your mind from the love of heavenly things and has inclined your heart to love the creature more than the Creator: and that one path alone leads, sooner than any other, to death.

PETRARCH: I pray you make no rash judgment. The love which I feel for her has most certainly led me to love God.

S. AUGUSTINE: But it has inverted the true order.

PETRARCH: How so?

S. AUGUSTINE: Because every creature should be dear to us because of our love for the Creator. But in your case, on the contrary, held captive by the charm of the creature, you have not loved the Creator as you ought. You have admired the Divine Artificer as though in all His works He had made nothing fairer than the object of your love, although in truth the beauty of the body should be reckoned last of all.

PETRARCH: I call Truth to witness as she stands here between us, and I take my conscience to witness also, as I said before, that the body of my lady has been less dear to me than her soul. The proof of it is here, that the further she has advanced in age (which for the beauty of the body is a fatal thunderstroke) the more firm has been my admiration; for albeit the flower of her youth has withered visibly with time, the beauty of her soul has grown with the years, and as it was the beginning of my love for her, even so has it been its sustainer. Otherwise if it had been her bodily form which attracted me, it was, ere this, time to make a change.

S. AUGUSTINE: Are you mocking me? Do you mean to assert that if the same soul had been lodged in a body ill-formed and poor to look upon, you would have taken equal delight therein?

PETRARCH: I dare not say that. For the soul itself cannot be discerned, and the image of a body like that would have given no indication of such a soul. But were it possible for the soul to be visible to my gaze, I should most certainly have loved its beauty even though its dwelling-place were poor.

S. AUGUSTINE: You are relying on mere words; for if you are only able to love that which is visible to your gaze, then what you love is the bodily form. However, I deny not that her soul and her character have helped to feed your flame, for (as I will show you before long) her name alone has both little and much kindled your mad passion; for, as in all the affections of the soul, it happens most of all in this one that oftentimes a very little spark will light a great fire.

PETRARCH: I see where you would drive me. You want to make me say with Ovid—

"I love at once her body and her soul."

S. AUGUSTINE: Yes, and you ought to confess this also, that neither in one or the other case has your love been temperate or what it should be.

PETRARCH: You will have to put me to the torture ere I will make any such confession.

S. AUGUSTINE: And you will allow that this love has also cast you into great miseries.

PETRARCH: Though you place me on the block itself, I will not acknowledge any such thing.

S. AUGUSTINE: If you do not ignore my questions and conclusions, you will soon make both those confessions. Tell me, then, can you recall the years when you were a little child, or have the crowding cares of your present life blotted all that time out?

PETRARCH: My childhood and youth are as vividly before my eyes as if they were yesterday.

S. AUGUSTINE: Do you remember, then, how in those times you had the fear of God, how you thought about Death, what love you had for Religion, how dear goodness and virtue were to you?

PETRARCH: Yes, I remember it all, and I am sorry when I see that as my years increased these virtues grew less and less in me.

S. AUGUSTINE: For my part I have ever been afraid lest the wind of Spring should cut that early blossom off, which, if only it might be left whole and unhurt, would have produced a wondrous fruitage.

PETRARCH: Pray do not wander from the subject; for what has this to do with the question we were discussing?

S. AUGUSTINE: I will tell you. Recall each step in your life, since your remembrance is so complete and fresh; recall all the course of your life, and recollect at what period this great change you speak of began.

PETRARCH: I have run over in my mind all the course and number of my years.

S. AUGUSTINE: And what do you find?

PETRARCH: I see that the doctrine in the treatise of Pythagoras, of which I have heard tell and have read, is by no means void of truth. For when travelling the right road, still temperate and modest, I had reached the parting of the ways and had been bidden to turn to the right hand, whether from carelessness or perversity I know not, behold I turned to the left; and what I had read in my boyhood was of no profit to me—

> "Here the ways part: the right will thee conduct
> To the walled palace of the mighty King
> And to Elysium, but the left will lead
> Where sin is punished and the malefactor
> Goes to his dreaded doom."

Although I had read of all this before, yet I understood it not until I found it by experience. Afterwards I went wrong, in this foul and crooked pathway, and often in mind went back with tears and sorrow, yet could not keep the right way; and it was when I left that way, yes, that was certainly the time when all this confusion in my life began.

S. AUGUSTINE: And in what period of your age did this take place?

PETRARCH: About the middle of my growing youth. But if you give me a minute or two, I think I can recall the exact year when it took place.

S. AUGUSTINE: I do not ask for the precise date, but tell me about when was it that you saw the form and feature of this woman for the first time?

PETRARCH: Never assuredly shall I forget that day.

S. AUGUSTINE: Well now, put two and two together; compare the two dates.

PETRARCH: I must confess in truth they coincide. I first saw her and I turned from my right course at one and the same time.

S. AUGUSTINE: That is all I wanted. You became infatuated. The unwonted dazzle blinded your eyes, so I believe. For they say the first effect of love is blindness. So one reads in the poet most conversant with Nature—

> "At the first sight was that Sidonian dame
> Blinded,"

and then he adds presently—

"With love was Dido burning."

And though, as you well know, the story is but an ancient fable, yet did the Poet in making it follow the order of Nature.

And when you had been struck blind by this meeting, if you chose the left-hand path it was because to you it seemed more broad and easy; for that to the right is steep and narrow, and of its hardship you were afraid. But that woman so renowned, whom you imagine as your most safe guide, wherefore did not she direct you upward, hesitating and trembling as you were? Why did she not take you by the hand as one does the blind, and set you in the way where you should walk?

PETRARCH: She certainly did so, as far as it was in her power. What but this was in her heart when, unmoved by my entreaties, unyielding to my caress, she safeguarded her woman's honour, and in spite of her youth and mine, in spite of a thousand circumstances that would have bent a heart of adamant, she stood her ground, resolute and unsubdued? Yes, this womanly soul taught me what should be the honour and duty of a man; and to preserve her chastity she did, as Seneca expresses it—

"What was to me at once an example and a reproach."

And at last, when she saw the reins of my chariot were broken and that I was rushing to the abyss, she chose rather to part from me than follow where I went.

S. AUGUSTINE: Base desires, then, sometimes you felt, though not long since you denied it? But it is the common folly of lovers, let me say of mad folk. One may say of them all alike—

"I would not, yet I would; I would, yet would not."

You know not, any of you, what you want or what you want not.

PETRARCH: Without seeing, I fell into the snare. But if in past days my feelings were other than they are now, love and youth were the cause. Now I know what I wish and what I desire, and I have at last made firm my staggering soul. She for her part has ever been firm in her mind and always the same. The more I understand this woman's constancy, the more I admire it; and if sometimes I regretted her resolution, now I rejoice in it and give her thanks.

S. AUGUSTINE: It is not easy to believe a man who has once taken you in. You may have changed the outside fashion of your life, but have not yet persuaded me that your soul is also changed.

If your flame is calmed and softened somewhat, yet it is not for certain quite put out. But you who set such price on her you love, do you not see how deeply by absolving her you condemn yourself? You delight in seeing in her the model of purity, and you avow yourself to be without any feeling and a criminal; and you protest that she is the most happy of women, while her love has made you the most unhappy of men. If you remember, it is just what I said at the beginning.

PETRARCH: Yes, I remember. I cannot deny that what you say is true, and I see whither you are gradually leading me.

S. AUGUSTINE: To see it better still, lend me all your attention. Nothing so much leads a man to forget or despise God as the love of things temporal, and most of all this passion that we call love; and to which, by the greatest of all desecrations, we even gave the name of God, without doubt only that we may throw a heavenly veil over our human follies and make a pretext of divine inspiration when we want to commit an enormous trangression. In the case of the other passions, the sight of the object, the hope of enjoying it, and the ardour of the will take us captive. Love also demands all that, but in addition it asks also a reciprocal passion, without which it will be forced to die away. So, whereas in the other cases one loves singly and alone, in this case we must give love for love, and thus man's heart is stung and stung again. Therefore, Cicero was right when he wrote that "Of all the passions of the soul, assuredly the most violent is love," and he must have been very certain of his ground when he added that "assuredly"—he who in four books shows he was aware how Plato's Academy doubted everything.

PETRARCH: I have often noticed that reference, and wondered that of the passions he should call this the most violent of all.

S. AUGUSTINE: Your surprise would have vanished if you had not lost your powers of memory. But I must recall you by a short admonition to a recollection of its many evils. Think what you were when that plague seized upon your soul; how suddenly you fell to bemoaning, and came to such a pitch of wretchedness that you felt a morbid pleasure in feeding on tears and sighs. Passing sleepless nights, and murmuring ever the name of your beloved, scorning everything, hating life, desiring death, with a melancholy love for being alone, avoiding all your fellow-men, one might well apply to you, for they exactly fit your case, the lines in which Homer describes Bellerophon—

> "There in the pleasant fields he wandered sad,
> Eating his heart, far from the ways of men."

What meant that pale face and wasted figure? that flower of your age withering before its time, those heavy eyes, ever bathed in tears, your mind in a state of agitation, your broken rest and troubled moans, even when you were asleep? Why was your voice weak and altered through your sorrow of heart, and the very sound of your words, indistinct and broken, with whatever other token can be imagined, of a heart distressed and in disorder? Do you call these the signs of one in good health? Was it not this lady with whom for you every day, whether feast or fast, began and ended? Was it not at her coming the sun shone forth, and when she left you, night returned? Every change of her countenance brought a change in your heart; and if she were sad, you forthwith were filled with sadness. In a word, your life became wholly dependent upon hers.

You know that I say but what is true and what is in every one's mouth.

And what could be more senseless than that, not content with the presence of her living face, the cause of all your woes, you must needs obtain a painted picture by an artist of high repute, that you might carry it everywhere with you, to have an everlasting spring of tears, fearing, I suppose, lest otherwise their fountain might dry up? Of all such things you were only too vigilant, and you neglected everything else. But to come to that which is the very crowning instance of your folly, and of which I gave you warning a little while ago, who could sufficiently utter his indignation and amazement at this sign of a distempered mind, that, infatuated as much by the beauty of her name as of her person, you have with perfectly incredible silliness paid honour to anything that has the remotest connection with that name itself? Had you any liking for the laurel of empire or of poetry, it was forsooth because the name they bore was hers; and from this time onwards there is hardly a verse from your pen but in it you have made mention of the laurel, as if indeed you were a denizen of Peneus' stream, or some priest on Cirrha's Mount.

And finally, discovering that the laurel of empire was beyond your reach, you have, with as little self-restraint as you showed in the case of your beloved herself, now coveted the laurel of Poetry of which the merit of your works seemed to give more promise.

Although to gain your reward you were borne up on the wings of genius, yet will you shudder to remember with what trouble you attained it. I clearly divine what excuse you will make, and I see your thought the moment you open your lips. You will allege that you were devoted to these studies some time before you became a lover at all, and that desire for the glory of the poet's crown had kindled your heart from childhood. I neither deny it or forget it; but the fact of the usage being obsolete for centuries, and this being an epoch very unfavourable for studies like yours, the dangers also of long voyages, which would have brought you to the threshold of prison and of death itself, not to mention other obstacles of fortune no less violent than those — all these difficulties, I say, would perhaps have broken your resolve entirely, if the remembrance of a name so sweet, always entwining itself with your inmost soul, had not banished every other care, and drawn you over sea, over land, across mountains of difficulty, to Rome and to Naples, where at length you attained what you had longed for with such ardour. If all this seems to you the token of but a moderate passion, then at least I shall be quite certain you are the victim of no moderate delusion.

I purposely leave out what Cicero was not ashamed to imitate from Terence when he wrote, "Wrongs, suspicions, fierce quarrels, jealousies, war, and then again peace — behold the miseries of love." Do you not recognize at once in his words the madness and, above all, the madness of jealousy which, as one knows too well, is the ruling power in love, as love is the ruling passion among all others?

Perhaps you may reply: "I admit it is so, but reason will be there to temper such excess." Terence himself had anticipated your answer when he added —

> "Such fickle things to settle by sane rule
> Is to be sanely insane."

The phrase, the truth of which you will scarcely question, puts an end, unless I am mistaken, to all those subterfuges of yours.

Such, then, are the miseries of love, the particulars of which it is needless to mention to those who have proved them, and which would not be believed by those who never tried. But the worst of them all, to come back to our subject, is that it engenders a forgetfulness of God and of man's real state. For how should the soul thus crushed beneath these weights ever arise to that one and only most pure fountain of true Good? And since it is so, you may lay aside your wonder that Cicero should tell us no passion of man's soul seemed to him more violent than love.

PETRARCH: I must own myself beaten; for it appears all you have said is taken from the very heart of the book of experience. And as you have quoted from the play of Terence, let me please myself by bringing from there also this sad complaint —

> "O deed of shame! now am I full of woe.
> Weary I burn with love; with open eyes,
> Brain clear, I am undone; and what to do
> I know not."

I would also call to mind this counsel from the same poet's words —

> "Think, while there's time, again and yet again."

S. AUGUSTINE: And I likewise from the lips of Terence will give you my reply —

> "What in itself contains no rule or reason,
> By rule or reason you can never hold."

PETRARCH: What is to be done, then? Am I to despair?

S. AUGUSTINE: That is the last thing in the world to do. However, let me briefly tell you the remedy I propose.

* * * * *

S. AUGUSTINE: Ambition still has too much hold on you. You seek too eagerly the praise of men, and to leave behind you an undying name.

PETRARCH: I freely confess it. I cannot beat down that passion in my soul. For it, as yet, I have found no cure.

S. AUGUSTINE: But I greatly fear lest this pursuit of a false immortality of fame may shut for you the way that leads to the true immortality of life.

PETRARCH: That is one of my fears also, but I await your discovering to me the means to save my life; you, of a truth, will do it, who have furnished me with means for the healing of evils greater still.

S. AUGUSTINE: Think not that any of your ills is greater than this one, though I deny not that some may be more vile.

But tell me, I pray you, what in your opinion is this thing called glory, that you so ardently covet?

PETRARCH: I know not if you ask me for a definition. But if so, who so capable to give one as yourself?

S. AUGUSTINE: The name of glory is well enough known to you; but to the real thing, if one may judge by your actions, you are a stranger. If you had known what it is you would not long for it so eagerly. Suppose you define glory, with Cicero, as being "the illustrious and world-wide renown of good services rendered to one's fellow citizens, to one's country, or to all mankind"; or as he expresses it elsewhere, "Public opinion uttering its voice about a man in words of praise." You will notice that in both these cases glory is said to be reputation. Now, do you know what this reputation is?

PETRARCH: I cannot say any good description of it occurs to me at the moment; and I shrink from putting forward things I do not understand. I think, therefore, the truer and better course is for me to keep silence.

S. AUGUSTINE: You act like a wise and modest man. In every serious question, and especially when the matter is ambiguous, one should pay much less attention to what one will say than to what one will not say, for the credit of having said well is something much less than the discredit of having said ill. Now I submit to you that reputation is nothing but talk about some one, passing from mouth to mouth of many people.

PETRARCH: I think your definition, or, if you prefer the word, your description, is a good one.

S. AUGUSTINE: It is, then, but a breath, a changing wind; and, what will disgust you more, it is the breath of a crowd. I know to whom I am speaking. I have observed that no man more than you abhors the manners and behaviour of the common herd. Now see what perversity is this! You let yourself be charmed with the applause of those whose conduct you abominate; and may Heaven grant you are only charmed, and that you put not in their power your own everlasting welfare! Why and wherefore, I ask, this perpetual toil, these ceaseless vigils, and this intense application to study? You will answer, perhaps, that you seek to find out what is profitable for life. But you have long since learned what is needful for life and for death.

What was now required of you was to try and put in practice what you know, instead of plunging deeper and deeper into laborious inquiries, where new problems are always meeting you, and insoluble mysteries, in which you never reach the end. Add to which the fact that you keep toiling and toiling to satisfy the public; wearying yourself to please the very people who, to you, are the most displeasing; gathering now a flower of poesy, now of history — in a word, employing all your genius of words to tickle the ears of the listening throng.

PETRARCH: I beg your pardon, but I cannot let that pass without saying a word. Never since I was a boy have I pleased myself with elegant extracts and flowerets of literature. For often have I noted what neat and excellent things Cicero has uttered against butchers of books, and especially, also, the phrase of Seneca in which he declares, "It is a disgrace for a man to keep hunting for flowers and prop himself up on familiar quotations, and only stand on what he knows by heart."

S. AUGUSTINE: In saying what I did, I neither accuse you of idleness nor scant memory. What I blame you for is that in your reading you have picked out the more flowery passages for the amusement of your cronies, and, as it were, packed up boxes of pretty things out of a great heap, for the benefit of your friends — which is nothing but pandering to a desire of vainglory; and, moreover, I say that, not being contented with your duty of every day (which, in spite of great expense of time, only promised you some celebrity among your contemporaries), you have let your thoughts run on ages of time and given yourself up to dreams of fame among those who come after. And in pursuit of this end, putting your hand to yet greater tasks, you entered on writing a history from the time of King Romulus to that of the Emperor Titus, an enormous undertaking that would swallow up an immensity of time and labour. Then, without waiting till this was finished, goaded by the pricks of your ambition for glory, you sailed off in your poetical barque towards Africa; and now on the aforesaid books of your *Africa* you are hard at work, without relinquishing the other. And in this way you devote your whole life to those two absorbing occupations — for I will not stop to mention the countless others that come in also — and throw utterly away what is of most concern and which, when lost, cannot be recovered. You write books on others, but yourself you quite forget. And who knows but what, before either of your works be finished, Death may snatch the pen from your tired hand, and while in your insatiable hunt for glory you hurry on first by one path, then the other, you may find at last that by neither of them have you reached your goal?

PETRARCH: Fears of that kind have sometimes come over me, I confess. And knowing I suffered from grave illness, I was afraid death might not be far off. Nothing then was more bitter to me than the thought of leaving my *Africa* half finished. Unwilling that another hand should put the finishing touch, I had determined that with my own I would cast it to the flames, for there was none of my friends whom I could trust to do me this service after I was gone. I knew that a request like that was the only one of our Virgil's which the Emperor Caesar Augustus declined to grant. To make a long story short, this land of Africa, burnt already by that fierce sun to which it is for ever exposed, already three times by the Roman torches devastated far and wide, had all but yet again, by my hands, been made a prey to the flames.

But of that we will say no more now, for too painful are the recollections that it brings.

S. AUGUSTINE: What you have said confirms my opinion. The day of reckoning is put off for a short time, but the account remains still to be paid. And what can be more foolish than thus to waste such enormous labor over a thing of uncertain issue? I know what prevents you abandoning the work is simply that you still hope you may complete it. As I see that there will be some difficulty (unless I am mistaken) in getting you to diminish this hope, I propose we try to magnify it and so set it out in words that you will see how disproportionate it is to toils like yours. Suppose, therefore, that you have full abundance of time, leisure, and freedom of mind; let there be no failure of intellect, no languor of body, none of those mischances of fortune which, by checking the first onrush of expression, so often stop the ready writer's pen; let all things go better even than you had dared to wish — still, what considerable work do you expect to achieve?

PETRARCH: Oh, certainly, one of great excellence, quite out of the common and likely to attract attention.

S. AUGUSTINE: I have no wish to seem contradictory: let us suppose it may be a work of great excellence. But if you knew of what greater excellence still is the work which this will hinder, you would abhor what you now desire. For I will go so far as to assert that this work of yours is, to begin with, taking off your attention from cares of a nobler kind; and, greatly excellent as you think it, has no wide scope nor long future before it, circumscribed as it must be by time and space.

PETRARCH: Well do I know that old story bandied about by the philosophers, how they declare that all the earth is but a tiny point, how the soul alone endures for infinite millions of years, how fame cannot fill either the earth or the soul, and other paltry pleas of this sort, by which they try to turn minds aside from the love of glory. But I beg you will produce some more solid arguments than these, if you know any; for experience has shown me that all this is more specious than convincing. I do not think to become as God, or to inhabit eternity, or embrace heaven and earth. Such glory as belongs to man is enough for me. That is all I sigh after. Mortal myself, it is but mortal blessings I desire.

S. AUGUSTINE: Oh, if that is what you truly mean, how wretched are you! If you have no desire for things immortal, if no regard for what is eternal, then you are indeed wholly of the earth earthy: then all is over for you; no hope at all is left.

PETRARCH: Heaven defend me from such folly! But my conscience is witness, and knows what have been my desires, that never have I ceased to love with burning zeal the things eternal. I said — or if, perchance, I am mistaken, I intended to say — that my wish was to use mortal things for what they were worth, to do no violence to nature by bringing to its good things a limitless and immoderate desire, and so to follow after human fame as knowing that both myself and it will perish.

S. AUGUSTINE: There you speak as a wise man. But when you declare you are willing to rob yourself of the riches that will endure merely for the sake of what you own is a perishing breath of applause — then you are a fool indeed.

PETRARCH: True, I may be postponing those riches, but not relinquishing them altogether.

S. AUGUSTINE: But how dangerous is such delay, remembering that time flies fast and how uncertain our short life is. Let me ask you a question, and I beg you to answer it. Suppose that He who alone can fix our time of life and death were this day to assign you one whole year, and you had the definite certainty of it — how would you propose to use that year?

PETRARCH: Assuredly I should use great economy of time, and be extremely careful to employ it on serious things; and I suppose no man alive would be so insolent or foolish as to answer your question in any other way.

S. AUGUSTINE: You have answered rightly. And yet the folly men display in this case is matter of astonishment, not to me only but to all those who have ever written on this subject. To set forth what they feel, they have combined every faculty they possess and employed all their eloquence, and even then the truth itself will leave their utmost efforts far behind.

PETRARCH: I fear I do not understand the motive of so great astonishment.

S. AUGUSTINE: It is because you are covetous of uncertain riches and altogether wasteful of those which are eternal, doing the very contrary of what you ought to do, if you were not quite devoid of wisdom.

So this space of a year, though short enough indeed, being promised you by Him who deceives not, neither is deceived, you would partition out and dissipate on any kind of folly, provided you could keep the last hour for the care of your salvation! The horrible and hateful madness of you all is just this, that you waste your time on ridiculous vanities, as if there were enough and to spare, and though you do not in the least know if what you have will be long enough for the supreme necessities of the soul in face of death. The man who has one year of life possesses something certain though short; whereas he who has no such promise and lies under the power of death (whose stroke may fall at any moment), which is the common lot of all men — this man, I say, is not sure of a year, a day; no, not even of one hour. He who has a year to live, if six months shall have slipped away, will still have another half-year left to run; but for you, if you lose the day that now is, who will promise you to-morrow?

It is Cicero who says: "It is certain that we must die: what is uncertain is whether it will be to-day; and there is none so young that he can be sure he will live until the evening." I ask, then, of you, and I ask it likewise of all those who stand gaping after the future and pay no heed to the present, "Who knows if the high gods will add even one morrow to this your little day of life?"

PETRARCH: If I am to answer for myself and for all: No one knows, of a truth. But let us hope for a year at least; on which, if we are still to follow Cicero, even the most aged reckons!

S. AUGUSTINE: Yes; and, as he also adds, not old men only but young ones too are fools in that they cherish false hope, and promise themselves uncertain goods as though they were certain.

But let us take for granted (what is quite impossible) that the duration of life will be long and assured: still, do you not find it is the height of madness to squander the best years and the best parts of your existence on pleasing only the eyes of others and tickling other men's ears, and to keep the last and worst — the years that are almost good for nothing — that bring nothing but distaste for life and then its end — to keep these, I say, for God and yourself, as though the welfare of your soul were the last thing you cared for?

Even supposing the time were certain, is it not reversing the true order to put off the best to the last?

PETRARCH: I do not think my way of looking at it is so unreasonable as you imagine. My principle is that, as concerning the glory which we may hope for here below, it is right for us to seek while we are here below. One may expect to enjoy that other more radiant glory in heaven, when we shall have there arrived, and when one will have no more care or wish for the glory of earth. Therefore, as I think, it is in the true order that mortal men should first care for mortal things; and that to things transitory things eternal should succeed; because to pass from those to these is to go forward in most certain accordance with what is ordained for us, although no way is open for us to pass back again from eternity to time.

S. AUGUSTINE: O man, little in yourself, and of little wisdom! Do you, then, dream that you shall enjoy every pleasure in heaven and earth, and everything will turn out fortunate and prosperous for you always and everywhere? But that delusion has betrayed thousands of men thousands of times, and has sunk into hell a countless host of souls. Thinking to have one foot on earth and one in heaven, they could neither stand here below nor mount on high. Therefore they fell miserably, and the moving breeze swept them suddenly away, some in the flower of their age, and some when they were in midst of their years and all their business.

And do you suppose what has befallen so many others may not befall you? Alas! if (which may God forefend!) in the midst of all your plans and projects you should be cut off — what grief, what shame, what remorse (then too late!) that you should have grasped at all and lost all!

PETRARCH: May the Most High in His mercy save me from that misery!

S. AUGUSTINE: Though Divine Mercy may deliver a man from his folly, yet it will not excuse it. Presume not upon this mercy overmuch. For if God abhors those who lose hope, He also laughs at those who in false hope put their trust. I was sorry when I heard fall from your lips that phrase about despising what you called the old story of the philosophers on this matter. Is it, then, an old story, pray, by figures of geometry, to show how small is all the earth, and to prove it but an island of little length and width? Is it an old story to divide the earth into five zones, the largest of which, lying in the centre, is burned by the heat of the sun, and the two utmost, to right and left, are a prey to binding frost and eternal snow, which leave not a corner where man can dwell; but those other two, between the middle and two utmost zones, are inhabited by man? Is it an old story that this habitable part is divided again into two parts, whereof one is placed under your feet, guarded by a vast sea, and the other is left you to inhabit everywhere, or, according to some authorities, is again in two parts subdivided, with but one part habitable and the other surrounded by the winding intricacies of the Northern Ocean, preventing all access to it? As to that part under your feet, called the antipodes, you are aware that for a long time the most learned men have been of two opinions whether it is inhabited or not: for myself, I have set forth my opinion in the book called *The City of God,* which you have doubtless read. Is it also an old story that your habitable part, already so restricted, is yet further diminished to such an extent by seas, marshes, forests, sand and deserts, that the little corner left you, of which you are so proud, is brought down to almost nothing? And, finally, is it an old story to point out to you that on this narrow strip, where you dwell, there are divers kinds of life, different religions which oppose one another, different languages and customs, which render it impossible to make the fame of your name go far?

But if these things are to you nought but fables, so, to me, all I had promised myself of your future greatness must be a fable also; for I had thought, hitherto, that no man had more knowledge of these things than you yourself. To say nothing of the conceptions of Cicero and Virgil and other systems of knowledge, physical or poetic, of which you seemed to have a competent knowledge, I knew that not long since, in your *Africa,* you had expressed the very same opinions in these pretty lines—

> "The Universe itself is but an isle
> Confined in narrow bounds, small, and begirt
> By Ocean's flowing waves."

You have added other developments later on, and now that I know you think them all fables, I am astonished you have put them forth with such hardihood.

What shall I say now of the brief existence of human fame, the short, short span of time, when you know too well how small and recent even the oldest memory of man is if compared to eternity? I spare to call to your mind those opinions of the men of old, laid up in Plato's *Timaeus* and in the sixth book of Cicero's *Republic,* where it is foretold what floods and conflagrations shall be coming not seldom on the earth. To many men such things have seemed probable; but they wear a different aspect to those who, like yourself, have come to know the true religion.

And besides these, how many other things there are that militate against, I do not say the eternity, but even the survival of one's name. First there is the death of those with whom one has passed one's life; and that forgetfulness which is the common bane of old age: then there is the rising fame, ever growing greater, of new men; which always, by its freshness, is somewhat derogatory to that of those who went before, and seems to mount up higher just in so far as it can depress this other down. Then you must add, also, that persistent envy which ever dogs the steps of those who embark on any glorious enterprise; and the hatred of Truth itself, and the fact that the very life of men of genius is odious to the crowd. Think, too, how fickle is the judgment of the multitude. And alas for the sepulchres of the dead! to shatter which—

> "The wild fig's barren branch is strong enough,"

as Juvenal has told us.

In your own *Africa* you call this, elegantly enough, "a second death"; and if I may here address to you the same words you have put in the mouth of another—

> "The animated bust and storied urn
> Shall fall, and with them fall thy memory,
> And thou, my son, thus taste a second death."

Lo, then, how excellent, how undying that glory must be which the fall of one poor stone can bring to nought!

And, then, consider the perishing of books wherein your name has been written, either by your own hand or another's. Even though that perishing may appear so much more delayed as books outlast monuments, nevertheless it is sooner or later inevitable; for, as is the case with everything else, there are countless natural or fortuitous calamities to which books are ever exposed. And even if they escape all these, they, like us, grow old and die—

> "For whatsoever mortal hand has made,
> With its vain labour, shall be mortal too,"

if one may be allowed, for choice, to refute your childish error by your own words.

What need to say more? I shall never cease to bring to your recollection lines of your own making which only too truly fit the case.

"When your books perish you shall perish too;
This is the third death, still to be endured."

And now you know what I think about glory.

Perhaps I have used more words in expressing it than was needful for you or me; and yet fewer, I believe, than the importance of the subject demands — unless perchance you still think all these things only an old story?

PETRARCH: No indeed. What you have been saying — so far from seeming to me like old stories — has stirred in me a new desire to get rid of my old delusions. For albeit that these things were known to me long ago, and that I have heard them oftentimes repeated, since, as Terence puts it —

"Everything that one can say
Has all been said before,"

nevertheless the stateliness of phrase, the orderly narration, the authority of him who speaks, cannot but move me deeply.

But I have yet a last request to make, which is that you will give me your definite judgment on this point. Is it your wish that I should put all my studies on one side and renounce every ambition, or would you advise some middle course?

S. AUGUSTINE: I will never advise you to live without ambition; but I would always urge you to put virtue before glory. You know that glory is in a sense the shadow of virtue. And therefore, just as it is impossible that your body should not cast a shadow if the sun is shining, so it is impossible also in the light of God Himself that virtues should exist and not make their glory to appear. Whoever, then, would take true glory away must of necessity take away virtue also; and when that is gone man's life is left bare, and only resembles that of the brute beasts that follow headlong their appetite, which to them is their only law. Here, therefore, is the rule for you to live by — follow after virtue, and let glory take care of itself; and as for this, as some one said of Cato, the less you seek it the more you will find it. I must once more allow myself to invoke your own witness —

"Thou shalt do well from Honour's self to flee,
For then shall Honour follow after thee."

Do you not recognise the verse? It is your own. One would surely think that man a fool who at midday should run here and there in the blaze of the sun, wearing himself out to see his shadow and point it out to others; now the man shows no more sense or reason who, amid the anxieties of life, takes huge trouble, first one way, then another, to spread his own glory abroad.

What then? Let a man march steadily to the goal set before him, his shadow will follow him step by step: let him so act that he shall make virtue his prize, and lo! glory also shall be found at his side. I speak of that glory which is virtue's true companion; as for that which comes by other means, whether from bodily grace or mere cleverness, in the countless ways men have invented, it does not seem to me worthy of the name. And so, in regard to yourself, while you are wearing your strength out by such great labours in writing books, if you will allow me to say so, you are shooting wide of the mark. For you are spending all your efforts on things that concern others, and neglecting those that are your own; and so, through this vain hope of glory, the time, so precious, though you know it not, is passing away.

* * * * *

PETRARCH: Ah! would that you had told me all this before I had surrendered myself over to these studies!

S. AUGUSTINE: I have told you, many a time and oft. From the moment when I saw you first take up your pen, I foresaw how short life would be, and how uncertain: how certain, too, and how long the toil. I saw the work would be great and the fruit little, and I warned you of all these things. But your ears were filled with the plaudits of the public, which, to my astonishment, took you captive, although you talked as if you despised them. But as we have now been conferring together long enough, I beg that if any of my counsels have seemed good to you, you will not allow them to come to nothing for want of energy or recollection; and if, on the other hand, I have sometimes been too rough, I pray you take it not amiss.

PETRARCH: Indeed I owe you a deep debt of gratitude, as for many other things, so, especially, for this three days' colloquy; for you have cleansed my darkened sight and scattered the thick clouds of error in which I was involved. And how shall I express my thankfulness to Her also, the Spirit of Truth, who, unwearied by our much talking, has waited upon us to the end? Had She turned away her face from us we should have wandered in darkness: your discourse had then contained no sure truth, neither would my understanding have embraced it. And now, as She and you have your dwelling-place in heaven, and I must still abide on earth, and, as you see, am greatly perplexed and troubled, not knowing for how long this must be, I implore you, of your goodness, not to forsake me, in spite of that great distance which separates me from such as you; for without you, O best of fathers, my life would be but one long sadness, and without Her I could not live at all.

S. AUGUSTINE: You may count your prayer already granted, if you will only to yourself be true: for how shall any one be constant to him who is inconstant to himself?

PETRARCH: I will be true to myself, so far as in me lies. I will pull myself together and collect my scattered wits, and make a great endeavour to possess my soul in patience. But even while we speak, a crowd of important affairs, though only of the world, is waiting my attention.

S. AUGUSTINE: For the common herd of men these may be what to them seem more important; but in reality there is nothing of more importance, and nothing ought to be esteemed of so much worth. For, of other trains of thought, you may reckon them to be not essential for the soul, but the end of life will prove that these we have been engaged in are of eternal necessity.

PETRARCH: I confess they are so. And I now return to attend to those other concerns only in order that, when they are discharged, I may come back to these.

I am not ignorant that, as you said a few minutes before, it would be much safer for me to attend only to the care of my soul, to relinquish altogether every bypath and follow the straight path of the way of salvation. But I have not strength to resist that old bent for study altogether.

S. AUGUSTINE: We are falling into our old controversy. Want of will you call want of power. Well, so it must be, if it cannot be otherwise. I pray God that He will go with you where you go, and that He will order your steps, even though they wander, into the way of truth.

PETRARCH: O may it indeed be as you have prayed! May God lead me safe and whole out of so many crooked ways; that I may follow the Voice that calls me; that I may raise up no cloud of dust before my eyes; and, with my mind calmed down and at peace, I may hear the world grow still and silent, and the winds of adversity die away.

THE LIFE OF SOLITUDE

Translated by Jacob Zeitlin

[Taken from *The Life of Solitude by Francis Petrarch,* translated by Jacob Zeitlin, University of Illinois Press, 1924.]

THE FIRST BOOK

THE FIRST TRACTATE

Introductory, noting certain things which contribute to the understanding of what follows.

Chapter 1. What is needful for them that desire to enjoy quiet

I believe that a noble spirit will never find repose save in God, in whom is our end, or in himself and his private thoughts, or in some intellect united by a close sympathy with his own. For though pleasure be covered with the most entangling lime and full of sweet and alluring baits, yet has it not the force to detain powerful wings very long upon the ground. But whether we are intent upon God, or upon ourselves and our serious studies, or whether we are seeking for a mind in harmony with our own, it behooves us to withdraw as far as may be from the haunts of men and crowded cities. That I speak truly, perhaps even they will hardly deny who find a charm in the stir and hum of many people, provided they are not so deeply whelmed and sunk in their false notions that they do not at times come to themselves, as it were, and return to the lofty path of truth, if only with a crawling motion. Would this were not the state of so many, and that men had at least as much concern for the cultivation of their minds as of their fields and many less important things; for the human mind teems with errors like a fat field overrun with brambles and if these are not diligently uprooted and with studious toil cleared away, the fruit in both cases will equally perish with the flower. But we sing to deaf ears. Yet, however lightly people in general may regard these matters, men of learning, I am sure, will second me in thought and word; and even if all should oppose me, you [1] at least will not — indeed you would be the first to confute my opponents. You will recognize your own thoughts in my words, and I shall appear to have attained the ultimate goal of all eloquence — to have moved the mind of the listener according to my wish, and that with no trouble. It is a sore task for the pleader when he is bent on dragging over to his own view a

1. In a foreword not here printed, Petrarch addressed this writing to Philip de Cabassolles, Bishop of Cavaillon, in whose diocese Vaucluse was situated.

mind that resists persuasion; but what trouble is there for an argument when it enters the ears of a person whose own thought chimes with what he hears and who, having the evidence of his own experience, in order to yield his assent requires neither concrete examples, nor weighty authority, nor pointed reasoning, but in silence says to himself, "It is true?"

Chapter 2. Of those who have written in praise of the life of solitude and whom the author in this work wished to imitate

I am aware that certain saintly men have written much on this theme. In particular the renowned Basil has composed a little book in praise of the life of solitude — from which I have borrowed nothing but the title. As I have met with it in some very old manuscripts sometimes thrust in among the writings of Peter Damianus, I have been doubtful whether it was the work of Basil or of Peter. But in this treatise I have in a large measure had my sole experience for guide, neither seeking any other leader nor disposed to accept one if he offered himself. For it is with a freer step, though perchance a less secure one, that I pursue my own route than I follow the traces of a stranger. You shall learn more from those who have had greater experience than I or who have searched further into the experience of others; from me you shall only hear whatever the moment may suggest. For I have not applied myself to this undertaking in a fastidious way, nor have I thought it necessary to do so, hardly fearing that matter would be wanting in so fertile a theme — at least in its superficial aspects — especially as I have often treated of it previously and the subject is variously and intimately wrought into my life. I have not composed my books with deliberation nor particularly polished my style, knowing that I am speaking to one who will like me even when I am tangled. Content with faithful and general observations and with a homely discourse, I have drawn forth what you here read partly from the present tenor of my life and partly from a past experience which is yet fresh in my memory. To you I appeal first as witness of these things, being frankly conscious that among the many causes which have won to you my all unforced affection, not the least has been that you were led by a love of solitude and the desire for freedom which accompanies it to flee what is called the Roman Court, now so near — almost adjacent — to you, where you might have attained no mean elevation if that Tartarean din and confusion had offered you as much pleasure as you always derive from blessed solitude.

Chapter 3. Of the manner of treating the substance of this work, and the differences between a life of solitude and a life spent in crowds

It seems to me that I can demonstrate the blessedness of solitude by exhibiting the troubles and afflictions of a populous environment, reviewing the actions of men whom one kind of life preserves in peace and tranquillity and the other kind keeps agitated and careworn and breathless. For there is a single idea underlying all these observations, that one kind of life is attended with happy leisure and the other with grievous worry. But if at any time some marvelous instance or some extraordinary concurrence of nature and chance, properly to be reckoned among miracles, should befall to change my opinion, I shall change it without shame and shall not be afraid to prefer the pleasant and reposeful assemblages of people to a pining and anxious seclusion. For it is not the mere name of solitude but the good things which are proper to it that I praise. And it is not so much the solitary recesses and the silence that delight me as the leisure and freedom that dwell within them. Nor am I so inhuman as to hate men, whom I am instructed by divine commandment to love as I love myself, but I hate the sins of men, especially my own, and the troubles and sad afflictions that reside among crowds. These things, unless I err, can be treated more suggestively not by discoursing separately what can be said on one side and on the other, but by mingling both, touching now this aspect and now the other, as the mind is by turns directed toward either, and, with alternate shift of the eye, as it were, from right to left, easily judges the difference between the very diverse objects which lie side by side. It is with intent that I have placed the bitter first, that I might follow it up with the sweet, and that the pleasanter taste, being felt the last wherever there was a division, should thereby prevail upon the mind.

THE THIRD TRACTATE

Of the difference in the lot of the busy man and the solitary man.

Chapter 2. Almost every busy man is unhappy, though there are some few who are worthily employed

And so, to dismiss the matter once for all, in my opinion practically every busy man is unhappy, and the man who is employed in the service of another is doubly unhappy because he has only his pains for his reward. Now I am not unaware that there have been, and perchance still are, very active men of a saintly nature who themselves go the way of Christ and lead straying souls along the same path. When this happens I acknowledge that it is a great and immeasurable good, a double blessing to be contrasted with the twofold misery of which I have said so much. For what is there more blessed, more worthy of a man, and more like divine goodness than to serve and assist as many as require help? Whoever is able to do so and does not, has repudiated, I think, the glorious duty of humanity and proved false to the name as well as the nature of man. If it should be proved that this is possible, I shall freely subordinate my private inclination to the public welfare and, abandoning the place of retirement in which I consulted only my own humor, I shall venture forth where I can be of use to the world, following the advice given by our Cicero. "It is more in accord with nature," he says, "to emulate the great Hercules and undergo the greatest toil and trouble for the sake of aiding or saving the world, if possible, than to live in seclusion, not only free from all care, but revelling in pleasures and abounding in wealth, while excelling others also in beauty and strength. Thus Hercules denied himself and underwent toil and tribulation for the world, and, out of gratitude for his services, popular belief has given him a place in the council of the gods. The better and more noble, therefore, the character with which a man is endowed, the more does he prefer the life of service to the life of pleasure." So says Cicero, and I yield an unconstrained assent, if things are as he says. But it is my view of the matter that the force of a general truth is not destroyed by a very few exceptional instances. There are many who profess to believe that employment is of general advantage and holier than any kind of retirement. I know. But how many, I ask you, do we see who carry out what they profess? There may be a few or there may be a great many; show me one and I shall hold my peace. I do not deny that there are learned and eloquent men who maintain the opposite view with great subtlety. But it is not so much a question of cleverness in arguing as of conduct. They go about the cities and deliver long harangues in public about vices and virtues. I could barely refrain from inserting here the satirist's biting tooth in a way which would be decidedly to the point, but I recalled to whom I was addressing myself and decided to sacrifice a vanity of style rather than be wanting in true respect. Yet these earnest persons, you observe, say many useful things which often are of advantage to their hearers. I grant it, but the physician is not necessarily in good health when he helps the patient with his advice; in fact, he often dies of the very ailment which he has cured in others. I do not disdain the careful choice and artful composition of words contrived for the salvation of men, and I honor the useful work regardless of the character of the workman, but this is a school of life and not of rhetoric, and our thoughts are now fixed not on the vainglory of eloquence but on the secure repose of the soul.

I am not unmindful of the sentence of Seneca: "Throw aside all hindrances and give up your time to attaining a sound mind," to which he promptly adds, "No man can attain it who is engrossed in other matters." Now what I maintain is not that solitude develops such a mind but that it is conducive to preserving and strengthening it, for I have not forgotten another observation of the same writer to the effect that the place in which one lives does not greatly contribute to one's tranquillity. Be it so, yet doubtless it contributes something. Otherwise why does he say elsewhere that "we ought to select abodes which are wholesome not only for the body but also for the character?" And in still another place he exclaims, "I shall flee far from the very sight and neighborhood of the Forum." For as a severe climate puts to the test even the sturdiest constitution, so there are some situations which are very unwholesome for a well-disposed mind before it has come to full maturity. Whence, pray, is the difference in the soundness of minds and habits of conduct if there is nothing in places? There is something in places, with Seneca's leave I would say a great deal, though not everything. I quite agree with his view that "it is the mind which must make everything agreeable to itself." That is well said, after his fashion. But whence comes the light of truth and right reason? Doubtless from a source without.

Chapter 4. How from the dangers of the shepherd's life it may be inferred that the busy life is less safe, and for that reason the author himself has chosen the retired life

Which mode of life is safer—this, my father, is what I shall examine in my discourse today. Tell me, therefore, if I may take my example from the occupation which I have had occasion to mention, how often does the shepherd lose his life in the course of his duties? How often does he fall into a trap while trying to find a sheep that has strayed, or tumble over a precipice while pursuing one that is running away? How often, do you think, does the healthy physician contract a mortal disease while he is making the round of his patients, or the gravedigger while he is burying the dead encounter the contagion which results in his own death? Let no one deceive himself that the contagions to which the mind is subject are less serious than those of the body; they are in fact more so, they afflict more heavily, they penetrate more deeply, they diffuse themselves more stealthily. But it is creditable, people say, to be helpful to great numbers, it is praiseworthy to be of service to as many as we can. Who denies it? Yet we know where a well-ordered charity begins. Take my word for it, it is a matter of no small assurance to promise aid to the struggling, counsel to the perplexed, light to the blind, joy to the grieving, safety to the terrified, hope to the depressed, health to the sick, rest to the weary, comfort to the afflicted; to show the path to the straying, to place your shoulders beneath the falling and to extend the hand to those that lie prostrate. These are great things if they are performed, trifling if only promised; for a large promise is of no more consequence than a small one, it is only the fulfilment that is more impressive. But I am not so much proposing a rule for others as exposing the principles of my own mind. If it commends itself to anyone, let him follow its suggestion. Whoever does not like it is free to reject it and, leaving us to our solitude, to embrace his own anxious cares and live to his own satisfaction in scorn of our rural retreat. I should not mind, I confess, to be of service to as many as possible or even, in Ovid's words, to be a bearer of health to the entire world; but the first is in the power of only a few, the last of Christ alone. I would yield so far to persons of a contrary opinion as to admit that whoever is in a place of safety sins against the law of nature if he does not offer what aid he can to the struggling. But for me, who have myself been hitherto struggling as in a great shipwreck, it is enough to pray for the aid of him who is alone able to provide aid in our need. My prayers are far-reaching, but I shall be content if they are fulfilled to a moderate degree. I could wish to have everybody, or at least as many as possible, gain salvation with me. But in the end what do you expect me to say? It is enough for me, yea, a cause of great happiness, if I do not perish myself. But for those who profess themselves guardians of the helpless sheep, alas, how much I fear that they are wolves eager to rend them alive.

THE FOURTH TRACTATE

What is proper for those who have decided to embark on the life of solitude.

Chapter 1. The retired life, especially to men unversed in literature, is heavier than death and seems calculated to bring on death

Let me not involve myself too long in reflections not pertinent to my argument, but let each man decide according to his own preference, for it is impossible that it should suit all men to follow a single road in life, even if they were all bound for the same ultimate destination. In this connection each man must seriously take into account the disposition with which nature has endowed him and the bent which by habit or training he has developed. For there are some for whom the life of solitude is more grievous than death and seems calculated to result in death, and this will happen particularly with persons who have no acquaintance with literature. Such men, if they have no one to talk to, are destitute of any resource for communion with themselves or with books, and necessarily remain dumb. And indeed isolation without literature is exile, prison, and torture; supply literature, and it becomes your country, freedom, and delight. "What is sweeter than lettered ease?" is a well known saying of Cicero. Not less familiar is Seneca's sentence, "Leisure without study is death; it is a tomb for the living man." Although I know full well that those two sweet solaces of philosophers, solitude and leisure, as I said at the outset, are at times annoying even to such as have an acquaintance with literature, the reason for it is evident. For with men of this class it sometimes happens that they are fettered by pleasure and in love with their prison, or seek to make their living in traffic with the multitude and in sordid business, or aspire to climb up the slippery steps of honors through the windy suffrages of the populace. For these — and their number in our times is great — literature is not a means of giving cultivation to the mind and refinement to life, but an instrument for procuring wealth. Children are sent by their parents to study literature not as to an academy but as to a market-place, at great expense to the family but with the hope of a much greater financial return, so that it need be no occasion for surprise if they make a venal and avaricious use of an education which they have pursued for purposes of sale and on which they have based the sinful expectation of a usury not of a hundred per cent but a thousand. All these things have to be carefully considered in selecting a mode of life, and so I would not invite to the life of solitude such men as I am describing nor willingly admit them if they came of their own accord. You may infer from this how numerous a lot I should exclude. For what shall a fish do out of water or these fellows at a distance from cities? That is what I formerly said to a certain enervated and effeminate lawyer who had begun to frequent this locality, not from any love of quiet, of which he had not the least notion, nor from any yearning after leisure, which he hated, but only from some itch of imitation. It is a question whether he was a greater nuisance to himself or to me, but he left suddenly, being overcome with the tedium of the place and the craving for the pleasures of the city. If I had not foreseen this outcome I should have withdrawn on my own part, so utterly destitute of conformity were our conditions and our ways of regarding things. It is true that he called himself my friend and that we had engaged since boyhood in the same studies, but our aims were far apart, as the event proved. I return, however, to my purpose.

Chapter 2. Although it were best that every man should recognize in his youth what is the proper kind of life for him, nevertheless if one fails to do it in youth, it is wise that he should at least do it in old age

It were an excellent thing, if want of counsel, the unavoidable concomitant of youth, did not stand in the way, that each one of us at the very beginning of his maturity should give careful and earnest thought to the selection of some particular kind of life, nor ever turn aside from the path he had once chosen, except for important reasons or for some grave necessity. Hercules did so on entering manhood, as is testified by Xenophon, the pupil of Socrates, and by Cicero. But because we fail to do it and live in most cases not by our own judgment but by that of the crowd, and are rushed along over tortuous paths, following the footsteps of others in the dark, we often emerge upon perilous and impassable roads and are carried so far that we have become some thing or other before we have had a chance to look about and consider what we wanted to be. And if one has not been able in youth to reflect on the role which nature or accident or some mistake has thrust upon him, let him ponder it in his old age, and like a wayfarer who has gone astray let him as far as he may look to his safety before nightfall, being assured that the potentialities of his nature cannot be completely suppressed. If a man has been illumined by the celestial light at his very entrance into life, when, as I have already said, not a spark of judgment is active, and has been able to find a safe road or one whose dangers are slight and easily avoided, he has reason for everlasting gratitude to God. For one whose fortune has been less auspicious greater trouble is in store. Yet once he has begun to open his eyes and to understand what a crooked path he is traveling, let him bend all his energy to correct, even though it be in old age, the follies and errors of his youth, and let him recall the old man in Terence, an excellent example of reformation in old age and a source at once of profit and delight. Though the undertaking is not particularly easy, it is notably profitable and by no means impossible. No action should be considered as coming too late when it is recognized as wholesome, and for this view there are some authorities not to be despised. Augustus Caesar, the most philosophical of princes, says, "What is done well enough is done speedily enough," and Plato, the prince of philosophers, says, "Happy is the man whose fortune it is even in old age to attain wisdom and truth."

Chapter 3. What course is to be kept in the order and plan of reformation

In every well-ordered plan for reforming one's life it is especially important to keep in view that we are to be guided not by idle wishes but by our character and predisposition, and that we are to follow not the road which looks most attractive but the one which is best suited to our needs. In this connection I require that a man shall be particularly honest and exacting in passing judgment on himself and not prone to be led astray by the delusive temptations of eye and ear. I know that it has happened to some men that in their admiration for the qualities of others they have lost the consciousness of their own limitations, and attempting actions that are remote from their powers, they have provided matter of mirth to strangers. One admonition that I have derived from the philosophers is that each man should note the relation between his own character and habits and a given mode of life, whether it be the retired life or life in the city or any other manner of life, and understand which is best suited for himself. If this is advantageous to those who are just entering upon life, how much more so must it be to those who have advanced in it, since in addition to the trouble of choosing they are also faced with the task of destroying old and firmly rooted notions. As for me, who, as far as I am aware, have nothing in common with the crowd and whose attainment in literature, while not so great as to puff up the mind, is enough to give it pleasure and to make me a friend of that solitude in which I acquired it without the intervention of a wordy teacher and without obstinate laziness, (would I could say without persecution from envy), whom neither sweetheart nor wife, neither bond nor interest nor guardianship nor chance of profit, neither the rostrum nor the bath, neither the tavern nor the banquet nor the public square could tie down to the city — as for me, I say, whose attitude, to tell the truth, was decided not so much by a deliberate resolve of my own or the advice of others as by a natural prompting of my disposition, my unusually retired life has been not only one of superior tranquillity but also of conspicuous dignity and security. My counsel to other men to take account of their condition is precisely what I have employed in arriving at an understanding of my own. I heartily embrace and cling to solitude and leisure, about which I have conversed with you so much today, as if they were ladders to the level toward which the mind strives to ascend, and I dread crowds and busy cares as though they were bolts and bars to my freedom.

But when some need compels me to dwell in the city, I have learned to create a solitude among people and a haven of refuge in the midst of a tempest, using a device, not generally known, of so controlling the senses that they do not perceive what they perceive. Long after I had developed it into a habit by my own experimentation, I discovered that it was also the advice of a very brilliant and learned writer, and I committed it to memory all the more eagerly because of my joy at finding that a practice of mine was supported by the authority of antiquity. It is Quintilian, in that book in which with great elegance he has put the finishing touches on the education of the orator, previously set forth with such beauty by Cicero, who says: "Study by the lamp, when we come to it fresh and vigorous, is the best kind of retirement. But silence and seclusion, and entire freedom of mind, though in the highest degree desirable, cannot always fall to our lot; and therefore we must not, if any noise disturbs us, immediately throw aside our books, and deplore the day as lost, but we must strive against inconveniences, and acquire such habits, that our application may set all interruptions at defiance; for if we direct our attention, with our whole mental energy, to the work actually before us, nothing of all that strikes our eyes or ears will penetrate into the mind. Does a casual train of thought often cause us not to see persons in our way, and to wander from our road, and shall we not attain the same abstraction if we resolve to do so? We must not yield to excuses for idleness; for if we fancy that we must not study except when we are fresh, except when we are in good spirits, except when we are free from all other cares, we shall always have some reason for self-indulgence. In the midst of crowds, therefore, on a journey, and even at festive meetings, let thought secure for herself privacy."

I have quoted this passage the more gladly because it is not too well known. Seneca's letter on the subject is more familiar, and I shall therefore cite only its conclusion. After discussing at length the way in which the mind of the student should endure the disturbances of the crowd, he finally asks himself, "Is it not sometimes a simpler matter just to avoid the uproar?" And answering his own question, he says, "I admit this. Accordingly I shall change from my present quarters," as if all that he had previously said was only by way of consolation in cases of compulsory sojourn, while his final advice was for voluntary withdrawal. And this is in fact the truth. For I also have found only this recourse in my need, that in the midst of the turmoil of cities I create for myself in thought, as far as I may, an imaginary solitude in some retreat and by an effort of the mind triumph over my situation. This manner of remedy I have often used hitherto, but whether I shall resort to it again I do not know, since the future is always uncertain. Assuredly, if my choice were free, I should seek solitude in her own retreat.

Chapter 4. The praise of solitude

This I have done while I could, and you shall see how eagerly I shall continue to do it. Solitude is indeed something holy, innocent, incorruptible, and the purest of all human possessions. To whom does she reveal herself amid forests, for whom does she display her charms and thorns? Whom, unless it be the fishes, does she deceive with a bait? Whom, apart from wild beasts and birds, does she entangle in her nets and snares? Whom does she allure with song or graceful motion? Whom does she fascinate with her colors? For whom does she weave the purple, to whom does she sell the oil, for whom wreathe garlands of flowery speech? With whom, finally, does she ingratiate herself, whom does she seek to please, except the person who has penetrated the inmost recesses of solitude and for whom therefore there is no solitude? She aims to deceive no one; she neither simulates nor dissimulates; she adorns nothing, she glosses nothing, she pretends nothing. She is utterly naked and unadorned, for she is averse to garish exhibitions and vulgar plaudits such as are poisonous to the life of the spirit and of all things. She has God for sole witness and puts her trust not in the voice of the blind and unreliable multitude but in her own conscience. At times she even reposes small faith in her conscience and remains perplexed, recalling that it is written, "Who can understand his errors?" and again, "If I am perfect, yet would I not know my soul." Nor is she forgetful that "the Lord is good to all and his tender mercies are over all his works," that "the Lord upholdeth all that fall and raiseth up all those that be bowed down," that he is "nigh unto all them that call upon him," that "he has not dealt with us after our sins nor rewarded us according to our iniquities. For as the heaven is high above the earth, so great is his mercy toward them that fear him. As far as the East is from the West, so far hath he removed our transgressions from us." Finally he looks upon us as a father and not as a judge, "Like as a father pitieth his children, so the Lord pitieth them that fear him. For he knoweth our frame, he remembereth that we are dust. As for man, his days are as grass; as a flower of the field, so he flourisheth," and his life is fleeting as a shadow. "But the mercy of the Lord is from everlasting to everlasting," since he has made us and none of the works of his hands is hateful to him. And so while the Scriptures breathe threats on the one hand and extend hope on the other, she remains doubtful of her merit and does not know whether she is deserving of love or hatred, but trembles and hopes and comforts herself with the assurance of the mercy of her king. Thus watchful of the devil's wiles and with her mind fixed on one thing only, she looks about her, and leaning on divine support she makes light of the danger. Thus she is happy and composed and, in a manner of speaking, a fortified citadel and a haven against storms. If any one fails to take advantage of such a refuge what result can he expect but to find himself without a haven, be tossed about in a sea of troubles, live upon rocks, and perish in the waves?

I am not, however, so unreasonable in my attitude or so narrowly attached to my view as to think all others foolish or to compel them to pledge fealty to my doctrine. Many may be brought to profess, but no one can be forced to believe. There is nothing more vital than independence of judgment; as I claim it for myself I would not deny it to others. I grant you (for it is possible) that every man's purpose is honorable and sacred; I would not constitute myself the judge of the deep and hidden mysteries of the human conscience. All men with the grace of God may lead a good life; the infinite clemency spurns none, though it is spurned by many. Even in the practice of human philosophy there are gradations of virtue. Everyone cannot hold the highest place, otherwise all the lower ones would be unoccupied. But all who have determined to lead their life, in whatsoever calling, out of the reach of ill report, must at least keep free from the indecency and sordidness which are generally found in low conditions. To avoid indecency is a duty, to have high aspiration is virtue, to attain it is felicity.

Chapter 5. On the fourfold distinction of virtues introduced by Plotinus and approved by Macrobius

I am not unaware of the celebrated distinction of the virtues into four kinds introduced by Plotinus, the great Platonist, and approved by Macrobius. Even with them, however, the political virtues occupy the lowest stage. These virtues may belong to busy men, but not to all of them, only to those the end of whose activity is their own virtue and, to a much greater extent, the welfare of the state. You see how with a single word the whole enormous host of busy men is reduced to a very small number. The purgatorial virtues occupy the next step above. These are the embellishment of those who, freely forsaking cities, become men of leisure and true followers of philosophy; they eradicate from the mind the passions which are only moderated in the case of the former. The virtues of the third stage are higher than those that are termed the virtues of a purified mind; their property is freedom from those passions which the political virtues have mitigated and the purgatorial ones removed. These are the virtues of perfect men. Where such men are to be found I know not, but if they have ever existed they have surely loved solitude, and if one of them still survives, though with his virtues for a rudder he may sail the high seas in safety, I think nevertheless that he too loves the haven of solitude. The fourth and highest is the place of the exemplary virtues, which are above the reach of man and dwell, as it is said, in the mind of God alone. It is maintained that the three other kinds of human virtue are derived from this fourth as from an immutable pattern, as its very name suggests, or, following Plato, from the ideas of the virtues which along with other ideas Plato fixed in the mind of God. It is not enough to say that these virtues do not exert the same influence on the passions as the others; to utter the word passion in connection with them is the height of profanity and sacrilege. I should have said nothing about them, for they have no connection with my theme, but since the occasion prompted me to say something about the political and purgatorial virtues I did not care to break and untwine the chain which Plotinus had woven with so much art.

Chapter 6. The delight and sweetness of the solitary life and the spiritual conflict of the solitary man

Do you see how I have striven with a roundabout profusion of words to reenter into favor with the man of action? But it is now time to set a limit to these digressions. I shall return to myself and to solitude. I could wish that I had drunk more deeply of its true and intimate sweetness, that I might more confidently converse with you in this discourse. A worldly mind is ashamed to speak of sacred things. Who indeed is able to express in words what he scarcely realizes in thought? It is presumptuous for an earthly—I might say a mere earthly—creature to speak of a life celestial and truly angelic, having been ravished by the sole enchantment of its name and the bare report of its perfection, and, to speak truly, having but faintly smelled its aroma without getting a taste of its flavor. It is exactly as if a shepherd who was born in the woods and brought up in the woods, accustomed to satisfy his thirst in the brook and his hunger on roots, to draw his food from the ground and take his rest in an overgrown cave, should blunder by some accident upon the walls of a vast and opulent city and, while he sits wearily at the entrance and turns his eyes eagerly in all directions and thrusts his gaze into the city itself, actually seeing only the houses of the watchmen or some alley that lies close to the gate, should return to the woods and recount to his friends what he had beheld in that city, in its palaces and streets, its courts and public squares, in the shops of the artisans and the halls of the nobility, and the business that was being transacted in its public and private conferences. Or it is as if one who has barely reached the threshold of some sacred temple should think that he knows in what secret recesses every vestment and holy vessel is kept concealed and understands all the forms of the books, the duties of the priests, and the whole sacred ceremonial. In reality how do I differ from this shepherd, except that he has approached the city or the temple but once while I have paid frequent visits to solitude; he has stood on the outside while I have ventured within; he has departed promptly while I have lingered? And yet what greater certainty have I as to the inner nature of the life of solitude? Caves, hills, and groves lie equally open to everybody; no one blocks the way when you would enter or expels you after you have entered; the wilderness has neither porter nor watchman. But of what avail is it merely to go to a place or to be carried along winding streams? What advantage is there in strolling through woods and what delight in sitting upon mountains, if wherever I go my mind follows me, the same among the woods as in the city? It is the mind that I must lay aside before all; it is the mind, I say, that I must leave at home, humbly imploring the Lord to make my heart pure within me and to establish an upright spirit in my body. Then at last shall I penetrate to the hidden recesses of the solitary life.

As for my present solitude — why should I boast of what I do not possess? It is not that solitary life for which I yearn, although outwardly it bears a near resemblance, being equally withdrawn from the human crowd but not equally emancipated from human passions. Oh, could I but behold that ineffable sweetness which is felt by blessed souls at the remembrance of the struggles they have passed through and the prospect of the joys to come, whether by those who have triumphed over the enemy or by those who, while they have often got the upper hand, have not yet vanquished him completely. These are still called upon to stand in battle array but not without sure hope of triumph, and to fight, not alone, but aided by the company of angels. And when they have put on the armor of God, wearing, if I may imitate the language of the Apostle, "the breast-plate of righteousness," "the shield of faith," "the sword of the spirit," and "the helmet of salvation," they go forth repeatedly to wrestle "against principalities, against powers, against the rulers of the darkness of this world," with no mortal looking on, but before a great presence of heavenly spirits who favor them with their countenance while Christ himself presides over the combat. What a welcome peace to the exhausted mind is there in those sighs rising out of the depths of the soul to highest heaven! What secret relief in the tears gushing from the purest fountain of the heart! What watches and vigils of the soldiers of Christ on the towers of Jerusalem and the ramparts of Zion against the hosts of Babylon as they sing their psalms through the entire night and maintain the guard over their walled encampment, knowing that they are in a strong and well fortified place where neither food nor drink is lacking, believing that while they may be assailed by the stratagems of the enemy, they cannot be overcome, and feeling themselves so exalted in grace that the fiercest onslaughts of the foe are a boon to them and a punishment to the assailants, as an action which is superfluous with regard to our safety may often be directed to the increase of our glory. And thus exercising itself, the army of Christ's champions, battling in the arena of this life, grows more wary, its victory becomes more impressive, its triumph more glorious.

Chapter 7. The comfort and joy of hoping for the perpetual company of the angels as a reward for the brief withdrawal from men

What a comfort and delight it is to enjoy the present and yet look forward to a better state, in place of a brief retirement from human society to partake of the perpetual companionship of the angels and the gaze of the divine countenance in which is the end of all holy longings and desires; instead of a few tears to have laughter without end, instead of earthly fasting eternal feasting, true and inestimable riches in lieu of self-imposed poverty, the freedom of the ethereal city in place of a forest habitation, the starry palaces of Christ in exchange for a smoky hut, the choiring of angels and the sweetness of celestial harmony in place of the silence of the woods, and, transcending all other melodies, to hear the voice of God as the faithful, trusted pledge of all these blessings when, after so many labors done, he calls his children to eternal rest! To reflect day after day upon what I have left and what I have gained, what I endure and what I look forward to, what I have sown and what I shall reap! To consider with what little waste of time — I should not say with waste but with what gain and escape from many irksome distractions, eternal felicity will soon be won, and that no sooner do we abandon the sickly appetites of men and the dangers of cities, in which exists that true hell of living men of which the Psalmist speaks, and hasten to our heavenly fatherland, than our happiness begins! Indeed the end of unhappiness is the beginning of happiness, since the nature of opposites demands that where one ceases the other should begin. Finally, there is the joy of having elevated thoughts, and conversing with comrades of the spirit, and beatific visions, and of often commanding the presence of Christ in intimate communion. For he is always present, since he is always in all places. Is it not he of whom it is written, "If I ascend up into heaven thou art there; if I make my bed in hell, behold thou art there. If I take up the wings of morning and dwell in the uttermost parts of the sea — "? He to whom it was easy to endow us with eyes and ears and understanding, surely finds it easier to see and hear and understand us. He sees us therefore and hears us even before we speak. For though Moses was silent the Lord said to him, "Wherefore criest thou unto me?" He forestalls our wishes and anticipates the movements of our hearts. He knows our thoughts from afar, long before they are formed. He answers our prayers before they are uttered and he beholds our needs before they appear. He sees the day of our death before we are born, but even though he finds us unworthy he regards us with pity, unless, which heaven forbid, we repel his mercy with headstrong contumacy.

Chapter 8. Having Christ for our faithful witness we need no imaginary witness

Having our Father therefore for witness and judge, we are not in need of that imaginary witness of whom I have written elsewhere and whom some philosophers have admonished us to seek. Epicurus, for example, who, though he stands in ill repute with some, is nevertheless held in great esteem by others who are themselves estimable men, writing to a friend, bids him act in all things as though Epicurus were looking on. Cicero, in the letter which he addresses to his brother Quinctus, after some impressive exhortations to virtue, ends as follows: "You will achieve this very easily if you think of me as being always with you and taking an interest in everything that you say and do, since it has always been your aim to please me more than all the rest of the world." He must have had very great confidence in the advantage of his real presence to his brother when he could regard the mere recollection of it as having such an influence on the pursuit of virtue. In imitation of these examples Seneca admonishes his Lucilius to imagine the presence of some illustrious persons, not venturing to offer himself as a model. "There is no real doubt," he says, "that it is good for one to have appointed a guardian over oneself, and to have some one whom you may look up to, some one whom you may regard as a witness of your thoughts." Shortly after he adds, "Act, in whatever you do, as you would act if anyone at all were looking on"; and a little further on, "Set as a guard over yourself the authority of some man, whether your choice be the great Cato, or Scipio, or Laelius, — or any man in whose presence even abandoned wretches would check their bad impulses." That it may be clear that he is here preaching Epicurean doctrine, I shall cite a remark of Seneca's from another place to this effect. "'Cherish some man of high character, and keep him ever before your eyes, living as if he were watching you, and ordering all your actions as if he beheld them.' Such, my dear Lucilius, is the counsel of Epicurus; he has quite properly given us a guardian and an attendant." Then, after inserting some examples in support of this advice, he adds, "Choose therefore a Cato; or, if Cato seems too severe a model, choose some Laelius, a gentler spirit. Choose a master whose life, conversation, and soul-expressing face have satisfied you." You see that he names a number of persons and leaves us free to choose whom we like, provided our choice falls upon one whom we admire not for his family, his power, or his wealth, but for his virtue and conversation, for a face which is the witness of a noble spirit, and for words which move the mind to worthy deeds. While this advice of the philosophers about an imaginary witness of one's life is not without profit to people in their condition, it is not necessary for us. I have given it this place in the book that by what I have said it may become clear that a Christian does not need such a witness, that he does not have to imagine the presence of Epicurus or Cicero or Cato or Scipio or

Laelius, since a good angel is provided for him as guardian and companion of his life, under whose gaze, if he has any sense of shame, he will not dare to do what he would not dare before a man. To say something even more impressive and awe-inspiring, Christ himself is present in all places and at all times, a faithful witness not only of our deeds but of all our thoughts as well, and thoughts could not be seen by Epicurus even if he were present in the flesh.

At this juncture I am inclined to arrest the current of my thought and reflect whether any person has ever been so close to the verge of madness and so abandoned in sin as not to put a tight rein upon his violent and careering lusts when he felt that he was in the presence, — I will not say of Christ — only of some friend of Christ. And yet there is absolutely no Christian who doubts that Christ himself is always present in the most secret recesses of the soul, examines what goes on there and sees everything as though it were openly exposed, and who does not refrain from every unseemly act on account of the dread and veneration of such a witness. What a delusion it is that, because we do not see with our eyes the presence which we acknowledge in our hearts, we should slip back into the error of which Cicero, who surely did not know Christ, arraigned the ancients when he said that they saw nothing with their minds but referred everything to their bodily eyes. And if we too fall into this case and look for counsel, we must give heed to the same Cicero, not because other authorities are lacking, even among writers of our own faith, (seeing that Augustine composed his book *On the True Religion* chiefly from this point of view), but because there is an advantage in hearing what a stranger, if I may call him so, has to say on this subject, especially since in a single passage he both exposes the wound and applies the remedy. "It is in the power of a large intellect," he says, "to free itself from the senses and draw our thoughts away from our prejudices." Let us too, therefore, apply ourselves with all our strength, and having subjugated our senses and got the better of our habits, view things with our intelligence. Let us open at last those inward eyes by which things invisible are beheld and clear away the mists that have obscured them and we shall see that Christ is actually with us. If Cato was ashamed to die with a groan because one was by to see, how much greater shame shall we feel, if Christ looks on, to live badly and die badly, or to commit any base or dishonorable deed in so awful a presence?

But to bring the discussion back to the subject, he is in truth our infallible and perpetual witness, and though he is present everywhere he never deigns to grace us more fully with his presence, to listen and converse with us more intimately than in solitude. And no wonder, for there no one breaks in with his clamor and nothing distracts the mind from its absorption, and so the human spirit accustoms itself to celestial contemplation, by continuous intercourse acquires confidence in its salvation, and from a guest and stranger becomes a member of God's household. For from great love and unremitting, faithful service there grows up an intimacy between

God and man such as is not known between man and man. Therefore, just as it is my faith that the restless men who are always entangled in worldly troubles and completely immersed in earthly affairs are already having a foretaste of their activities in the life immortal and of the labors of hell, so I believe it to be equally true that the solitary souls who are the friends of God and habituated to pious moods begin in this life to feel the delights of the life eternal. Nor should I say that it was beyond belief that any one of their number, to whom there clings no trace of the dust of this world, should be raised up with the assistance of the divine mercy to such a height that, though still confined to earth, he may hear the chorus of angels singing harmoniously in heaven and behold in an ecstasy of mind what he is unable to express when he comes back to himself. But what can I know or say about all these things, unhappy sinner that I am, dragging about with me the ball and chain of my iniquities? My love of a spot favorable to literary leisure springs no doubt from my love of books, or perhaps I seek to escape from the crowd because of an aversion arising from a discrepancy in our tastes, or it may even be that from a squeamishness of conscience I like to avoid a many-tongued witness of my life.

Chapter 9. Of the freedom of the solitary man and of mental employments

Therefore let us pass over these considerations, although, beloved Jesus, we have been created by you to the end that we may find our peace in you; for this we were born and without it our life is unhappy and unavailing. How much value, my father, do you set upon these common things: to live according to your pleasure, to go where you will, to stay where you will; in the spring to repose amid purple beds of flowers, in the autumn amid heaps of fallen leaves; to cheat the winter by basking in the sun and the summer by taking refuge in cool shades, and to feel the force of neither unless it is your choice! To belong to yourself in all seasons and wherever you are to be ever with yourself, far from evil, far from examples of wickedness! Not to be driven along, not to be dashed aside, not to be tormented, not to be pressed, not to be dragged to a banquet when you prefer not to eat, or to be forced to speak when you would rather be silent, not to be held up at crossings with importunate greetings and handshaking, and with a crude and tasteless kind of urbanity to linger in torture for days at a time making obeisance to passers-by! What fellow looks with gaping mouth upon you as though you were some monster? Who comes to a halt when he meets you? Who turns around and sticks at your heels, either whispering something hoarsely in the ear of his companion or questioning a passer-by concerning you? Who is there that offensively jostles you in a crowd or somewhat more offensively gives place to you? Who extends his hand to you or puts it to his head in recognition? Who sets himself to hold long talk with you in the narrow streets? Who signals to you silently with the eye and goes by with lips compressed? Finally, think what it means not to grow old among objects of disgust, to squeeze and to be squeezed amid dancing throngs, to have your breath cut short or inflated with noxious mists, to sweat, though it is the middle of winter; not to unlearn humanity among men, and through satiety of feeling to hate things, hate people, hate business, hate whom you love, hate yourself; not to forget your own concerns that you may be free to serve the ungrateful many! Yet all this is without prejudice to the saying of the Apostle in his letter to the Romans, that "none of us liveth to himself and no man dieth to himself, for whether we live, we live unto the Lord, and whether we die, we die unto the Lord." And so you must live and die as if you lived and died unto the Lord and to no other. To stand meanwhile as though on a high tower watching the troubled actions of men beneath your feet, to see all things in this world and yourself along with them passing away, not to feel old age as an affliction which has silently stolen upon you before you suspected that it was so close, as generally happens with busy men, but to expect it long in advance and be prepared for it with a sound body and a serene mind; to know that this life is but the shadow of life, that it is not home but an inn, not the fatherland but a road, not a chamber of rest but an arena; not to love fleeting things but to desire things that endure and to submit patiently to circumstances; always to remember that you are a mortal but one who enjoys the promise of immortality; to travel back in memory and to range in imagination through all ages and all lands; to move about at will and converse with all the glorious men of the past and so to lose consciousness of those who work all evils in the present; sometimes to rise, with thoughts that are lifted above yourself, to the ethereal region, to meditate on what goes on there and by meditation to inflame your desire, and in turn to encourage and admonish yourself with a fervent spirit as though with the power of burning words—these are not the least important fruits of the solitary life, though those who are without experience in it do not appreciate it. While I am speaking of these, however, let me not pass over in silence the more obvious pleasures: to devote oneself to reading and writing, alternately finding employment and relief in each, to read what our forerunners have written and to write what later generations may wish to read, to pay to posterity the debt which we cannot pay to the dead for the gift of their writings, and yet not remain altogether ungrateful to the dead but to make their names more popular if they are little known, to restore them if they have been forgotten, to dig them out if they have been buried in the ruins of time and to hand them down to our grandchildren as objects of veneration, to carry them in the heart and as something sweet in the mouth, and finally, by cherishing, remembering, and celebrating their fame in every way, to pay them the homage that is due to their genius even though it is not commensurate with their greatness.

Chapter 10. How divine honors were awarded to the inventors of certain arts

We hear that the inventors of certain arts after their death have been worshipped with the honors of deity. This shows more of gratitude than of piety, for there is no piety in any act that offends God; but the ill-advised gratitude of mortals, not content with bestowing human honors to commemorate benefits to the human race, has committed the folly of sacrilege. The harp has made a god of Apollo, medicine has made gods of both Apollo and Aesculapius, agriculture of Saturn, Bacchus, and Ceres, the forge of Vulcan. Egypt worships Osiris and the learned city of Athens Minerva, because the former is reported to have discovered the use of flax, the latter that of oil as well as the art of weaving. It would be a long task to particularize, for there is no limit to this sort of vanity among the ancients. The greatest and most careful of their poets does not dare openly to condemn it, fearing perhaps the punishment that would be visited on him, but secretly he has not been afraid to mock it, and with no little refinement, since he has placed in the lower regions the souls of those beings who have advanced human life by the arts they have invented and whose names the false multitude, the fountain of all errors, has raised to heaven in spite of the anger of the Lord of heaven. He recites specifically how the discoverer of healing himself was hurled down to the Stygian waters by the thunder of almighty God. But let this remain a question among the ancients; among us there is no talk of gods. And yet I can never cease marvelling that men in all other respects so perfect should be so foolish in their superstitions, like very swift runners moving in the wrong direction and not seeing the good directly before their eyes. I marvel at their perversity, but I pity their blindness.

If in truth some honor is due to the discoverers of things of this sort — and I do not deny that great honor is due, provided it be human and reasonable — what glory shall be showered upon the inventors of literature and the noble arts, who have provided us not with a plow to make furrows, nor woven garments for our bodies, nor tinkling lyres for our ears, nor oil and wine for our gullets — though to be sure our ears and gullets take pleasure in the sounds and tastes — but have furnished us with nobler instruments wherewith to procure nourishment, raiment, instruction, and healing for the mind? Moreover, I ask, where can this debt most effectively be paid? Who doubts that this pursuit of literature, by means of which we consecrate our own name or that of another, carving statutes of illustrious men much more enduring than bronze or marble, can be carried on nowhere more successfully or more freely than in solitude? Here at least I speak from experience, for I know what spurs it supplies to the mind, what wings for the spirit, what leisure time for work — things which I know not where to seek save in solitude. And if you do not take my word for it when I say that leisure or freedom, call it what you will, is the source of literature and the arts, you may trust Aristotle who in the first book of the *Metaphysics,* declaring the reason why the mathematical arts were so highly celebrated among the Egyptians, says that it was because of the leisure that was offered to the race of priests. Plato too has not omitted to note, speaking of these people in the *Timaeus,* that being entrusted with priestly functions they remain apart from the rest of the people in order to preserve their purity unpolluted from profane contact. One of our own priests, Cheremon the Stoic, a very eloquent writer, describing their mode of life, says that they put aside all business and thoughts of the world and lived always in the temple, studying nature and its causes and making computations of the stars, that they never consorted with women, never saw their near kin or even their children after they had once entered upon the service of the divine cult, and regularly abstained from flesh and wine. He adds that they were accustomed severely to suppress and correct the bodily humors which might develop from idleness or inaction by not eating for two or three days, and he relates many other things about their food, drink, and sleep. By habits like these I can easily believe that they acquired a certain divine fertility of intellect.

LETTERS

Translated by James Harvey Robinson
and Henry Winchester Rolfe

[Taken from *Petrarch. The First Modern Scholar and Man of Letters,* by James Harvey Robinson and Henry Winchester Rolfe, G. P. Putnam's Sons, New York, second edition, 1914.]

DE REBUS FAMILIARIBUS

IV, 1. To Dionisio da Borgo San Sepolcro

[THE ASCENT OF MOUNT VENTOUX]

To-day I made the ascent of the highest mountain in this region, which is not improperly called Ventosum. My only motive was the wish to see what so great an elevation had to offer. I have had the expedition in mind for many years; for, as you know, I have lived in this region from infancy, having been cast here by that fate which determines the affairs of men. Consequently the mountain, which is visible from a great distance, was ever before my eyes, and I conceived the plan of some time doing what I have at last accomplished to-day. The idea took hold upon me with especial force when, in re-reading Livy's *History of Rome,* yesterday, I happened upon the place where Philip of Macedon, the same who waged war against the Romans, ascended Mount Haemus in Thessaly, from whose summit he was able, it is said, to see two seas, the Adriatic and the Euxine. Whether this be true or false I have not been able to determine, for the mountain is too far away, and writers disagree. Pomponius Mela, the cosmographer — not to mention others who have spoken of this occurrence — admits its truth without hesitation; Titus Livius, on the other hand, considers it false. I, assuredly, should not have left the question long in doubt, had that mountain been as easy to explore as this one. Let us leave this matter one side, however, and return to my mountain here, — it seems to me that a young man in private life may well be excused for attempting what an aged king could undertake without arousing criticism.

When I came to look about for a companion I found, strangely enough, that hardly one among my friends seemed suitable, so rarely do we meet with just the right combination of personal tastes and characteristics, even among those who are dearest to us. This one was too apathetic, that one over-anxious; this one too slow, that one too hasty; one was too sad, another over-cheerful; one more simple, another more sagacious, than I desired. I feared this one's taciturnity and that one's loquacity. The heavy deliberation of some repelled me as much as the lean incapacity of others. I rejected those who were likely to irritate me by a cold want of interest, as well as those who might weary me by their excessive enthusiasm. Such defects, however grave, could be borne with at home, for charity suffereth all things, and friendship accepts any burden; but it is quite otherwise on a journey, where every weakness becomes much more serious. So, as I was bent upon pleasure and anxious that my enjoyment should be unalloyed, I looked about me with unusual care, balanced against one another the various characteristics of my friends, and without committing any breach of friendship I silently condemned every trait which might prove disagreeable on the way. And — would you believe it? — I finally turned homeward for aid, and proposed the ascent to my only brother, who is younger than I, and with whom you are well acquainted. He was delighted and gratified beyond measure by the thought of holding the place of a friend as well as of a brother.

At the time fixed we left the house, and by evening reached Malaucène, which lies at the foot of the mountain, to the north. Having rested there a day, we finally made the ascent this morning, with no companions except two servants; and a most difficult task it was. The mountain is a very steep and almost inaccessible mass of stony soil. But, as the poet has well said, "Remorseless toil conquers all." It was a long day, the air fine. We enjoyed the advantages of vigour of mind and strength and agility of body, and everything else essential to those engaged in such an undertaking, and so had no other difficulties to face than those of the region itself. We found an old shepherd in one of the mountain dales, who tried, at great length, to dissuade us from the ascent, saying that some fifty years before he had, in the same ardour of youth, reached the summit, but had gotten for his pains nothing except fatigue and regret, and clothes and body torn by the rocks and briars. No one, so far as he or his companions knew, had ever tried the ascent before or after him. But his counsels increased rather than diminished our desire to proceed, since youth is suspicious of warnings. So the old man, finding that his efforts were in vain, went a little way with us, and pointed out a rough path among the rocks, uttering many admonitions, which he continued to send after us even after we had left him behind. Surrendering to him all such garments or other possessions as might prove burdensome to us, we made ready for the ascent, and started off at a good pace. But, as usually happens, fatigue quickly followed upon our excessive exertion, and we soon came to a halt at the top of a certain cliff. Upon starting on again we went more slowly, and I especially advanced along the rocky way with a more deliberate step. While my brother chose a direct path straight up the ridge, I weakly took an easier one which really descended. When I was called back, and the right road was shown me, I replied that I hoped to find a better way round on the other side, and that I did not mind going farther if the path were only less steep. This was just an excuse for my laziness; and when the others had already reached a considerable height I was still wandering in the valleys. I had failed to find an easier path, and had only increased the distance and difficulty of the ascent. At last I became disgusted with the intricate way I had chosen, and resolved to ascend without more ado. When I reached my brother, who, while waiting for me, had had ample opportunity for rest, I was tired and irritated. We walked along together for a time, but hardly had we passed the first spur when I forgot about the circuitous route which I had just tried, and took a lower one again. Once more I followed an easy, roundabout path through winding valleys, only to find myself soon in my old difficulty. I was simply trying to avoid the exertion of the ascent; but no human ingenuity can alter the nature of things, or cause anything to reach a height by going down. Suffice it to say that, much to my vexation and my brother's amusement, I made this same mistake three times or more during a few hours.

After being frequently misled in this way, I finally sat down in a valley and transferred my winged thoughts from things corporeal to the immaterial, addressing myself as follows: — "What thou hast repeatedly experienced to-day in the ascent of this mountain, happens to thee, as to many, in the journey toward the blessed life. But this is not so readily perceived by men, since the motions of the body are obvious and external while those of the soul are invisible and hidden. Yes, the life which we call blessed is to be sought for on a high eminence, and strait is the way that leads to it. Many, also, are the hills that lie between, and we must ascend, by a glorious stairway, from strength to strength. At the top is at once the end of our struggles and the goal for which we are bound. All wish to reach this goal, but, as Ovid says, 'To wish is little; we must long with the utmost eagerness to gain our end.' Thou certainly dost ardently desire, as well as simply wish, unless thou deceivest thyself in this matter, as in so many others. What, then, doth hold thee back? Nothing, assuredly, except that thou wouldst take a path which seems, at first thought, more easy, leading through low and worldly pleasures. But nevertheless in the end, after long wanderings, thou must perforce either climb the steeper path, under the burden of tasks foolishly deferred, to its blessed culmination, or lie down in the valley of thy sins, and (I shudder to think of it!), if the shadow of death overtake thee, spend an eternal night amid constant torments." These thoughts stimulated both body and mind in a wonderful degree for facing the difficulties which yet remained. Oh, that I might traverse in spirit that other road for which I long day and night, even as to-day I overcame material obstacles by my bodily exertions! And I know not why it should not be far easier, since the swift immortal soul can reach its goal in the twinkling of an eye, without passing through space, while my progress to-day was necessarily slow, dependent as I was upon a failing body weighed down by heavy members.

One peak of the mountain, the highest of all, the country people call "Sonny," why, I do not know, unless by antiphrasis, as I have sometimes suspected in other instances; for the peak in question would seem to be the father of all the surrounding ones. On its top is a little level place, and here we could at last rest our tired bodies.

Now, my father, since you have followed the thoughts that spurred me on in my ascent, listen to the rest of the story, and devote one hour, I pray you, to reviewing the experiences of my entire day. At first, owing to the unaccustomed quality of the air and the effect of the great sweep of view spread out before me, I stood like one dazed. I beheld the clouds under our feet, and what I had read of Athos and Olympus seemed less incredible as I myself witnessed the same things from a mountain of less fame. I turned my eyes toward Italy, whither my heart most inclined. The Alps, rugged and snow-capped, seemed to rise close by, although they were really at a great distance; the very same Alps through which that fierce enemy of the Roman name once made his way, bursting the rocks, if we may believe the report, by the application of vinegar. I sighed, I must confess, for the skies of Italy, which I beheld rather with my mind than with my eyes. An inexpressible longing came over me to see once more my friend and my country. At the same time I reproached myself for this double weakness, springing, as it did, from a soul not yet steeled to manly resistance. And yet there were excuses for both of these cravings, and a number of distinguished writers might be summoned to support me.

Then a new idea took possession of me, and I shifted my thoughts to a consideration of time rather than place. "To-day it is ten years since, having completed thy youthful studies, thou didst leave Bologna. Eternal God! In the name of immutable wisdom, think what alterations in thy character this intervening period has beheld! I pass over a thousand instances. I am not yet in a safe harbour where I can calmly recall past storms. The time may come when I can review in due order all the experiences of the past, saying with St. Augustine, 'I desire to recall my foul actions and the carnal corruption of my soul, not because I love them, but that I may the more love thee, O my God.' Much that is doubtful and evil still clings to me, but what I once loved, that I love no longer. And yet what am I saying? I still love it, but with shame, but with heaviness of heart. Now, at last, I have confessed the truth. So it is. I love, but love what I would not love, what I would that I might hate. Though loath to do so, though constrained, though sad and sorrowing, still I do love, and I feel in my miserable self the truth of the well known words, 'I will hate if I can; if not, I will love against my will.' Three years have not yet passed since that perverse and wicked passion which had a firm grasp upon me and held undisputed sway in my heart began to discover a rebellious opponent, who was unwilling longer to yield obedience. These two adversaries have joined in close combat for the supremacy, and for a long time now a harassing and doubtful war has been waged in the field of my thoughts."

Thus I turned over the last ten years in my mind, and then, fixing my anxious gaze on the future, I asked myself, "If, perchance, thou shouldst prolong this uncertain life of thine for yet two lustres, and shouldst make an advance toward virtue proportionate to the distance to which thou hast departed from thine original infatuation during the past two years, since the new longing first encountered the old, couldst thou, on reaching thy fortieth year, face death, if not with complete assurance, at least with hopefulness, calmly dismissing from thy thoughts the residuum of life as it faded into old age?"

These and similar reflections occurred to me, my father. I rejoiced in my progress, mourned my weaknesses, and commiserated the universal instability of human conduct. I had well-nigh forgotten where I was and our object in coming; but at last I dismissed my anxieties, which were better suited to other surroundings, and resolved to look about me and see what we had come to see. The sinking sun and the lengthening shadows of the mountain were already warning us that the time was near at hand when we must go. As if suddenly wakened from sleep, I turned about and gazed toward the west. I was unable to discern the summits of the Pyrenees, which form the barrier between France and Spain; not because of any intervening obstacle that I know of but owing simply to the insufficiency of our mortal vision. But I could see with the utmost clearness, off to the right, the mountains of the region about Lyons, and to the left the bay of Marseilles and the waters that lash the shores of Aigues Mortes, altho' all these places were so distant that it would require a journey of several days to reach them. Under our very eyes flowed the Rhone.

While I was thus dividing my thoughts, now turning my attention to some terrestrial object that lay before me, now raising my soul, as I had done my body, to higher planes, it occurred to me to look into my copy of St. Augustine's *Confessions,* a gift that I owe to your love, and that I always have about me, in memory of both the author and the giver. I opened the compact little volume, small indeed in size, but of infinite charm, with the intention of reading whatever came to hand, for I could happen upon nothing that would be otherwise than edifying and devout. Now it chanced that the tenth book presented itself. My brother, waiting to hear something of St. Augustine's from my lips, stood attentively by. I call him, and God too, to witness that where I first fixed my eyes it was written: "And men go about to wonder at the heights of the mountains, and the mighty waves of the sea, and the wide sweep of rivers, and the circuit of the ocean, and the revolution of the stars, but themselves they consider not." I was abashed, and, asking my brother (who was anxious to hear more), not to annoy me, I closed the book, angry with myself that I should still be admiring earthly things who might long ago have learned from even the pagan philosophers that nothing is wonderful but the soul, which, when great itself, finds nothing great outside itself. Then, in truth, I was satisfied that I had seen enough of the mountain; I turned my inward eye upon myself, and from that time not a syllable fell from my lips until we had reached the bottom again. Those words had given me occupation enough, for I could not believe that it was by a mere accident that I happened upon them. What I had there read I believed to be addressed to me and to no other, remembering that St. Augustine had once suspected the same thing in his own case, when, on opening the book of the Apostle, as he himself tells us, the first words that he saw there were, "Not in rioting and drunkenness, not in chambering and wantonness, not in strife and envying. But put ye on the Lord Jesus Christ, and make not provision for the flesh, to fulfil the lusts thereof."

The same thing happened earlier to St. Anthony, when he was listening to the Gospel where it is written, "If thou wilt be perfect, go and sell that thou hast, and give to the poor, and thou shalt have treasure in heaven: and come and follow me." Believing this scripture to have been read for his especial benefit, as his biographer Athanasius says, he guided himself by its aid to the Kingdom of Heaven. And as Anthony on hearing these words waited for nothing more, and as Augustine upon reading the Apostle's admonition sought no farther, so I concluded my reading in the few words which I have given. I thought in silence of the lack of good counsel in us mortals, who neglect what is noblest in ourselves, scatter our energies in all directions, and waste ourselves in a vain show, because we look about us for what is to be found only within. I wondered at the natural nobility of our soul, save when it debases itself of its own free will, and deserts its original estate, turning what God has given it for its honour into dishonour. How many times, think you, did I turn back that day, to glance at the summit of the mountain, which seemed scarcely a cubit high compared with the range of human contemplation, — when it is not immersed in the foul mire of earth? With every downward step I asked myself this: If we are ready to endure so much sweat and labour in order that we may bring our bodies a little nearer heaven, how can a soul struggling toward God, up the steeps of human pride and human destiny, fear any cross or prison or sting of fortune? How few, I thought, but are diverted from their path by the fear of difficulties or the love of ease! How happy the lot of those few, if any such there be! It is of them, assuredly, that the poet was thinking, when he wrote:

> Happy the man who is skilled to understand
> Nature's hid causes; who beneath his feet
> All terrors casts, and death's relentless doom,
> And the loud roar of greedy Acheron.

How earnestly should we strive, not to stand on mountain-tops, but to trample beneath us those appetites which spring from earthly impulses.

With no consciousness of the difficulties of the way, amidst these preoccupations which I have so frankly revealed, we came, long after dark, but with the full moon lending us its friendly light, to the little inn which we had left that morning before dawn. The time during which the servants have been occupied in preparing our supper, I have spent in a secluded part of the house, hurriedly jotting down these experiences on the spur of the moment, lest, in case my task were postponed, my mood should change on leaving the place, and so my interest in writing flag.

You will see, my dearest father, that I wish nothing to be concealed from you, for I am careful to describe to you not only my life in general but even my individual reflections. And I beseech you, in turn, to pray that these vague and wandering thoughts of mine may some time become firmly fixed, and, after having been vainly tossed about from one interest to another, may direct themselves at last toward the single, true, certain, and everlasting good.

Malaucène, April 26.

XXI, 15. To Boccaccio

[Petrarch disclaims all jealousy of Dante]

There are many things in your letter which do not require any answer; those, for example, which we have lately settled face to face. Two points there were, however, which it seemed to me should not be passed over in silence, and I will briefly write down such reflections concerning them as may occur to me. In the first place, you excuse yourself with some heat for seeming to praise unduly a certain poet, a fellow-citizen of ours, who in point of style is very popular, and who has certainly chosen a noble theme. You beg my pardon for this, as if I regarded anything said in his, or anyone else's praise, as detracting from my own. You assert, for instance, that if I will only look closely at what you say of him, I shall find that it all reflects glory upon me. You take pains to explain, in extenuation of your favourable attitude towards him, that he was your first light and guide in your early studies. Your praise is certainly only a just and dutiful acknowledgement of his services, an expression of what I may call filial piety. If we owe all to those who begot and brought us forth, and much to those who are the authors of our fortunes, what shall we say of our debt to the parents and fashioners of our minds? How much more, indeed, is due to those who refine the mind than to those who tend the body, he will perceive who assigns to each its just value; for the one, it will be seen, is an immortal gift, the other, corruptible and destined to pass away.

Continue, then, not by my sufferance simply, but with my approbation, to extol and cherish this poet, the guiding star of your intellect, who has afforded you courage and light in the arduous way by which you are pressing stoutly on towards a most glorious goal. He has long been buffeted and wearied by the windy plaudits of the multitude. Honour him now and exalt him by sincere praise worthy alike of you and of him, and, you may be sure, not unpleasing to me. He is worthy of such a herald, while you, as you say, are the natural one to assume the office. I therefore accept your song of praise with all my heart, and join with you in extolling the poet you celebrate therein.

Hence there was nothing in your letter of explanation to disturb me except the discovery that I am still so ill understood by you who, as I firmly believed, knew me thoroughly. You think, then, that I do not take pleasure in the praises of illustrious men and glory in them? Believe me, nothing is more foreign to me than jealousy; there is no scourge of which I know less. On the contrary, in order that you may see how far I am from such feelings, I call upon Him before whom all hearts are open to witness that few things in life have caused me more pain than to see the meritorious passed by, utterly without recognition or reward. Not that I am deploring my own lot, or looking for personal gain; I am mourning the common fate of mankind, as I behold the reward of the nobler arts falling to the meaner. I am not unaware that although the reputation which attaches to right conduct may stimulate the mind to deserve it, true virtue is, as the philosophers say, a stimulus to itself; it is its own reward, its own guide, its own end and aim. Nevertheless, now that you have yourself suggested a theme which I should not voluntarily have chosen, I shall proceed to refute for you, and through you for others, the commonly accepted notion of my judgment of this poet. It is not only false, as Quintilian says of the construction put upon his criticism of Seneca, but it is insidious and, with many, out-and-out malevolent. My enemies say that I hate and despise him, and in this way stir up the common herd against me, for with them he is extremely popular. This is indeed a novel kind of perversity, and shows a marvellous aptitude for harming others. But truth herself shall defend me.

In the first place, there can be no possible cause for ill-will towards a man whom I never saw but once, and that in my very earliest childhood. He lived with my grandfather and my father, being younger than the former, but older than my father, with whom, on the same day and by the same civil commotion, he was driven from his country into exile. At such a time strong friendships are often formed between companions in misery. This proved especially true of these two men, since in their case not only a similar fate but a community of taste and a love for the same studies, served to bring them together. My father, however, forced by other cares and by regard for his family, succumbed to the natural influences of exile, while his friend resisted, throwing himself, indeed, with even greater ardour into what he had undertaken, neglecting everything else and desirous alone of future fame. In this I can scarce admire and praise him enough, — that neither the injustice of his fellow-citizens, nor exile, nor poverty, nor the attacks of his enemies, neither the love of wife, nor solicitude for his children, could divert him from the path he had once decided upon, when so many who are highly endowed are yet so weak of purpose that they are swerved from their course by the least disturbance. And this most often happens to writers of verse, for silence and quiet are especially requisite for those who have to care not only for the thought and the words but the felicitous turn as well. Thus you will see that my supposed hate for this poet, which has been trumped up by I know not whom, is an odious and ridiculous invention, since there is absolutely no reason for such repugnance, but, on the contrary, every reason for partiality, on account of our common country, his friendship with my father, his genius, and his style, the best of its kind, which must always raise him far above contempt.

This brings us to the second reproach cast upon me, which is based upon the fact that, although in my early years I was very eager in my search for books of all kinds, I never possessed a copy of this poet's work, which would naturally have attracted me most at that age. While exceedingly anxious to obtain other books which I had little hope of finding, I showed a strange indifference, quite foreign to me, towards this one, although it was readily procurable. The fact I admit, but I deny the motives which are urged by my enemies. At that time I too was devoting my powers to compositions in the vernacular; I was convinced that nothing could be finer, and had not yet learned to look higher. I feared, however, in view of the impressionableness of youth and its readiness to admire everything, that, if I should imbue myself with his or any other writer's verses, I might perhaps unconsciously and against my will come to be an imitator. In the ardour of youth this thought filled me with aversion. Such was my self-confidence and enthusiasm that I deemed my own powers quite sufficient, without any mortal aid, to produce an original style all my own, in the species of production upon which I was engaged. It is for others to judge whether I was right in this. But I must add that if anything should be discovered in my Italian writings resembling, or even identical with, what has been said by him or others, it cannot be attributed to secret or conscious imitation. This rock I have always endeavoured to avoid, especially in my writings in the vernacular, although it is possible that, either by accident or, as Cicero says, owing to similar ways of thinking, I may ignorantly have traversed the same path as others. If you ever believe me, believe me now; accept this as the real explanation of my conduct. Nothing can be more strictly true; and if my modesty and sense of propriety did not seem to you sufficient to vouch for this, my youthful pride at any rate certainly might have explained it.

To-day, however, I have left these anxieties far behind, and, having done so, I am freed from my former apprehension, and can now unreservedly admire other writers, him above all. At that time I was submitting work of my own to the verdict of others, whereas now I am merely passing my own silent verdicts upon my fellows. I find that my opinion varies as regards all the rest, but in his case there can be no room for doubt; without hesitation I yield him the palm for skill in the use of the vulgar tongue. They lie, then, who assert that I carp at his renown; I, who probably understand better than the majority of these foolish and immoderate admirers of his what it is that merely tickles their ears, without their knowing why, but cannot penetrate their thick heads, because the avenues of intelligence are obstructed. They belong to the same class that Cicero brands in his *Rhetoric,* who "read fine orations or beautiful poems, and praise the orators or poets, and yet do not know what it is that has aroused their admiration, for they lack the ability to see where the thing is that most pleases them, or what it is, or how it is produced." If this happens with Demosthenes and Cicero, Homer and Virgil, among learned men and in the schools, how will it fare with our poet among the rude fellows who frequent the taverns and public squares?

As for me, far from scorning his work, I admire and love him, and in justice to myself I may venture to add that if he had been permitted to live until this time he would have found few friends more devoted to him than myself, provided, of course, that I had found his character as attractive as his genius. On the other hand, there are none to whom he would have been more obnoxious than these same silly admirers, who, in general, know equally little about what they praise and what they condemn, and who so mispronounce and lacerate his verses that they do him the greatest injury that a poet can suffer. I might even strive to the best of my powers to rescue him from this abuse, did not my own productions give me enough to think about. As it is, I can only give voice to my irritation, when I hear the common herd befouling with their stupid mouths the noble beauty of his lines.

Just here it may not be out of place to say that this was not the least of the considerations which led me to give up a style of composition to which I devoted myself in my early years. I feared for my writings the same fate which I had seen overtake those of others, especially those of the poet of whom we are speaking. I could not in my own case look for more musical tongues or more flexible minds among the common people than I noted in the rendering of those authors whom long favour and habit have made popular in the theatres and public squares. That my apprehensions were not idle is clear from the fact that I am continually tortured by the tongues of the people, as they sing the few productions which I allowed to escape me in my youth. I indignantly reject and hate what I once loved; and day by day walk the streets with vexation and execrate my own talents. Everywhere a crowd of ignorant fellows, everywhere I find my Damoetas ready at the street corner "to murder with his screeching reed" my poor song.

However, I have already said more than enough concerning a trifling matter which I ought not to have taken so seriously, for this hour, which will never return, should have been devoted to other things. And yet your excuse did seem to me to have just a little in common with the accusations of these critics, some of whom are constantly asserting that I hate, some that I despise, this person,— whose name I have intentionally refrained to-day from mentioning, lest the mob, who catch up everything without understanding it, should cry out that I was defaming it. Others again claim that I am actuated by envy;— men who are jealous of me and my fame; for, although I scarcely am an object for envy, I yet have noticed late in life that there are those who entertain this feeling towards me, a thing that at one time I could not have believed possible. In answer to this charge of envy brought against me, I might reply that, many years ago, in the ardour of youth, and with an approving conscience, I ventured to assert, not in any ordinary manner, but in a poem addressed to a certain illustrious personage, that I envied no man. Suppose, though, that I am not worthy of belief. Still, even then, what probability is there that I should be jealous of a writer who devoted his whole life to those things which with me were but the flower and first-fruits of my youth. What to him was, if not his only occupation, certainly the supreme object of his life, to me was mere sport, a pastime, the first essay of my powers.

What occasion is there here for rancour? What ground is there for even a suspicion of jealousy? When you say, in praising him, that he might have devoted himself to another kind of composition, had he wished, I heartily agree with you. I have the highest opinion of his ability, for it is obvious from what he has done that he would have succeeded in anything he might have chosen to undertake. But suppose that he had turned his powers in another direction, and successfully— what then? What would there be in that to make me jealous? Why should it not rather be a source of satisfaction to me? Who indeed could excite envy in me, who do not envy even Virgil?— unless perhaps I should be jealous of the hoarse applause which our poet enjoys from the tavern-keepers, fullers, butchers, and others of that class, who dishonour those whom they would praise. But, far from desiring such popular recognition, I congratulate myself, on the contrary, that, along with Virgil and Homer, I am free from it, inasmuch as I fully realise how little the plaudits of the unschooled multitude weigh with scholars. Should it be suggested that the citizen of Mantua is, when all is said, dearer to me than my fellow-citizen of Florence, I must urge that, although I will not deny that jealousy does flourish most rankly between neighbours, the mere fact of common origin cannot by itself justify such an inference. Indeed the simple fact of our belonging to different generations would make this latter supposition absurd, for as one has elegantly said, who never speaks otherwise than elegantly, "The dead are neither hated nor envied."

You will accept my solemn affirmation that I delight in both the thought and style of our poet, nor do I ever refer to him except with the greatest admiration. It is true that I have sometimes said to those who wished to know precisely what I thought, that his style was unequal, for he rises to a higher plane of excellence in the vernacular than in poetry or prose. But you will not deny this, nor will it, if rightly understood, carry with it any disparagement of his fame and glory. Who, indeed — I will not say at the present time, when eloquence has so long been mourned as dead, but at the time when it flourished most — who, I say, ever excelled in all its various branches? Witness Seneca's *Declamations!* No one dreams of attributing inexhaustible versatility even to Cicero, Virgil, Sallust, or Plato. Who would lay claim to a degree of praise which must be denied even to such genius? It is enough to have excelled in one kind of composition. This being true, let those be silent who attempt to twist my words into calumnies, and let those who have believed my calumniators read here, if they will, my opinion of them.

Having disposed thus of one matter which has been troubling me, I come now to a second. You thank me for my solicitude for your health. While you do this from courtesy, and in accordance with conventional usage, you well know that such acknowledgment is quite unnecessary. For who is ever thanked for his interest in himself, or his own affairs? and you, dear friend, are part and parcel of myself.

Although, next to virtue, friendship is the most sacred, the most God-like and divine thing in human intercourse, yet I think that it makes a difference whether one begins by loving or by being loved, and that those friendships should be more carefully fostered where we return love for love than where we simply receive it. I have been overwhelmed in a thousand instances by your kindness and friendly offices, but among them all there is one that I can never forget.

In days gone by, I was hurrying across central Italy in mid-winter; you hastened to greet me, not only with affectionate longings, which are the wings of the soul, but in person, impelled by a wondrous desire to behold one whom you had never yet seen, but whom you were nevertheless resolved to love. You had sent before you a piece of beautiful verse, thus showing me first the aspect of your genius, and then of your person. It was evening, and the light was fading, when, returning from my long exile, I found myself at last within my native walls. You welcomed me with a courtesy and respect greater than I merited, recalling the poetic meeting of Anchises and the King of Arcadia, who, "in the ardour of youth, longed to speak with the hero and to press his hand." Although I did not, like him, stand "above all others," but rather beneath, your zeal was none the less ardent. You introduced me, not within the walls of Pheneus, but into the sacred penetralia of your friendship. Nor did I present you with "a superb quiver and arrows of Lycia," but rather with my sincere and unchangeable affection. While acknowledging my inferiority in many respects, I will never willingly concede it in this, either to Nisus, or to Pythias, or to Laelius. Farewell.

DE REBUS SENILIBUS

I, 4. To Boccaccio

[CONCERNING A CERTAIN MONK OF SIENA]

Your letter, my brother, filled me with the saddest forebodings. As I ran through it amazement and profound grief struggled for the supremacy in my heart, but when I had finished, both gave way to other feelings. As long as I was ignorant of the facts, and attended only to the words, how indeed could I read, with dry eyes, of your tears and approaching death? For at first glance I quite failed to see the real state of affairs. A little thought, however, served to put me in quite a different frame of mind, and to banish both grief and surprise.

But before I proceed I must touch upon the matter to which you refer in the earlier part of your letter. You dare not deprecate, you say with the utmost deference, the plan of your illustrious master — as you too humbly call me — for migrating to Germany, or far-off Sarmatia (I quote your words), carrying with me, as you would have it, all the Muses, and Helicon itself, as if I deemed the Italians unworthy longer to enjoy my presence or the fruits of my labour. You well know, however, that I have never been other than an obscure and lowly dweller on Helicon, and that I have been so distracted by outside cares as to have become by this time almost an exile. I must admit that your method of holding me back from such a venture is more efficacious than a flood of satirical eloquence would have been. I am much gratified by such tokens of your esteem, and by the keen interest you exhibit. I should much prefer to see signs of exaggerated apprehension on your part (*omnia tuta timens,* as Virgil says) than any suggestion of waning affection.

I have no desire to conceal any of my plans from you, dear friend, and will freely tell you the whole secret of my poor wounded heart. I can never see enough of this land of Italy; but, by Hercules! I am so utterly disgusted with Italian affairs that, as I recently wrote to our Simonides, I must confess that I have sometimes harboured the idea of betaking myself — not to Germany, certainly, but to some secluded part of the world. There I might hope to escape this eternal hubbub, as well as the storms of jealousy to which I am exposed not so much by my lot in life (which to my thinking might rather excite contempt than envy) as by a certain renown which I have acquired in some way or other. Thus secluded I should have done what I could to live an upright life and die a righteous death. This design I should have carried out had not fortune prevented. But as to turning my thoughts northward, that was by no means done with the intention which you imagine. I did not think of seeking repose in that barbarous and uninviting land, with its inclement sky. I was only submitting, from motives of respect and propriety, to the solicitations of our Emperor, who had repeatedly urged me to come and see him, with such insistence that my refusal to visit him, for a short time at least, might have been regarded as an exhibition of pride and rebellion, or even as a species of sacrilege. For, as you have read in Valerius, our ancestors were wont to regard those who could not venerate princes as capable of any form of crime. But you may dismiss your fears, and cease your laments; for — to my not very great regret — I have found this road, too, blocked by war. Anomalously enough, I am glad not to go where I should with even greater gladness have gone if I had been able. To have wished to go is enough to satisfy both my ruler's desires and my own scruples; for the rest fortune was responsible.

Leaving this matter, I come back to that part of your letter which so affected me on first reading. You say that a certain Peter, a native of Siena, noted for his piety and for the miracles which he performed, has recently died; that on his death-bed, among many predictions relating to various persons, he had something to say of both of us; and that, moreover, he sent a messenger to you to communicate his last words. When you inquired how this holy man, of whom we had never heard, happened to know so much about us, the messenger replied that the deceased had, it is understood, undertaken a certain work of piety; but when, having been told as I surmise that death was near, he saw himself unable to accomplish his proposed mission, he prayed a prayer of great efficacy, which could not fail to make its way to Heaven, that proper substitutes might be designated, who should bring to a successful close the chosen task which it was not the will of God that he himself should complete. With that intimacy of intercourse which exists between God and the soul of the just, Heaven ordained that he should see Christ in person, and thus know that his petition had been heard and granted. And in Christ's face it was conceded to him to read *"the things that are, the things that have been, and the things that are to come,"* not as Proteus does in Virgil, but far more perfectly, clearly, and fully; for what could escape one who was permitted to look upon the face of him to whom all things owe their being?

It is certainly a most astounding thing, this seeing Christ with mortal eyes, if only it be true. For it is an old and much-used device, to drape one's own lying inventions with the veil of religion and sanctity, in order to give the appearance of divine sanction to human fraud. But I cannot pronounce upon this case at present, nor until the messenger of the deceased presents himself to me in person. For you tell me that he visited you first because you were nearest, and, having delivered his message, departed for Naples, intending to go thence by sea to France and England, and lastly to visit me and impart such of his instructions as related to my case. I can then see for myself how much faith he succeeds in arousing in me. I shall closely interrogate everything about him, — his age, face, eyes, dress, bearing, gait, even his tone of voice, movements, style of address, and, above all, his apparent object and the upshot of his discourse.

The gist of the whole matter is then, as I infer, that the holy man as he was dying had a vision of us two, and along with us of several others as well, and intrusted certain secret messages for us all to this zealous and, as he seems to you, faithful executor of his last wishes. Now what messages the other persons may have received we do not know. But you yourself received the following communications, both relating to the general course and conduct of your life. If there were others you suppress them. You were first informed that your life is approaching its end, and that but a few years remain to you. Secondly, you were bidden to renounce the study of poetry. Hence your consternation and sorrow, which I shared at first as I read, but which a little reflection served to efface, as it will in your case too, if you will but lend me your ears, or listen to the utterances of your own better reason. You will see that, instead of being a source of grief, the message ought to give you joy.

I do not belittle the authority of prophesy. What comes to us from Christ must indeed be true. Truth itself cannot lie. But I venture to question whether Christ was the author of this particular prophesy, whether it may not be, as often happens, a fabrication attributed to him in order to insure its acceptance. And what of the fact that similar phenomena have been recorded among those who are quite ignorant of his name? If we may believe the pagan poets and philosophers, it was not at all unusual for dying men to utter prophesies; both the Greek literature and our own mention many such instances. Note, for example, that Homer makes Hector foretell the death of Achilles; Virgil tells us how Orodes warns Mezentius of his doom; Cicero mentions the same prophetic power in the cases of Theramenes, who foresaw the death of Critias, and of Calanus, who foretold that of Alexander. Another example, more like that which troubles you, is mentioned by Posidonius, the most celebrated philosopher of his time. He tells us of a certain inhabitant of Rhodes who, on his death-bed, indicated six of his contemporaries who were shortly to follow him to the grave; and, what is more, he actually foretold the order in which those people would die. This is not the place to consider either the authenticity or the explanation of such cases. Suppose, though, that we do grant their trustworthiness, as well as that of other similar prophecies which are reported to us, including the one by which you have recently been terrified; what is there, after all, which need fill you with such apprehension? We are usually indifferent to those things with which we are familiar, and are excited and disturbed only by the unexpected. Did you not know well enough, without hearing it from this man, that you had but a short span of life before you? . . .

I might commend to you, in your perplexity, the reflections of Virgil, as not only helpful but as the only advice to be followed at this juncture, were it not that I wished to spare the ears of one to whom poetry is absolutely forbidden. This prohibition filled me with much more astonishment than the first part of the dying man's message. If it had been addressed to an old man who was, so to speak, just learning his letters, I might have put up with it, but I cannot understand why such advice should be given to an educated person in the full possession of his faculties, . . . one who realises what can be derived from such studies for the fuller understanding of natural things, for the advancement of morals and of eloquence, and for the defence of our religion. (We have seen with what signal success those whom I have just enumerated used their learning.) I am speaking now only of the man of ripe years, who knows what is due to Jupiter the adulterer, Mercury the pander, Mars the manslayer, Hercules the brigand, and—to cite the less guilty—to the leech Aesculapius, and his father, Apollo the cither-player, to the smith Vulcan, the spinner Minerva; and, on the other hand, to Mary the virgin-mother, and to her son, our Redeemer, very God and very man. If, indeed, we must avoid the poets and other writers who did not know of Christ, and consequently do not mention his name, how much more dangerous must it be to read the books of heretics, who only speak of Christ to attack him. Nevertheless the defenders of the true faith do read them, and with the greatest attention.

Believe me, many things are attributed to gravity and wisdom which are really due to incapacity and sloth. Men often despise what they despair of obtaining. It is in the very nature of ignorance to scorn what it cannot understand, and to desire to keep others from attaining what it cannot reach. Hence the false judgments upon matters of which we know nothing, by which we evince our envy quite as clearly as our stupidity.

Neither exhortations to virtue nor the argument of approaching death should divert us from literature; for in a good mind it excites the love of virtue, and dissipates, or at least diminishes, the fear of death. To desert our studies shows want of self-confidence rather than wisdom, for letters do not hinder but aid the properly constituted mind which possesses them; they facilitate our life, they do not retard it. Just as many kinds of food which lie heavy on an enfeebled and nauseated stomach furnish excellent nourishment for one who is well but famishing, so in our studies many things which are deadly to the weak mind may prove most salutary to an acute and healthy intellect, especially if in our use of both food and learning we exercise proper discretion. If it were otherwise, surely the zeal of certain persons who persevered to the end could not have roused such admiration. Cato, I never forget, acquainted himself with Latin literature as he was growing old, and Greek when he had really become an old man. Varro, who reached his hundredth year still reading and writing, parted from life sooner than from his love of study. Livius Drusus, although weakened by age and afflicted with blindness, did not give up his interpretation of the civil law, which he carried on to the great advantage of the state. . . .

Besides these and innumerable others like them, have not all those of our own religion whom we should wish most to imitate devoted their whole lives to literature, and grown old and died in the same pursuit? Some, indeed, were overtaken by death while still at work reading or writing. To none of them, so far as I know, did it prove a disadvantage to be noted for secular learning, except to Jerome, whom I mentioned above; while to many, and Jerome himself not least, it was a source of glory. I do not forget that Benedict was praised by Gregory for deserting the studies which he had begun, to devote himself to a solitary and ascetic mode of life. Benedict, however, had renounced, not the poets especially, but literature altogether. Moreover, I very much doubt if his admirer would have been himself admired had he proceeded to adopt the same plan. It is one thing to have learned, another to be in the process of learning. It is only the hope of acquisition which the boy renounces, — quite a different thing from the learning itself, which an older person gives up; the former but turns away from an obstacle, while the latter sacrifices an ornament. The trials and uncertainties of acquisition are alone surrendered in one case; in the other the man sacrifices the sure and sweet fruit of long, laborious years, and turns his back upon the precious treasure of learning which he has gathered together with great effort.

While I know that many have become famous for piety without learning, at the same time I know of no one who has been prevented by literature from following the path of holiness. The apostle Paul was, to be sure, accused of having his head turned by study, but the world has long ago passed its verdict upon this accusation. If I may be allowed to speak for myself, it seems to me that, although the path to virtue by the way of ignorance may be plain, it fosters sloth. The goal of all good people is the same, but the ways of reaching it are many and various. Some advance slowly, others with more spirit; some obscurely, others again conspicuously. One takes a lower, another a higher path. Although all alike are on the road to happiness, certainly the more elevated path is the more glorious. Hence ignorance, however devout, is by no means to be put on a plane with the enlightened devoutness of one familiar with literature. Nor can you pick me out from the whole array of unlettered saints, an example so holy that I cannot match it with a still holier one from the other group.

But I will trouble you no longer with these matters, as I have already been led by the nature of the subject to discuss them often. I will add only this: if you persist in your resolution to give up those studies which I turned my back upon so long ago, as well as literature in general, and, by scattering your books, to rid yourself of the very means of study, — if this is your firm intention, I am glad indeed that you have decided to give me the preference before everyone else in this sale. As you say, I am most covetous of books. I could hardly venture to deny that without being refuted by my works. Although I might seem in a sense to be purchasing what is already my own, I should not like to see the books of such a distinguished man scattered here and there, or falling, as will often happen, into profane hands. In this way, just as we have been of one mind, although separated in the flesh, I trust that our instruments of study may, if God will grant my prayer, be deposited all together in some sacred spot where they may remain a perpetual memorial to us both. I came to this decision upon the day on which he died who I hoped might succeed me in my studies. I cannot, however, fix the prices of the books, as you most kindly would have me do. I do not know their titles and number, or their value. You can arrange this by letter, and on the understanding that if it should ever occur to you to spend with me the little time which remains to us, as I have always wished, and you at one time seemed to promise, you will find the books you send with those that I have recently gathered together here, all of them equally yours, so that you will seem to have lost nothing, but rather gained, by the transaction.

Lastly, you assert that you owe money to many, to me among others. I deny that it is true in my case. I am surprised at so unfounded and even absurd a scruple of conscience on your part. I might apply Terence's saying, that you seem "to be looking for a joint in a reed." You owe me nothing but love, and not even that, since you long ago paid me in full, — unless it be that you always are owing, because you are always receiving. Still, one who pays back so promptly cannot properly be said ever to owe.

As to the complaint of poverty, which I have frequently heard from you before, I will not attempt to furnish any consolation or to cite any illustrious examples of indigence. You know them already. I will only say plainly what I have always said: I congratulate you for preferring liberty of mind and tranquil poverty to the opulence which I might have procured for you, even though tardily. But I cannot praise you for scorning the oft-repeated invitation of a friend. I am not in a position to endow you. If I were, I should not confine myself to pen or words, but should address you with the thing itself. But I am amply supplied with all that two would need, if, with a single heart, they dwelt beneath a single roof. You insult me if you scorn my offers, still more so, if you are suspicious of their sincerity.

Padua, May 28 [1362].

GIOVANNI BOCCACCIO

(1313–1375)

Boccaccio was the third of the writers to establish the beginnings of modern literature. In their works which have lived most among men, Dante was the mystic, Petrarch the artist, and Boccaccio—although at first sight a novelist—was essentially the poet. Upon his tomb at Certaldo he chose to have inscribed in his epitaph—"studium fuit alma poesis"; his absorbing study was divine poetry. Two living individuals powerfully influenced the course of his life: Maria d'Aquino at the court of Naples, and his master of poetry and scholarship Francis Petrarch. Both of them in different ways fired his passion for poetry. He wrote poetry in his own tongue. He studied the poetry of the past, defended it, and compiled works to promote its study and influence in his own day. He conceived the poet as a leader of highest genius.

The material of poetry lay immediately in his own life, the story of which holds a deeper human interest than any narrative that came from his own pen. His father was Boccaccio or Boccaccino di Chellino from Certaldo in the Valdelsa. He came with his brother to Florence and became a merchant or money-changer associated with the wealthy banking house of the Bardi, whose business at times brought him to Naples and to Paris. Giovanni was his natural son, born in Paris in 1313. Very little is known of the poet's mother, but she is thought to have been of semi-noble birth, perhaps of the De la Roche family; her name may have been Jeanne.

Boccaccino deserted the poet's mother, and Giovanni's earliest memories were of Florence and its countryside. His earliest schooling was at Florence, where his father married; it was intended to prepare him ultimately for the world of business. His father's home did not remain pleasant for him, however; his life opened out only upon his going to Naples. It was probably in 1328, when he was fifteen years of age, that Boccaccino placed him as an apprentice in the commercial house of one of his associates in Naples. He remained there for six years, which he considered wasted; his father then permitted him to turn to the study of Canon Law for six years more.

But the Naples of Boccaccio's youth under King Robert of Anjou was joyous, rich, and magnificent above all other Italian cities. His real education was obtained in the atmosphere of its court, its university, and its seaside. He received instruction in astronomy from the court astrologer Andalò de' Negri, perhaps in classical antiquity from the king's librarian Paolo di Perugia, in his first Greek from the Calabrian monk Barlaam; at the same time in large measure he was self-educated. The experience which molded his entire life is recorded for us only in his romances and there indirectly. It was probably in 1336, on the Saturday before Easter in the Church of San Lorenzo, that he first saw the one whom he represented as Fiammetta. Her name was Maria d'Aquino, but she was the natural daughter of King Robert. Her mother was the Countess of Aquino, a Provençal lady. Maria was, probably contrary to her own wishes, married to a noble of the court. The tale woven into the romances is one of a brief period of ecstatic joy, followed by suspicions and jealousy on Boccaccio's part; then her growing coldness, and final abandonment of him. She deserted him in 1338. In disillusionment and despair, Boccaccio withdrew into a study of the Latin poets — Ovid, Virgil, Statius, in a house outside the city near the Tomb of Virgil where he seems then to have been living. Then, in 1340, he was recalled to Florence because of his father's financial downfall.

Boccaccio's love of Maria made him a poet. In one form or another, the experience is reflected in six of his youthful works. The *Filocolo,* a long novel in prose of the love of Florio and Biancofiore, was begun at her request in Naples, although later completed at Florence. The *Filostrato,* a poem in *ottava rima,* the story of Troilo and Criseida, was written to express his suffering when she had left Naples for Sannio; Chaucer was to use it for his *Troilus and Criseyda.* The *Teseide,* also in *ottava rima,* the story of the loves of Arcita and Palemone for Emilia, was written at Naples for her; it later appeared in Chaucer's *Knight's Tale.* Later, at Florence, he wrote the *Ameto,* a pastoral romance and allegory in prose and verse, on the subject of the civilizing power of love; the *Amorosa Visione,* an allegorical poem in *terza rima,* in which Love and Maria are glorified; and the *Elegia di Madonna Fiammetta,* a psychological novel in prose, in which the circumstances are reversed and Fiammetta is made to experience his own sufferings.

Boccaccio's return to Florence and his father was sad and dispiriting. Our information concerning the decade 1340–50 is all too little. Perhaps he sought for consolation vainly in new loves; his little daughter Violante, whose early loss he lamented so tenderly, was probably born at this time. We know that he occupied himself much with studies and writing. In addition to the works mentioned above, he wrote the charming pastoral romance, *Ninfale Fiesolano,* at this time. Late in 1346, however, he was in Ravenna. Late in 1347 or early in 1348, he was at Forlì, apparently in the service of Francesco degli Ordelaffi, lord of that city. In 1348, the Black Death swept through Florence; in the *Decameron* he says that he saw it with his own eyes. Fiammetta died of it in Naples. His father died in 1349. In 1350 he took charge of the instruction of his half-brother, Jacopo. The world of Boccaccio's youth had vanished and with it his own youth had gone. It was under these conditions that the *Decameron* was begun late in 1348 and finished in 1353. It thus belongs to the middle period of his life. No longer do we find his personal experience enshrined in his work. The idealization and passion of youth are supplanted by the detached outlook of the observer, at times perhaps somewhat sardonic, at times with that laughter of the intellect which George Meredith called the Spirit of Comedy. His artistic power, here at its height, created the greatest work in Italian prose, and wrought a series of tales — the pageant of his century, with all its human comedy, irony, and tragedy — which has become a part of world literature.

In the years that followed the Black Death, Boccaccio's growing fame and his own need secured for him offices and missions of honor from his fellow citizens. In 1350, he was sent as ambassador to the lords of Romagna. In the same year he was sent as special messenger from the captains of the Company of Or San Michele to carry ten gold florins "to sister Beatrice, daughter of Dante Alighiere, nun in Santo Stefano dell'Uliva in Ravenna." With the deep-seated reverence he held for his greatest predecessor, he must have found this a very moving experience. In 1351, he was entrusted with negotiations with the queen of Naples, and on another occasion with Louis of Bavaria. In 1354, with a single colleague, he was sent to Pope Innocent VI at Avignon. In 1355, he served in the Ufficio della Condotta. In these latter years he wrote the intense and bitter prose work, *Il Corbaccio,* which shows the inner reactions from the experience of his youth.

For many years, Boccaccio had admired ardently the career and doctrines of Francis Petrarch. He hastened to meet him for the first time as Petrarch passed through Florence on his way to Rome in the autumn of 1350. There began the crowning friendship of Boccaccio's life, which lasted until death. In it Boccaccio acted as disciple to his glorious master. In letters to others he confessed to have owed to Petrarch whatever of good was in him, that his master had persuaded him "to direct the mind toward eternal things, leaving aside the delight of the temporal." In 1351, he carried to Petrarch at Padua the letter in which Florence offered the distinguished humanist a chair in her newly-founded university and the restitution of his father's property. In 1362, after Boccaccio had received from a dying Sienese monk a warning to forsake poetry in the presence of imminent death, his perspective was restored by the advice and wisdom of Petrarch, who persuaded Boccaccio to live with him for three golden summer months in his house in Venice in 1363.

Under the influence of Petrarch's classical scholarship, Boccaccio wrote his own humanistic works. From 1360–62 Boccaccio entertained the Greek Leontius Pilatus in his house at Florence, where they carried on the first translation of Homer into Latin, and where Pilatus lectured in the university. Boccaccio's own Latin works were compiled as handbooks for poets and for students of classical poetry and history. Four in number, they were of wide influence in his time: the *De Genealogiis Deorum Gentilium, The Genealogy of the Gentile Gods,* an encyclopaedia of classical mythology, the two last books of which comprise Boccaccio's important defense of poets and poetry; *De Casibus Virorum Illustrium,* which John Lydgate used for his *Falls of Princes; De Claris Mulieribus,* lives of famous women of antiquity and of more recent times; and *De Montibus, Silvis, Fontibus, et Lacubus,* a geographical dictionary.

Despite Boccaccio's services for the Florentine Commune, however, he complained increasingly of poverty and sought some definite settlement of his life. Late in 1362, he accepted the invitations of Niccolò Acciaiuoli and Francesco Nelli to come to Naples, but left after six months, unable to endure the living conditions they provided. Finally, in 1363, returning from the Venetian summer spent with Petrarch, he took refuge at Certaldo. From here he wrote the *Epistola a messer Pino de'Rossi,* in which he denounced the wealthy citizens then in control in Florence and described the peace of his own refuge. Certaldo proved to be the central place of sojourn during his last years. He was called by Florence in 1365 and in 1367 upon embassies to Pope Urban V, first to Avignon and then to Rome. In 1367, he went to Venice, called there to attend "to a certain somewhat difficult affair" in which friends were involved; he had hoped to see Petrarch, but in his absence was entertained graciously by Petrarch's daughter Francesca and her husband. The delightful letter to Petrarch which followed expressed glowing praise of his host and hostess and of their little Eletta who reminded him of his own lost Violante. He was in Naples late in 1370 and in 1371 but, declining further invitations, was back in Tuscany in the spring of 1371, probably at Certaldo.

The last work of Boccaccio's life proved to be an act of veneration. He had lived with Dante's writings from early years, had taken every opportunity to gather information about him from those still living in Florence and Ravenna who had known him, and had already written the first *Vita di Dante.* In 1373, Florence called him to give the first public lectures on the *Divine Comedy* in Santo Stefano della Badia. He was then sixty years of age. He was obliged to discontinue them after a few months, owing to his poor health and perhaps also to clerical opposition to the public revelation of Dante's divine mysteries. In October 1374 he received at Certaldo the news of Petrarch's death. He himself died at Certaldo on the 21st of December 1375, and was buried there in the Church of San Jacopo as he had wished.

It is difficult to know whether Boccaccio attained philosophic serenity in his last years. Fiammetta's betrayal inflicted a wound which was never healed. Even though his love for her passed into the inner sanctuary of his life, her betrayal gave rise to an increasingly bitter attitude toward women. The friendship of Petrarch came to supplant Fiammetta's love. And the devotion to divine Poetry remained the enduring passion of his life.

SELECTED BIBLIOGRAPHY

EDITIONS

Opere Volgari di Giovanni Boccaccio, ed. Ignazio Moutier, Florence, Magheri, 17 vols., 1827–34; to be superseded by the edition now in process of publication in "Scrittori d'Italia," Bari, Laterza: *Il Filostrato,* ed. V. Pernicone, 1937; *Il Decameron,* ed. A. F. Massèra, 2 vols., 1927. *Il De-*

camerone, ed. M. Scherillo, Milan, Hoepli, 1914, 1 vol., annotated, for general use.

TRANSLATIONS

Thirteen Most Pleasant and Delectable Questions [Fragment of *Il Filocolo*], Englished 1566 by H. G., introd. E. Hutton, London, Davies, 1927; *Il Filostrato,* trans. Hubertis Cummings, Princeton Univ. Press, 1924; *The Filostrato,* trans. N. E. Griffin and A. B. Myrick, Univ. of Penn. Press, 1929; *Il Filostrato,* in *The Story of Troilus,* by R. K. Gordon, London, Dent, 1934; *Amorous Fiammetta,* trans. Bartholomew Young (1587), introd. E. Hutton, London, Navarre Soc., 1926; *Decameron,* trans. John Payne, London, Villon Soc., 1886, also in Modern Lib.; *Decameron,* trans. J. M. Rigg, London, Bullen, 1903, also in Everyman's Lib.; *De Genealogia Deorum Gentilium,* Books XIV and XV, in *Boccaccio on Poetry,* trans. Charles G. Osgood, Princeton Univ. Press, 1930; *Life of Dante,* trans. J. R. Smith, in *Aids to the Study of Dante,* by C. A. Dinsmore, 70–111, Boston, Houghton Mifflin, 1903; *De Claris Mulieribus, Forty-six Lives,* trans. Henry Parker, Lord Morley, ed. H. G. Wright, E. E. T. Soc., London, Oxford Univ. Press, 1943.

BIOGRAPHY AND CRITICISM

Francesco Torraca, *Per la Biografia di G. Boccaccio,* Rome, Albrighi, 1912; Henri Hauvette, *Boccace, Étude Biographique et Littéraire,* Paris, Colin, 1914; G. Lipparini, *La Vita e l'Opera di G. Boccaccio,* Florence, Monnier, 1927; Letterio di Francia, "G. Boccaccio," in *Enciclopedia Italiana,* VII, 219–29, 1930.

Edward Hutton, *Giovanni Boccaccio. A Biographical Study,* London, John Lane, 1910; Walter Raleigh, "Boccaccio," in *Some Authors,* 1–26, Oxford, Clarendon Press, 1923; J. W. Krutch, "Boccaccio," in *Five Masters,* New York, Cape & Smith, 1930; Thomas C. Chubb, *The Life of G. Boccaccio,* New York, Boni, 1930; Catherine Carswell, *The Tranquil Heart. Portrait of G. Boccaccio,* New York, Harcourt Brace, 1937; Francis MacManus, *Boccaccio,* New York, Sheed & Ward, 1947.

SPECIAL STUDIES

Karl Young, *The Origin and Development of the Story of Troilus and Criseyde,* Chaucer Soc., Second Series, XLI, London, 1908; A. C. Lee, *The Decameron: Its Sources and Analogues,* London, Nutt, 1909; E. H. Wilkins, "The Enamorment of Boccaccio," *Mod. Philol.,* XI (1913), 39–55; H. M. Cummings, *The Indebtedness of Chaucer's Works to the Italian Works of Boccaccio,* Univ. of Cincinnati Studies, Vol. 10, Part 2, 1916; V. Cioffari, "The Conception of Fortune in the Decameron," *Italica,* XVII (1940), 129–37; Angelo Lipari, "The Structure and Real Significance of the Decameron," in *Essays in Honor of A. Feuillerat,* 43–83, Yale Univ. Press, 1943; see also Singleton, *Italica,* XXI (1944), 117–24, and Lipari, *Italica,* XXII (1945), 101–8; Cornelia C. Coulter, "'A Song for Men in Days to Come,'" *Am. Jour. of Archaeol.,* LIV (1950), 193–202; Edith G. Kern, "The Gardens of the *Decameron* Cornice," *Pub. Mod. Lang. Assoc.,* LXVI (1951), 505–23; Enrico De' Negri, "The Legendary Style of the *Decameron,*" *Rom. Rev.,* XLIII (1952), 166–89.

IL FILOSTRATO

Translated by Hubertis Cummings

[Taken from *Il Filostrato by Giovanni Boccaccio,* translated by Hubertis Cummings, Princeton University Press, 1924.]

CANTO ONE

1

Some poets, Lady, still of Jove do crave
Fair favour for poetic enterprise;
Others invoke Apollo's aid to save
Their fragile verse. E'en I, with frequent sighs,
Besought Parnassian Muses, all too grave,
My theme to lift through music to the skies;
But Love, who changed old use, doth now require
I seek thine aid alone my true song to inspire.

2

Thou, Lady, art that clear and lovely light
Which in the darkness still my life illumes;
And thou that only star serenely bright
Whose ray, across the mountains, sweet assumes
The guidance of my bark from storm and night
Till anchored there, where joyous comfort blooms,—
With thee,—who art my Phoebus,—art my Jove,—
My Muse,—and all the good I feel and know of Love!

3

Lady, thy absence now, to me a woe
Greater than death itself, constrains my will
To write the grievous life of Troilo
Whenafter Criseis, who caused him ill,
Was forced, yet all in love with him, to go
Outside the Trojan walls, ere either fill
Of amorous delights had known; so, wise,
Thy puissant aid I seek for this my enterprise!

4

Whence, Lady fair,—whose faithful servitor
I e'er have been, whose subject ever hence
Shall be,—and thy fair eyes' refulgent store

Of light, where Love my every joy of sense
Hath placed,— my only hope,— I thee implore,
As one who loves thee than himself much more,—
With perfect love,— guide thou my hand aright,
Direct my mind in what my soul hath come to write.

5

In my sad heart thou art so effigied
Thou hast become more potent there than I.
O bring my voice then from my heart, I plead,
So sad it shall through sorrow's tones descry
My own deep grief in Troil's woes, and start
Whoever hears to pity of my need.
And if men listen, be the honour thine,
The praise thy words shall win — the labour be but mine!

6

And ye, O lovers, now I pray attend
The tale my tear-brimmed cantos would rehearse;
And, if perchance in your hearts doth extend
A spirit rising piteous to my verse,
I pray you pray that Amor succour lend
To me, like Troil, neath a heavy curse
Of grief, in that I live afar from her
Who would in every mind sweet joy and pleasaunce stir.

7

The kings of Greece besieged in full array
The ample walls of Troy, and all in pride
Of armour blazoned rich abode the fray,
Ardent and eager-proud (as each descried
The power Greece acquired from day to day).
They showed themselves in one great wish allied —
T' avenge the insult and the bold rapine
By Paris done, of Helen, Menelaus' queen.

8

When Calchas (that famed seer whose science high
Had merited full oft Apollo's trust
And won him sager knowledge from the sky)
With will to learn inquired which party must
Expect to win at last,— if victory
To Trojans' suffering long or Grecians' lust
In battle, meed should be; and, waiting, heard
The war assured Troy's doom, a bitter cruel word!

9

And, knowing now her hosts would all be slain
And Troy ere long destroyed, the cunning seer
Resolved on sudden flight, and, counsel ta'en

Duly of time and place, rode slyly near
The Grecian lines; and there upon the plain
Full many Greeks, on seeing him appear,
Arose to welcome him with faces bright,—
Hoping his wit might help, should theirs come evil plight.

10

Great was the uproar in the Trojan town
When Rumour on her eager wings had sped
The news abroad: "Our wary prophet's frown
No more can warn us now, for he is fled,—
A traitor proved and to the Greeks gone down!"
Then, by his crime inflamed and fury-led,
The crowd was scarce restrained from vengeance dire,—
And feeling flared up quick to set his house on fire.

11

Calchas in that ill hour's evil case,
All uninformed of his intended flight,
Had left behind in that quick-hostile place
An only widowed daughter, fair as light,—
No mortal thing but one of angel's grace
She seemed, and Criseis named, to human sight
The loveliest of all Troy's womanhood,
Dainty and lissome, wise, most chastely true and good.

12

Who, learning soon all dolorous the cause
Of that rude outcry,—Calchas' treachery,
For all that furious hubbub made no pause
But rose, donned mourning habit tearfully,—
Like one who tow'rd an altar suppliant draws,
And, seeking Hector, fell to bended knee
Bemoaning Calchas' guilt with piteous face—
The while she guiltless begged the prince might lend her grace.

13

Great Hector was by nature pitiful,
And, hearing there that lady's weeping plaint
(Fairer than ladies fair by every rule
She was), with measured speech and sweet restraint,
Bade Criseis comfort take: "Thy father, fool
In evil erring, be dismissed and faint
Amid the Greeks!" quoth he, "But in security
Dwell thou, fair lady, here as long as pleaseth thee.

14

"Such favours as thou wilt and honours, too,
As if Sage Calchas still were here, receive

For certain now; we grant them as thy due
In every future need. Cease hence to grieve!
But him may God with condign shame pursue!"
And more to press her thanks, ere taking leave,
He suffered Criseis not; whereat she rose
And sought her mansion out and there more safe repose.

15

Such household there as fitted her estate,
And to her honour, Criseis maintained
The while she dwelt in Troy without debate,
Modest in custom and in life unstained,
Marvel of chasteness in her widow's state,
Sans any child to be in 'haviour trained
She was as free as maid still unpossessed —
By all who knew her loved and by all richly blest.

16

So things progressed (as in war usually)
Twixt Greeks and Trojans ever much the same;
Ofttimes the Trojans came out valiantly,
And, driving back the Greeks, earned praise and fame;
Ofttimes the Greeks, — unless much history
Doth err, — went at their foes with lusty game
Up to their very moat, — and e'en inside
They robbed, burned hall and villa, plundered far and wide.

17

And still the Trojans, hard as they were pressed
By the high daring of their Grecian foes,
Failed never once their reverence to attest
In holy rites; but evermore they chose
To keep their customs, and, as suppliants dressed,
Crowded good Pallas' temple; where arose
Many a solemn anthem in high praise,
Many a Trojan's vow, his prayer, his reverent gaze!

18

For now fair spring had come, whose potent sway
Reclothes the meads with flowers and grasses new,
When every beast becomes both blithe and gay,
And brings by divers acts his loves to view;
When Trojan sires had bid such honours pay
To the divine Palladium as were due.
Ladies and knights joined that festivity
In equal manner, — coming all most willingly.

19

Mongst others Calchas' daughter Criseis moved,
Apparelled chastely in her russet weeds,
Wherein, just as the rose hath ever proved
Still fairer than the violet (which leads
In beauty other flowers), that lady loved,
Surpassed the fairest in her modest deeds
And, by her presence near the temple door,
Made goodlier yet that great fête's rich and goodly store.

20

When mid the throng, as youths are wont to do,
Peering about the temple here and there,
Prince Troilo approached with other few,
And stopped and stood Troy's ladies to compare:
"This one," he gan, "was fair, that one a shrew!"
So praised or blamed, — like one who did not care,
Like one to whom no maid could give delight
Or youth who'd keep him free in every maid's despite.

21

In such a mood of scorn proceeding free,
If he beheld a youth with languorous sigh
Gazing upon a lady fixedly,
The prince would to his comrades jesting cry:
"Lo there a wretch who to his liberty
Would set a bound, — it vexes him so nigh, —
And in yon damsel's hand would bind it fain;
Mark ye his thoughts, how idle-fond they are and vain!

22

"What is't in womankind faith to repose?
Whose heart turns in one day a thousand ways,
Like to a leaf if breeze upon it blows?
Nor doth a lover's care within her raise
One pang of grief; nor is there one who knows
What silly whim shall next command her praise.
O happy is the man who's never ta'en
With idle love for her — who's brave yet to abstain!

23

'From mine own folly I have knowledge gained,
Who suffered his curst flames in me to burn;
So, said I now Love ne'er with me maintained
A gracious mien but rather did me spurn,
Giving me naught, my words were false and feigned;
Yet Love's gifts, gathered, prove a poor return, —
His cheer affords no boon of certain joy
Compared with lovers' woes and lovers' sad annoy!

24

"That I am free my thanks I him accord
Whose mercy proved far higher than my own,
Almighty Jove, true deity and lord
Of every grace to me, — who not o'erthrown
By Love must live, but, glad to see adored
Fair maids by other youths, may move alone
Steering an easy course, and laugh to scorn
All such pale, troubled lovers with their moods forlorn!"

25

O blindness of man's dull and earthly mind!
Too oft the end will man's forethought belie
And bring effect of far contrary kind!
Satiric Troilo would fain decry
Their silly faults whom love doth anxious bind,
Nor dreams that Heav'n doth even now espy
Some means to break his pride — that Love's sharp darts
Will pierce him ere he from that festive temple parts.

26

Pursuing then Love's followers to deride,
This one or that, — the while his idle gaze
Reviewed the damsels there on every side,
Perchance his wandering eye, with great amaze,
Mid ladies fair hath Criseis espied
Traversing daintily those througéd ways,
Her garb still russet neath a veil milkwhite, —
In that so solemn festival a pleasing sight!

27

This Criseis was tall — of stately height
Whereto her members were proportioned well;
A beauty born of fair celestial might
Adorned her winsome face, sans parallel.
Yea, for her features shone serenely bright
With womanly noblesse, when — subtly — fell,
Touched by her arm, her mantle from her face,
As 'twere to awe the crowd that swarmed about the place!

28

Which graceful gesture pleased young Troilo,
So in the movement showed her dainty pride, —
As if she said: "May not a wight stand so?" —
And mute he gazed upon her face and stride,
Which, as he looked, did ever fairer grow, —
More worthy praise, — and now first he espied
How sweet it is to gaze, in joy and grace,
From soul to soul, — on lucent eyes and heavenly face.

29

And he no jot perceived, who'd been so shrewd
Before to censure love in other men,
That Amor, dwelling in the ray unviewed
Of her bright eyes, aimed true his dart just then;
Nor did that weapon, deep with love imbrued,
Of his late taunts remind him once again
What time he scorned Love's languorous retinue,
For still of Love's sweet sting the prince but little knew.

30

Beneath her mantle's folds so pleasingly
And peerless, too, the face of Criseis shone
That Troil gazed thereon in ecstasy,
Held by a cause he could not name, if known;
Only he knew a high will now to see
To be less far — to keep his thoughts his own —
To love and win! When Pallas' rites were past
He stood there still — hardly his comrades stirred him at the last.

31

Not as he entered there so free and gay,
The prince made exit from the temple now,
But pensive, all enamoured, — went his way, —
Beyond his own belief, with solemn vow
To keep well hid his new desire, and say
No word, nor that, his recent prate, allow
Henceforth expressed, lest on himself be turned
The ridicule his ardour would have meetly earned.

32

When from that spacious temple now had moved
This Criseis, too, then changéd Troilo
Joined his companions and the hours improved
By making with them blithe and merry show,
And tarried long — and that, his wound beloved,
Better to hide, kept all his jests aglow
O'er men that love, saying how differently
His own heart fared; and bade all go and be as free.

33

At length, his comrades separating all,
The prince sought out alone his chamber-room,
And there to sighing let his fancy fall,
Stretched on his bed, and now would fain resume
The pleasure of his morning, fain recall
The charming aspect of sweet Criseis' bloom,
Counting the beauties of her lovely face,
Commending this or that part for its charm and grace.

34

He praised her conduct and her stately size,
Saying she showed her heart's munificence
Both in her mien and gait; what high emprise
To win a lady of such excellence,
And have her love! O matchless, matchless prize,
If to his wooing in pure innocence
She could consent, could love as he loved now,
And, smiling on her servant, accept her servant's vow!

35

He told himself no labour and no sigh
Expended in her service could be lost,
Thought his desire would win applause most high
If told to friends who chanced him to accost,
Reasoned his fellows would not now decry
His love, knowing the pain wherein he tossed;
Then gladly argued he could hold his peace,
Unwitting how soon cheer and joyaunce cease.

36

Disposed to follow, then, such fair fortune,
To act in everything discreet he planned,
With thought to hide his ardour as a boon
Too rich for common use by vulgar hand,—
A thing conceived in amorous mind and tune,—
From every friend, from every servant bland,
Unless some need compel; for love, in truth,
To many known brings joy with much commingled ruth.

37

Such thoughts and others now he entertained,
How to disclose his love and how attract
The favour of sweet Criseis, undisdained,—
And, after this, conformed his every act
To songs of hope and passion unrestrained;
To love one lady only is his pact,
Holding at naught all ladies seen before,—
However they had pleased, they could not please him more.

* * * * *

45

From reveries of love he was not stirred
E'en by his sharing in those battles fought
And stern assaults fierce-joined at Hector's word,
Wherein he with his brothers moved; but, caught
With growing wonder, now the Trojans heard

Or, as they followed, cheered his fierce onslaught,
Or stopped to see the marvel flash in arms,
His courage never daunted in the great alarms.

46

But 'twas no hate for Greeks that moved him so,
Nor victory desired great Troy to free
(Troy which he saw so straitened by her foe
In that great siege); but in him, secretly
His will still clutched at glory, urged him go
Down in the field for Love's felicity,—
Criseis' favour won! And, if the story's true,
His mere approach the Greeks in mortal terrour threw.

47

And so had Amor robbed him of his sleep,
His appetite depressed, and earnest thought
So in him multiplied,— that pallour deep
Spread o'er his face the while he toiled and fought
As if it would belie his deeds and weep.
But spite of it, with laughter feigned he sought,
And speaking blithe, to cover up his pain,
Till Troy believed 'twas only war he felt as bane.

48

Whate'er in all this still remains unsure,
Whether Criseis did not once suspect
The love this Troil strove to hide secure,
Or feigning not to know it did elect,—
This much is clear and must as truth endure
That nothing, it appeared, the lady recked
Of all the love her lover tow'rd her bore,
But stood, like one unloved,— unsoftened,— evermore.

49

Whence Troilo such grievous dolour knew
He could not name it e'en, and much he sighed
Lest Criseis should with greater favour view
Some other knight and therefore should deride
His love, if known, and all his service true
Reject; and now a myriad ways he tried,
In his mind's eye to make his lady feel
How honest was his love, how fervid and how real.

50

And then, when it had stung him thus a space,
The prince began of Love to make a moan,

Saying within: "Lo, Troil, there thy place,—
Where thou didst others mock,—to stand alone!
Ne'er was a lover brought so in disgrace
Since how to keep from Love he had not known!
Thou'rt taken in the net thou censured hast:
Because thou didst not wisely guard thee at the last!

51

"What will be said of thee mid other knights
Who love, if this thy love becometh known?
Will they not revel in new gibes and slights
Or cry at thee: 'The railer's overthrown;
No more so seer-like proud the prince indicts
Our sighs and every low-breathed amorous moan;
Behold the bitter bitten! Love be praised,
Who to such end hath brought the scorner lately crazed!'

* * * * *

55

"O aid me, Love, I plead! And thou for whom,
Enchained now more than other knights, I weep,
Vouchsafe some pity for thy lover's doom,
Who more than life loves thee with ardour deep;
Turn thou thy face's power to illume
Upon thy knight; grant Love his way to keep,
For in these sighs for thee he holds me strait;
Refuse not kindness to my sad-despairéd state.

56

"Yet if thou must refuse my poor request,
Like vernal bloom I'll early fade away;
Waiting shall then no more my peace molest
Nor seeing thy high pride my soul dismay;
But should such course aggrieve thee, this behest,
Ready in all to please, I crave today;—
Cry, cruel: 'Slay thyself, Sir Troilo.'
And I, to give thee pleasaunce, will do even so!"

57

This and full many other pleas he made
Deep-plunged in sighs and weeping, calling out
Her name like one whose love is undismayed
Even in the uttermost of grief and doubt;
But to his plaints he found no mercy stayed;
All were but leaves, blown in the wind about
And lost, none reaching Criseis' ear;
And thence grew every day his torment and his fear.

CANTO TWO

1

So lasted many moons his pensive mood
Till one day, in his chamber all alone,
A Trojan youth, of courage high imbued
And ancient lineage born, slipped in unknown
And there his friend the woeful prince first viewed
Melted to wretched tears and lying prone
Upon his couch: and "How now, friend," he cried,
"Doth this our bitter hour so conquering o'er thee ride?"

2

And him the prince quick queried, "Pandaro,
What chance hath led thee here to see me die?
If to our friendship any debt thou owe,
Away with thee! Begone! O let me lie
Disconsolate, for this of truth I know,
Of all my friends thou wouldst to see me die
Be saddened most; and I thrive not in life
So conquered is my strength, so battered by its strife.

3

"Yet do not think it is the siege of Troy
Or any task of arms or any fear
Occasions me my present great annoy;
Mid other cares that one doth least appear.
'Tis other grief that would my life destroy—
That makes me craven neath its wounds severe:
But what it is, seek not to know, my friend;
'Twere best I speak it not but hide it to the end."

4

In Pandaro an instant pity grew
And earnest wish sad Troil's pain to know;
Whence he once appealed, "Let friendship true,
As formerly 'twas wont, reveal thy woe
To me, thy friend, lest further ill ensue,—
Wherefore so fain to join the shades below?
It cannot be thou hold it friendly act
To hide from me, thy friend, the cause thou art so racked!

5

"Fain would I share with thee this grief and woe
If I can bring no ease to thine annoy,
Because friends must them ever willing show
To share all things, their sorrows and their joy;
That I have loved thee thou dost truly know,
Methinks, in good and ill with fair employ,—
Dost truly know I'd render any feat
Thou might'st require of me or as a friend entreat."

6

The prince sighed deep before he answer made:
"O Pandar mine, since nothing thee can please
Except thou know what woe hath me dismayed,
I'll yield and tell thee briefly my disease,—
Not in the hope that through thy proffered aid
I may somehow secure my spirit peace,—
But feeling I must satisfy thy prayer,
To which I know not how to make denial fair.

7

"Love,—gainst whom, if any try defence,
Too soon he's caught and finds his efforts vain,—
Flames now my heart with such all pleasant sense
I have no pow'r thence to remove his reign
Henceforth; and this now me so sore repents,
As thou canst see, my hand I scarce restrain,
And scarce have checked its thousandth trial
And fervent wish somehow to end my life most vile.

8

"Let this suffice thee, sweet and worthy friend,
To know then these my griefs, which hitherto
I have revealed to none, and God forfend,
If to my love thou'ldst hold thee loyal-true,
That thou disclose my eager amorous end
And fervent wish, lest added ill ensue!
Thou knowst now what I will; go thou, I pray,
And let me fight alone my anxious fears today."

9

And Pandar answered: "Couldst thou hope to hide
So long from me thy great love's secret fire?
From me, who would my wits have glad applied
And found some means thy comfort to inspire
And sense of peace?" But Troilo replied,
"Comes aid from thee, whom ever love's desire
I see tormenting? O thou hapless wight,
Who thinkst with thine own frailty to relieve my plight!"

10

Whereto Pandaro urged: "I know, my lord;
'Tis sooth thou speakst, yet oftentimes 'twill fall
Who doth to other's counsel him accord
From venom saves himself and other gall;
And sure it is the blind can ill afford
To take those paths which seeing men appall;
And though no man may for himself prove wise,
He can give others aid when others' perils rise.

11

"I too have loved through much despairing hap,
And still I love of my perversity;
And must perforce keep me within the trap
Because I have not loved in secrecy
Like thee. And God my folly wills, mayhap!
But that all-loyal love I've given thee,
I bear thee still and will preserve so well
No man shall ever know the secret thou shalt tell.

12

"Rest then in me, my friend, thy trust secure,
And tell me all that causes this thy plight,—
What makes thy life so noxious to endure.
Fear not I shall assume the scorner's right
To mock thy love, for men that feel most sure
Within their wisdom would all deem it light
To claim love can be wrested from the heart
Ere long-besieging time hath willed it to depart.

13

"Leave then thine anguish, cease thy sighs,
And, reasoning, alleviate thy grief;
So make thy sufferings in fear arise
And pass, their pain becoming yet more brief;
They who feel love alike make best allies
Whene'er a lover's seen, 'tis my belief;
And I, as thou too knowst, against my will
Do love, and nothing can allay or soothe my ill!—

14

"Perchance the lovely one that troubles thee
I can e'en to thy pleasure somehow bend;
More gladly thy will satisfied I'd see,—
If so might be,—than mine own pleased, my friend.
Wouldst thou perceive it so, declare to me
Her name whose charms do so much pain portend.
Up, youth! Lie not so prone! Think, thou canst speak
With me as to thyself in trust both firm and meek."

15

Some time the anxious Troilo refrained,
Breathed deep,—but could not check his bitter sighs,
While shame his countenance with blushes stained,—
Then answered: "Pandar, friend,—true friend and wise,—
Of honest cause my will were best constrained—
I should not speak my love before thy eyes,
For she from whom I trace my grief so sore
Is of thy kin"— And, shame-faced, he could say no more.

16

And thereat Troil on his bed supine
Fell wild with weeping and there hid his face.
To whom good Pandar cried: "O comrade mine,
Should fear so easy over trust gain place
Within thy breast? Cease, craven, to repine,
Lest to thy weeping I my death should trace,—
Should she thou lovest my own sister prove,
Gladly with all my power I'd help thee win her love.

17

"Up then, my friend, and tell me who is she;
Tell me at once that I may see straightway
To thy sweet comfort, sweetest care for me.
In mine own mansion doth this lady stay?
Tell me I pray, whoever she may be
(For I go pond'ring who should be the may),
And I'll be certain scarce six days shall speed
Ere I shall wrest thee from this grievous state and need."

18

To these pleas Troilo would answer naught
And every moment closed his lips more tight,
But, as his ears Pandaro's promise caught,
Within himself he felt his hopes more bright;
And now he yearned to speak, and now he fought
His silence to maintain with all his might,
Ashamed to loose his tongue,—but Pandar urged;
At last he turned; and, weeping, forth his words now surged:

19

"My Pandar, I could wish that I were dead
Rather than thinking of Love's wound in me;
If by concealing it no pain were bred,
No wrong to thee, I'd still act feigningly;
But more I cannot; and, if thou art led
Wisely as is thy wont, well canst thou see
Love doth not wish that man should love by law
Save that one law which man's own appetite doth draw.

20

"For lawless Love makes men sometimes desire
Their sisters, girls their brothers wickedly;
Makes daughters love their fathers, and with fire
For sons-in-law fills beldames sans degree,
Making poor wights despite themselves aspire,
For good or ill, to know Love's ecstasy.
I love your cousin Criseis," he said,
Mouthing his words, and wept and fell back on his bed.

21

When Pandar now had heard the lady's name,
At first he laughed, then answered: "Troilo,
By Heaven I beg thee, friend, to change thy game
Of idly weeping, since Love hath loved thee so
Pointing tow'rd such a place thy amorous flame
It could not tow'rd a worthier lady blow.
The may, such beauteous grace is hers and rare,
In all her soul is worthy of thy love, I'd swear.

22

"No lover's friend was ever worthier,
More affable or sweeter in converse;
No lady could more grateful pleasaunce stir;
And poet could not of a queen rehearse
Virtues more rare than those that dwell in her;
Yea, of a truth they would transcend all verse.
For she is peerless! ne'er a king could hold
His heart in check should she her love to him unfold!

23

"Besides these graces named, another one,
To thee of evil omen, doth my cousin vaunt, —
Lady more chaste than she there liveth none,
And all Love's charms fall scorned beneath her taunt:
But gainst this virtue I'll find words to run, —
If other mishap enter not to daunt
Our hopes, — and win thy need. Have patience now
And curb thy ardent love with every act and vow.

24

"Well canst thou see, therefore, that Love hath stirred
Thy passion for one worth thy valiant name;
Stand therefore steadfast, both in act and word;
Expect, too, full success in thy new game,
Which presently on thee will be conferred,
Should not thy weeping its rare price disclaim;
Worthy thou art of her and she of thee,
And I will work the thing with ingenuity.

* * * * *

33

Thereat the prince leaped lightly from his bed,
Kissed and embraced full ardently his friend,
Swearing to win the war the Greek hosts led
Was no such task to him as to contend
Against that ardour which his passion fed:
"O Pandaro, my heart I recommend

To thy best aid, thou shrewd and prudent knight,
Who canst bring end to sorrow — means to love's delight!"

34

Desirous then to serve the royal youth,
Whom much he loved, this Pandar took his leave,
Hoping some pleasure might afford him ruth,
And sought out Criseis, — him to relieve, —
Who, as she saw him come, arose in sooth
And with fair greetings did her guest receive.
First Pandar hath her fingers lightly caught
And with her then a sheltered *loggia* sought.

35

And there with laughter, in parleying sweet,
With merry words and all that gay converse
Which kin are wont to use, and which most meet
Those close in blood do knowingly rehearse,
Pandaro played a while, with will to treat
His cherished scheme as if 't were the reverse,
Or of but trifling worth; then, sudden, gazed
So fixed in Criseis' face she might well grow amazed.

36

And, as she caught, thus fixed, his gaze, she smiled, —
Then cried: "Hast never seen my face before?
What subtlety hath now thy mind beguiled?
To what intent?" And Pandaro but swore:
"Thou knowst I've viewed thy beauty from a child,
But never hath it charmed my vision more
Than now; and Heaven thou mayest praise and thank
No fairer dame than thou appears in any rank!"

37

Whereto the lady begged: "What praise is this?
Wherefore pronounce me fairer than of yore?"
To whom he quickly answered, full of bliss:
"Because thy face would make all men adore,
None being in the world so fair, ywis!
And now, unless I am deceived the more,
It doth a well-made knight so wholly please
He boasts his love for thee e'en though from Love he flees!"

38

And Criseis thereon blushed so modestly,
Hearing the words her cousin Pandar spake,
She seemed a morning rose so fair was she;
Then from her lips such words as these did break:
"Make not thy mock of me, who joyous see

Whatever gifts to thee the kind gods make;
He must have little gear, this man I please;
Since birth, I have not charmed a wight with equal ease!"

39

"Let be thy words," our Pandar made reply,
"Declare if of his love thou art aware."
To whom she answered: "If I do not die,
No one man more than other hold I fair;
True 'tis from time to time I do espy
A passing knave who at my door will stare;
But whether he is looking there for me
Or of another dreams I know not certainly."

40

In answer Pandar queried, "Who is he?"
And Criseis replied again, "In sooth
I know him not, nor can I tell to thee
More than I've told." And, inward, "Of a truth,"
Pandaro reasoned, "The prince this cannot be;
Some other woos!" Then, quick to serve the youth,
He ventured more, "This man thou'st set in flame
Is known of all — and one, too, that deserves his fame."

41

"Who can," then Criseis quoth, "take such delight
In merely seeing me, — if I may ask?"
Whereto this Pandar with evasion slight:
"O damsel, since God wrought Creation's task, —
Made the first man, — there breathed no truer wight
Nor held more perfect soul in human mask
Than he whom I shall name, — whose love is such
One could not say a man had ever loved so much!"

42

"He is of spirit and of lineage proud,
An honest man who holds his honour dear;
With natural wit is no man more endowed,
Nor lives in other science e'en his peer,
Valour and zeal are in his face avowed;
I cannot tell you all his virtue clear;
O happy is thy beauty, which hath stirred
A man, so made, to hold thee to all dames preferred!

43

"Well is the jewel suited to the ring
If, as thou beauteous art, so provest thou wise;
If thou become his fief in anything
As he has thine become, a star will rise

In union with the sun; no luck could bring
To fairer *damoiseau* in amorous ties
A fairer *damoiselle!* Be thou but coy!
Blessed art thou, if thou wilt consummate thy joy.

44

"One only opportunity appears
To every one who lives that he may seize;
And whoe'er lets it come and pass, in tears
That man must grieve that it so rapid flees,
Blaming himself; and now to thee it nears,
Drawn by the might of thy fair face to please.
Employ thou it, — while I, more luckless born,
Weep that God, Fate, the World allowed me only scorn!"

45

"Are these true words, or wouldst thou tempt me ill?
Or art thou from thy wits?" gasped Criseis dumb;
"What man or knight should of me have his will
Save he had first my married lord become?
Yet say What man is this, — an alien still
Or citizen, on whom such pain hath come
For love of me? Speak, — if thou oughtest, speak,
And do not merely cry thy bootless sighs so meek."

46

And Pandar answered: "Citizen is he,
Yet none of mean degree, — my greatest friend,
From whose full breast, perhaps through Destiny,
This secret I've disclosed, I late did rend;
And now he lives in plaint and misery
Such fire thy glorious face doth in him send.
Know therefore now that he that loves thee so, —
Desires thee so, — is no man less than Troilo!"

47

Some time Criseis stood in mute amaze
Her eyes on Pandaro, until she grew
Pale as a dawn's most gray and sunless rays,
Wishing her tear-bright eyes were less in view.
Afraid her tears should flow their several ways
Or, unstemmed in their course, her cheeks endew:
Then, gaining speech, she murmured in surprise
With many a halting breath and many fearful sighs:

48

"I had believed, my cousin Pandaro,
If e'er I had so far in folly run
As redelessly to love Prince Troilo,

Thou wouldst have whipped me as a shameless one,
Thou wouldst have sworn I shamed my kindred so,
Disgraced my parents with the deed I'd done:
Now thou dost urge I follow Love's mad way;
Could strangers urge me worser rede than that, I pray?

49

"Troil, I know, is valorous and great,—
So brave a queen should find in him content;
But since my dear lord's death (unhappy fate!)
Always my heart has vowed with true intent
Never to love again; my widow's state
Always must be of grief and deep lament;
My only joy is memory of him—
My only wish that memory may never dim:

50

"Yet were there living man my love might win,
Surely that man should be thy Troilo
Could I be sure he felt true joy therein,
Once it was giv'n; but, Cousin, thou must know
Such ecstasies as Troil now is in
Do commonly befall, and even so
Last but four days or six—for o'er the night
Men's thoughts do change their love and men seek new delight.

51

"Let me continue such a life to lead
As Fate hath thought it fair to offer me;
And he will find some lady fair indeed
Whom he may love at will; for modesty
'Tis meet I save my honour for my need;
And Pandaro, let not this answer be,
For God's sweet sake, to thee a cause of grief;
But seek thou other pleasures to yield thy prince relief!"

52

Within him Pandar felt his cousin's scorn
The while the lady's speech he patient heard,
Then rose as one who thought his cause forlorn,—
As if to go, paused, turned, resumed his word,
And cried: "Sweet coz, to thee in praise I've borne
Such honour as with joy I'd see conferred
On my own sister, daughter, even wife—
If with such pleasant kindred God had blessed my life.

53

"And since I feel the prince is worth much more
Than e'er thy love could be, and yesterday

Because I saw him for it in a plight so sore,
I am myself much grieved, — alack the day!
Believe thou wilt not, nor his pain deplore:
But yet I know thy hardness would give way
If thou, like me, didst all his ardour know;
Then wouldst thou, for my sake, take pity on his woe.

54

"Discreet as he or of a faith as great,
I do not think in all the world is knight, —
Nor loyal friend as he in any state, —
And friend could not desire thee with more might!
'Tis meet thou love him, cease thy foolish prate
Of widow's weeds, and grant thy youth its right.
Waste not thy time; remember how dull death
Or age may catch thy charms away like idle breath."

55

"Alack," quoth Criseis, "thou speakest true;
The years recede and youth's frail charms decay
And, ere love's path in full celestial hue
Hath bloomed, we pass in dusty death away;
But let me still in thought this truth review
And tell me if of love at this late day
I yet may joy and solace have — and how —
And why — thou learn'dst the love of Troilo but now?"

* * * * *

65

At length Criseis answered: "Unaware
His secret thou hast caught from out his breast,
The while he mused, though firm he held it there,
Until thou foundst him to his tears addressed,
Prone on his bed! May God now yield him fair!
Make me no less than him to feel I'm blest!
For, through thy speech, strange pity stirs in me,
Who am in naught so harsh as I may seem to be."

66

Some time she paused; then, sighing deep, pursued
Almost transfixed: "Alas, I see it well,
Where leads thy pious wish when closely viewed;
But that I grant it *devoir* doth compel —
And pleasing thee; and he is worthily endued. —
Suffice it thee I see him, and then tell
How I, if he be sage, may scape all shame, —
Escape e'en worse perhaps, — and seem in naught to blame."

67

"Sweet sister mine," quick Pandar then replied,
"Thou sayest well; his shrewdness I'll demand
Though I am sure he hath no guile inside,—
So courteous he is, his heart so grand,—
Save some mischance hath newly changed its pride.
God save him aye from every lawless stand!
But I'll find thee such grace 'twill pleasure thee;
Dwell thou secure in God and to thy *devoir* see."

68

Pandaro went, and Criseis moved apart,
Pond'ring the news and every tiniest word
Brought by her cousin with his pleasant art,—
Then sought her room, where deep her fancies stirred;
How all was said she mused deep in her heart;
She reasoned joy like hers but rare occurred,
Talking within herself, and oft she sighed,
Picturing the prince in all his fame and pride:

69

"Young am I yet, noble and blithe and fair,
Widowed indeed, but rich and still admired,—
Nay even loved,—childless and free as air;
May I not then by love again be fired?
And though my honour should perchance declare,
'This must thou not,' I'll act as one inspired,
Be shrewd, conceal my will, and none will know
My heart hath willed new love, sad pleasaunce and sweet woe.

70

"My youth, as all youth, speeds it tow'rd decay,
And should I lose it then so wretchedly?
In all this world I cannot find to-day
Woman without a lover; nay more, I see
And know it well,—to love is all men's way:
And shall I lose my time in nullity?
To act as other mortals is no sin,
And blame from any one my actions cannot win.

71

"What man will want me, grown to older age?
No one, forsooth! In late years to repent
Will add but more woes to a grievous stage,
And futile prove my hours in mourning spent;
Alack words then, 'Why felt I not love's rage?'
Wise it will be to act full provident.
Fair is this man who loves thee, gentle, wise,
Fresh as the charm that in a garden lily lies.

72

"For royal blood and valour too supreme,
Pandar, thy cousin, praises Troilo?
Why then to thee should it unworthy seem,
To take him to thy heart and let him know?
Why not accord him every love and dream?
Dost not thou hear the pity of his woe?
O what rare bliss thou mightest with him see,
Couldst thou but love him now as he in sooth loves thee!

73

"Yet 'tis no time of marriage-ties for me;
And were it so, one's freedom to maintain
To use at will is wiser rule, I see;
Always that love proves lover's richer gain
Which grows from friendship's sweet felicity;
And howe'er great one's beauty may remain,
How sure are we 'twill not our husbands tire,
Who have each-every day some fresh thing in desire?

74

"As furtive water gives a sweeter taste
Than wine that's drunk too copiously, to one,
So is love's joy, that hides long unembraced
By any husband, the sweeter felt when won.
'Tis meet then thou, sans proving thee less chaste,
Receive this prince so sweet to look upon,
Whom God hath yielded thee by sov'reign grace,
And to his ardent love grant him a fairer place."

75

Some time she stood, then sudden turned about
And softly cried, "O wretched one," within,
"What wilt thou do? The evil life, no doubt,
That moves with love in love's sweet languid sin
Thou knowst and all its sighs,—a dreary rout,—
And all the plaints and griefs that dwell therein?
And to them all, so close-joined jealousy
That worse than churlish death our living comes to be!

76

"And as for him who so doth love thee now
He is a prince of loftiest birth and rank—
Out of thy star—his wish to keep Love's vow
May burn away and, if it fadeth blank,
Sorrow will be thy portion—thou wilt bow
Broken beneath thy shame, with him to thank,
Only for having scorned thee! O beware,
Wisdom that follows scandal hath no value rare!

77

"And even if this love should long endure,
How canst thou know it will remain concealed?
Foolish it is to trust to Fortune's lure;
And whate'er profit human counsel yield,
'Tis well to scan it close; of this be sure, —
If this thy love be e'er to men revealed,
Then is thy good fame lost eternally —
Lost here in Troy which so much praised thy chastity.

78

"Then let such love henceforth for them remain,
Whom it doth please." Such were the words she said,
And thereupon began her sighs again;
From her chaste breast with all her hardihead
She strove to drive Troilo's face. (In vain!)
Blame turned to praise and praise to blame instead,
The while she weighed his charms in reverie
Or raised within herself sweet doubts with subtlety.

[At Pandaro's urging, Troilo writes a letter which Pandaro carries to Criseis.]

108

Pandaro then the pious letter took
And, parting, sought out Criseis' abode;
Who, as she saw him come, her guests forsook,
Meeting him ere he o'er her threshold strode;
And like an orient pearl then she did look,
Poised between wish and trembling in her mode.
Each greeted other while they were afar
And then they clasped their hands as who most cordial are.

109

A moment's pause — then Criseis began;
"What business brings thee here? Is't tidings new?"
And to her Pandar's answer glibly ran:
"Lady, I have for thee good news and true,
But not for others' ears, — as, shouldst thou scan
These notes, they'll prove most quickly to thy view,
For he who wrote them soon will die of woe,
If thou'lt not soon on him some little love bestow!

110

"Take them, pursue them through with diligence;
And soon, I ween, reply will make him glad."
Criseis paused in timorous reticence,
Nor took them yet, the while to colour sad
Her face was changed, until with diffidence

She cried in plaintive note: "O Pandar mad,
Desist; if love puts thee in quiet truth,
Have some respect for me, not only for the youth.

111

"Thyself be judge, consider thou and see;
Ask thyself dost thou ask a seemly thing.
Can I do well to take immediately
Such letters as from Troil thou mayst bring?
Should e'er a woman through dishonesty
Think to cure pains that in her lover spring?
Leave not his letters here, I pray;
For God's love, Pandar, take them back — away! away!"

112

Pandaro, though disturbed, still urged his case:
"This is a matter ever strange in thought,
That what they most desire all dames abase,
And toward it ever each one feels she ought, —
Beyond her sex, — prove harsh in every place;
So oft before this truth to thee I've brought
Thou shouldst now be ashamed at hearing me;
But still I do beseech thou'lt not deny my plea."

113

A while Criseis listened ere she smiled,
And took and placed his letter in her breast;
"When I have leisure," she then murmured mild,
"Well as I can I'll scan what he's confessed;
And, if for doing so I am reviled,
The blame must be that I have been oppressed
By thy ill power; may God the cause observe,
And for my simple heart some honest way preserve!"

114

Pandar, the letter given, took his leave,
And Criseis, to know what words it said
Eagerly seized a time (one may believe)
To leave her maids, and to her room she sped.
There long she scanned the writing, sans reprieve,
And deep in pleasure, read it and re-read
Till she was ware so much Troilo burned
It seemed in no act could his love be e'er returned.

115

Then dear became the thought to her, to know
Love had so sudden pierced his heart and soul,
Though that thought, too, was smit with living woe,
So that she felt herself in nothing whole:

And each word writ, when noted, moved her so
She praised and thanked Love with an ample toll,
Urging within, "This fire to quench some way
'Tis meet for me to find the hour, place, and day.

116

"For, if I leave it in too great a flame
Increasing, it may hap incontinent
My face, discoloured to the point of blame,
May show the hid desire within me pent,
Which would be no small scar to my fair name;
Myself to die I have no great intent
Nor wish that others die, when, with such joy,
I can avoid my own and Troilo's annoy.

117

" 'Tis sure I shall not tow'rd him be disposed
Henceforth, as I have been until this hour;
If Pandaro returns, he'll find composed
My answer; I'll smile and give it to his power
E'en if there be therewith high cost imposed.
Nor shall they say I pine within my bower,
Despised by Troilo; nay, his embrace
Would I felt now, drawn to him even face to face!"

118

Pandaro, oft of Troilo desired,
At length returned to Criseis the fair,
And smiling asked, "Have aught thee yet inspired
The words which from my friend I late did bear?"
At once her face a crimson colour fired,
And "God knows!" she could only then declare.
Yet Pandar urged the more, "Hast thou replied?"
Whereto "So soon?" she echoed 'tween her smiles and sighed.

119

"If e'er I shall be free to act for thee,"
Pandaro pressed, "Grant that I be it now."
And she to him, "My way I cannot see";
While he coaxed still; "To please him think thou now,
Is not Love wont to teach us well, pardee?
I wish so much to comfort him, I vow,
Thou couldst not e'er i' faith my wish conceive
Without thou sent at once thy answer, I believe."

120

"I'll do it then to pleasure thee," she cried,
"And Heaven grant the matter may chance well!"
"It will fare thus," Pandaro blithe replied,—

"So far as pleasing him it doth excel,"
And parted then; while Criseis moved aside,
And in a corner where it so befell
Her maids had little custom to resort
She sat her down and wrote long words to this import:

121

"On thee, discreet and shrewdly potent friend,
Whom love for me so flagrantly beguiles, —
As now on one who to an undue end
Is seized with love for her, — Criseis smiles,
And doth, her honour saved, now recommend
Her to thy valour which no sin defiles,
Bidding thee, humbly, hail, to pleasure thee
If but my name be safe — and eek my chastity!

122

"From him who loves thee so he hath no care
For my pure honour — even for my fame —,
I've had thy letter in thy writing fair;
Reading wherein of thy life sad and lame,
I sorrow as I read (by Heav'n I swear!
And as my hopes of future bliss I frame!)
And, though thy pages are all stained with tears,
I have looked o'er them much — although with many fears.

123

"For pond'ring all things in my reason deep, —
Thy sore affliction and thy mute request, —
Seeing thy faith and how thy hope doth leap,
I know not how I now may please thee best
Or thy demand, and yet in safety keep,
As I would e'er, what I have aye confessed, —
That mundane thing that most doth satisfy, —
My will to live full chaste and no less chaste to die!

124

"For me to pleasure thee were well enough
If e'er the world were what the world should be;
But, as it is, we may not use it rough
But must observe its views obediently,
Lest other deeds should bring us its rebuff
And other ills; yet pity grows for thee
And, malgree me, I'll have to grant it place
That thou may seem to gain more freely joy and grace.

125

"But such great worth I feel in thee resides
I know that thou wilt fully comprehend

What acts for me are meet, and that, besides,
Thou'lt be content whatever I extend
To thee in answer; what grief thee now bestrides
Thou'lt curb, — thy grief that doth my heart offend, —
Yet felt I not it was forbidden me,
Most gladly I should do whate'er might pleasure thee.

126

"Slight is the art; as thou full well canst see,
And mean the writing in this letter wrote,
Which much I wish brought greater cheer to thee,
But all it wills it cannot clear denote;
Although good-will may give it potency
Unless thou think it evilly doth quote.
Yet may it to thy pain some respite bring,
Even if it hath not made the fullest answering.

127

"For thine own offer here I make no place,
For I am sure thou'lt keep all faithfully;
And I forsooth, poor as I am and base,
More than a thousand times do promise me
To be thine own, if love doth not efface
With flame my very soul, which certainly
Thou wilt not wish; no more, — but God I pray
He may content thy wish and mine some happy day!"

128

And, after she had writ him in such wise,
She folded, sealed, and gave to Pandaro
That letter sweet. He, not delaying, hies
Away with it in search of Troilo,
And gives him it with joy and great surprise;
And, taking it, in haste that prince of woe
Reads what was writ and gins to sigh anew,
His heart aquiver as her words appear to view.

129

But, having well considered all she wrote,
At last he mused: "If right I understand,
Love binds her; but, as if of evil note,
She seeks a shield to hide her from his hand,
And shelter her from those great blows he smote;
But that to do she cannot power command,
For Venus makes me bear love and endure,
And so must Criseis change to other talk for sure."

* * * * *

133

Pandar, who felt how deep the amorous flame
Burned in the breast of his beloved friend,
With frequent courtesy to Criseis came
And frequent prayers, and told her to the end
All that she saw herself of Troil's fame;
Who yet, although she gladly ear would lend,
Opposed: "Do I not now already do
The things thou askedst, brother? Why, then, more pursue?"

134

"They'll not suffice," Pandaro made reply;
"I wish thou comfort him with fairer speech."
And him Criseis answered with a sigh:
"Myself to do his will I ne'er can teach,
For that I should my virtue's crown lay by
I'll never wish — through any cause thou preach;
But like a brother, for his goodness rare,
I will him always love — and for his honour fair."

135

"This crown," Pandar replied, "the priests will praise
In them from whom they cannot rob it e'er;
All men like saints their brows and speech may raise,
But, when the world's asleep, they little care.
No one shall ever know Prince Troil's ways; —
Relieve his pain, — to do him well but dare.
They do great ill who can, but do no good, —
And they all waste their time who live in scornful mood."

136

And Criseis said: "I know his virtue well,
That tender for my honour it will be,
Nor will he ask, — if right his worth I spell, —
Other than due and honest things of me;
And thee I, by my safety, swear and tell,
That I am his, for whom thou askst this fee,
More now a thousand times than I am mine,
So sweet I find his courtesies — so true and fine."

137

"If sweet they seem, what more then shouldst thou seek,
I pray thee let all this thy shyness go.
Wouldst thou he died for loving thee so meek?
Dear thou must hold thy beauty, valued so
Thou slayest such a man for it! But speak,
When wouldst thou that he come? Thou whom, I know,
He prizes more than Heaven or God? How? Where?
Think not to use with him thine every test and care!"

138

"O wretched me! Where wilt thou lead me now,
My Pandaro, and what more have me do?
Thou hast despised and broke my chastest vow;
To look thee in thy face I soon must rue;
O wretched me! 'twill never mend, I trow;
And in my heart the blood will freeze anew,
The while I think of that he asks of me,—
And thee it nothing grieves,—as thou dost clearly see!

139

"Would I had died upon that idle day,
When in this *loggia* first I harked to thee,
Thou madest my heart to yearn in such a way
I doubt if e'er again it may be free;
Rather my honour thou'lt to loss betray
And me, alack, to sighing endlessly!
I can no more appeal, and thee to please
I will incline to do whate'er shall give thee ease.

140

"But (if before thy presence prayer may rise),
I pray thee, gentle, precious kinsman mine,
Our acts and words be hid from all men's eyes
And secret kept; for sure the power is thine
To see what might ensue if, to surprise,
Such deeds should come to light; give him this sign—
Bid him be sage—and, when the time draws nigh,
I'll do whatever will his pleasure satisfy."

141

And Pandar answer made, "Thy lips guard well;
Nor he nor I shall ever thee betray."
And she: "So mute thou hast me in thy spell
Thou canst perceive what fear doth me affray—
Of what I hardly know; yet thee I tell
My honour and my shame no less to-day
Touch thee than me; I'll pass from them in peace,
And thou canst do with them whatever thee may please!"

142

And Pandar then: "Have thou no idle fear
Lest we in this shall not good caution use,
When wilt thou let the prince talk with thee here?
Now let us draw the threads 'twere best we choose;—
To do it soon doth better far appear
Since 't must be done, for sure our little ruse
Is better hid, once ye in love have met
And both together planned what acts await you yet."

143

"Thou knowst," said Criseis, "what ladies dwell
And other servants in my house with me,
A part of whom must go ere long, they tell,
T' attend the fête; then with him I will be.
May this delay in him no grief compel!
How he shall come, I'll show betimes to thee;
Urge him to act in all things more than shrewd
And keep his hardihood well hidden and subdued."

CANTO THREE

1

O sweet and fervent Light, whose subtle ray
Up to this point through fair Love's beauteous hall
Hath guided, as I craved, my poem's way,
It now befits thy doubled beam I call
To guide my genius and so give it sway
That in my verse may be declaréd all,
No parcel missed, the good of Love's sweet reign,
Which hath made Troilo a worthy man again.

2

For every man can to this reign draw nigh
Who will Love's passion all entire endure
With knowledge, truth, and other virtues high;
But to arrive no other way is sure,
Whoe'er attempt. Therefore, I pray, be by,
O Lady fair, my wishes high and pure;
Fill with thy grace whatever I demand,
And bravely I will sing thy praise on every hand.

3

To Troil, though his ardour still burned keen,
It seemed his fortune showed itself more fair;
He only knew Criseis, pleased, had seen
And answered with a sweet and lowly air
What letters he had written her, I ween;
And often as he saw that lady rare,
She looked on him with face so soft and bright
He knew he felt in him the most supreme delight.

4

Pandar had gone, as elsewhere I have told,
Leaving the prince's lady to her peace,
And, glad at heart and of his face quite bold,
He sought the youth he'd left so ill at ease
Between fair hope and sad plaints manifold,

When he had gone fair Criseis t' appease;
And, seeking for a time now here now there,
He found him in a temple thinking and in prayer.

5

Soon as he came upon him thus in thought,
He drew him thence apart and gan to say:
"My friend, so deep with pain my heart was fraught,
What time I saw thee languishing away
So cruelly for love, on me was brought
No small part of thy sorrow that sad day;
To seek thee comfort I have never ceased,
Since then; e'en though I have not found thy woe decreased.

6

"For thee I have become a go-between,
For thee mine honour clear I've cast away,
For thee my sister's breast, that late was clean,
I've made corrupt till in her heart doth play,
Deep placed, a love for thee; and her, I ween,
Ere time grows long thou'lt see as fair as day—
With greater pleasaunce than thou hear'st me speak
Thou'lt have thy Criseis in thy arms, full meek.

7

"But, as God knows, who all things yet doth see,
And thou thyself, it was a hope full poor
First sped my efforts and my loyalty,
Alone, to thee my friend,—made them endure
Till by my toil the prize I'd won for thee;
So now, if of thy wished boon thou'ldst make sure
Nor have base Fortune catch it quick away,
In all thy love schemes show thee wise, my prince, I pray.

8

"Thou knowst through Troy town Criseis' repute
Is yet most fair and sacred; not a deed
Of else than good do men to her impute;
And, now thou hast her in thy hands, take heed,—
For thou canst take whatever thee may suit,
Yet if her name she lose, 'twere evil speed,
And more than shame to me, her kith and kin,
Who evermore should guard lest villain's name I win.

9

"Therefore I pray thee now as I can best
That 'tween ourselves we keep this business still;
From Criseis' heart I have, with happy hest,
Removed all modest fear and every will

That checked at thee, and hold it now so stressed
With speaking of thy true love's fill
That quite she loves thee and inclines to do
Whatever it may please thee to command her to.

10

"Yet but a little time, before success
Thou shalt enjoy complete, and I shall place
Her in thine arms for thy delight to bless!
But, 'fore God, act with such a quiet grace
That naught escapes thy heart through carelessness;
O dear my friend, despise not my dull face
If many times I make my prayer to thee,
Seeing that what I beg is begged in honesty."

11

O who could tell in verse the joy complete
Which Troil's soul, now hearing Pandar, knew?
Or how, receding far, its pain did fleet,
The more he spake, away from every view?
The sighs that he had breathed to riches sweet
Yielded their place most gently; caitiff rue
Departed; and his lately tearful face
Bright new hope did reveal with signs of joyous grace.

12

And, as it chances in the new born spring
That trees and shrubs in leaves and blossoms new
Smile at the robes the sudden hours bring
To hide their limbs late nude to wintry view;
As meadows, hills, and eke the rivers too
Smile, clothed in green and every flower's hue;
So with a newer joy 'twas easy seen
Troilo smiled and laughed now with a face serene.

13

And softly in sweet rapture first he sighed,
Gazing in glad content at Pandar's face:
"Ah, how thou must remember," then he cried,
"The tears thou foundst me in — my bitter case,
When still methought it best my love to hide!
Ah, how thou must recall that time and place
Where thy demands and urgent wish to know
Forced from my woeful breast the reason of my woe!

14

"Aware, then, how I tried to keep it hid
Even from thee, my only friend, although
To tell it thee no peril did forbid —

Save that I seemed immodest doing so;
Think how, when I consent, — as late I did, —
To tell't — think how I dread lest others know!
Forget not how I fear lest men suspect;
God keep that misadventure from poor me deject!

15

"But natheless, by highest Jove I swear,
The God who heaven and earth rules equally,
That if in Agamemnon's hands to fare
Prove not my evil chance, I swear it thee,
That were my life not mortal but more rare, —
Eternal e'en, — thou canst assuréd be
Thy trust with all my power will be preserved,
And she who wounds my heart full honestly be served.

16

"Full well I wot all thou hast said and done,
And all thy grace to me I see it clear;
And that no act of mine, howe'er begun
Or rendered, could repay thee mine arrear,
For out of Hell, — and worse, — to Heaven I'm won
And drawn by thee; so, by our friendship near,
I beg, take not the villain's name to thee
But rather think thou servest friend's necessity.

17

"The name of villain let those wretches claim
Whom love of gold doth spur to villainy;
What thou hast done thou didst, sans any blame,
To draw me from my bitter plaints, I see;
And from those hostile thoughts that ever came
To fight and scatter all sweet peace in me —
Just as 'tis meet that for a friend one do
When one beholds his fellow overcome with rue.

18

"And, that thou mayest fully realize
The gracious thanks I'd like to yield thee now,
Know that I have a sister, beauty's prize,
Polyxena, whose charms are praised, I vow,
Scarce less than those of Helen in a wise;
Open thy heart, seek love of her somehow —
Or e'en of Helen, my own brother's wife —
And, thee to win thy choice, I'll work with all my life.

19

"But, since thou hast achieved me so much more
Than I could beg of thee, see to the end

My sweet desire, when time fits, I implore;
To thee I have recourse; all can depend
Only on thee; in thee my joys, and more —
My comfort, solace, health, delight — do blend; —
Yet, an thou bid it not, I'll do no deed; —
Be my delight, and thence thou'lt see thy joy proceed."

20

Pandar by Troil's word was satisfied,
And both resumed their ordinary care;
But in each day now Troilo espied
A hundred days (with her so ill aware)
And, suffering in them all, could scarce abide
Those flames of love which all in him did tear;
So gave to thoughts of love the hours of night
And with his comrades spent the day in martial fight.

21

With matters thus, the time so much desired
Of those two lovers neared; whence Criseis made
To summon Pandar and it so transpired
She showed him all her wish; but Pandar played,
Grieving that Troilo that day was hired
With others for some special martial raid
Or deed of war — was far away from cry,
"Although 'twas very like he'd come back by and by."

22

This news, the while she heard, proved grief to her,
And sad she turned; but with most friendly zeal
Pandar declared he'd find some messenger
To send the prince (she need make no appeal),
And, thereupon, with but the briefest stir
Nor any let, the man had proved him leal
And Troil found, — who listened with surprise,
Then hurried back to Troy in blithe and joyous wise.

23

And, come to Pandaro, from him he learned
In full the needful steps that he must take;
And now impatiently the young prince burned,
Awaiting night that ever seemed to break
In flight before his gaze; quiet he turned
And took his way with Pandaro, his make,
For that sweet spot where lovely Criseis stood
Lonely expectant, with fear and subtle dread subdued.

24

At length the night fell clouded and obscure,
As Troil wished, who, gazing full intent,
Examined all to be the more secure,
The while he moved, in hope that no event
Should make his eager love new pain endure
Or cheat it now when from its great torment
It seemed it should escape; and soon, — alone —
Secret — he entered Criseis' house, now quiet grown;

25

And in a secret, safe-removéd place,
As had been him instructed, stayed in wait;
Nor seemed his waiting now an evil grace,
Nor failing yet to see clear, — harsh in fate;
But often with a sure, courageous face
He urged within: "My love, ere very late,
Will come to me, and I'll be happier then
Than were I, all alone, the Lord of Earth and Men."

26

Criseis, who his coming well had heard,
That he might now the better understand
How 'twas arranged, coughed once and no more stirred;
Then, lest his waiting wearily expand,
She gan to speak, with oft a quickened word,
Till all her maids she'd hastened (well she planned)
Off to their beds, declaring that such sleep
Had never fallen on her, — awake she could not keep!

27

After that each and all had gone to rest
And the whole house grown quiet everywhere,
To Lady Criseis it did first seem best
Toward Troil's hiding place in haste to fare;
Who, as he heard her footsteps thither pressed,
Rose up and, starting tow'rd her, passed from there
With joyful face — and mute expectancy
To be prepared for all the lady might decree.

28

And now, a lighted torch within her hand,
The lady quite alone came down the stair
And found the prince, with all his ardour fanned,
Awaiting her; whom, with full courteous air,
She greeted as she could: "My lord, command
If aught I did offend thee, hidden there,
And thy high royal love in any way;
Or, sweet my love, for God's sake grant me pardon, pray."

29

And her her Troil answered: "Lady bright,
Sole hope and good and blessing of my heart,
Thy face hath so long been before my sight
A lucent star, so splendid in each part
And each dear ray of it such glorious light,
That all my palace seems of poorer art;
And to ask pardon more is mine than thine."
Then he embraced her and they kissed in rapture fine.

30

And now, ere they could part from that charmed place,
With dalliance sweet and eager-joyous play
They clasped their arms in many a glad embrace;
A thousand times they kissed in amorous way,
For in them fire burned of an equal pace,
And each the other felt was dear as day;
But, when their greetings ended at the last,
They climbed the stairs and to an inner chamber passed.

31

Long would it need to tell now of their bliss
And no man could express that rich delight
They had together when they entered this,
Free for sweet nuptials and sans hindrance quite
Save that at Troil's side fair Criseis
Trembled a moment and must cry in fright,
"O Troil, lord and love, when brides are new
They are abashed to meet, the first night, lovers' view."

32

To whom the prince then: "Sweet, O sweet my soul,
Yield that my arms do now thee closelier take
And have, as Lord Love wills, more perfect toll
Of love." And she: "Behold, for thy sweet sake,
I rid me of all fear and seek my goal
In thine arms only." Then courteously her make
Drew her more close and close in his embrace
That they might win of Love more high and richer grace.

33

O sweet, most sweet and most desiréd night,
How lavish wert thou to those lovers gay,
If all the knowledge were made mine of right
Which all the poets owned, I could not say
Nor truly yet explain their joyaunce bright;
But he who knows the favour of Love's way
And boons hath had of him, can guess or know
In part at least the joy that Love to these did show.

34

And all night long from one another's arms
They stirred not, nor released their sweet embrace;
Yet still believed, in one another's arms,
It could not quite be real, their sweet embrace,—
They could not be in one another's arms,—
But only dreamed they were in sweet embrace;
And each the other asked with frequent care,
"Is mine a true embrace? or dream? or art thou there?"

35

And so they gazed with such enraptured will
That neither could from other turn his eyes,
But each the other cried with voice athrill,
"My love, is't true I'm with thee in this wise?";
And "Yes, heart of my heart," each answered still,
"And God have thanks for it," in amorous sighs;
And then each drew the other in embrace
And sweetly kissed again the other's lovely face.

36

And oft upon her eyes, for love aglow,
Troil would press a soft, enraptured kiss,
Crying, "My heart ye have enflamed so
With Love's sweet darts that burning now seems bliss,—
And, caught, I cannot hide nor find it woe,
Nor flee, as those are wont who fare amiss;
Ye hold, and e'er may hold, mine eyes and me
Meshed in the net of Love's own sweet intricacy."

37

A second time he kissed them, and once more,
Till in response the lady kissed his eyes;
Then he o'er all her face and breast did kisses pour;
And no hour passed without a thousand sighs,—
Not those that come from souls with anguish sore,—
But out of reverent souls, which prove them wise,
Showing thereby the love that's in the breast;
Then, sighing o'er, themselves to joy they new addressed.

38

Such scenes should make the caitiff misers pause,
Who so themselves have given all to gold,
A-counting pence, they reckon love but cause
For scorn and laughter—and him who loves, too bold;
Let them but ponder if by any laws
They can from all their wealth such pleasure hold—
In any single point—as Love doth give
To those who joined for his grand venture love and live.

39

'Tis like they'll say they can and, willing, lie,—
Calling with many a wanton mock and jest
"Love is a wretched folly best passed by,"
Without once seeing that, by Fate's behest,
A single hour may come their souls to try
And they, their gold lost, live thence never blest
By joy in life or love. God make them sad,—
And give to lovers all the wealth they might have had!

40

But these two lovers, feeling comforted,
Began together hopefully to speak,
Telling each other of their pains now fled,—
Their plaints, their sighs, their anguish cruel—bleak!
And oft, when such speech had been wholly said,
Again they would more fervent kisses seek;
And now, forgetting all their past annoy,
They took together thus a most delirious joy.

41

So here I have no tale to tell of sleep,
For theirs was all desire the night should last;
Such pleasure did they from their waking reap
They could not sate each other while it passed;
And all they did and said they thought to keep,
Through such an act of waking, long and fast
And not to let their fair chance lapse in vain
They made full use of it all night in glad refrain.

42

But, as the cocks gan crow and day drew nigh
And in the east the purple dawn arose,
Their will t'embrace again once more burned high;
And in that hour they felt were dolorous woes,
Which made them part, and in it pain did lie
Of such a kind none yet had known its throes,
To torture them, so hard 't would be to part
While Love flamed more than ever in each eager heart.

43

And, hearing them thus all too early crow,
Fair Criseis called out sad: "O love of mine,
Now 'tis ordained we rise by Fate, our foe,
Would we keep hidden well our love's design;
But yet I wish once more, before thou go,
To kiss thy lips—to say that I am thine
With one more kiss—that, after thou art sped,
My pain, O sweet my life, may feel diminished."

44

Prince Troilo embraced her weeping thus,
And, drawn within his arms, her kissed again,
Cursing the day which came so envious
And, churlish, made them part so early then;
And after, he began in words as dolorous;
"Lady, unmeasured grief comes oft to men,
But parting from thee brings e'en greater woe,
Since every joy I feel—that joy to thee I owe.

45

"I know not how I can do else than stay
For thought of how much going thwarts my will,
And that, now I have ta'en life's pain away,
Pale death o'er me its power holdeth still;
Nor if I may return nor when I may;
O Fate, why hast thou such a pleasured thrill
In taking me from there where most I joy?
Why wilt thou now my solace and my peace destroy?

46

"Alack, what shall I do? If now desire,
When first we part, constrains me to return
Till life can hardly bear 't? O pain most dire!
And why, O hateful day, dost thou so yearn
And come so soon our parting to require?
How soon will't be that once again I learn
Thou art restored? Alack, I cannot know."
Then, turning back, he kissed fair Criseis' face in woe,

47

Saying: "O lady mine, if I believed
That in thy heart my image were to stay
So sure as thine will rest in mine received,
More dear 'twould be to give Troy's rule away
Than lose thy love, and less I should feel grieved
At parting thus,—which gainst my will doth sway,—
And hope that time and place might come again
For us to soothe, as now, our cruel fire and pain."

48

And, sighing, him fair Criseis answered then
While closelier she her arms about him cast:
"Have done thy talk, my soul, for oft mid men
I've heard it said (if well my memory last!)
Love's greedy spirit doth ne'er release again
What once 't has caught, but holds it hard and fast,
And pressed and closed in its embrace so tight
That counsel to release 't hath then no power or might.

49

"And through thee Love hath grown so whole in me,
O dear my precious lord, that if I sought
Loveless, as I was late, again to be,
I could not even wrest thee from my thought;
Morning and evening, always, shall I see
Thy image in my heart entirely wrought;
And, could I think myself so wholly thine,
I should more blessed feel than knowledge can define.

50

"Then live thou, therefore, of my love secure,
Which ne'er for other have I felt so great;
If to return thou wish with fervour pure,
I too desire it more than thou canst state;
And happy hour will not be mine, I'm sure,
Ere thou return, return thou soon or late;
Heart of my body, I commend me thee."
She spake and sighed, and kissed her prince most tenderly.

51

And Troil, all against his will, arose
When now the hundredth time he'd kissed her face;
For then, like one who well his *devoir* knows,
He fought not Fate but clad himself with grace,
And then a thousand pledges did propose:
"I'll do thy will nor break it in no case;
Thy promise keep. I yield thee to God's care—
And mine own spirit, lady, to thy keeping rare!"

52

But Criseis had no voice to answer more
So fast pain for his parting her had caught;
And Troil with swift step, as ne'er before,
Turned toward his house, now happy in his thought,
Knowing in Love was even greater store
To kindle love than e'er his will had sought—
So much more he had found in Criseis
Than he erewhile had dreamed could ever be in bliss.

* * * * *

72

And Troilo now lived in mighty bliss,
Singing his lady's charms as in a dream;
Feeling he should himself prove all remiss,
Should he another lady's face esteem;
And that all other men lived but amiss
Who loved not such a one, it him did seem;

So matchless did his lady now appear—
Such fair fortune the thought of her drew near!

73

And often he would seize Pandaro's hand,
And oft his fellow to some garden lead,
Where deep absorbed in thought of her he'd stand
Or praise his lady's worth and courteous rede;
Till joy, it seemed, did so his soul command
It must disown all melancholic breed,
And he would sing such songs in joyous wise
As scarce a poet could by any means devise.

* * * * *

90

Then did this Troil in each chance of war,
Prove him first chief in arms in every deed;
And he upon the Greeks so fiercely bore,—
So bold and brave, if true's the tale I read,—
They were affrayed by him as ne'er before
By any man; for now 'twas Love did feed
With courage high his lofty spirit proud,—
Great Love, whose servitor he had him late avowed.

91

Or he would go to hunt in times of truce
With falcon, gerfalcon, or eagle e'en, in hand;
And, oftentimes, it was with dogs his use
To chase great bears, boars, lions through the land,
For smaller game he spurned and did refuse;
And at such times he would for joy expand,—
If Criseis he saw,—as blithe and free
As falcon from a hood new set at liberty.

92

And then of love his speech was all entire,
Of gracious mien, and full of courtesy;
To praise all honest men was his desire,
And from all caitiffs still to keep him free;
And whate'er youths excelled in youthful fire,
Adorned with honours 'twas his will to see;
But them that loved not, much he held in scorn—
Lost souls, whose villain state was hardly to be borne!

93

And though of royal blood was this our knight,
And though at will he might in much command,
Humble he made himself as any wight,—
As modest as the lowliest in the land;

For so Love willed, in whom dwells subtle might,
To make men more for others' pleasure stand;
Pride, envy, avarice he held in ire
And from all taint of these he made himself retire.

94

But such great joy could last but little space,
Thanks to Dame Fortune, cruel and envious,
Who in this world leaves nothing firm in place.
For some new chance (and oft it cometh thus!)
She turned from Troilo her cruel face;
And all the joy he felt so copious,
The fruits of Criseis' love, she tore away,
And for them did him but a bitter grief repay.

CANTO FOUR

1

Since that the Greeks still held in mighty siege
The Trojan town, Prince Hector, in whose hand
Was all the war, sought out from Trojans liege,—
And from the bravest allies in the land,—
And picked a group for valour's privilege,
And with them in the open fields took stand
Against the Greeks, as oft before he'd done;
And all the varied chance of melee they did run.

2

The Greeks advanced and square the encounter met,
And all that day in battle hard they spent;
Until the Trojan knights, too sore beset,—
Their sally failing,—when occasion lent,
Turned them to flight, as loss and travail let;
But in that fight by Death were many hent;
And others still were taken prisoner then,—
Famed kings, great lords, and numerous noble valiant men.

3

Mongst these were that great hero, Antenor,
Polydamas his son, and Menesteus,
Xantippus, Sarpedon, Polynestor,—
Polites too, and Trojan-keen Rifeus,—
And others whom to save the brave Hector
Tried all his might. But 'twas to little use;
Retreat was forced, and plaints filled all of Troy,
Though auguries foretold a greater yet annoy.

4

King Priam asked a truce and 'twas declared;
Whereat for the exchange they gan to treat;
Ransoms of heavy gold were now prepared,
Man or a gift should buy man from defeat.
Soon then as Calchas saw how matters fared,
He changed his face, and mid the Greeks full fleet
He got, roaring his plaints,—and howled until
He had obtained that they would listen to his will.

5

"Trojan I was, my lords," the seer began,
"As all of you, methinks, are full aware;
And if you will recall, I am the man
Who first brought hope unto your thirst and care,
And said, when to its end the season ran
And the due hour came, then should your trumpets blare
The victory you had won for high emprise,
When Troy should burn and fall before your watching eyes.

6

"The order and the means thereof you know
And hold from me, as I did demonstrate;
But though all your desires in time proved so,—
And at the looked for hour, as I did state,—
Still in no word of mine your faith you'd show
If ta'en from sealed or opened book of late,
However much it seemed my coming here
Was willed to give you counsel and provide new cheer.

7

"And, since Fate wished it so, 'twas fortunate
That I by my own skill should find the way
T' escape the town—so keep the secret great
That none should know a word of it to say—
And bring me here alone, when day was late
And clear sky turning light to brown and gray.
For come I have and hither with me brought,
Of all the things I owned, no greater thing than naught.

8

"But for my leaving all I nothing care,
Save for that only daughter young and frail,
Whom I left back: O parent sans compare
For cruelty, his offspring so to fail!
Would God I'd led her safe from there!
But fear and fury made my courage pale:—
That is my cause of grief for leaving Troy,
'Tis that hath robbed from me all of my cheer and joy.

9

"Long days I've made myself in silence wait,
Seeing no time when I could make demands
Of you to ransom her, but now — though late —
I come to ask this favour of your hands;
And if you cannot give't, — if 'tis my fate
I ne'er shall see her more, — more these lands
I'll wander ne'er again; my life I'll scorn;
Careless to live or die, in all things then forlorn.

10

"Here in your camp is many a Trojan peer,
Baron and lesser man ye would exchange
For captured Greeks the Trojans hold in fear;
To give me one you could with ease arrange,
And for the price of him, a price not dear,
Criseis ransom: O thus, I beg, estrange
From grief, for God's sweet sake, a wretched wight,
Grown old — and of all solace void and empty quite.

11

"And let no wish, by Heaven I conjure you,
For great wealth gained through ransoms of these lords,
Delay you now, when 'tis most certain-true
That all Troy's strength and all Troy's richest hoards
Are in your hands; and (if I err not too)
The might of him whose courage yet affords
To keep Troy locked against your wish, will fail,
And Hector soon, methinks, in violent death fall pale."

12

And, as he spoke these words, the ancient priest,
Humble in speech and with a face downcast,
Watered his cheeks with tears most free released;
Over his hoary beard and breast they passed,
Endewing all: and ne'er his prayers he ceased
Until their piteousness gained ears at last;
For, when they heard, the Greeks began to shrill,
"Send Antenor to Troy, let Calchas have his will."

13

Such compact made they; Calchas felt content;
And envoys for the task they soon had chose:
These came to Priam, told why they were sent,
And to his sons and lords made honest shows,
Till Troy's grave king had called a parliament
The thing to weigh, and answer brief was lent:
If Greeks to Trojans firm their pledge will hold,
Trojans will hand to Greeks what prisoners they are told.

14

Troil stood near at that great conference
And heard the Greeks for Criseis make request.
Sudden his heart was pierced without defense;
Then Sorrow's quickened thrust him sore oppressed,
And on his soul grief fell so stern-intense
He felt he must die, sitting there distressed;
Only with labour did he keep confined
As it behooved, the love and sad complainings in his mind.

15

Then he grew full of anguish and proud fear,
And he began to wait the dread reply;
Unwonted was the care fell on him here,
The while he pondered what was best and why,
Whether his secret to his brother's ear
He dared entrust when fortune ill was nigh,—
If Criseis were to Calchas rendered now,
How he might hinder that by any deed or vow.

16

On one hand came then Love, that made him feel
Ready to offer him gainst any fate;
While on the other Reason's stern repeal
Gave such proud-high emprise a doubtful rate,
For might not Criseis (the thought was real)
Be brought thereby to fears most desolate?—
So, will-he? nill-he? in his tristful woe
Between two fires he stood,—the fearful *damoiseau.*

17

And while he brooded in such doleful wise,
Yet all suspense, the barons still conferred,
Discussing much whatever did arise,
What most was needful for what had occurred;
And when they spake, it was with no surprise
To him who waited for their answering word,—
Criseis should be giv'n incontinent,—
She ne'er had been in any durance held or pent.

18

As a field-lily, then, by plough-share caught
And notched, falls low beneath the intense sun
And fades, its late rich colour changed to naught,
And paleness covering all; so pallour won
(When into words their counsel full was wrought,
And Greek and Trojan pledges had begun)
Till Troil swooned away, struck low by grief
For peril boundless quite—and loss sans all relief.

19

Then him old Priam seized in quick embrace,
And Hector and his brothers, too, for fear
Now moved them all lest worse should prove his case;
Each sought to succour him to death so near;
One rubbed his pulse, another bathed his face,
And each a prudent wight with love sincere
Laboured to call his spirit back again,
Though for some little time it naught availed their pain.

20

He lay among his kindred vanquished quite,
And little breath was left in his pale frame,
His face showed lifeless, — tinged a deathlike white, —
Like dead he seemed, and living but in name;
(Such sorry guise was his in that sad plight
None saw that wept not for the pain that came),
For all too cruel was that lofty tone
He heard, when 'twas declared the Greeks should Criseis own.

21

A long time did his stricken spirit stray,
In darkness lost, ere it recovered all;
Then, coming back, returned in quiet way;
Whence he, like one who waked at sudden call,
Rose sudden to his feet in deep dismay,
A moment dazed; then, ere wight could fall
On him and ask what pain 'twas hurt him so,
He feigned some cause, and scaped with his new bitter woe.

22

And tow'rd his palace quickly then he sped,
Without appeal or sign to any wight;
So deep on sighs and sorrows had he fed,
He wished no comrade in his dismal plight,
And, come unto his room, Prince Troil said
He so lacked sleep that now of every knight
He must needs be excused — his servants, too, might leave,
Closing the windows first; he would not light perceive!

23

To witness what then followed, lady fair,
I cannot wish at all that thou be near;
And yet my soul must know such heavy care,
As fills both memory and mind with fear,
Though, of itself oppressed, 'twill little dare
(For so my parting from thee keeps it drear)
One jot to tell, unless thou give it aid, —
Thou who hast caused the wound by which 'tis still affrayed.

24

To this time blithely have I sung in joy
All the rich favour Love gave Troilo,
And what was mingled in it of annoy;
Now I must turn from joy to sombre woe,
And even though thou like not mine employ,
I cannot yet refrain — perforce I know
Thy heart will change and with new pity view
Mine own life, given up so whole to grief and rue.

25

But if my wishes ever reach thine ears,
I pray thee by the love I bear to thee,
Give respite to my grievous woes and fears,
And so restore my wonted joy to me,
Which at our parting turned itself to tears:
Yea, if my death thou'dst bear aught heavily,
Return thou soon; for it is cherished naught,
The life thou leftest me when parting pleased thy thought.

26

Prince Troil in his chamber barred and dark
Stayed desolate, — without that any man
Suspected aught, — sans fear that men could hark, —
And there the grief that in his breast now ran
And made, through misadventure, such sad mark,
To give release the caitiff then began,
Opening his heart in such a crazéd way
He seemed not man but frenzied beast, thou wouldest say.

* * * * *

63

Thus wept in deep lament Prince Troilo,
And Pandar likewise did, for very grief,
Yet often sought to ease his friend's deep woe
And piteously he offered him relief;
But comfort nothing helped the cruel blow,
While still his weeping grew beyond belief
Continually — and thereto, his lament,
So much for his sad fate had swelled his discontent.

64

And Pandar answered him: "My dearest friend,
If my appeals in nothing pleasure thee,
And if to thee it seems too cruel end
To part from her, anon or presently,
Why not accept the power gods do lend
Now to thy life and seize her instantly

To bear away, as Paris stole from Greece
Helen, that flower of dames, who wrecked the world's long peace?

65

"Wilt thou in thine own Troy not venture e'en
To carry off a dame that pleaseth thee?
Thou wilt, — if trust at all on me thou lean:
Chase off thy grief; chase 't off and so make flee
Thine anguish and these woes too plainly seen;
Dry up thy tears and let thy face be free;
Let thy great spirit show itself once more,
To make sweet Criseis ours, my prince, I do implore."

66

And then to Pandar Troil made reply:
"I see, my friend, to drive away my pain
Thou wilt at nothing stop but all must try:
Yet all thou urgest, with other things as plain,
I've thought on much and raised before mine eye,
The while I'd weep and yield to grief again, —
To grief which somehow doth increase my power,
Keen though its shock hath been to make me pause and cower;

67

"But not therefore could I feel aught constrained
Good counsel, in love's fervour e'en, to scorn;
Rather I thought and saw no whit was gained,
The time forbade such errour to be born;
For, if a citizen could be regained,
And Antenor at that, I much should mourn
To break my oath and fealty unto Troy:
Hap then what might, I never could such means employ.

68

"Besides I fear with rapine violent
Much I should harm her honour and her fame;
Nor do I know she'd therewith be content.
I only know she loves me, sans all blame.
Therefore my heart feels it in no way bent
To try such means as wish that her good name
Be safe, on one side; on the other, fear
To like unpleasant things they would not have appear.

69

"Then had I weened to ask by special grace
My father Priam should give her to me;
Then thought that were like accusation base,
And making known things done in secrecy;
I dared not hope he'd hearken to my case

And give her me through breaking utterly
The things he pledged; but knew he'd try to say
She was not of my rank,—he'd find some royal may.

70

"So still I weep and in love's maze remain,
Weary and unaware what I may do;
Because my might, whatever it may gain
Through strength in love, I feel is failing too;
On every side my hope flees off in pain
And causes of my grief grow ever new:
I wish that I had died that luckless day
When I was first inflamed with passion in this way."

71

And Pandar answered then: "Do as thou please;
But, were I now enamoured as thou art,
With show of truth, I'd bid farewell to ease,
And, whatsoever guilt became my part,
Did I possess the power thou canst seize,
(Unless that power some strange force rose to thwart),
I'd use it all and bear her safe away—
Whoso might be displeased or whoso might gainsay.

72

"Do not conceal thy love so subtilely,
As now appears thou wouldst, when love's good still
Heats the enamoured soul incessantly,
While love plagues yet with wild and hearty will,
Hath his own way, and then so forcibly
Exposes thee to every torment ill;
Wish rather thou to be checked by restraint
Than die with torture in thy sad and sore complaint.

73

"And thine is not the task a dame to steal
Who would be distant from thy high intent,
But such a one as seeks no greater weal;
And if for this, great ill to thee were lent
Or blame assigned, thou hast the power, I feel,
Soon to succeed in it to thy content,
Or yet to give her back; and Fate doth aid
Him who is brave, who makes the timid more afraid.

74

"And if this thing should bring her any grief,
Quite soon thou'lt have thy peace with her again;
And that she'd suffer not, is my belief,
So much thy love for her would ease her pain:

And for her fame she would soon feel relief
For that she lost, and little time complain:
To speak thee sooth, the shame that Helen bore
This lady glad would bear could she thus please thee more.

75

"Pluck ardour then, be valorous once more,
Love holds no idle laws of faith or care;
Show of thy courage now its greatest store,
And for thyself reward more rich prepare.
I'll stand with thee each peril new before,
As valiant as my power lets me dare.
Deign but to act, my gracious friend, and lo!
The gods will aid our cause with every well-struck blow."

76

The prince, who each word understood full well,
Replied then to his friend: "I am content
If in me now flames hotter yet did dwell
By twice a thousand times,—if my torment
Were greater than it is,—this must I tell,
To satisfy 't I'd ne'er let my intent
Do any courteous dame one tiny ill,
'Twere better die than have her feel my selfish will.

77

"Then up, and let us stand no longer here;
Bathe thou thy face; return we both to court;
Beneath our laughter let no grief appear
(The people nothing know of any sort,
And we should bring them all to marvelling near
By telling what both know); observe thy part;
Keep thou my secret hid; I'll find a way
So that this very eve with Criseis I may speak and stay."

* * * * *

95

O who could ever tell in words complete
The sighs this Criseis breathed in her lament?
(In sooth not I, whose speech fails of the feat,
So cruel was her grief and great torment.)
But, while she her complaints did so repeat,
Pandaro came, gainst whom no door stayed pent;
And right into her bower then he passed,
Where still he found her weeping bitter tears and fast.

96

He saw her lying prostrate on her bed,
All given o'er to sobs and moans and sighs,

Her face and breast wet with the tears she shed;
And still, it seemed, desire was in her eyes
Yet more to weep; and all dishevelléd
She lay, her torture shown without disguise;
Yet, when she saw him coming in apace,
She raised her arms for shame and hid from view her face.

97

And Pandaro began: "Sad was the hour
That let me rise to-day to see such grief;
For everywhere seems torment come to power,—
Lament and anguish, woe without relief,
Sighs and annoy, and languishing most sour;
O Jove, what wouldest thou? 'Tis my belief
Thou dost thy tears from Heaven's heights outpour
Because our deeds have grieved thee worse then e'er before.

98

"But thou, my sister so disconsolate,
What meanest thou? To war with Destiny?
Why treat thy body's beauty with such hate,
With sad lament and boundless cruelty?
Rise up, turn, turn about; speak, talk, narrate;
Lift up thy face; dry, dry immediately
Thy sorrowing eyes; and hark to what I say
Of words entrusted to me by thy friend to-day."

99

Criseis turned thereat, still weeping so
No poet's words could true describe the sight,
And spake, the while she gazed at Pandaro:
"Alas me now! What will my soul aright?
Save leave me now and flee to weep in woe?
Such, wicked chance declares should be her plight,—
Chance, that doth wish me all these sighs,—these tears,
Chance, that permits I shall own nothing but my fears!"

100

To see her face was little otherwise
Than viewing close a corse, borne to the grave;
Her countenance, shaped true in Paradise,
An aspect all transformed now sadly gave;
Her beauty and the smile once in her eyes
Had both deserted her—their fairness so to save;
And now about each eye a purple ring
Bare witness true to Lady Criseis's suffering.

101

And this, when Pandar saw, who all that day
Had spent in weeping sad with Troilo,
He sought no more to keep his tears away,
But gan, like Criseis to vent his woe,
Keeping in check what most he wished to say
He let his tears with his fair cousin's flow;
At last, when both had long wept sans restraint,
Our Pandar tempered first the grief of his complaint,

102

And spake: "Lady, I trust the news I've heard—
But am not sure—thy father asked for thee,
And Priam King hath, ere this, pledged his word
Thee to deliver; so it may well be
Thou wilt ere noon to-morrow be transferred,—
If truth I've learned. And oh, how cruelly
This thing hath touched thy Troil, none can tell,—
Who, for his grief at it, prays death to come—and hell.

103

"And so much he and I have wept to-day
That I have marvelled whence our tears could flow;
Though now at length, my counsel to obey,
He hath in some sort checked his cries of woe,
And wish to be with thee him more doth sway;
To pleasure him I've come to tell thee so,
In order that, before ye separate,
Ye may together meet somehow in fair estate."

104

And Criseis answered: "Great as is the pain
Of one who loves self less than Troilo,
When I hear for my sake he death would gain,
Then less my pain seems than my love's great woe.
And now, if e'er heart opened up again
Through stress of grief, mine shall it open show;
Now envious Fate exults above my loss,
Now I behold her secrets freed of guile and gloss.

105

"Parting is hard for me, as Heaven knows,
But 'tis more hard my Troilo to see,
In faith to me, afflicted by such woes
As make death near and dear to hapless me;
And death, sans hope of gain, less wretched grows
The more I know how pierced with grief is he;
Bid Troil, when he will, come hither then—
And let my anguish have supreme comfort again!"

106

And, that said, back she fell once more supine,
And to her closed arms did her plaints renew,
While Pandar called: "Alas, poor cousin mine,
What wilt thou now? Cannot some cheer ensue
From thinking that the hour so near is thine,
When he thou lovest will come before thy view—
To take thee to his arms? Rise, comfort thee,
Lest in this thriftless state thy knight discover thee.

107

"And, if he knew that thou wert acting so,
He'd slay himself, and no wight could restrain;
And, if I thought to me should come that blow,
My feet would never lead me here again;
But, if I could, I'd slay me too, I know,
And make my soul pursue my friend's in pain.
Then up, my lady, make thee calm and still
That thou relieve and not more, thus, provoke his ill."

108

And Criseis answered: "Go; I promise thee,
My cousin Pandar, to be more controlled;
When thou art gone, I will immediately
Rise from this bed and more my courage hold;
My pain and all delight, now lost to me,
Close in my bolted heart for him I'll fold:
Then make him come in this accustomed way,
And here he'll find the door still propped, thou mayest say."

109

Pandar found Troilo in anxious thought,
His face once more so darkened by his fears
That pity in his friend a new grief wrought;
But yet he called: "Art thou, as now appears,
So caitiff, youth, who once so valiant fought?
Thy blessing hath not gone—to cause these tears;
Why dost thou then so keep thyself in pain?
Thy very eyes seem eyes of one already slain!

110

"Art not, without her, still alive and sound?
Canst not give to thy heart strength to endure?
Wast born to earth but to her to be bound?
Show thee a man; make more thy courage sure.
Dismiss these griefs and sighs to some new ground:
I have not made delay,—naught could allure
Me from the place where I might tell to thee
What time I spent with her and what she said to me.

111

"And thou, methinks, dost not one moment feel
Half of the pain thy mistress, grieving, knows;
Her sighs so fervid hot themselves reveal,
Since so this parting gainst her will doth close,
Twenty to one thy sighs they overpeal;
Wherefore thou shouldst thee more to peace compose,
For in thy bitter plight this grace is thine,
How dear thou art to her more clearly to define.

112

"I have of her, too, now won thee consent
Thou shouldest go to her this very eve;
Exhibit, then, whate'er was thine intent,
The best demeanour she could wish perceive;
Soon wilt thou see whatever most is meant
To give her pleasaunce, and her mind relieve:
And more, — perchance the two of you will find
Ways to assuage your woes and make them seem more kind."

113

And Troilo made answer with a sigh:
"Good is thy speech, I'll try to bear me so."
And other things he said, but time drew nigh
When good it seemed to Criseis to go.
Then, quickly slipping his friend Pandar by,
He made him on his way, so free from woe
It seemed a thousand years he'd been embraced
In Criseis' arms with joy, ere Fate had him displaced.

114

And Criseis, when the usual time was near,
Came to him with her torch illumined bright,
And in her arms received her lover dear;
And he took her in his (as was his right),
Though sore by grief oppressed; and, dumb with fear,
The two could not conceal their heart's wild plight;
And, speechless both, they kissed in sad constraint, —
Then recommenced their weeping and excessive plaint.

115

And each clung to the other very tight,
Each bathed in tears that would incessant flow;
And, though they tried, to speak they had no might,
So much their weeping hindered and their woe, —
Their sobs and sighs, their sorrows grim as night;
And long their sweet-sad kissing lasted so,
The while each seemed to drink the other's tears,
Careless how bitter was their nature, it appears.

116

Then, soon as their vexed spirits were returned
From th' anguish of their weeping and their sighs,
Back to the places that they late had spurned,
Their souls gan soften their despondent cries;
And Criseis her eyes to Troil turned,
Sad with her grief's desire — in piteous wise;
When, broken-voiced, she cried: "Lord of my heart,
Who wrests thee from me now? How from thee can I part?"

117

Then, once again, she fell, head on his breast,
And swooned away, till all her strength was fled,
So sore with grief her heart had been oppressed;
The while her soul tried scape as from one dead;
And Troil, gazing in her face distressed
And calling her and hearing no word said,
Saw that her eyes were veiled and fallen to —
As those that have assumed death's pale and sombre hue.

118

And, as he that beheld, in double grief
The anguished youth hath down his Criseis laid,
Kissing her tear-wet face, as for relief,
And sought if sign of life might be displayed,
In any part of her, till sad belief
Told him no life at all within her stayed, —
So quite devoid of breath she did appear;
And then that all was past he cried, and wept in fear.

119

For cold she was and showed no sentiment;
Wherefore her Troilo, in sooth, he knew
(For that seemed him the truest argument)
Her days were ended now of bitter rue;
Then first he gave him to a long lament,
And, after, gave him to a service new, —
He bathed her face, her frail frame did compose,
And did the wonted things that follow death's last blows.

120

These done, he drew his sword from out his sheath
With that grave courage which was e'er his wont,
In full prepared to seize on bitter death, —
So that his soul, which nothing else could daunt,
Might follow ill-starred Criseis o'er the heath
And with her there th' infernal regions haunt,
Since Fate had proved so cruel, Love so hard, —
And woe persuaded him in life was no regard!

121

But first he called, inflamed with high disdain:
"Most cruel Jove, and thou accurséd Fate,
To what ye willed behold me come in pain;
For Criseis, giv'n me I thought of late
By your especial favour, now is ta'en,
Caught from my life by your immortal hate;
And where she dwells, I know not in this hour,
Only I see her slain here by your evil power!

122

"And now I leave the world to follow her
And with her spirit wend, as pleaseth you;
Perhaps in hell things better may occur
And I my peace may gain in sighs and rue—
If, there beyond, men love, as tales defer
Sometimes, in telling what the pale shades do;
O, since you do not wish to see me live,
At least to be with her my soul permission give.

123

"And thou, my city, whom at war I leave,
And thou, Priam, and ye, my brothers dear,
Act so with God I burial receive,
Not far, but to my Criseis' fair eyes near;
And thou, for whom such dolour doth me grieve
That from my body now my soul I tear,
Criseis, welcome me!" he tried to say,
With breast bared to his sword and ready him to slay.

124

When lo! reviving, Criseis heaved a sigh
Full of great pain, and called for Troilo;
And "Sweet, my love" again he gan to cry,
"Art thou alive?" and wept once more for woe;
Then raised her in his arms and gan to try
To soothe her pain through words with love aglow,
Offered her comfort; till her bruiséd soul
Back to the heart returned whence late it frightened stole.

125

But some time yet her spirit, lately strayed,
Kept silence; till her eyes his sword espied,
When she began: "Thy weapon, why is't made
Free of its sheath?" And he, in tears, replied
And told her how his life escaped its blade;
And she: "O me, to hear of such a tide!
If my lost soul had longer stayed away,
Within this very place thou'ldst slain thyself this day.

126

"O woe to me, O heavy dole thou'st said!
I should not in this life have wished to be,
After my lord; my breast would soon have bled,
Pierced by thy sword; great thanks in this I see
For praising God; but seek we now our bed,
Where we may speak our woes more quietly:
When I consider how my torch burns low,
Then, that the night is almost gone, I know."

127

And there, as other times they had embraced,
They kissed again, though now 'twas much in tears,
For joy by bitterness had been replaced;
Yet peaceful speech and sad, despite their fears,
Could sans delay on their quick lips be traced,
Whisp'ring the words that only lover hears;
Till Criseis began: "O sweet my friend,
To all the words I say, see that thou well attend.

128

"Since I have learned those tidings ill
How my cursed father turned him traitor all,
If to deprive me now be Heaven's will
Of thy fair face, I'll say on none did fall
Such pain as I have felt and suffer still;
For now in city gay or palace tall
I find no cheer; but aye to dwell with thee
Only can give me joy, and thou to dwell with me!

129

"Of late my will of all things did despair,
Believing nevermore I thee should see;
But, since thou'st seen my spirit free as air
Wander away, and then return to me,
I feel my mind more certain thoughts doth bear,—
Useful perhaps, and which I'll ope to thee
Before now further in our souls we grieve,
For, perchance even now, we may in hope believe!

130

"Thou knowst my father for me makes demand,
And, though him fain I would in naught obey,
I must yet go, for Priam doth command,
Whose faith must still be kept in every way;
So go I must, thou seest, from Trojan land
With Diomed, the Greeks' envoy, they say,
When he comes here again. Would Heaven willed
He would no more return in times so evil-filled!

131

"Thou knowest, too, that all my kin dwell here—
My father save; and all the goods I own
Must stay in Troy; and (if my mind is clear
And quite returned to me)—'twill soon be shown
That peace is sought from peril drawn too near
Twixt Troy and Greece; and, once the Greeks have known
King Menelaus can his wife regain,
Troy shall have peace, and thou and I be near again.

132

"For here I shall return when Troy makes peace,
Since otherwhere I do not have to go;
And, if perchance from war Troy scorns release,
Yet, in a time of truce, I'll manage so
I come to town, for, then, much as they please
Ladies, thou knowest, pass 'tween foe and foe;
And all my kin will gladly welcome me,
And cordially desire I visit them, we'll see.

133

"Then can we both some comfort find again,
However waiting for it prove annoy;
For he must seem with courage to sustain
Life's loads of grief who'd find life's gifts of joy,
Which, after, come in still more pleasant train;
But now only I see we are in Troy,
And nothing else, save that more days must go
While we continue grieving in our paths of woe.

134

"Yet more than this, a greater hope is mine,
Peace made or not, of soon returning here:
My father, doubtless, now hath this design,
Because he thinks some ill to me is near
Through his late fault,—some force, some blame condign,—
May, hence, be hurled on me to make him fear;—
But, once he knows how much Troy honours me,
He will not much repine if I return to thee.

135

"And wherefore mid the Greeks me shall he hold?
They, as thou seest, are always armed for fight.
And if not there, where else can he be bold
To leave his child? (I cannot see aright.)
With Greeks he will not trust me, young or old,
Or feel it safe to let me from his sight;
So here to send me back, when time allows,
Will be his wish, I see, whate'er oppose his vows.

136

"He is, thou knowest too, quite miserly
And, having left goods here, he will incline
His ear to what I'll say of them, we'll see;
Yea since they're dear, he'll yield to my design
Of coming back for their recovery
Once I have shown him that such power is mine;
Yea, he will all his avarice employ,
Spite of all things, and view my coming back with joy!"

137

Then Troil to his lady quite intent
Listened, and deep her words impressed his mind;
And all she said, it seemed incontinent
It must prove true; but faith lagged slow behind
(So much he loved and feared for his content
He could not hope so soon his joys to find);
Yet, in the end, however dim it seemed,
He bravely sought to trust like one who fought and dreamed.

138

A part, thus, of their grief was soothed away,
And, as it sped, they found new esperance;
And, feeling less of evil Fate the prey,
Both of them gan again their amorous dance;
And, as a bird in spring will lightly sway
From leaf to leaf and sing for dalliance,
So did these lovers blithe their joy renew,
And many happy things did in their talk review.

139

But, since from Troil's mind the weary thought
Could not escape, that they must separate,
In such a wise as this new words he caught;
"O Criseis mine, loved more by me, thy mate,
Than any goddess to whom praise is brought,—
And more to be adored! I have of late
Thinking thee dead, prepared myself to slay,—
For what life could be mine if thine were not, I pray?

140

"And, certain as is death, of this live sure,
I yet will slay myself, if to return
Thou dost not every effort try t' endure.
And, how I'll fare, I cannot yet discern,
Sans bitter languishment and grief in pure,
Knowing thee gone; and doubt will ever burn
In me anew, lest Calchas keep thee there,
And all not hap, as now thou sayst, so bright and fair.

141

"I do not know if peace tween us will be;
And, peace or not, I cannot e'er believe
Calchas will come again to Troy, with thee;
For, if I do not much myself deceive,
He could not hope to scape his infamy
In dwelling here, so much must he retrieve;
And, if so urgently he seeks thee now,
He will not instant wish to send thee back, I trow.

142

"Rather he'll make thee some Greek lord to wed,
Or prove to thee besieged Troy cannot stand,
Doubting her doom comes soon to evil head;
And lie he will, and say on every hand
Thou art, of all the Greeks, much honouréd;
And he is so revered in Grecian land, —
His virtue so much praised, — that, sans annoy,
I still must fear thou canst not then return to Troy.

143

"And very much they irk me, thoughts like these,
More than my heart can say, O fair my soul!
Thou hast, now gathered to thy hands, the keys
Both of my life and death, and hast them whole,
And that key, too, to use as thou shalt please,
Gently or not, to bring me to my goal.
O radiant star, through whom I find my port,
Know, if thou leave me now, death soon must be my sort!

144

"Therefore, pardee, we must find means and way
To stay thy going hence, if that can be;
To some strange clime we'll bear ourselves away,
Nor care how Priam's promises agree
With future acts, if we escape to-day
His wrath and ire; and, far beyond the sea,
Welcome mid other people we shall find, —
Nations that will us take as lords amid their kind.

145

"Then thither let us flee in secrecy, —
Go there together thou, my love, and I;
And what is left in life to thee and me,
Heart of my body, thou sans whom I die,
There let me live it joyous and carefree!
That is my wish, and that my heart's deep cry —
If thou deem well — and that is end most sure
When every other means is too hard to endure."

146

Criseis sighed and spake assuringly:
"Dear all my good and all my heart's delight,
These things and more may happen presently
All in such form as thou dost fair recite;
But, by the darts of Love, I swear it thee,
That entered have my heart and filled it quite,
My sire's commands, his lies, — a Grecian lord, —
Nothing can turn my love from thee, my soul-adored!

147

"But what thou sayst of fleeing now from here,
Is not, in my own view, good counseling:
One must think much in times, like these, severe,
And to one's thought, both self and kindred bring;
For three great faults would to thy sight appear,
Once we had gone, as thou wouldst urge the thing;
And one through broken faith we should perceive,
Which portends more of ill than any men believe.

148

"And, then, 'twould be with peril to thy kin,
For if, sans aid and counsel, thou them leave
For one poor woman's love, they'll have within
A fear lest others' treasons soon them grieve;
And, — if my wits I really sharpen thin, —
Thou wilt thereon the foulest blame receive,
And then the truth will never be believed
Save by our only friend, who hath our love perceived.

149

"And if the time require no loyalty,
Still war's great needs abide on every hand;
And none his own puissance clear can see
Or hope, of his own self, secure to stand:
And many men unite them hopefully,
For what they risk with others of their land,
They risk more sure; who in themselves much trust,
And in their goods, soon see their hopes decay to dust.

150

"And more, — bethink thee now, what would be said
Among the common folk if thou shouldst go?
That 'twas not Love, with burning darts, that sped
Thy flight, but fear and cowardice, I trow.
Beware that such thoughts take then further head
In thee, and let thy heart no more them know
If to thy soul thy fame was ever dear,
Which of thy valour still doth sound so clear.

151

"And further, think thou of my honour too,
And of my chastity, supremely prized,—
How infamy would stain their spotless hue,
Both be undone, both lost and both despised,
And never raised again so pure in view
Through any plea or any virtue realized
In aught I hence might do, if I should tell
A hundred thousand years of living nobly well.

152

"And yet one more thing,—see thou realize
A truth that chanceth aye in man's affairs:
There is no thing so vile, as see the wise,
As wishing that for which one nothing dares;—
The more one yearns to own that with one's eyes,
The sooner in one's heart one evil bears,
If one, with power large the ill to see
What hath been done, still holds the evil inwardly.

153

"And this our love, that thee doth so delight,
Doth so because we love in secrecy
And rarely come to have its peace aright;
Yea, if thou once shouldst have me wholly free,
The burning fires would be extinguished quite
That now flame thee—and me no less than thee;
Wherefore, if we would have our love stay real,
As much we wish, we must it more in secret steal.

154

"Therefore take cheer, and vanquish Fortune quite,
Render her weak and make her turn her back;
Subject to her control hath stayed no wight
Who never of a free will felt the lack;
Pursue her course and measure, in this plight,
Such steps for thee as make thy sighs more slack,
For ten days hence, sans any failing thee,
I will return to stay in Troy continually."

155

"If thou," then answered Troilo, "return
Within the tenth day, I'll abide content.
But who, in that long time, some means will learn
To soothe my grievous woes and languishment?
Already as thou canst quite well discern,
I pass no single hour sans grave torment
If thou'rt not near. O how, then, can I spend
Ten long, long days before thy steps tow'rd Troy do bend?

156

"For God's sweet sake then find a means to stay
And go not, if thou any means canst see;
I know thou art full subtle in thy way,
If true I grasp reports I hear of thee;
And that no thought now more doth on me prey,
Thou seest clear, if true thou lovest me,
Than this, — that thou dost go; thou canst perceive,
Once thou art gone away, how sore my life will grieve."

157

"Alack," cried Criseis, "thou wilt me slay;
Too much, in thy beliefs, thou givest me
Of black wanhope; I cannot trust to-day
As, when I promised, once I trusted thee;
Alas, my love, what makes thee fear this way?
Why lose thy strength of will so utterly?
Who could believe a man, so brave in war,
Would so a ten days absence of his love deplore?

158

"I think thou canst far better it afford
To take resolve as to thee I have said;
Be more content with it, O sweet my lord,
And know for sure that my breast, too, hath bled,
That my soul, too, and heart weep in accord
As from thy countenance they see me led;
For more than thou dost think now or suppose
I feel, as I have felt, my griefs about me close.

159

"Awaiting time hath often recompense
In gaining time, my love, my Troilo;
Nor am I, as thou claimst, now wrested hence,
Because it is to Calchas that I go;
And do not think in mind I am so dense
I cannot find a way among the foe
For coming back to thee, whom more I love
Than life, and treasure — far all other good above!

160

"And so I pray, — if aught my prayers avail, —
By that great love I know thou hast for me,
By my own love, which nothing thee doth fail, —
For this, my parting now, thou comfort thee;
For seeing still thy tears and sighs prevail,
Thou knowest, brings the deepest hurt to me;
'Tis pity that thou let them plague thee so,
Thou oughtest rid thee of them by some potent blow.

161

"For thee I hope in sweet desire and joy
To live, and hope for thee soon to return,—
And then some means to our delight employ;
But let me in such guise now thee discern
As will, before I go, soothe mine annoy
That then no other pain may in me burn
Than that great flame of love within my heart;
Be blithe then, Troil, who my peace and comfort art.

162

"And this I pray,—while I shall absent be,—
Thou in no other lady take delight,
Nor let a stranger's charms take hold on thee;
For, if I learned, thou must believe of right
I'd slay myself in mad insanity,
Superlatively grieving in my plight.
Oh, couldst thou leave me for another love,
Thou whom I love as woman ne'er loved man above?"

163

And to her last words Troilo with sighs
Made answer then: "If I should wish to do
That that thou touchest on in fearful wise,
I know not how I could such crime pursue;
So hath my love for thee grown great in size
I could not live, should I such evil view.
The love I bear to thee, and all its cause,
Unfold I will, and tell in words its noble laws.

164

" 'Twas not thy beauty urged my loving thee,
Which oft is wont to other men ensnare;
Nor yet thy breeding and thy courtesy,
Which often seize men's wills all unaware;
Nor yet thy richesse nor thy jewelry
Caused in my heart the love that stirreth there;
And still 'tis true, thou art more rich in these
Than ever lady was who lived in Love's fair ease.

165

" 'Twas thy high acts of peerless sov'reignty,—
Thy worth, thy lofty speech in lordly strain,
Thy manners wrought of fair gentility,
Thy charming and thy feminine disdain,
Which make all lust seem more than vile to thee,
And more than vile all deeds of vulgar stain,—
So pure thou art, O potent lady mine,—
'Twas these that made my heart to thee incline.

166

"And such things years can never wrench away,
Nor fickle Fortune; and thence 'tis I aspire
Through anguish, travail, every toil-paved way,—
Always to have thee close to my desire.
Alack then, what repose my loss can stay,
Once thou art gone, my love, my heart's sweet fire?
I ne'er shall find repose, except in death,
And only when my woes cease with my mortal breath."

167

And, after much the two had reasoned so
And wept together, when the dawn drew near,
They broke off talking of their heart-felt woe,
And close they both embraced and held them dear;
And, when the cocks had much begun to crow,
After a thousand kisses sweet and clear,
Each rose and to the other spake farewell;
And they two parted with more tears than I can tell.

CANTO FIVE

1

Upon the same day came, then, Diomed
To give Antenor to his kin in Troy;
And to him Priam bade Criseis lead,
So full of dolour, sighs, and sad annoy
She made the hearts of those who saw her bleed;
And Troil stood nearby,—and all sans joy
To sorrow given o'er as never wight
Was giv'n who dwelt upon this earth and knew its light.

2

Yet true it is, he in his breast did hide
The battle that was waging furious there,
So marv'llously that not a man espied
His sighs or deep lament;—no trace of care
Showed on his countenance, now fair and wide,
Although he wished he might alone repair
To breathe his plaint in some close-hid retreat,
And at his ease there furiously his woes repeat.

3

And many things came in his lofty soul
At seeing Criseis sent to her sire;
And at *him* most, the cause of all his dole,
His anger raged and all of Troil's ire;
Grief gnawed within, and pain without control,
While he complained: "What more do I require?

O caitiff wight, 'tis better once to die
Than live and languish weeping to eternity.

4

"Why not with these my arms, the pact destroy?
And why not here this Diomede slay?
Or fell the old man, cause of mine annoy?
And why not these my brothers here betray?
Or why not turn to weeping all of Troy,
To dolorous shrieks? And bring all ills this day?
O why not carry off my Criseis
And in some new abode provide my cure and bliss?

5

"Who will gainsay if what I wish I do?
Why should I not to e'en the Greeks make cry,
Ask that they Criseis leave with gentle rue?
Why more delay? Why run not there more nigh,
And so let all my friends my madness view?"
But that proud thought and lofty purpose high,
Fear made him leave, lest Criseis be killed
And in th' ensuing fray her warm red blood be spilled.

6

And Criseis, when she saw to part was need,
Just as she was, in that sad company,
Mounted the horse that stood there as her steed,
Since go she must, and then full piteously
She gan, within, with Heav'n to intercede:
"O cruel Jove, and Fortune cruel to me,
Where do ye bear me now against my will?
Why so much doth it pleasure you to see my ill?

7

"Ye wrest me hence, O cruel and pitiless,
From the one joy that entered e'er my soul;
Haply ye think to you I shall address
Honour and sacrifice to slack my dole,
But in that wish ye are deceivéd whole;
For I shall henceforth in my woes express
Only my scorn of you, while I sojourn
Afar, and Troil's noble face cannot discern."

8

And then she turned, in her proud high disdain,
To Diomed and said: "Then go we now,
Let me be shown to thy Greek host more plain,—
A host that hopes t' escape its woes, I vow,
When they so subtly gaze on her they gain,—

And honourable exchange thou mak'st, I trow,—
A woman rendered for a mighty king,
A woman for a man, a brave and much feared thing."

9

These things she said, and forward spurred her mount
And only bade her closest friends goodbye;
But all the lords there clearly could recount
With what great scorn the lady made her cry:
Then she was gone,—to take no further count
Of speech or gossip,—with unseeing eye,
Away from Troy, where ne'er she should return
To be with Troilo, as much her soul did yearn.

10

But Troil, in the guise of courtesy,
With more companions, mounted his great steed,
A falcon on his wrist, and company
He gave her, far as the wall allowed the deed
(Though he had gone the whole way willingly
To Criseis' new home if Priam had agreed);
But, through that, too much might discovered be,
And his repute for wit he held in slight degree.

11

Meanwhile there came surrendered Antenor
Back from the Greeks; and Troy's brave youths with fest
Received their friend to show him honour more;
And, though that coming back proved sad behest
To Troil's heart, which Criseis did deplore,
The prince a fair good mien expressed,
Making his brother welcome cordially
And bidding Pandar ride with him for chivalry.

12

And, being now where they must take their leave,
He and Criseis somewhat nearer drew
And gazed each in the other's eyes to grieve,
Nor could the lady check her plaint and rue,
When each the other's right hand did receive
And Troilo accosted her anew
In soft accents (but such that she could hear)
And said, "Return, lest I should die in pain and fear."

13

He spake no more but turned his gallant steed,
While all his face grew crimson deep, and red;
Nor breathed one little word to Diomed,
Who, shrewdly all the pretty business read

Of the two lovers' love in very deed,
With diverse thoughts arising in his head.
But what he thought himself he softly told,
Resolving secretly to keep his plans in hold.

14

Her father welcomed her with much ado,
As if his love to her had been most great;
But she stood still and modest in his view,
Tortured within, in life made desolate,
Grief filling every vein with bitter rue,
For still she kept her heart to Troil true;
Which, all too soon, was bound to change its view
And him relinquish for another lover new.

15

And back to Troy now turned Prince Troilo
Sadder of soul than e'er was mortal wight—
And sure ne'er tortured fellow showed such woe
As Troil did in face, poor broken knight!
Dismounted at his palace, sad and slow,
Pensive as ne'er before in any plight,
He would not bear what any man might say,
But in his lonely chamber hid himself away.

[By Pandaro's advice, Troilo and Pandaro go to spend some days with Sarpedon to pass the time in an attempt to relieve Troilo of his suffering.]

40

The comrades two then set them on their way
And after some four miles of journeying,
Arrived at Sarpedon's and there made stay;
Who proved most cordial in his welcoming
To Troil, and his friend alike, that day;
And they, though more inclined to sigh than sing,
With merry cheer and playful-laughing boast,
Made gay and blithe their mien before their baron-host.

41

The latter, like a man of mighty heart,
In all more gracious far than any man,
Showed both great honour in his marvellous art;
They made great fête or in the chase they ran
With ladies fair-esteemed, in every part,
With song and shout—or great feasts he began
In pomp and regal hospitality,
Greater than men in Troy before might ever see.

42

But yet what joyed these things sad Troilo,
Whose heart went not to them, but silent stayed?
Where his desire had gazed, his thoughts would go
And of his love they often image made;—
Then Criseis seemed no highest god below,
But stood before his mind's eyes bright arrayed;—
Now one thing, now another, fancy tried;
But ever and anon for love the young prince sighed.

43

And every other dame 'twas grief to see,
However she was prized, however she was fair;
All comfort, every gentle song of glee
Was pain to him, who saw not Criseis there,
In whose hands Love had placed the holy key
Of all his life of fear and fretful care:
The more they made him cheer, the more he thought
Or her, and spurned all other things as things of naught.

44

Meantime no morning, no nor evening passed,
When he called not on Criseis in sighs,
"O light most fair, and star of dawn stedfast!"
And then, as though she was before his eyes,
Listening, a thousand times and more, at last
He'd call her *rose* and ask a kiss for prize,
Until he had again to stop pretence
And end his feignéd greetings in more impotence.

45

And now no hour in the day went by
When he a thousand times breathed not her name;
Always upon his lips was that sweet cry;
In heart and mind he fashioned e'er the same
Fair face, and all her words adorned and high;—
And letters, too, that from his lady came
He turned and read a hundred times a day,
So much he joyed to see what matter in them lay.

46

And when they had there three long days delayed,
To Pandaro our Troil gan to sigh:
"What boots it here? Were we two bound and made
Only to live here tediously, and die?
To take our leave must we be so afraid?
To speak thee sooth, I can no more deny
My wish t' escape; with Sarpedon we've fared
Now long enough, and seen his sumptuous cheer prepared."

47

And Pandar then: "Have we been treated here
Aught churlishly, or hath the tenth day sped?
Our going hence would sure affront appear,—
Restrain thee more, be more by reason led.
Where couldst thou go? What other place seek near
For feasts as rich as these with which we're fed?
Yet two more days, then, stay we ere we go
And, after, take us home if still thou wishest so."

48

And Troil, gainst his will, continued there,
But ever clinging to his wonted thought,
And all that Pandar urged was lost in air
Until the fifth day mood for leaving brought;
When both, though Sarpedon objection bare,
Departed home; but Troil, still distraught,
Called much upon the way, "O God of Grace,
Shall I now find my love returned and see her face?"

49

But Pandar to himself spake otherwise,
As one who knew the whole of Calchas' bent
And all his subtle schemes could realize:
"The youth's wild will and fiery-hot intent
May well grow cool, unless I ill surmise
The things I heard ere Criseis from him went;
Ten days will pass, — nay more, — a month, a year
Before, methinks, the prince will see his lady here."

50

Soon as they were to Troil's house returned,
Both sought the prince's room incontinent;
And, seated there, they both could be discerned
With still their speech on Criseis wholly bent;
While in Prince Troil sighs, as ever, burned;
And, when again they rose and forward went,
Once more he wailed, "The house, at least, we'll see,
Though we can nothing else with any certainty."

51

This said, he caught the hand of Pandaro,
Forced o'er his countenance a feignéd smile,
Drew from the palace doors his comrade slow;
And other pretexts used then to beguile
The friends they met, that he might hide the woe
That yet he felt of love; but, in short while,
His eyes caught sight of Criseis' closed abode
And quick, anew disturbed, his feelings overflowed.

52

He felt his heart had been most rudely split
When door and window both he saw were closed;
And, so far was he carried by the sudden fit
Of sudden pain again on him imposed,
He knew not how to rise, stand, walk, or sit.
Then on his face, so late by guile composed,
A change came, with its signs so manifest
That any wight who gazed had sure his secret guessed.

53

A while he could not speak for that new grief,
But presently began to Pandaro:
"Alas, this place was bright beyond belief
And joyous, too, when I could come and go
Finding her beauty here, who let relief
And all my peace from her fair eyes to flow:
Now is it grown obscure, sans her, as night,
And I can never hope to see her in this light."

54

Then off they rode along the Trojan ways,
Where each spot brought his lady back to mind:
Whence he went musing much in praise:
"There once I saw her smiling blithe and kind;
Here saw her turn and at me sweetly gaze;
There gentle greeting 'twas my joy to find;
Here I beheld her feasting, there saw her stand
In pensive mood, and piteous to my sighs' demand.

55

" 'Twas there she stood when first the blessed look
Of her bright eyes and fair, moved my desire;
And here, when in a sigh's red flame she took
My heart from me to burn't in greater fire;
And there, when she could not now longer brook
To stay my pleasure — woman-like retire;
And here I saw her proud; here, lowly-willed,
My gentle lady showed she was with meekness filled."

* * * * *

58

And in those days he oft approached the gate
Whence Criseis had gone, and pondered there:
" 'Twas hence my comfort issued, driv'n by Fate,
'Twas hence she went, my life, my love, my fair;
As far as this I did escort her late,
And here I parted from her full of care;

Here, wearily, I pressed her fingers white,
Here, weeping, held her hand in our last sad delight.

59

"Thou wentest hence, my heart, my being's fire;
When shall it be thou canst again return,
O dear my blessing, sweet my life's desire?
In those ten days I can, at least, discern
A thousand years; must I so long aspire
To see thee coming back — and yearn and yearn?
Come, comfort me, — as thou hast pledged thy word, —
And be thy coming now not one day more deferred!"

60

And, as he thought, his face had grown more pale
And colourless than e'er its wont had been;
He fancied now men would each other hail
And then point at him with their fingers thin,
Demanding, "Why is Troil grown so frail,
So stricken sore, so cruelly battered in?" —
But no man had so pointed, in good sooth:
He oft suspects such things who in him knows the truth.

* * * * *

68

Each day seemed long, and longer yet each night;
And both grew ever in unwonted mode:
For from the instant when the dawn flushed white
He counted seconds till the fixed stars showed
Clear in the dark; or, while the sun stayed bright,
He vowed so long, so wide, it never rode
There in the sky. And in the hours of night
He counted quite the same until the dawn was white.

69

At Criseis' parting he had seen the moon
Not altogether full but hornéd quite,
Riding the sky at morn by some fortune;
Whence oft he said, remembering that sight:
"When she returns, — and may that time be soon, —
With her two horns both new and clear and white,
As fair she shone when Criseis went away,
Then shall my soul return and here then with me stay."

70

He saw the Greeks' tents stretched outside of Troy,
And, though much formerly that martial sight
Had him disturbed and filled him with annoy,
His gazing now was tempered with delight;

And he would fancy with a lonesome joy,
Whene'er the soft winds touched his face aright,
They came as Criseis' sighs, and then would say
Or here or there his charmful lady now did stray.

71

In such a wise, or even ways more vain,
He sought to while the weary hours away;
And Pandaro, to soothe his Troil's pain,
Always would reason with him, blithe and gay,
Leaving untried no alley of his brain,
Whence he might find a means good cheer to say,—
Giving his Troil hope and esperance
Of some shrewd means which Criseis must find perchance.

CANTO SIX

1

Outside the walls, down on the broad seacoast,
Dwelt Criseis now, a few maids at her side;
And there, amid the Greeks' great armèd host,
She spent her nights in tears she needs must hide,
For in the day she had to check them most;
Wherefore her cheeks, once fresh and rosy-dyed,
Grew both most meager-pale and thin to see—
Far from her love, far from her heart's sweet certainty.

2

She wept and murmured much in reverie
Of Troil, now, it seemed, a lost delight,
And all their acts she cast in memory
And went recording all their words aright,
Prizing his vows and hers in all entirety,
Whenever time she had and power and might:
Whence, knowing her so far from joy and him,
She made her eyes a fountain bitter to the brim.

3

And no one could have been so hard of soul
Who, if he heard her weep in that torment,
He had not of his own tears lost control,
So bitterly she wept in her lament
Whenever time gave her one moment's dole;
And, though no one could write her woe's extent,
Criseis had grief much harder yet to bear—
She had no cousin near who might her sorrows share!

4

She gazed in sorrow on the walls of Troy,
On palace, tower, mighty fortresses,
And inward cried: "What measures, there, of joy!
What sweets of love and all its richnesses,
Alas, were mine! But now in sad annoy
I waste my charms to sombre palenesses.
Alas, my Troilo, how fares it thee?
Dost thou still hold thy Criseis in true memory?

5

"Ah me, alas! Had I thee but believed,
Had we twain but together lately fled,
And in what kingdom pleased thee been received!
Then had I on such dolour never fed
As now I feel, nor such lost time perceived
When Fate shall grant I back to thee be led!
And none would e'er have spoken ill of me
Because, with such a man, I once had chose to flee.

6

"Ah me, alas! that realize so slow
How my own bosom turns my enemy!
I'd flee one ill, to follow worser woe—
Beggar my heart still more in penury,
Hoping that joy might follow death's fell blow!
Alas, dear Troil whom no more I see
(And fear I ne'er shall see!), I wish in vain,
Wishing the Greeks would leave this Trojan plain.

7

"Yet I shall try my best from them to flee,
If Fate will not another means bestow
Of going back to Troy to be with thee,
As I have promised: for the smoke doth go
Where the smoke lists, and so 'twill prove with me,
For what would follow me must follow slow.
Yea, though I die of grief, I still will say,
No wight can stop me now—and no wight bar my way."

8

But from such lofty-pure and high intent
Another lover soon had turned the dame;
For Diomed plied every argument
And quite to win her heart he made his game;
Nor did it fail him long, that hoped event,
For soon he drave her mind from Troil's name,
From thoughts of Troy,—from every other dream,
False love or true, whatever love might to her seem.

9

The fourth full day was not yet onward hied
Since she had parted in her bitter woe,
When Diomed an honest means espied
To come and find her lonely, sobbing low,
Transformed from when he rode at her fair side
The day when Fate from Troy had made her go;
The day when he had brought her thence to here;
And this to him did marvel more than great appear.

10

And to himself he said at that first view:
"Vain will my efforts be, I must believe;
'Tis for some other's love she feels this rue,
For some man else I see her sigh and grieve;
And I with sov'reign art must me indue
If I would win her that man's love to leave
And take up mine. Oh evil was the day
When this sweet Criseis from Troy I led away!"

11

But like a man of ardour great possessed,
And of great heart, he firm resolved in mind
(Though death itself should prove his sure behest),
Since he was come, he would a method find
To show her how he was with love oppressed,
What pains he'd suffer till she proved more kind;
Then, agilely, the Greek knight took his seat,
Resolved, though 'twere at length, he would achieve the feat.

12

And first, then, in his talk he spake amain
Of that hard war by Greeks and Trojans fought,
Demanding if she deemed its purpose vain—
(If winning it was but a frivolous thought!)
Ventured so far in words that were more plain
To ask if Greek ways seemed in strangeness wrought—
Only refrained from asking her forthright
Why Calchas did not wed her to some Grecian knight.

13

But Criseis, whose mind was still on Troil bent,
On him who had appeared such lover sweet,
Saw naught of Diomed's astute intent;
But, since great Amor held the answer meet,
Amor, who ruled the day, she answer lent,
And oftentimes to him her heart would fleet
In pitying mood,—and, thus, much hope she gave
To Diomed of that he sought so ardent-brave.

14

Then, of his speech assured and bolder grown,
"Fair lady, blithe and young," he gan to say,
"If well I saw, then none hath ever known,
Even in angel's face, a look more gay,—
A visage that with greater pleasaunce shone,—
Than yours the day we drew from Troy away
And did, as well you know, then hither come;
But now I see your look transformed—in martyrdom!

15

"Nor do I know what can thereof be cause
If 'tis not love, the which, if you are wise,
You'll cast away, obeying reason's laws;
Therefore, as now I speak, act in that guise;
Methinks doom on the Trojans nearer draws,
Held now our prisoners in war's hard vise;
And we, to raise our siege, have no desire
Until it mean we sack Troy Town with sword and fire.

16

"For do not think that any wight in Troy
Shall find Greek then to treat him pityingly:
Never was Greek who folly did employ,
And never, though the world should last eternally
Will Greek refuse his just right to destroy
The friends of Paris' mad iniquity.—
Yea, if we can, we'll give such punishment
As Paris' deed requires—though all of Troy be shent.

17

"If twelve Hectors instead of one, were there
And sixty brothers each as brave as he
(If Calchas doth us not with errours snare
Or ply his tricks for us unequally),
Though high prized are the honours now they bear,
Soon shall we make them ours, with death the fee
That soon these things will chance, you may be sure;
For not false is our hope, but true and high and pure.

18

"Believe not Calchas had demanded you
With half the great persistence that he showed,
Had he not known the things I say are true;
I talked it with him in his own abode
Before he brought that wish to common view,
And I saw deep the cause that in it rode,—
Why he would bring you from your perils great,
Why so he counseled him ere it should prove too late.

19

"And him as I consoled, of you I learned,—
Your marvelous virtue and your every grace:
When, feeling Antenor might be returned,
I offered me as agent in the case;
And Calchas, since my faith he well discerned,
Left me the task, which I performed apace,
Going and coming ever tirelessly
In speech and conference, and holding audience free.

20

"Wherefore I bid you, lady fair and dear,
To cast all Trojans' bootless love aside;
Expel whatever bitter hope draws near;
Observe your sighs how vainly they are sighed;
Recall, and let your beauty shine out clear,
Which pleases well whoever has't espied;
For now such fate is closely come to Troy
As must her warriors' hopes in full destroy.

21

"And e'en if Troy should always stand secure,
Hers is a race of barbarous, uncouth men,
Her king, his sons, her citizens, impure,
And nothing like the Greeks in might or ken,
Who well surpass all men in prowess sure,
In customs high and honours, twice again;
Here shall you dwell mid men of courtesy;
There ye abode midst gross and dull brutality.

22

"Suppose not love as high and perfect-great
Is not found here with us, as there in Troy;
Your own high worth, your beauteous estate,
Your face angelic, aspect sweet and coy,
Will find a worthy lover here not late;
And, should it not displease you, I would be,
More than a king in Greece, that lover willingly."

23

This said, his face did all vermilion grow,
Red as a fire; and sudden he him checked;
Trembling, his eyelids toward the earth dropped low
And suffered not his eyes to gaze direct.
Then counsel smote on him, as 'twere a blow,
And quick he spake again to this effect;
"Fair lady, do not deem this great annoy,
I am as gentle-born as any man in Troy.

24

"Were Tydeus, my sire, alive to-day,
Who died with them that gainst Thebes nobly fought,
Argo and Calydon would know his sway
As king; and to be king there is my thought.
For no usurper there, he made his way,
But native-born, revered, with ancient honours fraught,
And, sooth to say, sprung from high deity;
So that I am not held, mid Greeks, of low degree.

25

"Wherefore I pray, if aught my prayers can do,
You drive away all black-browed listlessness,
And take me as a servant unto you
If aught I seem to fit your worthiness
In my deserts; and I shall serve most true
Whate'er your honour ask, — or graciousness, —
For ne'er in wight did both so much appear, —
If you poor Diomed will only hold more dear!"

26

Criseis listened long; then modestly,
Her words both slow and few, made answering
To what his many words had asked should be;
And, hearing what he said as latest thing,
She told herself she could great ardour see, —
Yet saw it vile and not worth treasuring
So firm did love for Troil yet endure.
At last she spake submissive, but in accents sure:

27

"I love much, Diomed, the land of Troy,
Where I was born and more than kindly bred;
So heavy on me weighs this war's annoy,
And glad I'd see my home deliveréd;
Since Fate forbids me there my life enjoy,
I feel I am, with reason, sore bestead;
But for each service that thou rend'rest me
I pray deserved reward be measured full to thee.

28

"The Greeks, I know, are of a noble race
And gentle breeding as thou dost assure;
But Trojan worth holds, therefore, no less place
Of honour — being quite as high and pure,
For oft hath Trojan valour shown its face
In Hector's deeds. Oh no, I'll not endure
A thought of praising Greece through blaming Troy;
So to compare the two could give me little joy!

29

"And love I have not known, since late he died,
My husband, whom I served most loyally
Ever as lord and master worth my pride;
And never could I in so high degree
Love Greek or Trojan, though full oft he sighed,
For Love's desire abides no more in me;
That thou art sprung of lofty royal blood,
I well believe and I have clearly understood.

30

"And that truth, with thy spirit high and great,
Moves admiration in a wight like me,
Born to a lowlier, far more humble, state;
While born more royal should thy consort be
And fair as Helen; I am desolate—
Too ill at heart to have such news of thee;
But this I do not say because I grieve
That now so clear confessed thy love I should perceive.

31

"The times are ill, and still in arms ye fight,—
Let nearer come the victory thou dost wait,
Then shall I better know what is my might;
Then less than now, perhaps, I'll find I hate
Pleasure—and then, perchance, some new delight
May spring in me, and what thou dost relate
Will grow more dear: a man must watch, 'tis said,
Time and the season if he would him wisely wed."

32

Quite dear her last words were to Diomed,
Who cheerly thought he now could hope more sure
And see, sans fail, reward from hope proceed,—
Some boon of pleasure that would long endure;
And so he answered: "Lady, to thy need
I pledge my greatest faith, my ardour pure;
At thy disposing am I, and shall be."
No more he said but went thereafter, instantly.

33

In figure he was tall, and fair of mien,
A fresh youth well endowed with pleasing grace,—
Proud, too, and brave, as in his speech was seen,—
As affable as all of Grecian race,—
And prone to love by nature, one would ween:
Which things fair Criseis' mind began to trace,
Once he was gone, much doubting which was meet:
Should she respond to it or flee from love so sweet?

34

And these things chilled in her that keen desire
Which she had felt so promptly to return;
They fixed them deep and bent her mind entire,
Where late her love for Troil bright did burn;
Then back inclined the flames of that great fire
Till torment vanished as new hope did yearn:
At last, it chanced, these things did so persuade
She broke her faith, and Troilo unkindly she betrayed.

CANTO SEVEN

1

But Troil passed the time, as hath been said,
Waiting in vain the tenth and promised day,
Which for his waiting was no earlier bred.
At last it came; when, feigning some new play,
Toward the gate he unattended sped—
Save for his Pandar—talking all the way;
And, gazing tow'rd the fields, the two moved coy
To see if any wight was coming back to Troy.

2

When ladies came, attended or alone,
It seemed each must be Criseis coming back,
Till, on approach, she proved some fair unknown
Who walked on openly sans haste or slack:
So stood they, till the midday sun had shone
And turned across the heavens on his track;
And oft they smiled at their credulity—
"As if experience showed things ever thus could be!"

3

And Troil said: "Of course, she would not start
Before she'd eaten dinner with her sire;
For she would have to use her subtlest art
To leave at all against his fond desire.
Yea, she had found a means from him to part
Had she not stayed to eat beside his fire!
Speak, then, what wilt thou say of my surmise?
She tried her wits in vain—old Calchas was too wise!"

4

And Pandar answered: "Thou dost truly say.
Go we a while and later we'll come here
Again." And finally they took their way,
Troil agreeing, as it would appear.
Then, though the time ere nones upon that day

Had seemed most long, they felt with inward fear
They'd not stood long enough, and stopped again,
Looking for her that came no way across the plain.

5

And Troil said: "Her sire doth her oppose,
Perhaps, and on tow'rd eve would her delay.
'Tis therefore her return so tardy grows;
Come, let us stand outside there on the way
So that the guards, who always look too close,
Shall not much hinder her return to-day,
For they are wont to parley endlessly
Sans thought to whom such treatment comes appropriately."

6

And vespers came and darker evening came,
And each hour crept on, mocking Troilo,
Who, eyes bent on the fields, stood e'er the same,
Regarding all that moved there to and fro
Approaching Troy, and (Never-ending game!)
Of each who came that way he sought to know
What new things chanced among the Greeks of late;
But naught he gleaned from all he asked importunate.

7

Then, turned to Pandaro, he made surmise:
"If in her methods well and true I see,
My lady once again hath acted wise;
She wishes to return in secrecy,
Therefore waits night, when all in darkness lies;
And I commend her that too curiously
She'll not have people gaze and idly sneer:
'For Antenor exchanged, and now returnéd here?'

8

"Nay, do not weary that so long we wait,
For God's sweet sake, my Pandar, I emplore!
We have naught else t' employ our idle state;
Granting my wish can grieve thee nothing sore.
Oh there methinks I see her coming late!
Look thou! Yea, we are seeing her once more!"
"No," answered Pandar, "if my eyes see clear
Thou pointest at a cart which cometh slowly near."

9

"Alas, that thou sayst true," sighed Troilo,
" 'Tis ever thus man's wish doth him deride,—
And her, as if she came, it clear did show."
At length the sunlight from the heaven died,

And, one by one, the stars renewed their glow;
"It comforts me," then Troil softly cried,
"To have my gentle thought and wishes pure
Make me so certain that she'll come ere long for sure."

10

But Pandar only then laughed inwardly
At that he heard Prince Troil raptly say,
For he, as no one else, could know and see
The cause that moved the young knight's lips that way;
But, not to make him more in grief to be
Than then he was, he made his semblance gay
And feigned belief, but mused, "The wretched wight
Awaits some great volcano wind to come to-night."

11

They waited still in vain, while at the gate
The keepers made above a furious din,
Calling for citizens and strangers late
And all who entrance wished, to come within,—
Herdsman and beast and other rabble great;
But Troil still delayed nor would come in
Until he saw the whole sky brightly starred,
When he returned with Pandar, still unbarred.

12

And, though full many times that idle day
With one or other hope he him deceived,
Ever anon it still was Amour's way
That in each hope in turn he much believed,
And none seemed foolish in the whole array:
Whence he him turned to Pandar, now relieved,
And once more venturéd: "O witless pair
Of youths, to wait all day her coming up from there!

13

"She said she would ten days with Calchas spend,
Nor would with her old sire one other stay,
But back to Troy she would thereafter wend;
To-day was then to be her last away.
Not till to-morrow doth her absence end—
If to count rightly still I know the way!
We have, want-wits, a whole day lingered here,
So hath desire forgot what she told me so clear!

14

"To-morrow morning we shall here return,
Pandaro, timely." And they promptly came;
But, up and down, they could no more discern.

Her thought was fixed now on another's name;
So that their idling did them nothing learn,
And that day proved as yesterday the same;
Night came, and both withdrew them into Troy,
Whence Troilo was filled with bitterest annoy.

15

And the glad hope he once had stoutly owned
Now had no place itself to fasten sure;
So, once again, the heart within him moaned,
As he commenced complaint that none could cure
Of her and Love, and, as his spirit groaned,
He felt in no sense could excuse be pure
For her delay, — return, she said she would,
And she had pledged her faith in goodly womanhood!

16

The third, the fourth, the fifth, the sixth day passed
After the ten already fled away, —
With Troil hopeful now, now sad downcast, —
But ever sighing through each bitter day:
And yet more time, when these were gone at last,
Hope kept in him an ever changing sway.
But all in vain! She never did return,
Wherefore the prince's heart must burn, and ache, and burn.

17

His tears, that had been lately much relieved
Through Pandar's comforting, and all his sighs
Came back uncalled for, while his spirit grieved
In an increasing hot and furious wise.
All of the hopes he had till then reprieved
And saved, died cruelly as martyr dies
(For, mocked in him, they found them tortured more
Than ever hopes had been), and fled the winds before.

18

In him all old desire returned anew,
No longer checked; and o'er him the deceit
It seemed he now saw true, — the hostile rue
Whose spirit holds in jealousy its seat, —
Weighed heavier than erst he ever knew,
Till, beggared of repose, he felt defeat,
More than all men to jealousy a prey;
And, as his eyes allowed, he wept both night and day.

19

Eating or drinking was no pleasure now
So full of anguish did he feel his breast;

And more, his conquering sighs would not allow
Sleep to approach his eyes; yea, sore distressed,
His life and self beneath his griefs did bow;
And then, like fire, fled all delight and rest.
And so, with might and main, the prince did flee
All festival and every jocund company.

20

And his pale face was grown so agonized,
He seemed less man than some poor wounded beast;
And no man could him well have recognized,
For wax-like pale he was — like one deceased.
All valour left his body as despised,
And in his members force dwelt now the least
That could beat up at all; and still he spurned
All comfort that to give him friend and kinsman yearned.

21

Priam, who saw his face so sad dismayed,
Called the prince often closely to his side
Asking, "What grief, my Troil, so hath weighed
On thee? Speak, that some cure may be applied.
Thou'rt not thyself — thy cheeks too wanly fade;
What makes thee look so ill, so mortified?
Speak out, my son, thou hidest some deep woe,
And too well do we see how weak thy cheer doth grow."

22

And Hector spake to him no otherwise;
Paris; his brothers, and his sisters too;
And all demanded whence should so arise
The grief he had and through what evils new.
But back to all he gave the same replies, —
His heart was ill, he felt strange forms of rue,
But, what these all were urgent questioning,
Could never from his lips more freely learn to bring.

* * * * *

49

And Pandar answered him: "It seems to me
We might, with letters writ, the lady try;
Because, if now she hath no love for thee,
I do not think we can expect reply,
Or, if she answers, we can clearly see,
From what she writes, if all thy hopes must die, —
Or still in her return thou mayst believe, —
Or if another's love she now doth glad receive.

50

"Since ye two parted, thou hast never wrote
Nor she writ back to thee. In such a case
She might perhaps hold (and thee justly quote!)
She had done well, awaiting time and place.
And surely were that so, 'twere best thy note
Chide her indifference — not that she is base
And otherwise offending. Go thou and write;
Seeking and doing well must bring the truth to light!"

51

And now so of himself he wearied Troilo
The prince believed him more than willingly,
And, drawn apart, he ordered some one go
And fetch him things to write, — and speedily.
That done, he fell to thinking safe and slow
How he should write, and then not terribly,
But calm — yet sans delay — the knight began
A letter to his lady that thus sober ran:

52

"O damsel sweet, to whom Love gave me late
And whose he keeps me now, and long shall keep, —
E'en all my life, — with faith inviolate,
Since at thy parting thou didst make it weep
In greater misery than wight can state,
My soul, still bruiséd with its wounds so deep,
Would recommend it to thy courtesy;
And other greeting now it cannot send to thee.

53

"Surely thou canst not now have turned so Greek
Thou wilt my letters wantonly refuse,
Or chide because it is of love they speak;
For from sweet memories, howe'er one choose,
Love cannot die — nor can those chains grow weak
Which held our love conjoined. We must not lose
Either those chains or love. So take, I pray,
These words that I have writ, and read thou all I say.

54

"If servant of his lord might e'er complain,
I should, I feel, have cause for chiding thee
And that I might, in fairness, show my pain
When I regard the pledge thou gavest to me, —
Thy pious passion, promises again,
Thy oaths, sworn me by every deity,
Thou wouldst return in ten days' little space; —
Forty of them have passed since I beheld thy face.

55

"Yet, since it seems that I should be content
With that that pleases thee, I dare not chide;
But, humbly as I can, 'tis mine intent
To write my thoughts no less by Love's fire tried;
To say my love is still upon thee bent,
As is my life; and wish I cannot hide—
To know what is thy life's experience
Since thou dost dwell, exchanged, amid the Grecian tents!

56

"Methinks, if now I do remember well,
Thy father's lies have had some pow'r with thee,
Or in thy soul new-entered love doth dwell;
Or yet mayhap, — a thing we seldom see, —
The old man is grown kind, and so it fell
Thou wert beholden to his courtesy;
'Tis thence thy inward purposes do show
All contrary, and bring us all lament and woe.

57

"So much beyond our compact thou hast stayed
Surely thou shouldst be thinking of return
To keep with faith the promise thou hast made!
Were't still the first or third day, I'd discern
It meant but this: I must still undismayed
Wait as I've waited and of patience learn!
Hadst thou wished only that, I know for sure
Thou'ldst seen how patiently thy Troil can endure.

58

"But now some new-had lover much I fear
Provides occasion for thy long delay;
Who, if he do, then greater dolour here
Is mine to feel than e'er I felt or may;
And if my fervour merits grief so dear,
'Tis only thine to know it, or to say:
Yet thought thereof so makes me live in dread
That joy and hope are robbed of me and wholly fled.

59

"This dread still makes me groan in hopeless ways, —
Despondent all, when I would quiet be;
This dread alone still conqu'ring on me preys, —
Deep in my thoughts, — and it I cannot flee;
This dread, alas, still haunts me, still me slays,
Nor from it can I ever succour me;
This dread hath brought me in such sad duress
I'm of no use to Venus — and to Mars still less.

60

"My grieving eyes have never ceased to weep
Since thou didst thy departure weary take;
All power to eat, to drink, to rest, to sleep
Is gone; and, speaking, all my words do break
Into sighs only; from my lips can leap
Only the sounds that name thee for my sake—
Sounds that to thee and Love for comfort call;
And they alone, methinks, have saved my life at all.

61

"Well canst thou image, then, the thing I'd do
If I were sure of that which much I fear:
Certain, I trust, I'd slay me in my rue
If ever I should see thy failure clear;
To what end, then, shall I life still pursue,
Once I have lost the hope, so fond and dear,
Of having thee, my soul, of whom I wait
My peace while I shall live—but wait in tearful state?

62

"Sweet song or dalliance with some blithe brigade,
The falcons, dogs, and all festivity,
Bright ladies, temples, all the gay parade,
Which I, of yore, was wont with joy to see,—
All these I shun, like snares in deep hate laid,
Whenever that sad thought comes back to me,
That thou art still so far away from here,
O sweet my life, my hope, and aye my sov'reign dear!

63

"The painted flowers and the verdure new
Which colour now the meads a thousand ways,
Cannot recall my soul from its sad rue,
So much for thee, my lady, burn Love's rays;
Only that coign of sky delights my view
'Neath which I think my Criseis dwells and stays;
Always to that coign do I look to cry:
'She sees it, too,—she now, in whom my hope doth lie.'

64

"I gaze out on the hills that round thee close,
Down on the place that keeps thee hid from me,
And sigh and sigh: 'Alas, 'tis that and those
Are privileged her love-lit face to see,
And her fair eyes, for which my longing grows,
Afar from them, a life of misery.'
O were I just that hill—or on that hill!
O that I dwelt where I might see her still!

65

"I gaze upon the streams bound for the sea,
To which my Criseis hath her dwelling near,
And say: 'These streams go where they can her see,
Go there, where they are seen of her, my dear,
In whom my own eyes' light hath gone to be,
Knowing it shines in her divinely clear;
Alas my life, why cannot streams and I
Change power to flow on there beneath sweet Criseis' eye?'

66

"And, when the sun sets, enviously I gaze,
Because, methinks, he yearns for my delight,
Drawn on toward thee in amorous amaze,
And so, more soon than wont, to seek thy sight
He hastens on; and then I hate his ways;
I sigh; my pains increase; I pray that night
Descend to earth and thereby rescue thee,
Lest the broad sun I fear, should steal thee thence from me.

67

"And oft to hear some one the place but name,
Where thou dost dwell, — or oft a man to see
Who comes from there, — relights in me the flame
That had seemed growing weak for grief of thee;
And then, methinks, I feel a hidden game
Of pleasure in my mind grow cheerily,
And I cry out: 'O might I come but there
Whence this man comes, and see my heart's delight so fair!'

68

"But thou, how dost thou mid those arméd knights?
Mid warlike men, mid rumours, neath their tents,
Amid great ambuscades and sundry frights?
Art thou not dazed by fury so intense?
By sounds of arms, by sea-storms in the nights,
To which thou dwellst so near, sans all defense?
Are these not cause, my love, of grave annoy? —
For thou wert wont to live more delicate in Troy!

69

"But true compassion I still have for thee, —
Greater than for myself, — as true I ought.
Return therefore; redeem thy pledge to me
Before I fall into more evil thought:
I pardon gladly, too, the injury
Thy too, too long delay hath on me brought;
Amends I ask none, — save to see thine eyes,
Thy beauteous face, where only dwells my paradise!

70

"I pray thee by that sov'reign high delight
Which thou of me, and I of thee did take,
And, thereto, by thy sweetness fair and bright,
Which flamed our hearts alike for dear Love's sake;
And then, my lady, by the beauty white,
Which thou dost courteous own, my prayer I make:
By those long sighs, that piteous lament
In which our mutual breath one time so much was spent.

71

"By kisses sweet and by the glad embrace
Which drew our hearts together, close and tight;
By all the joyaunce and the talk in grace,
Which ever made more blithe our high delight;
By that faith, too, it pleased thee so to place
In all the words of love thou didst recite,
When last we met (and parted sadly then—
And have not, ever since, the other met again!).

72

"I pray thee, so recall and here return:
And, if perchance some cause prohibits thee,
Then write who, after thy ten day sojourn,
Still holds thee there from coming back to me.
O be not in thy fair speech harsh and stern;
In this, at least, content my life of dree;
And say if I may henceforth hope to have
Any sweet love of thee before I seek my grave.

73

"Give me but hope, and I will wait and pray,
Though that is ever more than misery;
Deny me hope, and I myself will slay,
And end this life so bitter-hard for me:—
Then still, whatever loss befall me may,
The shame is thine and evermore will be,
That thou didst do to death a servant true,
Who ne'er had done thee ill nor giv'n thee cause of rue.

74

"Pardon, if now I do not well endite
But fail in speech, or if here stain on stain
Thou find in this sad letter that I write;
For both offences spring from out my pain,
Because I live and dwell in sore despite,
And nothing me from weeping can restrain;
And all these stains that o'er my letter spread
Are tears, all tears in grief and tristful dolour shed.

75

"I'll say no more, though much remains to say,
Until I see thee coming back to me;
Then act, my soul! Thou canst do much to-day
If, as thou couldst, thou wouldest labour thee.
Alas, so am I changed by grief's hard sway
Thou wilt not know me henceforth for my dree;
I'll say no more, save 'God thee save, my sweet';
And God soon grant that thou and I once more may meet."

76

He sealed and gave his words to Pandaro,
Who sent them her. And then whole days in vain
The prince awaited answer to his woe.
His dolour grew to more than human pain;
And everything did confirmation show
Of that dim forecast of his dream insane;
But not, therefore, did he all hoping cease,
For yet to love his Criseis did young Troil please.

* * * * *

104

So grief continued for our Troilo
Until he grew inured and, patiently,
Was able more to bear his pain and woe;
Then once again the prince most ardently
His valour gainst the Greeks desired to show;
And that restored his old strength presently, —
Strength he had lost, what time he sore complained
Through the excess of pain he had so long sustained.

105

And then, too, Criseis had writ him now;
Who, that she loved him more than ever, swore;
And her excuses, which she did endow
With reasons why she had not come before,
And her demands he further time allow
For her return (which was not evermore!) —
All moved him so they gave him hope again
To see his Criseis — though, alack, he knew not when!

106

So he made battle once more on his foes
And all his worth in arms did demonstrate;
And all those sighs, and other bitter woes
The Greeks, he felt, had done upon him late
He sold them dear, when he renewed his blows;
But nothing would thereon his wrath abate;

Until destroying death should bring him peace,
And from both love and fighting grant his soul release.

CANTO EIGHT

1

He grew inured to pain, as we have said,
And only seemed to draw more valiant breath,
When higher grief than pen hath e'er portrayed
Fell upon Troy in mighty Hector's death,—
In whom his sire and brothers all had laid
Their sov'reign hopes, their strength, their last of faith,—
The walls and gates of Troy,—a cureless blow
That kept them all lamenting long in pain and woe.

2

Yet e'en for this he'd not from Love depart,
However much, then, hope might seem to lose;
Rather he sought by every means and art,—
As still among fond lovers is the use,—
To have again what once had pleased his heart,
All that sweet essence which from love ensues;
And that she came not pardoned Criseis,
Deeming the cause of her delay was this—or this.

3

And letters more he wrote her presently,
Which told her how he felt by night or day,
Praising sweet times of cherished memory.
Oft of her pledge to come he'd tell the may;
And oft he chided, though most courteously,
Her sad postponement and her long delay,
Through Pandar, whom he always sent to her
Whene'er times set for truce or treaty would recur.

4

And likewise often he had thought to go,
Dressed in some pilgrim's habit gray;
But how to counterfeit he did not know,
Or how conceal the truth by such a way;
And much, conviction did within him grow
He could not find a good excuse to say
If ever he were known and recognized,
Why he had gone in that strange garb disguised.

5

And nothing more than words came from her now—
Fair, but their promises, had no effect;
So that his mind began more to allow

These were but tricks, and he did much suspect
Truth for the bitter truth (as oft, I trow,
It chanceth him, whoe'er without defect
Will look into the things that sway his mind
Because, through seeing clear, no man e'er yet went blind!)

6

That new love was the cause, at length he knew,
She sent such frequent and such reckless lies;
Then full conviction in the poor prince grew
'Twas not her father's falsehoods, — crafty, wise, —
Nor filial cares that kept her from his view;
And further proof he asked not for his eyes,
He knew the truth as well as truth is known
Through that dread spectre which his evil dream [1] had shown.

7

And that new love made faith in him recede, —
As happens oft with those that hope in vain
And show at first an all too willing creed
In things that, while they love, increase their pain.
Yet that this was the truth of Diomed,
As erewhile he had feared, he learned more plain
Soon after, by a chance that took away
All semblance of excuse; and he believed that day.

8

While standing, still in torment, pensively,
His heart yet timid and with love distraught,
He heard the rabble calling noisily —
That Greeks and Trojans had new battle fought, —
Deifebo had met right valiantly
With Diomed and now his vestment brought,
A captured prize worth showing all of Troy,
And here the victor marched in solemn pomp and joy.

9

This coat was borne before Deifebo
Throughout all Troy and came to Troil's view,
Who praised with others the triumphant show,
Then, closer it to see, the vestment drew;
And, as he moved his eyes quick to and fro,
Gazing at all, he found new cause for rue,
For on the breast of it a clasp of gold,
Set as a buckle there, the prince chanced to behold.

1. In this dream, Troilo had seen within a wood a great boar which held Criseis beneath its feet and which, with its snout, tore her heart forth from her side. It seemed to Troilo that Criseis cared little for the hurt it caused her, but almost took pleasure in it. The account of this dream is given in Canto Seven, stanzas 23 ff., omitted in this volume.

10

And that he recognized immediately
As one he gave to parting Criseis
The morning that he bore her company
Beyond the gates, in those last hours of bliss
Which followed their last night of revelry, —
That last night they had met to love and kiss;
But now he only said, "My dream was true,
I see — and all my long suspicion, all my thoughts of rue!"

11

He parted thence, and sent for Pandaro,
Who as of old now thither kindly came;
And straight the prince began to cry his woe,
Bewailing all the love he bore the dame,
And, how he learned her treason, gan to show,
Nor sought to longer shield his Criseis' name;
Mourning so bitter in his mighty grief
He only thought that death could bring him sure relief.

12

And, as he wept, the prince began to say:
"O Criseis mine, where is thy loyalty?
Thy faith? thy love? desire of fervid ray?
Where are those gracious favours promised me
When we two parted and thou wentst away?
Doth Diomed now have them all from thee?
And I, who loved thee more, through thy deceit
Must I be left to weep my trouble and defeat?

13

"Who will hereafter trust in any vow,
Have faith in Love or woman ever more
Seeing such perjury as I see now?
Nay, I knew not that any woman bore
A heart so rigid-hard as that which thou
Dost bear, letting another enter at that door
Whence Troil is dismissed, who loved thee so,
Waited and was deceived and came to utter woe!

14

"And hadst thou, too, no other jewelry
On thy new lover careless to bestow —
On Diomed — save what I gave to thee
With many tears and in the depths of woe
That it might be remembrancer of me,
When thou shouldst dwell with Calchas there below?
Nay, nothing could so move thee but vile spite —
Some mean desire to show thy soul in truer light.

15

"Therefore I see me now expelled in scorn
Out of thy heart, although against my will,
Deep in my heart thy image yet is worn,—
Thy fair face wrecking grief upon me still:
Woe, woe is me,—in evil hour born!
These thoughts despoil me quite, the while they kill,
Of all my esperance for future joy,
And are, at once, the cause of anguish and annoy.

16

"Thy heart hath wickedly discarded me,—
Who aye in it had thought to dwell and stay,—
And ta'en in place of me, through perfidy,
This Diomed; but Venus hear, I pray,
The oath I swear to bring high grief on thee
With this my sword, when comes the first melee!
If Heaven grant I find thy Diomed
And let me use my strength in one victorious deed!

17

"Or let him kill me—and be dear to thee!—
Still, 'tis my hope, true Justice and divine
Will take fair view of this my agony,
And likewise see what evil sins are thine!
O Jove supreme, in whom is remedy
For injured Right, and from whom, at thy sign,
High Virtue rises, lives, and moves her fair,
Are thy just eyes completely turned now otherwhere?

18

"Do now thy fervent thunderbolts repose?
And of thine eyes are they no longer seen,
The sins of men—our griefs and human woes?
O very Light, O Lucid Rays serene,
Through whom the earthly mind rejoicing knows,
Cast into darkness her in whom have been
All lies and treasons, all deceits and guile,
Show her no pardon more—not e'en a moment's while!

19

"O Pandar mine, who blamédst so of late
The faith I had in dreams and augury,
Now canst thou see what clear truths they relate,—
Thy Criseis makes thee trust them certainly!
The gods, to mortal men compassionate,
In divers wise do show them openly
Secrets by Heaven seen, to us unknown,
That through their kindness we may fuller knowledge own.

20

"And sleep is one mode that the gods pursue
In revelation, oft I have perceived,—
With mind kept firmly on the things in view;
So now I wish me dead, so am I grieved
Because naught waits me hence but bitter rue,—
No solace hence, no joy with mirth inweaved!
Yet, through thy counsel, I consent to pause
And mid my foes,—in arms,—await death's hateful jaws.

21

"God send before me, then, this Diomed
When first I issue to renew the fight!
Let this great wish my sorrows supersede,
So I may make him taste my weapon's might,
May make him rue with death his caitiff deed
There in the fields; nor care I, then, what wight
May slay poor me, if only first he die
And I, on reaching hell, find him in misery!"

22

Pandaro listened, torn twixt grief and rue;
Felt all was true; and knew not what to say:
Love of his friend in one direction drew;
Shame in another bade him flee away
As all of Criseis' treason came to view,—
Somehow, at least, his cousin's guilt repay;
But what and how, he could not clear perceive,
And love and shame both made him sorer yet to grieve.

23

But in the end he spake, mid weeping sore:
"Troil, I know not what I ought to say,
Rightly thy lady's foulness to deplore
Or give her due of blame in proper way;
Her falseness I'll not try excusing more;
I'll never wish to go where she doth stay!
The things I did, I did for love of thee
Smirching my own good name quite unreservédly!

24

"When once I pleased thee, I felt pleasure true;
But in the ill done now I cannot act,
For, like thee, I am overcome with rue:
Yet, if I saw a means to mend the fact,
Be certain I should quick that means pursue:
Only I pray that God, whose high impact
Makes all things turn or be, shall punish her
That in so false a wise she may not hence bestir."

25

Great was their lamentation and complaint,
But Fortune kept the road of destiny;
Criseis loved Diomed now sans constraint,
And Troilo wept on in misery:
The Greek praised Heav'n with praises never faint;
The Trojan grieved on unconsolédly;
In all Troy's battles Troil gladly fought
And more than others always Diomed he sought.

26

And when they met, as so about he ranged,
They cried out taunts of caitiff villainy,
Or mighty warlike blows the two exchanged,
Hurtling together both, most savagely,
Their swords in hand, and for that heart estranged
They sold each other hate most furiously;
Yet Fortune had not so in Heav'n disposed
Either should do the deed he for himself proposed.

27

At divers times the wrath of Troilo
Worked on the Greeks such skilful hurt and hate
That few did then against the sad knight go
Who did not meet, unhorsed, their death and fate
(If e'er they paused to let him strike his blow!).
And, after long he so for death did wait,
And after he a thousand men did slay,
Achilles smote and slew him wretchedly one day.

28

So ended then the love of Troilo
For Criseis, in evil hour conceived;
So ended then his more than wretched woe,
Wherein, in equal wise, none ever grieved;
So ended then that splendid light and show
Which e'en the throne deserved, as men believed;
So ended Troil's faith in vanity;
So hope in Criseis false forever ceased to be!

29

O youths in whom, with life's increasing age,
Love comes with all too amorous desire,
I pray by Heav'n ye bravely do assuage
The first swift flames of Love's perverting fire!
Behold how mad poor Troil's love did rage,
Which you to show, my verses did aspire,
O read them now with free and open heart!
If ye would not trust lightly in false Amor's art!

30

Maidens are fickle (as young men should see);
Delight in many lovers; estimate
Their beauties high as glasses; haughtily
Take much vain glory in their youthful state,—
The which the more its charms and pleasaunce be,
The higher in themselves they name its rate;
Virtue they never know, nor sense of mind;
They are as volatile as leaves blown in the wind!

31

And oft, because they spring of lofty lineage
Or many grandsires can enumerate,
They think they should be favoured in Love's rage,—
Count lovers more, than dames of lesser state;
They think pure custom is a mere outrage,
Tilt noses, and in scorn all good berate.—
O loathe these, youths! Hold them for mean and vile,
For they are beasts, not gentle ladies free from guile!

32

A perfect lady hath more true desire
To be beloved, and to love doth delight;
Clear she discerns what must be shunned like fire,
Bravely avoids, elects, foresees what things are right,
Keeps faith and promise, as the gods require.
Her kind pursue; yet not if she be light
Or hope a hasty choice.— Not all are wise,
And often, when mature, they are the less to prize.

33

Have foresight then and pity Troilo,
And even for yourselves compassion bear;
Demean you well; and with a piteous woe
For him beseech the god of Love in prayer,
That he full peace may in that region know
Where'er he dwell; and pray Love's grace and care
Be granted you to make you love aright,
Lest ye, too, perish wretched through some wanton's spite.

CANTO NINE

1

Glad times are wont to be the cause
Of soft-writ verse, O song, my piteous canto!
But thee, neath stern affliction's hard-forced laws,
Love drew from out a soul deep sunk in woe,—
Gainst nature so it gives the understanding pause,

Unless some hidden virtue aimed the blow
At our transfixéd heart, inspired and stirred
Through our sweet lady's potent worth and word.

2

She, as I know from oft felt sentiment,
Can make me naught or she can make me great—
Whiche'er she choose; and so the argument
Of all the tragic story I relate
Was born, methinks; and so I am content
That more from this than grief I did create
Thee, little song; but, howe'er that may be,
We're both come to the noble end desired by me.

3

We now have reached the port which long we sought,
There by the rocks, there on the open sea;
With wind and tempest we have sailed and fought,
Seeking, amid the sea's uncertainty,
That pure star's sign with light and radiance fraught
(Worthy our reverence in high degree),
Which makes our every aim to bearings true,
And came and comes so timely to our clearer view.

4

Here, then, I think we may our anchors throw
And make end to our ways of journeying;
Here we may breathe those thanks with love aglow
Returning pilgrims always ought to bring
To her who guided them through weal and woe;
There, by the shore so near, with garlanding
And with the many other honours due
We will our love's good ship adorn before her view!

5

Then thou, somewhat reposed, mayst presently
Unto my soul's kind lady freely go:
O happy thou, who shalt my bright love see,
A thing I cannot do, (whence springs my woe!).
And, if her hands accept thee festively,
Then in a humble wise, and soft and low,
Commend me to her noble virtues high,
In which alone I can my heart's salvation spy.

6

And, in the mournful weeds thou now dost wear,
I pray thee go and make my lady see,
In Troil's griefs, what ills my life doth bear—
The woes, the sighs, the plaints of misery

And other things that caused, and cause, my care
Since her clear radiant eyes are hid from me
Because she parted, too, and went away
Although I only lived when near me she would stay.

7

And if thou find she listen kind to thee,—
Or if her angel face show pitying sign,
Or if she sigh for my hard misery,—
Pray her return and prove her heart benign,—
When pleasures her, or else command from me
My soul depart and be no longer mine,
For where she is, my soul and heart must go,
And better than such life 'twould be to die in woe!

8

Beware thou do not try thine embassy
Without the aid of Love, lest thou shouldst fail
Through misadventure that would fall on thee,—
Or lest, sans him, thou to no good avail.
If thou go with him, thou shalt honoured be;
Then haste; while I in prayer Apollo hail,
Beseeching first he win thee ready ear,
Then send thee back to me with answer of good cheer!

THE DECAMERON

Translated by J. M. Rigg

[Taken from *The Decameron of Giovanni Boccaccio*, translated by J. M. Rigg, Everyman's Library, 2 vols., E. P. Dutton & Co., New York, and J. M. Dent & Sons, London.]

Beginneth here the first day of the Decameron, in which, when the author has set forth, how it came to pass that the persons, who appear hereafter, met together for interchange of discourse, they, under the rule of Pampinea, discourse of such matters as most commend themselves to each in turn.

As often, most gracious ladies, as I bethink me, how compassionate you are by nature one and all, I do not disguise from myself that the present work must seem to you to have but a heavy and distressful prelude, in that it bears upon its very front what must needs revive the sorrowful memory of the late mortal pestilence, the course whereof was grievous not merely to eye-witnesses but to all who in any other wise had cognisance of it. But I would have you know, that you need not therefore be fearful to read further, as if your reading were ever to be accompanied by sighs and tears. This horrid beginning will be to you even such as to wayfarers is a steep and rugged mountain, beyond which stretches a plain most fair and delectable, which the toil of the ascent and descent does but serve to render more agreeable to them; for, as the last degree of joy brings with it sorrow, so misery has ever its sequel of happiness. To this brief exordium of woe — brief, I say, inasmuch as it can be put within the compass of a few letters — succeed forthwith the sweets and delights which I have promised you, and which, perhaps, had I not done so, were not to have been expected from it. In truth, had it been honestly possible to guide you whither I would bring you by a road less rough than this will be, I would gladly have so done. But, because without this review of the past, it would not be in my power to shew how the matters, of which you will hereafter read, came to pass, I am almost bound of necessity to enter upon it, if I would write of them at all.

I say, then, that the years of the beatific incarnation of the Son of God had reached the tale of one thousand three hundred and forty-eight, when in the illustrious city of Florence, the fairest of all the cities of Italy, there made its appearance that deadly pestilence, which, whether disseminated by the influence of the celestial bodies, or sent upon us mortals by God in His just wrath by way of retribution for our iniquities, had had its origin some years before in the East, whence, after destroying an innumerable multitude of living beings, it had propagated itself without respite from place to place, and so, calamitously, had spread into the West.

In Florence, despite all that human wisdom and forethought could devise to avert it, as the cleansing of the city from many impurities by officials appointed for the purpose, the refusal of entrance to all sick folk, and the adoption of many precautions for the preservation of health; despite also humble supplications addressed to God, and often repeated both in public procession and otherwise, by the devout; towards the beginning of the spring of the said year the doleful effects of the pestilence began to be horribly apparent by symptoms that shewed as if miraculous.

Not such were they as in the East, where an issue of blood from the nose was a manifest sign of inevitable death; but in men and women alike it first betrayed itself by the emergence of certain tumours in the groin or the armpits, some of which grew as large as a common apple, others as an egg, some more, some less, which the common folk called gavoccioli. From the two said parts of the body this deadly gavocciolo soon began to propagate and spread itself in all directions indifferently; after which the form of the malady began to change, black spots or livid making their appearance in many cases on the arm or the thigh or elsewhere, now few and large, now minute and numerous. And as the gavocciolo had been and still was an infallible token of approaching death, such also were these spots on whomsoever they shewed themselves. Which maladies seemed to set entirely at naught both the art of the physician and the virtues of physic; indeed, whether it was that the disorder was of a nature to defy such treatment, or that the physicians were at fault — besides the qualified there was now a multitude both of men and of women who practised without having received the slightest tincture of medical science — and, being in ignorance of its source, failed to apply the proper remedies; in either case, not merely were those that recovered few, but almost all within three days from the appearance of the said symptoms, sooner or later, died, and in most cases without any fever or other attendant malady.

Moreover, the virulence of the pest was the greater by reason that intercourse was apt to convey it from the sick to the whole, just as fire devours things dry or greasy when they are brought close to it. Nay, the evil went yet further, for not merely by speech or association with the sick was the malady communicated to the healthy with consequent peril of common death; but any that touched the clothes of the sick or aught else that had been touched or used by them, seemed thereby to contract the disease.

So marvellous sounds that which I have now to relate, that, had not many, and I among them, observed it with their own eyes, I had hardly dared to credit it, much less to set it down in writing, though I had had it from the lips of a credible witness.

I say, then, that such was the energy of the contagion of the said pestilence, that it was not merely propagated from man to man, but, what is much more startling, it was frequently observed, that things which had belonged to one sick or dead of the disease, if touched by some other living creature, not of the human species, were the occasion, not merely of sickening, but of an almost instantaneous death. Whereof my own eyes (as I said a little before) had cognisance, one day among others, by the following experience. The rags of a poor man who had died of the disease being strewn about the open street, two hogs came thither, and after, as is their wont, no little trifling with their snouts, took the rags between their teeth and tossed them to and fro about their chaps; whereupon, almost immediately, they gave a few turns, and fell down dead, as if by poison, upon the rags which in an evil hour they had disturbed.

In which circumstances, not to speak of many others of a similar or even graver complexion, divers apprehensions and imaginations were engendered in the minds of such as were left alive, inclining almost all of them to the same harsh resolution, to wit, to shun and abhor all contact with the sick and all that belonged to them, thinking thereby to make each his own health secure. Among whom there were those who thought that to live temperately and avoid all excess would count for much as a preservative against seizures of this kind. Wherefore they banded together, and, dissociating themselves from all others, formed communities in houses where there were no sick, and lived a separate and secluded life, which they regulated with the utmost care, avoiding every kind of luxury, but eating and drinking very moderately of the most delicate viands and the finest wines, holding converse with none but one another, lest tidings of sickness or death should reach them, and diverting their minds with music and such other delights as they could devise. Others, the bias of whose minds was in the opposite direction, maintained, that to drink freely, frequent places of public resort, and take their pleasure with song and revel, sparing to satisfy no appetite, and to laugh and mock at no event, was the sovereign remedy for so great an evil: and that which they affirmed they also put in practice, so far as they were able, resorting day and night, now to this tavern, now to that, drinking with an entire disregard of rule or measure, and by preference making the houses of others, as it were, their inns, if they but saw in them aught that was particularly to their taste or liking; which they were readily able to do, because the owners, seeing death imminent, had become as reckless of their property as of their lives; so that most of the houses were open to all comers, and no distinction was observed between the stranger who presented himself and the rightful lord. Thus, adhering ever to their inhuman determination to shun the sick, as far as possible, they ordered their life. In this extremity of our city's suffering and tribulation the venerable authority of laws, human and divine, was abased and all but totally dissolved, for lack of those who should have administered and enforced them, most of whom, like the rest of the citizens, were either dead or sick, or so hard bested for servants that they were unable to execute any office; whereby every man was free to do what was right in his own eyes.

Not a few there were who belonged to neither of the two said parties, but kept a middle course between them, neither laying the same restraint upon their diet as the former, nor allowing themselves the same license in drinking and other dissipations as the latter, but living with a degree of freedom sufficient to satisfy their appetites, and not as recluses. They therefore walked abroad, carrying in their hands flowers or fragrant herbs or divers sorts of spices, which they frequently raised to their noses, deeming it an excellent thing thus to comfort the brain with such perfumes, because the air seemed to be everywhere laden and reeking with the stench emitted by the dead and the dying, and the odours of drugs.

Some again, the most sound, perhaps, in judgment, as they were also the most harsh in temper, of all, affirmed that there was no medicine for the disease superior or equal in efficacy to flight; following which prescription a multitude of men and women, negligent of all but themselves, deserted their city, their houses, their estates, their kinsfolk, their goods, and went into voluntary exile, or migrated to the country parts, as if God in visiting men with this pestilence in requital of their iniquities would not pursue them with His wrath wherever they might be, but intended the destruction of such alone as remained within the circuit of the walls of the city; or deeming, perchance, that it was now time for all to flee from it, and that its last hour was come.

Of the adherents of these divers opinions not all died, neither did all escape; but rather there were, of each sort and in every place, many that sickened, and by those who retained their health were treated after the example which they themselves, while whole, had set, being everywhere left to languish in almost total neglect. Tedious were it to recount, how citizen avoided citizen, how among neighbours was scarce found any that shewed fellow-feeling for another, how kinsfolk held aloof, and never met, or but rarely; enough that this sore affliction entered so deep into the minds of men and women, that in the horror thereof brother was forsaken by brother, nephew by uncle, brother by sister, and oftentimes husband by wife; nay, what is more, and scarcely to be believed, fathers and mothers were found to abandon their own children, untended, unvisited, to their fate, as if they had been strangers. Wherefore the sick of both sexes, whose number could not be estimated, were left without resource but in the charity of friends (and few such there were), or the interest of servants, who were hardly to be had at high rates and on unseemly terms, and being, moreover, one and all, men and women of gross understanding, and for the most part unused to such offices, concerned themselves no further than to supply the immediate and expressed wants of the sick, and to watch them die; in which service they themselves not seldom perished with their gains. In consequence of which dearth of servants and dereliction of the sick by neighbours, kinsfolk and friends, it came to pass — a thing, perhaps, never before heard of — that no woman, however dainty, fair or well-born she might be, shrank, when stricken with the disease, from the ministrations of a man, no matter whether he were young or no, or scrupled to expose to him every part of her body, with no more shame than if he had been a woman, submitting of necessity to that which her malady required; wherefrom, perchance, there resulted in after time some loss of modesty in such as recovered. Besides which many succumbed, who with proper attendance, would, perhaps, have escaped death; so that, what with the virulence of the plague and the lack of due tendance of the sick, the multitude of the deaths, that daily and nightly took place in the city, was such that those who heard the tale — not to say witnessed the fact — were struck dumb with amazement. Whereby, practices contrary to the former habits of the citizens could hardly fail to grow up among the survivors.

It had been, as to-day it still is, the custom for the women that were neighbours and of kin to the deceased to gather in his house with the women that were most closely connected with him, to wail with them in common, while on the other hand his male kinsfolk and neighbours, with not a few of the other citizens, and a due proportion of the clergy according to his quality, assembled without, in front of the house, to receive the corpse; and so the dead man was borne on the shoulders of his peers, with funeral pomp of taper and dirge, to the church selected by him before his death. Which rites, as the pestilence waxed in fury, were either in whole or in great part disused, and gave way to others of a novel order. For not only did no crowd of women surround the bed of the dying, but many passed from this life unregarded, and few indeed were they to whom were accorded the lamentations and bitter tears of sorrowing relations; nay, for the most part, their place was taken by the laugh, the jest, the festal gathering; observances which the women, domestic piety in large measure set aside, had adopted with very great advantage to their health. Few also there were whose bodies were attended to the church by more than ten or twelve of their neighbours, and those not the honourable and respected citizens; but a sort of corpse-carriers drawn from the baser ranks, who called themselves becchini and performed such offices for hire, would shoulder the bier, and with hurried steps carry it, not to the church of the dead man's choice, but to that which was nearest at hand, with four or six priests in front and a candle or two, or, perhaps, none; nor did the priests distress themselves with too long and solemn an office, but with the aid of the becchini hastily consigned the corpse to the first tomb which they found untenanted. The condition of the lower, and, perhaps, in great measure of the middle ranks, of the people shewed even worse and more deplorable; for, deluded by hope or constrained by poverty, they stayed in their quarters, in their houses, where they sickened by thousands a day, and, being without service or help of any kind, were, so to speak, irredeemably devoted to the death which overtook them. Many died daily or nightly in the public streets; of many others, who died at home, the departure was hardly observed by their neighbours, until the stench of their putrefying bodies carried the tidings; and what with their corpses and the corpses of others who died on every hand the whole place was a sepulchre.

It was the common practice of most of the neighbours, moved no less by fear of contamination by the putrefying bodies than by charity towards the deceased, to drag the corpses out of the houses with their own hands, aided, perhaps, by a porter, if a porter was to be had, and to lay them in front of the doors, where any one who made the round might have seen, especially in the morning, more of them than he could count; afterwards they would have biers brought up, or, in default, planks, whereon they laid them. Nor was it once or twice only that one and the same bier carried two or three corpses at once; but quite a considerable number of such cases occurred, one bier sufficing for husband and wife, two or three brothers, father and son, and so forth. And times without number it happened, that, as two priests, bearing the cross, were on their way to perform the last office for some one, three or four biers were brought up by the porters in rear of them, so that, whereas the priests supposed that they had but one corpse to bury, they discovered that there were six or eight, or sometimes more. Nor, for all their number, were their obsequies honoured by either tears or lights or crowds of mourners; rather, it was come to this, that a dead man was then of no more account than a dead goat would be to-day. From all which it is abundantly manifest, that that lesson of patient resignation, which the sages were never able to learn from the slight and infrequent mishaps which occur in the natural course of events, was now brought home even to the minds of the simple by the magnitude of their disasters, so that they became indifferent to them.

As consecrated ground there was not in extent sufficient to provide tombs for the vast multitude of corpses which day and night, and almost every hour, were brought in eager haste to the churches for interment, least of all, if ancient custom were to be observed and a separate resting-place assigned to each, they dug, for each grave-yard, as soon as it was full, a huge trench, in which they laid the corpses as they arrived by hundreds at a time, piling them up as merchandise is stowed in the hold of a ship, tier upon tier, each covered with a little earth, until the trench would hold no more. But I spare to rehearse with minute particularity each of the woes that came upon our city, and say in brief, that, harsh as was the tenor of her fortunes, the surrounding country knew no mitigation; for there — not to speak of the castles, each, as it were, a little city in itself — in sequestered village, or on the open champaign, by the wayside, on the farm, in the homestead, the poor hapless husbandmen and their families, forlorn of physicians' care or servants' tendance, perished day and night alike, not as men, but rather as beasts. Wherefore, they too, like the citizens, abandoned all rule of life, all habit of industry, all counsel of prudence; nay, one and all, as if expecting each day to be their last, not merely ceased to aid Nature to yield her fruit in due season of their beasts and their lands and their past labours, but left no means unused, which ingenuity could devise, to waste their accumulated store; denying shelter to their oxen, asses, sheep, goats, pigs, fowls, nay, even to their dogs, man's most faithful companions, and driving them out into the fields to roam at large amid the unsheaved, nay, unreaped corn. Many of which, as if endowed with reason, took their fill during the day, and returned home at night without any guidance of herdsman. But enough of the country! What need we add, but (reverting to the city) that such and so grievous was the harshness of heaven, and perhaps in some degree of man, that, what with the fury of the pestilence, the panic of those whom it spared, and their consequent neglect or desertion of not a few of the stricken in their need, it is believed without any manner of doubt, that between March and the ensuing July upwards of a hundred thousand human beings lost their lives within the walls of the city of Florence, which before the deadly visitation would not have been supposed to contain so many people! How many grand palaces, how many stately homes, how many splendid residences, once full of retainers, of lords, of ladies, were now left desolate of all, even to the meanest servant! How many families of historic fame, of vast ancestral domains, and wealth proverbial, found now no scion to continue the succession! How many brave men, how many fair ladies, how many gallant youths, whom any physician, were he Galen, Hippocrates, or Æsculapius himself, would have pronounced in the soundest of health, broke fast with their kinsfolk, comrades and friends in the morning, and when evening came, supped with their forefathers in the other world!

Irksome it is to myself to rehearse in detail so sorrowful a history. Wherefore, being minded to pass over so much thereof as I fairly can, I say, that our city, being thus well-nigh depopulated, it so happened, as I afterwards learned from one worthy of credit, that on a Tuesday morning after Divine Service the venerable church of Santa Maria Novella was almost deserted save for the presence of seven young ladies habited sadly in keeping with the season. All were connected either by blood or at least as friends or neighbours; and fair and of good understanding were they all, as also of noble birth, gentle manners, and a modest sprightliness. In age none exceeded twenty-eight, or fell short of eighteen years. Their names I would set down in due form, had I not good reason to withhold them, being solicitous lest the matters which here ensue, as told and heard by them, should in after time be occasion of reproach to any of them, in view of the ample indulgence which was then, for the reasons heretofore set forth, accorded to the lighter hours of persons of much riper years than they, but which the manners of to-day have somewhat restricted; nor would I furnish material to detractors, ever ready to bestow their bite where praise is due, to cast by invidious speech the least slur upon the honour of these noble ladies. Wherefore, that what each says may be apprehended without confusion, I intend to give them names more or less appropriate to the character of each. The first, then, being the eldest of the seven, we will call Pampinea, the second Fiammetta, the third Filomena, the fourth Emilia, the fifth we will distinguish as Lauretta, the sixth as Neifile, and the last, not without reason, shall be named Elisa.

'Twas not of set purpose but by mere chance that these ladies met in the same part of the church; but at length grouping themselves into a sort of circle, after heaving a few sighs, they gave up saying paternosters, and began to converse (among other topics) on the times.

So they continued for a while, and then Pampinea, the rest listening in silent attention, thus began:—"Dear ladies mine, often have I heard it said, and you doubtless as well as I, that wrong is done to none by whoso but honestly uses his reason. And to fortify, preserve, and defend his life to the utmost of his power is the dictate of natural reason in every one that is born. Which right is accorded in such measure that in defence thereof men have been held blameless in taking life. And if this be allowed by the laws, albeit on their stringency depends the well-being of every mortal, how much more exempt from censure should we, and all other honest folk, be in taking such means as we may for the preservation of our life? As often as I bethink me how we have been occupied this morning, and not this morning only, and what has been the tenor of our conversation, I perceive—and you will readily do the like—that each of us is apprehensive on her own account; nor thereat do I marvel, but at this I do marvel greatly, that, though none of us lacks a woman's wit, yet none of us has recourse to any means to avert that which we all justly fear. Here we tarry, as if, methinks, for no other purpose than to bear witness to the number of the corpses that are brought hither for interment, or to hearken if the brothers there within, whose number is now almost reduced to nought, chant their offices at the canonical hours, or, by our weeds of woe, to obtrude on the attention of every one that enters, the nature and degree of our sufferings.

"And if we quit the church, we see dead or sick folk carried about, or we see those, who for their crimes were of late condemned to exile by the outraged majesty of the public laws, but who now, in contempt of those laws, well knowing that their ministers are a prey to death or disease, have returned, and traverse the city in packs, making it hideous with their riotous antics; or else we see the refuse of the people, fostered on our blood, becchini, as they call themselves, who for our torment go prancing about here and there and everywhere, making mock of our miseries in scurrilous songs. Nor hear we aught but:—Such and such are dead; or, Such and such are dying; and should hear dolorous wailing on every hand, were there but any to wail. Or go we home, what see we there? I know not if you are in like case with me; but there, where once were servants in plenty, I find none left but my maid, and shudder with terror, and feel the very hairs of my head to stand on end; and turn or tarry where I may, I encounter the ghosts of the departed, not with their wonted mien, but with something horrible in their aspect that appals me. For which reasons church and street and home are alike distressful to me, and the more so that none, methinks, having means and place of retirement as we have, abides here save only we; or if any such there be, they are of those, as my senses too often have borne witness, who make no distinction between things honourable and their opposites, so they but answer the cravings of appetite, and, alone or in company, do daily and nightly what things soever give promise of most gratification. Nor are these secular persons alone; but such as live recluse in monasteries break their rule, and give themselves up to carnal pleasures, persuading themselves that they are permissible to them, and only forbidden to others, and, thereby thinking to escape, are become unchaste and dissolute. If such be our circumstances — and such most manifestly they are — what do we here? what wait we for? what dream we of? why are we less prompt to provide for our own safety than the rest of the citizens? Is life less dear to us than to all other women? or think we that the bond which unites soul and body is stronger in us than in others, so that there is no blow that may light upon it, of which we need be apprehensive? If so, we err, we are deceived. What insensate folly were it in us so to believe! We have but to call to mind the number and condition of those, young as we, and of both sexes, who have succumbed to this cruel pestilence, to find therein conclusive evidence to the contrary. And lest from lethargy or indolence we fall into the vain imagination that by some lucky accident we may in some way or another, when we would, escape — I know not if your opinion accord with mine — I should deem it most wise in us, our case being what it is, if, as many others have done before us, and are still doing, we were to quit this place, and, shunning like death the evil example of others, betake ourselves to the country, and there live as honourable women on one of the estates, of which none of us has any lack, with all cheer of festal gathering and other delights, so long as in no particular we overstep the bounds of reason. There we shall hear the chant of birds, have sight of verdant hills and plains, of cornfields undulating like the sea, of trees of a thousand sorts; there also we shall have a larger view of the heavens, which, however harsh to usward, yet deny not their eternal beauty; things fairer far for eye to rest on than the desolate walls of our city. Moreover, we shall there breathe a fresher air, find ampler store of things meet for such as live in these times, have fewer causes of annoy. For, though the husbandmen die there, even as here the citizens, they are dispersed in scattered homesteads, and 'tis thus less painful to witness. Nor, so far as I can see, is there a soul here whom we shall desert; rather we may truly say, that we are ourselves deserted; for, our kinsfolk being either dead or fled in fear of death, no more regardful of us than if we were strangers, we are left alone in our great affliction. No censure, then, can fall on us if we do as I propose; and otherwise grievous suffering, perhaps death, may ensue. Wherefore, if you agree, 'tis my advice, that, attended by our maids with all things needful, we sojourn, now on this, now on the other estate, and in such way of life continue, until we see — if death should not first overtake us — the end which Heaven reserves for these events. And I remind you that it will be at least as seemly in us to leave with honour, as in others, of whom there are not a few, to stay with dishonour."

The other ladies praised Pampinea's plan, and indeed were so prompt to follow it, that they had already begun to discuss the manner in some detail, as if they were forthwith to rise from their seats and take the road, when Filomena, whose judgment was excellent, interposed, saying: — "Ladies, though Pampinea has spoken to most excellent effect, yet it were not well to be so precipitate as you seem disposed to be. Bethink you that we are all women; nor is there any here so young, but she is of years to understand how women are minded towards one another, when they are alone together, and how ill they are able to rule themselves without the guidance of some man. We are sensitive, perverse, suspicious, pusillanimous and timid; wherefore I much misdoubt, that, if we find no other guidance than our own, this company is like to break up sooner, and with less credit to us, than it should. Against which it were well to provide at the outset." Said then Elisa: — "Without doubt man is woman's head, and, without man's governance, it is seldom that aught that we do is brought to a commendable conclusion. But how are we to come by the men? Every one of us here knows that her kinsmen are for the most part dead, and that the survivors are dispersed, one here, one there, we know not where, bent each on escaping the same fate as ourselves; nor were it seemly to seek the aid of strangers; for, as we are in quest of health, we must find some means so to order matters that, wherever we seek diversion or repose, trouble and scandal do not follow us."

While the ladies were thus conversing, there came into the church three young men, young, I say, but not so young that the age of the youngest was less than twenty-five years; in whom neither the sinister course of events, nor the loss of friends or kinsfolk, nor fear for their own safety, had availed to quench, or even temper, the ardour of their love. The first was called Pamfilo, the second Filostrato, and the third Dioneo. Very debonair and chivalrous were they all; and in this troublous time they were seeking if haply, to their exceeding great solace, they might have sight of their fair friends, all three of whom chanced to be among the said seven ladies, besides some that were of kin to the young men. At one and the same moment they recognised the ladies and were recognised by them: wherefore, with a gracious smile, Pampinea thus began: — "Lo, fortune is propitious to our enterprise, having vouchsafed us the good offices of these young men, who are as gallant as they are discreet, and will gladly give us their guidance and escort, so we but take them into our service." Whereupon Neifile, crimson from brow to neck with the blush of modesty, being one of those that had a lover among the young men, said:—"For God's sake, Pampinea, have a care what you say. Well assured am I that nought but good can be said of any of them, and I deem them fit for office far more onerous than this which you propose for them, and their good and honourable company worthy of ladies fairer by far and more tenderly to be cherished than such as we. But 'tis no secret that they love some of us here; wherefore I misdoubt that, if we take them with us, we may thereby give occasion for scandal and censure merited neither by us nor by them." "That," said Filomena, "is of no consequence; so I but live honestly, my conscience gives me no disquietude; if others asperse me, God and the truth will take arms in my defence. Now, should they be disposed to attend us, of a truth we might say with Pampinea, that fortune favours our enterprise." The silence which followed betokened consent on the part of the other ladies, who then with one accord resolved to call the young men, and acquaint them with their purpose, and pray them to be of their company. So without further parley Pampinea, who had a kinsman among the young men, rose and approached them where they stood intently regarding them; and greeting them gaily, she opened to them their plan, and besought them on the part of herself and her friends to join their company on terms of honourable and fraternal comradeship. At first the young men thought she did but trifle with them; but when they saw that she was in earnest, they answered with alacrity that they were ready, and promptly, even before they left the church, set matters in train for their departure. So all things meet being first sent forward in due order to their intended place of sojourn, the ladies with some of their maids, and the three young men, each attended by a man-servant, sallied forth of the city on the morrow, being Wednesday, about daybreak, and took the road; nor had they journeyed more than two short miles when they arrived at their destination. The estate lay upon a little hill some distance from the nearest highway, and, embowered in shrubberies of divers hues, and other greenery, afforded the eye a pleasant prospect. On the summit of the hill was a palace with galleries, halls and chambers, disposed around a fair and spacious court, each very fair in itself, and the goodlier to see for the gladsome pictures with which it was adorned; the whole set amidst meads and gardens laid out with marvellous art, wells of the coolest water, and vaults of the finest wines, things more suited to dainty drinkers than to sober and honourable women. On their arrival the company, to their no small delight, found their beds already made, the rooms well swept and garnished with flowers of every sort that the season could afford, and the floors carpeted with rushes. When they were seated, Dioneo, a gallant who had not his match for courtesy and wit, spoke thus:—"My ladies, 'tis not our forethought so much as your own mother-wit that has guided us hither. How you mean to dispose of your cares I know not; mine I left behind me within the city-gate when I issued thence with you a brief while ago. Wherefore, I pray you, either address yourselves to make merry, to laugh and sing with me (so far, I mean, as may consist with your dignity), or give me leave to hie me back to the stricken city, there to abide with my cares." To whom blithely Pampinea replied, as if she too had cast off all her cares:—"Well sayest thou, Dioneo, excellent well; gaily we mean to live; 'twas a refuge from sorrow that here we sought, nor had we other cause to come hither. But, as no anarchy can long endure, I who initiated the deliberations of which this fair company is the fruit, do now, to the end that our joy may be lasting, deem it expedient, that there be one among us in chief authority, honoured and obeyed by us as our superior, whose exclusive care it shall be to devise how we may pass our time blithely. And that each in turn may prove the weight of the care, as well as enjoy the pleasure, of sovereignty, and, no distinction being made of sex, envy be felt by none by reason of exclusion from the office; I propose, that the weight and honour be borne by each one for a day; and let the first to bear sway be chosen by us all, those that follow to be appointed towards the vesper hour by him or her who shall have had the signory for that day; and let each holder of the signory be, for the time, sole arbiter of the place and manner in which we are to pass our time."

Pampinea's speech was received with the utmost applause, and with one accord she was chosen queen for the first day. Whereupon Filomena hied her lightly to a bay-tree, having often heard of the great honour in which its leaves, and such as were deservedly crowned therewith, were worthy to be holden; and having gathered a few sprays, she made thereof a goodly wreath of honour, and set it on Pampinea's head; which wreath was thenceforth, while their company endured, the visible sign of the wearer's sway and sovereignty.

No sooner was Queen Pampinea crowned than she bade all be silent. She then caused summon to her presence their four maids, and the servants of the three young men, and, all keeping silence, said to them:—"That I may shew you all at once, how, well still giving place to better, our company may flourish and endure, as long as it shall pleasure us, with order meet and assured delight and without reproach, I first of all constitute Dioneo's man, Parmeno, my seneschal, and entrust him with the care and control of all our household, and all that belongs to the service of the hall. Pamfilo's man, Sirisco, I appoint treasurer and chancellor of our exchequer; and be he ever answerable to Parmeno. While Parmeno and Sirisco are too busy about their duties to serve their masters, let Filostrato's man, Tindaro, have charge of the chambers of all three. My maid, Misia, and Filomena's maid, Licisca, will keep in the kitchen, and with all due diligence prepare such dishes as Parmeno shall bid them. Lauretta's maid, Chimera, and Fiammetta's maid, Stratilia we make answerable for the ladies' chambers, and wherever we may take up our quarters, let them see that all is spotless. And now we enjoin you, one and all alike, as you value our favour, that none of you, go where you may, return whence you may, hear or see what you may, bring us any tidings but such as be cheerful." These orders thus succinctly given were received with universal approval. Whereupon Pampinea rose, and said gaily: — "Here are gardens, meads, other places delightsome enough, where you may wander at will, and take your pleasure; but on the stroke of tierce, let all be here to breakfast in the shade."

Thus dismissed by their new queen the gay company sauntered gently through a garden, the young men saying sweet things to the fair ladies, who wove fair garlands of divers sorts of leaves and sang love-songs.

Having thus spent the time allowed them by the queen, they returned to the house, where they found that Parmeno had entered on his office with zeal; for in a hall on the ground-floor they saw tables covered with the whitest of cloths, and beakers that shone like silver, and sprays of broom scattered everywhere. So, at the bidding of the queen, they washed their hands, and all took their places as marshalled by Parmeno. Dishes, daintily prepared, were served, and the finest wines were at hand; the three serving-men did their office noiselessly; in a word all was fair and ordered in a seemly manner; whereby the spirits of the company rose, and they seasoned their viands with pleasant jests and sprightly sallies. Breakfast done, the tables were removed, and the queen bade fetch instruments of music; for all, ladies and young men alike, knew how to tread a measure, and some of them played and sang with great skill: so, at her command, Dioneo having taken a lute, and Fiammetta a viol, they struck up a dance in sweet concert; and, the servants being dismissed to their repast, the queen, attended by the other ladies and the two young men, led off a stately carol; which ended they fell to singing ditties dainty and gay. Thus they diverted themselves until the queen, deeming it time to retire to rest, dismissed them all for the night. So the three young men and the ladies withdrew to their several quarters, which were in different parts of the palace. There they found the beds well made, and abundance of flowers, as in the hall; and so they undressed, and went to bed.

Shortly after none the queen rose, and roused the rest of the ladies, as also the young men, averring that it was injurious to the health to sleep long in the daytime. They therefore hied them to a meadow, where the grass grew green and luxuriant, being nowhere scorched by the sun, and a light breeze gently fanned them. So at the queen's command they all ranged themselves in a circle on the grass, and hearkened while she thus spoke: —

"You mark that the sun is high, the heat intense, and the silence unbroken save by the cicalas among the olive-trees. It were therefore the height of folly to quit this spot at present. Here the air is cool and the prospect fair, and here, observe, are dice and chess.

Take, then, your pleasure as you may be severally minded; but, if you take my advice, you will find pastime for the hot hours before us, not in play, in which the loser must needs be vexed, and neither the winner nor the onlooker much the better pleased, but in telling of stories, in which the invention of one may afford solace to all the company of his hearers. You will not each have told a story before the sun will be low, and the heat abated, so that we shall be able to go and severally take our pleasure where it may seem best to each. Wherefore, if my proposal meet with your approval—for in this I am disposed to consult your pleasure—let us adopt it; if not, divert yourselves as best you may, until the vesper hour."

The queen's proposal being approved by all, ladies and men alike, she added:—"So please you, then, I ordain, that, for this first day, we be free to discourse of such matters as most commend themselves to each in turn." She then addressed Pamfilo, who sat on her right hand, bidding him with a gracious air to lead off with one of his stories. And prompt at the word of command, Pamfilo, while all listened intently, thus began:—

[FIRST DAY]

NOVEL I

Ser Ciappelletto cheats a holy friar by a false confession, and dies; and, having lived as a very bad man, is, on his death, reputed a saint, and called San Ciappelletto.

A seemly thing it is, dearest ladies, that whatever we do, it be begun in the holy and awful name of Him who was the maker of all. Wherefore, as it falls to me to lead the way in this your enterprise of story-telling, I intend to begin with one of His wondrous works, that, by hearing thereof, our hopes in Him, in whom is no change, may be established, and His name be by us forever lauded. 'Tis manifest that, as things temporal are all doomed to pass and perish, so within and without they abound with trouble and anguish and travail, and are subject to infinite perils; nor, save for the especial grace of God, should we, whose being is bound up with and forms part of theirs, have either the strength to endure or the wisdom to combat their adverse influences. By which grace we are visited and penetrated (so we must believe) not by reason of any merit of our own, but solely out of the fulness of God's own goodness, and in answer to the prayers of those who, being mortal like ourselves, did faithfully observe His ordinances during their lives, and are now become blessed for ever with Him in heaven. To whom, as to advocates taught by experience all that belongs to our frailty, we, not daring, perchance, to present our petitions in the presence of so great a Judge, make known our requests for such things as we deem expedient for us. And of His mercy richly abounding to usward we have further proof herein, that, no keenness of mortal vision being able in any degree to penetrate the secret counsels of the Divine mind, it sometimes, perchance, happens, that, in error of judgment, we make one our advocate before His Majesty, who is banished from His presence in eternal exile, and yet He to whom nothing is hidden, having regard rather to the sincerity of our prayers than to our ignorance or the banishment of the intercessor, hears us no less than if the intercessor were in truth one of the blest who enjoy the light of His countenance. Which the story that I am about to relate may serve to make apparent; apparent, I mean, according to the standard of the judgment of man, not of God.

The story goes, then, that Musciatto Franzesi, a great and wealthy merchant, being made a knight in France, and being to attend Charles Sansterre, brother of the King of France, when he came into Tuscany at the instance and with the support of Pope Boniface, found his affairs, as often happens to merchants, to be much involved in divers quarters, and neither easily nor suddenly to be adjusted; wherefore he determined to place them in the hands of commissioners, and found no difficulty except as to certain credits given to some Burgundians, for the recovery of which he doubted whether he could come by a competent agent; for well he knew that the Burgundians were violent men and ill-conditioned and faithless; nor could he call to mind any man so bad that he could with confidence oppose his guile to theirs. After long pondering the matter, he recollected one Ser Ciapperello da Prato, who much frequented his house in Paris. Who being short of stature and very affected, the French who knew not the meaning of Cepparello, but supposed that it meant the same as Cappello, *i.e.* garland, in their vernacular, called him not Cappello, but Ciappelletto by reason of his diminutive size; and as Ciappelletto he was known everywhere, whereas few people knew him as Ciapperello. Now Ciappelletto's manner of life was thus. He was by profession a notary, and his pride was to make false documents; he would have made them as often as he was asked, and more readily without fee than another at a great price; few indeed he made that were not false, and great was his shame when they were discovered. False witness he bore, solicited or unsolicited, with boundless delight; and, as oaths were in those days had in very great respect in France, he, scrupling not to forswear himself, corruptly carried the day in every case in which he was summoned faithfully to attest the truth. He took inordinate delight, and bestirred himself with great zeal, in fomenting ill-feeling, enmities, dissensions between friends, kinsfolk and all other folk; and the more calamitous were the consequences the better he was pleased. Set him on murder, or any other foul crime, and he never hesitated, but went about it with alacrity; he had been known on more than one occasion to inflict wounds or death by preference with his own hands. He was a profuse blasphemer of God and His saints, and that on the most trifling occasions, being of all men the most irascible. He was never seen at church, held all the sacraments vile things, and derided them in language of horrible ribaldry. On the other hand he resorted readily to the tavern and other places of evil repute, and frequented them. He was as fond of women as a dog is of the stick: in the use against nature he had not his match among the most abandoned. He would have pilfered and stolen as a matter of conscience, as a holy man would make an oblation. Most gluttonous he was and inordinately fond of his cups, whereby he sometimes brought upon himself both shame and suffering. He was also a practised gamester and thrower of false dice. But why enlarge so much upon him? Enough that he was, perhaps, the worst man that ever was born.

The rank and power of Musciatto Franzesi had long been this reprobate's mainstay, serving in many instances to secure him considerate treatment on the part of the private persons whom he frequently, and the court which he unremittingly, outraged. So Musciatto, having bethought him of this Ser Cepparello, with whose way of life he was very well acquainted, judged him to be the very sort of person to cope with the guile of the Burgundians. He therefore sent for him, and thus addressed him:—"Ser Ciappelletto, I am, as thou knowest, about to leave this place for good; and among those with whom I have to settle accounts are certain Burgundians, very wily knaves; nor know I the man whom I could more fitly entrust with the recovery of my money than thyself. Wherefore, as thou hast nothing to do at present, if thou wilt undertake this business, I will procure thee the favour of the court, and give thee a reasonable part of what thou shalt recover." Ser Ciappelletto, being out of employment, and by no means in easy circumstances, and about to lose Musciatto, so long his mainstay and support, without the least demur, for in truth he had hardly any choice, made his mind up and answered that he was ready to go. So the bargain was struck. Armed with the power of attorney and the royal letters commendatory, Ser Ciappelletto took leave of Messer Musciatto and hied him to Burgundy, where he was hardly known to a soul. He set about the business which had brought him thither, the recovery of the money, in a manner amicable and considerate, foreign to his nature, as if he were minded to reserve his severity to the last. While thus occupied, he was frequently at the house of two Florentine usurers, who treated him with great distinction out of regard for Messer Musciatto; and there it so happened that he fell sick. The two brothers forthwith placed physicians and servants in attendance upon him, and omitted no means meet and apt for the restoration of his health. But all remedies proved unavailing; for being now old, and having led, as the physicians reported, a disorderly life, he went daily from bad to worse like one stricken with a mortal disease. This greatly disconcerted the two brothers; and one day, hard by the room in which Ser Ciappelletto lay sick, they began to talk about him; saying one to the other:—"What shall we do with this man? We are hard bested indeed on his account. If we turn him out of the house, sick as he is, we shall not only incur grave censure, but shall evince a signal want of sense; for folk must know the welcome we gave him in the first instance, the solicitude with which we have had him treated and tended since his illness, during which time he could not possibly do aught to displease us, and yet they would see him suddenly turned out of our house sick unto death. On the other hand he has been so bad a man that he is sure not to confess or receive any of the Church's sacraments; and dying thus unconfessed, he will be denied burial in church, but will be cast out into some ditch like a dog; nay, 'twill be all one if he do confess, for such and so horrible have been his crimes that no friar or priest either will or can absolve him; and so, dying without absolution, he will still be cast out into the ditch. In which case the folk of these parts, who reprobate our trade as iniquitous and revile it all day long, and would fain rob us, will seize their opportunity, and raise a tumult, and make a raid upon our houses, crying:—'Away with these Lombard dogs, whom the Church excludes from her pale'; and will certainly strip us of our goods, and perhaps take our lives also; so that in any case we stand to lose if this man die."

Ser Ciappelletto, who, as we said, lay close at hand while they thus spoke, and whose hearing was sharpened, as is often the case, by his malady, overheard all that they said about him. So he called them to him, and said to them:—"I would not have you disquiet yourselves in regard of me, or apprehend loss to befall you by my death. I have heard what you have said of me and have no doubt that 'twould be as you say, if matters took the course you anticipate; but I am minded that it shall be otherwise. I have committed so many offences against God in the course of my life, that one more in the hour of my death will make no difference whatever to the account. So seek out and bring hither the worthiest and most holy friar you can find, and leave me to settle your affairs and mine upon a sound and solid basis, with which you may rest satisfied." The two brothers had not much hope of the result, but yet they went to a friary and asked for a holy and discreet man to hear the confession of a Lombard that was sick in their house, and returned with an aged man of just and holy life, very learned in the Scriptures, and venerable and held in very great and especial reverence by all the citizens. As soon as he had entered the room where Ser Ciappelletto was lying, and had taken his place by his side, he began gently to comfort him: then he asked him how long it was since he was confessed. Whereto Ser Ciappelletto, who had never been confessed, answered:—"Father, it is my constant practice to be confessed at least once a week, and many a week I am confessed more often; but true it is, that, since I have been sick, now eight days, I have made no confession, so sore has been my affliction." "Son," said the friar, "thou hast well done, and well for thee, if so thou continue to do; as thou dost confess so often, I see that my labour of hearkening and questioning will be slight." "Nay but, master friar," said Ser Ciappelletto, "say not so; I have not confessed so often but that I would fain make a general confession of all my sins that I have committed, so far as I can recall them, from the day of my birth to the present time; and therefore I pray you, my good father, to question me precisely in every particular just as if I had never been confessed. And spare me not by reason of my sickness, for I had far rather do despite to my flesh than, sparing it, risk the perdition of my soul, which my Saviour redeemed with His precious blood."

The holy man was mightily delighted with these words, which seemed to him to betoken a soul in a state of grace. He therefore signified to Ser Ciappelletto his high approval of this practice; and then began by asking him whether he had ever sinned carnally with a woman. Whereto Ser Ciappelletto answered with a sigh:—"My father, I scruple to tell you the truth in this matter, fearing lest I sin in vain-glory." "Nay, but," said the friar, "speak boldly; none ever sinned by telling the truth, either in confession or otherwise." "Then," said Ser Ciappelletto, "as you bid me speak boldly, I will tell you the truth of this matter. I am virgin even as when I issued from my mother's womb." "Now God's blessing on thee," said the friar, "well done; and the greater is thy merit in that, hadst thou so willed, thou mightest have done otherwise far more readily than we who are under constraint of rule." He then proceeded to ask, whether he had offended God by gluttony. Whereto Ser Ciappelletto, heaving a heavy sigh, answered that he had frequently so offended; for, being wont to fast not only in Lent like other devout persons, but at least three days in every week, taking nothing but bread and water, he had quaffed the water with as good a gusto and as much enjoyment, more particularly when fatigued by devotion or pilgrimage, as great drinkers quaff their wine; and oftentimes he had felt a craving for such dainty dishes of herbs as ladies make when they go into the country, and now and again he had relished his food more than seemed to him meet in one who fasted, as he did, for devotion. "Son," said the friar, "these sins are natural and very trifling; and therefore I would not have thee burden thy conscience too much with them. There is no man, however holy he may be, but must sometimes find it pleasant to eat after a long fast and to drink after exertion." "O, my father," said Ser Ciappelletto, "say not this to comfort me. You know well that I know, that the things which are done in the service of God ought to be done in perfect purity of an unsullied spirit; and whoever does otherwise sins." The friar, well content, replied:—"Glad I am that thou dost think so, and I am mightily pleased with thy pure and good conscience which therein appears; but tell me: hast thou sinned by avarice, coveting more than was reasonable, or withholding more than was right?" "My father," replied Ser Ciappelletto, "I would not have you disquiet yourself, because I am in the house of these usurers: no part have I in their concerns; nay, I did but come here to admonish and reprehend them, and wean them from this abominable traffic; and so, I believe, I had done, had not God sent me this visitation. But you must know, that my father left me a fortune, of which I dedicated the greater part to God; and since then for my own support and the relief of Christ's poor I have done a little trading, whereof I have desired to make gain; and all that I have gotten I have shared with God's poor, reserving one half for my own needs and giving the other half to them; and so well has my Maker prospered me, that I have ever managed my affairs to better and better account." "Well done," said the friar; "but how? hast thou often given way to anger?" "Often indeed, I assure you," said Ser Ciappelletto. "And who could refrain therefrom, seeing men doing frowardly all day long, breaking the commandments of God and recking nought of His judgments? Many a time in the course of a single day I had rather be dead than alive, to see the young men going after vanity, swearing and forswearing themselves, haunting taverns, avoiding the churches, and in short walking in the way of the world rather than in God's way." "My son," said the friar, "this is a righteous wrath; nor could I find occasion therein to lay a penance upon thee. But did anger ever by any chance betray thee into taking human life, or affronting or otherwise wronging any?" "Alas," replied Ser Ciappelletto, "alas, sir, man of God though you seem to me, how come you to speak after this manner? If I had had so much as the least thought of doing any of the things of which you speak, should I believe, think you, that I had been thus supported of God? These are the deeds of robbers and such like evil men, to whom I have ever said, when any I saw:—'Go, God change your heart.'" Said then the friar:—"Now, my son, as thou hopest to be blest of God, tell me, hast thou never borne false witness against any, or spoken evil of another, or taken the goods of another without his leave?" "Yes, master friar," answered Ser Ciappelletto, "most true it is that I have spoken evil of another; for I had once a neighbour who without the least excuse in the world was ever beating his wife, and so great was my pity of the poor creature, whom, when he was in his cups, he would thrash as God alone knows how, that once I spoke evil of him to his wife's kinsfolk." "Well, well," said the friar, "thou tellest me thou hast been a merchant; hast thou ever cheated any, as merchants use to do?" "I'faith, yes, master friar," said Ser Ciappelletto; "but I know not who he was; only that he brought me some money which he owed me for some cloth that I had sold him, and I put it in a box without counting it, where a month afterwards I found four farthings more than there should have been, which I kept for a year to return to him, but not seeing him again, I bestowed them in alms for the love of God." "This," said the friar, "was a small matter; and thou didst well to bestow them as thou didst." The holy friar went on to ask him many other questions, to which he made answer in each case in this sort. Then, as the friar was about to give him absolution, Ser Ciappelletto interposed:—"Sir, I have yet a sin to confess." "What?" asked the friar. "I remember," he said, "that I once caused my servant to sweep my house on a Saturday after none; and that my observance of Sunday was less devout than it should have been." "O, my son," said the friar, "this is a light matter." "No," said Ser Ciappelletto, "say not a light matter; for Sunday is the more to be had in honour because on that day our Lord rose from the dead." Then said the holy friar:—"Now is there aught else that thou hast done?" "Yes, master friar," replied Ser Ciappelletto, "once by inadvertence I spat in the church of God." At this the friar began to smile, and said:—"My son, this is not a matter to trouble about; we, who are religious, spit there all day long." "And great impiety it is when you so do," replied Ser Ciappelletto, "for there is nothing that is so worthy to be kept from all impurity as the holy temple in which sacrifice is offered to God." More he said in the same strain, which I pass over; and then at last he began to sigh, and by and by to weep bitterly, as he was well able to do when he chose. And the friar demanding:—"My son, why weepest thou?" "Alas, master friar," answered Ser Ciappelletto, "a sin yet remains, which I have never confessed, such shame were it to me to tell it; and as often as I call it to mind, I weep as you now see me weep, being well assured that God will never forgive me this sin." Then said the holy friar:—"Come, come, son, what is this that thou sayst? If all the sins of all the men, that ever were or ever shall be, as long as the world shall endure, were concentrated in one man, so great is the goodness of God that He would freely pardon them all, were he but penitent and contrite as I see thou art, and confessed them: wherefore tell me thy sin with a good courage." Then said Ser Ciappelletto, still weeping bitterly:—"Alas, my father, mine is too great a sin, and scarce can I believe, if your prayers do not co-operate, that God will ever grant me His pardon thereof." "Tell it with a good courage," said the friar; "I promise thee to pray God for thee." Ser Ciappelletto, however, continued to weep, and would not speak, for all the friar's encouragement. When he had kept him for a good while in suspense, he heaved a mighty sigh, and said:—"My father, as you promise me to pray God for me, I will tell it you. Know, then, that once, when I was a little child, I cursed my mother"; and having so said he began again to weep bitterly. "O, my son," said the friar, "does this seem to thee so great a sin? Men curse God all day long, and He pardons them freely, if they repent them of having so done; and thinkest thou He will not pardon thee this? Weep not, be comforted, for truly, hadst thou been one of them that set Him on the Cross, with the contrition that I see in thee, thou wouldst not fail of His pardon." "Alas! my father," rejoined Ser Ciappelletto, "what is this you say? To curse my sweet mother that carried me in her womb for nine months day and night, and afterwards on her shoulder more than a hundred times! Heinous indeed was my offence; 'tis too great a sin; nor will it be pardoned, unless you pray God for me."

The friar now perceiving that Ser Ciappelletto had nothing more to say, gave him absolution and his blessing, reputing him for a most holy man, fully believing that all that he had said was true. And who would not have so believed, hearing him so speak at the point of death? Then, when all was done, he said:—"Ser Ciappelletto, if God so will, you will soon be well; but should it so come to pass that God call your blessed soul to Himself in this state of grace, is it well pleasing to you that your body be buried in our convent?" "Yea, verily, master friar," replied Ser Ciappelletto; "there would I be, and nowhere else, since you have promised to pray God for me; besides which I have ever had a special devotion to your order. Wherefore I pray you, that, on your return to your convent, you cause to be sent me that very Body of Christ, which you consecrate in the morning on the altar; because (unworthy though I be) I purpose with your leave to take it, and afterwards the holy and extreme unction, that, though I have lived as a sinner, I may die at any rate as a Christian." The holy man said that he was greatly delighted, that it was well said of Ser Ciappelletto, and that he would cause the Host to be forthwith brought to him; and so it was.

The two brothers, who much misdoubted Ser Ciappelletto's power to deceive the friar, had taken their stand on the other side of a wooden partition which divided the room in which Ser Ciappelletto lay from another, and hearkening there they readily heard and understood what Ser Ciappelletto said to the friar; and at times could scarce refrain their laughter as they followed his confession; and now and again they said one to another: — "What manner of man is this, whom neither age nor sickness, nor fear of death, on the threshold of which he now stands, nor yet of God, before whose judgment-seat he must soon appear, has been able to turn from his wicked ways, that he die not even as he has lived?" But seeing that his confession had secured the interment of his body in church, they troubled themselves no further. Ser Ciappelletto soon afterwards communicated, and growing immensely worse, received the extreme unction, and died shortly after vespers on the same day on which he had made his good confession. So the two brothers, having from his own moneys provided the wherewith to procure him honourable sepulture, and sent word to the friars to come at even to observe the usual vigil, and in the morning to fetch the corpse, set all things in order accordingly. The holy friar who had confessed him, hearing that he was dead, had audience of the prior of the friary; a chapter was convened and the assembled brothers heard from the confessor's own mouth how Ser Ciappelletto had been a holy man, as had appeared by his confession, and were exhorted to receive the body with the utmost veneration and pious care, as one by which there was good hope that God would work many miracles. To this the prior and the rest of the credulous confraternity assenting, they went in a body in the evening to the place where the corpse of Ser Ciappelletto lay, and kept a great and solemn vigil over it; and in the morning they made a procession habited in their surplices and copes, with books in their hands and crosses in front; and chanting as they went, they fetched the corpse and brought it back to their church with the utmost pomp and solemnity, being followed by almost all the folk of the city, men and women alike. So it was laid in the church, and then the holy friar who had heard the confession got up in the pulpit and began to preach marvellous things of Ser Ciappelletto's life, his fasts, his virginity, his simplicity and guilelessness and holiness; narrating among other matters that of which Ser Ciappelletto had made tearful confession as his greatest sin, and how he had hardly been able to make him conceive that God would pardon him; from which he took occasion to reprove his hearers; saying:—"And you, accursed of God, on the least pretext, blaspheme God and His Mother, and all the celestial court." And much beside he told of his loyalty and purity; and, in short, so wrought upon the people by his words, to which they gave entire credence, that they all conceived a great veneration for Ser Ciappelletto, and at the close of the office came pressing forward with the utmost vehemence to kiss the feet and the hands of the corpse, from which they tore off the cerements, each thinking himself blessed to have but a scrap thereof in his possession; and so it was arranged that it should be kept there all day long, so as to be visible and accessible to all. At nightfall it was honourably interred in a marble tomb in one of the chapels, where on the morrow, one by one, folk came and lit tapers and prayed and paid their vows, setting there the waxen images which they had dedicated. And the fame of Ciappelletto's holiness and the devotion to him grew in such measure that scarce any there was that in any adversity would vow aught to any saint but he, and they called him and still call him San Ciappelletto, affirming that many miracles have been and daily are wrought by God through him for such as devoutly crave his intercession.

So lived, so died Ser Cepperello da Prato, and came to be reputed a saint, as you have heard. Nor would I deny that it is possible that he is of the number of the blessed in the presence of God, seeing that, though his life was evil and depraved, yet he might in his last moments have made so complete an act of contrition that perchance God had mercy on him and received him into His kingdom. But, as this is hidden from us, I speak according to that which appears, and I say that he ought rather to be in the hands of the devil in hell than in Paradise. Which, if so it be, is a manifest token of the superabundance of the goodness of God to usward, inasmuch as He regards not our error but the sincerity of our faith, and hearkens unto us when, mistaking one who is at enmity with Him for a friend, we have recourse to him, as to one holy indeed, as our intercessor for His grace. Wherefore, that we of this gay company may by His grace be preserved safe and sound throughout this time of adversity, commend we ourselves in our need to Him, whose name we began by invoking, with lauds and reverent devotion and good confidence that we shall be heard.

And so he was silent.

[THIRD DAY]

Endeth here the second day of the Decameron, beginneth the third, in which, under the rule of Neifile, discourse is had of the fortune of such as have painfully acquired some much-coveted thing, or, having lost, have recovered it.

The dawn of Sunday was already changing from vermillion to orange, as the sun hasted to the horizon, when the queen rose and roused all the company. The seneschal had early sent forward to their next place of sojourn ample store of things meet with folk to make all things ready, and now seeing the queen on the road, and the decampment, as it were, begun, he hastily completed the equipment of the baggage-train, and set off therewith, attended by the rest of the servants, in rear of the ladies and gentlemen. So, to the chant of, perhaps, a score of nightingales and other birds, the queen, her ladies and the three young men trooping beside or after her, paced leisurely westward by a path little frequented and overgrown with herbage and flowers, which, as they caught the sunlight, began one and all to unfold their petals. So fared she on with her train, while the quirk and the jest and the laugh passed from mouth to mouth; nor had they completed more than two thousand paces when, well before half tierce, they arrived at a palace most fair and sumptuous, which stood out somewhat from the plain, being situate upon a low eminence. On entering, they first traversed its great halls and dainty chambers furnished throughout with all brave and meet appointments; and finding all most commendable, they reputed its lord a magnifico. Then descending, they surveyed its spacious and cheerful court, its vaults of excellent wines and copious springs of most cool water, and found it still more commendable. After which, being fain of rest, they sat them down in a gallery which commanded the court, and was close imbosked with leafage and such flowers as the season afforded, and thither the discreet seneschal brought comfits and wines most choice and excellent, wherewith they were refreshed. Whereupon they hied them to a walled garden adjoining the palace; which, the gate being opened, they entered, and wonder-struck by the beauty of the whole passed on to examine more attentively the several parts. It was bordered and traversed in many parts by alleys, each very wide and straight as an arrow and roofed in with trellis of vines, which gave good promise of bearing clusters that year, and, being all in flower, dispersed such fragrance throughout the garden as blended with that exhaled by many another plant that grew therein made the garden seem redolent of all the spices that ever grew in the East. The sides of the alleys were all, as it were, walled in with roses white and red and jasmine; insomuch that there was no part of the garden but one might walk there not merely in the morning but at high noon in grateful shade and fragrance, completely screened from the sun. As for the plants that were in the garden, 'twere long to enumerate them, to specify their sorts, to describe the order of their arrangement; enough, in brief, that there was abundance of every rarer species that our climate allows. In the middle of the garden, a thing not less but much more to be commended than ought else, was a lawn of the finest turf, and so green that it seemed almost black, pranked with flowers of, perhaps, a thousand sorts, and girt about with the richest living verdure of orange-trees and cedars, which shewed not only flowers but fruits both new and old, and were no less grateful to the smell by their fragrance than to the eye by their shade. In the middle of the lawn was a basin of whitest marble, graven with marvellous art; in the centre whereof — whether the spring were natural or artificial I know not — rose a column supporting a figure which sent forth a jet of water of such volume and to such an altitude that it fell, not without a delicious plash, into the basin in quantity amply sufficient to turn a mill-wheel. The overflow was carried away from the lawn by a hidden conduit, and then, re-emerging, was distributed through tiny channels, very fair and cunningly contrived, in such sort as to flow round the entire lawn, and by similar derivative channels to penetrate almost every part of the fair garden, until, re-uniting at a certain point, it issued thence, and, clear as crystal, slid down towards the plain, turning by the way two mill-wheels with extreme velocity to the no small profit of the lord. The aspect of this garden, its fair order, the plants and the fountain and the rivulets that flowed from it, so charmed the ladies and the three young men that with one accord they affirmed that they knew not how it could receive any accession of beauty, or what other form could be given to Paradise, if it were to be planted on earth. So, excellently well pleased, they roved about it, plucking sprays from the trees, and weaving them into the fairest of garlands, while songsters of, perhaps, a score of different sorts warbled as if in mutual emulation, when suddenly a sight as fair and delightsome as novel, which, engrossed by the other beauties of the place, they had hitherto overlooked, met their eyes. For the garden, they now saw, was peopled with a host of living creatures, fair and of, perhaps, a hundred sorts; and they pointed out to one another how here emerged a cony, or there scampered a hare, or couched a goat, or grazed a fawn, or many another harmless, all but domesticated, creature roved carelessly seeking his pleasure at his own sweet will. All which served immensely to reinforce their already abundant delight. At length, however, they had enough of wandering about the garden and observing this thing and that: wherefore they repaired to the beautiful fountain, around which were ranged the tables, and there, after they had sung half-a-dozen songs and trod some measures, they sat them down, at the queen's command, to breakfast, which was served with all celerity and in fair and orderly manner, the viands being both good and delicate; whereby their spirits rose, and up they got, and betook themselves again to music and song and dance, and so sped the hours, until, as the heat increased, the queen deemed it time that whoso was so minded should go to sleep. Some there were that did so; others were too charmed by the beauty of the place to think of leaving it; but tarried there, and, while the rest slept, amused themselves with reading romances or playing at chess or dice. However, after none, there was a general *levée;* and, with faces laved and refreshed with cold water, they gathered by the queen's command upon the lawn, and, having sat them down in their wonted order by the fountain, waited for the story-telling to begin upon the theme assigned by the queen. With this duty the queen first charged Filostrato, who began on this wise.

[FOURTH DAY]

NOVEL I

Tancred, Prince of Salerno, slays his daughter's lover, and sends her his heart in a golden cup: she pours upon it a poisonous distillation, which she drinks and dies.

A direful theme has our king allotted us for to-day's discourse; seeing that, whereas we are here met for our common delectation, needs must we now tell of others' tears, whereby, whether telling or hearing, we cannot but be moved to pity. Perchance 'twas to temper in some degree the gaiety of the past days that he so ordained, but, whatever may have been his intent, his will must be to me immutable law; wherefore I will narrate to you a matter that befell piteously, nay woefully, and so as you may well weep thereat.

Tancred, Prince of Salerno, a lord most humane and kind of heart, but that in his old age he imbrued his hands in the blood of a lover, had in the whole course of his life but one daughter; and had he not had her, he had been more fortunate.

Never was daughter more tenderly beloved of father than she of the Prince, who, for that cause not knowing how to part with her, kept her unmarried for many a year after she had come of marriageable age: then at last he gave her to a son of the Duke of Capua, with whom she had lived but a short while, when he died and she returned to her father. Most lovely was she of form and feature (never woman more so), and young and light of heart, and more knowing, perchance, than beseemed a woman. Dwelling thus with her loving father, as a great lady, in no small luxury, nor failing to see that the Prince, for the great love he bore her, was at no pains to provide her with another husband, and deeming it unseemly on her part to ask one of him, she cast about how she might come by a gallant to be her secret lover. And seeing at her father's court not a few men, both gentle and simple, that resorted thither, as we know men use to frequent courts, and closely scanning their mien and manners, she preferred before all others the Prince's page, Guiscardo by name, a man of very humble origin, but pre-eminent for native worth and noble bearing; of whom, seeing him frequently, she became hotly enamoured, hourly extolling his qualities more and more highly. The young man, who for all his youth by no means lacked shrewdness, read her heart, and gave her his own on such wise that his love for her engrossed his mind to the exclusion of almost everything else. While thus they burned in secret for one another, the lady, desiring of all things a meeting with Guiscardo, but being shy of making any her confidant, hit upon a novel expedient to concert the affair with him. She wrote him a letter containing her commands for the ensuing day, and thrust it into a cane in the space between two of the knots, which cane she gave to Guiscardo, saying:—"Thou canst let thy servant have it for a bellows to blow thy fire up to-night." Guiscardo took it, and feeling sure that 'twas not unadvisedly that she made him such a present, accompanied with such words, hied him straight home, where, carefully examining the cane, he observed that it was cleft, and, opening it, found the letter; which he had no sooner read, and learned what he was to do, than, pleased as ne'er another, he fell to devising how to set all in order that he might not fail to meet the lady on the following day, after the manner she had prescribed.

Now hard by the Prince's palace was a grotto, hewn in days of old in the solid rock, and now long disused, so that an artificial orifice, by which it received a little light, was all but choked with brambles and plants that grew about and overspread it. From one of the ground-floor rooms of the palace, which room was part of the lady's suite, a secret stair led to the grotto, though the entrance was barred by a very strong door. This stair, having been from time immemorial disused, had passed out of mind so completely that there was scarce any that remembered that it was there: but Love, whose eyes nothing, however secret, may escape, had brought it to the mind of the enamoured lady. For many a day, using all secrecy, that none should discover her, she had wrought with her tools, until she had succeeded in opening the door; which done, she had gone down into the grotto alone, and having observed the orifice, had by her letter apprised Guiscardo of its apparent height above the floor of the grotto, and bidden him contrive some means of descending thereby. Eager to carry the affair through, Guiscardo lost no time in rigging up a ladder of ropes, whereby he might ascend and descend; and having put on a suit of leather to protect him from the brambles, he hied him the following night (keeping the affair close from all) to the orifice, made the ladder fast by one of its ends to a massive trunk that was rooted in the mouth of the orifice, climbed down the ladder, and awaited the lady. On the morrow, making as if she would fain sleep, the lady dismissed her damsels, and locked herself into her room: she then opened the door of the grotto, hied her down, and met Guiscardo, to their marvellous mutual satisfaction. The lovers then repaired to her room, where in exceeding great joyance they spent no small part of the day. Nor were they neglectful of the precautions needful to prevent discovery of their amour; but in due time Guiscardo returned to the grotto; whereupon the lady locked the door and rejoined her damsels. At nightfall Guiscardo reascended his ladder, and, issuing forth of the orifice, hied him home; nor, knowing now the way, did he fail to revisit the grotto many a time thereafter.

But Fortune, noting with envious eye a happiness of such degree and duration, gave to events a dolorous turn, whereby the joy of the two lovers was converted into bitter lamentation. 'Twas Tancred's custom to come from time to time quite alone to his daughter's room, and tarry talking with her a while. Whereby it so befell that he came down there one day after breakfast, while Ghismonda—

such was the lady's name — was in her garden with her damsels; so that none saw or heard him enter; nor would he call his daughter, for he was minded that she should not forgo her pleasure. But, finding the windows closed and the bed-curtains drawn down, he seated himself on a divan that stood at one of the corners of the bed, rested his head on the bed, drew the curtain over him, and thus, hidden as if of set purpose, fell asleep. As he slept Ghismonda, who, as it happened, had caused Guiscardo to come that day, left her damsels in the garden, softly entered the room, and having locked herself in, unwitting that there was another in the room, opened the door to Guiscardo, who was in waiting. Straightway they got them to bed, as was their wont; and, while they there solaced and disported them together, it so befell that Tancred awoke, and heard and saw what they did: whereat he was troubled beyond measure, and at first was minded to upbraid them; but on second thoughts he deemed it best to hold his peace, and avoid discovery, if so he might with greater stealth and less dishonour carry out the design which was already in his mind. The two lovers continued long together, as they were wont, all unwitting of Tancred; but at length they saw fit to get out of bed, when Guiscardo went back to the grotto, and the lady hied her forth of the room. Whereupon Tancred, old though he was, got out at one of the windows, clambered down into the garden, and, seen by none, returned sorely troubled to his room. By his command two men took Guiscardo early that same night, as he issued forth of the orifice accoutred in his suit of leather, and brought him privily to Tancred; who, as he saw him, all but wept, and said: — "Guiscardo, my kindness to thee is ill requited by the outrage and dishonour which thou hast done me in the person of my daughter, as to-day I have seen with my own eyes." To whom Guiscardo could answer nought but: — "Love is more potent than either you or I." Tancred then gave order to keep him privily under watch and ward in a room within the palace; and so 'twas done. Next day, while Ghismonda wotted nought of these matters, Tancred, after pondering divers novel expedients, hied him after breakfast, according to his wont, to his daughter's room, where, having called her to him and locked himself in with her, he began, not without tears, to speak on this wise: — "Ghismonda, conceiving that I knew thy virtue and honour, never, though it had been reported to me, would I have credited, had I not seen with my own eyes, that thou wouldst so much as in idea, not to say fact, have ever yielded thyself to any man but thy husband: wherefore, for the brief residue of life that my age has in store for me, the memory of thy fall will ever be grievous to me. And would to God, as thou must needs demean thyself to such dishonour, thou hadst taken a man that matched thy nobility; but of all the men that frequent my court, thou must needs choose Guiscardo, a young man of the lowest condition, a fellow whom we brought up in charity from his tender years; for whose sake thou hast plunged me into the abyss of mental tribulation, insomuch that I know not what course to take in regard of thee. As to Guiscardo, whom I caused to be arrested last night as he issued from the orifice, and keep in durance, my course is already taken, but how I am to deal with thee, God knows, I know not. I am distraught between the love which I have ever borne thee, love such as no father ever bare to daughter, and the most just indignation evoked in me by thy signal folly; my love prompts me to pardon thee, my indignation bids me harden my heart against thee, though I do violence to my nature. But before I decide upon my course, I would fain hear what thou hast to say to this." So saying, he bent his head, and wept as bitterly as any child that had been soundly thrashed.

Her father's words, and the tidings they conveyed that not only was her secret passion discovered, but Guiscardo taken, caused Ghismonda immeasurable grief, which she was again and again on the point of evincing, as most women do, by cries and tears; but her high spirit triumphed over this weakness; by a prodigious effort she composed her countenance, and taking it for granted that her Guiscardo was no more, she inly devoted herself to death rather than a single prayer for herself should escape her lips. Wherefore, not as a woman stricken with grief or chidden for a fault, but unconcerned and unabashed, with tearless eyes, and frank and utterly dauntless mien, thus answered she her father:—"Tancred, your accusation I shall not deny, neither will I cry you mercy, for nought should I gain by denial, nor aught would I gain by supplication: nay more; there is nought I will do to conciliate thy humanity and love; my only care is to confess the truth, to defend my honour by words of sound reason, and then by deeds most resolute to give effect to the promptings of my high soul. True it is that I have loved and love Guiscardo, and during the brief while I have yet to live shall love him, nor after death, so there be then love, shall I cease to love him; but that I love him, is not imputable to my womanly frailty so much as to the little zeal thou shewedst for my bestowal in marriage, and to Guiscardo's own worth. It should not have escaped thee, Tancred, creature of flesh and blood as thou art, that thy daughter was also a creature of flesh and blood, and not of stone or iron; it was, and is, thy duty to bear in mind (old though thou art) the nature and the might of the laws to which youth is subject; and, though thou hast spent part of thy best years in martial exercise, thou shouldst nevertheless have not been ignorant how potent is the influence even upon the aged—to say nothing of the young—of ease and luxury. And not only am I, as being thy daughter, a creature of flesh and blood, but my life is not so far spent but that I am still young, and thus doubly fraught with fleshly appetite, the vehemence whereof is marvellously enhanced by reason that, having been married, I have known the pleasure that ensues upon the satisfaction of such desire. Which forces being powerless to withstand, I did but act as was natural in a young woman, when I gave way to them, and yielded myself to love. Nor in sooth did I fail to the utmost of my power so to order the indulgence of my natural propensity that my sin should bring shame neither upon thee nor upon me. To which end Love in his pity, and Fortune in a friendly mood, found and discovered to me a secret way, whereby, none witting, I attained my desire: this, from whomsoever thou hast learned it, howsoever thou comest to know it, I deny not. 'Twas not at random, as many women do, that I loved Guiscardo; but by deliberate choice I preferred him before all other men, and of determinate forethought I lured him to my love, whereof, through his and my discretion and constancy, I have long had joyance. Wherein 'twould seem that thou, following rather the opinion of the vulgar than the dictates of truth, find cause to chide me more severely than in my sinful love, for, as if thou wouldst not have been vexed, had my choice fallen on a nobleman, thou complainest that I have forgathered with a man of low condition; and dost not see that therein thou censurest not my fault but that of Fortune, which not seldom raises the unworthy to high place and leaves the worthiest in low estate. But leave we this: consider a little the principles of things: thou seest that in regard of our flesh we are all moulded of the same substance, and that all souls are endowed by one and the same Creator with equal faculties, equal powers, equal virtues. 'Twas merit that made the first distinction between us, born as we were, nay, as we are, all equal, and those whose merits were and were approved in act the greatest were called noble, and the rest were not so denoted. Which law, albeit overlaid by the contrary usage of after times, is not yet abrogated, nor so impaired but that it is still traceable in nature and good manners; for which cause whoso with merit acts, does plainly shew himself a gentleman; and if any denote him otherwise, the default is his own and not his whom he so denotes. Pass in review all thy nobles, weigh their merits, their manners and bearing, and then compare Guiscardo's qualities with theirs: if thou wilt judge without prejudice, thou wilt pronounce him noble in the highest degree, and thy nobles one and all churls. As to Guiscardo's merits and worth I did but trust the verdict which thou thyself didst utter in words, and which mine own eyes confirmed. Of whom had he such commendation as of thee for all those excellences whereby a good man and true merits commendation? And in sooth thou didst him but justice; for, unless mine eyes have played me false, there was nought for which thou didst commend him but I had seen him practise it, and that more admirably than words of thine might express; and had I been at all deceived in this matter, 'twould have been by thee. Wilt thou say then that I have forgathered with a man of low condition? If so, thou wilt not say true. Didst thou say with a poor man, the impeachment might be allowed, to thy shame, that thou so ill hast known how to requite a good man and true that is thy servant; but poverty, though it take away all else, deprives no man of gentilesse. Many kings, many great princes, were once poor, and many a ditcher or herdsman has been and is very wealthy. As for thy last perpended doubt, to wit, how thou shouldst deal with me, banish it utterly from thy thoughts. If in thy extreme old age thou art minded to manifest a harshness unwonted in thy youth, wreak thy harshness on me, resolved as I am to cry thee no mercy, prime cause as I am that this sin, if sin it be, has been committed; for of this I warrant thee, that as thou mayst have done or shalt do to Guiscardo, if to me thou do not the like, I with my own hands will do it. Now get thee gone to shed thy tears with the women, and when thy melting mood is over, ruthlessly destroy Guiscardo and me, if such thou deem our merited doom, by one and the same blow."

The loftiness of his daughter's spirit was not unknown to the Prince; but still he did not credit her with a resolve quite as firmly fixed as her words implied, to carry their purport into effect. So, parting from her without the least intention of using harshness towards her in her own person, he determined to quench the heat of her love by wreaking his vengeance on her lover, and bade the two men that had charge of Guiscardo to strangle him noiselessly that same night, take the heart out of the body, and send it to him. The men did his bidding: and on the morrow the Prince had a large and beautiful cup of gold brought to him, and having put Guiscardo's heart therein, sent it by the hand of one of his most trusted servants to his daughter, charging the servant to say, as he gave it to her:—"Thy father sends thee this to give thee joy of that which thou lovest best, even as thou hast given him joy of that which he loved best."

Now when her father had left her, Ghismonda, wavering not a jot in her stern resolve, had sent for poisonous herbs and roots, and therefrom had distilled a water, to have it ready for use, if that which she apprehended should come to pass. And when the servant appeared with the Prince's present and message, she took the cup unblenchingly, and having lifted the lid, and seen the heart, and apprehended the meaning of the words, and that the heart was beyond a doubt Guiscardo's, she raised her head, and looking straight at the servant, said:—"Sepulture less honourable than of gold had ill befitted heart such as this: herein has my father done wisely." Which said, she raised it to her lips, and kissed it, saying:—"In all things and at all times, even to this last hour of my life, have I found my father most tender in his love, but now more so than ever before; wherefore I now render him the last thanks which will ever be due from me to him for this goodly present." So she spoke, and straining the cup to her, bowed her head over it, and gazing at the heart, said:—"Ah! sojourn most sweet of all my joys, accursed be he by whose ruthless act I see thee with the bodily eye: 'twas enough that to the mind's eye thou wert hourly presently. Thou hast run thy course; thou hast closed the span that Fortune allotted thee; thou hast reached the goal of all; thou hast left behind thee the woes and weariness of the world; and thy enemy has himself granted thee sepulture accordant with thy deserts. No circumstance was wanting to duly celebrate thy obsequies, save the tears of her whom, while thou livedst, thou didst so dearly love; which that thou shouldst not lack, my remorseless father was prompted of God to send thee to me, and, albeit my resolve was fixed to die with eyes unmoistened and front all unperturbed by fear, yet will I accord thee my tears; which done, my care shall be forthwith by thy means to join my soul to that most precious soul which thou didst once enshrine. And is there other company than hers, in which with more of joy and peace I might fare to the abodes unknown? She is yet here within, I doubt not, contemplating the abodes of her and my delights, and — for sure I am that she loves me — awaiting my soul that loves her before all else."

Having thus spoken, she bowed herself low over the cup; and, while no womanish cry escaped her, 'twas as if a fountain of water were unloosed within her head, so wondrous a flood of tears gushed from her eyes, while times without number she kissed the dead heart. Her damsels that stood around her knew not whose the heart might be or what her words might mean, but melting in sympathy, they all wept, and compassionately, as vainly, enquired the cause of her lamentation, and in many other ways sought to comfort her to the best of their understanding and power. When she had wept her fill, she raised her head, and dried her eyes. Then: "O heart," said she, "much cherished heart, discharged is my every duty towards thee; nought now remains for me to do but to come and unite my soul with thine." So saying, she sent for the vase that held the water which the day before she had distilled, and emptied it into the cup where lay the heart bathed in her tears; then, nowise afraid, she set her mouth to the cup, and drained it dry, and so with the cup in her hand she got her upon her bed, and having there disposed her person in guise as seemly as she might, laid her dead lover's heart upon her own, and silently awaited death. Meanwhile the damsels, seeing and hearing what passed, but knowing not what the water was that she had drunk, had sent word of each particular to Tancred; who, apprehensive of that which came to pass, came down with all haste to his daughter's room, where he arrived just as she got her upon her bed, and, now too late, addressed himself to comfort her with soft words, and seeing in what plight she was, burst into a flood of bitter tears. To whom the lady: — "Reserve thy tears, Tancred, till Fortune send thee hap less longed for than this: waste them not on me who care not for them. Whoever yet saw any but thee bewail the consummation of his desire? But, if of the love thou once didst bear me any spark still lives in thee, be it thy parting grace to me, that, as thou brookedst not that I should live with Guiscardo in privity and seclusion, so wherever thou mayst have caused Guiscardo's body to be cast, mine may be united with it in the common view of all." The Prince replied not for excess of grief; and the lady, feeling that her end was come, strained the dead heart to her bosom, saying: — "Fare ye well; I take my leave of you"; and with eyelids drooped and every sense evanished departed this life of woe. Such was the lamentable end of the loves of Guiscardo and Ghismonda; whom Tancred, tardily repentant of his harshness, mourned not a little, as did also all the folk of Salerno, and had honourably interred side by side in the same tomb.

[FIFTH DAY]

NOVEL I

Cimon, by loving, waxes wise, wins his wife Iphigenia by capture on the high seas, and is imprisoned at Rhodes. He is delivered by Lysimachus; and the twain capture Cassandra and recapture Iphigenia in the hour of their marriage. They flee with their ladies to Crete, and having there married them, are brought back to their homes.

Many stories, sweet my ladies, occur to me as meet for me to tell by way of ushering in a day so joyous as this will be: of which one does most commend itself to my mind, because not only has it one of those happy endings of which to-day we are in quest, but 'twill enable you to understand how holy, how mighty and how salutary are the forces of Love, which not a few, witting not what they say, do most unjustly reprobate and revile: which, if I err not, should to you, for that I take you to be enamoured, be indeed welcome.

Once upon a time, then, as we have read in the ancient histories of the Cypriotes, there was in the island of Cyprus a very great noble named Aristippus, a man rich in all worldly goods beyond all other of his countrymen, and who might have deemed himself incomparably blessed, but for a single sore affliction that Fortune had allotted him. Which was that among his sons he had one, the best grown and handsomest of them all, that was well-nigh a hopeless imbecile. His true name was Galesus; but, as neither his tutor's pains, nor his father's coaxing or chastisement, nor any other method had availed to imbue him with any tincture of letters or manners, but he still remained gruff and savage of voice, and in his bearing liker to a beast than to a man, all, as in derision, were wont to call him Cimon, which in their language signifies the same as "bestione" (brute) in ours. The father, grieved beyond measure to see his son's life thus blighted, and having abandoned all hope of his recovery, nor caring to have the cause of his mortification ever before his eyes, bade him betake him to the farm, and there keep with his husbandmen. To Cimon the change was very welcome, because the manners and habits of the uncouth hinds were more to his taste than those of the citizens. So to the farm Cimon hied him, and addressed himself to the work thereof; and being thus employed, he chanced one afternoon as he passed, staff on shoulder, from one domain to another, to enter a plantation, the like of which for beauty there was not in those parts, and which was then — for 'twas the month of May — a mass of greenery; and, as he traversed it, he came, as Fortune was pleased to guide him, to a meadow girt in with trees exceeding tall, and having in one of its corners a fountain most fair and cool, beside which he espied a most beautiful girl lying asleep on the green grass, clad only in a vest of such fine stuff that it scarce in any measure veiled the whiteness of her flesh, and below the waist nought but an apron most white and fine of texture; and likewise at her feet there slept two women and a man, her slaves. No sooner did Cimon catch sight of her, than, as if he had never before seen form of woman, he stopped short, and leaning on his cudgel, regarded her intently, saying never a word, and lost in admiration. And in his rude soul, which, despite a thousand lessons, had hitherto remained impervious to every delight that belongs to urbane life, he felt the awakening of an idea, that bade his gross and coarse mind acknowledge, that this girl was the fairest creature that had ever been seen by mortal eye. And thereupon he began to distinguish her several parts, praising her hair, which shewed to him as gold, her brow, her nose and mouth, her throat and arms, and above all her bosom, which was as yet but in bud, and as he gazed, he changed of a sudden from a husbandman into a judge of beauty, and desired of all things to see her eyes, which the weight of her deep slumber kept close shut, and many a time he would fain have wakened her, that he might see them. But so much fairer seemed she to him than any other woman that he had seen, that he doubted she must be a goddess; and as he was not so devoid of sense but that he deemed things divine more worthy of reverence than things mundane, he forbore, and waited until she should awake of her own accord; and though he found the delay overlong, yet, enthralled by so unwonted a delight, he knew not how to be going. However, after he had tarried a long while, it so befell that Iphigenia — such was the girl's name — her slaves still sleeping, awoke, and raised her head, and opened her eyes, and seeing Cimon standing before her, leaning on his staff, was not a little surprised, and said: — "Cimon, what seekest thou in this wood at this hour?" For Cimon she knew well, as indeed did almost all the countryside, by reason alike of his uncouth appearance as of the rank and wealth of his father. To Iphigenia's question he answered never a word; but as soon as her eyes were open, nought could he do but intently regard them, for it seemed to him that a soft influence emanated from them, which filled his soul with a delight that he had never before known. Which the girl marking began to misdoubt that by so fixed a scrutiny his boorish temper might be prompted to some act that should cause her dishonour: wherefore she roused her women, and got up, saying: — "Keep thy distance, Cimon, in God's name." Whereto Cimon made answer: — "I will come with thee." And, albeit the girl refused his escort, being still in fear of him, she could not get quit of him; but he attended her home; after which he hied him straight to his father's house, and announced that he was minded on no account to go back to the farm: which intelligence was far from welcome to his father and kinsmen; but nevertheless they suffered him to stay, and waited to see what might be the reason of his change of mind. So Cimon, whose heart, closed to all teaching, love's shaft, sped by the beauty of Iphigenia, had penetrated, did now graduate in wisdom with such celerity as to astonish his father and kinsmen, and all that knew him. He began by requesting his father to let him go clad in the like apparel, and with, in all respects, the like personal equipment as his brothers: which his father very gladly did. Mixing thus with the gallants, and becoming familiar with the manners proper to gentlemen, and especially to lovers, he very soon, to the exceeding great wonder of all, not only acquired the rudiments of letters, but waxed most eminent among the philosophic wits. After which (for no other cause than the love he bore to Iphigenia) he not only modulated his gruff and boorish voice to a degree of smoothness suitable to urbane life, but made himself accomplished in singing and music; in riding also and in all matters belonging to war, as well by sea as by land, he waxed most expert and hardy. And in sum (that I go not about to enumerate each of his virtues in detail) he had not completed the fourth year from the day of his first becoming enamoured before he was grown the most gallant, and courteous, ay, and the most perfect in particular accomplishments, of the younger cavaliers that were in the island of Cyprus. What then, gracious ladies, are we to say of Cimon? Verily nought else but that the high faculties, with which Heaven had endowed his noble soul, invidious Fortune had bound with the strongest of cords, and circumscribed within a very narrow region of his heart; all which cords Love, more potent than Fortune, burst and brake in pieces; and then with the might, wherewith he awakens dormant powers, he brought them forth of the cruel obfuscation, in which they lay, into clear light, plainly shewing thereby, whence he may draw, and whither he may guide, by his beams the souls that are subject to his sway.

Now, albeit by his love for Iphigenia Cimon was betrayed, as young lovers very frequently are, into some peccadillos, yet Aristippus, reflecting that it had turned him from a booby into a man, not only bore patiently with him, but exhorted him with all his heart to continue steadfast in his love. And Cimon, who still refused to be called Galesus, because 'twas as Cimon that Iphigenia had first addressed him, being desirous to accomplish his desire by honourable means, did many a time urge his suit upon her father, Cipseus, that he would give her him to wife: whereto Cipseus always made the same answer, to wit, that he had promised her to Pasimondas, a young Rhodian noble, and was not minded to break faith with him. However, the time appointed for Iphigenia's wedding being come, and the bridegroom having sent for her, Cimon said to himself:—'Tis now for me to shew thee, O Iphigenia, how great is my love for thee: 'tis by thee that I am grown a man, nor doubt I, if I shall have thee, that I shall wax more glorious than a god, and verily thee will I have, or die. Having so said, he privily enlisted in his cause certain young nobles that were his friends, and secretly fitted out a ship with all equipment meet for combat, and put to sea on the look-out for the ship that was to bear Iphigenia to Rhodes and her husband. And at length, when her father had done lavishing honours upon her husband's friends, Iphigenia embarked, and, the mariners shaping their course for Rhodes, put to sea. Cimon was on the alert, and overhauled them the very next day, and standing on his ship's prow shouted amain to those that were aboard Iphigenia's ship:—"Bring to; strike sails, or look to be conquered and sunk in the sea." Then, seeing that the enemy had gotten their arms above deck, and were making ready to make a fight of it, he followed up his words by casting a grapnel upon the poop of the Rhodians, who were making great way; and having thus made their poop fast to his prow, he sprang, fierce as a lion, reckless whether he were followed or no, on to the Rhodians' ship, making, as it were, no account of them, and animated by love, hurled himself, sword in hand, with prodigious force among the enemy, and cutting and thrusting right and left, slaughtered them like sheep; insomuch that the Rhodians, marking the fury of his onset, threw down their arms, and as with one voice did all acknowledge themselves his prisoners. To whom Cimon:—"Gallants," quoth he, "'twas neither lust of booty nor enmity to you that caused me to put out from Cyprus to attack you here with force of arms on the high seas. Moved was I thereto by that which to gain is to me a matter great indeed, which peaceably to yield me is to you but a slight matter; for 'tis even Iphigenia, whom more than aught else I love; whom, as I might not have her of her father in peaceable and friendly sort, Love has constrained me to take from you in this high-handed fashion and by force of arms; to whom I mean to be even such as would have been your Pasimondas: wherefore give her to me, and go your way, and God's grace go with you."

Yielding rather to force than prompted by generosity, the Rhodians surrendered Iphigenia, all tears, to Cimon; who, marking her tears, said to her:—"Grieve not, noble lady; thy Cimon am I, who, by my long love, have established a far better right to thee than Pasimondas by the faith that was plighted to him." So saying, he sent her aboard his ship, whither he followed her, touching nought that belonged to the Rhodians, and suffering them to go their way. To have gotten so dear a prize made him the happiest man in the world, but for a time 'twas all he could do to assuage her grief: then, after taking counsel with his comrades, he deemed it best not to return to Cyprus for the present: and so, by common consent they shaped their course for Crete, where most of them, and especially Cimon, had alliances of old or recent date, and friends not a few, whereby they deemed that there they might tarry with Iphigenia in security. But Fortune, that had accorded Cimon so gladsome a capture of the lady, suddenly proved fickle, and converted the boundless joy of the enamoured gallant into woeful and bitter lamentation. 'Twas not yet full four hours since Cimon had parted from the Rhodians, when with the approach of night, that night from which Cimon hoped such joyance as he had never known, came weather most turbulent and tempestuous, which wrapped the heavens in cloud, and swept the sea with scathing blasts; whereby 'twas not possible for any to see how the ship was to be worked or steered, or to steady himself so as to do any duty upon her deck. Whereat what grief was Cimon's, it boots not to ask. Indeed it seemed to him that the gods had granted his heart's desire only that it might be harder for him to die, which had else been to him but a light matter. Not less downcast were his comrades; but most of all Iphigenia, who, weeping bitterly and shuddering at every wave that struck the ship, did cruelly curse Cimon's love and censure his rashness, averring that this tempest was come upon them for no other cause than that the gods had decreed, that, as 'twas in despite of their will that he purposed to espouse her, he should be frustrate of his presumptuous intent, and having lived to see her expire, should then himself meet a woeful death.

While thus and yet more bitterly they bewailed them, and the mariners were at their wits' end, as the gale grew hourly more violent, nor knew they, nor might conjecture, whither they went, they drew nigh the island of Rhodes, albeit that Rhodes it was they wist not, and set themselves, as best and most skilfully they might, to run the ship aground. In which enterprise Fortune favoured them, bringing them into a little bay, where, shortly before them, was arrived the Rhodian ship that Cimon had let go. Nor were they sooner ware that 'twas Rhodes they had made, than day broke, and, the sky thus brightening a little, they saw that they were about a bow-shot from the ship that they had released on the preceding day. Whereupon Cimon, vexed beyond measure, being apprehensive of that which in fact befell them, bade make every effort to win out of the bay, and let Fortune carry them whither she would, for nowhere might they be in worse plight than there. So might and main they strove to bring the ship out, but all in vain: the violence of the gale thwarted them to such purpose as not only to preclude their passage out of the bay but to drive them, willing nilling, ashore. Whither no sooner were they come, than they were recognized by the Rhodian mariners, who were already landed. Of whom one ran with all speed to a farm hard by, whither the Rhodian gallants were gone, and told them that Fortune had brought Cimon and Iphigenia aboard their ship into the same bay to which she had guided them. Whereat the gallants were overjoyed, and taking with them not a few of the farm-servants, hied them in hot haste to the shore, where, Cimon and his men being already landed with intent to take refuge in a neighbouring wood, they took them all (with Iphigenia) and brought them to the farm. Whence, pursuant to an order of the Senate of Rhodes, to which, so soon as he received the news, Pasimondas made his complaint, Cimon and his men were all marched off to prison by Lysimachus, chief magistrate of the Rhodians for that year, who came down from the city for the purpose with an exceeding great company of men at arms. On such wise did our hapless and enamoured Cimon lose his so lately won Iphigenia before he had had of her more than a kiss or two. Iphigenia was entertained and comforted of the annoy, occasioned as well by her recent capture as by the fury of the sea, by not a few noble ladies of Rhodes, with whom she tarried until the day appointed for her marriage. In recompense of the release of the Rhodian gallants on the preceding day the lives of Cimon and his men were spared, notwithstanding that Pasimondas pressed might and main for their execution; and instead they were condemned to perpetual imprisonment: wherein, as may be supposed, they abode in dolorous plight, and despaired of ever again knowing happiness.

However, it so befell that, Pasimondas accelerating his nuptials to the best of his power, Fortune, as if repenting her that in her haste she had done Cimon so evil a turn, did now by a fresh disposition of events compass his deliverance. Pasimondas had a brother, by name Hormisdas, his equal in all respects save in years, who had long been contract to marry Cassandra, a fair and noble damsel of Rhodes, of whom Lysimachus was in the last degree enamoured; but owing to divers accidents the marriage had been from time to time put off. Now Pasimondas, being about to celebrate his nuptials with exceeding great pomp, bethought him that he could not do better than, to avoid a repetition of the pomp and expense, arrange, if so he might, that his brother should be wedded on the same day with himself. So, having consulted anew with Cassandra's kinsfolk, and come to an understanding with them, he and his brother and they conferred together, and agreed that on the same day that Pasimondas married Iphigenia, Hormisdas should marry Cassandra. Lysimachus, getting wind of this arrangement, was mortified beyond measure, seeing himself thereby deprived of the hope which he cherished of marrying Cassandra himself, if Hormisdas should not forestall him. But like a wise man he concealed his chagrin, and cast about how he might frustrate the arrangement: to which end he saw no other possible means but to carry Cassandra off. It did not escape him that the office which he held would render this easily feasible, but he deemed it all the more dishonourable than if he had not held the office; but, in short, after much pondering, honour yielded place to love, and he made up his mind that, come what might, he would carry Cassandra off. Then, as he took thought what company he should take with him, and how he should go about the affair, he remembered Cimon, whom he had in prison with his men, and it occurred to him that he could not possibly have a better or more trusty associate in such an enterprise than Cimon. Wherefore the same night he caused Cimon to be brought privily to him in his own room, and thus addressed him: — "Cimon, as the gods are most generous and liberal to bestow their gifts on men, so are they also most sagacious to try their virtue; and those whom they find to be firm and steadfast in all circumstances they honour, as the most worthy, with the highest rewards. They have been minded to be certified of thy worth by better proofs than thou couldst afford them, as long as thy life was bounded by thy father's house amid the superabundant wealth which I know him to possess: wherefore in the first place they so wrought upon thee with the shrewd incitements of Love that from an insensate brute, as I have heard, thou grewest to be a man; since when, it has been and is their intent to try whether evil fortune and harsh imprisonment may avail to change thee from the temper that was thine when for a short while thou hadst joyance of the prize thou hadst won. And so thou prove the same that thou wast then, they have in store for thee a boon incomparably greater than aught that they vouchsafed thee before: what that boon is, to the end thou mayst recover heart and thy wonted energies, I will now explain to thee. Pasimondas, exultant in thy misfortune and eager to compass thy death, hastens to the best of his power his nuptials with thy Iphigenia; that so he may enjoy the prize that Fortune, erstwhile smiling, gave thee, and forthwith, frowning, reft from thee. Whereat how sore must be thy grief, if rightly I gauge thy love, I know by my own case, seeing that his brother Hormisdas addresses himself to do me on the same day a like wrong in regard of Cassandra, whom I love more than aught else in the world. Nor see I that Fortune has left us any way of escape from this her unjust and cruel spite, save what we may make for ourselves by a resolved spirit and the might of our right hands: take we then the sword, and therewith make we, each, prize of his lady, thou for the second, I for the first time: for so thou value the recovery, I say not of thy liberty, for without thy lady I doubt thou wouldst hold it cheap, but of thy lady, the gods have placed it in thine own hands, if thou art but minded to join me in my enterprise."

These words restored to Cimon all that he had lost of heart and hope, nor pondered he long, before he replied: — "Lysimachus, comrade stouter or more staunch than I thou mightst not have in such an enterprise, if such indeed it be as thou sayst: wherefore lay upon me such behest as thou shalt deem meet, and thou shalt marvel to witness the vigour of my performance." Whereupon Lysimachus: — "On the third day from now," quoth he, "their husbands' houses will be newly entered by the brides, and on the same day at even we too will enter them in arms, thou with thy men, and I with some of mine, in whom I place great trust, and forcing our way among the guests and slaughtering all that dare to oppose us, will bear the ladies off to a ship which I have had privily got ready." Cimon approved the plan, and kept quiet in prison until the appointed time; which being come, the nuptials were celebrated with great pomp and magnificence, that filled the houses of the two brothers with festal cheer. Then Lysimachus having made ready all things meet, and fired Cimon and his men and his own friends for the enterprise by a long harangue, disposed them in due time, all bearing arms under their cloaks, in three companies; and having privily despatched one company to the port, that, when the time should come to embark, he might meet with no let, he marched with the other two companies to the house of Pasimondas, posted the one company at the gate, that, being entered, they might not be shut in or debarred their egress, and, with the other company and Cimon, ascended the stairs, and gained the saloon, where the brides and not a few other ladies were set at several tables to sup in meet order: whereupon in they rushed, and overthrew the tables and seized each his own lady, and placed them in charge of their men, whom they bade bear them off forthwith to the ship that lay ready to receive them. Whereupon the brides and the other ladies and the servants with one accord fell a sobbing and shrieking, insomuch that a confused din and lamentation filled the whole place. Cimon, Lysimachus and their band, none withstanding, but all giving way before them, gained the stairs, which they were already descending when they encountered Pasimondas, who, carrying a great staff in his hand, was making in the direction of the noise; but one doughty stroke of Cimon's sword sufficed to cleave his skull in twain, and lay him dead at Cimon's feet, and another stroke disposed of hapless Hormisdas, as he came running to his brother's aid. Some others who ventured to approach them were wounded and beaten off by the retinue. So forth of the house, that reeked with blood and resounded with tumult and lamentation and woe, sped Cimon and Lysimachus with all their company, and without any let, in close order, with their fair booty in their midst, made good their retreat to the ship; whereon with the ladies they one and all embarked, for the shore was now full of armed men come to rescue the ladies, and, the oarsmen giving way, put to sea elate. Arrived at Crete, they met with a hearty welcome on the part of their many friends and kinsfolk; and, having married their ladies, they made greatly merry, and had gladsome joyance of their fair booty. Their doings occasioned, both in Cyprus and in Rhodes, no small stir and commotion, which lasted for a long while: but in the end, by the good offices of their friends and kinsfolk in both islands, 'twas so ordered as that after a certain term of exile Cimon returned with Iphigenia to Cyprus, and in like manner Lysimachus returned with Cassandra to Rhodes; and long and blithely thereafter lived they, each well contented with his own wife in his own land.

NOVEL IX

Federigo degli Alberighi loves and is not loved in return: he wastes his substance by lavishness until nought is left but a single falcon, which, his lady being come to see him at his house, he gives her to eat: she, knowing his case, changes her mind, takes him to husband and makes him rich.

So ended Filomena; and the queen, being ware that besides herself only Dioneo (by virtue of his privilege) was left to speak, said with gladsome mien:—'Tis now for me to take up my parable; which, dearest ladies, I will do with a story like in some degree to the foregoing, and that, not only that you may know how potent are your charms to sway the gentle heart, but that you may also learn how upon fitting occasions to make bestowal of your guerdons of your own accord, instead of always waiting for the guidance of

Fortune, which most times, not wisely, but without rule or measure, scatters her gifts.

You are then to know, that Coppo di Borghese Domenichi, a man that in our day was, and perchance still is, had in respect and great reverence in our city, being not only by reason of his noble lineage, but, and yet more, for manners and merit most illustrious and worthy of eternal renown, was in his old age not seldom wont to amuse himself by discoursing of things past with his neighbours and other folk; wherein he had not his match for accuracy and compass of memory and concinnity of speech. Among other good stories, he would tell, how that there was of yore in Florence a gallant named Federigo di Messer Filippo Alberighi, who for feats of arms and courtesy had not his peer in Tuscany; who, as is the common lot of gentlemen, became enamoured of a lady named Monna Giovanna, who in her day held rank among the fairest and most elegant ladies of Florence; to gain whose love he jousted, tilted, gave entertainments, scattered largess, and in short set no bounds to his expenditure. However the lady, no less virtuous than fair, cared not a jot for what he did for her sake, nor yet for him.

Spending thus greatly beyond his means, and making nothing, Federigo could hardly fail to come to lack, and was at length reduced to such poverty that he had nothing left but a little estate, on the rents of which he lived very straitly, and a single falcon, the best in the world. The estate was at Campi, and thither, deeming it no longer possible for him to live in the city as he desired, he repaired, more in love than ever before; and there, in complete seclusion, diverting himself with hawking, he bore his poverty as patiently as he might.

Now, Federigo being thus reduced to extreme poverty, it so happened that one day Monna Giovanna's husband, who was very rich, fell ill, and, seeing that he was nearing his end, made his will, whereby he left his estate to his son, who was now growing up, and in the event of his death without lawful heir named Monna Giovanna, whom he dearly loved, heir in his stead; and having made these dispositions he died.

Monna Giovanna, being thus left a widow, did as our ladies are wont, and repaired in the summer to one of her estates in the country which lay very near to that of Federigo. And so it befell that the urchin began to make friends with Federigo, and to shew a fondness for hawks and dogs, and having seen Federigo's falcon fly not a few times, took a singular fancy to him, and greatly longed to have him for his own, but still did not dare to ask him of Federigo, knowing that Federigo prized him so much. So the matter stood when by chance the boy fell sick; whereby the mother was sore distressed, for he was her only son, and she loved him as much as might be, insomuch that all day long she was beside him, and ceased not to comfort him, and again and again asked him if there were aught that he wished for, imploring him to say the word, and, if it might by any means be had, she would assuredly do her utmost to procure it for him. Thus repeatedly exhorted, the boy said: — "Mother mine, do but get me Federigo's falcon, and I doubt not I shall soon be well." Whereupon the lady was silent a while, bethinking her what she should do. She knew that Federigo had long loved her, and had never had so much as a single kind look from her: wherefore she said to herself: — How can I send or go to beg of him this falcon, which by what I hear is the best that ever flew, and moreover is his sole comfort? And how could I be so unfeeling as to seek to deprive a gentleman of the one solace that is now left him? And so, albeit she very well knew that she might have the falcon for the asking, she was perplexed, and knew not what to say, and gave her son no answer. At length, however, the love she bore the boy carried the day, and she made up her mind, for his contentment, come what might, not to send, but to go herself and fetch him the falcon. So: — "Be of good cheer, my son," she said, "and doubt not thou wilt soon be well; for I promise thee that the very first thing that I shall do tomorrow morning will be to go and fetch thee the falcon." Whereat the child was so pleased that he began to mend that very day.

On the morrow the lady, as if for pleasure, hied her with another lady to Federigo's little house, and asked to see him. 'Twas still, as for some days past, no weather for hawking, and Federigo was in his garden, busy about some small matters which needed to be set right there. When he heard that Monna Giovanna was at the door, asking to see him, he was not a little surprised and pleased, and hied him to her with all speed. As soon as she saw him, she came forward to meet him with womanly grace, and having received his respectful salutation, said to him: — "Good morrow, Federigo," and continued: — "I am come to requite thee for what thou hast lost by loving me more than thou shouldst: which compensation is this, that I and this lady that accompanies me will breakfast with thee without ceremony this morning." "Madam," Federigo replied with all humility, "I mind not ever to have lost aught by loving you, but rather to have been so much profited that, if I ever deserved well in aught, 'twas to your merit that I owed it, and to the love that I bore you. And of a surety had I still as much to spend as I have spent in the past, I should not prize it so much as this visit you so frankly pay me, come as you are to one who can afford you but a sorry sort of hospitality." Which said, with some confusion, he bade her welcome to his house, and then led her into his garden, where, having none else to present to her by way of companion, he said: — "Madam, as there is none other here, this good woman, wife of this husbandman, will bear you company, while I go to have the table set." Now, albeit his poverty was extreme, yet he had not known as yet how sore was the need to which his extravagance had reduced him; but this morning 'twas brought home to him, for that he could find nought wherewith to do honour to the lady, for love of whom he had done the honours of his house to men without number: wherefore, distressed beyond measure, and inwardly cursing his evil fortune, he sped hither and thither like one beside himself, but never a coin found he, nor yet aught to pledge. Meanwhile it grew late, and sorely he longed that the lady might not leave his house altogether unhonoured, and yet to crave help of his own husbandman was more than his pride could brook. In these desperate straits his glance happened to fall on his brave falcon on his perch in his little parlour. And so, as a last resource, he took him, and finding him plump, deemed that he would make a dish meet for such a lady. Wherefore, without thinking twice about it, he wrung the bird's neck, and caused his maid forthwith pluck him and set him on a spit, and roast him carefully; and having still some spotless table-linen, he had the table laid therewith, and with a cheerful countenance hied him back to his lady in the garden, and told her that such breakfast as he could give her was ready. So the lady and her companion rose and came to table, and there, with Federigo, who waited on them most faithfully, ate the brave falcon, knowing not what they ate.

When they were risen from table, and had dallied a while in gay converse with him, the lady deemed it time to tell the reason of her visit: wherefore, graciously addressing Federigo, thus began she:—"Federigo, by what thou rememberest of thy past life and my virtue, which, perchance, thou hast deemed harshness and cruelty, I doubt not thou must marvel at my presumption, when thou hearest the main purpose of my visit; but if thou hadst sons, or hadst had them, so that thou mightest know the full force of the love that is borne them, I should make no doubt that thou wouldst hold me in part excused. Nor, having a son, may I, for that thou hast none, claim exemption from the laws to which all other mothers are subject, and, being thus bound to own their sway, I must, though fain were I not, and though 'tis neither meet nor right, crave of thee that which I know thou dost of all things and with justice prize most highly, seeing that this extremity of thy adverse fortune has left thee nought else wherewith to delight, divert and console thee; which gift is no other than thy falcon, on which my boy has so set his heart that, if I bring him it not, I fear lest he grow so much worse of the malady that he has, that thereby it may come to pass that I lose him. And so, not for the love which thou dost bear me, and which may nowise bind thee, but for that nobleness of temper, whereof in courtesy more conspicuously than in aught else thou hast given proof, I implore thee that thou be pleased to give me the bird, that thereby I may say that I have kept my son alive, and thus made him for aye thy debtor."

No sooner had Federigo apprehended what the lady wanted, than, for grief that 'twas not in his power to serve her, because he had given her the falcon to eat, he fell a weeping in her presence, before he could so much as utter a word. At first the lady supposed that 'twas only because he was loath to part with the brave falcon that he wept, and as good as made up her mind that he would refuse her: however, she awaited with patience Federigo's answer, which was on this wise: — "Madam, since it pleased God that I should set my affections upon you there have been matters not a few, in which to my sorrow I have deemed Fortune adverse to me; but they have all been trifles in comparison of the trick that she now plays me: the which I shall never forgive her, seeing that you are come here to my poor house, where, while I was rich, you deigned not to come, and ask a trifling favour of me, which she has put it out of my power to grant: how 'tis so, I will briefly tell you. When I learned that you, of your grace, were minded to breakfast with me, having respect to your high dignity and desert, I deemed it due and seemly that in your honour I should regale you, to the best of my power, with fare of a more excellent quality than is commonly set before others; and, calling to mind the falcon which you now ask of me, and his excellence, I judged him meet food for you, and so you have had him roasted on the trencher this morning; and well indeed I thought I had bestowed him; but, as now I see that you would fain have had him in another guise, so mortified am I that I am not able to serve you, that I doubt I shall never know peace of mind more." In witness whereof he had the feathers and feet and beak of the bird brought in and laid before her.

The first thing the lady did, when she had heard Federigo's story, and seen the relics of the bird, was to chide him that he had killed so fine a falcon to furnish a woman with a breakfast; after which the magnanimity of her host, which poverty had been and was powerless to impair, elicited no small share of inward commendation. Then, frustrate of her hope of possessing the falcon, and doubting of her son's recovery, she took her leave with the heaviest of hearts, and hied her back to the boy: who, whether for fretting, that he might not have the falcon, or by the unaided energy of his disorder, departed this life not many days after, to the exceeding great grief of his mother. For a while she would do nought but weep and bitterly bewail herself; but being still young, and left very wealthy, she was often urged by her brothers to marry again, and though she would rather have not done so, yet being importuned, and remembering Federigo's high desert, and the magnificent generosity with which he had finally killed his falcon to do her honour, she said to her brothers: — "Gladly, with your consent, would I remain a widow, but if you will not be satisfied except I take a husband, rest assured that none other will I ever take save Federigo degli Alberighi." Whereupon her brothers derided her, saying: — "Foolish woman, what is 't thou sayst? How shouldst thou want Federigo, who has not a thing in the world?" To whom she answered: — "My brothers, well wot I that 'tis as you say; but I had rather have a man without wealth than wealth without a man." The brothers, perceiving that her mind was made up, and knowing Federigo for a good man and true, poor though he was, gave her to him with all her wealth. And so Federigo, being mated with such a wife, and one that he had so much loved, and being very wealthy to boot, lived happily, keeping more exact accounts, to the end of his days.

[SIXTH DAY]

NOVEL X

Fra Cipolla promises to shew certain country-folk a feather of the Angel Gabriel, in lieu of which he finds coals, which he avers to be of those with which St. Lawrence was roasted.

All the company save Dioneo being delivered of their several stories, he wist that 'twas his turn to speak. Wherefore, without awaiting any very express command, he enjoined silence on those that were commending Guido's pithy quip, and thus began: — Sweet my ladies, albeit 'tis my privilege to speak of what likes me most, I purpose not to-day to deviate from that theme whereon you have all discoursed most appositely; but, following in your footsteps, I am minded to shew you with what adroitness and readiness of resource one of the Friars of St. Antony avoided a pickle that two young men had in readiness for him. Nor, if, in order to do the story full justice, I be somewhat prolix of speech, should it be burdensome to you, if you will but glance at the sun, which is yet in mid-heaven.

Certaldo, as perchance you may have heard, is a town of Val d'Elsa within our country-side, which, small though it is, had in it aforetime people of rank and wealth. Thither, for that there he found good pasture, 'twas long the wont of one of the Friars of St. Antony to resort once every year, to collect the alms that fools gave them. Fra Cipolla — so hight the friar — met with a hearty welcome, no less, perchance, by reason of his name than for other cause, the onions produced in that district being famous throughout Tuscany. He was little of person, red-haired, jolly-visaged, and the very best of good fellows; and therewithal, though learning he had none, he was so excellent and ready a speaker that whoso knew him not would not only have esteemed him a great rhetorician, but would have pronounced him Tully himself or, perchance, Quintilian; and in all the country-side there was scarce a soul to whom he was not either gossip or friend or lover. Being thus wont from time to time to visit Certaldo, the friar came there once upon a time in the month of August, and on a Sunday morning, all the good folk of the neighbouring farms being come to mass in the parish church, he took occasion to come forward and say: — "Ladies and gentlemen, you wot 'tis your custom to send year by year to the poor of Baron Master St. Antony somewhat of your wheat and oats, more or less, according to the ability and the devoutness of each, that blessed St. Antony may save your oxen and asses and pigs and sheep from harm; and you are also accustomed, and especially those whose names are on the books of our confraternity, to pay your trifling annual dues. To collect which offerings, I am hither sent by my superior, to wit, Master Abbot; wherefore, with the blessing of God, after none, when you hear the bells ring, you will come out of the church to the place where in the usual way I shall deliver you my sermon, and you will kiss the cross; and therewithal, knowing, as I do, that you are one and all most devoted to Baron Master St. Antony, I will by way of especial grace shew you a most holy and goodly relic, which I brought myself from the Holy Land overseas, which is none other than one of the feathers of the Angel Gabriel, which he left behind him in the room of the Virgin Mary, when he came to make her the annunciation in Nazareth." And having said thus much, he ceased, and went on with the mass. Now among the many that were in the church, while Fra Cipolla made this speech, were two very wily young wags, the one Giovanni del Bragoniera by name, the other Biagio Pizzini; who, albeit they were on the best of terms with Fra Cipolla and much in his company, had a sly laugh together over the relic, and resolved to make game of him and his feather. So, having learned that Fra Cipolla was to breakfast that morning in the town with one of his friends, as soon as they knew that he was at table, down they hied them into the street, and to the inn where the friar lodged, having complotted that Biagio should keep the friar's servant in play, while Giovanni made search among the friar's goods and chattels for this feather, whatever it might be, to carry it off, that they might see how the friar would afterwards explain the matter to the people. Now Fra Cipolla had for servant one Guccio, whom some called by way of addition Balena, others Imbratta, others again Porco, and who was such a rascallion that sure it is that Lippo Topo himself never painted his like. Concerning whom Fra Cipolla would ofttimes make merry with his familiars, saying: — "My servant has nine qualities, any one of which in Solomon, Aristotle, or Seneca, would have been enough to spoil all their virtue, wisdom and holiness. Consider, then, what sort of a man he must be that has these nine qualities, and yet never a spark of either virtue or wisdom or holiness." And being asked upon divers occasions what these nine qualities might be, he strung them together in rhyme, and answered: — "I will tell you. Lazy and uncleanly and a liar he is, Negligent, disobedient and foul-mouthed, iwis, And reckless and witless and mannerless: and therewithal he has some other petty vices, which 'twere best to pass over. And the most amusing thing about him is, that, wherever he goes, he is for taking a wife and renting a house, and on the strength of a big, black, greasy beard he deems himself so very handsome a fellow and seductive, that he takes all the women that see him to be in love with him, and, if he were left alone, he would slip his girdle and run after them all. True it is that he is of great use to me, for that, be any minded to speak with me never so secretly, he must still have his share of the audience; and, if perchance aught is demanded of me, such is his fear lest I should be at a loss what answer to make, that he presently replies, ay or no, as he deems meet."

Now, when he left this knave at the inn, Fra Cipolla had strictly enjoined him on no account to suffer any one to touch aught of his, and least of all his wallet, because it contained the holy things. But Guccio Imbratta, who was fonder of the kitchen than any nightingale of the green boughs, and most particularly if he espied there a maid, and in the host's kitchen had caught sight of a coarse fat woman, short and misshapen, with a pair of breasts that shewed as two buckets of muck and a face that might have belonged to one of the Baronci, all reeking with sweat and grease and smoke, left Fra Cipolla's room and all his things to take care of themselves, and like a vulture swooping down upon the carrion, was in the kitchen in a trice. Where, though 'twas August, he sat him down by a fire, and fell a gossiping with Nuta — such was the maid's name — and told her that he was a gentleman by procuration, and had more florins than could be reckoned, besides those that he had to give away, which were rather more than less, and that he could do and say such things as never were or might be seen or heard forever, good Lord! and a day. And all heedless of his cowl, which had as much grease upon it as would have furnished forth the caldron of Altopascio, and of his rent and patched doublet, inlaid with filth about the neck and under the armpits, and so stained that it shewed hues more various than ever did silk from Tartary or the Indies, and of his shoes that were all to pieces, and of his hose that were all in tatters, he told her in a tone that would have become the Sieur de Châtillon, that he was minded to rehabit her and put her in trim, and raise her from her abject condition, and place her where, though she would not have much to call her own, at any rate she would have hope of better things, with much more to the like effect; which professions, though made with every appearance of good will, proved, like most of his schemes, insubstantial as air, and came to nothing.

Finding Guccio Porco thus occupied with Nuta, the two young men gleefully accounted their work half done, and, none gainsaying them, entered Fra Cipolla's room, which was open, and lit at once upon the wallet, in which was the feather. The wallet opened, they found, wrapt up in many folds of taffeta, a little casket, on opening which they discovered one of the tail-feathers of a parrot, which they deemed must be that which the friar had promised to shew the good folk of Certaldo. And in sooth he might well have so imposed upon them, for in those days the luxuries of Egypt had scarce been introduced into Tuscany, though they have since been brought over in prodigious abundance, to the grave hurt of all Italy. And though some conversance with them there was, yet in those parts folk knew next to nothing of them; but, adhering to the honest, simple ways of their forefathers, had not seen, nay for the most part had not so much as heard tell of, a parrot.

So the young men, having found the feather, took it out with great glee; and looking around for something to replace it, they espied in a corner of the room some pieces of coal, wherewith they filled the casket; which they then closed, and having set the room in order exactly as they had found it, they quitted it unperceived, and hied them merrily off with the feather, and posted themselves where they might hear what Fra Cipolla would say when he found the coals in its stead. Mass said, the simple folk that were in the church went home with the tidings that the feather of the Angel Gabriel was to be seen after none; and this goodman telling his neighbour, and that goodwife her gossip, by the time every one had breakfasted, the town could scarce hold the multitude of men and women that flocked thither all agog to see this feather.

Fra Cipolla, having made a hearty breakfast and had a little nap, got up shortly after none, and marking the great concourse of country-folk that were come to see the feather, sent word to Guccio Imbratta to go up there with the bells, and bring with him the wallet. Guccio, though 'twas with difficulty that he tore himself away from the kitchen and Nuta, hied him up with the things required; and though, when he got up, he was winded, for he was corpulent with drinking nought but water, he did Fra Cipolla's bidding by going to the church door and ringing the bells amain. When all the people were gathered about the door, Fra Cipolla, all unwitting that aught of his was missing, began his sermon, and after much said in glorification of himself, caused the confiteor to be recited with great solemnity, and two torches to be lit by way of preliminary to the shewing of the feather of the Angel Gabriel: he then bared his head, carefully unfolded the taffeta, and took out the casket, which, after a few prefatory words in praise and laudation of the Angel Gabriel and his relic, he opened. When he saw that it contained nought but coals, he did not suspect Guccio Balena of playing the trick, for he knew that he was not clever enough, nor did he curse him, that his carelessness had allowed another to play it, but he inly imprecated himself, that he had committed his things to the keeping of one whom he knew to be "negligent and disobedient, reckless and witless." Nevertheless, he changed not colour, but with face and hands upturned to heaven, he said in a voice that all might hear:—"O God, blessed be Thy might for ever and ever." Then, closing the casket, and turning to the people:—"Ladies and gentlemen," he said, "you are to know, that when I was yet a very young man, I was sent by my superior into those parts where the sun rises, and I was expressly bidden to search until I should find the Privileges of Porcellana, which, though they cost nothing to seal, are of much more use to others than to us. On which errand I set forth, taking my departure from Venice, and traversing the Borgo de' Greci, and thence on horseback the realm of Algarve, and so by Baldacca I came to Parione, whence, somewhat athirst, I after a while got on to Sardinia. But wherefore go I about to enumerate all the lands in which I pursued my quest? Having passed the straits of San Giorgio, I arrived at Truffia and Buffia, countries thickly populated and with great nations, whence I pursued my journey to Menzogna, where I met with many of our own brethren, and of other religious not a few, intent one and all on eschewing hardship for the love of God, making little account of others' toil, so they might ensue their own advantage, and paying in nought but unminted coin throughout the length and breadth of the country; and so I came to the land of Abruzzi, where the men and women go in pattens on the mountains, and clothe the hogs with their own entrails; and a little further on I found folk that carried bread in staves and wine in sacks. And leaving them, I arrived at the mountains of the Bachi, where all the waters run downwards. In short I penetrated so far that I came at last to India Pastinaca, where I swear to you by the habit that I wear, that I saw pruning-hooks fly: a thing that none would believe that had not seen it. Whereof be my witness that I lie not Maso del Saggio, that great merchant, whom I found there cracking nuts, and selling the shells by retail! However, not being able to find that whereof I was in quest, because from thence one must travel by water, I turned back, and so came at length to the Holy Land, where in summer cold bread costs four deniers, and hot bread is to be had for nothing. And there I found the venerable father Nonmiblasmetesevoipiace, the most worshipful Patriarch of Jerusalem; who out of respect for the habit that I have ever worn, to wit, that of Baron Master St. Antony, was pleased to let me see all the holy relics that he had by him, which were so many, that, were I to enumerate them all, I should not come to the end of them in some miles. However, not to disappoint you, I will tell you a few of them. In the first place, then, he shewed me the finger of the Holy Spirit, as whole and entire as it ever was, and the tuft of the Seraph that appeared to St. Francis, and one of the nails of the Cherubim, and one of the ribs of the Verbum Caro hie thee to the casement, and some of the vestments of the Holy Catholic Faith, and some of the rays of the star that appeared to the Magi in the East, and a phial of the sweat of St. Michael a battling with the Devil and the jaws of death of St. Lazarus, and other relics. And for that I gave him a liberal supply of the acclivities of Monte Morello in the vulgar and some chapters of Caprezio, of which he had long been in quest, he was pleased to let me participate in his holy relics, and gave me one of the teeth of the Holy Cross, and in a small phial a bit of the sound of the bells of Solomon's temple, and this feather of the Angel Gabriel, whereof I have told you, and one of the pattens of San Gherardo da Villa Magna, which, not long ago, I gave at Florence to Gherardo di Bonsi, who holds him in prodigious veneration. He also gave me some of the coals with which the most blessed martyr, St. Lawrence, was roasted. All which things I devoutly brought thence, and have them all safe. True it is that my superior has not hitherto permitted me to shew them, until he should be certified that they are genuine. However, now that this is avouched by certain miracles wrought by them, of which we have tidings by letter from the Patriarch, he has given me leave to shew them. But, fearing to trust them to another, I always carry them with me; and to tell you the truth I carry the feather of the Angel Gabriel, lest it should get spoiled, in a casket, and the coals, with which St. Lawrence was roasted, in another casket; which caskets are so like the one to the other, that not seldom I mistake one for the other, which has befallen me on this occasion; for, whereas I thought to have brought with me the casket wherein is the feather, I have brought instead that which contains the coals. Nor deem I this a mischance; nay, methinks, 'tis by interposition of God, and that He Himself put the casket of coals in my hand, for I mind me that the feast of St. Lawrence falls but two days hence. Wherefore God, being minded that by shewing you the coals, with which he was roasted, I should rekindle in your souls the devotion that you ought to feel towards him, guided my hand, not to the feather which I meant to take, but to the blessed coals that were extinguished by the humours that exuded from that most holy body. And so, blessed children, bare your heads and devoutly draw nigh to see them. But first of all I would have you know, that whoso has the sign of the cross made upon him with these coals, may live secure for the whole of the ensuing year, that fire shall not touch him, that he feel it not."

Having so said, the friar, chanting a hymn in praise of St. Lawrence, opened the casket, and shewed the coals. Whereon the foolish crowd gazed a while in awe and reverent wonder, and then came pressing forward in a mighty throng about Fra Cipolla with offerings beyond their wont, each and all praying him to touch them with the coals. Wherefore Fra Cipolla took the coals in his hand, and set about making on their white blouses, and on their doublets, and on the veils of the women crosses as big as might be, averring the while that whatever the coals might thus lose would be made good to them again in the casket, as he had often proved. On this wise, to his exceeding great profit, he marked all the folk of Certaldo with the cross, and, thanks to his ready wit and resource, had his laugh at those, who by robbing him of the feather thought to make a laughing-stock of him. They, indeed, being among his hearers, and marking his novel expedient, and how voluble he was, and what a long story he made of it, laughed till they thought their jaws would break; and, when the congregation was dispersed, they went up to him, and never so merrily told him what they had done, and returned him his feather; which next year proved no less lucrative to him than that day the coals had been.

[SEVENTH DAY]

NOVEL VII

Lodovico discovers to Madonna Beatrice the love that he bears her: she sends Egano, her husband, into a garden disguised as herself, and lies with Lodovico; who thereafter, being risen, hies him to the garden and cudgels Egano.

This device of Madonna Isabella, thus recounted by Pampinea, was held nothing short of marvellous by all the company. But, being bidden by the king to tell the next story, thus spake Filomena: — Loving ladies, if I mistake not, the device, of which you shall presently hear from me, will prove to be no less excellent than the last.

You are to know, then, that there dwelt aforetime at Paris a Florentine gentleman, who, being by reason of poverty turned merchant, had prospered so well in his affairs that he was become very wealthy; and having by his lady an only son, Lodovico by name, whose nobility disrelished trade, he would not put him in any shop; but that he might be with other gentlemen, he caused him to enter the service of the King of France, whereby he acquired very fine manners and other accomplishments. Being in this service, Lodovico was one day with some other young gallants that talked of the fair ladies of France, and England, and other parts of the world, when they were joined by certain knights that were returned from the Holy Sepulchre; and hearing their discourse, one of the knights fell a saying, that of a surety in the whole world, so far as he had explored it, there was not any lady, of all that he had ever seen, that might compare for beauty with Madonna Beatrice, the wife of Egano de' Galluzzi, of Bologna: wherein all his companions, who in common with him had seen the lady at Bologna, concurred. Which report Lodovico, who was as yet fancy-free, no sooner heard, than he burned with such a yearning to see the lady that he was able to think of nought else: insomuch that he made up his mind to betake him to Bologna to see her, and if she pleased him, to remain there; to which end he gave his father to understand that he would fain visit the Holy Sepulchre, whereto his father after no little demur consented.

So to Bologna Anichino — for so he now called himself — came; and, as Fortune would have it, the very next day, he saw the lady at a festal gathering, and deemed her vastly more beautiful than he had expected: wherefore he waxed most ardently enamoured of her, and resolved never to quit Bologna, until he had gained her love. So, casting about how he should proceed, he could devise no other way but to enter her husband's service, which was the more easy that he kept not a few retainers: on this wise Lodovico surmised that, peradventure, he might compass his end. He therefore sold his horses and meetly bestowed his servants, bidding them make as if they knew him not; and being pretty familiar with his host, he told him that he was minded to take service with some worthy lord, if any such he might find. "Thou wouldst make," quoth the host, "the very sort of retainer to suit a gentleman of this city, Egano by name, who keeps not a few of them, and will have all of them presentable like thee: I will mention the matter to him." And so he accordingly did, and before he took leave of Egano had placed Anichino with him, to Egano's complete satisfaction.

Being thus resident with Egano, and having abundant opportunities of seeing the fair lady, Anichino set himself to serve Egano with no little zeal; wherein he succeeded so well, that Egano was more than satisfied, insomuch that by and by there was nought he could do without his advice, and he entrusted to him the guidance not only of himself, but of all his affairs. Now it so befell that one day when Egano was gone a hawking, having left Anichino at home, Madonna Beatrice, who as yet wist not of his love, albeit she had from time to time taken note of him and his manners, and had not a little approved and commended them, sat herself down with him to a game of chess, which, to please her, Anichino most dexterously contrived to lose, to the lady's prodigious delight. After a while, the lady's women, one and all, gave over watching their play, and left them to it; whereupon Anichino heaved a mighty sigh. The lady, looking hard at him, said:—"What ails thee, Anichino? Is it, then, such a mortification to thee to be conquered by me?" "Nay, Madam," replied Anichino, "my sigh was prompted by a much graver matter." "Then, if thou hast any regard for me," quoth the lady, "tell me what it is." Hearing himself thus adjured by "any regard" he had for her whom he loved more than aught else, Anichino heaved a yet mightier sigh, which caused the lady to renew her request that he would be pleased to tell her the occasion of his sighs. Whereupon:—"Madam," said Anichino, "I greatly fear me, that, were I to tell it you, 'twould but vex you; and, moreover, I doubt you might repeat it to some one else." "Rest assured," returned the lady, "that I shall neither be annoyed, nor, without thy leave, ever repeat to any other soul aught that thou mayst say." "Then," said Anichino, "having this pledge from you, I will tell it you." And, while the tears all but stood in his eyes, he told her, who he was, the report he had heard of her, and where and how he had become enamoured of her, and with what intent he had taken service with her husband: after which, he humbly besought her, that, if it might be, she would have pity on him, and gratify this his secret and ardent desire; and that, if she were not minded so to do, she would suffer him to retain his place there, and love her. Ah! Bologna! how sweetly mixed are the elements in thy women! How commendable in such a case are they all! No delight have they in sighs and tears, but are ever inclinable to prayers, and ready to yield to the solicitations of Love. Had I but words apt to praise them as they deserve, my eloquence were inexhaustible.

The gentlewoman's gaze was fixed on Anichino as he spoke; she made no doubt that all he said was true, and yielding to his appeal, she entertained his love within her heart in such measure that she too began to sigh, and after a sigh or two made answer:—"Sweet my Anichino, be of good cheer; neither presents nor promises, nor any courting by gentleman, or lord, or whoso else (for I have been and am still courted by not a few) was ever able to sway my soul to love any of them: but thou, by the few words that thou hast said, hast so wrought with me that, brief though the time has been, I am already in far greater measure thine than mine. My love I deem thee to have won right worthily; and so I give it thee, and vow to give thee joyance thereof before the coming night be past. To which end thou wilt come to my room about midnight; I will leave the door open; thou knowest the side of the bed on which I sleep; thou wilt come there; should I be asleep, thou hast but to touch me, and I shall awake, and give thee solace of thy long-pent desire. In earnest whereof I will even give thee a kiss." So saying, she threw her arms about his neck, and lovingly kissed him, as Anichino her.

Their colloquy thus ended, Anichino betook him elsewhere about some matters which he had to attend to, looking forward to midnight with boundless exultation. Egano came in from his hawking; and after supper, being weary, went straight to bed, whither the lady soon followed him, leaving, as she had promised, the door of the chamber open. Thither accordingly, at the appointed hour, came Anichino, and having softly entered the chamber, and closed the door behind him, stole up to where the lady lay, and laying his hand upon her breast, found that she was awake. Now, as soon as she wist that Anichino was come, she took his hand in both her own; and keeping fast hold of him, she turned about in the bed, until she awoke Egano; whereupon:—"Husband," quoth she, "I would not say aught of this to thee, yestereve, because I judged thou wast weary; but tell me, upon thy hope of salvation, Egano, whom deemest thou thy best and most loyal retainer, and the most attached to thee, of all that thou hast in the house?" "What a question is this, wife?" returned Egano. "Dost not know him? Retainer I have none, nor ever had, so trusted, or loved, as Anichino. But wherefore put such a question?"

Now, when Anichino wist that Egano was awake, and heard them talk of himself, he more than once tried to withdraw his hand, being mightily afraid lest the lady meant to play him false; but she held it so tightly that he might not get free, while thus she made answer to Egano:—"I will tell thee what he is. I thought that he was all thou sayst, and that none was so loyal to thee as he, but he has undeceived me, for that yesterday, when thou wast out a hawking, he, being here, chose this time, and had the shamelessness to crave of me compliance with his wanton desires: and I, that I might not need other evidence than that of thine own senses to prove his guilt to thee, I made answer, that I was well content, and that to-night, after midnight, I would get me into the garden, and await him there at the foot of the pine. Now go thither I shall certainly not; but, if thou wouldst prove the loyalty of thy retainer, thou canst readily do so, if thou but slip on one of my loose robes, and cover thy face with a veil, and go down and attend his coming, for come, I doubt not, he will." Whereto Egano:—"Meet indeed it is," quoth he, "that I should go see"; and straightway up he got, and, as best he might in the dark, he put on one of the lady's loose robes and veiled his face, and then hied him to the garden, and sate down at the foot of the pine to await Anichino. The lady no sooner wist that he was out of the room, than she rose, and locked the door. Anichino, who had never been so terrified in all his life, and had struggled with all his might to disengage his hand from the lady's clasp, and had inwardly cursed her and his love, and himself for trusting her, a hundred thousand times, was overjoyed beyond measure at this last turn that she had given the affair. And so, the lady having got her to bed again, and he, at her bidding, having stripped and laid him down beside her, they had solace and joyance of one another for a good while. Then, the lady, deeming it unmeet for

Anichino to tarry longer with her, caused him to get up and resume his clothes, saying to him:—"Sweet my mouth, thou wilt take a stout cudgel, and get thee to the garden, and making as if I were there, and thy suit to me had been but to try me, thou wilt give Egano a sound rating with thy tongue and a sound belabouring with thy cudgel, the sequel whereof will be wondrously gladsome and delightful." Whereupon Anichino hied him off to the garden, armed with a staff of wild willow; and as he drew nigh the pine, Egano saw him, and rose and came forward to meet him as if he would receive him with the heartiest of cheer. But:—"Ah! wicked woman!" quoth Anichino; "so thou art come! Thou didst verily believe, then, that I was, that I am, minded thus to wrong my lord? Foul fall thee a thousand times!" And therewith he raised his cudgel, and began to lay about him. Egano, however, had heard and seen enough, and without a word took to flight, while Anichino pursued him, crying out:—"Away with thee! God send thee a bad year, lewd woman that thou art; nor doubt that Egano shall hear of this to-morrow." Egano, having received sundry round knocks, got him back to his chamber with what speed he might; and being asked by the lady, whether Anichino had come into the garden:—"Would to God he had not!" quoth he, "for that, taking me for thee, he has beaten me black and blue with his cudgel, and rated me like the vilest woman that ever was: passing strange, indeed, it had seemed to me that he should have said those words to thee with intent to dishonour me; and now 'tis plain that 'twas but that, seeing thee so blithe and frolicsome, he was minded to prove thee." Whereto:—"God be praised," returned the lady, "that he proved me by words, as thee by acts: and I doubt not he may say that I bear his words with more patience than thou his acts. But since he is so loyal to thee, we must make much of him and do him honour." "Ay, indeed," quoth Egano, "thou sayst sooth."

Thus was Egano fortified in the belief that never had any gentleman wife so true, or retainer so loyal, as he; and many a hearty laugh had he with Anichino and his lady over this affair, which to them was the occasion that, with far less let than might else have been, they were able to have solace and joyance of one another, so long as it pleased Anichino to tarry at Bologna.

[EIGHTH DAY]

NOVEL VI

Bruno and Buffalmacco steal a pig from Calandrino, and induce him to essay its recovery by means of pills of ginger and vernaccia. Of the said pills they give him two, one after the other, made of dog-ginger compounded with aloes; and it then appearing as if he had had the pig himself, they constrain him to buy them off, if he would not have them tell his wife.

Filostrato's story, which elicited not a little laughter, was no sooner ended, than the queen bade Filomena follow suit. Wherefore thus Filomena began:—As, gracious ladies, 'twas the name of Maso del Saggio that prompted Filostrato to tell the story that you have but now heard, even so 'tis with me in regard of Calandrino and his comrades, of whom I am minded to tell you another story, which you will, I think, find entertaining. Who Calandrino, Bruno and Buffalmacco were, I need not explain; you know them well enough from the former story; and therefore I will tarry no longer than to say that Calandrino had a little estate not far from Florence, which his wife had brought him by way of dowry, and which yielded them yearly, among other matters, a pig; and 'twas his custom every year in the month of December to resort to the farm with his wife, there to see to the killing and salting of the said pig. Now, one of these years it so happened that his wife being unwell, Calandrino went thither alone to kill the pig. And Bruno and Buffalmacco learning that he was gone to the farm, and that his wife was not with him, betook them to the house of a priest that was their especial friend and a neighbour of Calandrino, there to tarry a while. Upon their arrival Calandrino, who had that very morning killed the pig, met them with the priest, and accosted them, saying:—"A hearty welcome to you. I should like you to see what an excellent manager I am"; and so he took them into his house, and shewed them the pig. They observed that 'twas a very fine pig; and learned from Calandrino that he was minded to salt it for household consumption. "Then thou art but a fool," quoth Bruno. "Sell it, man, and let us have a jolly time with the money; and tell thy wife that 'twas stolen." "Not I," replied Calandrino: "she would never believe me, and would drive me out of the house. Urge me no further, for I will never do it." The others said a great deal more, but to no purpose; and Calandrino bade them to supper, but so coldly that they declined, and left him.

Presently:—"Should we not steal this pig from him to-night?" quoth Bruno to Buffalmacco. "Could we so?" returned Buffalmacco. "How?" "Why as to that," rejoined Bruno, "I have already marked how it may be done, if he bestow not the pig elsewhere." "So be it, then," said Buffalmacco: "we will steal it; and then, perchance, our good host, Master Priest, will join us in doing honour to such good cheer?" "That right gladly will I," quoth the priest. Whereupon:—"Some address, though," quoth Bruno, "will be needful: thou knowest, Buffalmacco, what a niggardly fellow Calandrino is, and how greedily he drinks at other folk's expense. Go we, therefore, and take him to the tavern, and there let the priest make as if, to do us honour, he would pay the whole score, and suffer Calandrino to pay never a soldo, and he will grow tipsy, and then we shall speed excellent well, because he is alone in the house."

As Bruno proposed, so they did: and Calandrino, finding that the priest would not suffer him to pay, drank amain, and took a great deal more aboard than he had need of; and the night being far spent when he left the tavern, he dispensed with supper, and went home, and thinking to have shut the door, got him to bed, leaving it open.

Buffalmacco and Bruno went to sup with the priest; and after supper, taking with them certain implements with which to enter Calandrino's house, where Bruno thought it most feasible, they stealthily approached it; but finding the door open, they entered, and took down the pig, and carried it away to the priest's house, and having there bestowed it safely, went to bed. In the morning when Calandrino, his head at length quit of the fumes of the wine, got up, and came downstairs and found that his pig was nowhere to be seen, and that the door was open, he asked this, that, and the other man, whether they wist who had taken the pig away, and getting no answer, he began to make a great outcry: — "Alas, alas! luckless man that I am, that my pig should have been stolen from me!" Meanwhile Bruno and Buffalmacco, being also risen, made up to him, to hear what he would say touching the pig. Whom he no sooner saw, than well-nigh weeping he called them, saying: — "Alas! my friends! my pig is stolen from me." Bruno stepped up to him and said in a low tone: — " 'Tis passing strange if thou art in the right for once." "Alas!" returned Calandrino, "what I say is but too true." "Why, then, out with it, man," quoth Bruno, "cry aloud, that all folk may know that 'tis so." Calandrino then raised his voice and said: — "By the body o' God I say of a truth that my pig has been stolen from me." "So!" quoth Bruno, "but publish it, man, publish it; lift up thy voice, make thyself well heard, that all may believe thy report." "Thou art enough to make me give my soul to the Enemy," replied Calandrino. "I say — dost not believe me? — that hang me by the neck if the pig is not stolen from me!" "Nay, but," quoth Bruno, "how can it be? I saw it here but yesterday. Dost think to make me believe that it has taken to itself wings and flown away?" "All the same 'tis as I tell thee," returned Calandrino. "Is it possible?" quoth Bruno. "Ay indeed," replied Calandrino; " 'tis even so: and I am undone, and know not how to go home. Never will my wife believe me; or if she do so, I shall know no peace this year." "Upon my hope of salvation," quoth Bruno, " 'tis indeed a bad business, if so it really is. But thou knowest, Calandrino, that 'twas but yesterday I counselled thee to make believe that 'twas so. I should be sorry to think thou didst befool thy wife and us at the same time." "Ah!" vociferated Calandrino, "wilt thou drive me to despair and provoke me to blaspheme God and the saints and all the company of heaven? I tell thee that the pig has been stolen from me in the night." Whereupon: — "If so it be," quoth Buffalmacco, "we must find a way, if we can, to recover it." "Find a way?" said Calandrino: "how can we compass that?" "Why," replied Buffalmacco, " 'tis certain that no one has come from India to steal thy pig: it must have been one of thy neighbours, and if thou couldst bring them together, I warrant thee, I know how to make the assay with bread and cheese, and we will find out in a trice who has had the pig." "Ay," struck in Bruno, "make thy assay with bread and cheese in the presence of these gentry hereabout, one of whom I am sure has had the pig! why, the thing would be seen through: and they would not come." "What shall we do, then?" said Buffalmacco. Whereto Bruno made answer:—"It must be done with good pills of ginger and good vernaccia; and they must be bidden come drink with us. They will suspect nothing, and will come; and pills of ginger can be blessed just as well as bread and cheese." "Beyond a doubt, thou art right," quoth Buffalmacco; "and thou, Calandrino, what sayst thou? Shall we do as Bruno says?" "Nay, I entreat you, for the love of God," quoth Calandrino, "do even so: for if I knew but who had had the pig, I should feel myself half consoled for my loss." "Go to, now," quoth Bruno, "I am willing to do thy errand to Florence for these commodities, if thou givest me the money."

Calandrino had some forty soldi upon him, which he gave to Bruno, who thereupon hied him to Florence to a friend of his that was an apothecary, and bought a pound of good pills of ginger, two of which, being of dog-ginger, he caused to be compounded with fresh hepatic aloes, and then to be coated with sugar like the others; and lest they should be lost, or any of the others mistaken for them, he had a slight mark set upon them by which he might readily recognize them. He also bought a flask of good vernaccia, and, thus laden, returned to the farm, and said to Calandrino:—"To-morrow morning thou wilt bid those whom thou suspectest come hither to drink with thee: as 'twill be a saint's day, they will all come readily enough; and to-night I and Buffalmacco will say the incantation over the pills, which in the morning I will bring to thee here, and for our friendship's sake will administer them myself, and do and say all that needs to be said and done." So Calandrino did as Bruno advised; and on the morrow a goodly company, as well of young men from Florence, that happened to be in the village, as of husbandmen, being assembled in front of the church around the elm, Bruno and Buffalmacco came, bearing a box containing the ginger, and the flask of wine, and ranged the folk in a circle. Whereupon:—"Gentlemen," said Bruno, "'tis meet I tell you the reason why you are gathered here, that if aught unpleasant to you should befall, you may have no ground for complaint against me. Calandrino here was the night before last robbed of a fine pig, and cannot discover who has had it; and, for that it must have been stolen by some one of us here, he would have each of you take and eat one of these pills and drink of this vernaccia. Wherefore I forthwith do you to wit, that whoso has had the pig will not be able to swallow the pill, but will find it more bitter than poison, and will spit it out; and so, rather than he should suffer this shame in the presence of so many, 'twere perhaps best that he that has had the pig should confess the fact to the priest, and I will wash my hands of the affair."

All professed themselves ready enough to eat the pills; and so, having set them in a row with Calandrino among them, Bruno, beginning at one end, proceeded to give each a pill, and when he came to Calandrino he chose one of the pills of dog-ginger and put it in his hand. Calandrino thrust it forthwith between his teeth and began to chew it; but no sooner was his tongue acquainted with the aloes, than, finding the bitterness intolerable, he spat it out. Now, the eyes of all the company being fixed on one another to see who should spit out his pill, Bruno, who, not having finished the distribution, feigned to be concerned with nought else, heard some one in his rear say:—"Ha! Calandrino, what means this?" and at once turning round, and marking that Calandrino had spit out his pill:—"Wait a while," quoth he, "perchance 'twas somewhat else that caused thee to spit: take another"; and thereupon whipping out the other pill of dog-ginger, he set it between Calandrino's teeth, and finished the distribution. Bitter as Calandrino had found the former pill, he found this tenfold more so; but being ashamed to spit it out, he kept it a while in his mouth and chewed it, and, as he did so, tears stood in his eyes that shewed as large as filberts, and at length, being unable to bear it any longer, he spat it out, as he had its predecessor. Which being observed by Buffalmacco and Bruno, who were then administering the wine, and by all the company, 'twas averred by common consent that Calandrino had committed the theft himself; for which cause certain of them took him severely to task.

However, the company being dispersed, and Bruno and Buffalmacco left alone with Calandrino, Buffalmacco began on this wise:—"I never doubted but that thou hadst had it thyself, and wast minded to make us believe that it had been stolen from thee, that we might not have of thee so much as a single drink out of the price which thou gottest for it." Calandrino, with the bitterness of the aloes still on his tongue, fell a swearing that he had not had it. Whereupon:—"Nay, but, comrade," quoth Buffalmacco, "upon thy honour, what did it fetch? Six florins?" Whereto, Calandrino being now on the verge of desperation, Bruno added:—"Now be reasonable, Calandrino; among the company that ate and drank with us there was one that told me that thou hadst up there a girl that thou didst keep for thy pleasure, giving her what by hook or by crook thou couldst get together, and that he held it for certain that thou hadst sent her this pig. And thou art grown expert in this sort of cozenage. Thou tookest us one while adown the Mugnone a gathering black stones, and having thus started us on a wild-goose chase, thou madest off; and then wouldst fain have us believe that thou hadst found the stone: and now, in like manner, thou thinkest by thine oaths to persuade us that this pig which thou hast given away or sold, has been stolen from thee. But we know thy tricks of old; never another couldst thou play us; and, to be round with thee, this spell has cost us some trouble: wherefore we mean that thou shalt give us two pair of capons, or we will let Monna Tessa know all." Seeing that he was not believed, and deeming his mortification ample without the addition of his wife's resentment, Calandrino gave them the two pair of capons, with which, when the pig was salted, they returned to Florence, leaving Calandrino with the loss and the laugh against him.

[TENTH DAY]

NOVEL V

Madonna Dianora craves of Messer Ansaldo a garden that shall be as fair in January as in May. Messer Ansaldo binds himself to a necromancer, and thereby gives her the garden. Her husband gives her leave to do Messer Ansaldo's pleasure: he, being apprised of her husband's liberality, releases her from her promise; and the necromancer releases Messer Ansaldo from his bond, and will take nought of his.

Each of the gay company had with superlative commendation extolled Messer Gentile to the skies, when the king bade Emilia follow suit; and with a good courage, as burning to speak, thus Emilia began: — Delicate my ladies, none can justly say that 'twas not magnificently done of Messer Gentile; but if it be alleged that 'twas the last degree of magnificence, 'twill perchance not be difficult to shew that more was possible, as is my purpose in the little story that I shall tell you.

In Friuli, a country which, though its air is shrewd, is pleasantly diversified by fine mountains and not a few rivers and clear fountains, is a city called Udine, where dwelt of yore a fair and noble lady, Madonna Dianora by name, wife of a wealthy grandee named Giliberto, a very pleasant gentleman, and debonair. Now this lady, for her high qualities, was in the last degree beloved by a great and noble baron, Messer Ansaldo Gradense by name, a man of no little consequence, and whose fame for feats of arms and courtesy was spread far and wide. But, though with all a lover's ardour he left nought undone that he might do to win her love, and to that end frequently plied her with his ambassages, 'twas all in vain. And the lady being distressed by his importunity, and that, refuse as she might all that he asked of her, he none the less continued to love her and press his suit upon her, bethought her how she might rid herself of him by requiring of him an extraordinary and, as she deemed, impossible feat. So one day, a woman that came oftentimes from him to her being with her: — "Good woman," quoth she, "thou hast many a time affirmed that Messer Ansaldo loves me above all else; and thou has made proffer to me on his part of wondrous rich gifts which I am minded he keep to himself, for that I could never bring myself to love him or pleasure him for their sake; but, if I might be certified that he loves me as much as thou sayst, then without a doubt I should not fail to love him, and do his pleasure; wherefore, so he give me the assurance that I shall require, I shall be at his command." "What is it, Madam," returned the good woman, "that you would have him do?" "This," replied the lady; "I would have this next ensuing January, hard by this city, a garden full of green grass and flowers and flowering trees, just as if it were May; and if he cannot provide me with this garden, bid him never again send either thee or any other to me, for that, should he harass me any further, I shall no longer keep silence, as I have hitherto done, but shall make my complaint to my husband and all my kinsmen, and it shall go hard but I will be quit of him."

The gentleman being apprised of his lady's stipulation and promise, notwithstanding that he deemed it no easy matter, nay, a thing almost impossible, to satisfy her, and knew besides that 'twas but to deprive him of all hope that she made the demand, did nevertheless resolve to do his endeavour to comply with it, and causing search to be made in divers parts of the world, if any he might find to afford him counsel or aid, he lit upon one, who for a substantial reward offered to do the thing by necromancy. So Messer Ansaldo, having struck the bargain with him for an exceeding great sum of money, gleefully expected the appointed time. Which being come with extreme cold, insomuch that there was nought but snow and ice, the adept on the night before the calends of January wrought with his spells to such purpose that on the morrow, as was averred by eyewitnesses, there appeared in a meadow hard by the city one of the most beautiful gardens that was ever seen, with no lack of grass and trees and fruits of all sorts. At sight whereof Messer Ansaldo was overjoyed, and caused some of the finest fruits and flowers that it contained to be gathered, and privily presented to his lady, whom he bade come and see the garden that she had craved, that thereby she might have assurance of his love, and mind her of the promise that she had given him and confirmed with an oath, and, as a loyal lady, take thought for its performance. When she saw the flowers and fruits, the lady, who had already heard not a few folk speak of the wondrous garden, began to repent her of her promise. But for all that, being fond of strange sights, she hied her with many other ladies of the city to see the garden, and having gazed on it with wonderment, and commended it not a little, she went home the saddest woman alive, bethinking her to what it bound her: and so great was her distress that she might not well conceal it; but, being written on her face, 'twas marked by her husband, who was minded by all means to know the cause thereof.

The lady long time kept silence: but at last she yielded to his urgency, and discovered to him the whole matter from first to last. Whereat Giliberto was at first very wroth; but on second thoughts, considering the purity of the lady's purpose, he was better advised, and dismissing his anger: — "Dianora," quoth he, "'tis not the act of a discreet or virtuous lady to give ear to messages of such a sort, nor to enter into any compact touching her chastity with any man on any terms. Words that the ears convey to the heart have a potency greater than is commonly supposed, and there is scarce aught that lovers will not find possible. 'Twas then ill done of thee in the first instance to hearken, as afterwards to make the compact; but, for that I know the purity of thy soul, that thou mayst be quit of thy promise, I will grant thee that which, perchance, no other man would grant, being also swayed thereto by fear of the necromancer, whom Messer Ansaldo, shouldst thou play him false, might, peradventure, cause to do us a mischief. I am minded, then, that thou go to him, and contrive, if on any wise thou canst, to get thee quit of this promise without loss of virtue; but if otherwise it may not be, then for the nonce thou mayst yield him thy body, but not thy soul." Whereat the lady, weeping, would none of such a favour at her husband's hands. But Giliberto, for all the lady's protestations, was minded that so it should be.

Accordingly, on the morrow about dawn, apparelled none too ornately, preceded by two servants and followed by a chambermaid, the lady hied her to Messer Ansaldo's house. Apprised that his lady was come to see him, Messer Ansaldo, marvelling not a little, rose, and having called the necromancer: — "I am minded," quoth he, "that thou see what goodly gain I have gotten by thine art." And the twain having met the lady, Ansaldo gave way to no unruly appetite, but received her with a seemly obeisance; and then the three repaired to a goodly chamber, where there was a great fire, and having caused the lady to be seated, thus spoke Ansaldo: — "Madam, if the love that I have so long borne you merit any guerdon, I pray you that it be not grievous to you to discover to me the true occasion of your coming to me at this hour, and thus accompanied." Shamefast, and the tears all but standing in her eyes, the lady made answer: — "Sir, 'tis neither love that I bear you; nor faith that I pledged you, that brings me hither, but the command of my husband, who, regarding rather the pains you have had of your unbridled passion than his own or my honour, has sent me hither; and for that he commands it, I, for the nonce, am entirely at your pleasure."

If Messer Ansaldo had marvelled to hear of the lady's coming, he now marvelled much more, and touched by Giliberto's liberality, and passing from passion to compassion: — "Now, God forbid, Madam," quoth he, "that, it being as you say, I should wound the honour of him that has compassion on my love; wherefore, no otherwise than as if you were my sister shall you abide here, while you are so minded, and be free to depart at your pleasure; nor crave I aught of you but that you shall convey from me to your husband such thanks as you shall deem meet for courtesy such as his has been, and entreat me ever henceforth as your brother and servant." Whereat overjoyed in the last degree: — "Nought," quoth the lady, "by what I noted of your behaviour, could ever have caused me to anticipate other sequel of my coming hither than this which I see is your will, and for which I shall ever be your debtor." She then took her leave, and, attended by a guard of honour, returned to Giliberto, and told him what had passed; between whom and Messer Ansaldo there was thenceforth a most close and loyal friendship.

Now the liberality shewn by Giliberto towards Messer Ansaldo, and by Messer Ansaldo towards the lady, having been marked by the necromancer, when Messer Ansaldo made ready to give him the promised reward: — "Now God forbid," quoth he, "that, as I have seen Giliberto liberal in regard of his honour, and you liberal in regard of your love, I be not in like manner liberal in regard of my reward, which accordingly, witting that 'tis in good hands, I am minded that you keep." The knight was abashed, and strove hard to induce him to take, if not the whole, at least a part of the money; but finding that his labour was in vain, and that the necromancer, having caused his garden to vanish after the third day, was minded to depart, he bade him adieu. And the carnal love he had borne the lady being spent, he burned for her thereafter with a flame of honourable affection. Now what shall be our verdict in this case, lovesome ladies? A lady, as it were dead, and a love grown lukewarm for utter hopelessness! Shall we set a liberality shewn in such a case above this liberalty of Messer Ansaldo, loving yet as ardently, and hoping, perchance, yet more ardently than ever, and holding in his hands the prize that he had so long pursued? Folly indeed should I deem it to compare that liberality with this.

NICCOLÒ MACHIAVELLI

(1469–1527)

Machiavelli's profession was the art of government, rather than of letters. He was essentially a man of action, the chancellor and diplomat. The two passions of his life were his love of his country, Florence, and his study of men and their motives, the character of governments, and the laws which operate in war and in peace. In his youth he grew up in the years of Lorenzo the Magnificent, the golden age of humanism and of Florence. He served for fourteen years the Florentine Republic that followed. It was his fortune to watch the decline of civic freedom which came with the return of the Medici, and then the downfall of Italy itself plundered by foreign armies. The acute analysis he made of power politics was construed for centuries as the cynicism of a subservient opportunist. In reality it was made in the passionate hope that a new prince might preserve the integrity of Florence and restore the ultimate freedom of its citizens.

He was born on the 3rd of May 1469 in Florence, in what is now No. 16, Via Guicciardini, not far from the Ponte Vecchio. His parents were Bernardo Machiavelli, a lawyer, and his wife Bartolomea di Stefano Nelli. He had one older brother, and two sisters who were younger. Although the family was then of moderate means, both parents had come from Tuscan nobility. Bernardo's forebears had been ancient lords of Montespèrtoli in the country south of Florence, who had later become members of the Guelf party in the Florentine Commune; several of them were elected to the highest office in the City-State, that of Gonfalonier of Justice. Their coat of arms bore a cross argent upon a field azure with a nail placed at each corner of the cross.

Of his education nothing is known except by inference from his later writings and activities. He knew the Latin writers well: Livy, Tacitus, Suetonius, Caesar, Cicero, as well as Virgil, and the poets of love — Ovid, Tibullus, and Catullus. He admired Dante, Petrarch, and Boccaccio. But it is probable that he was no bookish scholar. He was largely self-taught in the street, the shop, and the market place, in a city of merchants and bankers, where men came and went from remote parts of Europe and Asia. It is likely that he developed in the give-and-take of those groups beloved by Florentines where acute discussion and argument alternated with witty jest or ribald story.

His mature life became sharply divided into two periods: the first, an active diplomatic career; the second, years of enforced retirement. Together they coincided with the gradual political disintegration of Italy. He was twenty-three when the age of Lorenzo ended. He then witnessed the intense career of Savonarola, and the march of Charles VIII of France into Italy which was the beginning of her downfall. He was twenty-nine when Savonarola was burned at the stake; in the same year, 1498, he was appointed Secretary in the Second Chancery of the Signoria and, a few months later, Secretary to the Ten of Liberty and Peace of the Florentine Republic.

As "Florentine Secretary," Machiavelli entered upon the central experience of his career, the experience that conditioned the thought of all his later political writings. Beyond his routine work in the Palazzo della Signoria, he was sent on countless embassies which gave him direct contact with the major figures of his time and close knowledge of the powerful forces maneuvering for the control of Italy. He found Florence weak, but inclined to keep faith; he found all others bent only upon self-interest and bound to hold to agreements only so long as they paid. Compelled to rely upon aid from France on the one hand, Florence was subjected to the rising power of the Papacy on the other; meanwhile, her strength was heavily taxed by the war with Pisa. Machiavelli acted as observer, negotiator, mediator in this international game of politics. He was sent four times to the Court of Louis XII in France. He followed the career of Cesare Borgia in his conquest of the Romagna. He went twice to Pope Julius II, and twice to the Emperor Maximilian. He was with the Florentine army before Pisa and was largely responsible for the military operations that brought her downfall. He was sent to Siena, Perugia, Mantua, and to other minor courts of Italy, and to many places in the Florentine domains. The many detailed reports he sent back are filed in the Florentine archives. They bespeak the faith, the diligence, and the prudence of one who was in reality a subordinate to officials clearly his inferiors.

The period of his legations lasted from 1498 to 1512. Machiavelli studied other, more powerful, rulers and states in order that he might build the security of his own. To this end he advocated and established a Florentine militia made up of her own citizens. But the Florentine policy of depending upon the French alliance proved inadequate. In 1512, the French were driven from Italy, the Spanish marched to the sensational sack of Prato, and Florence lay open to the invaders. Inevitably, the Medici, despotic rulers of the new order, returned, and the Florentine Republic was at its end.

Machiavelli was immediately deprived of all positions he held under the Republic and was banished for one year from the city but required to live in Florentine territory. He was forty-three years of age. He retired to a country place he owned near San Casciano to the south, where he lived with his wife, Marietta Corsini, and their five children.

His life in the years that followed is pictured in the letters he wrote to his friends, the Florentine ambassador Francesco Vettori, and the high papal official and historian Francesco Guicciardini. To the former he wrote on the 10th of December 1513:

> I have been setting snares for the thrushes with my own hands; I get up before daylight, prepare my birdlime, and go out with a bundle of cages on my back . . .

I go out into a grove that I am having cut; there I remain a couple of hours to look over the work of the past day and kill some time with the woodmen, who always have on hand some dispute . . .

When I leave the grove, I go to a spring, and from there into my aviary. I have a book in my pocket, either Dante or Petrarch or one of the minor poets, as Tibullus, Ovid, and the like . . . Then I go along the road to the inn, talk with those who pass by, ask the news of their villages, learn various things, and note the varied tastes and different fancies of men . . . After dinner, I return to the inn; there I usually find the host, a butcher, a miller, and two furnace-tenders. With these fellows I sink into vulgarity for the rest of the day . . . So, involved in these trifles, I keep my brain from getting mouldy . . .

In the evening, I return to my house, and go into my study. At the door I take off the clothes I have worn all day, mud spotted and dirty, and put on regal and courtly garments. Thus appropriately clothed, I enter into the ancient courts of ancient men, where, being lovingly received, I feed on that food which alone is mine, and which I was born for; I am not ashamed to speak with them and to ask the reasons for their actions, and they courteously answer me. For four hours I feel no boredom and forget my worry; I do not fear poverty, and death does not terrify me . . . [Gilbert translation]

To this period of enforced idleness we owe his greatest works, *The Prince,* and the *Discourses on the First Decade of Livy.* He had given his lifework to the Republic of Florence, which based its policy upon freedom and keeping faith. He had seen the powerful and unscrupulous conquer. In the effort to meet the insoluble problems of the present, he turned to a study of the Roman Republic of the past in Livy, and to the career of Cesare Borgia of his own day which, he believed, afforded an example in meeting the desperate situation. Why should not the reigning princes of the Medici revive the genius of Lorenzo the Magnificent of his own youth? In his vision he saw their opportunity. In a period of brilliant inspiration in 1513 he wrote *The Prince* and dedicated it to the Lorenzo then in control of Florence. It has been Machiavelli's great misfortune that the centuries since have been blind to the situation that called his book forth. The shrewd analysis of political power for a new prince, written to meet a desperate emergency, must be combined with his study of republican government, the *Discourses on Livy,* begun in the same year, to see what a passionate patriot and a republican Machiavelli was in reality. This latter work purports to be a commentary upon the first ten books of Livy's *History of Rome.* It actually took Roman history only as a point of departure for a series of reflections upon politics. The work is much longer and far less readable than *The Prince,* but study reveals it to be a more considered piece of work and a far more comprehensive expression of Machiavelli's thought as a whole.

His efforts to regain position and the use of his abilities under the Medici, however, brought only few and delayed results, and his return to Florence was only gradual. In 1518, he participated in the discussions in the Oricellari Gardens in the circle called together by Cosimo Rucellai; here was placed the setting for his dialogue, *The Art of War.* There were missions to Genoa, to Lucca, in the business interests of Florentine merchants, and one to Carpi to the General Assembly of the Franciscans in the interest of the monks of Florence. While at Lucca, he wrote the *Life of Castruccio Castracani,* virtually an historic romance presenting an idealized ruler. In 1519, at the request of Pope Leo X and of Cardinal Giulio de' Medici, he wrote the *Discourse on Reforming the Government of Florence.* In 1520, through influence of Cardinal Giulio, he was commissioned to write the *History of Florence,* with a salary of a hundred florins a year. Five years later, he presented it to Giulio, then Pope Clement VII, and was received graciously and given a further subsidy of a hundred ducats. In his last years he went on missions to Guicciardini, Papal Governor in the Romagna, and Papal Lieutenant in the Army of the League in the war against the Emperor Charles V. Finally in 1526, in the movement to strengthen the walls of Florence, at the instance of Clement VII, he was made Secretary to the Five Procurators of the Walls. He seemed to have entered again upon his official life. But in the following year came the tragic Sack of Rome; revolution immediately broke out in Florence, the Medicean party was cast out, and Machiavelli was dismissed. He had spent his life in the service of Florence, and in the interests of Florentine democracy; but now that the Republic was again proclaimed, he was considered as a sympathizer with the Medici. He died in Florence a month later in May 1527 and was buried in Santa Croce. He did not live to see the final collapse of Florentine liberty which followed in a few years.

Of Machiavelli's works not already mentioned, first importance should be attached to the *Mandragola,* in five acts, commonly considered one of the greatest of Italian comedies. This seems to have been written during the years of his most active diplomatic life; it was performed in the early 1520's. His second comedy, the *Clizia,* was performed in 1525. Mention should also be made among other writings of his novella *Belfagor,* and of his *Capitoli* on Ingratitude, Fortune, Ambition, and Opportunity. His *Familiar Letters* are of great interest and charm; they afford a picture of the last thirty years of his life, and a direct expression of his personal spirit.

Our knowledge of his personal appearance has been derived from busts, from the engravings in the early editions of his works, and from portraits. There we see him spare in figure, with a rather small head, and black hair; but of lasting impression are the vivid eyes, the tightly closed lips, and the enigmatic smile. "Whenever I have been able to do honor to my native city, even with difficulty and danger to myself, I have been glad to do it," he once wrote, "because a man has no greater obligation in life than to his country, because he is indebted to her first for his being and then for everything good that fortune and nature have bestowed on him; and this obligation is greatest in those whose native city is most noble." And, on another occasion — "of my faith and goodness, my poverty is testimony." With such a temperament, it was not his fortune to prosper in the complex world of his time; but his relentless analysis of the way men actually live as distinguished from the way they ought to live, the penetrating power of his political realism, and — in George Meredith's sense — the comic temper and detachment of his spirit, endure.

SELECTED BIBLIOGRAPHY

EDITIONS

Opere di Niccolò Machiavelli, 8 vols., Florence, Italia, 1813; *Tutte le Opere Storiche e Letterarie di N. Machiavelli,* ed. G. Mazzoni and M. Casella, 1 vol., Florence, Barbèra, 1929; *Il Principe,* ed. Arthur L. Burd, Oxford, 1891; *Il Principe,* ed. Giuseppe Lisio, Florence, Sansoni, 1899.

TRANSLATIONS

The Historical, Political, and Diplomatic Writings, trans. C. E. Detmold, 4 vols., Boston, Osgood, 1882; *Works: The Art of War,* trans. P. Whiteborne (1560), *The Prince,* trans. E. Dacres (1640), *The Florentine History,* trans. T. Bedingfeld (1595), 2 vols., Tudor Translations, London, Nutt, 1905; *The Prince,* trans. L. Ricci, rev. E. R. P. Vincent, *The Discourses,* trans. C. E. Detmold, introd. Max Lerner, Modern Lib., New York, Random House, 1940; *The Prince and Other Works,* trans. Allan H. Gilbert, Chicago, Packard, 1941; translations of *The Prince* also in Everyman's Lib. and World's Classics; *Discourses,* trans. N. H. Thomson, London, Kegan Paul, 1883; *The Discourses of N. Machiavelli,* trans. L. J. Walker, 2 vols., Yale Univ. Press, 1950; *Mandragola,* trans. Stark Young, New York, Macaulay, 1927.

BIOGRAPHY AND CRITICISM

Oreste Tommasini, *La Vita e gli Scritti di N. Machiavelli,* 2 vols., Rome, 1883–1911.

Pasquale Villari, *The Life and Times of N. Machiavelli* (1877–82), trans. Linda Villari, London, 1929; A. L. Burd, "Machiavelli," in *Camb. Mod. History,* I, 190–218, 1902; Giuseppi Prezzolini, *N. Machiavelli the Florentine,* New York, Brentano, 1928; Orestes Ferrara, *The Private Correspondence of N. Machiavelli,* Johns Hopkins Press, 1929; Ettore Janni, *Machiavelli,* London, Harrap, 1930; Ralph Roeder, *The Man of the Renaissance,* parts 2–3, Garden City Pub. Co., 1933; D. Erskine Muir, *Machiavelli and His Times,* New York, Dutton, 1936; Jeffrey Pulver, *Machiavelli. The Man, His Work and His Times,* London, Herbert Joseph, 1937; Allan H. Gilbert, *Machiavelli's Prince and Its Forerunners,* Duke Univ. Press, 1938; Valeriu Marcu, *Accent on Power. The Life and Times of Machiavelli,* New York, Farrar & Rinehart, 1939; H. Butterfield, *The Statecraft of Machiavelli,* London, Bell, 1940; Count Carlo Sforza, *The Living Thoughts of Machiavelli,* New York, Longmans, 1940; Leonardo Olschki, *Machiavelli the Scientist,* Berkeley, Gillick Press, 1945; Ernst Cassirer, *The Myth of the State,* chaps. X–XII, Yale Univ. Press, 1946; J. H. Whitfield, *Machiavelli,* Oxford, Blackwell, 1947.

SPECIAL STUDIES

Mario Praz, *Machiavelli and the Elizabethans,* Oxford Univ. Press, 1928; H. L. Stewart, "Machiavelli and Fascism," *Univ. of Toronto Quar.,* VI (1936), 33–48; also "Machiavelli and 'Twofold Truth,'" *Personalist,* XIX (1938), 187–97; F. Gilbert, "The Humanist Concept of the Prince and The Prince of Machiavelli," *Jour. of Mod. Hist.,* XI (1939), 449–83; G. A. Borgese, "Political Creeds and Machiavellian Heresy," *Am. Scholar,* IX (1940), 31–50; S. Marck, "Neo-Machiavellism and Ethical Nihilism," *Ethics,* LI (1941), 185–99; C. N. R. McCoy, "The Place of Machiavelli in the History of Political Thought," *Am. Pol. Science Rev.,* XXXVII (1943), 626–41; V. Cioffari, "The Function of Fortune in Dante, Boccaccio and Machiavelli," *Italica,* XXIV (1947), 1–13; H. L. Stewart, "Machiavelli and History," *Queen's Quar.,* LV (1948), 270–81; I. Ribner, "Machiavelli and Sidney's *Discourse to the Queenes Majesty,*" *Italica,* XXVI (1949), 177–87; also "Sidney's *Arcadia* and the Machiavelli Legend," *Italica,* XXVII (1950), 225–35; also "Machiavelli and Sidney: The *Arcadia* of 1590," *Stud. in Philol.,* XLVII (1950), 152–72; J. Kraft, "Truth and Poetry in Machiavelli," *Jour. of Mod. Hist.,* XXIII (1951), 109–21; F. Gilbert, "The Composition and Structure of Machiavelli's *Discorsi,*" *Journ. Hist. of Ideas,* XIV (1953), 136–56; I. Ribner, "Marlowe and Machiavelli," *Compar. Lit.,* VI (1954), 348–56.

THE PRINCE

Translated by Allan H. Gilbert

[Taken from *Machiavelli. The Prince and Other Works,* translated by Allan H. Gilbert, University Classics, Hendricks House, Packard and Company, Chicago.]

NICCOLÒ MACHIAVELLI

TO THE

MAGNIFICENT LORENZO DE' MEDICI

In most instances, those who wish to gain favor with a prince come into his presence with the things among their possessions that they hold most dear or in which they see that he takes most pleasure. Hence it is seen that many times horses, arms, cloth of gold, precious stones and similar ornaments worthy of their greatness are presented to them. I, then, desiring to come before Your Magnificence with some proof of my desire to serve you, do not find among my treasures anything that I hold more dear or estimate so high as my knowledge of the actions of great men, learned by me through long experience of recent things and continual reading of ancient ones. Having long thought over and considered these with great diligence, and having now collected them in a little volume, I send them to Your Magnificence. And though I judge this work unworthy of your presence, yet I fully trust that in your kindness you will accept it, considering that I cannot make a greater gift than to give you the means of being able in a very short time to learn all that I have found out and learned in so many years with so many troubles and perils to myself.

I have not adorned this work nor filled it with swelling phrases, or with bombastic and magnificent words, or with any other meretricious or extrinsic ornament, with which many are in the habit of writing out and dressing up their things, because I have decided either that nothing should beautify it or that merely the variety of the matter and the weight of the subject should make it pleasing.

And I hope it will not be thought presumption if a man of low and humble station dares to discuss the conduct of princes and give rules for it, because, just as those who draw maps of countries put themselves low on the plain to observe the nature of the mountains and of the high places, and to observe that of the low regions put themselves high on the mountains, so likewise, in order to understand well the nature of the people, it is necessary to be a prince, and to understand well that of princes, it is necessary to be of the people.

May Your Magnificence, then, take this little gift in that spirit in which I send it. If you consider it carefully and read it, you will observe in it my extreme desire that you will come to that greatness which Fortune and your other distinctions promise you. And if from the summit of your lofty station, Your Magnificence will sometimes turn your eyes to these low places, you will observe to what extent I am undeservedly enduring the same great and steady spite of Fortune.

CHAPTER 3

ON MIXED PRINCEDOMS

The difficulties lie in the new princedom. And first, if it is not wholly new but a sort of limb (such that the whole thing can almost be called mixed), its variations originate in the first place from a natural difficulty found in all new princedoms. This is, that men gladly change their ruler when they think to better themselves; and this belief makes them take arms against him; in this they deceive themselves, because later they see through experience that they are worse off. This results from another natural and normal necessity, namely, that one always has to harm those over whom one becomes a new prince both with soldiers and with countless other injuries that follow the new conquest. Hence you have as enemies all those you have damaged in taking possession of that princedom, and you cannot hold as friends those who have put you there, because you cannot satisfy them in such a way as they had expected and because you cannot use strong medicines against them, since you are under obligation to them. For always, even though one has very strong armies, one needs the favor of the inhabitants on entering a region. For these reasons Louis XII, the king of France, quickly seized Milan and quickly lost it. And the first time the forces of Lodovico himself were enough to take it from him, because the people who had opened the gates, finding that they were deceived in their judgment and in that future good they had counted on, were not able to endure the annoyances caused by the new prince.

It is indeed true that when countries that have rebelled are gained the second time, they are lost with more difficulty, because the ruler, taking opportunity from the rebellion, is less hesitant about securing himself by punishing the delinquent, by making evident those who are suspected, by taking precautions in the weaker places. Hence, if to make France lose Milan the first time, a Duke Lodovico making a noise on the borders was enough, to make him lose it the second time, he needed to have all the world against him and to have his armies destroyed or driven from Italy. This came from the causes mentioned above. Nevertheless it was taken from him the first time and the second.

The general causes of the first have been gone through. It now remains to tell those of the second and to see what resources he had and what one in his situation could have, in order to be able to maintain himself in his acquisition better than France did. I say, then, that those states that, when they are gained, are united to an old state belonging to the one who gains them, either are of the same region and of the same language or they are not. When they are, it is very easy to hold them, especially when they are not used to being free; and to keep them securely it is enough to have destroyed the line of the prince who ruled them, because in other things, if their old conditions are kept and there is no lack of conformity in customs, men live quietly, as one sees that Burgundy, Brittany, Gascony, and Normandy have done, which have been with France so long a time; and though there is some lack of conformity in language, nevertheless the customs are similar, and they can get on easily with one another. And he who gains them and hopes to keep them ought to observe two cautions: one, that the family of the old prince is blotted out; the other, not to change their laws or their taxes, so that in a very short time they get to be all one body with his old government.

But when states are gained in a region that lacks conformity in language, customs, and laws, here the difficulties come up, and here one has to have great good fortune and great sagacity to keep them. And one of the greatest and vital remedies is that the person who gains them should go there to live. This will make that possession more secure and more lasting. So the Turk has done about Greece, which, even with all the other methods followed by him for holding that state, he could not possibly have held, if he had not gone there to live. Because, if one is there, disorders can be seen as they spring up and you can quickly cure them; if one is not there, they are known about when they get big and there is no longer any remedy for them. Besides this, the region is not plundered by your officials; the subjects are satisfied with their immediate access to the prince; from it they have more cause to love him, if they intend to be good, and to fear him if they intend to be other than that. Any foreigner who might intend to attack that state is more hesitant about it. Altogether, if one lives there, it is possible for the loss to be very difficult.

Another good remedy is to send colonies into one or two places, to be like fetters to that state, because it is necessary to do this or to keep there many cavalry and infantry. Not much is spent on colonies; and without expense to himself, or with but little, the prince sends them there and keeps them. And he damages only those from whom he takes away their fields and their houses in order to give them to new inhabitants, and they are a very small part of that state. And those whom he damages, since they continue to be scattered and poor, are never able to harm him, and all the others continue on the one hand to be uninjured, and therefore are likely to be quiet, and on the other in terror of making a mistake, for fear that the same will happen to them as to those who have been plundered. I conclude that these colonies are not expensive, are more faithful, do less damage; those who are made angry cannot do harm, since they are poor and scattered, as I have said.

In this connection, it is to be noted that men ought either to be pampered or to be wiped out; for they take vengeance for slight injuries, for heavy ones they cannot; so that an offense caused to a man ought to be of such a sort that vengeance for it is not to be feared. But if instead of colonies he keeps men-at-arms there, much more is spent, since he has to use up all the income of that state on the guards; hence the gain becomes a loss to him. And he causes much more indignation, because he harms all that state by transferring his army with its quarters. Everyone feels this trouble and everyone becomes his enemy; and they are enemies who can injure him, since, though put down, they continue in their abode. In every way, then, this guard is unserviceable, as that of colonies is serviceable.

He who is in a region differing in the way that has been spoken of, ought also to make himself head and defender of the neighboring lesser powers, to strive to weaken the powers of the region, and to keep on the watch so that through some accident a foreigner as powerful as himself will not come in there. And it will always happen that one will be put there by those in that region who are malcontent either through too much ambition or through fear, as it was once seen that the Aetolians put the Romans in Greece; and in every other region that they entered they were put there by the natives. And such is the order of things that as soon as a powerful foreigner enters a region, all those in it who are less powerful join him, moved by their envy against him who has been powerful over them; hence, with respect to these lesser powers, he does not have to go to any trouble in gaining them, because at once they all together gladly form one body with the party that he has gained there. He has only to take care that they do not get too large forces and too great authority; and he can easily, with his forces and with their aid, put down all who are powerful, in order to remain, in everything, master of that region. And he who does not manage this matter well will quickly lose what he has gained; and while he holds it he will have within it countless difficulties and vexations.

The Romans, in the regions they took, observed these matters well, for they sent colonies, showed favor to the less powerful without increasing their power, put down the powerful, and did not allow powerful foreigners to get reputation there. And I am sure the land of Greece alone is enough as an example. The Achaeans and the Aetolians were favored by them; the kingdom of the Macedonians was put down; Antiochus was driven out; and never did the merits of the Achaeans and the Aetolians bring it about that they allowed them to make additions to any state; nor did the persuasions of Philip ever induce them to be his friends without weakening him; nor was the power of Antiochus able to make them consent that he should hold any position in that region.

For in these cases the Roman did what all wise princes should do; they have to take thought not merely for present discords but for future ones, and to forestall them with every effort; for if they are foreseen when they are far off, they can easily be remedied, but if you wait until they are upon you, the medicine is not in time, because the malady has become incurable. And it is with this as the physicians say about the hectic fever: in the beginning of the disease it is easy to cure and hard to recognize, but in the course of time, since it has not been recognized and treated in the beginning, it becomes easy to recognize and hard to cure. So it happens in things of state, because, if the ills that spring up in a state are recognized when far off (something that is given only to a prudent man) they are at once cured, but when, because they are not recognized, they are allowed to increase in such a way that everybody recognizes them, there is no longer a remedy for them. Hence the Romans, seeing difficulties when they were far off, always provided a remedy for them; and they never let them go on in order to avoid a war, because they knew that the war is not avoided but is deferred to the advantage of others. Hence they decided to make war on Philip and Antiochus in Greece in order not to have to make it on them in Italy; yet they were able for the time being to avoid both the one and the other—something they did not choose to do. Nor were they pleased with that which all day is in the mouths of the wise men of our times — about enjoying the benefit of the hour — but very much so that of their own vigor and prudence; because Time drives everything before him, and can carry with him good as well as bad, bad as well as good.

But let us come back to France, and see if he has done any of the things spoken of. And I shall speak of Louis and not of Charles, as of one whose methods, since he longer held territory in Italy, are better seen; and you will see that he has done the contrary to those things that ought to be done in order to hold a state in a region that lacks conformity. King Louis was put in Italy by the ambition of the Venetians, who planned to gain through his coming half the state of Lombardy. I do not mean to blame this decision that was made by the King. Because, since he wished to begin to plant one foot in Italy and had no friends in that region — for on the contrary all the gates were locked against him because of the actions of King Charles — he was forced to lay hold of those friendships that he could, and his resolution would in the end have appeared well taken, if he had made no error in the rest of his management. Having, then, secured Lombardy, the King at once regained that reputation that Charles had taken from him; Genoa yielded, the Florentines became his friends; the Marquis of Mantua, the Duke of Ferrara, Bentivogli, the Lady of Forlì, the Lords of Faenza, of Pesaro, of Rimini, of Camerino, of Piombino, the Lucchese, the Pisans, the Sienese — every one of them presented himself to him to be his friend. And then the Venetians were able to observe the folly of the plan they adopted; to gain two towns in Lombardy, they made the King lord of a third of Italy.

Now let anyone consider with how little difficulty the King would have been able to keep his reputation in Italy, if he had observed the rules given above and kept secure and protected all those friends of his who, being in large numbers, and weak and afraid — one of the Church, another of the Venetians — were always under the necessity of standing with him; and he by means of them could easily have secured himself against anybody who continued to be great there. But he was no sooner in Milan than he did the opposite, giving aid to Pope Alexander in order that he might occupy the Romagna. Nor did he understand that by this decision he was making himself weak, by taking from himself his friends and those who had thrown themselves into his arms, and making the Church strong, by adding to the spiritual, which gives her so much authority, so much temporal power. And having made a first error, he was obliged to go on so far that in order to put an end to the ambition of Alexander and that he might not become lord of Tuscany, he was obliged to come into Italy. It was not enough for him to have made the Church strong and to have taken away from himself his own friends, for, because he wanted the kingdom of Naples, he divided it with the King of Spain; and whereas he had been at first master of Italy, he gave himself an equal there, so that the ambitious men of that land and those dissatisfied with him would have somewhere to turn; and whereas he was able to leave in that kingdom a king who was his pensioner, he took him away and put there one who would be able to drive himself out of it.

It is truly a very natural and ordinary thing to wish to make conquests, and always, when men do it who are able to, they will be praised and blamed. But when they are not able to and set out to do it all the same, here is the error and the blame. If France, then, was able with his own forces to attack Naples, he should have done it; if he was not able to, he should not have divided it. And if the division he made of Lombardy with the Venetians deserves excuse because by means of it he planted his foot in Italy, this one deserves blame because it was not excused by that necessity.

Louis had, then, made these five mistakes: the lesser powers destroyed; the might of one power increased in Italy; a very powerful foreigner put into the land; not coming to live there; colonies not put there. Which errors, while he lived, still possibly would not have injured him, if he had not made the sixth one, that of taking their territory from the Venetians. For if he had not made the Church great nor put Spain into Italy, it was indeed reasonable and necessary to humble them, but having taken these first resolutions, he should never have agreed to their ruin. Because while they were powerful, they would always have kept the others far from an attempt on Lombardy, both because the Venetians would not have agreed to it without becoming masters there themselves, and because the others would not have wished to take it from France to give it to them, and would not have had the courage to undertake to butt against both of them. And if anybody says that King Louis yielded the Romagna to Alexander and the Kingdom to Spain to avoid a war, I answer with the reasons given above: that an evil ought not to be allowed to go on in order to avoid a war, because it is not escaped but put off to your disadvantage. And if some others may allege the faith that the King had pledged to the Pope, that he would carry on that affair for him because of the dissolution of his marriage and the hat for Rouen, I answer with what I shall say below on the faith of princes and how it ought to be kept. King Louis has lost Lombardy, then, through not having observed any of those rules observed by others who have taken regions and wished to hold them. Nor is this any miracle but very ordinary and reasonable.

And I spoke about this matter with Rouen, at Nantes, when Valentino (for so Cesare Borgia, son of Pope Alexander, was popularly called) took possession of the Romagna. Because, when the Cardinal of Rouen said to me that the Italians did not understand war, I answered that the French did not understand about the state, because, if they had understood it, they would not have let the Church come to such greatness. And it is seen by experience that her greatness in Italy and that of Spain has been caused by France, and his ruin has been caused by them.

From this is got a general rule that is never or seldom wrong: namely, he falls who is the reason why some one becomes powerful; because that power is caused by him either with sagacity or with force, and both of these are suspected by him who has become powerful.

CHAPTER 7

ON NEW PRINCEDOMS THAT ARE GAINED BY THE FORCES OF OTHERS AND THROUGH FORTUNE

Those who merely through fortune change themselves from private persons into princes, become so with little labor but maintain themselves with much. And they do not have any difficulty along the road because they fly there. But all the difficulties come up when they are settled. And such as these are to be found when a state is granted to somebody either for money or as a favor by him who grants it, as happened to many in Greece in the cities of Ionia and the Hellespont, where they were made princes by Darius, in order that they might hold them for his security and glory; so were made also those emperors who by bribery of the soldiers came from private stations to the empire. These depend merely on the will and fortune of him who has granted it to them, which are two things most uncertain and unstable; and they do not know how and are not able to hold that rank. They do not know how because, if a man is not of great native ability and vigor, it is not reasonable that, since he has always lived in a private station, he should know how to command; they are not able because they do not have forces that can be friendly and faithful to them. Hence states that come quickly, like all other things in nature that spring up and grow rapidly, are not able to have their roots and corresponding parts; hence the first unfavorable weather destroys them. Unless indeed, as has been said, those of this sort who have suddenly become princes are of so great vigor that they are able at once to fit themselves to keep what Fortune has put in their laps, and will lay afterward those foundations that the others laid before they became princes.

I plan to bring forward two examples, which have existed within the days of our memory, of the first and of the second of these ways that have been mentioned with regard to becoming prince through vigor or through fortune. And these are Francesco Sforza and Cesare Borgia.

Francesco, by the methods required and through his great vigor, changed himself a private person into duke of Milan; and what he had gained with a thousand anxieties, he kept with little effort.

On the other side Cesare Borgia, called by the people Duke Valentino, gained his state through the fortune of his father and through that lost it, notwithstanding that he made use of every action and did all those things that would be done by a prudent and vigorous man for putting down his roots in those states that the arms and fortune of others had bestowed on him. Because, as is said above, he who does not lay his foundations beforehand, may be able because of his great vigor to lay them afterward, though they are laid with trouble for the architect and danger for the building. If, then, one examines all the steps taken by the Duke, one will see that he had laid great foundations for his future power, which I do not consider it superfluous to discuss, because I would not know what better precepts I for my part could give to a new prince than the example of his actions. And if his arrangements did not profit him, that was not his fault, because it came from an unusual and extreme malice of Fortune.

In his attempt to make a great man of his son the Duke, Alexander VI had many difficulties, present and future. First, he did not see a way in which he could make him lord of any state that was not a state of the Church; and if he tried to take that from the Church, he knew that the Duke of Milan and the Venetians would not allow him to, for Faenza and Rimini were already under the protection of the Venetians. He saw, besides this, that the weapons of Italy, and especially those of which he could have made use, were in the hands of those who had reason to fear the greatness of the Pope; and therefore he could not rely on them, since they were all among the Orsini and the Colonnesi and their helpers. It was, then, needful that those conditions should be upset, and the states of those powers thrown into confusion, so that he could safely make himself master of part of them. This was easy for him because he found that the Venetians, moved by other reasons, had set out to make the French come again into Italy; this he not merely did not oppose, but made more easy by the dissolution of the early marriage of King Louis. The King, then, went into Italy with the aid of the Venetians and the consent of Alexander; he was no sooner in Milan than the Pope had from him soldiers for the enterprise in the Romagna; this was allowed him for the sake of the King's reputation.

When the Duke had conquered the Romagna and put down the Colonnesi, if he wished to keep that province and to go further, two things hindered him: one, his forces that did not seem to him faithful; the other, the will of France. That is, the Orsini forces which he had made use of, would fail him, and not merely would hinder his conquering but would take from him what he had conquered, and the King also would do the same thing to him. He had a warning about the Orsini when after the capture of Faenza he attacked Bologna, for he saw that they turned cold over that attack. And as for the King, he learned his inclination when, after taking the dukedom of Urbino, he assailed Tuscany, from which undertaking the King made him desist. As a result the Duke determined not to depend further on the armed forces and fortune of others. And the first thing, he weakened the Orsini and Colonnesi parties in Rome; for all their adherents that were men of rank he gained to himself, making them his own men of rank and giving them large subsidies; and he honored them, according to their stations, with offices and governments; so that in a few months the affection of their hearts for the parties was extinguished and it was all turned to the Duke. After this, he waited for a chance to get rid of the leaders of the Orsini, having scattered those of the house of Colonna; this came to him well and he used it better. For when the Orsini found out, though late, that the greatness of the Duke and of the Church was their overthrow, they held a meeting at Magione, in the Perugino. From that came the rebellion of Urbino and the insurrections in the Romagna and countless dangers for the Duke, all of which he overcame with the aid of the French. And having got back his reputation but not trusting France or other outside forces, in order not to put them to a test he turned to trickery. And he knew so well how to dissimulate his mind that the Orsini themselves became reconciled with him, by means of Lord Paulo (with him the Duke did not fail in every sort of method for making sure of him, giving him money, clothing, and horses), so completely that their innocence took them to Sinigaglia into his hands. When these heads, then, were got rid of and their partizans made his friends, the Duke had formed very good foundations for his power, having all the Romagna together with the dukedom of Urbino, for it seemed to him that especially he had made the Romagna his friend and gained for himself all those peoples, since they had begun to get the flavor of well-being.

And because this matter is worthy of notice and of being imitated by others, I do not wish to let it go by. When the Duke had taken the Romagna and found it was controlled by weak lords who had plundered their subjects rather than governed them, and given them reason for disunion, not of union, so that that province was all full of stealing, of contentions, and of every other sort of disorder, he judged it was necessary, if he intended to make it peaceful and obedient to the ruling arm, to give it good government. Hence he put in charge of it Messer Remirro de Orco, a cruel and decided man, to whom he gave the most complete power. This man in a short time made it peaceful and united, with the greatest honor to himself. Thereupon the Duke decided that such excessive authority was not useful, because he feared it would become hated, and he set up a civil court in the midst of the province, with a very excellent president, where every city would have its lawyer. And because he knew that the past severities had produced some hatred against him, he determined, in order to purge the minds of these people and to win them over entirely to himself, to show that if any cruelty had gone on, it did not originate in him but in the harsh nature of his minister. And having taken an opportunity about this, at Cesena one morning he had him laid out in two pieces on the public square. The savagery of this spectacle made those people at the same time contented and amazed.

But let us turn back to where we left off. I say that when the Duke found himself very powerful and in part made secure against the present perils, since he was armed as he wished and had in great part destroyed those forces that, being nearby, could injure him, there remained to him, if he intended to continue his conquest, the matter of the King of France, because he knew that it would not be allowed him by the King, who had, though late, realized his error. And he began for this reason to seek for new friendships and to waver in his dealings with France, in the expedition that the French made to the kingdom of Naples against the Spaniards who besieged Gaeta. And his intention was to make himself secure against them, in which he would soon have succeeded if Alexander had lived. And these were his ways of acting as to the present things.

But as to future ones, he had to fear, first, that a new successor to the Church would not be friendly to him and would try to take from him what Alexander had given him. Against this he planned to make himself secure in four ways: first, to extinguish all the families of those lords he had plundered, in order to take that opportunity away from the Pope; second, to win to his side all the men of rank in Rome, as has been said, in order to be able by their means to keep the Pope in check; third, to make the College as much his as he could; fourth, to gain so much power, before the Pope died, that he would be able by himself to resist a first attack. Of these four things, at the death of Alexander he had completed three; the fourth was almost as good as complete: because of the plundered rulers he killed as many as he could reach and very few escaped; he had gained the men of rank in Rome, and he had a very large party in the College; and as to new conquest, he had planned to become lord of Tuscany, and he already possessed Perugia and Piombino and had undertaken the protection of Pisa. And as soon as he did not have to have regard for the French (for he was not going to have to have it for them in the future, since the French were already deprived of the Kingdom by the Spaniards, in such a way that each of them was obliged to buy his friendship), he was going to jump into Pisa. After this, Lucca and Siena would have yielded at once, partly through envy of the Florentines, partly through fear. The Florentines would have had no remedy. If he had carried this through (and he was going to carry it through the very year when Alexander died) he would have got himself such strong forces and such great reputation that he would have kept himself up just by himself, and would not have been any longer dependent on the fortune and forces of others but on his own power and vigor.

But Alexander died five years after he had begun to draw the sword. He left him with the state of the Romagna alone made solid, with all the others in the air, between two very powerful hostile armies, and sick unto death. Yet there was in the Duke so much courage and so much vigor, and he knew so well how men are to be gained or lost, and so strong were the foundations that he had laid in so short a time, that if he had not had those armies upon him, or if he had been in good health, he would have mastered every difficulty. And that his foundations were good can be seen, because the Romagna waited for him more than a month; in Rome, though but half alive, he was secure; and though the Baglioni, Vitelli, and Orsini came into Rome, they had not gone farther against him; he had power, if not to make the one he wanted pope, at least to make sure that the one he did not want should not be. But if on the death of Alexander he had been in good health, everything would have been easy for him. And he said to me himself, on the day that Julius II was made pope, that he had thought of what could happen if his father died, and he had found a remedy for everything, except that he did not ever think that at his death he too would be close to dying.

Having brought together, then, all the actions of the Duke, I should not be able to censure him; rather it seems fitting to me to set him up, as I have done, for imitation by all those who through fortune and with the arms of others have risen to a ruling position. For, since his courage was great and his purpose high, he could not have conducted himself otherwise; and his plans were opposed only by the shortness of the life of Alexander and his own sickness. He then who thinks it necessary in his new princedom to secure himself against his enemies, to gain friends, to conquer by force or by fraud, to make himself loved and feared by the people, followed and respected by the soldiers, to wipe out those who can or are likely to injure you, to replace the ancient customs with new laws, to be severe and agreeable, magnanimous and liberal, to wipe out unfaithful soldiers, to raise new ones, to keep the friendship of kings and of princes in such a way that they treat you as one either to be conciliated with kindness or injured with hesitation, cannot find fresher instances than the actions of this man.

He can be blamed only in the election of Julius as pope, in which he made a bad choice; because, as has been said, if he was not able to make a pope as he would, he was able to keep any man from being pope. And he ought never to have consented to the popedom of those cardinals whom he had injured or who, if they became pope, were going to fear him. Because men do injury either through fear or through hate. Those whom he had injured were, among the others, San Piero ad Vincula, Colonna, San Giorgio, Ascanio; all the others, if they became pope, would have to fear him, except Rouen and the Spaniards, the latter because of connection and indebtedness, the former because of his power, since the kingdom of France was connected with him. Therefore the Duke, before everything else, should have made a Spaniard pope, and if he could not, he should have agreed that it should be Rouen and not San Piero ad Vincula. And he who believes that in great persons new benefits cause old injuries to be forgotten, deceives himself. The Duke, then, erred in this choice; and it was the cause of his final downfall.

CHAPTER 8

ON THOSE WHO THROUGH WICKED DEEDS HAVE COME TO THE PRINCEDOM

But because one in a private station may become a prince in two ways besides, which cannot be attributed altogether to Fortune or to vigor, it does not seem to me proper to leave them out, though it is possible to discuss one of them more at length where we deal with republics. They are when either through some wicked and criminal way one rises to the princedom, or when a private citizen with the aid of the other citizens becomes prince of his native land. And speaking of the first manner, it will be shown with two examples, the one old, the other recent, without entering otherwise into the merits of this situation, because I judge that it is enough for him who is forced to it to imitate them.

Agathocles the Sicilian, not merely of private but of low and abject station, became king of Syracuse. He, the son of a potter, always lived a wicked life throughout the stages of his career. Nevertheless, he joined his wickedness with such vigor of mind and of body that, entering the army, he rose through its grades to be praetor of Syracuse. Being settled in this rank and having determined to become prince and to keep with violence and without obligation to others what had been granted to him by agreement, and having an understanding as to his plan with Hamilcar the Carthaginian, who was campaigning with his armies in Sicily, one morning he assembled the people and the senate of Syracuse, as if he needed to consider things relating to the state; and at a given sign he had all the senators and the richest of the people killed by his soldiers. When they had been slain, he took and held the rule of that city without any civil strife. And though he was twice defeated by the Carthaginians and finally besieged, he was able not merely to defend his city, but having left part of his soldiers for defense against the siege, with the others he attacked Africa and in a short time freed Syracuse from the siege and brought the Carthaginians into the utmost straits; and they were obliged to make peace with him, to be content with the possession of Africa, and to leave Sicily to Agathocles.

He who will consider, then, the actions and the life of this man, will see nothing, or but little, that he can attribute to Fortune, since, as was said above, he came to the princedom not through the favor of anybody but through the grades of the army, which he had won for himself with a thousand hardships and perils, and he then kept the princedom for himself with many spirited and dangerous actions. It cannot, however, be called virtue to kill fellow citizens, to betray friends, to be without faith, without mercy, without religion; such ways can cause one to gain command but not glory. Because, if the vigor of Agathocles in entering into and getting out of dangers is considered, and his greatness of mind in enduring and overcoming adverse things, it cannot be seen why he must be judged inferior to any of the most excellent generals. Nevertheless, his outrageous cruelty and inhumanity, together with his countless acts of wickedness, do not allow him to be famed among the most excellent men. One cannot, then, attribute to Fortune or to virtue that which he carried through without either one.

In our times, when Alexander VI was reigning, Liverotto of Fermo, who many years before, when he was little, had been left without a father, was brought up by his maternal uncle, named Giovanni Fogliani, and in the early years of his youth had been put out to serve as a soldier under Paulo Vitelli, in order that, being accomplished in that discipline, he might attain some excellent military position. After Paulo died, he served under Vitellozzo his brother, and in a very short time, because he was gifted, and vigorous in body and mind, he became the first man in his army. But since it seemed to him a servile thing to remain under the control of others, he determined, with the aid of some citizens of Fermo to whom the slavery of their native city was dearer than her liberty, and with the aid of the Vitelleschi, to occupy Fermo; and he wrote to Giovanni Fogliani that, since he had been many years away from home, he wished to come to see him and his native city, and in some matters to inspect his inheritance; and because he had not labored for the sake of anything except the gaining of honor, he wished to come honorably and accompanied by a hundred horsemen from among his friends and servants, in order that his fellow citizens might see that he had not spent his time in vain; and he begged that he would be so kind as to arrange that he should be received with honor by the Firmani; this would bring honor not merely to Liverotto but to Giovanni himself, since he was his foster child. Giovanni, therefore, did not fail in any duty he owed to his nephew, and after he had had him honorably received by the Firmani, he was lodged in his own houses. There, after he had passed some days and attended to arranging secretly what was necessary to his future wickedness, he gave a splendid banquet, to which he invited Giovanni Fogliani and all the leading men of Fermo. When the victuals were dispatched and all the other matters usual in such banquets, Liverotto, according to plan, set about certain serious discourses, talking of the greatness of Pope Alexander and of Cesare his son and of their enterprises. When Giovanni and the others replied to these discourses, he at once rose up, saying these were things to be spoken of in a more secret place; and retired to a chamber, to which Giovanni and all the other citizens followed him. No sooner were they seated than from secret places in it soldiers came out, who slew Giovanni and all the others. After this slaughter, Liverotto mounted his horse and rode through the city and besieged in the palace the supreme magistracy, so that for fear they were obliged to obey him, and to confirm a government of which he made himself prince.

And since all those had been put to death who, if they were discontented, could injure him, he strengthened himself with new civil and military ordinances, in such a way that for the length of a year during which he held the princedom, he was not merely safe in the city of Fermo, but had become an object of fear to all his neighbors. And an attack on him would have been difficult as on Agathocles, if he had not let himself be deceived by Cesare Borgia when he took the Orsini and Vitelli at Sinigaglia, as was said above; where, since he was also taken, in the year after the parricide he committed, he was strangled, along with Vitellozzo, whom he had had as master in his virtues and his crimes.

One might wonder whence it came that Agathocles or anybody like him, after countless betrayals and cruelties, was able to live safe in his native city a long time and to defend himself from foreign enemies, and was never conspired against by the citizens, although many others have not been able by means of cruelty to keep their positions even in peaceful times, much less in the uncertain times of war. I believe this comes from cruelties badly used or well used. Those can be called well used (if it is permitted to say *well* of the bad) that are done promptly, because of a necessity for making oneself secure, and then one does not persist in them, but they are changed into the greatest benefit to the subjects that is possible. Badly used are those that, though they may be few in the beginning, rather increase with time than are extinguished. Those who follow the first method are able to have with God and men some remedy for their position, such as Agathocles had; it is impossible for the others to maintain themselves.

From this it is to be noted that in seizing a state the usurper ought to consider all the injuries that it is necessary for him to do; and to do them promptly, in order not to have to renew them every day, but to be able, since he does not renew them, to make men feel safe and to win them to himself by benefitting them. He who does otherwise, either through timidity or through ill counsel, is obliged always to hold his knife in his hand; he can never rely on his subjects, and they, because of fresh and continual injuries, cannot be secure about him. Because injuries should be done all together, in order that, since their flavor is less perceived, they may cause less anger; benefits ought to be conferred little by little, in order that their flavor may be perceived better. And above all, a prince ought to live with his subjects in such a way that no happening whether bad or good is able to make him vary; because when necessities come, on account of adverse times, you are not in time for the bad, and the good you do does not help you because it is looked upon as forced, and no gratitude to you is felt because of it.

CHAPTER 14

HOW A PRINCE SHOULD ACT ABOUT MILITARY AFFAIRS

A prince, then, should have no other object and no other thought and should not take for his own specialty anything else than war and its laws and discipline; because it is the only art expected from him who commands; and it is of such efficacy that it not merely maintains those who are born princes, but many times makes men rise from a private station to that rank. And on the contrary, it is seen that princes, when they have thought more about pleasures than about arms have lost their positions. And the first cause that makes them lose them is neglecting this art, and the cause that makes them acquire them is being expert in this art.

Francesco Sforza, because he was armed, became no longer a private individual but duke of Milan; his sons, through avoiding the discomforts of arms, became no longer dukes but private individuals. Because among the other causes of evil that being unarmed brings upon you, it makes you despised, which is one of the stigmas that a prince ought to guard himself against, as will be said below. Because there is no equality between an armed and an unarmed man, and it is not reasonable that one who is armed should willingly obey one who is unarmed and that the unarmed should be safe among servants who are armed, for since there is contempt in one and suspicion in the other, it is not possible that they should work well together. And for this reason, besides other drawbacks such as have been mentioned, a prince who does not understand warfare cannot be esteemed by his soldiers or trust them.

He ought, then, never to withdraw his thought from this business of war, and in time of peace he ought to exercise himself in it more than in time of war. This he can do in two ways, one with his actions, the other with his mind. And as to his actions, besides keeping his soldiers well organized and trained, he ought always to be hunting and thereby accustoming his body to hardships; and incidentally learning topography, and finding out how the mountains rise, how the valleys are hollowed out, how the plains lie, and observing the nature of rivers and swamps; and on this to put the greatest effort. This knowledge is useful in two ways: he teaches himself, first, to know his country and is able better to understand its defenses; next by means of his knowledge and experience of these places, to understand easily any other place which it may be necessary for him to look at for the first time. Because the hills, the valleys, the plains, the rivers, the swamps that are in Tuscany, for instance, have some likeness to those of other regions, so that from the knowledge of the lie of one region he can easily arrive at knowledge of others. And the prince who lacks this expertness lacks the first faculty that a general needs to have, because this teaches him to find the enemy, to choose encampments, to lead his armies, to plan battles, to besiege towns to advantage.

Philopoemon, prince of the Achaeans, among the other things for which writers praise him, is said in times of peace never to have meditated on anything except the methods of war, and when he was in the country with his friends he often stopped and talked with them: "If the enemy were on that hill and we were here with our army, which of us would have the advantage? How would we be able, keeping our organization, to go to attack them? If we should wish to retire, how could we do it? If they should retire, how could we follow them?" And he would set before them, as they walked along, all the accidents that could come about in an army; he would learn their opinions, tell his own, back it up with reasons; so that on account of this continual reflection, no event could ever come about, when he was leading his armies, for which he would not have the remedy.

But as to the exercise of the mind, the prince should read histories, and consider in them the actions of excellent men; see how they have conducted themselves in wars, examine the causes of their victories and defeats, to be able to escape the latter and imitate the former. And above all, he ought to act as in the past some excellent men have done, who, if some earlier man has been praised and honored, have chosen him for imitation and have always kept his deeds and actions before them, as it is said that Alexander the Great imitated Achilles; Caesar, Alexander; Scipio, Cyrus. And whoever reads the life of Cyrus written by Xenophon recognizes afterward in the life of Scipio how glorious that imitation was to him, and how closely Scipio conformed in chastity, affability, humanity, liberality, with those things that are written about Cyrus by Xenophon.

A wise prince ought to follow such methods as these and never be lazy in times of peace but industriously make capital of them, in order to be able to use them in adverse conditions, so that when Fortune changes he may be prepared to resist her.

CHAPTER 15

ON THOSE THINGS FOR WHICH MEN AND ESPECIALLY PRINCES ARE PRAISED OR CENSURED

It now remains to see of what sort ought to be the ways and conduct of a prince with subjects or with his friends. And because I know that many have written about this, I fear that I shall be thought presumptuous when I write about it too, since, in debating this matter, I depart very far from the methods of the others. But since it is my purpose to write something useful to him who comprehends it, it has seemed to me fitting to pursue the working truth of the matter rather than a fancy about it. And many have imagined for themselves republics and principalities that have never been seen or known to exist in reality. For there is such a difference between how men live and how they ought to live, that he who leaves what is done for what ought to be done is learning his ruin rather than his preservation; because he who chooses in all ways to act in the character of a good man must needs come to ruin among so many who are not good. Hence if a prince expects to maintain himself, it is necessary for him to acquire the power of being not good, and of using it and not using it in accord with necessity.

Omitting, then, things that have been imagined about a prince and discussing those things that are true, I say that all men, when they are spoken of, and especially princes, because they are set higher, are stamped with some of these qualities that bring them either blame or praise. And this means that one is thought liberal, one stingy (I use a Tuscan word, because the *avaricious* man in our tongue is still he who wishes to get by means of violence; *stingy* we call him who holds back too much from using his own); one is thought a giver, one grasping; one cruel, one merciful; one a breaker of faith, the other faithful; one effeminate and cowardly, the other bold and spirited; one kindly, the other proud; one lascivious, the other chaste; one of integrity, the other crafty; one firm, the other yielding; one serious, the other light-minded; one religious, the other unbelieving; and the like.

And I know that everyone will admit that it would be a most praiseworthy thing if, among all the qualities given above, those that are thought to be good should be found in a prince. But because they cannot be had or entirely observed, on account of human conditions that do not allow it, it is necessary for him to be so prudent that he will be able to avoid a bad name for those vices that would take his position away from him, and to guard himself, if it is possible, from those that would not take it away; but if he cannot, they can be let slide with less concern. And he should not even care about getting a bad name for those vices without which it will be difficult for him to preserve his position. Because, if the whole is well considered, something or other will be found that will seem a virtue — yet if it is followed, it will be his ruin —, and something else that will seem a vice — yet if it is followed, his own security and well-being will result from it.

CHAPTER 17

ON CRUELTY AND MERCY; AND WHETHER IT IS BETTER TO BE LOVED THAN TO BE FEARED, OR THE REVERSE

Coming next to the other qualities mentioned above, I say that every prince ought to wish to be thought merciful and not cruel. Nevertheless, he ought to look out that he does not use this mercy badly. Cesare Borgia was thought cruel; nevertheless this cruelty of his had reorganized the Romagna, united it, brought it to peace and fidelity. If this is considered well, it will be seen that he was much more merciful than the Florentine people, who, to escape the name of cruel, allowed Pistoia to be destroyed. A prince, then, ought not to care about the stigma of cruelty, for the sake of keeping his subjects united and faithful; because, with a very few instances, he will be more merciful than those who, through too much mercy, let evils continue, from which result slaughters or plunder; because the latter commonly injure a whole group, but those executions that come from the prince injure one individual. And it is impossible for the new prince, above all other princes, to escape the name of cruel, because new states are full of perils. As Virgil says by the mouth of Dido, "My hard condition and my new kingdom force me to do such things, and to set guards over my boundaries far and wide."

Nevertheless he should be cautious in believing and in moving, and should not himself produce fear within himself, and should proceed in such a way, moderated by prudence and kindness, that too much trust does not make him incautious and too much distrust does not make him unbearable.

From this rises a debate: Is it better to be loved than feared, or the reverse? The answer is that one would like to be both, but because it is difficult to fit them together, it is much more secure to be feared than loved, if it is necessary to do without one of the two. Because this can generally be said of men: they are ungrateful, changeable, simulators and dissimulators, escapers from dangers, eager for gain; while you do well by them they are all yours; they offer you their blood, their property, their lives, their children, as was said above, when need is far off; but when it comes near you, they turn about. And that prince who has based himself entirely on their words, if he is bare of other preparations, falls; because friendships that are gained with money and not with greatness and nobility of spirit are earned but not possessed, and they cannot be spent at the right time. And men have less hesitation in injuring one who makes himself loved than one who makes himself feared. For love is held by a chain of duty, which, because men are bad, is broken by every chance for their own profit; but fear is held by a dread of punishment that never forsakes you.

Still, the prince should make himself feared in such a way that if he does not gain love he escapes hate, because being feared and not being hated are very well able to dwell together; he will always achieve this if he abstains from the property of his citizens and of his subjects and from their women. And when it really is necessary for him to put somebody on trial for his life, he is to do it when he has a fitting justification and a clear case. But above all, he is to abstain from the property of others; because men forget the death of a father more quickly than the loss of a paternal estate. Besides, legal pretexts for taking away property are never lacking; and, always, he who begins to live on plunder finds a pretext for taking what belongs to some one; but on the contrary pretexts for taking life are rarer and fail sooner.

But when the prince is with his armies and has a multitude of soldiers in his charge, then it is altogether needful not to trouble about the name of cruel, for without this name no army was ever kept united or fit for any action. Among the wonderful deeds of Hannibal this is included, that, though he had a very large army, a mixture of men of countless sorts, led to service in foreign lands, there never sprang up any dissension, either among themselves or against their commander, no more in his bad than in his good fortune. This could not come from anything other than that inhuman cruelty of his, which, together with his numberless abilities, made him always respected and terrible in the sight of his soldiers; but without that, his other abilities would not have been enough for getting that result. And the writers, who have thought little on this, on one side admire this conduct of his, and on the other condemn the chief cause for it.

And that it is true that his other capacities would not have been enough can be observed in Scipio — a very unusual man not merely in his days but in all the record of things that are known — against whom his armies in Spain rebelled. This did not rise from anything else than his too great mercy, which had given his soldiers more license than befits military discipline. He was reproached for this thing in the Roman senate by Fabius Maximus, who called him the corrupter of the Roman soldiers. When the Locrians had been destroyed by a legate of Scipio's, they were not avenged by him nor was the arrogance of that legate punished, all as a result of that yielding disposition of his; hence some one in the Senate, wishing to excuse him, said there were many men better able not to err than to punish errors. That disposition would in time have spoiled the fame and glory of Scipio if, with it, he had kept on in supreme command; but since he lived under the control of the Senate, this harmful quality of his not merely was concealed but was a glory to him.

I conclude, then, returning to being feared and loved, that since men love at their own choice and fear at the choice of the prince, a wise prince ought to base himself on what is his own, not on what is in the power of another; he ought to strive only to avoid hatred, as has been said.

CHAPTER 18

IN WHAT WAY FAITH SHOULD BE KEPT BY PRINCES

Everybody knows how praiseworthy it is in a prince to keep faith and to live in sincerity and not in craft. Nonetheless, we see through experience in our times that those princes have done great things who have taken little account of faith and have known how to addle the brains of men with craft; and in the end they have overcome those who have founded themselves on integrity.

You ought, then, to know that there are two ways of fighting: one with the laws, the other with force. The first is suited to man, the second to the animals; but because the first many times is not enough, one must have recourse to the second. Hence it is necessary for a prince to know well how to act both the animal and the man. This method has been allegorically taught to princes by the ancient writers, who wrote that Achilles and many others of those ancient princes were given for education to Chiron the Centaur, who kept them under his discipline. This — that is, to have as teacher one who is half animal and half man — does not mean anything else than that it is necessary for a prince to know how to use either nature, and one without the other is not lasting.

Since, then, a prince is obliged to know well how to act the animal, he ought to choose from them the fox and the lion, because the lion does not protect himself from traps; the fox does not protect himself from the wolves. It is needful, then, to be a fox to recognize the traps and a lion to frighten the wolves. Those who reckon only on the lion do not understand things. Indeed a prudent ruler cannot and should not observe faith if such observance runs counter to him, and the reasons that made him promise are annulled. And if men were all good, this precept would not be good, but because they are bad, and do not observe it to you, you too do not have to observe it to them. Nor will legitimate reasons to excuse this lack of observance ever be wanting to a prince. It would be possible to give countless modern examples of this and to show how many pacts, how many promises have been made null and empty through princes' lack of faith; and he who has been able to play the fox best has come out best. But one must be able to disguise this nature well and to be a great simulator and dissimulator. And men are so simple and comply so much with present necessities that he who deceives will always find those who will let themselves be deceived.

I do not wish, among recent instances, to keep still about one. Alexander VI never did anything else and did not think of anything else than deceiving men, and he always found a subject to work on. And there was never a man more efficient in swearing and who affirmed a thing with greater oaths, who observed it less. Nonetheless, his deceptions always succeeded as he hoped, because he knew well this characteristic of the world.

It is not necessary, then, for a prince actually to have all the abovementioned qualities, but it is very necessary to seem to have them. I shall even dare to say this, that if one has them and always observes them, they are harmful; and if one seems to have them, they are useful; that is, to seem merciful, trustworthy, humane, blameless, religious, and to be so; but to have the mind built up in such a way that if you find it necessary not to be so, you are able and know how to change to the contrary. And this must be understood, that a prince, and especially a new prince, is unable to observe all those things because of which men are thought good, since he is often obliged, in order to keep his position, to act contrary to faith, contrary to charity, contrary to humanity, contrary to religion. And therefore it is needful that he have a spirit disposed to shift itself as the winds of Fortune and the variations of things command it, and, as I said above, not to depart from the good, when possible, but to know how to enter into evil when necessary.

A prince, then, ought to take great care that there never comes out of his mouth one thing that is not full of the above-mentioned five qualities, and, to look at him and to see him, he should appear all mercy, all faith, all integrity, all humanity, all religion. There is nothing that it is more necessary to seem to have than this last quality. And men, in general, judge more with their eyes than with their hands; because it is the part of everybody to see, of few to perceive. Everybody sees what you appear to be, few perceive what you are. And those few do not dare to oppose themselves to the opinion of the many who have the majesty of the state to defend them. And in the actions of all men, and especially of princes, where there is no judgment to which to appeal, we look at the outcome. Let a prince manage to conquer and to hold his place, his means will always be judged honorable and praised by everybody, because the mob is always taken by what seems and by the outcome of a thing; and in the world there is nothing but the mob, and the few have no place there when the many have where to cling. A certain prince of the present time, whom it is not well to name, never preaches anything other than peace and faith, and is most hostile to both of them. And either one, if he had observed it, would many times have taken away either his reputation or his position.

CHAPTER 21

WHAT IS ADVISABLE FOR A PRINCE THAT HE MAY BE THOUGHT EXCELLENT

Nothing makes a prince so much esteemed as great undertakings and the giving of striking displays of himself. In our times we have Ferdinand of Aragon, the present king of Spain. He can be called almost a new prince because, once a weak king, he has become in fame and glory the foremost king among the Christians; and if you will consider all his actions you will find them all very great and some of them extraordinary. In the beginning of his reign he attacked Granada; and this undertaking was the foundation of his greatness. First he did it when he was at leisure and without fear of being impeded; he kept occupied in it the minds of those barons of Castile, who, thinking of that war, did not think of rebelling. And he gained by means of it reputation and rule over them, when they did not realize it. He was able, with money from the Church and from the people, to support armies, and in that long war to lay a foundation for his army, which has afterward done him honor. Besides this, in order to be able to undertake greater enterprises, availing himself always of religion, he turned to a pious cruelty, driving out the Moors and stripping his kingdom of them. Nor can this instance be more worthy of pity or more striking. Under this same cloak, he attacked Africa, he carried on his Italian enterprise, he recently has attacked France, and so he always has done and laid out great things, which have always kept the minds of his subjects in suspense and admiration and busied over their outcome. And his actions have come from one another in such a way that, between one and the next, he has never given space to men to be able quietly to work against him.

It is also useful to a prince to give striking displays of himself in his conduct in internal affairs (like those that are told about Messer Bernabò of Milan) whenever an opportunity is given by somebody who does something unusual, either good or bad, in the life of the city, — and to find a way for rewarding or punishing him that is sure to be talked about a great deal. And above all a prince ought to strive to give himself in every act the fame of a great man and one of excellent ability.

A prince is also esteemed when he is a true friend and a true enemy, that is, when without any reservation he shows himself in favor of one against another. This course will always be more useful than standing neutral, because if two powerful neighbours of yours come to blows, either they are of such a sort that if one or the other of them conquers, you must fear the conqueror, or they are not. In either of these two cases, it will always be more useful to reveal yourself and to make genuine war. Because, in the first case, if you do not reveal yourself, you will always be the prey of the one who conquers, with the pleasure and satisfaction of the one who has been conquered, and you do not have any reason or anything that will protect you or that will receive you, because he who conquers does not wish friends he suspects and who do not aid him in adversity; he who loses does not receive you because you have not wished to share his fortune with weapons in your hand.

Antiochus had gone into Greece, brought there by the Aetolians to drive out the Romans. Antiochus sent ambassadors to the Achaians, who were friends of the Romans, to encourage them to take a middle ground; and on the other side the Romans were urging them to take up arms for them. This matter came up for decision in the council of the Achaians, where the envoy from Antiochus urged them to remain neutral. To this the Roman envoy answered: "As to what these men say about not getting yourselves into the war, nothing is more remote from your interests; without thanks, without dignity, you will be the booty of the victor."

And it will always happen that he who is not your friend will ask for neutrality, and he who is your friend will ask that you reveal yourself with your weapons. And princes of weak resolution, in order to escape present dangers, most of the time follow the neutral road and most of the time fail. But when the prince reveals himself vigorously in favor of one side, if the one to whom you adhere wins, even if he is powerful and you remain at his discretion, he has a duty to you and has formed love for you; and men are never so dishonorable that with so great an example of ingratitude they will oppress you. Then victories are never so unmixed that the victor does not have to have some scruples and especially as to justice. But if that one to whom you attach yourself loses, you are received by him, and while he can, he aids you, and you become companion of a fortune that can rise again.

In the second case, when those who fight together are of such a sort that you do not have to fear the one who conquers, it is so much the greater prudence to join, because you go to the ruin of one with the aid of him who, if he were wise, would save him, and if you win, he remains at your discretion, and it is impossible, with your aid, that he will not win.

And here it is to be noted that a prudent prince ought to watch out that he never makes an alliance with one more powerful than himself, in order to attack another, except when necessity compels it, as was said above, because, if he conquers, you remain his prisoner, and princes ought to avoid, all they can, being at the discretion of others. The Venetians allied themselves with France against the duke of Milan and they could have avoided entering that alliance from which came their downfall. But when it cannot be avoided (as happened to the Florentines when the Pope and Spain went with their armies to attack Lombardy) then the prince ought to join in, for the reasons given above. Nor should any state ever believe it can always take safe courses; on the contrary, it should realize that all those it must take are doubtful, because it is in the order of things that a man never tries to escape from one disadvantage without running into another; but prudence consists in being able to recognize the nature of the disadvantages and to take the less bad for good.

A prince ought also to show himself a lover of ability by giving shelter to able men and honoring those who are excellent in some art. Besides, he ought to encourage his citizens in thinking that they can quietly busy themselves in their businesses, both in commerce and in agriculture and in every other business of men; so that one man is not afraid to increase his possessions because of his dread that they will be taken from him, and another to open a trade for fear of the taxes; but he ought to prepare rewards for those who try to do these things and for anyone who plans in any way to make his city or his state greater. Besides this, he ought, at proper times of the year, to keep the people occupied with festivals and shows. And because every city is divided into guilds or into wards, he ought to take account of those bodies, to meet with them sometimes, to make himself an example of humanity and munificence — nevertheless always keeping firm the majesty of his position, because this ought never to be lacking in any situation.

CHAPTER 22

ON THOSE WHOM PRINCES EMPLOY FOR SECRET BUSINESS

The choice of ministers is not of slight importance to a prince. They are good or not according to the prudence of the prince. And the first conjecture that is made about the brain of the prince is by seeing the men he has around him; and when they are competent and faithful, it can always be reckoned that he is prudent, because he has been able to recognize the competent and to keep them faithful. But when they are otherwise, a low estimate can always be made of him, because the chief mistake he makes, he makes in this choice.

There was nobody who knew Messer Antonio da Venafro as the minister of Pandolfo Petrucci, prince of Siena, who did not judge Pandolfo a very able man, since he had the other as his minister. And because there are three sorts of brains (one understands of itself, the second sees what another understands, the third does not understand either by itself or through another — the first is very excellent, the second is excellent, the third useless —) it must therefore have been necessary that, if Pandolfo was not in the first class, he was in the second; because every time that one has judgment to recognize the good or the ill that one does or says, even though he himself does not have originality, he recognizes the bad deeds and the good ones of the minister, and praises the latter and censures the others; and the minister cannot hope to deceive him and keeps himself good.

But as to how a prince can be certain about his minister, there is this method that never fails: when you see the minister thinking more about himself than about you and in all his actions seeking, within himself, for his own advantage, this man is of such a sort that he will never be a good minister, and you will never be able to trust him, because he who has the position of one in his hands ought never to think of himself but of his prince and never ought to suggest to the latter anything that does not concern him especially.

And on the other side the prince, to keep him good, ought to think of the minister, honoring him, making him rich, putting him under obligation to himself, sharing with him honors and great offices, so that he will see that he cannot stand without the prince, and so that his adequate honors will make him not wish more honors, his adequate riches will make him not wish more riches, his adequate offices will make him fear changes. When, finally, the ministers and the princes in relation to the ministers are of such a sort, they are able to have faith in each other; and when it is otherwise, the end will always be damaging either to the one or to the other.

CHAPTER 23

IN WHAT WAY FLATTERERS ARE TO BE AVOIDED

I do not wish to omit an important subject and an error from which princes protect themselves with difficulty, if they are not very prudent or if they do not have a good selection. And these are the flatterers, of whom the courts are full. For men are so complacent about their own affairs and deceive themselves about them in such a way that with difficulty they protect themselves against this pest; and in trying to defend oneself from it, one runs the risk of becoming despised. Because there is no other way of guarding oneself from flatteries except that men should understand that they do not offend you by telling you the truth; but when everybody is able to speak the truth to you, respect for you is wanting. Hence a prudent prince ought to employ a third way, choosing in his state wise men, and to them alone he ought to give freedom of judgment to speak the truth to him, but only on those things that he asks about, and not on anything else. But he ought to ask them about everything and listen to their opinions; and then decide for himself, in his own way. And with these advisers and with each of them, he should bear himself in such a way that every one may know that the more freely he speaks the more acceptable he will be. Except these, he ought not to consent to hear anybody; he should follow up the thing decided on and be firm in his decisions. He who does otherwise either falls because of flatterers or changes often according to the variation of opinions. This gives rise to a low estimate of him.

I wish in this matter to bring up a modern example. Pre' Luca, servant to Maximilian, the present emperor, speaking of His Majesty, said that he did not take counsel with anybody and that he never acted in his own way in anything. This came from using a method the opposite of what has been mentioned above. For the emperor is a secretive man, does not impart his plans to anybody, does not get any opinion on them. But when, as they are put into effect, they begin to be known and to be revealed, they begin to be opposed by those he has around him, and he, being yielding, is pulled away from them. From this it comes that what he does one day he destroys the next, and that what he wishes or intends to do is never understood, and that it is not possible to rely on his decisions.

A prince, then, ought always to get advice, but when he wishes and not when somebody else wishes; on the contrary, he ought to deprive everybody of intention to advise him about anything if he does not ask it from him. But he surely ought to be a big asker and then a patient hearer of the truth about the things asked. Yet more, if he learns that anybody for any reason does not tell it to him, he ought to be vexed about it.

And because many think that some prince or other who gives the impression that he himself is prudent is thought to be so not by reason of his nature but by reason of the good advisers whom he has around him, without question they are fooling themselves. Because this is a general rule that never fails: a prince who is not wise himself cannot be well advised, unless indeed by chance he turns himself over to one only, who entirely controls him, who is a very prudent man. In this case, he surely can be, but it will not last long, because that tutor in a short time will take his position from him. But if he takes counsel with more than one, a prince who is not wise will never have unified counsels, nor will he know for himself how to unite them; of the counsellors, each will think in his own individual way; the prince will not be able to control them or to understand them. And they cannot be otherwise; because men always turn out bad for you unless they are made good by some necessity. Therefore it is to be concluded that good counsels, from whomsoever they come, must have their source in the prudence of the prince and not the prudence of the prince in the good counsels.

CHAPTER 24

WHY THE PRINCES OF ITALY HAVE LOST SOVEREIGNTY

The things written above, if prudently observed, make a new prince seem old and make him quickly more secure and more firm in his state than if he had grown old in it. Because the acts of a new prince are much more observed than those of a hereditary one; and when these are recognized as effective, they gain men much better and bind them with obligations much more than the ancient blood does. For men are much more taken by present things than by past ones; and when in present things they find good, they are happy in it and do not seek for anything else; more than that, they will undertake every sort of defence for him, if in other things he does not fail himself. And so he will have a double glory, that of having begun a new princedom, and of having enriched it and strengthened it with good laws, good arms, and good examples. Just as he has a double shame who, born a prince, has lost it through his imprudence.

And if one considers those lords in Italy who have lost their sovereignty in our times, as the king of Naples, the duke of Milan, and others, there will be found in them, first, a common defect as to arms, for the reasons that have been discussed above at length. Then some of them will be seen to whom the people have been hostile, or if people have not been hostile to them, they have not been able to secure themselves against the aristocrats. Because, without these defects, states are not lost that have so much strength as to be able to keep an army in the field. Philip of Macedon, not the father of Alexander, but the one who was conquered by Titus Quintus, did not have a large state, in comparison with the greatness of the Romans and of Greece, who attacked him. Nonetheless, because he was a soldierly man and knew how to get the support of the people and to secure himself against the aristocrats, he kept up the war against them for many years, and if at the end he lost the control of some cities, nevertheless his kingdom remained to him.

Therefore these princes of ours, who have been many years in their princedoms, should blame for their loss of them in the end not Fortune but their own laziness; because in quiet times they never considered that there could be changes (it is a common defect of men not, in fair weather, to reckon on a storm); hence when adverse times came at last, they thought about running away and not about defending themselves; and they hoped that the people, sickened by the arrogance of the conquerors, would call them back. This plan, when others are lacking, is good, but it is certainly bad to have abandoned other remedies for it; for one should never consent to fall because of believing you will find somebody who will pick you up. That either does not happen, or if it happens, it does not bring security for you, because that protection has been abject and does not depend upon yourself. And only those protections are good, are certain, are durable, that depend on yourself and your own abilities.

CHAPTER 25

HOW POWERFUL FORTUNE IS IN HUMAN AFFAIRS, AND IN WHAT WAY SHE SHOULD BE OPPOSED

It is not unknown to me that many have had and have the opinion that the things of the world are in such a way controlled by Fortune and by God that men with their prudence are not able to guide them; even more, that they have no remedy against them, and that because of this they can decide that one is not to sweat much over things but to let oneself be controlled by chance. This opinion has been the more believed in our times because of the great changes in things that have been seen and are seen every day, beyond all human conjecture. Thinking on this, I myself, sometimes, have inclined in some respects to their opinion. Nonetheless, in order that our free will should not be annulled, I judge it can be true that Fortune is the arbitress of half of our actions, but that even she leaves the control of the other half, or nearly that, to us.

And I compare her with one of these destructive rivers of ours which, when they are angry, make lakes of the plains, throw down the trees and the buildings, take away earth from this side, put it on that side; everyone flees before them; everyone yields to their fury, without being able at any point to resist. And though they are of that sort, it does not for that reason follow that, when the weather is quiet, men are not able to take precautions against them, with banks and dykes, in such a way that when afterwards they rise, either they will go off by a canal or their fury will not be either so wild or so damaging. It goes in the same way with Fortune. She shows her power where nothing effective is prepared to resist her, and turns her attacks where she knows that no dykes or banks are made to hold her. And if you consider Italy, who is the seat of these variations and that which has given motion to them, you will see that she is a plain without dykes and without any bank; but if she were dyked with adequate effectiveness, like Germany, Spain, and France, either this flood would not have made the great changes it has or it would not have come here. And I think this is enough to have said on opposing oneself to Fortune, in general.

But limiting myself more to particulars, I say that the same prince is seen living happily today and falling tomorrow, without having been seen changing his nature or any of his qualities. This I believe arises, first, from the causes that have been discussed above at such length, that is, that that prince who bases himself wholly on his Fortune falls when she varies. I believe, also, that he is lucky who adapts his way of procedure to the nature of the times, and likewise he is unlucky with whose procedure the times are not in harmony. Because men are seen proceeding in different ways in the things that lead them to the end that each one has before him, that is, fame and wealth: one with caution, the other rashly; one with violence, the other with art; one with patience, the other with its contrary; and each one with those differing methods is able to get there. Moreover, two cautious men may be seen, one reaching his goal, the other not; and likewise two who are equally lucky with two diverse methods, one being cautious and the other rash.

This comes from nothing else than the nature of the times, which are harmonious or not with their procedure. From this comes what I have said: two, working differently, produce the same effect; and of two working the same way, one attains his end, the other not. On this besides depends the variation in what is good: namely, if, for one who conducts himself with caution and patience, the times and their affairs circle about in such a way that his conduct is good, he keeps on being lucky; but if the times and their affairs change, he falls, because he does not change his way of proceeding. No man is found so prudent that he knows how to accommodate himself to this, both because he cannot deviate from that to which Nature inclines him, and also because, having always prospered while walking in one road, he cannot persuade himself to depart from it. And therefore the cautious man, when it is time to turn to rashness, cannot do it; hence he falls; yet if he could change his nature with the times and with affairs, his Fortune would not change.

Pope Julius II proceeded rashly in every affair of his, and he found the times and affairs so harmonious with his method of proceeding that a lucky result always emerged. Consider the first expedition he made, that of Bologna, while Messer Giovanni Bentivogli was still living. The Venetians were not pleased with it; the King of Spain felt the same; with France he was having conversations about that enterprise; and nonetheless, in his energy and rashness, he started in person on that expedition. This start made Spain and the Venetians stand uncertain and motionless, the latter for fear, and the other because of the desire he had to recover the entire kingdom of Naples. And on the other side, the King of France was dragged after him, because that king, seeing that he had started and wishing to make him a friend in order to humble the Venetians, judged he could not deny him his soldiers without doing him obvious injury. With his rash start, then, Julius brought about that which any other pope, with all human prudence, would never have brought about; because, if he had waited until he could depart from Rome with his terms fixed and all things in order, as any other pontiff would have done, he would never have succeeded, because the King of France would have had a thousand excuses and the others would have brought out a thousand fears. I intend to omit his other acts, which were all of the same sort and all came out well for him. And the shortness of his life did not allow him to know the opposite; because if times had come when it was needful to proceed with caution, his ruin would have resulted from them. Nor would he ever have deviated from those methods to which his nature inclined him.

I conclude, then, that since Fortune varies and men are set in their ways, they are prosperous while they agree, and as soon as they disagree, not prosperous. Even though I do think this: it is better to be rash than cautious, because Fortune is a woman and it is necessary, if you wish to keep her under, to beat her and pound her. And it can be seen that she lets herself be more often overcome by these than by those who proceed coldly; and therefore, like a woman, she is the friend of young men, because they are less cautious, more headstrong, and command her with more boldness.

CHAPTER 26

AN EXHORTATION TO SEIZE ITALY AND SET HER FREE FROM THE BARBARIANS

Taking account, then, of all the things discussed above, and considering within myself whether in Italy at present the times are suited for the honoring of a new prince, and if there is matter there that would give a prudent and able one opportunity to introduce into it a form that would do honor to himself and good to the generality of the men of that land, it seems to me that so many things come together for the advantage of a new prince, that I do not know what time has ever been more apt for this. And if, as I said, it was needful, if the vigor of Moses was to be seen, that the people of Israel should be enslaved in Egypt; and for recognizing the greatness of Cyrus' spirit, that the Persians should be oppressed by the Medes; and Theseus' excellence, that the Athenians should be dispersed; so, at present, if the efficacy of an Italian spirit is to be recognized, it is necessary that Italy should be reduced to the extremity in which she is at present, and that she should be more slave than the Hebrews, more servant than the Persians, more dispersed than the Athenians, without head, without order, beaten, despoiled, lacerated, devastated; and that she should have endured ruin of every sort.

And though up to now some gleams have appeared in a certain one that have made it possible to judge that he was ordained by God for her redemption, nevertheless it has later been seen how, in the highest course of his actions, he has been cast off by Fortune. Hence, being as though without life, she awaits whoever he may be who can cure her wounds, and put an end to the plunderings of Lombardy, to the tribute moneys of the Kingdom and of Tuscany, and cure her of those sores that now for a long time have been festering. We see how she prays God that he will send someone who will redeem her from this barbarous cruelty and arrogance; we see her all ready and willing to follow a banner, if only there be one here who will take it.

Nor is he to be seen at present in whom she is more able to hope than in your illustrious house, which through its fortune and its vigor, favored by God and by the Church, of which it is now leader, can make itself head of this redemption. This will not be very difficult if you bring before you the actions and the lives of those named above. And though those men were unusual and marvelous, nevertheless they were men, and each of them had a poorer opportunity than the present one, because their undertaking was not more just than this, nor more easy, nor was God more friendly to them than to you. Here justice is great, "for war is just for those to whom it is necessary and arms are holy when there is no hope except in arms." The order of things is now very favorable, and when the order is favorable there cannot be great difficulty, if only your house will take some of the methods of those whom I have set up to be aimed at. Besides this, we now see extraordinary leadings by God, without example: the sea has divided; a cloud has guided you on the road; the rock has poured out water; manna has rained here; everything has united for your greatness. The rest is for you to do. God does not wish to do everything, in order not to take from us free will and part of that glory that pertains to us.

And it is no marvel if none of the Italians mentioned above has been able to do what one can hope your illustrious house will do, and if, in so many revolutions in Italy and in so many affairs of war, it always seems that military vigor has been brought to an end in that land. The cause of this is that her old customs were not good and there has not been anybody who has been able to discover new ones; and nothing does so much honor to a man who rises anew as the new laws and new customs discovered by him. These things, when they are well based and have greatness in them, make him revered and wondered at. And in Italy matter is not lacking into which forms of every sort can be put; there is great efficacy here in the limbs if it is not lacking in the heads. Observe in duels and in combats by a few how superior the Italians are in strength, in skill, in intelligence; but when one comes to armies, they make no showing. And all proceeds from the weakness of the heads; because those who know are not obeyed, and it seems to each one that he knows, for up to now there has been no one there who has understood how to raise himself up, through both vigor and fortune, so that the others would yield to him. From this it comes that in so long a time, in such a number of wars as have been waged in the past twenty years, when there has been an army all Italian, it has always come out badly. Testimony of this is first the Taro, then Alessandria, Capua, Genoa, Vaila, Bologna, Mestri.

If your illustrious house, then, intends to follow those excellent men who redeemed their countries, it is necessary, before everything else, as the true foundation of every undertaking, that it be provided with its own military forces, because one cannot have more faithful, nor truer, nor better soldiers. And though each one of them may be good, all together would become better if they should see themselves commanded by their prince, and honored and maintained by him. It is necessary, therefore, for these forces to be made ready, if your house is to be able to defend itself against foreigners with Italian might.

And though the Swiss and the Spanish infantry be considered formidable, nonetheless there is a defect in both, because of which a third type would be able not merely to oppose them but to be sure of conquering them. Because the Spanish are not able to resist cavalry and the Swiss have to be afraid of infantry when they meet those as obstinate in fighting as themselves. Hence it has been seen and will be seen in experience that the Spanish are not able to resist cavalry like that of the French, and the Swiss are ruined by infantry like that of the Spanish. And though we have not seen a complete demonstration of this last, yet part of a test appeared in the battle of Ravenna, when the Spanish infantry were face to face with the German battalions, which use the same order of battle as the Swiss; there the Spanish, with the agility of their bodies and the aid of their bucklers, got within the pikes, underneath them, and attacked the Germans safely, without the latter having any remedy against it, and if it had not been for the cavalry that charged them, they would have destroyed all of them. It is possible then, knowing the defect of both of these types of infantry, to plan a new one that will resist cavalry and will not be afraid of infantry. The nature of their weapons and the variety of their tactics will effect this. And these are among the things that, newly arranged, give reputation and greatness to a new prince.

This opportunity, then, should not be allowed to pass by, in order that Italy, after so long a time, may see him who is to redeem her. I cannot express with what love he will be received in all those regions that have suffered from these foreign floods, with what thirst for vengeance, with what firm fidelity, with what piety, with what tears. What gates will be locked against him? what peoples will deny him obedience? what envy will oppose itself to him? what Italian will refuse to follow him? This barbarian rule stinks for everybody. May your illustrious house, then, take up this charge with that spirit and that hope with which just enterprises are taken up, in order that, under its ensign, our native land may be ennobled by it and, under its auspices, that saying by Petrarch may come true:

Valor against fury
Will take up arms, and the combat will be brief;
Because the ancient courage
Is not yet dead in Italian hearts.

DISCOURSES ON LIVY

Translated by ALLAN H. GILBERT

[Taken from *Machiavelli. The Prince and Other Works,* translated by Allan H. Gilbert, University Classics, Hendricks House, Packard and Company, Chicago.]

FIRST BOOK

CHAPTER 9

THAT IT IS NECESSARY TO BE ALONE TO BE ABLE TO ORGANIZE A REPUBLIC AFRESH AND TO REMAKE IT COMPLETELY CONTRARY TO ITS OLD LAWS

It perhaps will appear to some that I have rushed too far into the midst of Roman history since I have not as yet made any mention of the founders of that state, or of the laws that relate to religion and military affairs. And therefore, since I do not wish to hold in suspense any longer the minds of those who wish to learn something on this matter, I say that possibly many will judge it a bad example that a founder of a civil society, like Romulus, should first have killed his brother and then been a party to the death of Titus Tatius the Sabine, whom he had chosen as his companion on the throne. They think that because of this the citizens, with the precedent of their prince, would be able in their ambition and desire to rule, to injure those who might resist their authority. This opinion would be true if the end for which he committed that homicide were not considered.

And this ought to be taken as a general rule: it never, or very rarely, happens that any state or kingdom is well organized from the beginning, or is altogether reformed, contrary to its old laws, if it is not organized by one man; on the contrary, it is essential that the pattern be given by one man only, and that on his mind any such reformation should depend. Therefore a prudent organizer of a state, and one who has a fixed intention of benefitting not himself but the common good, and not his own descendants but the common fatherland, ought to strive to have the authority for himself alone. Nor will a prudent man ever censure anybody for an irregular action he carries out in order to found a kingdom or set up a republic. It is necessary, indeed, that even if he blames the action he should excuse its effect; and if it is good, like that of Romulus, he always will excuse it; because he who is violent in order to destroy, not he who is violent in order to restore, should be blamed.

He ought, indeed, to be so prudent and virtuous as not to leave the authority he has seized to someone else as an inheritance; for since men are more prone to evil than to good, his successor may use ambitiously what he has used virtuously. Besides this, though one man is best for organizing, the thing organized will not last long if it rests on the shoulders of one man only, but it will last if it is left to the care of many and many have the task of keeping it up. Because, just as many are not fit to organize a thing, because they do not know what is best for it, on account of their diverse opinions, so, after they have recognized it, they do not agree to abandon it. And that Romulus was among those, that he deserved excuse for the death of his brother and his companion, and that what he did was for the common good, and not by reason of his own ambition, is shown by his having at once established a senate, with which he would confer, and according to the opinion of which he would decide. And he who will consider well the authority Romulus kept for himself, will see that he retained nothing except the command of the armies when war had been decided on, and the power of summoning the senate. This was seen at the time when Rome became free by the expulsion of the Tarquins, when no arrangement from the past was changed by the Romans, except that in place of a king for life there were two annual consuls. This testifies that all the early fundamental laws of that city had been more in harmony with a life according to law and freedom than with an absolute and tyrannical one.

Numerous examples can be given in support of what I have said above, as Moses, Lycurgus, Solon, and other founders of kingdoms and republics, who were able, by appropriating individual authority, to form laws suited to the common good; but I intend to pass them by, as things generally known. I shall bring up just one, not so famous, but worthy to be considered by those who wish to establish good laws. This is that when Agis, king of Sparta, wished to bring the Spartans back within the limits set by the laws of Lycurgus (because it seemed to him that by deviating from them the city had lost much of its ancient efficiency, and consequently much of its military power and its empire), he was killed by the Spartan Ephors at the very outset, as a man who intended to seize the tyranny. But when Cleomenes came after him in the kingdom and there grew up in him the same wish (because of the memorials and writings by Agis that he found, where it appeared of what sort his mind and intention were), he knew that he could not do this good to his native city if he did not become the only one in authority, and, because of the ambition of men, it seemed to him that he could not benefit the many against the will of the few. And taking a suitable occasion, he killed all the Ephors and anyone else able to oppose him; then he completely restored the laws of Lycurgus. This decision would have been enough to revivify Sparta and give Cleomenes the same reputation Lycurgus had, if it had not been for the power of the Macedonians, and the weakness of the other Greek states. For after his reform he was attacked by the Macedonians and conquered by them because he was himself inferior in force and had no one to whom he could turn for aid. Hence his plan, though well laid and worthy of praise, remained imperfect.

Considering all these things then, I conclude that in order to organize a state, it is necessary to govern alone. Hence Romulus deserves to be excused rather than blamed for the deaths of Remus and Titus Tatius.

CHAPTER 10

THE FOUNDERS OF A REPUBLIC OR A KINGDOM DESERVE PRAISE JUST AS MUCH AS THE FOUNDERS OF A DESPOTISM DESERVE INFAMY

Among all praiseworthy men those are most praised who have been the heads and founders of religions. Next are those who have founded republics or kingdoms. After them, those are known to fame who as leaders of armies have increased their own dominion or that of their native land. Next to these are to be put men of letters. And because these men are of several sorts, each of them is famous according to his degree. To various other men, the number of whom is countless, some measure of praise is given, as their arts and their occupations secure it. On the other side, infamous and worthy to be detested are destroyers of religions, wasters of kingdoms and republics, enemies of the virtues, of letters, and of every other art that brings utility and honor to the human race, such as are the irreligious, the oppressive, the ignorant, the worthless, the lazy, and the cowardly. There never will be anyone so silly or so wise, so bad or so good that, if the choice between these two kinds of men is offered to him, he will not praise the kind that deserves praise, and blame the kind that deserves blame. Nonetheless, almost all men, deceived by a false good and a false glory, let themselves go, either willingly or ignorantly, into the ranks of those who merit blame rather than praise, and though they are able to establish a republic or a kingdom, to their lasting honor, yet they turn to a tyranny. They do not realize what great renown, what great glory, what great honor, security, quiet, and satisfaction of mind they abandon by this decision, and what great infamy, abuse, censure, peril, and disquiet they incur.

Those who live in a private station in a republic, or who through fortune or prowess become princes of it, if they read history and get anything of value from the records of the past, cannot possibly, if they are private citizens, wish to do other than live in their native cities rather as Scipios than as Caesars; or if they are princes, they must prefer Agesilaus, Timoleon, and Dion to Nabis, Phalaris, and Dionysius, because they will see that the latter are always strongly censured and the former very much praised. They will see also that Timoleon and the others did not have less authority in their native cities than did Dionysius and Phalaris, and that they had far more security there.

Nor should anybody be deceived by the glory of Caesar, especially on seeing him lauded by the historians, for those who praise him have been bribed by his good fortune, and terrified by the long duration of the Empire, which, since it was conducted under his name, did not permit literary men to speak freely of him. But he who would like to know what free writers would say of him may read what they say of Catiline. For Caesar is so much the more to be blamed in proportion as he who has done an evil deed is more blameworthy than he who has planned to do it. He may see also with what praises they honor the name of Brutus, for since they are unable to censure Caesar on account of his power, they give honor to his enemy.

He who has become prince in a state should also consider that after Rome became an Empire those emperors who lived according to the laws, as good rulers should, deserved much greater praise than those who lived in the opposite way. He will see that Titus, Nerva, Trajan, Hadrian, Antoninus, and Marcus did not need the praetorian soldiers nor the masses of the legions to protect them, because their habits, the good will of the people, and the love of the Senate were their defence. He will see, too, that Caligula, Nero, Vitellius, and the many other wicked emperors did not find the eastern and the western armies enough to protect them against the enemies which their evil habits and their impious lives had raised up against them. And if the history of these emperors were well considered, it would be a sufficient body of instruction for any prince, to show him the road to glory or to censure, to security or to fear on his part. Because, of twenty-six emperors between Caesar and Maximinus, sixteen were killed and ten died naturally; and if some of those who were killed were good, as Galba and Pertinax, they were killed by that corruption their predecessors had left among the soldiers. And if among those who died naturally there was one wicked, like Severus, it happened because of his very great good fortune and personal ability —two things that are companions to few men. One will see also through the reading of this history how a good kingdom can be established, because all the emperors who came to the throne through heredity, except Titus, were bad; those through adoption were all good, as were those five from Nerva to Marcus; and when the Empire was left to heirs, it went back to its ruin.

Let a prince put before himself, then, the times from Nerva to Marcus, and compare them with those that had been before and those that were later, and then he can choose in which he would prefer to be born, or over which he would choose to be put in charge. Because in those governed by the good ones he will see a prince secure in the midst of his secure citizens; the world full of peace and justice; he will see the Senate with its authority; the magistrates with their honors; the rich citizens enjoying their riches; nobility and virtue exalted; he will see everybody quiet and everybody good. And on the other hand, all hatred, all licentiousness, corruption, and ambition are blotted out; he will see times of gold, when each man can hold and defend what opinion he wishes. He will see, in short, the world rejoicing; the prince abounding in reverence and glory, the people in love and security. If after that he will consider carefully the days of the other emperors, he will see them horrible by wars, torn by seditions, cruel in peace and in war; many princes slain with the sword; many civil wars and foreign wars; Italy distressed and full of new misfortunes; her cities ruined and plundered. He will see Rome burned, the Capitol laid waste by its citizens, the ancient temples desolate, the ceremonies of religion corrupted, the city full of adulteries; he will behold the sea covered with exiles, the rocks covered with blood. In Rome he will behold countless cruelties come to pass, and nobility, riches, former honors, and above all virtue, counted as capital sins. He will see false accusers rewarded, servants bribed against their masters, and freedmen against their former owners, and those who lack enemies oppressed by their friends. He will then recognize very well what heavy obligations Rome, Italy, and the world owe Caesar.

Without doubt, if he is of human birth, he will be horrified by every imitation of wicked days, and will be fired with a tremendous desire to follow the ways of good times. Of a truth, if a prince seeks glory in this world, he should desire to possess a corrupt city, not to ruin it completely as did Caesar, but to reform it as did Romulus. Certainly Heaven cannot give men a greater opportunity for glory, nor can men wish for a greater one. And if indeed, to be able to organize a city well, it should be necessary to lay down the princedom, he would deserve some excuse who would not organize it, in order not to fall from his position; but if he is able to keep his princedom for himself and to reform his city, he deserves no excuse. And in short, those to whom Heaven gives such an opportunity should observe that two roads are put before them: one of these causes them to live in security and renders them glorious after their deaths; the other causes them to live in continual anxiety, and after their deaths to leave unending infamy for themselves.

CHAPTER 12

OF HOW MUCH IMPORTANCE IT IS TO TAKE ACCOUNT OF RELIGION, AND THAT ITALY, HAVING BEEN WITHOUT IT BECAUSE OF THE ROMAN CHURCH, IS RUINED

Those princes and republican governments that wish to keep themselves uncorrupted must above everything else keep the ceremonies of their religions uncorrupted, and always respect them, because there can be no clearer sign of the ruin of a land than to see divine worship undervalued. This is easy to understand when one knows on what the religion in which a man is born is based; for every religion has the basis of its life in some important institution of its own. The life of the heathen religion was based on the responses of the oracles, and on the group of diviners and soothsayers; all their other ceremonies, sacrifices, and rites depended on these, because they easily believed that God who could predict future good or future ill could also give it. From this came sacrifices, prayers, and every ceremony in veneration of them; this was the reason for the oracle of Delos, the temple of Jupiter Ammon, and other celebrated oracles, which filled the world with admiration and devotion. Then when these oracles began to speak to suit the powerful, and this falsity was discovered by the people, men became unbelieving and ready to disturb every good custom. The rulers of a republic or a kingdom ought, then, to preserve the fundamentals of the religion they adhere to. If they do this, it will be easy for them to keep their country religious, and as a result to keep it good and united. And they ought to favor and magnify all happenings that seem to favor religion, even though they think them false. And they ought to do it the more in proportion as they are more prudent and have a better understanding of natural science. And because this method has been practised by wise men, there has sprung up belief in miracles, which are renowned in religions even though false, because the prudent aggrandize them, from whatever origin they come, and their authority then gives the miracles credence with everybody.

There were many of these miracles at Rome. Among them was this: When the Roman soldiers were sacking the city of Veii, some of them entered the temple of Juno, went up to the image of the goddess, and said: "Do you wish to come to Rome?" To some it appeared that the image nodded, and to others that it said "Yes." These soldiers were very religious, as Titus Livius shows by saying that when they entered the temple they were not disorderly but were all devout and reverent. Hence they heard the response to their question which they probably expected. This opinion and belief was favored and added to in every way by Camillus and the other chief men of the city.

If the rulers of Christendom had kept their religion in the form in which its founder established it, Christian states and republics would be much more united and more prosperous than they are. One cannot form a better estimate of the decline of Christianity than by seeing that those people who are nearest to the Roman Church, the head of our religion, have least religion. And anybody who considers its fundamentals, and sees how different its practice is at the present time, must decide that, beyond doubt, overthrow or punishment is near at hand.

And because many are of the opinion that the well-being of the cities of Italy is derived from the Roman Church, I wish to give the reasons that occur to me on the other side. I will mention two very strong arguments, which, so far as I can see, cannot be refuted. The first is that because of the bad example of that papal court, this land has lost all piety and all religion. This has resulted in numerous troubles and disorders, because, just as every good thing is taken for granted where there is religion, so where it is lacking, the contrary is taken for granted. We Italians, then, have this first obligation to the Church and the priests that we have become without religion and vile.

But we have one still greater to them, which is the second cause of our ruin. This is that the Church has kept this country divided and still keeps it so. And certainly no land was ever united or prosperous if it was not wholly under the rule of one republican government or one prince, as has happened in France and Spain. The cause why Italy is not in that same position, and has neither one republic nor one prince to govern her, is the Church alone. Because, though the Church has had her seat here and has held temporal power, yet she has never been so strong or vigorous that she has been able to seize sole authority over Italy and make herself ruler of the land. Yet, on the other hand, she has not been so weak that, for fear of losing her power over her temporal possessions, she has not been able to call in some strong man to defend her against anyone in Italy who became too powerful. This was seen long ago in various instances: by means of Charlemagne, she drove out the Lombards, who were then almost king of Italy; in our times, she deprived the Venetians of power with the aid of France; later she drove away the French with the help of the Swiss.

Since the Church has not, then, been powerful enough to be able to take possession of Italy, and has not permitted any one else to sieze it, she has been the cause that the land has been unable to unite under one ruler. But it has been under many princes and lords, who have caused such disunion and weakness that she has been brought to be the prey not merely of powerful barbarians, but of anybody who assails her. For this we Italians owe our thanks to the Church, and to nobody else. And he who would like to see the truth of this more plainly by a sure test, would need to be so powerful that he could send the Roman court, with the authority it has in Italy, to live in the cities of the Swiss, who today are the only people who live as the ancients did, as to religion and military customs. And he would see that in a short time the wicked habits of the papal court would make more trouble in the land than any other event that could occur there at any time.

CHAPTER 34

THE AUTHORITY OF THE DICTATOR DID GOOD AND NOT HARM TO THE ROMAN REPUBLIC; AND THAT THE POWERS THAT CITIZENS TAKE FOR THEMSELVES, NOT THOSE GIVEN TO THEM BY FREE VOTES, ARE HARMFUL TO FREE GOVERNMENT

Some writers have condemned those Romans who devised in that city the scheme of setting up a Dictator, as a thing that was in time the cause of the tyranny over Rome; for they allege that the first tyrant in that city ruled it under this title of Dictator; and they say that if this had not existed, Caesar would not have been able to make his tyranny respectable under any lawful title. But this thing has not been well examined by those who hold this opinion and has been believed contrary to all reason. Because it was not the name of the rank of Dictator that made Rome a slave, but it was the power taken by citizens because of prolonged authority. And if the name of Dictator had been lacking in Rome, they would have taken some other, because forces easily get themselves names, not names forces. And it is to be seen that as long as the Dictator was set up according to the general laws and not by his own authority, he always did good to the city. Because magistrates that set themselves up and powers that are given in abnormal ways do harm to republics, not those that come in regular ways; just as it can be seen that it was true in Rome that in so long a course of time never any Dictator did anything but good to the state.

There are very obvious reasons for this. First, in order to make it possible for a citizen to do harm and seize irregular authority for himself, it is necessary that he have many qualities that he can never have in a state that is not corrupt. For he needs to be very rich and to have many adherents and partisans, which he cannot have where the laws are observed. And when he does have them, such men are so dangerous that free votes do not unite on them. Besides this the Dictator was set up for a time and not for life, and merely to dispose of that cause because of which he was set up; and his authority included the power to decide for himself about the remedies for that urgent peril and to do everything without consultation and to punish without appeal, but he was not able to do things that tended toward weakening the state, such as taking power away from the Senate and the people, undoing the laws of the city and making new ones. Therefore, since there came together the short time of his dictatorship and the limited authority he had and the uncorrupted Roman people, it was impossible for the Dictator to go beyond his bounds and injure the city; and it is seen from experience that he always helped.

And truly among the other Roman laws, this is one that deserves to be considered and counted among those that were the cause of the greatness of so mighty an empire, because without such a law the citizens will emerge with difficulty from unusual events. Because the habitual arrangements of republics have a slow motion (since no council and no magistrate has power by himself to do anything, but in many things one has need of another, and in getting these wills into union, time is spent), their remedies are very perilous, when they have to remedy a thing that does not wait for time. And therefore republics should have among their laws such a method. And the Venetian republic, which stands high among modern republics, has reserved power to a few citizens, who in urgent needs, if all agree, have power to decide without further consultation. Because, when a republic lacks such a method, it must fall, if the laws are to be kept, or it must break them in order not to fall. And in a republic nothing should ever happen that must be managed with unlawful methods. Because, though the unlawful method may benefit at that time, nonetheless the example does harm, because it brings in a habit of breaking the laws for the sake of a benefit, and then, with that excuse, they are broken for the sake of an injury. Hence a republic never will be perfect if it has not with its laws provided for everything and laid out a remedy for every accident and given the method for controlling it. And for that reason I say in conclusion that those republics that in urgent perils do not have a resource either in the Dictator or in some like authority, always fall when conditions are difficult.

It is to be observed how wisely the mode of choosing the Dictator was provided by the Romans in this new law. Because, since setting him up meant some indignity for the consuls, who, though they were the heads of the city, had to come under command like the others, and since it was foreseen that some envy of him might appear among the citizens, they determined that power to choose him should rest in the consuls, imagining that when such an event happened that Rome had need of this kingly power, they would be able to establish it willingly, and since they did it themselves, it would grieve them less. Because wounds and all other evils that a man inflicts on himself of his own will and by choice pain him very much less than those that are inflicted by others. Yet afterward, in their last days, the Romans were wont to give such authority to the consuls instead of to a Dictator, with these words: "Let the consul see to it that the republic receives no harm."

And to return to my subject, I conclude that the neighbors of Rome, by trying to crush her, made her take measures such that she was able not merely to defend herself but was also able to attack them with more force, better planning, and more power.

SECOND BOOK

CHAPTER 2

WITH WHAT KINDS OF PEOPLE THE ROMANS HAD TO FIGHT, AND HOW STUBBORNLY THOSE DEFENDED THEIR FREEDOM [WITH DISCUSSION OF THE EFFECTS OF CHRISTIANITY]

Nothing made it harder for the Romans to conquer the peoples around them and parts of the lands at a distance than the love that in those times many peoples had for their freedom, which they defended so stubbornly that they would never have been subjugated except by immense vigor. From many instances we can learn in what perils they put themselves in order to maintain or regain that freedom, what vengeance they took on those who had taken it from them. We also learn from the reading of histories what injuries peoples and cities receive from servitude. And whereas in these times there is but a single land that can be said to have free cities in it, in ancient times there were many completely free peoples in all lands. It can be seen that in those times of which we are speaking at present, in Italy, from the Alps that now divide Tuscany from Lombardy all the way to the point of Italy, the peoples were all free, such as the Tuscans, the Romans, the Samnites, and many other peoples that lived in that section of Italy. Nor is it said that there was ever any king there except those that ruled in Rome, and Porsenna king of Tuscany. How his family was wiped out, history does not tell, but it is very plain that in the times when the Romans went to besiege Veii, Tuscany was free, and it so much enjoyed its liberty and so much hated the name of prince that when the Veientians had established one in Veii and asked aid against the Romans from the Tuscans, the last, after holding many consultations, determined not to give aid to the Veientians so long as they lived under the king, thinking it not good to defend the country of those who had already submitted it to another.

And it is easy to learn why this love for free government springs up in peoples, for experience shows that cities never have increased in dominion or in riches except while they have been at liberty. And truly it is a marvelous thing to consider to what greatness Athens came in the space of a hundred years when she freed herself from the tyranny of Pisistratus. But above all it is very wonderful to observe what greatness Rome attained after she freed herself from her kings. The cause is easy to understand, because not individual good but common good is what makes cities great. And without doubt this common good is not attended to except in republics, because everything that advances it is attended to, and though it acts to the harm of this or that private citizen, those whom the said good benefits are so many that they are able to carry it forward against the inclination of those few who are injured by it.

It happens in the opposite way when there is a prince; in that case what benefits him almost always injures the city, and what benefits the city injures him. For that reason, as soon as a tyranny over a free community grows up, the least ill that results from it for those cities is that they no longer go forward and no longer increase in power or in riches; but most of the time, in fact always, it happens that they go backward. And if chance brings about that there rises up an efficient tyrant, who through courage and through force of arms increases his dominion, no advantage comes from it for that republic, but only to himself, because he cannot honor any of those citizens whom he tyrannizes over who are strong and good, if he does not wish to have suspicion of them. Nor can he subordinate or make tributary to the city where he is tyrant the cities he conquers, because making it powerful does not make for his advantage, but it does make for it to keep the state disunited and to have each city and each province recognize him. Hence he alone, and not his country, profits from his conquests. And let him who wishes to support this opinion with countless other reasons read Xenophon in the tractate he composed *On Tyranny*.

It is no wonder, then, that the ancient peoples with such great hatred pursued tyrants and loved free government and that the name of liberty was so highly esteemed by them. This was shown when Hieronymus, the grandson of Hiero of Syracuse, was killed in Syracuse, for when the news of his death came to his army, which was not very far from Syracuse, at first they began to riot and to take arms against his murderers, but when they heard that freedom was being proclaimed in Syracuse, they were attracted by that name, became entirely quiet, laid aside their anger against the tyrannicides, and decided that it would be possible to organize a free government in that city.

It is also not strange that the peoples should inflict strange vengeance on those who have taken away their liberty. There have been many examples of this, of which I intend to mention but one, that happened in Corcyra, a city in Greece, in the times of the Peloponnesian War. That country being then divided into two parties, of which one followed the Athenians, the other the Spartans, it came about that in many cities that were divided within themselves one party sought the friendship of Sparta, the other of Athens. And when it happened that in the said city the nobles were stronger and took away the freedom of the people, the popular party by means of the Athenians regained its powers and, laying hands on all the nobility, shut them up in a prison that would hold them all. From this they took them out eight or ten at a time, under the pretext of sending them into exile in different places, and caused them to die with many cruel punishments. Those who remained, being aware of this, determined, in so far as it was possible for them, to escape that shameful death, and arming themselves with what they could, they fought with those who tried to enter and defended the entrance of the prison. Thereupon the people, having assembled at this noise, unroofed the upper part of that place and smothered them with those ruins. In the said country many other similar horrible and noteworthy events also occurred, so that it is seen to be true that freedom which has been taken away from you is avenged with greater fury than that which somebody has planned to take from you.

Thinking then whence it could have come that in those ancient times the peoples were greater lovers of freedom than in these, I believe it comes from the same cause that makes men now less vigorous, which I believe is the difference of our education from the ancient, based on the difference of our religion from the ancient. Because, since our religion has shown us the truth and the true way, it makes us have less esteem for the honor of the world; whereas the pagans, greatly esteeming it and having placed their greatest good in it, were more vigorous in their actions. This can be inferred from many of their customs, beginning with the magnificence of their sacrifices, compared with the modesty of ours, where there is some pomp, more delicate than magnificent, but no fierce and vigorous action. In theirs the pomp and the magnificence of the ceremonies were not lacking, but to them was joined the act of sacrifice, full of blood and ferocity, since they killed a multitude of animals in it; this sight, being terrible, made the men like to it. The ancient religion, besides this, gave divine honor only to men laden with worldly glory, such as generals of armies and princes of states. Our religion has glorified humble and contemplative men rather than active ones. It has, then, put the greatest good in humility, abjectness, and contempt for human things; the other puts it in greatness of mind, in strength of body, and in all the other things apt to make men exceedingly vigorous. And if our religion asks that you have fortitude within you, it prefers that you be adapted to suffering rather than to doing something vigorous.

This way of living, then, seems to have made the world weak and given it as a prey to wicked men, who in security are able to control it, seeing that the generality of men, in order to go to Heaven, think more about enduring their injuries than about avenging them. And though it may appear that the world has grown effeminate, and Heaven has laid aside her arms, it is without doubt caused more by the worthlessness of men, who have interpreted our religion according to sloth and not according to vigor. For if they would consider that it allows us the aggrandizement and the defense of our country, they would see that it intends that we love and honor her and prepare ourselves to be such that we can defend her.

This education, then, and such false interpretations bring about that we do not see in the world so many republics as were seen in ancient times, nor, as a result, do we see in the peoples such great love for freedom as then. Still I believe that the cause of this is rather that the Roman Empire with her arms and her greatness wiped out all the republics and all the self-governing communities. And though later that Empire was liquidated, the cities have not yet been able to put themselves together or to reorganize themselves for government according to law, except in a few places in that Empire.

However that may be, the Romans did find in every smallest part of the world a league of republics well armed and very stubborn in the defense of their freedom. This shows that the Roman people without unusual and immense efficiency never would have been able to overcome them. And in order to give an example of some parts of it, I think the instance of the Samnites is enough. About them it seems a wonderful thing — and Titus Livius confesses it — that they were so powerful and their armies so strong that as late as the time of Papirius Cursor the consul, the son of the first Papirius (which was a space of forty-six years) they were able to resist the Romans, after so many defeats, ruins of cities, and so many slaughters that they suffered in their country, especially when one sees that that country, where there were so many cities and so many men, is almost uninhabited; and then there was such good organization and such force there that it was unconquerable, if it had not been assailed with Roman efficiency.

It is an easy thing to determine where that organization took its rise and whence this confusion is derived, because it all comes from living in freedom then and living in slavery now. Because all the cities and the provinces that live in freedom in every region, as I said above, make very great gains. For there larger populations are seen, on account of marriages being freer, more desirable to men, for each man gladly begets those children he thinks he can bring up, without fear that his patrimony will be taken from him; and he knows not merely that they are born free and not slaves but that by means of their ability they can become leading men. Riches are seen to multiply there to a greater extent, both those that come from agriculture and those that come from industry. For each man gladly increases in that thing and seeks to gain those goods that he believes he can enjoy when he has gained them. Thence it comes that men in emulation give thought to private and public advantages; and both of them continue to increase marvelously.

The opposite of all this happens in those countries that live as slaves; and the more they fall away from their wonted good, the harder their slavery is. And of all hard slaveries, that is hardest that subjects you to a republic: first, because it is more lasting and there is less hope of being able to escape from it; second, because the purpose of a republic is to enfeeble and weaken all other bodies in order to increase its own. This is not done by a prince who subjugates you, if that prince is not some barbarian prince, a destroyer of cities and a waster of all the civilization of men, as are the oriental princes. But if he has in himself human and ordinary qualities, he usually loves equally the cities subject to him and leaves them all their industries and almost all their ancient customs. Hence, if they are not able to prosper like free men, they also do not go to ruin like slaves. I refer to the slavery into which cities come by serving a foreigner, because of those serving one of their own citizens I have spoken above.

He who considers, then, all that has been said, will not be astonished at the power the Samnites had when they were free, and at the weakness into which they came later, when they were slaves. And Titus Livius gives us assurance of it in several places and especially in the war with Hannibal, where he shows that when the Samnites were oppressed by a legion of men that was in Nola, they sent ambassadors to Hannibal to beg him to rescue them; and they said in their speech that they had for a hundred years fought the Romans with their own soldiers and their own generals, and many times had resisted two consular armies and two consuls, and that then they had come to such a low condition that they were scarcely able to defend themselves from a little Roman legion that was in Nola.

BALDASSARE CASTIGLIONE

(1478–1529)

The Book of the Courtier presents a picture of the court in the little Umbrian city of Urbino in the year 1507. From the discussions carried on in that court circle, there emerges the humanist ideal of the development of the individual evolved by the culture of the Renaissance. At first circulated in manuscript, and finally printed in 1528, the book immediately became read over all of Western Europe.

Its author, Baldassare Castiglione, soldier, scholar, and diplomat, demonstrated in his own life the ideal his book portrayed. Although he was a descendant of an ancient and noble family of Milanese territory, he was born at Casatico near Mantua in 1478. His father, Cristoforo, was a captain in the military service of Francesco Gonzaga, Marquis of Mantua; his mother was a member of the Gonzaga family itself.

At the age of thirteen, he was sent to complete his education at Milan and later entered court service there during the most flourishing years of the Duke Lodovico Sforza and his charming duchess Beatrice d'Este. There he obtained the humanist training of the age: he studied Greek with the Athenian Demetrius Chalcondylas, Latin with Giorgio Merula, also the writings of the Italian poets; he was trained in the feats of horsemanship and of military exercises; he cultivated the taste for music and painting. Thus early he became a favorite in the kind of court life he was later to glorify by his writing.

In 1499, at the age of twenty-one, he was recalled to Mantua by the death of his father, and himself entered the service of the Marquis Francesco Gonzaga. Here his superior qualities of intelligence and tact were at once recognized and employed by the Marquis and his accomplished duchess Isabella d'Este; indeed the friendship which the Duchess gave him continued to the end of his life. When, in 1503, Francesco marched in command of the French forces of Louis XII to the campaign against Naples, Castiglione gave military service with him in the unsuccessful battle of the Garigliano.

On the return from the Naples campaign, he stopped at Rome soon after the election of Pope Julius II and there found the Duke Guidobaldo di Montefeltro from Urbino. Castiglione had known the Duke when the latter was an exile at the Mantuan court. Such a mutual regard now arose between them that it was decided to ask Castiglione's release from the Marquis of Mantua that he might enter Guidobaldo's service at Urbino. Francesco consented with a curt reply, but he harbored a personal resentment that kept Castiglione away from Mantua for some years to come.

There followed immediately, however, the four golden years of Castiglione's life in the court at Urbino which inspired him to the end and which have lived in his prose ever since. Situated on the slopes of the Apennines toward the Adriatic Sea, almost in the center of Italy, the little city had been ruled for half a century by the princes of the Montefeltro family. The Duke Federico di Montefeltro, pupil of the distinguished humanist educator Vittorino da Feltre, powerful *condottiere,* and learned patron of the arts, had built there the magnificent palace which may be visited today, had collected one of the choicest libraries in Italy, and had attracted noted scholars and artists from many parts of Europe. He had died in 1482, and his son Guidobaldo and the Duchess Elisabetta Gonzaga had ruled since over perhaps the most attractive court in Renaissance Italy. Castiglione came on the 6th of September 1504; Guidobaldo died in April 1508. During these four years, Castiglione's service was largely diplomatic and personal: he went to the court of Henry VII at London and received for Guidobaldo the Order of the Garter at Windsor; he was sent to pay homage to the French king Louis XII at Milan. But he had ample leisure for the cultural pursuits and associations of the court in an atmosphere of peace and tranquillity. His writing is eloquent of the graciousness of the Duchess Elisabetta and of his devotion to her. And to the court, among many others, came Giuliano de'Medici, an exile from Florence; the distinguished humanist and later cardinal, Pietro Bembo; Bernardo, later Cardinal Bibbiena; and the youthful artist Raphael. At this time Castiglione wrote many of his Latin elegies and Italian *canzoni* and sonnets, and in 1506 his pastoral eclogue the *Tirsi* was given during the carnival. The discussions of *The Book of the Courtier* are represented as having taken place on four successive evenings in early March 1507.

With the death of Guidobaldo in 1508 and the accession of Francesco Maria della Rovere, change came at Urbino. Pope Leo X was elected in 1513; he proceeded to surround himself with scholars, artists, and poets, so that it seemed the Golden Age had returned to Rome. The Duke Francesco invested Castiglione with the castle and countship of Novillara in 1513 and made him envoy at the Vatican where many members of the circle at Urbino were now papal officials. But in 1516 Leo deprived Francesco of his duchy, the papal forces invaded Urbino, and the ducal family took refuge at Mantua.

In 1516, after having long subordinated any consideration of marriage, Castiglione was married to Ippolita Torelli, of a noble family of Modena. At the fall of Urbino he now retired to his family estate at Casatico. His marriage was most fortunate; but his young bride, who was fifteen years of age, died four years later after the birth of a second daughter, one son having also been born.

When, in 1519, Federico Gonzaga became Marquis of Mantua, Castiglione entered his service and became his ambassador at Rome. He enjoyed the cultured society of the last years of Leo X: his friend Raphael was at the height of his fame, and before the end Leo admitted Castiglione into his confidence and intimate association.

By this time, however, the European situation, in which Francis I, the Emperor Charles V, and the Pope were so deeply involved, was becoming more and more acute. Finally in 1524, Clement VII requested the service of Castiglione from the Marquis that he might send him upon what proved his last and most difficult mission, as papal nuncio at the Emperor's court in Spain. He arrived in Madrid in March 1525 during one of the most critical times in the history of the Papacy and of Italy. He followed the Emperor's court to Toledo, Seville, Granada; in association with the Venetian ambassador Andrea Navagero, he responded to the soft climate and Moorish culture of Andalusia. From the beginning he enjoyed the esteem of the Emperor. He labored with complete loyalty and integrity to the end. No doubt he placed too much confidence in both the Emperor and the Pope; but Clement, who was playing a double game with both Francis and Charles, vacillated, temporized, and withheld communication with his nuncio, leaving him without direction. When, in the spring of 1527, the soldiers of the Imperial army marched south and sacked Rome for eight days, Castiglione was left discredited and broken by his diplomatic defeat.

The Book of the Courtier had been conceived in Urbino soon after the death of Guidobaldo in 1508; Castiglione had written much of it at Rome during his years as envoy to Leo X, virtually completing it by 1516, although he continued to revise it. It had since been read by his friends in manuscript. He now gave it its final revision in Spain, and it was printed by the Aldine Press in Venice in 1528. Shortly before his death the Emperor conferred upon him the bishopric of Avila. He died on the 7th of February 1529 in Toledo. The Emperor declared to his courtiers, "I tell you that one of the finest gentlemen in the world is dead." He was buried with royal honors in the Cathedral of Toledo, although his body was later transferred and placed with the ashes of his wife Ippolita in the sarcophagus in Santa Maria delle Grazie near Mantua.

Raphael left as one of his masterpieces the portrait of Castiglione which now hangs in the Louvre. From it one catches the true spirit of the man. He maintained the esteem and friendship of the highest princes, churchmen, scholars, and artists of his time. But by blood and nurture he belonged to the chivalric and feudal aristocracy of an age that had passed. In him were united the qualities of the humanist and the courtier, and his conception of the courtier and of the prince has the high seriousness of his chivalric tradition. For a few brief years that tradition flourished at Urbino. Thereafter, Castiglione's very nature handicapped him for the part he was called upon to play in the world so shrewdly understood by Machiavelli. Consequently, in his book, as in his personality, the noble gravity and refinement of his nature remain tempered by a subtle tone of melancholy.

SELECTED BIBLIOGRAPHY

EDITIONS

Opere Volgari e Latine de Conte Baldassare Castiglione, ed. G. A. and G. Volpi, Padua, 1733; *Opere. Baldassare Castiglione e Giovanni della Casa,* ed. Giuseppe Prezzolini, Milan, Rizzoli, 1937; *Il Cortegiano,* ed. Vittorio Cian, 4th edit., Florence, Sansoni, 1947; *Lettere del Conte Baldassare Castiglione,* ed. Pierantonio Serassi, 2 vols., Padua, 1769–71.

TRANSLATIONS

The Book of the Courtier, trans. (1561) Sir Thomas Hoby, introd. Walter Raleigh, Tudor Translations, London, Nutt, 1900, also in Everyman's Lib.; *The Book of the Courtier,* trans. Leonard Eckstein Opdycke, New York, Scribner, 1901, also in Black and Gold Library, New York, Liveright, 1929.

BIOGRAPHY AND CRITICISM

C. Martinati, *Notizie Storico-Biografiche intorno al Conte B. Castiglione,* Florence, 1890; V. Cian, "B. Castiglione," in *Enciclopedia Italiana,* IX, 374–76, 1931.

Christopher Hare, *Courts and Camps of the Ital. Renaissance,* New York, Scribner, 1908; Julia Cartwright, *B. Castiglione. His Life and Letters,* 2 vols., New York, Dutton, 1908; James Dennistoun, *Memoirs of the Dukes of Urbino,* 3 vols., new edit. ed. E. Hutton, London, John Lane, 1909; Walter Raleigh, "Sir Thomas Hoby," in *Some Authors,* 41–121, Oxford, Clarendon Press, 1923; Ralph Roeder, *The Man of the Renaissance,* parts 3–4, New York, Garden City Pub. Co., 1933.

SPECIAL STUDIES

Ruth Kelso, *The Doctrine of the English Gentleman in the Sixteenth Century,* Univ. of Illinois Stud. in Lang. and Lit., XIV (1929), nos. 1–2; A. C. Judson, "Spenser's Theory of Courtesy," *Pub. Mod. Lang. Assoc.,* XLVII (1932), 122–36; A. D. Menut, "Castiglione and the Nicomachean Ethics," *Pub. Mod. Lang. Assoc.,* LVIII (1943), 309–21; E. Williamson, "The Concept of Grace in the Work of Raphael and Castiglione," *Italica,* XXIV (1947), 316–24; W. Schenk, "The *Cortegiano* and the Civilization of the Renaissance," *Scrutiny,* XVI (1949), 93–103; T. M. Pearce, "Marlowe and Castiglione," *Mod. Lang. Quar.,* XII (1951), 3–12.

THE BOOK OF THE COURTIER

Translated and with notes by
LEONARD ECKSTEIN OPDYCKE

[Taken from *The Book of the Courtier by Count Baldesar Castiglione,* translated by Leonard Eckstein Opdycke, Charles Scribner's Sons, New York, 1903.]

THE AUTHOR'S DEDICATORY LETTER

To the Reverend and Illustrious
Lord Dom Miguel de Silva
Bishop of Viseu

When my lord Guidobaldo di Montefeltro,[1] Duke of Urbino, passed from this life, I, together with several other cavaliers who had served him, remained in the service of Duke Francesco Maria della Rovere, his heir and successor in the State. And as the recollection of Duke Guido's character was fresh in my mind, and the delight I had during those years in the kind companionship of the notable persons who at that time frequented the Court of Urbino, I was moved by their memory to write these books of the Courtier, which I did in a few days, purposing in time to correct those errours that arose from the wish to pay this debt speedily. But for many years past fortune has burdened me with toil so constant that I never could find leisure to make the book such as would content even my poor judgment.

Now being in Spain, and learning from Italy that my lady Vittoria della Colonna, Marchioness of Pescara, to whom I gave a copy of the book, had against her word caused a large part of it to be transcribed, I could not but feel some annoyance, fearing the many inconveniences that may befall in such cases. Still, I relied upon the wit and good sense of this lady (whose character I have always held in veneration as a thing divine) to prevent any mischief coming to me from having obeyed her wishes. Finally I was informed that this part of the book was in the hands of many people at Naples; and as men are always eager for anything new, it seemed likely that someone might try to have it printed. Alarmed at this peril, then, I resolved to revise the book at once so far as I had time, with intent to publish it; for I thought better to let it be seen imperfectly corrected by my own hand than grievously mutilated by the hand of others.

And so, to carry out this plan, I began to read the book again; and touched at the very outset by the title, I was saddened not a little, and far more so as I went on, by the thought that most of the personages introduced in the discussion were already dead; for besides those mentioned in the proem of the last Book, messer Alfonso Ariosto (to whom the work is dedicated) is also dead, a gracious youth, considerate, of the highest breeding, and apt in everything proper to a man who lives at court. Likewise Duke Giuliano de' Medici,[2] whose kindness and noble courtesy deserved to be enjoyed longer by the world. Messer Bernardo,[3] Cardinal of Santa Maria in Portico, who for his keen and playful readiness of wit was most delightful to all that knew him, he, too, is dead. Dead also is my lord Ottaviano Fregoso,[4] a man very rare in our times; magnanimous, devout, full of kindness, talent, good sense, and courtesy, a true lover of honour and merit, and so worthy of praise that his very enemies were ever forced to praise him; and the misadventures that he bore so bravely were enough to prove that fortune is still, as always, adverse to merit. And of those mentioned in my book many more besides are dead, to whom nature seemed to promise very long life.

But what should not be told without tears is that my lady Duchess,[5] too, is dead. And if my heart mourns the loss of so many friends and patrons, who have left me in this life as in a solitude full of sorrows, it is meet that I grieve more bitterly for the death of my lady Duchess than of all the others; for she was more precious than they, and I more bound to her than to all the others. Not to delay, then, the tribute that I owe the memory of so excellent a Lady and of the others who are no more, and moved also by the danger to my book, I have had it printed and published in such state as the shortness of time permitted.

And since you had no knowledge in their lifetime either of my lady Duchess or of the others who are dead (except Duke Giuliano and the Cardinal of Santa Maria in Portico), in order to give you that knowledge after their death as far as I can, I send you this book as a picture of the Court of Urbino, not by the hand of Raphael or Michelangelo, but of a humble painter, who knows only how to trace the chief lines, and cannot adorn truth with bright colouring, or by perspective art make that which is not seem to be. And although I tried to show forth in their discourse the qualities and character of my personages, I own I failed to express or even to suggest the excellences of my lady Duchess, not only because my style is inadequate to describe them, but because my intelligence fails even to conceive of them; and if I be censured for this or any other matter worthy of censure (for I well know that my book contains many such), I shall not gainsay the truth.

But as men sometimes so delight in finding fault that they reprehend even that which does not merit reprehension, to such as blame me because I did not imitate Boccaccio or conform to the usages of present Tuscan speech, I shall not refrain from saying that while, for his time, Boccaccio had a charming faculty and often wrote with care and diligence, yet he wrote far better when he followed only the guidance of his natural wit and instinct, without further thought or care to polish his writings, than when he strove industriously and laboriously to be more refined and correct. For this reason even his followers declare that he greatly erred in judgment concerning his own works, holding cheap what did him honour and prizing what was worthless. Therefore, if I had imitated that manner of writing which in Boccaccio is censured by those who elsewise praise him, I should not have been able to escape those same aspersions that were cast on him in this regard; and I should have more deserved them, because he committed his faults thinking he was doing well, while I should have known I was doing ill. Again, if I had imitated the style now admired by many but less esteemed by him, it seemed to me that by such imitation I should show myself at variance with him whom I was imitating, a thing I deemed unseemly. And again, if this consideration had not moved me, I was not able to imitate him in my subject-matter, for he never wrote anything at all in the manner of these books of the Courtier; and I thought I ought not to imitate him in language, because the power and true law of good speech consist rather in usage than in aught else, and it is always a bad habit to employ words not in use. Therefore it was not meet for me to borrow many of Boccaccio's words that were used in his day, but are not now used even by the Tuscans themselves.

Nor was I willing to limit myself to the Tuscan usage of today, because intercourse between different nations has always had the effect to transport, as it were like merchandise, new forms of speech from one to the other; and these endure or fail according as custom accepts or rejects them. Besides being attested by the ancients, this is clearly seen in Boccaccio, who used so many French, Spanish, and Provençal words (some of them perhaps not very intelligible to modern Tuscans) that if they were all omitted his work would be far shorter.

And since, in my opinion, we ought not to despise the idiom of the other noble cities of Italy, whither men resort who are wise, witty, and eloquent, wont to discourse on weighty matters of statecraft, letters, war, and commerce, I think that, of the words used in the speech of these places, I could fitly use in writing such as are graceful in themselves, elegant to pronounce, and commonly deemed good and expressive, although they might not be Tuscan or even of Italian origin. Moreover, in Tuscany, many words are used which are plainly corruptions of the Latin, but which in Lombardy and other parts of Italy have remained pure and unchanged, and are so generally employed by everyone that they are accepted by the gentle and easily understood by the vulgar. Hence I think I did not err if in writing I used some of these words, or preferred what is whole and true speech of my own country rather than what is corrupt and mutilated from abroad.

Neither do I regard as sound the maxim laid down by many, that our common speech is the more beautiful the less it is like Latin; nor do I understand why one fashion of speech should be accorded so much greater authority than another, that, if the Tuscan tongue can ennoble debased and mutilated Latin words and lend them such grace that, mutilated as they are, they may be used by anyone without reproach (which is not denied), the Lombard or any other tongue may not support these same Latin words, pure, whole, precise, and quite unchanged, so that they be tolerable. And truly, just as to undertake, in spite of usage, to coin new words or to preserve old ones may be called bold presumption, so also, besides being difficult, it seems almost impious to undertake, against the force of that same usage, to suppress and bury alive, as it were, words that have already endured for many centuries, protected by the shield of custom against the envy of time, and have maintained their dignity and splendour through the changes in language, in buildings, in habits and in customs, wrought by the wars and disasters of Italy.

Hence if in writing I have chosen not to use those words of Boccaccio that are no longer used in Tuscany, nor to conform to the rule of those who deem it not permissible to use any words that the Tuscans of to-day do not use, I seem to myself excusable. And I think that both in the matter and in the language of my book (so far as one language can aid another), I have followed authors as worthy of praise as is Boccaccio. Nor do I believe that it ought to be counted against me as a fault that I have elected to make myself known rather as a Lombard speaking Lombard, than as a non-Tuscan speaking Tuscan too precisely, in order that I might not resemble Theophrastus, who was detected as non-Athenian by a simple old woman, because he spoke the Athenian dialect with excess of care.

But as this subject is sufficiently treated of in my first Book, I shall say no more, except that, to prevent all possible discussion, I grant my critics that I do not know this Tuscan dialect of theirs, which is so difficult and recondite. And I declare that I have written in my own dialect, just as I speak and for those who speak as I do; and in this I think I have wronged no man, because it seems to me that no one is forbidden to write and speak in his own language; nor is anyone bound to read or listen to what does not please him. Therefore if these folk do not care to read my Courtier, I shall not hold myself in the least wronged by them.

Others say that since it is so very hard and well nigh impossible to find a man as perfect as I wish the Courtier to be, it was superfluous to write of him, because it is folly to teach what cannot be learned. To these I make answer that I am content to have erred in company with Plato, Xenophon and Marcus Tullius, leaving on one side all discussion about the Intelligible World and Ideals; among which, just as are included (according to those authors) the ideal of the perfect State, of the perfect King and of the perfect Orator, so also is the ideal of the perfect Courtier. And if in my style I have failed to approach the image of this ideal, it will be so much the easier for courtiers to approach in deeds the aim and goal that I have set them by my writing; and even if they fail to attain the perfection, such as it is, that I have tried to express, he that approaches nearest to it will be the most perfect; just as when many archers shoot at a target and none hit the very mark, surely he that comes nearest to it is better than the rest.

Still others say that I thought to paint my own portrait, as if I were convinced that I possessed all the qualities that I attribute to the Courtier.[6] To these I shall not indeed deny having essayed everything that I should wish the Courtier to know; and I think that a man, however learned, who did not know something of the matters treated of in the book, could not well have written of them; but I am not so lacking in self-discernment as to fancy that I know everything I have the wit to desire.

My defence then against these and perhaps many other accusations, I leave for the present to the verdict of public opinion; for while the many may not perfectly understand, yet oftener than not they scent by natural instinct the savour of good and bad, and without being able to explain why, they relish one thing and like it, and reject another and hate it. Therefore if my book wins general favour, I shall think it must be good and ought to live; but if it fails to please, I shall think it must be bad and soon to be forgot. And if my censors be not satisfied with the common verdict of opinion, let them rest content with that of time, which in the end reveals the hidden defects of everything, and being father of truth and judge without passion, ever passes on men's writings just sentence of life or death.

Baldesar Castiglione.

NOTES TO THE DEDICATORY LETTER

1. Guidobaldo di Montefeltro, Duke of Urbino, (born 1472; died 1508), was the only son of Duke Federico di Montefeltro and Battista Sforza, an accomplished niece of the first Sforza duke of Milan. Precocious as a child, he was elaborately yet judiciously educated, and much of the praise bestowed upon him in *The Courtier* is shown by contemporary evidence to have been just. . .

In 1489 Guidobaldo married Elisabetta Gonzaga, a sister of the Marquess of Mantua. All hopes, however, of an heir were soon abandoned, apparently owing to the young duke's physical infirmities, which were increased by over exercise and in time unfitted him for all active occupations. Nevertheless he was able to take part in the vain resistance to Charles VIII's invasion of Italy, and later in the expulsion of the French from the kingdom of Naples. While fighting in the service of Pope Alexander VI in 1497, he was taken prisoner and forced to pay a ransom of 30,000 ducats . . . In 1501 he aided rather than opposed Louis XII's invasion of Naples.

In 1502 the pope's son Cesare Borgia treacherously seized the Duchy of Urbino. To spare his people bloodshed and ruin, Guidobaldo fled in disguise to his brother-in-law at Mantua, and after a vain appeal to Louis XII, found an honourable asylum at Venice. In the same year he regained his dominions for a short time, but was again forced to take flight. On the death of Alexander VI (August 1503), Cesare's power crumbled, Guidobaldo easily recovered his duchy, and his position was soon assured by the election of Julius II, who was not only his personal friend, but also the brother of his sister Giovanna's husband. In 1504 he formally adopted as his heir this sister's son, Francesco Maria della Rovere, and took into his service the future author of *The Courtier*. His learning, amiability and munificence attracted choice spirits to his court, which came to be regarded as the first in Italy. Pope Julius was splendidly entertained there on his way both to and from his Bologna campaign, and the Courtier dialogues are represented as taking place immediately after his departure for Rome in March 1507.

Long an invalid. Guidobaldo became more and more a martyr to his gout, which was aggravated by a season of exceptional drought and cold and brought him final relief from suffering in April 1508. His fame rests, not upon his military and political achievements, but upon the beauty of his character, the variety of his intellectual accomplishments, the patience with which he endured reverses, illness and forced inaction, and upon the culture and refinement that characterized his court.

2. Giuliano de' Medici, (born 1478; died 1516), was the third son of Lorenzo the Magnificent and Clarice Orsini. His education seems to have been for a time entrusted to the famous scholar-poet Poliziano. During his family's exile from Florence (1494–1512), he resided much at the court of Urbino, where he was known as "the Magnifico Giuliano," and where one wing of the great palace was reserved to his use and is still called by his name. . . On the restoration of the Medici, Giuliano was placed at the head of affairs in his native city and succeeded in winning the good will of the Florentines, but his gentle disposition and love of ease thwarted other ambitious projects formed for his advancement by his brother Leo X, and he was too grateful to the dukes of Urbino for their hospitality to accept the pope's intended appropriation of their duchy for his benefit. In 1515 he married Filiberta of Savoy and was created Duke of Nemours by her nephew Francis I of France. In the same year he was appointed Captain General of the Church, but failing health prevented his actual service, and he soon died of fever at Florence, not without suspicion of poison at the hands of his nephew Lorenzo. . .

Apart, however, from his appearance as an interlocutor in *The Courtier* and in Bembo's *Prose,* his memory is best preserved by Michelangelo's famous tomb at Florence.

3. "Messer Bernardo" (Dovizi), better known by the name of his birthplace Bibbiena, (born 1470; died 1520), was of humble parentage. His elder brother Pietro was secretary to Lorenzo de' Medici, and secured his admission to the Magnifico's household, where he shared the education of the young Giovanni and became a devoted friend of that future pope. Following the Medici into exile, he travelled about Europe with Giovanni and attended Giuliano to Urbino, where he received the warm welcome always accorded there to such as combined learning with courtly manners. By the Duke of Urbino he seems to have been so commended to the favour of Julius II, that he was able to aid Michelangelo in securing part payment for the Sistine Chapel frescoes, of which payment, however, he accepted five per cent, as a gift from the painter. At the death of Julius, he was secretary to his friend Cardinal Giovanni de' Medici, and in that capacity had access to the conclave, where his adroitness was largely helpful in effecting his patron's election as pope. Leo at once made him Cardinal of Santa Maria in Portico and loaded him with lucrative offices. During the Medicean usurpation of the Duchy of Urbino, he showed no gratitude for the kindness enjoyed by him at that

court. He became very rich, and was a liberal patron of authors and artists. . .

It was to Bibbiena, a few weeks before his death in 1520, that Isabella d'Este, dowager Marchioness of Mantua, entrusted the duty of breaking as gently as possible to Castiglione (then Mantuan ambassador at Rome) the news of the sudden death of the latter's young wife. "We told him the sad news," wrote Bibbiena, "as best we could, . . . none of us could keep back our tears, and we all wept together for some time."

4. Ottaviano Fregoso, (died 1524), belonged to a noble Genoese family that had long distinguished itself in public service and had furnished several doges to the Republic. His parents were Agostino Fregoso and Gentile di Montefeltro, a half-sister of Duke Guidobaldo. Driven from Genoa as early as 1497, he entered his uncle's court at Urbino and rendered important military services, especially during the struggle with Cesare Borgia, in which he gallantly defended the fortress of San Leo, and was rewarded with the lordship of Santa Agata in the Apennines. In 1506 he commanded the papal forces for the recovery of Bologna, and later in the League of Cambray against Venice. In 1513 he succeeded in putting an end to French domination in Genoa, was elected doge, and ruled so beneficently for two years that when Francis I regained the city, Fregoso was continued as governor. In 1522 Genoa was captured and sacked by Spanish and German troops, and Fregoso given over to the Marquess of Pescara, treated harshly (despite Castiglione's intercession on his behalf), and carried to Ischia, where he died.

5. "My lady Duchess," Elisabetta Gonzaga, (born 1471; died 1526), was the second daughter of the Marquess Federico Gonzaga of Mantua and Margarita of Bavaria. She married Duke Guidobaldo in 1489. In 1502 she reluctantly attended the festivities for the marriage, at Ferrara, of Lucrezia Borgia to Alfonso d'Este, and some of her costumes are thus described by an eye-witness: On entering Ferrara, she rode a black mule caparisoned in black velvet embroidered with woven gold, and wore a mantle of black velvet strewn with triangles of beaten gold, a string of pearls about her neck, and a cap of gold; another day indoors she wore a mantle of brown velvet slashed, and caught up with chains of massive gold; another day a gown of black velvet striped with gold, with a jewelled necklace and diadem; and still another day, a black velvet robe embroidered with gold ciphers.

During the Borgian usurpation of their duchy in the same year, she shared her husband's exile at Venice, and on returning to Urbino earlier than Guidobaldo, she amused herself with a scenic representation of the chief events that had occurred during their absence. She cared for her husband tenderly in his illnesses, administered his government wisely when he was called away, and on his death acted as regent and guardian for his nephew and successor, with whom she maintained affectionate relations as long as she lived, and from appropriating whose dominions she strove to the utmost to dissuade Leo X.

Next to her husband's niece by marriage, Emilia Pia, her closest friend seems to have been her brother's wife, the famous Isabella d'Este, with whom she often travelled and continually corresponded by letter. Although still young and accounted beautiful at her husband's death, she remained faithful to his memory, and the years of her widowhood were cheered by the companionship of her niece, the young duchess Eleanora of Urbino. If we may trust universal contemporary opinion of her virtues and beauty, the author of *The Courtier* flattered her as little as did the painter of her portait in the Uffizi Gallery.

6. In the letter Vittoria Colonna wrote: "I do not marvel at your portraying a perfect courtier well, for by merely holding a mirrour before you and considering your inward and outward parts, you could describe him as you have; but our greatest difficulty being to know ourselves, I say that it was more difficult for you to portray yourself than another man."

THE FIRST BOOK OF THE COURTIER

To Messer Alfonso Ariosto

Within myself I have long doubted, dearest messer Alfonso, which of two things were the harder for me: to deny you what you have often begged of me so urgently, or to do it. For while it seemed to me very hard to deny anything (and especially a thing in the highest degree laudable) to one whom I love most dearly and by whom I feel myself to be most dearly loved, yet to set about an enterprise that I was not sure of being able to finish, seemed to me ill befitting a man who esteems just censure as it ought to be esteemed. At last, after much thought, I am resolved to try in this matter how much aid my assiduity may gain from that affection and intense desire to please, which in other things are so wont to stimulate the industry of man.

You ask me then to write what is to my thinking the form of Courtiership [1] most befitting a gentleman who lives at the court of princes, by which he may have the ability and knowledge perfectly to serve them in every reasonable thing, winning from them favour, and praise from other men; in short, what manner of man he ought to be who may deserve to be called a perfect Courtier without flaw. Wherefore, considering your request, I say that had it not seemed to me more blameworthy to be reputed somewhat unamiable by you than too conceited by everyone else, I should have avoided this task, for fear of being held over bold by all who know how hard a thing it is, from among such a variety of customs as are in use at the courts of Christendom, to choose the perfect form and as it were the flower of Courtiership. For custom often makes the same thing pleasing and displeasing to us; whence it sometimes follows that customs, habits, ceremonies and fashions that once were prized, become vulgar, and contrariwise the vulgar become prized. Thus it is clearly seen that use rather than reason has power to introduce new things among us, and to do away with the old; and he will often err who seeks to determine which are perfect. Therefore being conscious of this and many other difficulties in the subject set before me to write of, I am constrained to offer some apology, and to testify that this errour (if errour it may indeed be called) is common to us both, to the end that if I be blamed for it, the blame may be shared by you also; for your offence in setting me a task beyond my powers should not be deemed less than mine in having accepted it.

So now let us make a beginning of our subject, and if possible let us form such a Courtier that any prince worthy to be served by him, although of but small estate,[2] might still be called a very great lord.

In these books we shall follow no fixed order or rule of distinct precepts, such as are usually employed in teaching anything whatever; but after the fashion of many ancient writers, we shall revive a pleasant memory and rehearse certain discussions that were held between men singularly competent in such matters; and although I had no part in them personally, being in England at the time they took place,[3] yet having received them soon after my return, from one who faithfully reported them to me, I will try to recall them as accurately as my memory will permit, so that you may know what was thought and believed on this subject by men who are worthy of highest praise, and to whose judgment implicit faith may be given in all things. Nor will it be amiss to tell the cause of these discussions, so that we may reach in orderly manner the end to which our discourse tends.

On the slopes of the Apennines towards the Adriatic sea, almost in the centre of Italy, there lies (as everyone knows) the little city of Urbino. Although amid mountains, and less pleasing ones than perhaps some others that we see in many places, it has yet enjoyed such favour of heaven that the country round about is very fertile and rich in crops; so that besides the wholesomeness of the air, there is great abundance of everything needful for human life. But among the greatest blessings that can be attributed to it, this I believe to be the chief, that for a long time it has ever been ruled by the best of lords; although in the calamities of the universal wars of Italy, it was for a season deprived of them. But without seeking further, we can give good proof of this by the glorious memory of Duke Federico,[4] who in his day was the light of Italy; nor is there lack of credible and abundant witnesses, who are still living, to his prudence, humanity, justice, liberality, unconquered courage,—and to his military discipline, which is conspicuously attested by his numerous victories, his capture of impregnable places, the sudden swiftness of his expeditions, the frequency with which he put to flight large and formidable armies by means of a very small force, and by his loss of no single battle whatever; so that we may not unreasonably compare him to many famous men of old.

Among his other praiseworthy deeds, he built on the rugged site of Urbino a palace regarded by many as the most beautiful to be found in all Italy; and he so well furnished it with everything suitable that it seemed not a palace but a city in the form of a palace; and not merely with what is ordinarily used,—such as silver vases, hangings of richest cloth-of-gold and silk, and other similar things,—but for ornament he added countless antique statues in marble and bronze, pictures most choice, and musical instruments of every sort, nor would he admit anything there that was not very rare and excellent. Then at very great cost he collected a goodly number of most excellent and rare books in Greek, Latin and Hebrew, all of which he adorned with gold and with silver, esteeming this to be the chiefest excellence of his great palace.[5]

Following then the course of nature, and already sixty-five years old, he died gloriously, as he had lived; and he left as his successor a motherless little boy of ten years, his only son Guidobaldo. Heir to the State, he seemed to be heir also to all his father's virtues, and soon his noble nature gave such promise as seemed not permissible to hope for from mortal man; so that men esteemed none among the notable deeds of Duke Federico to be greater than to have begotten such a son. But envious of so much virtue, fortune thwarted this glorious beginning with all her power; so that before Duke Guido reached the age of twenty years, he fell ill of the gout, which grew upon him with grievous pain, and in a short space of time so crippled all his members that he could neither stand upon his feet nor move; and thus one of the fairest and most promising forms in the world was distorted and spoiled in tender youth.

And not content even with this, fortune was so contrary to him in all his purposes, that he could seldom carry into effect anything that he desired; and although he was very wise of counsel and unconquered in spirit, it seemed that what he undertook, both in war and in everything else whether small or great, always ended ill for him. And proof of this is found in his many and diverse calamities, which he ever bore with such strength of mind, that his spirit was never vanquished by fortune; nay, scorning her assaults with unbroken courage, he lived in illness as if in health and in adversity as if fortunate, with perfect dignity and universal esteem; so that although he was thus infirm of body, he fought with most honourable rank in the service of their Serene Highnesses the Kings of Naples, Alfonso and Ferdinand the Younger; later with Pope Alexander VI, and with the Venetian and Florentine signories.

Upon the accession of Julius II to the pontificate, he was made Captain of the Church; at which time, following his accustomed habit, above all else he took care to fill his household with very noble and valiant gentlemen, with whom he lived most familiarly, delighting in their intercourse: wherein the pleasure he gave to others was not less than that he received from others, he being well versed in both the [learned] languages, and uniting affability and pleasantness to a knowledge of things without number. And besides this, the greatness of his spirit so set him on, that although he could not practise in person the exercises of chivalry, as he once had done, yet he took the utmost pleasure in witnessing them in others; and by his words, now correcting now praising every man according to desert, he clearly showed his judgment in those matters; wherefore, in jousts and tournaments, in riding, in the handling of every sort of weapon, as well as in pastimes, games, music, — in short, in all the exercises proper to noble cavaliers, — everyone strove so to show himself, as to merit being deemed worthy of such noble fellowship.

Thus all the hours of the day were assigned to honourable and pleasant exercises as well for the body as for the mind; but since my lord Duke was always wont by reason of his infirmity to retire to sleep very early after supper, everyone usually betook himself at that hour to the presence of my lady Duchess, Elisabetta Gonzaga; where also was ever to be found my lady Emilia Pia,[6] who was endowed with such lively wit and judgment that, as you know, it seemed as if she were the Mistress of us all, and as if everyone gained wisdom and worth from her. Here then, gentle discussions and innocent pleasantries were heard, and on the face of everyone a jocund gaiety was seen depicted, so that the house could truly be called the very abode of mirth: nor ever elsewhere, I think, was so relished, as once was here, how great sweetness may flow from dear and cherished companionship; for not to speak of the honour it was to each of us to serve such a lord as he of whom I have just spoken, there was born in the hearts of all a supreme contentment every time we came into the presence of my lady Duchess; and it seemed as if this were a chain that held us all linked in love, so that never was concord of will or cordial love between brothers greater than that which here was between us all.

The same was it among the ladies, with whom there was intercourse most free and honourable; for everyone was permitted to talk, sit, jest and laugh with whom he pleased; but such was the reverence paid to the wish of my lady Duchess, that this same liberty was a very great check; nor was there anyone who did not esteem it the utmost pleasure he could have in the world, to please her, and the utmost pain to displease her. And thus, most decorous manners were here joined with greatest liberty, and games and laughter in her presence were seasoned not only with witty jests, but with gracious and sober dignity; for that modesty and loftiness which governed all the acts, words and gestures of my lady Duchess, bantering and laughing, were such that she would have been known for a lady of noblest rank by anyone who saw her even but once. And impressing herself thus upon those about her, she seemed to attune us all to her own quality and tone; accordingly every man strove to follow this pattern, taking as it were a rule of beautiful behaviour from the presence of so great and virtuous a lady; whose highest qualities I do not now purpose to recount, they not being my theme and being well known to all the world, and far more because I could not express them with either tongue or pen; and those that perhaps might have been somewhat hid, fortune, as if wondering at such rare virtue, chose to reveal through many adversities and stings of calamity, so as to give proof that in the tender breast of woman, in company with singular beauty, there may abide prudence and strength of soul, and all those virtues that even among stern men are very rare.

But leaving this aside, I say that the custom of all the gentlemen of the house was to betake themselves straightway after supper to my lady Duchess; where, among the other pleasant pastimes and music and dancing that continually were practised, sometimes neat questions were proposed, sometimes ingenious games were devised at the choice of one or another, in which under various disguises the company disclosed their thoughts figuratively to whom they liked best. Sometimes other discussions arose about different matters, or biting retorts passed lightly back and forth. Often "devices" (*imprese*), as we now call them, were displayed;[7] in discussing which there was wonderful diversion, the house being (as I have said) full of very noble talents; among whom (as you know) the most famous were my lord Ottaviano Fregoso, his brother messer Federico,[8] the Magnifico Giuliano de' Medici, messer Pietro Bembo,[9] messer Cesare Gonzaga,[10] Count Ludovico da Canossa,[11] my lord Gaspar Pallavicino,[12] my lord Ludovico Pio, my lord Morello da Ortona,[13] Pietro da Napoli, messer Roberto da Bari, and countless other very noble cavaliers. Moreover there were many, who, although usually they did not dwell there constantly, yet spent most of the time there: like messer Bernardo Bibbiena, the Unico Aretino,[14] Giancristoforo Romano, Pietro Monte, Terpandro, messer Niccolò Frisio; so that there always flocked thither poets, musicians and all sorts of agreeable men, and in every walk the most excellent that were to be found in Italy.

Now Pope Julius II, having by his presence and the aid of the French brought Bologna under subjection to the apostolic see in the year 1506, and being on his way back to Rome, passed through Urbino; where he was received with all possible honour and with as magnificent and splendid state as could have been prepared in any other noble city of Italy: so that besides the pope, all the lord cardinals and other courtiers were most highly gratified. And some there were, attracted by the charm of this society, who tarried at Urbino many days after the departure of the pope and his court; during which time not only were the ordinary pastimes and diversions continued in the usual manner, but every man strove to contribute something new, and expecially in the games, to which almost every evening was devoted. And the order of them was such that immediately after reaching the presence of my lady Duchess, everyone sat down in a circle as he pleased or as chance decided; and in sitting they were arranged alternately, a man and a woman, as long as there were women, for nearly always the number of men was by far the greater; then they were governed as seemed best to my lady Duchess, who for the most part left this charge to my lady Emilia.

So, the day after the pope's departure,[15] the company being assembled at the wonted hour and place, after much pleasant talk, my lady Duchess desired my lady Emilia to begin the games; and she, after having for a time refused the task, spoke thus:

"My Lady, since it pleases you that I shall be the one to begin the games this evening, not being able in reason to fail to obey you, I will propose a game in which I think I ought to have little blame and less labour; and this shall be for everyone to propose after his liking a game that has never been given; and then we will choose the one that seems best worthy to be played in this company."

And so saying, she turned to my lord Gaspar Pallavicino, requiring him to tell his choice; and he at once replied:

"It is for you, my Lady, first to tell your own."

"But I have already told it," said my lady Emilia; "now do you, my lady Duchess, bid him be obedient."

Then my lady Duchess said, smiling:

"To the end that everyone may be bound to obey you, I make you my deputy and give you all my authority."

"It is a remarkable thing," replied my lord Gaspar, "that women should always be allowed this exemption from toil, and it certainly would not be unreasonable to wish in some way to learn the reason why; but not to be the first to disobey, I will leave this for another time, and will tell what is required of me;" and he began: "It seems to me that in love, as in everything else, our minds judge diversely; and thus it often happens that what is very delightful to one man, is very hateful to another; but none the less we all are ever alike in this, that every man holds his beloved very dear; so that the over fondness of lovers often cheats their judgment to such a degree, that they esteem the person whom they love to be the only one in the world adorned with every excellent virtue and wholly without defect; but since human nature does not admit such complete perfection, and since there is no one to be found who does not lack something, it cannot be said that such men do not cheat themselves, and that the lover does not become blind concerning the beloved. I would therefore that this evening our game might be that each of us should tell what virtue above others he would have the person whom he loves adorned with; and then, as all must have some blemish, what fault he would have in her; in order that we may see who can find the most praiseworthy and useful virtues, and the most excusable faults and least harmful to lover and beloved."

My lord Gaspar having spoken thus, my lady Emilia made sign to madonna Costanza Fregosa to follow after, because she sat next in order, and she was preparing to speak; but my lady Duchess said quickly:

"Since my lady Emilia will not make the effort to invent a game, it were only fair that the other ladies share this ease and that they too be exempt from such exertion for this evening, especially as there are here so many men that there is no danger of lack of games."

"So be it," replied my lady Emilia; and imposing silence on madonna Costanza, she turned to messer Cesare Gonzaga, who sat next, and bade him speak; and he began thus:

"Whoso will carefully consider all our actions, will ever find various defects in them; the reason whereof is that nature, variable in this as in other things, has given to one man the light of reason in one thing, to another man in another thing; and so it happens that, the one knowing what the other does not know and being ignorant of what the other understands, each readily perceives his neighbour's fault and not his own, and we all seem to ourselves very wise and perhaps most of all in that wherein we most are foolish. Thus we have seen it happen in this house that many, at first accounted very wise, were in course of time recognized as very foolish, which came about from nothing else but our own watchfulness. For, as they say that in Apulia musical instruments are used for those bitten by the tarantula, and various tunes are tried until the humour that causes the malady (through a certain affinity it has for some one of those tunes) is suddenly stirred by the sound, and so excites the sick man that he is restored to health by virtue of that excitement: so when we have perceived a hidden touch of folly, we have stimulated it so artfully and with such various persuasions and diverse means, that at length we have learned whither it tended; then, the humour once recognized, so well have we excited it that it has always reached the perfection of open folly. Thus one man has waxed foolish over poetry, another over music, another over love, another over dancing, another over inventing mimes, another over riding, another over fencing,—each according to the native quality of his metal; whence, as you know, great amusement has been derived. I hold it then as certain that there is some grain of folly in each of us, which being quickened can multiply almost infinitely.

"Therefore I would that this evening our game might be a discussion upon this subject, and that each one tell with what kind of folly, and about what thing, he thinks I should make a fool of myself if I had to make a fool of myself openly, judging of this outburst by the sparks of folly that are daily seen to issue from me. Let the same be told of all the rest, keeping to the order of our games, and let each one try to found his opinion upon some actual sign and argument. And thus we shall each derive from our game the advantage of learning our defects, and so shall be better able to guard against them; and if the vein of folly that is discovered proves so rich that it seems incurable, we will assist it, and according to fra Mariano's teaching, we shall have saved a soul, which will be no small gain."

There was much laughter at this game, nor were there any who could keep from talking; one said, "I should make a fool of myself over thinking;" another, "Over looking;" another said, "I have already made a fool of myself over loving;" and the like.

Then fra Serafino [16] said, laughing after his manner:

"That would take too long; but if you want a fine game, let everyone give his opinion why it is that nearly all women hold rats in hatred, and are fond of snakes; and you will see that no one will guess the reason except myself, who learned this secret in a strange way." And he began to tell his stories; but my lady Emilia bade him be silent, and passing over the lady who sat next, made sign to the Unico Aretino whose turn it was; and he, without waiting for further command, said:

"I would I were a judge with power to search the heart of evildoers by every sort of torture; and this that I might fathom the deceits of an ingrate with angel eyes and serpent heart, who never lets her tongue reveal her soul, and with deceitful pity feigned has no thought but of dissecting hearts. Nor is there in sandy Libya to be found a serpent so venomous and eager for human blood as is this false one; who not only in the sweetness of her voice and honeyed words, but in her eyes, her smiles, her aspect and in all her ways, is a very siren.

"But since I am not suffered, as I would I were, to use chains, rope and fire to learn a certain truth, I fain would learn it by a game,— which is this: let each one tell what he believes to be the meaning of that letter S which my lady Duchess wears upon her brow; for, although this too is surely an artful veil to aid deceit, perchance there will be given it some interpretation unthought of by her perhaps, and it will be found that fortune, compassionate spectatress of men's martyrdoms, has led her against her will to disclose by this small token her secret wish to slay and bury alive in calamity everyone who beholds her or serves her."

My lady Duchess laughed, and the Unico, seeing that she wished to defend herself against this imputation, said:

"Nay, my Lady, do not speak, for it is not now your turn to speak."

My Lady Emilia then turned and said:

"Sir Unico, there is no one of us here who does not yield to you in everything, but above all in knowledge of my lady Duchess's mind; and since you know it better than the others (thanks to your divine genius), you love it better than the others, who like those weak-sighted birds that fix not their eyes upon the sun's orb, cannot so justly know how perfect it is; wherefore every effort to clear this doubt would be vain, save your own judgment. To you alone then be left this task, as to him who alone can perform it."

The Unico remained silent for a while, then being urged to speak, at last recited a sonnet upon the aforesaid subject, declaring what that letter S meant; which was by many believed to be done impromptu, but as it was more ingenious and finished than seemed to accord with the shortness of the time, it was thought rather to have been prepared.[17]

Then having bestowed a merry plaudit in praise of the sonnet, and talked of it awhile, my lord Ottaviano Fregoso, whose turn it was, smilingly began as follows:

"My Lords, if I were to affirm that I had never felt the passion of love, I am sure that my lady Duchess and my lady Emilia would feign to believe it even though they believed it not, and would say that it was because I mistrusted ever being able to prevail upon any woman to love me; whereof indeed I have not made trial hitherto with such persistence as reasonably to despair of being able sometime to succeed. But yet I have not refrained because I rate myself so high, or women so low, that I do not deem many of them worthy to be loved and served by me; but made timorous rather by the continual laments of some lovers, who — pallid, gloomy and taciturn — seem always to wear their unhappiness depicted in their eyes; and if they speak, they accompany every word with triple sighs, and discourse of nothing but tears, torments, despairings and longings for death; so that if an amourous spark has sometimes kindled in my heart, I have at once striven with all my might to quench it, not from any hate I bear to women as these ladies think, but for my own good.

"I have also known some others quite different from these dolourous souls,— lovers who not only give thanks and praise for the kind looks, tender words and gentle bearing of their mistresses, but flavour all evils with sweetness, so that they call their ladies' warrings, anger and disdain, most sweet. Wherefore such as these seem to me far more than happy. For if they find such sweetness in lovers' quarrels, which those others deem far more bitter than death, I think that in loving endearments they must enjoy that supreme beatitude which we vainly seek in this world. So I would that this evening our game might be, that each man tell, if she whom he loves must needs be angry with him, by what cause he would have her anger roused. Because if there be any here who have enjoyed this sweet anger, I am sure that out of courtesy they will choose one of those causes that make it so sweet; and perhaps I shall take courage to advance a little farther in love, hoping that I too may find this sweetness where some find bitterness; and then these ladies will be no longer able to cast shame upon me because I do not love."

This game found much favour and everyone made ready to speak upon the subject, but as my lady Emilia made no further mention of it, messer Pietro Bembo, who sat next in order, spoke thus:

"My Lords, no small uncertainty has been awakened in my mind by the game proposed by my lord Ottaviano in his discourse about love's anger: the which, however varied it be, has in my case always been most bitter, nor do I believe that any seasoning could be learned from me that would avail to sweeten it; but perhaps it is more or less bitter according to the cause from which it springs. For I remember once to have seen the lady whom I served wrought up against me, either by some idle suspicion that she had herself conceived as to my loyalty, or by some other false notion awakened in her by what others had said to my injury; insomuch that I believed no pain could equal mine, and it seemed to me that the greatest suffering I felt was to endure that which I had not deserved, and to have this affliction come upon me not from my fault but from her lack of love. At other times I saw her angered by some errour of mine, and knew her ire to proceed from my fault; and then I deemed that my former woe was very light compared with that which now I felt; and it seemed to me that to have displeased, and through my own guilt, the person whom alone I desired and so zealously strove to please, was the greatest torment and above all others. I would therefore that our game might be that each man tell, if she whom he loves must needs be angry with him, from which of the two he would have her anger spring, from her or from himself; so that we may know which is the greater suffering, to give displeasure to her who is loved, or to receive it from her who is loved."

Everyone waited for my lady Emilia to reply; but she, saying nothing more to Bembo, turned and made sign to messer Federico Fregoso that he should tell his game; and he at once began as follows:

"My Lady, I would it were permitted me, as it sometimes is, to assent to another's proposal; since for my part I would readily approve any of the games proposed by these gentlemen, for I really think that all of them would be amusing. But not to break our rule, I say that anyone who wished to praise our court, — laying aside the merit of our lady Duchess, which with her divine virtue would suffice to lift from earth to heaven the meanest souls that are in the world, — might well say without suspicion of flattery, that in all Italy it would perhaps be hard to find so many cavaliers so singularly admirable and so excellent in divers other matters besides the chief concerns of chivalry, as are now to be found here: wherefore if anywhere there be men who deserve to be called good Courtiers and who are able to judge of what pertains to the perfection of Courtiership, it is reasonable to believe that they are here. So, to repress the many fools who by impudence and folly think to win the name of good Courtier, I would that this evening's game might be, that we select some one of the company and give him the task of portraying a perfect Courtier, explaining all the conditions and special qualities requisite in one who deserves this title; and as to those things that shall not appear sound, let everyone be allowed to contradict, as in the schools of the philosophers it is allowed to contradict anyone who proposes a thesis."

Messer Federico was continuing his discourse still further, when my lady Emilia interrupted him and said:

"This, if it pleases my lady Duchess, shall for the present be our game."

My lady Duchess answered:

"It does please me."

Then nearly all those present began to say, both to my lady Duchess and among themselves, that this was the finest game that could possibly be; and without waiting for each other's answer, they entreated my lady Emilia to decide who should begin. She turned to my lady Duchess and said:

"Command, my Lady, him who it best pleases you should have this task; for I do not wish, by selecting one rather than another, to seem to decide whom I think more competent in this matter than the rest, and so do wrong to anyone."

My lady Duchess replied:

"Nay, make this choice yourself, and take heed lest by not obeying you give an example to the others, so that they too prove disobedient in their turn."

At this my lady Emilia laughed and said to Count Ludovico da Canossa:

"Then not to lose more time, you, Count, shall be the one to take this enterprise after the manner that messer Federico has described; not indeed because we account you so good a Courtier that you know what befits one, but because, if you say everything wrong as we hope you will, the game will be more lively, for everyone will then have something to answer you; while if someone else had this task who knew more than you, it would be impossible to contradict him in anything, because he would tell the truth, and so the game would be tedious."

The Count answered quickly:

"Whoever told the truth, my Lady, would run no risk of lacking contradiction, so long as you were present;" and after some laughter at this retort, he continued: "But truly I would fain escape this burden, it seeming to me too heavy, and I being conscious that what you said in jest is very true; that is, that I do not know what befits a good Courtier: and I do not seek to prove this with further argument, because, as I do not practice the rules of Courtiership, one may judge that I do not know them; and I think my blame may be the less, for sure it is worse not to wish to do well than not to know how. Yet, since it so happens that you are pleased to have me bear this burden, I neither can nor will refuse it, in order not to contravene our rule and your judgment, which I rate far higher than my own."

Then messer Cesare Gonzaga said:

"As the early evening is now spent and many other kinds of entertainment are ready, perhaps it will be well to put off this discussion until to-morrow and give the Count time to think of what he has to say; for it is difficult indeed to speak unprepared on such a subject."

The Count replied:

"I do not wish to be like the fellow who, when stripped to his shirt, vaulted less well than he had done in his doublet; hence it seems to me good fortune that the hour is late, for I shall be obliged by the shortness of the time to say but little, and my not having taken thought will excuse me, so that I shall be allowed to say without blame whatever first comes to my lips.

"Therefore, not to carry this burden of duty longer on my shoulders, I say that in everything it is so hard to know the true perfection as to be well nigh impossible; and this because of the variety of opinions. Thus there are many that will like a man who speaks much, and will call him pleasing; some will prefer modesty; some others, an active and restless man; still others, one who shows calmness and deliberation in everything; and so every man praises or decries according to his mind, always clothing vice with the name of its kindred virtue, or virtue with the name of its kindred vice; for example, calling an impudent man frank, a modest man dull, an ignorant man good, a knave discreet; and so in all things else. Yet I believe that there exists in everything its own perfection, although concealed; and that this can be determined through rational discussion by any having knowledge of the thing in hand. And since, as I have said, the truth often lies concealed, and I do not profess to have this knowledge, I can only praise the kind of Courtier that I most esteem, and approve him who seems to me nearest right, according to my poor judgment; the which you will follow if you find it good, or you will hold to your own if it differs from mine. Nor shall I at all insist that mine is better than yours; not only because you may think one thing and I another, but I myself may sometimes think one thing, and sometimes another.

"I wish, then, that this Courtier of ours should be nobly born and of gentle race; because it is far less unseemly for one of ignoble birth to fail in worthy deeds, than for one of noble birth, who, if he strays from the path of his predecessors, stains his family name, and not only fails to achieve but loses what has been achieved already; for noble birth is like a bright lamp that manifests and makes visible good and evil deeds, and kindles and stimulates to virtue both by fear of shame and by hope of praise. And since his splendour of nobility does not illumine the deeds of the humbly born, they lack that stimulus and fear of shame, nor do they feel any obligation to advance beyond what their predecessors have done; while to the nobly born it seems a reproach not to reach at least the goal set them by their ancestors. And thus it nearly always happens that both in the profession of arms and in other worthy pursuits the most famous men have been of noble birth, because nature has implanted in everything that hidden seed which gives a certain force and quality of its own essence to all things that are derived from it, and makes them like itself: as we see not only in the breeds of horses and of other animals, but also in trees, the shoots of which nearly always resemble the trunk; and if they sometimes degenerate, it arises from poor cultivation. And so it is with men, who if rightly trained are nearly always like those from whom they spring, and often better; but if there be no one to give them proper care, they become like savages and never reach perfection.

"It is true that, by favour of the stars or of nature, some men are endowed at birth with such graces that they seem not to have been born, but rather as if some god had formed them with his very hands and adorned them with every excellence of mind and body. So too there are many men so foolish and rude that one cannot but think that nature brought them into the world out of contempt or mockery. Just as these can usually accomplish little even with constant diligence and good training, so with slight pains those others reach the highest summit of excellence. And to give you an instance; you see my lord Don Ippolito d'Este, Cardinal of Ferrara, who has enjoyed such fortune from his birth, that his person, his aspect, his words and all his movements are so disposed and imbued with this grace, that — although he is young — he exhibits among the most aged prelates such weight of character that he seems fitter to teach than to be taught; likewise in conversation with men and women of every rank, in games, in pleasantry and in banter, he has a certain sweetness and manners so gracious, that whoso speaks with him or even sees him, must needs remain attached to him forever.

"But to return to our subject: I say that there is a middle state between perfect grace on the one hand and senseless folly on the other; and those who are not thus perfectly endowed by nature, with study and toil can in great part polish and amend their natural defects. Besides his noble birth, then, I would have the Courtier favoured in this regard also, and endowed by nature not only with talent and beauty of person and feature, but with a certain grace and (as we say) air that shall make him at first sight pleasing and agreeable to all who see him; and I would have this an ornament that should dispose and unite all his actions, and in his outward aspect give promise of whatever is worthy the society and favour of every great lord."

Here, without waiting longer, my lord Gaspar Pallavicino said:

"In order that our game may have the form prescribed, and that we may not seem to slight the privilege given us to contradict, I say that this nobility of birth does not appear to me so essential in the Courtier; and if I thought I were saying what was new to any of us, I should cite instances of many men born of the noblest blood who have been full of vices; and on the other hand, of many men among the humbly born who by their virtue have made their posterity illustrious. And if what you just said be true, namely that there is in everything this occult influence of the original seed, then we should all be in the same case, because we had the same origin, nor would any man be more noble than another. But as to our differences and grades of eminence and obscurity, I believe there are many other causes: among which I rate fortune to be chief; for we see her holding sway in all mundane affairs, often amusing herself by lifting to heaven whom she pleases (although wholly without merit), and burying in the depths those most worthy to be exalted.

"I quite agree with what you say as to the good fortune of those endowed from birth with advantages of mind and body: but this is seen as well among the humbly born as among the nobly born, since nature has no such subtle distinctions as these; and often, as I said, the highest gifts of nature are found among the most obscure. Therefore, since this nobility of birth is won neither by talent nor by strength nor by craft, and is rather the merit of our predecessors than our own, it seems to me too extravagant to maintain that if our Courtier's parents be humbly born, all his good qualities are spoiled, and that all those other qualifications that you mentioned do not avail to raise him to the summit of perfection; I mean talent, beauty of feature, comeliness of person, and that grace which makes him always charming to everyone at first sight."

Then Count Ludovico replied:

"I do not deny that the same virtues may rule the low-born and the noble: but (not to repeat what we have said already or the many other arguments that could be adduced in praise of noble birth, which is honoured always and by everyone, it being reasonable that good should beget good), since we have to form a Courtier without flaw and endowed with every praiseworthy quality, it seems to me necessary to make him nobly born, as well for many other reasons as for universal opinion, which is at once disposed in favour of noble birth. For if there be two Courtiers who have as yet given no impression of themselves by good or evil acts, as soon as the one is known to have been born a gentleman and the other not, he who is low-born will be far less esteemed by everyone than he who is high-born, and will need much effort and time to make upon men's minds that good impression which the other will have achieved in a moment and merely by being a gentleman. And how important these impressions are, everyone can easily understand: for in our own case we have seen men present themselves in this house, who, being silly and awkward in the extreme, yet had throughout Italy the reputation of very great Courtiers; and although they were detected and recognized at last, still they imposed upon us for many days, and maintained in our minds that opinion of them which they first found impressed there, although they conducted themselves after the slightness of their worth. We have seen others, held at first in small esteem, then admirably successful at the last.

"And of these mistakes there are various causes: and among others, the regard of princes, who in their wish to perform miracles sometimes undertake to bestow favour on a man who seems to them to merit disfavour. And often too they are themselves deceived; but since they always have a host of imitators, their favour begets very great fame, which chiefly guides our judgments: and if we find anything that seems contrary to common opinion, we suspect that it is we ourselves who are wrong, and always seek for something hidden: because it seems that these universal opinions must after all be founded on fact and spring from rational causes; and because our minds are very prone to love and hate, as is seen in battle-shows and games and every other sort of contest, wherein the spectators without apparent cause become partisans of one side, with eager wish that it may win and the other lose. In our opinion of men's character also, good or evil fame sways our minds to one of these two passions from the start; and thus it happens that we usually judge with love or hate. You see then how important this first impression is, and how he ought to strive to make a good one at the outset, who thinks to hold the rank and name of good Courtier.

"But to come to some details, I am of opinion that the principal and true profession of the Courtier ought to be that of arms; which I would have him follow actively above all else, and be known among others as bold and strong, and loyal to whomsoever he serves. And he will win a reputation for these good qualities by exercising them at all times and in all places, since one may never fail in this without severest censure. And just as among women, their fair fame once sullied never recovers its first lustre, so the reputation of a gentleman who bears arms, if once it be in the least tarnished with cowardice or other disgrace, remains forever infamous before the world and full of ignominy. Therefore the more our Courtier excels in this art, the more he will be worthy of praise; and yet I do not deem essential in him that perfect knowledge of things and those other qualities that befit a commander; since this would be too wide a sea, let us be content, as we have said, with perfect loyalty and unconquered courage, and that he be always seen to possess them. For the courageous are often recognized even more in small things than in great; and frequently in perils of importance and where there are many spectators, some men are to be found, who, although their hearts be dead within them, yet, moved by shame or by the presence of others, press forward almost with their eyes shut, and do their duty God knows how. While on occasions of little moment, when they think they can avoid putting themselves in danger without being detected, they are glad to keep safe. But those who, even when they do not expect to be observed or seen or recognized by anyone, show their ardour and neglect nothing, however paltry, that may be laid to their charge, — they have that strength of mind which we seek in our Courtier.

"Not that we would have him look so fierce, or go about blustering, or say that he has taken his cuirass to wife, or threaten with those grim scowls that we have often seen in Berto; because to such men as this, one might justly say that which a brave lady jestingly said in gentle company to one whom I will not name at present; who, being invited by her out of compliment to dance, refused not only that, but to listen to the music, and many other entertainments proposed to him, — saying always that such silly trifles were not his business; so that at last the lady said, 'What is your business, then?' He replied with a sour look, 'To fight.' Then the lady at once said, 'Now that you are in no war and out of fighting trim, I should think it were a good thing to have yourself well oiled, and to stow yourself with all your battle harness in a closet until you be needed, lest you grow more rusty than you are;' and so, amid much laughter from the bystanders, she left the discomfited fellow to his silly presumption.

"Therefore let the man we are seeking, be very bold, stern, and always among the first, where the enemy are to be seen; and in every other place, gentle, modest, reserved, above all things avoiding ostentation and that impudent self-praise by which men ever excite hatred and disgust in all who hear them."

Then my lord Gaspar replied:

"As for me, I have known few men excellent in anything whatever, who do not praise themselves; and it seems to me that this may well be permitted them; for when anyone who feels himself to be of worth, sees that he is not known to the ignorant by his works, he is offended that his worth should lie buried, and needs must in some way hold it up to view, in order that he may not be cheated of the fame that is the true reward of worthy effort. Thus among the ancient authors, whoever carries weight seldom fails to praise himself. They indeed are insufferable who do this without desert, but such we do not presume our Courtier to be."

The Count then said:

"If you heard what I said, it was impudent and indiscriminate self-praise that I censured: and as you say, we surely ought not to form a bad opinion of a brave man who praises himself modestly, nay we ought rather to regard such praise as better evidence than if it came from the mouth of others. I say, however, that he, who in praising himself runs into no errour and incurs no annoyance or envy at the hands of those that hear him, is a very discreet man indeed and merits praise from others in addition to that which he bestows upon himself; because it is a very difficult matter."

Then my lord Gaspar said:

"You must teach us that."

The Count replied:

"Among the ancient authors there is no lack of those who have taught it; but to my thinking, the whole art consists in saying things in such a way that they shall not seem to be said to that end, but let fall so naturally that it was impossible not to say them, and while seeming always to avoid self-praise, yet to achieve it; but not after the manner of those boasters, who open their mouths and let the words come forth haphazard. Like one of our friends a few days ago, who, being quite run through the thigh with a spear at Pisa, said he thought it was a fly that had stung him; and another man said he kept no mirrour in his room because, when angry, he became so terrible to look at, that the sight of himself would have frightened him too much."

Everyone laughed at this, but messer Cesare Gonzaga added:

"Why do you laugh? Do you not know that Alexander the Great, on hearing the opinion of a philosopher to be that there was an infinite number of worlds, began to weep, and being asked why he wept, replied, 'Because I have not yet conquered one of them;' as if he would fain have vanquished all? Does not this seem to you a greater boast than that about the fly-sting?"

Then the Count said:

"Yes, and Alexander was a greater man than he who made the other speech. But extraordinary men are surely to be pardoned when they assume much; for he who has great things to do must needs have daring to do them, and confidence in himself, and must not be abject or mean in spirit, yet very modest in speech, showing less confidence in himself than he has, lest his self-confidence lead to rashness."

The Count now paused a little, and messer Bernardo Bibbiena said, laughing:

"I remember what you said earlier, that this Courtier of ours must be endowed by nature with beauty of countenance and person, and with a grace that shall make him so agreeable. Grace and beauty of countenance I think I certainly possess, and this is the reason why so many ladies are ardently in love with me, as you know; but I am rather doubtful as to the beauty of my person, especially as regards these legs of mine, which seem to me decidedly less well proportioned than I should wish: as to my bust and other members however, I am quite content. Pray, now, describe a little more in particular the sort of body that the Courtier is to have, so that I may dismiss this doubt and set my mind at rest."

After some laughter at this, the Count continued:

"Of a certainty that grace of countenance can be truly said to be yours, nor need I cite further example than this to show what manner of thing it is, for we unquestionably perceive your aspect to be most agreeable and pleasing to everyone, albeit the lineaments of it are not very delicate. Still it is of a manly cast and at the same time full of grace; and this characteristic is to be found in many different types of countenance. And of such sort I would have our Courtier's aspect; not so soft and effeminate as is sought by many, who not only curl their hair and pluck their brows, but gloss their faces with all those arts employed by the most wanton and unchaste women in the world; and in their walk, posture and every act, they seem so limp and languid that their limbs are like to fall apart; and they pronounce their words so mournfully that they appear about to expire upon the spot: and the more they find themselves with men of rank, the more they affect such tricks. Since nature has not made them women, as they seem to wish to appear and be, they should be treated not as good women but as public harlots, and driven not merely from the courts of great lords but from the society of honest men.

"Then coming to the bodily frame, I say it is enough if this be neither extremely short nor tall, for both of these conditions excite a certain contemptuous surprise, and men of either sort are gazed upon in much the same way that we gaze on monsters. Yet if we must offend in one of the two extremes, it is preferable to fall a little short of the just measure of height than to exceed it, for besides often being dull of intellect, men thus huge of body are also unfit for every exercise of agility, which thing I should much wish in the Courtier. And so I would have him well built and shapely of limb, and would have him show strength and lightness and suppleness, and know all bodily exercises that befit a man of war: whereof I think the first should be to handle every sort of weapon well on foot and on horse, to understand the advantages of each, and especially to be familiar with those weapons that are ordinarily used among gentlemen; for besides the use of them in war, where such subtlety in contrivance is perhaps not needful, there frequently arise differences between one gentleman and another, which afterwards result in duels often fought with such weapons as happen at the moment to be within reach: thus knowledge of this kind is a very safe thing. Nor am I one of those who say that skill is forgotten in the hour of need; for he whose skill forsakes him at such a time, indeed gives token that he has already lost heart and head through fear.

"Moreover I deem it very important to know how to wrestle, for it is a great help in the use of all kinds of weapons on foot. Then, both for his own sake and for that of his friends, he must understand the quarrels and differences that may arise, and must be quick to seize an advantage, always showing courage and prudence in all things. Nor should he be too ready to fight except when honour demands it; for besides the great danger that the uncertainty of fate entails, he who rushes into such affairs recklessly and without urgent cause, merits the severest censure even though he be successful. But when he finds himself so far engaged that he cannot withdraw without reproach, he ought to be most deliberate, both in the preliminaries to the duel and in the duel itself, and always show readiness and daring. Nor must he act like some, who fritter the affair away in disputes and controversies, and who, having the choice of weapons, select those that neither cut nor pierce, and arm themselves as if they were expecting a cannonade; and thinking it enough not to be defeated, stand ever on the defensive and retreat, — showing therein their utter cowardice. And thus they make themselves a laughing-stock for boys, like those two men of Ancona who fought at Perugia not long since, and made everyone laugh who saw them."

"And who were they?" asked my lord Gaspar Pallavicino.

"Two cousins," replied messer Cesare.

Then the Count said:

"In their fighting they were as like as two brothers;" and soon continued: "Even in time of peace weapons are often used in various exercises, and gentlemen appear in public shows before the people and ladies and great lords. For this reason I would have our Courtier a perfect horseman in every kind of seat; and besides understanding horses and what pertains to riding, I would have him use all possible care and diligence to lift himself a little beyond the rest in everything, so that he may be ever recognized as eminent above all others. And as we read of Alcibiades that he surpassed all the nations with whom he lived, each in their particular province, so I would have this Courtier of ours excel all others, and each in that which is most their profession. And as it is the especial pride of the Italians to ride well with the rein, to govern wild horses with consummate skill, and to play at tilting and jousting, — in these things let him be among the best of the Italians. In tourneys and in the arts of defence and attack, let him shine among the best in France. In stick-throwing, bull-fighting, and in casting spears and darts, let him excel among the Spaniards. But above everything he should temper all his movements with a certain good judgment and grace, if he wishes to merit that universal favour which is so greatly prized.

"There are also many other exercises, which although not immediately dependent upon arms, yet are closely connected therewith, and greatly foster manly sturdiness; and one of the chief among these seems to me to be the chase, because it bears a certain likeness to war: and truly it is an amusement for great lords and befitting a man at court, and furthermore it is seen to have been much cultivated among the ancients. It is fitting also to know how to swim, to leap, to run, to throw stones, for besides the use that may be made of this in war, a man often has occasion to show what he can do in such matters; whence good esteem is to be won, especially with the multitude, who must be taken into account withal. Another admirable exercise, and one very befitting a man at court, is the game of tennis, in which are well shown the disposition of the body, the quickness and suppleness of every member, and all those qualities that are seen in nearly every other exercise. Nor less highly do I esteem vaulting on horse, which although it be fatiguing and difficult, makes a man very light and dexterous more than any other thing; and besides its utility, if this lightness is accompanied by grace, it is to my thinking a finer show than any of the others.

"Our Courtier having once become more than fairly expert in these exercises, I think he should leave the others on one side: such as turning summersaults, rope-walking, and the like, which savour of the mountebank and little befit a gentleman.

"But since one cannot devote himself to such fatiguing exercises continually, and since repetition becomes very tiresome and abates the admiration felt for what is rare, we must always diversify our life with various occupations. For this reason I would have our Courtier sometimes descend to quieter and more tranquil exercises, and in order to escape envy and to entertain himself agreeably with everyone, let him do whatever others do, yet never departing from praiseworthy deeds, and governing himself with that good judgment which will keep him from all folly; but let him laugh, jest, banter, frolic and dance, yet in such fashion that he shall always appear genial and discreet, and that everything he may do or say shall be stamped with grace."

Then messer Cesare Gonzaga said:

"We certainly ought on no account to hinder the course of this discussion; but if I were to keep silence, I should be neglectful both of the right I have to speak and of my desire to know one thing: and let me be pardoned if I ask a question instead of contradicting; for this I think may be permitted me, after the precedent of messer Bernardo here, who in his over desire to be held comely, broke the rules of our game by asking a question instead of contradicting."

Then my lady Duchess said:

"You see how one errour begets many. Therefore he who transgresses and sets a bad example, like messer Bernardo, deserves to be punished not only for his own transgression but also for the others'."

Then messer Cesare replied:

"In that case, my Lady, I shall be exempt from penalty, since messer Bernardo is to be punished for his own fault as well as mine."

"Nay," said my lady Duchess, "you both ought to have double punishment: he for his own transgression and for leading you to transgress; you for your own transgression and for imitating him."

"My Lady," replied messer Cesare, "as yet I have not transgressed; so, to leave all this punishment to messer Bernardo alone, I will keep silence."

And indeed he remained silent; when my lady Emilia laughed and said:

"Say whatever you like, for under leave of my lady Duchess I pardon him that has transgressed and him that shall transgress, in so small a degree."

"I consent," continued my lady Duchess. "But take care lest perchance you fall into the mistake of thinking to gain more by being merciful than by being just; for to pardon him too easily that has transgressed is to wrong him that transgresses not. Yet I would not have my severity reproach your indulgence, and thus be the cause of our not hearing this question of messer Cesare."

And so, being given the signal by my lady Duchess and by my lady Emilia, he at once said:

"If I remember rightly, Sir Count, I think you have repeated several times this evening that the Courtier must accompany his actions, gestures, habits, in short his every movement, with grace; and this you seem to regard as an universal seasoning, without which all other properties and good qualities are of little worth. And indeed I think that in this everyone would allow himself to be persuaded easily, since from the very force of the word, it may be said that he who has grace finds grace. But since you said that this is oftentimes the gift of nature and of heaven and, even when not thus perfect, can with care and pains be made much greater,—those men who are born so fortunate and so rich in this treasure as are some we see, seem to me in this to have little need of other master; because that benign favour of heaven almost in despite of themselves leads them higher than they will, and makes them not only pleasing but admirable to all the world. Therefore I do not discuss this, it not being in our power to acquire it of ourselves. But they who have received from nature only so much, that they are capable of becoming graceful by pains, industry and care,—I long to know by what art, by what training, by what method, they can acquire this grace, as well in bodily exercises (in which you esteem it to be so necessary) as also in everything else that they may do or say. Therefore, since by much praise of this quality you have aroused in all of us, I think, an ardent thirst to pursue it, you are further bound, by the charge that my lady Emilia laid upon you, to satisfy that thirst by teaching us how to attain it."

"I am not bound," said the Count, "to teach you how to become graceful, or anything else; but only to show you what manner of man a perfect Courtier ought to be. Nor would I in any case undertake the task of teaching you this perfection; especially having said a little while ago that the Courtier must know how to wrestle, vault, and do many other things, which I am sure you all know quite as well as if I, who have never learned them, were to teach you. For just as a good soldier knows how to tell the smith what fashion, shape and quality his armour ought to have, but cannot show how it is to be made or forged or tempered; so I perhaps may be able to tell you what manner of man a perfect Courtier ought to be, but cannot teach you what you must do to become one.

"Yet to comply with your request as far as is within my power,—although it is almost a proverb that grace is not to be learned,—I say that whoever would acquire grace in bodily exercises (assuming first that he be by nature not incapable), ought to begin early and learn the rudiments from the best masters. And how important this seemed to King Philip of Macedon, may be seen from the fact that he chose Aristotle, the famous philosopher and perhaps the greatest that has ever been in the world, to teach his son Alexander the first elements of letters. And of the men whom we know at the present day, consider how well and how gracefully my lord Galeazzo Sanseverino, Grand Equerry of France, performs all bodily exercises; and this because in addition to the natural aptitude of person that he possesses, he has taken the utmost pains to study with good masters, and always to have about him men who excel and to select from each the best of what they know: for just as in wrestling, vaulting and in the use of many sorts of weapons, he has taken for his guide our friend messer Pietro Monte, who (as you know) is the true and only master of every form of trained strength and agility,—so in riding, jousting and all else, he has ever had before his eyes the most proficient men that were known in those matters.

"Therefore he who wishes to be a good pupil, besides performing his tasks well, must put forth every effort to resemble his master, and, if it were possible, to transform himself into his master. And when he feels that he has made some progress, it will be very profitable to observe different men of the same calling, and governing himself with that good judgment which must ever be his guide, to go about selecting now this thing from one and that thing from another. And as the bee in the green meadows is ever wont to rob the flowers among the grass, so our Courtier must steal this grace from all who seem to possess it, taking from each that part which shall most be worthy praise; and not act like a friend of ours whom you all know, who thought he greatly resembled King Ferdinand the Younger of Aragon, and made it his care to imitate the latter in nothing but a certain trick of continually raising the head and twisting one side of the mouth, which the king had contracted from some infirmity. And there are many such, who think they gain a point if only they be like a great man in some thing; and frequently they devote themselves to that which is his only fault.

"But having before now often considered whence this grace springs, laying aside those men who have it by nature, I find one universal rule concerning it, which seems to me worth more in this matter than any other in all things human that are done or said: and that is to avoid affectation to the uttermost and as it were a very sharp and dangerous rock; and, to use possibly a new word, to practise in everything a certain nonchalance [18] that shall conceal design and show that what is done and said is done without effort and almost without thought. From this I believe grace is in large measure derived, because everyone knows the difficulty of those things that are rare and well done, and therefore facility in them excites the highest admiration; while on the other hand, to strive and as the saying is to drag by the hair, is extremely ungraceful, and makes us esteem everything slightly, however great it be.

"Accordingly we may affirm that to be true art which does not appear to be art; nor to anything must we give greater care than to conceal art, for if it is discovered, it quite destroys our credit and brings us into small esteem. And I remember having once read that there were several very excellent orators of antiquity, who among their other devices strove to make everyone believe that they had no knowledge of letters; and hiding their knowledge they pretended that their orations were composed very simply and as if springing rather from nature and truth than from study and art; the which, if it had been detected, would have made men wary of being duped by it.

"Thus you see how the exhibition of art and study so intense destroys the grace in everything. Which of you is there who does not laugh when our friend messer Pierpaolo dances in his peculiar way, with those capers of his,—legs stiff to the toe and head motionless, as if he were a stick, and with such intentness that he actually seems to be counting the steps? What eye so blind as not to see in this the ungracefulness of affectation,—and in many men and women who are here present, the grace of that nonchalant ease (for in the case of bodily movements many call it thus), showing by word or laugh or gesture that they have no care and are thinking more of everything else than of that, to make the onlooker think they can hardly go amiss?"

Messer Bernardo Bibbiena here said, without waiting:

"Now at last our friend messer Roberto has found someone to praise the manner of his dancing, as all the rest of you seem to value it lightly; because if this merit consists in nonchalance, and in appearing to take no heed and to be thinking more of everything else than of what you are doing, messer Roberto in dancing has no peer on earth; for to show plainly that he is not thinking about it, he often lets the cloak drop from his shoulders and the slippers from his feet, and still goes on dancing without picking up either the one or the other."

Then the Count replied:

"Since you insist on my talking, I will speak further of our faults. Do you not perceive that what you call nonchalance in messer Roberto, is really affectation? For it is clearly seen that he is striving with all his might to seem to be taking no thought, and this is taking too much thought; and since it passes the true limits of moderation, his nonchalance is affected and unbecoming; and it is a thing that works precisely the reverse of the effect intended, that is the concealment of art. Thus in nonchalance (which is praiseworthy in itself), I do not think that it is less a vice of affectation to let the clothes fall from one's back, than in care of dress (which also is praiseworthy in itself) to hold the head stiff for fear of disarranging one's locks, or to carry a mirrour in the peak of one's cap and a comb in one's sleeve, and to have a valet follow one about the streets with sponge and brush: for such care in dress and such nonchalance both touch upon excess, which is always offensive and contrary to that pure and charming simplicity which is so pleasing to the human mind.

"You see how ungraceful a rider is who strives to sit bolt upright in the saddle after the manner we are wont to call Venetian, — as compared with another who seems not to be thinking about it, and sits his horse as free and steady as if he were afoot. How much more pleasing and how much more praised is a gentleman who carries arms, if he be modest, speak little and boast little, than another who is forever sounding his own praises, and with blasphemy and bluster seems to be hurling defiance at the world! This too is naught but affectation of wishing to appear bold. And so it is with every exercise, nay with everything that can be done or said in the world."

Then my lord Magnifico said:

"This is true also with music, wherein it is a very great fault to place two perfect consonances one after the other, so that our very sense of hearing abhors it and often enjoys a second or seventh, which in itself is a harsh and intolerable discord. And the reason is that repetition of perfect consonances begets satiety and exhibits a too affected harmony; which is avoided by introducing imperfect consonances, and thus a kind of contrast is given, whereby our ears are held more in suspense, and more eagerly await and enjoy the perfect consonances, and sometimes delight in that discord of the second or seventh, as in something unpremeditated."

"You see then," replied the Count, "the harmful effect of affectation in this as in other things. It is said also to have been proverbial among some very excellent painters of antiquity, that over diligence is harmful, and Protogenes is said to have been censured by Apelles because he did not know when to take his hand from the tablet."

Then messer Cesare said:

"Methinks our friend fra Serafino has this same fault, of not knowing when to take his hands from the table, at least until all the food has been taken from it too." [19]

The Count laughed, and continued:

"Apelles meant that in his painting Protogenes did not know when he had finished, which was the same thing as reproving him for being affected in his work. Thus this excellence, which is the opposite of affectation and which for the present we call nonchalance, besides being the true fountain from which grace springs, carries with it another ornament, which, in accompanying any human action whatever and however trifling it be, not only at once reveals the knowledge of him who performs it, but often leads us to rate his knowledge as much greater than in fact it is; because it impresses upon the minds of the bystanders the idea that he who does well so easily, knows much more than he does, and that if he were to use care and effort in what he did, he could do it far better.

"And to multiply like examples, here is a man who handles weapons, either about to throw a dart or holding a sword in his hand or other weapon; if he nimbly and without thinking puts himself in an attitude of readiness, with such ease that his body and all his members seem to fall into that posture naturally and quite without effort, — although he do no more, he will prove himself to everyone to be perfect in that exercise. Likewise in dancing, a single step, a single movement of the person that is graceful and not forced, soon shows the knowledge of the dancer. A musician who in singing utters a single note ending with sweet tone in a little group of four notes with such ease as to seem spontaneous, shows by that single touch that he can do much more than he is doing. Often too in painting, a single line not laboured, a single brush-stroke easily drawn, so that it seems as if the hand moves unbidden to its aim according to the painter's wish, without being guided by care or any skill, clearly reveals the excellence of the craftsman, which every man appreciates according to his capacity for judging. And the same is true of nearly everything else.

"Our Courtier then will be esteemed excellent and will attain grace in everything, particularly in speaking, if he avoids affectation; into which fault many fall, and often more than others, some of us Lombards, who, if they have been a year away from home, on their return at once begin to speak Roman, sometimes Spanish or French, and God knows how. And all this comes from over zeal to appear widely informed; in such fashion do men devote care and assiduity to acquiring a very odious fault. And truly it would be no light task for me, if I were to try in these discussions of ours to use those antique Tuscan words that are quite rejected by the usage of the Tuscans of to-day; and besides I think everyone would laugh at me."

* * * * *

"My Lady," replied the Count, "I fear the thread is broken; yet if I am not wrong, methinks we were saying that the pest of affectation imparts extreme ungracefulness to everything, while on the other hand simplicity and nonchalance produce the height of grace: in praise of which, and in blame of affectation, we might cite many other arguments; but of these I wish to add only one, and no more. Women are always very eager to be — and when they cannot be, at least to seem — beautiful. So where nature is somewhat at fault in this regard, they try to piece it out by artifice; whence arise that painting of the face with so much care and sometimes pains, that plucking of the eyebrows and forehead, and the use of all those devices and the endurance of that trouble, which you ladies think to keep very secret from men, but which are all well known."

Here madonna Costanza Fregosa laughed and said:

"It would be far more courteous for you to keep to your discussion, and tell us of what grace is born, and talk about Courtiership, — than to try to unveil the weaknesses of women, which are not to the purpose."

"Nay, much to the purpose," replied the Count: "for these weaknesses of yours I am speaking of, deprive you of grace because they spring from nothing but affectation, wherein you openly make known to everyone your over-eagerness to be beautiful.

"Do you not see how much more grace a lady has who paints (if at all) so sparingly and so little, that whoever sees her is in doubt whether she be painted or not; than another lady so plastered that she seems to have put a mask upon her face and dares not laugh for fear of cracking it, nor ever changes colour but when she dresses in the morning, and then stands motionless all the rest of the day like a wooden image, showing herself only by candle-light, like wily merchants who display their cloths in a dark place? Again, how much more pleasing than all others is one (I mean not ill-favoured) who is plainly seen to have nothing on her face, although it be neither very white nor very red, but by nature a little pale and sometimes tinged with an honest flush from shame or other accident,—with hair artlessly unadorned and hardly confined, her gestures simple and free, without showing care or wish to be beautiful! This is that nonchalant simplicity most pleasing to the eyes and minds of men, who are ever fearful of being deceived by art.

"Beautiful teeth are very charming in a woman, for since they are not so much in view as the face is, but lie hidden most of the time, we may believe that less care is taken to make them beautiful than with the face. Yet if one were to laugh without cause and solely to display the teeth, he would betray his art, and however beautiful they were, would seem most ungraceful to all, like Catullus's Egnatius. It is the same with the hands; which, if they are delicate and beautiful, and occasionally left bare when there is need to use them, and not in order to display their beauty, they leave a very great desire to see more of them, and especially if covered with gloves again; for whoever covers them seems to have little care or thought whether they be seen or not, and to have them thus beautiful more by nature than by any effort or pains.

"Have you ever noticed when a woman, in passing through the street to church or elsewhere, thoughtlessly happens (either in frolic or from other cause) to lift her dress high enough to show the foot and often a little of the leg? Does this not seem to you full of grace, when you see her tricked out with a touch of feminine daintiness in velvet shoes and neat stockings? I for one delight in it and believe you all do, for everyone is persuaded that elegance, in matters thus hidden and rarely seen, is natural and instinctive to the lady rather than forced, and that she does not think to win any praise by it.

"In this way we avoid and hide affectation, and you can now see how opposed and destructive it is to grace in every office as well of the body as the mind: whereof we have thus far spoken little, and yet we must not omit it, for since the mind is of far more worth than the body, it deserves to be more cultivated and adorned. And as to what ought to be done in the case of our Courtier, we will lay aside the precepts of the many sage philosophers who write of this matter and define the properties of the mind and discuss so subtly about their rank,—and keeping to our subject, we will in a few words declare it to be enough that he be (as we say) an honest and upright man; for in this are included prudence, goodness, strength and temperance of mind, and all the other qualities that are proper to a name so honoured. And I esteem him alone to be a true moral philosopher, who wishes to be good; and in this regard he needs few other precepts than that wish. And therefore Socrates was right in saying that he thought his teachings bore good fruit indeed whenever they incited anyone to understand and teach virtue: for they who have reached the goal of desiring nothing more ardently than to be good, easily acquire knowledge of everything needful therefor; so we will discuss this no further.

"Yet besides goodness, I think that letters are for everyone the true and principal ornament of the mind: although the French recognize only the nobility of arms and esteem all else as naught. Thus they not only fail to prize but they abhor letters, and hold all men of letters most base, and think they speak very basely of any man when they call him a clerk."

Then the Magnifico Giuliano replied:

"You say truly, that this fault has long been prevalent among the French. But if kind fate decrees that Monseigneur d'Angoulême shall succeed to the crown, as is hoped, I think that just as the glory of arms flourishes and shines in France, so too ought that of letters to flourish in highest state; for it is not long since I, being at the court, saw this prince, and it seemed to me that besides the grace of his person and the beauty of his face, he had in his aspect such loftiness, joined however with a certain gracious humanity, that the realm of France must always seem small for him. I heard afterwards from many gentlemen, both French and Italian, of his very noble manner of life, of his loftiness of mind, of his valour and liberality. And among other things I was told that he loved and esteemed letters especially and held all men of letters in greatest honour; and he condemned the French themselves for being so hostile to this profession, especially as they have within their borders such a noble school as that of Paris, frequented by all the world."

Then the Count said:

"It is a great marvel that in such tender youth, solely by natural instinct and against the usage of his country, he has of himself chosen so worthy a path. And as subjects always copy the customs of their superiors, it may be that, as you say, the French will yet come to esteem letters at their true worth: whereto they may easily be persuaded, if they will but listen to reason; since nothing is by nature more desirable for men, or more proper to them, than knowledge, which it is great folly to say or believe is not always a good thing.

"And if I were speaking with them, or with others who had an opinion contrary to mine, I should strive to show them how useful and necessary letters are to our life and dignity, having indeed been granted by God to men as a crowning gift. Nor should I lack instances of many excellent commanders of antiquity, who all added the ornament of letters to the valour of their arms.

"Thus you know Alexander held Homer in such veneration that he always kept the Iliad by his bedside; and he devoted the greatest attention not only to these studies but to philosophical speculation under Aristotle's guidance. Alcibiades enlarged his natural aptitudes and made them greater by means of letters and the teachings of Socrates. The care that Caesar gave to study is also attested by the surviving works that he divinely wrote. It is said that Scipio Africanus always kept in hand the works of Xenophon, wherein the perfect king is portrayed under the name of Cyrus. I could tell you of Lucullus, Sulla, Pompey, Brutus, and many other Romans and Greeks; but I will merely remind you that Hannibal, the illustrious commander, — although fierce by nature and a stranger to all humanity, faithless and a despiser of both men and God, — yet had knowledge of letters and was conversant with the Greek language; and if I mistake not, I once read that he even left a book composed by him in Greek.

"However it is superfluous to tell you this, for I well know that you all see how wrong the French are in thinking that letters are injurious to arms. You know that glory is the true stimulus to great and hazardous deeds of war, and whoso is moved thereto by gain or other motive, besides doing nothing good, deserves not to be called a gentleman, but a base trafficker. And true glory is that which is preserved in the sacred treasure-house of letters, as everyone may understand except those unfortunates who have never enjoyed them.

"What soul is there so abject, timid and humble, that when he reads of the deeds of Caesar, Alexander, Scipio, Hannibal, and many others, is not inflamed by an ardent desire to be like them, and does not make small account of this frail two days' life, in order to win the almost eternal life of fame, which in spite of death makes him live in far greater glory than before? But he who does not feel the delight of letters, cannot either know how great is the glory they so so long preserve, and measures it by the life of one man or two, because his memory runs no further. Hence he cannot esteem this short-lived glory so much as he would that almost eternal glory if knowledge of it were unhappily not denied him, and as he does not esteem it so much, we may reasonably believe that he will not run such danger to pursue it as one who knew it would.

"I should be far from willing to have an antagonist cite instances to the contrary in refutation of my view, and urge upon me that with all their knowledge of letters the Italians have for some time since shown little martial valour, — which is alas only too true. But it very certainly might be said that the fault of a few has brought not only grievous harm but eternal obloquy upon all the rest; and from them was derived the true cause of our ruin and of the decadence if not the death of valour in our souls: yet it would be far more shameful in us to publish it, than for the French to be ignorant of letters. Therefore it is better to pass over in silence that which cannot be recalled without pain: and avoiding this subject (upon which I entered against my will) to return to our Courtier.

"I would have him more than passably accomplished in letters, at least in those studies that are called the humanities, and conversant not only with the Latin language but with the Greek, for the sake of the many different things that have been admirably written therein. Let him be well versed in the poets, and not less in the orators and historians, and also proficient in writing verse and prose, especially in this vulgar tongue of ours; for besides the enjoyment he will find in it, he will by this means never lack agreeable entertainment with ladies, who are usually fond of such things. And if other occupations or want of study prevent his reaching such perfection as to render his writings worthy of great praise, let him be careful to suppress them so that others may not laugh at him, and let him show them only to a friend whom he can trust: because they will at least be of this service to him, that the exercise will enable him to judge the work of others. For it very rarely happens that a man who is not accustomed to write, however learned he may be, can ever quite appreciate the toil and industry of writers, or taste the sweetness and excellence of style, and those latent niceties that are often found in the ancients.

"Moreover these studies will also make him fluent, and as Aristippus said to the tyrant, confident and assured in speaking with everyone. Hence I would have our Courtier keep one precept fixed in mind; which is that in this and everything else he should be always on his guard, and diffident rather than forward, and that he should keep from falsely persuading himself that he knows that which he does not know. For by nature we all are fonder of praise than we ought to be, and our ears love the melody of words that praise us more than any other sweet song or sound; and thus, like sirens' voices, they are often the cause of shipwreck to him who does not close his ears to such deceptive harmony. Among the ancient sages this danger was recognized, and books were written showing in what way the true friend may be distinguished from the flatterer. But what does this avail, if there be many, nay a host, of those who clearly perceive that they are flattered, yet love him who flatters them, and hold him in hatred who tells them the truth? And often when they find him who praises them too sparing in his words, they even help him and say such things of themselves, that the flatterer is put to shame, most impudent though he be.

"Let us leave these blind ones to their errour, and have our Courtier of such good judgment that he will not take black for white, or have more self-confidence than he clearly knows to be well founded; and especially in those peculiarities which (if you remember) messer Cesare in his game said we had often used as an instrument to bring men's folly to light. On the contrary, even if he well knows the praises bestowed upon him to be true, let him not err by accepting them too openly or confirming them without some protest; but rather let him as it were disclaim them modestly, always showing and really esteeming arms as his chief profession, and all other good accomplishments as an ornament thereto. And particularly among soldiers let him not act like those who insist on seeming soldiers in learning, and learned men among soldiers. In this way, for the reasons we have alleged, he will avoid affectation, and even the middling things that he does, shall seem very great."

Messer Pietro Bembo here replied:

"Count, I do not see why you insist that this Courtier, being lettered and endowed with so many other admirable accomplishments, should hold everything as an ornament of arms, and not arms and the rest as an ornament of letters; which without other accompaniment are as superior in dignity to arms, as the mind is to the body, for the practice of them properly pertains to the mind, as that of arms does to the body."

Then the Count replied:

"Nay, the practice of arms pertains to both mind and body. But I would not have you judge in such a cause, messer Pietro, for you would be too much suspected of bias by one of the two sides: and as the controversy has already been long waged by very wise men, there is no need to renew it; but I regard it as settled in favour of arms, and would have our Courtier so regard it too, since I may form him as I wish. And if you are of contrary mind, wait till you hear of a contest wherein he who defends the cause of arms is allowed to use arms, just as those who defend letters make use of letters in their defence; for if everyone avails himself of his proper weapons, you shall see that men of letters will be worsted."

"Ah," said messer Pietro, "a while ago you blamed the French for prizing letters little, and told what glorious lustre is shed on man by letters and how they make him immortal; and now it seems you have changed your mind. Do you not remember that

> Before the famous tomb of brave Achilles
> Thus spake the mighty Alexander, sighing:
> 'O happy youth, who found so clear a trumpet,
> And lofty bard to make thy deeds undying!'

And if Alexander envied Achilles not for his deeds, but for the fortune that had granted him the happiness of having his exploits celebrated by Homer, we may conclude that Alexander esteemed Homer's poems above Achilles's arms. For what other judge do you wait then, or for what other sentence upon the dignity of arms and letters, than that pronounced by one of the greatest commanders that have ever been?"

Then the Count replied:

"I blame the French for thinking that letters are a hindrance to the profession of arms, and I hold that learning is more proper to no one than to a warrior; and in our Courtier I would have these two accomplishments joined and each aided by the other, as is most proper: nor do I think I have changed my mind in this. But as I said, I do not wish to discuss which of the two is more worthy of praise. It is enough that men of letters almost never select for praise any but great men and glorious deeds, which in themselves merit praise for the mere essential quality from which they spring; besides this they are very noble material for writers: which is a great ornament, and in part the cause of perpetuating writings, which perhaps would not be so much read and appreciated if they lacked their noble theme, but vain and of little moment.

"And if Alexander was envious that Achilles should be praised by Homer, it does not therefore follow that he esteemed letters above arms; wherein if he had felt himself as far behind Achilles as he deemed all those who wrote of him were behind Homer, I am sure he would far rather have desired fine acts on his part than fine speeches on the part of others. Hence I believe that saying of his to have been a tacit eulogy of himself, and that he was expressing a desire for what he thought he did not possess (that is, the supreme excellence of a writer), and not for what he believed he already had attained (that is, prowess in arms, wherein he did not deem Achilles at all his superior). Thus he called Achilles happy, as if hinting that although his own fame had hitherto not been so celebrated in the world as Achilles's, which was made bright and illustrious by that poem so divine, — it was not because his valour and merits were less or deserving of less praise, but because fortune bestowed upon Achilles that miracle of nature as a glorious trumpet for his achievements. Perhaps also he wished to incite some noble genius to write about him, by showing that this must be as pleasing to him as were his love and veneration for the sacred monuments of letters: whereof we have spoken long enough for the present."

"Nay, too long," replied my lord Ludovico Pio; "for I believe that in the whole world it would be impossible to find a receptacle large enough to hold all the things you would have in our Courtier."

Then the Count said:

"Wait a little, for there are many more that he must have."

"In that case," replied Pietro da Napoli, "Grasso de' Medici would have a great advantage over messer Pietro Bembo."

Here everyone laughed, and the Count began anew and said:

"My lords, you must know that I am not content with the Courtier unless he be also a musician and unless, besides understanding and being able to read notes, he can play upon divers instruments. For if we consider rightly, there is to be found no rest from toil or medicine for the troubled spirit more becoming and praiseworthy in time of leisure, than this; and especially in courts, where besides the relief from tedium that music affords us all, many things are done to please the ladies, whose tender and gentle spirit is easily penetrated by harmony and filled with sweetness. Thus it is no marvel that in both ancient and modern times they have always been inclined to favour musicians, and have found refreshing spiritual food in music."

Then my lord Gaspar said:

"I admit that music as well as many other vanities may be proper to women and perhaps to some that have the semblance of men, but not to those who really are men; for these ought not to enervate their mind with delights and thus induce therein a fear of death."

"Say not so," replied the Count; "for I shall enter upon a vast sea in praise of music. And I shall call to mind how it was always celebrated and held sacred among the ancients, and how very sage philosophers were of opinion that the world is composed of music, that the heavens make harmony in their moving, and that the soul, being ordered in like fashion, awakes and as it were revives its powers through music.

"Thus it is written that Alexander was sometimes excited by it so passionately, that he was forced almost against his will to leave the banquet table and rush to arms; and when the musician changed the temper of the tune, he grew calm again, lay aside his arms, and returned to the banquet table. Moreover I will tell you that grave Socrates learned to play the cithern at a very advanced age. And I remember having once heard that Plato and Aristotle would have the man of culture a musician also; and they show by a host of arguments that the power of music over us is very great, and (for many reasons which would be too long to tell now) that it must needs be taught from childhood, not so much for the mere melody that we hear, but for the power it has to induce in us a fresh and good habit of mind and an habitual tendency to virtue, which renders the soul more capable of happiness, just as bodily exercise renders the body more robust; and that music is not only no hindrance in the pursuits of peace and war, but is very helpful therein.

"Again, Lycurgus approved of music in his harsh laws. And we read that in their battles the very warlike Lacedemonians and Cretans used the cithern and other dulcet instruments; that many very excellent commanders of antiquity, like Epaminondas, practised music; and that those who were ignorant of it, like Themistocles, were far less esteemed. Have you not read that music was among the first accomplishments which the worthy old Chiron taught Achilles in tender youth, whom he reared from the age of nurse and cradle? and that the sage preceptor insisted that the hands which were to shed so much Trojan blood, should be often busied with the cithern? Where is the soldier who would be ashamed to imitate Achilles,—to say nothing of many other famous commanders whom I could cite?

"Therefore seek not to deprive our Courtier of music, which not only soothes men's minds, but often tames wild beasts; and he who enjoys it not, may be sure that his spirit is ill attuned. See what power it has, to make (as once it did) a fish submit to be ridden by a man upon the boisterous sea. We find it used in holy temples to render praise and thanks to God; and we must believe that it is pleasing to Him and that He has given it to us as most sweet alleviation for our fatigues and troubles. Wherefore rough toilers of the field under a burning sun often cheat their weariness with crude and rustic song. With music the rude peasant lass, who is up before the day to spin or weave, wards off her drowsiness and makes her toil a pleasure; music is very cheering pastime for poor sailors after rain, wind and tempest: a solace to tired pilgrims on their long and weary journeys, and often to sorrowing captives in their chains and fetters. Thus, as stronger proof that melody even if rude is very great relief from every human toil and care, nature seems to have taught it to the nurse as chief remedy for the continual wailing of frail children, who by the sound of her voice are brought restful and placid sleep, forgetful of the tears so proper to them and given us in that age by nature as a presage of our after life."

As the Count now remained silent for a little, the Magnifico Giuliano said:

"I do not at all agree with my lord Gaspar. Nay I think, for the reasons you give and for many others, that music is not only an ornament but a necessity to the Courtier. Yet I would have you declare in what way this and the other accomplishments that you prescribe for him, are to be practised, and at what time and in what manner. For many things that are praiseworthy in themselves often become very inappropriate when practised out of season, and on the other hand, some that seem of little moment are highly esteemed when made use of opportunely."

Then the Count said:

"Before we enter upon that subject, I wish to discuss another matter, which I deem of great importance and therefore think our Courtier ought by no means to omit: and this is to know how to draw and to have acquaintance with the very art of painting.

"And do not marvel that I desire this art, which to-day may seem to savour of the artisan and little to befit a gentleman; for I remember having read that the ancients, especially throughout Greece, had their boys of gentle birth study painting in school as an honourable and necessary thing, and it was admitted to the first rank of liberal arts; while by public edict they forbade that it be taught to slaves. Among the Romans too, it was held in highest honour, and the very noble family of the Fabii took their name from it; for the first Fabius was given the name *Pictor,* because,—being indeed a most excellent painter, and so devoted to painting that when he painted the walls of the temple of Health,—he inscribed his own name thereon; for although he was born of a family thus renowned and honoured with so many consular titles, triumphs and other dignities, and although he was a man of letters and learned in the law, and numbered among the orators,—yet he thought to add splendour and ornament to his fame by leaving a memorial that he had been a painter. Nor is there lack of many other men of illustrious family, celebrated in this art; which besides being very noble and worthy in itself, is of great utility, and especially in war for drawing places, sites, rivers, bridges, rocks, fortresses, and the like; since however well we may keep them in memory (which is very difficult), we cannot show them to others.

"And truly he who does not esteem this art, seems to me very unreasonable; for this universal fabric that we see, — with the vast heaven so richly adorned with shining stars, and in the midst the earth girdled by the seas, varied with mountains, valleys and rivers, and bedecked with so many divers trees, beautiful flowers and grasses, — may be said to be a great and noble picture, composed by the hand of nature and of God; and whoever is able to imitate it, seems to me deserving of great praise: nor can it be imitated without knowledge of many things, as he knows well who tries. Hence the ancients greatly prized both the art and the artist, which thus attained the summit of highest excellence; very sure proof of which may be found in the antique marble and bronze statues that yet are seen. And although painting is different from sculpture, both the one and the other spring from the same source, which is good design. Therefore, as the statues are divine, so we may believe the pictures were also; the more indeed because they are susceptible of greater skill."

Then my lady Emilia turned to Giancristoforo Romano, who was sitting with the others there, and said:

"What think you of this opinion? Do you admit that painting is susceptible of greater skill than sculpture?"

Giancristoforo replied:

"I, my Lady, think that sculpture needs more pains, more skill, and is of greater dignity than painting."

The Count rejoined:

"In that statues are more enduring, perhaps we might say they are of greater dignity; for being made as memorials, they fulfil better than painting the purpose for which they are made. But besides serving as memorials, both painting and sculpture serve also to beautify, and in this respect painting is much superior; for if less diuturnal (so to speak) than sculpture, yet it is of very long life, and is far more charming so long as it endures."

Then Giancristoforo replied:

"I really think that you are speaking against your convictions and that you are doing so solely for the sake of your friend Raphael; and perhaps too the excellence you find in his painting seems to you so consummate that sculpture cannot rival it: but consider that this is praise of an artist and not of his art."

Then he continued:

"It seems clear to me that both the one and the other are artificial imitations of nature; but I do not see how you can say that truth, such as nature makes it, is not better imitated in a marble or bronze statue, — wherein the members are round, formed and measured, as nature makes them, — than in a painting, where we see nothing but the surface and those colours that cheat the eyes; nor will you tell me, surely, that being is not nearer truth than seeming. Moreover

I think sculpture is more difficult, because if a slip is made, it cannot be corrected (since marble cannot be patched again), but another statue must be made anew; which does not happen with painting, for one may change a thousand times, and add and take away, improving always."

The Count said, laughing:

"I am not speaking for Raphael's sake; nor ought you to repute me so ignorant as not to know the excellence of Michelangelo in sculpture, your own, and others'. But I am speaking of the art, and not of the artists.

"You say very truly that both the one and the other are imitations of nature; but it is not true that painting seems, and sculpure is. For while statues are round as in life and painting is seen only on the surface, statues lack many things that paintings do not lack, and especially light and shade. Thus flesh has one tone and marble another; and this the painter imitates to the life by chiaroscuro, greater or less according to the need, — which the sculptor cannot do. And although the painter does not make his figure round, he presents the muscles and members rounded in such fashion as to join the parts which are not seen, that we can discern very well that the painter knows and understands these also. And in this, another and greater skill is needed to represent those members that are foreshortened and grow smaller in proportion to the distance by reason of perspective; which, by means of measured lines, colours, lights and shades, shows you foreground and distance all on the single surface of an upright wall, in such proportion as he chooses. Do you really think it of small moment to imitate the natural colours, in representing flesh or stuffs or any other coloured thing? The sculptor certainly cannot do this, or express the grace of black eyes or blue, with the splendour of their amourous beams. He cannot show the colour of fair hair, or the gleam of weapons, or a dark night, or a storm at sea, or its lightnings and thunderbolts, or the burning of a city, or the birth of rosy dawn with its rays of gold and purple. In short, he cannot show sky, sea, earth, mountains, woods, meadows, gardens, rivers, cities, or houses, — all of which the painter shows.

"Therefore painting seems to me nobler and more susceptible of skill, than sculpture. And I think that it, like other things, reached the summit of excellence among the ancients: which still is seen in the few slight remains that are left, especially in the grottoes of Rome; but much more clearly may it be perceived in the ancient authors, wherein is such honoured and frequent mention both of works and of masters, and whereby we learn how highly they were always honoured by great lords and by commonwealths.

"Thus we read that Alexander loved Apelles of Ephesus dearly, — so dearly, that having caused the artist to paint a portrait of his favourite slave undraped, and hearing that the worthy painter had become most ardently enamoured of her by reason of her marvellous beauty, he gave her to Apelles without hesitation: — munificence truly worthy of Alexander, to sacrifice not only treasure and states but his very affections and desires; and sign of exceeding love for Apelles, in order to please the artist, not to hesitate at displeasing the woman he dearly loved, who (we may believe) was sorely grieved to change so great a king for a painter. Many other signs also are told of Alexander's favour to Apelles; but he very clearly showed how highly he esteemed the painter, in commanding by public edict that none other should presume to paint his portrait.

"Here I could tell you of the rivalries of many noble painters, which filled nearly the whole world with praise and wonderment. I could tell you with what solemnity ancient emperors adorned their triumphs with pictures, and set them up in public places, and how dearly bought them; and that there were some painters who gave their works as gifts, esteeming gold and silver inadequate to pay for them; and how a painting by Protogenes was prized so highly, that when Demetrius laid siege to Rhodes and could have gained an entrance by setting fire to the quarter where he knew the painting was, he refrained from giving battle so that it might not be burned, and thus did not capture the place; and that Metrodorus, a philosopher and very excellent painter, was sent by the Athenians to Lucius Paulus to teach his children and to adorn the triumph that he was about to receive. Moreover many noble authors have written about this art, which is a great sign of the esteem in which it was held; but I do not wish to enlarge further upon it in this discussion.

"So let it be enough to say that it is fitting for our Courtier to have knowledge of painting also, as being honourable and useful and highly prized in those times when men were of far greater worth than now they are. And if he should never derive from it other use or pleasure than the help it affords in judging the merit of statues ancient and modern, of vases, buildings, medals, cameos, intaglios, and the like, — it also enables him to appreciate the beauty of living bodies, not only as to delicacy of face but as to symmetry of all the other parts, both in men and in every other creature. Thus you see how a knowledge of painting is a source of very great pleasure. And let those think of this, who so delight in contemplating a woman's beauty that they seem to be in paradise, and yet cannot paint; which if they could do, they would have much greater pleasure, because they would more perfectly appreciate that beauty which engenders such satisfaction in their hearts."

Here messer Cesare Gonzaga laughed, and said:

"Certainly I am no painter; yet I am sure I have greater pleasure in looking upon a woman than that admirable Apelles, whom you just mentioned, would have if he were now come back to life."

The Count replied:

"This pleasure of yours is not derived wholly from her beauty, but from the affection that perhaps you bear her; and if you will say the truth, the first time you saw that woman you did not feel a thousandth part of the pleasure that you did afterwards, although her beauty was the same. Thus you may see how much more affection had to do with your pleasure, than beauty had."

"I do not deny this," said messer Cesare; "but just as my pleasure is born of affection, so is affection born of beauty. Thus it may still be said that beauty is the cause of my pleasure."

The Count replied:

"Many other causes also inflame our minds, besides beauty: such as manners, knowledge, speech, gesture, and a thousand other things which in a way perhaps might also be called beauties; but above all, the consciousness of being loved. So it is possible to love very ardently even without that beauty you speak of; but the love that springs from the outward bodily beauty which we see, will doubtless give far greater pleasure to him who appreciates it more than to him who appreciates it less. Therefore, to return to our subject, I think that Apelles enjoyed the contemplation of Campaspe's beauty far more than Alexander did: for we may easily believe that both men's love sprang only from her beauty; and perhaps it was partly on this account that Alexander resolved to give her to him who seemed fitted to appreciate her most perfectly.

"Have you not read that those five maidens of Crotona, whom the painter Zeuxis chose above the others of that city for the purpose of forming from them all a single type of surpassing beauty, were celebrated by many poets as having been adjudged beautiful by one who must have been a consummate judge of beauty?"

Messer Cesare here seemed ill satisfied and unwilling to admit for a moment that anyone but himself could taste that pleasure which he felt in contemplating a woman's beauty, and he began to speak. But just then a great tramping of feet was heard, and the sound of loud talking; whereupon everyone turned, and a glare of torches was seen at the door of the room, and soon there arrived, with a numerous and noble company, my lord Prefect, who returned from attending the pope part way on the journey. At once on entering the palace he had asked what my lady Duchess was doing, and had learned of what manner the game was that evening, and the charge imposed on Count Ludovico to speak about Courtiership. Therefore he came as fast as he could, so as to arrive in season to hear something. Then, immediately after having made his reverence to my lady Duchess and bidden the others to be seated (for everyone had risen when he came in), — he too sat down in the circle with some of his gentlemen; among whom were the Marquess Febus di Ceva and his brother Gerardino, messer Ettore Romano, Vincenzo Calmeta, Orazio Florido, and many others; and as everyone remained silent, my lord Prefect said:

"Gentlemen, my coming here would be indeed a pity, if I were to interrupt such a fine discussion as I think you were just now engaged in; so do me not this wrong of depriving yourselves and me of such a pleasure."

Then Count Ludovico said:

"Nay, my Lord, I think we all must be far better pleased to be silent than to speak; for this burden having fallen more to me than to the others this evening, I have at last grown weary of speaking, and I think all the others are weary of listening, for my talk has not been worthy of this company or adequate to the lofty theme that I was charged with; in which, having little satisfied myself, I think I have satisfied the others still less. So you were fortunate, my Lord, to come in at the end. And for the rest of the discussion, it would indeed be well to appoint someone else to take my place, because whoever he may be, I know he will fill it far better than I should even if I were willing to go on, being now tired as I am."

The Magnifico Giuliano replied:

"I certainly shall not submit to be cheated of the promise that you made me, and am sure my lord Prefect too will not be sorry to hear that part of our discussion."

"And what promise was it?" said the Count.

"To tell us in what way the Courtier must make use of those good qualities that you have said befit him," replied the Magnifico.

Although but a boy, my lord Prefect was wise and sensible beyond what seemed natural to his tender years, and in his every movement he showed a loftiness of mind and a certain vivacity of temper that gave true presage of the high pitch of manliness that he was to attain. So he said quickly:

"If all this is to be told, I think I have come just in time; for by hearing in what way the Courtier must use his good qualities, I shall hear also what they are, and thus shall come to learn everything that has been said before. So do not refuse, Count, to fulfil the obligation of which you have already performed a part."

"I should not have so heavy an obligation to fulfil," replied the Count, "if the labour were more evenly divided; but the mistake was made of giving the right of command to a too partial lady;" and then laughing he turned to my lady Emilia, who quickly said:

"It is not you who ought to complain of my partiality; but since you do so without reason, we will give someone else a share of this honour, which you call labour;" and turning to messer Federico Fregoso, she said: "You proposed the game of the Courtier, hence it is right that you should bear some share in it; and this shall be to comply with my lord Magnifico's request, by declaring in what way, manner and time, the Courtier ought to make use of his good qualities and practise those things which the Count has said it is fitting he should know."

Then messer Federico said:

"My Lady, in trying to separate the way and the time and the manner of the Courtier's good qualities and good practice, you try to separate that which cannot be separated, because these are the very things that make his qualities good, and his practice good. Therefore, since the Count has spoken so much and so well, and has touched somewhat upon these matters and arranged in his mind the rest of what he has to say, it was only right that he should continue to the end."

"Account yourself to be the Count," said my lady Emilia, "and say what you think he would say; and thus all will be right."

Then Calmeta said:

"My Lords, since the hour is late, and in order that messer Federico may have no excuse for not telling what he knows, I think it would be well to postpone the rest of the discussion until tomorrow, and let the little time we have left, be spent in some other quiet diversion."

As everyone approved, my lady Duchess desired madonna Margarita and madonna Costanza Fregosa to dance. Whereupon Barletta, a very charming musician and excellent dancer, who always kept the whole court in good humour, began to play upon his instruments; and joining hands, the two ladies danced first a basset and then a *roegarze,* with consummate grace and to the great delight of those who saw them. Then the night being already far spent, my lady Duchess rose to her feet, and so everyone reverently took leave and retired to sleep.

NOTES TO THE FIRST BOOK OF THE COURTIER

1. "Courtiership" is a sadly awkward rendering of the Italian *cortegiania,* which implies not only courtesy and courtliness, but all the many other qualities and accomplishments essential to the perfect Courtier or (what in Castiglione's time was the same) the perfect Gentleman.

2. The extreme dimensions of the Duchy of Urbino were 64 miles from east to west, and 60 miles from north to south. Its population did not much exceed 150,000.

3. The first of the four dialogues is represented as having been held on the evening of the day after the close of a certain visit paid by Pope Julius II to Urbino on his return from a successful campaign against Bologna. This visit is known to have lasted from 3 March to 7 March 1507. Castiglione returned from England as early as 5 March, on which date he wrote to his mother from Urbino: "We have had his Holiness here for two days." It seems probable that this fictitious prolongation of his absence in England was simply a graceful excuse for not himself appearing in the dialogues.

4. "Duke Federico" di Montefeltro, (born 1422; died 1482), was a natural son of Count Guidantonio di Montefeltro . . . In his boyhood he resided fifteen months as a hostage at Venice. Later he studied the theory and practice of war at the Mantuan court, and was trained in the humanities by the famous Vittorino da Feltre. In 1437 he married Gentile Brancaleone, who died childless in 1457. Nearly the whole of his life was spent in military service, as paid ally, now of one prince, now of another. In this capacity he became not only the most noted commander of his time, but always displayed perfect and exceptional fidelity to the causes that he undertook. In 1450 he lost an eye and suffered a fracture of the nose in a tournament; contemporary portraits represent his features in profile. In 1454 he began the construction of the great palace at Urbino. In 1460, at the suggestion of Francesco Sforza (whom he had aided to become Duke of Milan), he married the latter's accomplished niece Battista Sforza, who bore him seven daughters and one son, Guidobaldo. In 1474 he was made Duke of Urbino and appointed Captain General of the Church by Pope Sixtus IV, and was unanimously elected

a Knight of the Garter. He died of fever contracted during military operations in the malarial country near Ferrara. The vast sums spent by him on public buildings, art objects and books, and upon the maintenance of his splendid household, were not extorted from his subjects, but were received from foreign states in return for war services. Thus at the close of his life he drew a yearly stipend equivalent to about £330,000. . .

5. Although long since despoiled of its treasures, the palace is still one of the architectural monuments of Italy. . . For more than fourteen years Duke Federico employed from thirty to forty copyists in transcribing Greek and Latin MSS. Not only the classics, but ecclesiastical and mediæval authors, as well as the Italian poets and humanists were represented in his library, which contained 792 MSS. Ultimately the collection was sent to Rome, where it forms part of the Vatican Library.

6. Emilia Pia, (died 1528), was the youngest daughter of Marco Pio, one of the lords of Carpi. Her brother Giberto married a natural daughter of Cardinal Ippolito d'Este, while her cousin Alberto Pio (1475–1530) was the pupil and became the patron and financial supporter of the scholar-printer Aldus Manutius. In 1487 she was married very young to the studious Count Antonio di Montefeltro (a natural half-brother of Duke Guidobaldo), who left her a widow in 1500. She resided at Urbino and became the trusted and inseparable companion of the Duchess Elisabetta, whom she accompanied on journeys and in exile, ever faithful in misfortune and sorrow. In the duchess's testament she was named as legatee and executrix. She seems to have died without the sacraments of the Church, while discussing passages of the newly published *Courtier* with Count Ludovico Canossa. The part taken by her in these dialogues evinces the charm of her winning manners as well as her possession of a variety of knowledge and graceful accomplishment rare even in that age of womanly genius. Always ready to lead or second the learned and sportive pastimes by which the court circle of Urbino gave zest to their intercourse and polish to their wit, she was of infinite service to the duchess, whose own acquirements were of a less brilliant kind.

7. These devices, so much in vogue during the 16th century in Italy, were the "inventions" which Giovio (a contemporary writer upon the subject) says "the great lords and noble cavaliers of our time like to wear on their armour, caparisons and banners, to signify a part of their generous thoughts." They consisted of a figure or a picture, and a motto nearly always in Latin. The fashion is said to have been copied from the French at the time of the invasions of Charles VIII and Louis XII.

8. Federico Fregoso, (born 1480; died 1541), was a younger brother of Ottaviano, and was educated for holy orders under the direction of his uncle Duke Guidobaldo, at whose court he also perfected himself in worldly accomplishments. In 1507 Julius II made him Archbishop of Salerno, in the kingdom of Naples, but, owing to his supposed French sympathies, he was not allowed to enjoy this benefice, and the next year was put in charge of the bishopric of Gubbio. In the same year he was sent by Julius with the latter's physician to attend Duke Guidobaldo's death-bed, but arrived too late. During the nine years that followed his brother's election as Doge of Genoa (1513), he by turns commanded the army of the Republic, led her fleet against the Barbary pirates (whom he routed in their own harbours), and represented her at the papal court. During the Spanish siege of Genoa in 1522, he escaped to France, was warmly received by Francis I, and made Abbot of St. Bénigne at Dijon,

where he devoted himself to theological study. In 1528 he returned to Italy and was appointed to the see of Gubbio. His piety and zeal for the welfare of his flock won for him the title of "father to the poor and refuge of the distressed." In 1539 he was made a cardinal, and two years later died at Gubbio, being succeeded in that see by his friend Bembo. . .

9. Pietro Bembo, (born at Venice 1470; died at Rome 1547), was the son of a noble Venetian, Bernardo Bembo (a man of much cultivation, who paid for the restoration of Dante's tomb at Ravenna), and Elena Marcella. Having received his early education at Florence, where his father was Venetian ambassador, he studied Greek at Messina under Lascaris (a native of Hellas, whose grammar of that tongue was the first Greek book ever printed, 1476), and philosophy at Padua and Ferrara, where his father was Venetian envoy and introduced him to the Este court. Here he became acquainted with Lucrezia Borgia, who had recently wedded Duke Ercole's son Alfonso, and to whom he dedicated his dialogues on love, *Gli Asolani.* By some writers indeed he is said to have been her lover, but the report is hardly confirmed by the character of the letters exchanged between the two, 1503–1516. Having been entertained at Urbino in 1505, he spent the larger part of the next six years at that court, where he profited by the fine library, delighted in many congenial spirits, and became the close friend of Giuliano de' Medici, who took him to Rome in 1512 and recommended him to the future pope, Leo X. On attaining the tiara, Leo at once appointed him and his friend Sadoleto papal secretaries, an office for which his learning and courtly accomplishments well fitted him. His laxity of morals and his paganism were no disqualification in the eyes of the pope, whom he served also in several diplomatic missions, and from whom he received benefices and pensions sufficient to enrich him for life. In 1518 his friend Castiglione sent him the MS. of *The Courtier,* requesting him to "take the trouble . . . to read it either wholly or in part," and to give his opinion of it. Ten years later, when the book was printed, it was Bembo to whom the proofs were sent for correction, the author being absent in Spain. Even before the death of Leo X in 1521, Bembo had entered upon a life of literary retirement at Padua, where his library and art collection, as well as the learned society that he drew about him, rendered his house famous. Nor was it less esteemed by reason of the presence, at its head, of an avowed mistress (Morosina), who bore him several children. After her death, he devoted himself to theology, entered holy orders, reluctantly accepted a cardinal's hat in 1539, and in 1541 succeeded his friend Fregoso in the bishopric of Gubbio, to which was added that of Bergamo. His death was occasioned by a fall from his horse, and he was buried at Rome in the Minerva church, between his patrons Leo X and Clement VII. . .

10. Cesare Gonzaga, (born 1475; died 1512), was a native of Mantua, being descended from a younger branch of the ruling family of that city, and a cousin of Castiglione, with whom he maintained a close friendship. Having received a courtly and martial education at Milan, and after spending some time with his relatives at Mantua, he entered the service of Duke Guidobaldo of Urbino. In 1504 he shared Castiglione's lodgings after their return from a campaign against Cesare Borgia's strongholds in Romagna, and in the carnival of 1506 they together recited Castiglione's eclogue *Tirsi,* in the authorship of which he is by some credited with a part. On Guidobaldo's death in 1508, the

two friends remained in the service of the new duke, Francesco Maria. In 1511 Cesare fought bravely against the French at Mirandola, and the next year took part in the reduction of Bologna, where he soon died of an acute fever. . .

11. Count Ludovico da Canossa, (born 1476; died 1532), belonged to a noble Veronese family (still honourably extant), and was a close friend of Castiglione and a cousin of the latter's mother. His boyhood was passed at Mantua, and his happiest years at Urbino, where he was received in 1496. In the pontificate of Julius II he went to Rome, and was made Bishop of Tricarico, in southern Italy, 1511. Under Leo X he was entrusted with several embassies, one of which (1514) was to England to reconcile Henry VIII with Louis XII, and another (1515) was to the new French king, Francis I, at whose court he continued to reside, and through whose influence he was made Bishop of Bayeux in 1516. In 1526 and 1527 he served as French ambassador to Venice. . .

12. Gaspar Pallavicino, (born 1486; died 1511), was a descendant of the marquesses of Cortemaggiore, near Piacenza. He appears in *The Courtier* as the youthful woman-hater of the company, and was friend of Castiglione and Bembo. . .

13. Sigismondo Morello da Ortona is presented in *The Courtier* as the only elderly member of the company, and the object of many youthful jests. . .

14. Bernardo Accolti, (born about 1465; died 1535), was generally known as the Unico Aretino, from the name of his birthplace (Arezzo) and in compliment to his "unique" faculty for extemporising verse. His poetical celebrity commended him to the court of Urbino, where (as at Rome and in other places) he was in the habit of reciting his verses to vast audiences of rich and poor alike. When an exhibition by him was announced, guards had to be set to restrain the crowds that rushed to secure places, the shops were closed, and the streets emptied. His life was a kind of lucrative poetic vagabondage: thus we find him flourishing, caressed and applauded, at the courts of Urbino, Mantua, Naples, and especially at that of Leo X, who bestowed many offices upon him, of which, however, his wealth (acquired by his recitations) rendered him independent, enabling him to indulge in a life of literary ease. . In *The Courtier* he poses as the sentimental and afflicted lover, the "slayer" of duchesses and other noble ladies, who (according to his own account) kept flocking in his train, but who more probably were often making sport of him.

15. This passage establishes the date of the first dialogue as 8 March 1507.

16. Fra Serafino was probably a Mantuan, and had a brother Sebastiano. He lived long at the Gonzaga court, where he was employed in organizing festivals, and at Urbino, where the few of his letters that have survived show him in familiar relations with other interlocutors in *The Courtier*. While at Rome in 1507, with the suite of the Duchess of Urbino, he was seriously wounded in the head by an unknown assailant, probably in return for some lampoon or scandal of his against the papal court.

17. This letter S was evidently one of the golden ciphers that ladies of the period were fond of wearing on a circlet about their heads. In her portrait the duchess is represented as wearing a narrow band, from which the image of a scorpion hangs upon her forehead. The S may have been used on this occasion as the initial letter of the word scorpion, and

seems in any case to have been an instance of the 'devices' mentioned. . .

18. The word *sprezzatura* (rendered "nonchalance") could hardly have been new to Castiglione's contemporaries, at least in its primary meaning of disprizement or contempt. He may, however, have been among the first to use it (as here and elsewhere in *The Courtier*) in its modified sense of unconcern or nonchalance. Compare Herrick's 'wild civility' in "Art above Nature" and "Delight in Disorder."

19. The play upon words here is untranslatable into English. The Italian *tavola* stands equally well for a dining-table and for the tablet or panel upon which pictures were painted.

THE FOURTH BOOK OF THE COURTIER

To Messer Alfonso Ariosto

* * * * *

Then my lord Gaspar said:

"I remember that in discussing the accomplishments of the Courtier last evening, these gentlemen desired that he should be in love; and since, by reviewing what has thus far been said, we might conclude that a Courtier who has to allure his prince to virtue by his worth and authority, must almost of necessity be old (because knowledge very rarely comes before years, and especially in those things that are learned by experience),—I do not know how becoming it is for him (being advanced in age) to be in love. For as has been said this evening, love does not sit well upon old men, and those things which in young men are delights, courtesies and elegances very pleasing to women, in old men are extravagances and ridiculous incongruities, and for him who practises them win hatred from women and derision from others.

"So if your friend Aristotle, the old Courtier, were in love, and did those things which young lovers do, like some whom we have seen in our days,—I fear he would forget to instruct his prince, and perhaps children would mock at him behind his back, and women would get little pleasure from him except to deride him."

Then my lord Ottaviano said:

"As all the other accomplishments ascribed to the Courtier befit him although he be old, methinks we ought by no means to deprive him of this enjoyment of loving."

"Nay," said my lord Gaspar, "to deprive him of love is to give him an added perfection, and to make him live at ease remote from misery and calamity."

Messer Pietro Bembo said:

"Do you not remember, my lord Gaspar, that although he is little skilled in love, yet in his game the other evening my lord Ottaviano seemed to know that there are some lovers who call sweet the scorns and ires and warrings and torments which they have from their ladies; whence he asked to be taught the cause of this sweetness? Therefore if our Courtier, although old, were inflamed with those loves that are sweet without bitterness, he would feel no calamity or misery in them; and if he were wise, as we suppose him to be, he would not deceive himself by thinking that all was befitting to him which befits young men; but if he loved, perhaps he would love in a way that would bring him not only no blame, but much praise and highest happiness unaccompanied by any pain, which rarely and almost never happens with young men; and thus he would not fail to instruct his prince, nor would he do aught to deserve the mockery of children."

Then my lady Duchess said:

"I am glad, messer Pietro, that you have had little fatigue in our discussion this evening, for now we shall with more assurance impose on you the burden of speaking, and of teaching the Courtier this love which is so happy that it brings with it neither blame nor discomfort; for perhaps it will be one of the most important and useful attributes that have thus far been ascribed to him: therefore tell us, on your faith, all you know about it."

Messer Pietro laughed, and said:

"I should be sorry, my Lady, that my saying it is permissible for old men to love should be a reason for these ladies to regard me as old; therefore please to give this task to someone else." [1]

My lady Duchess replied:

"You ought not to shun being reputed old in wisdom, even if you are young in years; so speak on, and make no more excuse."

Messer Pietro said:

"Indeed, my Lady, if I must talk about this matter, I should need to go take counsel with my Lavinello's Hermit." [2]

Then my lady Emilia said, half vexed:

"Messer Pietro, there is no one in the company who is more disobedient than you; therefore it will be well for my lady Duchess to inflict some chastisement upon you."

Messer Pietro said, again smiling:

"Be not angry with me, my Lady, for love of God; for I will tell what you wish."

"Then tell it at once," replied my lady Emilia.

Whereupon messer Pietro, having first remained silent awhile, then settled himself a little as if about to speak of something important, and spoke thus: [3]

"My Lords, in order to prove that old men can love not only without blame but sometimes more happily than young men, it will be needful for me to make a little discourse to explain what love is, and in what consists the happiness that lovers may enjoy. So I pray you hear me with attention, for I hope to make you see that there is no man here whom it does not become to be in love, even though he were fifteen or twenty years older than my lord Morello."

And then after some laughter, messer Pietro continued:

"I say, then, that according to the definition of the ancient sages love is naught but a certain desire to enjoy beauty; and as desire longs only for things that are perceived, perception must needs always precede desire, which by its nature wishes good things, but

"Hence it is not beyond reason to say further that the old can love without blame and more happily than the young; taking this word old, however, not in the sense of decrepit, nor when the bodily organs have already become so weak that the soul cannot perform its functions through them, but when our knowledge is at its true prime.

"I will not refrain from saying also this: which is, that I think that although sensual love is evil at every age, yet in the young it deserves excuse, and is perhaps in a measure permitted. For although it gives them anguish, dangers, toils, and those woes that have been told, still there are many who, to win the favour of the ladies of their love, do worthy acts, which (although not directed to a good end) are intrinsically good; and thus from that mass of bitterness they extract a little sweet, and through the adversities which they endure they at last perceive their errour. Hence, just as I deem those youths divine who control their appetites and love in reason, so I excuse those who allow themselves to be overcome by sensual love, to which they are so strongly inclined by human frailty: provided they show therein gentleness, courtesy and worth, and the other noble qualities of which these gentlemen have told; and provided that when they are no longer of youthful age, they abandon it altogether, shunning this sensual desire as it were the lowest round of the ladder by which true love can be attained. But if, even after they are old, they preserve the fire of appetite in their chill heart and subject stout reason to frail sense, it is not possible to say how much they are to be blamed. For like fools they deserve to be numbered with perpetual infamy among the unreasoning animals, since the thoughts and ways of sensual love are too unbecoming to mature age."

Here Bembo paused a little, as if to rest; and as everyone remained silent, my lord Morello da Ortona said:

"And if an old man were found more vigourous and sturdy and of better looks than many youths, why would you not have him allowed to love with that love wherewith young men love?"

My lady Duchess laughed, and said:

"If young men's love is so unhappy, my lord Morello, why do you wish to have old men love thus unhappily also? But if you were old, as these gentlemen say, you would not thus contrive evil for old men."

My lord Morello replied:

"Methinks it is messer Pietro Bembo who is contriving evil for old men, in that he wishes to have them love in a certain way which I for my part do not understand; and methinks that to possess this beauty which he so highly praises, without the body, is a dream."

Then Count Ludovico said:

"Do you believe, my lord Morello, that beauty is always as good as messer Pietro Bembo says?"

"Not I indeed," replied my lord Morello; "nay, I remember having seen many beautiful women who were very bad, cruel and spiteful; and this seems to be almost always so, for beauty makes them proud, and pride makes them cruel."

Count Ludovico said, laughing:

"To you, perhaps, they seem cruel because they do not grant you what you would have; but have yourself taught by messer Pietro Bembo in what way old men ought to desire beauty, and what they ought to seek from women, and with what they ought to be content; and if you do not exceed these limits, you shall see that they will not be either proud or cruel, and will grant you what you wish."

Then my lord Morello seemed a little vexed, and said:

"I have no wish to know what does not concern me; but do you have yourself taught how this beauty ought to be desired by young men who are less vigourous and sturdy than their elders."

Here messer Federico, to quiet my lord Morello and turn the conversation, did not allow Count Ludovico to reply, but interrupted him and said:

"Perhaps my lord Morello is not altogether wrong in saying that beauty is not always good; for women's beauty is often the cause that brings upon the world countless evils, hatreds, wars, deaths and destructions; of which good proof can be found in the fall of Troy. And beautiful women are for the most part either proud or cruel, or (as has been said) immodest; but this would not seem to my lord Morello a fault. There are also many wicked men who have the gift of fair looks, and it seems that nature made them thus to the end that they should be better fitted to deceive, and that this gracious seeming is like the bait upon the hook."

Then Messer Pietro Bembo said:

"Do not believe that beauty is not always good."

Here Count Ludovico, in order to return to the original subject, interrupted and said:

"Since my lord Morello does not care to know what so deeply concerns him, teach it to me, and show me how old men attain this happiness in love, for I shall not mind having myself thought old, provided it help me."

Messer Pietro laughed, and said:

"I wish first to free these gentlemen's minds from their errour; then I will satisfy you too." Resuming thus, he said:

"My Lords, I would not have any of us, like profane and sacrilegious men, incur God's wrath by speaking ill of beauty, which is a sacred thing. Therefore, to the end that my lord Morello and messer Federico may be warned, and not lose their sight, like Stesichorus (which is a very fitting punishment for one who scorns beauty), I say that beauty springs from God, and is like a circle of which goodness is the centre. And hence, as there can be no circle without a centre, there can be no beauty without goodness. Thus a wicked soul rarely inhabits a beautiful body, and for that reason outward beauty is a true sign of inward goodness. And this grace is impressed upon bodies, more or less, as an index of the soul, whereby she is known outwardly, as in the case of trees, in which the beauty of the blossom gives token of the excellence of the fruit. The same is true in the case of human bodies, as we see that the Physiognomists often recognize in the face the character and sometimes the thoughts of men; and what is more, in beasts also we discern from the aspect the quality of the mind, which is expressed as much as possible in the body. Think how clearly we read anger, ferocity and pride in the face of the lion, the horse, the eagle; a pure and simple innocence in lambs and doves; cunning malice in foxes and wolves, and so of nearly all other animals.

"The ugly are therefore for the most part wicked too, and the beautiful are good: and we may say that beauty is the pleasant, gay, acceptable and desirable face of good, and that ugliness is the dark, disagreeable, unpleasant and sad face of evil. And if you will consider all things, you will find that those which are good and useful always have a charm of beauty also.

"Look at the state of this great fabric of the world, which was made by God for the health and preservation of every created thing. The round firmament, adorned with so many heavenly lights, and the earth in the centre, surrounded by the elements and sustained by its own weight; the sun, which in its revolving illumines the whole, and in winter approaches the lowest sign, then little by little mounts to the other side; the moon, which derives her light from it, according as it approaches her or withdraws from her; and the five other stars, which separately travel the same course. These things have such influence upon one another through the linking of an order thus precisely framed, that if they were changed for an instant, they could not hold together, and would wreck the world; they have also such beauty and grace that human wit cannot imagine anything more beautiful.

"Think now of the shape of man, which may be called a little world; wherein we see every part of the body precisely composed with skill, and not by chance; and then the whole form together so beautiful that we could hardly decide whether more utility or more grace is given to the human features and the rest of the body by all the members, such as the eyes, nose, mouth, ears, arms, breast, and other parts withal. The same can be said of all the animals. Look at the feathers of birds, the leaves and branches of trees, which are given them by nature to preserve their being, and yet have also very great loveliness.

"Leave nature, and come to art. What thing is so necessary in ships as the prow, the sides, the yards, the masts, the sails, the helm, the oars, the anchors and the cordage? Yet all these things have so much comeliness, that it seems to him who looks upon them that they are thus devised as much for beauty as for use. Columns and architraves support lofty galleries and palaces, yet they are not on that account less pleasing to the eyes of him who looks upon them, than useful to the buildings. When men first began to build, they set that middle ridge in their temples and houses, not in order that the buildings might have more grace, but to the end that the water might flow off conveniently on either side; yet to utility soon was added comeliness, so that if a temple were built under a sky where no hail or rain falls, it would not seem able to have any dignity or beauty without the ridge.

"Much praise is therefore bestowed, not only upon other things, but upon the world, by saying that it is beautiful. We praise when we say: 'Beautiful sky, beautiful earth, beautiful sea, beautiful rivers, beautiful lands, beautiful woods, trees, gardens; beautiful cities, beautiful churches, houses, armies.' In short, this gracious and sacred beauty gives highest ornament to everything; and we may say that the good and the beautiful are in a way one and the same thing, and especially in the human body; of whose beauty I think the most immediate cause is beauty of the soul, which (as partaker of true divine beauty) brightens and beautifies whatever it touches, and especially if the body wherein it dwells is not of such base material that it cannot impress thereon its quality. Therefore beauty is the true trophy of the soul's victory, when with power divine she holds sway over material nature, and by her light overcomes the darkness of the body.

"Hence we must not say that beauty makes women proud or cruel, although it may seem so to my lord Morello; nor yet ought we to ascribe to beautiful women those enmities, deaths and destructions of which the immoderate appetites of men are the cause. I do not by any means deny that it is possible to find beautiful women in the world who are also immodest, but it is not at all because their beauty inclines them to immodesty; nay, it turns them therefrom and leads them to the path of virtuous behaviour, by the connection that beauty has with goodness. But sometimes evil training, the continual urgence of their lovers, gifts, poverty, hope, deceits, fear and a thousand other causes, overcome the steadfastness even of beautiful and good women; and through these or similar causes beautiful men also may become wicked."

Then messer Cesare said:

"If that is true which my lord Gaspar alleged yesterday, there is no doubt that beautiful women are more chaste than ugly women."

"And what did I allege?" said my lord Gaspar.

Messer Cesare replied:

"If I remember rightly, you said that women who are wooed always refuse to satisfy him who wooes them, and that those who are not wooed woo others. Certain it is that the beautiful are always more wooed and besought in love than are the ugly; therefore the beautiful always refuse, and hence are more chaste than the ugly, who, not being wooed, woo others."

Bembo laughed, and said:

"To this argument no answer can be made." Then he added: "It often happens also that our sight deceives us like our other senses, and accounts a face beautiful which in truth is not beautiful; and since in some women's eyes and whole aspect a certain wantonness is seen depicted, together with unseemly blandishments,—many (who like such manner because it promises them ease in attaining what they desire) call it beauty: but in truth it is disguised immodesty, unworthy a name so honoured and so sacred."

Messer Pietro Bembo was silent, and those gentlemen still urged him to speak further of this love and of the mode of enjoying beauty truly; and he at last said:

"Methinks I have shown clearly enough that old men can love more happily than young, which was my thesis; therefore it does not become me to go further."

Count Ludovico replied:

"You have better shown the unhappiness of youths than the happiness of old men, whom as yet you have not taught what road to follow in this love of theirs, but have only told them to be guided by reason; and by many it is thought impossible for love to abide with reason."

Bembo still sought to put an end to his discourse, but my lady Duchess begged him to speak; and he began anew thus:

"Too unhappy would human nature be, if our soul (wherein such ardent desire can spring up easily) were forced to feed it solely upon that which is common to her with the beasts, and could not direct it to that other nobler part which is peculiar to herself. Therefore, since so indeed it pleases you, I have no wish to avoid discoursing upon this noble subject. And as I feel myself unworthy to speak of Love's most sacred mysteries, I pray him so to inspire my thought and tongue that I may be able to show this excellent Courtier how to love beyond the manner of the vulgar crowd; and since from boyhood up I have dedicated my whole life to him, so now also may my words comport with this intent and with his praise.

"I say, then, that as in youth human nature is so greatly prone to sense, the Courtier may be allowed to love sensually while he is young. But if afterwards in maturer years he chances still to be kindled with this amourous desire, he must be very wary and take care not to deceive himself by allowing himself to be led into those calamities which in the young merit more compassion than blame, and, on the contrary, in the old more blame than compassion.

"Therefore when the gracious aspect of some fair woman meets his view, accompanied with such sweet behaviour and gentle manners that he, as an adept in love, feels that his spirit accords with hers: as soon as he finds that his eyes lay hold upon her image and carry it to his heart; and that his soul begins to contemplate her with pleasure and to feel that influence within which stirs and warms it little by little; and that those quick spirits which shine out through the eyes continually add fresh tinder to the fire; — he ought at this first stage to provide a speedy cure, and arouse his reason, and therewith arm the fortress of his heart, and so shut the way to sense and appetite that they cannot enter there by force or trickery. Thus, if the flame is extinguished, the danger is extinguished also; but if it survives or grows, then the Courtier, feeling himself caught, must resolve on shunning wholly every stain of vulgar love, and thus enter on the path of divine love, with reason for guide. And first he must consider that the body wherein this beauty shines is not the fountain whence it springs, but rather that beauty (being an incorporeal thing and, as we have said, a heavenly beam) loses much of its dignity when it finds itself joined to vile and corruptible matter; for the more perfect it is the less it partakes thereof, and is most perfect when wholly separate therefrom. And he must consider that just as one cannot hear with the palate or smell with the ears, so too can beauty in no wise be enjoyed, nor can the desire which it excites in our minds be satisfied, by means of touch, but by that sense of which this beauty is the very object, namely, the power of vision.

"Therefore let him shun the blind judgment of sense, and with his eyes enjoy the splendour of his lady, her grace, her amourous sparkle, the laughs, the ways and all the other pleasant ornaments of her beauty. Likewise with his hearing let him enjoy the sweetness of her voice, the concord of her words, the harmony of her music (if his beloved be a musician). Thus will he feed his soul on sweetest food by means of these two senses—which have little of the corporeal and are ministers of reason—without passing in his desire for the body to any appetite less than seemly.

"Next let him obey, please and honour his lady with all reverence, and hold her dearer than himself, and prefer her convenience and pleasures to his own, and love in her not less the beauty of mind than that of body. Therefore let him take care not to leave her to fall into any kind of errour, but by admonition and good advice let him always seek to lead her on to modesty, to temperance, to true chastity, and see to it that no thoughts find place in her except those that are pure and free from every stain of vice; and by thus sowing virtue in the garden of her fair mind, he will gather fruits of fairest behaviour too, and will taste them with wonderful delight. And this will be the true engendering and manifesting of beauty in beauty, which by some is said to be the end of love.

"In such fashion will our Courtier be most acceptable to his lady, and she will always show herself obedient, sweet and affable to him, and as desirous of pleasing him as of being loved by him; and the wishes of both will be most virtuous and harmonious, and they themselves will thus be very happy."

Here my lord Morello said:

"To engender beauty in beauty, forsooth, would be to beget a beautiful child in a beautiful woman; and pleasing him in this would seem to me a much clearer token that she loved her lover than treating him with the affability of which you speak."

Bembo laughed, and said:

"You must not go beyond bounds, my lord Morello; nor does a woman give small token of her love when she gives her lover her beauty, which is so precious a thing, and by the ways that are the avenues to her soul (that is, sight and hearing) sends the glances of her eyes, the image of her face, her voice, her words, which strike home to the lover's heart and give him proof of her love."

My lord Morello said:

"Glances and words may be, and often are, false proofs; therefore he who has no better pledge of love is, in my judgment, far from sure; and truly I quite expected you to make this lady of yours a little more courteous and generous to the Courtier than my lord Magnifico made his; but methinks that both of you are in like case with those judges who pronounce sentence against their friends for the sake of appearing wise."

Bembo said:

"I am very willing that this lady should be much more courteous to my unyouthful Courtier, than my lord Magnifico's is to the youthful Courtier; and with reason, for my Courtier will desire only seemly things, and therefore the lady can grant him all of them without blame; while my lord Magnifico's lady, who is not so sure of the youthful Courtier's modesty, ought to grant him only seemly things, and to refuse him the unseemly. Hence my Courtier, to whom is granted what he asks, is more happy than the other, to whom part is granted and part refused.

"And to the end that you may still better understand that rational love is happier than sensual, I say that the same things ought sometimes to be refused in sensual love and granted in rational love, because they are unseemly in the one and seemly in the other. Thus, to please her worthy lover, besides granting him pleasant smiles, familiar and secret discourse, and leave to joke and jest with her and to touch her hand, the lady may in reason even go so far as kissing without blame, which is not permitted in sensual love according to my lord Magnifico's rules. For since the kiss is the union of body and soul, there is danger lest the sensual lover incline more in the direction of the body than in that of the soul; while the rational lover perceives that although the mouth is part of the body, yet it gives issue to words, which are interpreters of the soul, and to that inward breath which is itself even called soul. Hence a man delights to join his mouth to that of his beloved in a kiss, not in order to arouse any unseemly desire in him, but because he feels that bond to be the opening of a passage between their souls, which, being each drawn by desire for the other, pour themselves each into the other's body by turn, and so commingle that each has two souls, and a single soul (thus composed of these two) rules as it were over two bodies. Hence the kiss may be oftener said to be a joining of soul than of body, because it has such power over the soul that it draws her to itself and separates her from the body. On this account all chaste lovers desire to kiss as a joining of the soul; and thus the divinely enamoured Plato says that in kissing the soul came to his lips to escape his body. And since the separation of the soul from things material, and its complete union with things spiritual, may be denoted by the kiss, Solomon, in his divine book of the Song, says: 'Let him kiss me with the kiss of his mouth,' to express desire that his soul might be so transported with divine love to the contemplation of celestial beauty, that by joining closely therewith she might forsake the body."

Everyone gave closest heed to Bembo's discourse; and he, having made a little pause and seeing that no one else spoke, said:

"As you have made me begin to teach our unyouthful Courtier happy love, I fain would lead him a little farther; for it is very dangerous to stop at this stage, seeing that the soul is very prone to the senses, as has many times been said; and although reason and argument choose well and perceive that beauty does not spring from the body, and although they therefore put a bridle upon unseemly desires, still, always contemplating beauty in the body often perverts sound judgment. And even if no other evil flowed therefrom, absence from the beloved object brings much suffering with it, because the influence of her beauty gives the lover wonderful delight when she is present, and by warming his heart wakens and melts certain dormant and frozen forces in his soul, which (being nourished by the warmth of love) spread and blossom about his heart, and send forth through the eyes those spirits that are very subtle vapours made of the purest and brightest part of the blood, which receive the image of her beauty and fashion it with a thousand various ornaments. Hence the soul delights, and trembles with awe and yet rejoices, and as in a stupour feels not only pleasure, but that fear and reverence which we are wont to have for sacred things, and speaks of being in paradise.

"Therefore the lover who considers beauty in the body only, loses this blessing and felicity as soon as his beloved lady by her absence leaves his eyes without their splendour, and his soul consequently widowed of its blessing. Because, her beauty being far away, that amourous influence does not warm his heart as it did in her presence; wherefore his pores become arid and dry, and still the memory of her beauty stirs a little those forces of his soul, so that they seek to scatter abroad the spirits; and these, finding the ways shut, have no exit, and yet seek to issue forth; and thus hemmed in by those goads, they sting the soul and give it keenest suffering, as in the case of children when the teeth begin to come through the tender gums. And from this proceed the tears, the sighs, the anguish and the torments of lovers, because the soul is ever in affliction and travail, and becomes almost raging until her dear beauty appears to it again; and then it suddenly is calmed and breathes, and all intent upon that beauty it feeds on sweetest food, nor would ever part from so delightful a spectacle.

"Hence, to escape the torment of this absence and to enjoy beauty without suffering, there is need that the Courtier should, with the aid of reason, wholly turn his desire from the body to the beauty alone, and contemplate it in itself simple and pure, as far as he can, and fashion it in his imagination apart from all matter; and thus make it lovely and dear to his soul, and enjoy it there, and have it with him day and night, in every time and place, without fear of ever losing it; bearing always in mind that the body is something very different from beauty, and not only does not enhance it, but diminishes its perfection.

"In this wise will our unyouthful Courtier be beyond all the bitterness and calamities that the young nearly always feel: such as jealousies, suspicions, disdainings, angers, despairings, and certain furies full of madness whereby they are often led into such errour that some of them not only beat the women whom they love, but deprive themselves of life. He will do no injury to the husband, father, brothers or kinsfolk of his beloved lady; he will put no infamy upon her; he will never be forced to bridle his eyes and tongue with such difficulty in order not to disclose his desires to others, or to endure suffering at partings or absences; — because he will always carry his precious treasure with him shut up in his heart, and also by force of his imagination he will inwardly fashion her beauty much more beautiful than in fact it is.

"But besides these blessings the lover will find another much greater still, if he will employ this love as a step to mount to one much higher; which he will succeed in doing if he continually considers within himself how narrow a restraint it is to be always occupied in contemplating the beauty of one body only; and therefore, in order to escape such close bounds as these, in his thought he will little by little add so many ornaments, that by heaping all beauties together he will form an universal concept, and will reduce the multitude of these beauties to the unity of that single beauty which is spread over human nature at large. In this way he will no longer contemplate the particular beauty of one woman, but that universal beauty which adorns all bodies; and thus, bewildered by this greater light, he will not heed the lesser, and glowing with a purer flame, he will esteem lightly that which at first he so greatly prized.

"This stage of love, although it be very noble and such as few attain, still cannot be called perfect; for since the imagination is merely a corporeal faculty and has no perception except through those means that are furnished it by the senses, it is not wholly purged of material darkness; and hence, although it considers this universal beauty in the abstract and intrinsically, yet it does not discern that beauty very clearly or without some ambiguity, because of the likeness which phantoms bear to substance. Thus those who attain this love are like tender birds beginning to put on feathers, which, although with their frail wings they lift themselves a little in flight, yet dare not go far from their nest or trust themselves to the winds and open sky.

"Therefore when our Courtier shall have reached this goal, although he may be called a very happy lover by comparison with those who are plunged in the misery of sensual love, still I would have him not rest content, but press boldly on following along the lofty path after the guide who leads him to the goal of true felicity. And thus, instead of going outside himself in thought (as all must needs do who choose to contemplate bodily beauty only), let him have recourse to himself, in order to contemplate that beauty which is seen by the eyes of the mind, which begin to be sharp and clear when those of the body lose the flower of their loveliness. Then the soul, — freed from vice, purged by studies of true philosophy, versed in spiritual life, and practised in matters of the intellect, devoted to the contemplation of her own substance, — as if awakened from deepest sleep, opens those eyes which all possess but few use, and sees in herself a ray of that light which is the true image of the angelic beauty communicated to her, and of which she then communicates a faint shadow to the body. Grown blind to things earthly, the soul thus becomes very keen-sighted to things heavenly; and sometimes, when the motive forces of the body are absorbed by earnest contemplation or fettered by sleep, being unhampered by them, she is conscious of a certain far-off perfume of true angelic beauty, and ravished by the splendour of that light, she begins to kindle and pursues it so eagerly that she almost becomes phrensied with desire to unite herself to that beauty, thinking that she has found God's footstep, in the contemplation of which she seeks to rest as in her beatific end. And thus, glowing in this most happy flame, she rises to her noblest part, which is the intellect; and here, no longer darkened by the gloomy night of things earthly, she sees the divine beauty; but still she does not yet quite enjoy it perfectly, because she contemplates it in her own particular intellect only, which cannot be capable of the vast universal beauty.

"Wherefore, not well content with this boon, love gives the soul a greater felicity; for just as from the particular beauty of one body it guides her to the universal beauty of all bodies, so in the highest stage of perfection it guides her from the particular to the universal intellect. Hence the soul, kindled by the most sacred fire of true divine love, flies to unite herself with the angelic nature, and not only quite forsakes sense, but has no longer need of reason's discourse; for, changed into an angel, she understands all things intelligible, and without veil or cloud views the wide sea of pure divine beauty, and receives it into herself, and enjoys that supreme felicity of which the senses are incapable.

"If, then, the beauties which with these dim eyes of ours we daily see in corruptible bodies (but which are naught but dreams and faintest shadows of beauty) seem to us so fair and gracious that they often kindle most ardent fire in us, and of such delight that we deem no felicity able to equal that which we sometimes feel at a single glance coming to us from a woman's beloved eyes, — what happy wonder, what blessed awe, shall we think is that which fills the souls that attain to the vision of divine beauty! What sweet flame, what delightful burning, must that be thought which springs from the fountain of supreme and true beauty! — which is the source of every other beauty, which never waxes nor wanes: ever fair, and of its own self most simple in every part alike; like only to itself, and partaking of none other; but fair in such wise that all other fair things are fair because they derive their beauty from it.

"This is that beauty identical with highest good, which by its light calls and attracts all things to itself, and not only gives intellect to the intellectual, reason to the rational, sense and desire for life to the sensual, but to plants also and to stones communicates motion and that natural instinct of their quality, as an imprint of itself.

"Therefore this love is as much greater and happier than the others, as the cause that moves it is more excellent; and hence, just as material fire refines gold, so does this most sacred fire in our souls destroy and consume that which is mortal there, and quickens and beautifies that celestial part which at first, by reason of the senses, was dead and buried in them. This is the Pyre whereon the poets write that Hercules was burned on the crest of Mount Œta, and by such burning became divine and immortal after death. This is the Burning Bush of Moses, the Cloven Tongues of fire, the Fiery Chariot of Elias, which doubles grace and felicity in the souls of those who are worthy to behold it, when they leave this earthly baseness and take flight towards heaven.

"Let us, then, direct all the thoughts and forces of our soul to this most sacred light, which shows us the way that leads to heaven; and following after it, let us lay aside the passions wherewith we were clothed at our fall, and by the stairway that bears the shadow of sensual beauty on its lowest step, let us mount to the lofty mansion where dwells the heavenly, lovely and true beauty, which lies hidden in the inmost secret recesses of God, so that profane eyes cannot behold it. Here we shall find a most happy end to our desires, true rest from our toil, certain cure for our miseries, most wholesome medicine for our diseases, safest refuge from the boisterous storms of this life's tempestuous sea.

"What mortal tongue, then, O most holy Love, can praise thee worthily? Most fair, most good, most wise, thou springest from the union of beauty and goodness and divine wisdom, and abidest in that union, and by that union returnest to that union as in a circle. Sweetest bond of the universe, joining things celestial to things terrestrial, thou with benignant sway inclinest the supernal powers to rule the lower powers, and turning the minds of mortals to their origin, joinest them thereto. Thou unitest the elements in concord, movest nature to produce — and that which is born, to the perpetuation of life. Thou unitest things that are separate, givest perfection to the imperfect, likeness to the unlike, friendship to the unfriendly, fruit to the earth, tranquillity to the sea, vital light to the heavens.

"Thou art father of true pleasure, of grace, of peace, of gentleness and good will, enemy to rustic savagery and sloth — in short, the beginning and the end of every good. And since thou delightest to inhabit the flower of beautiful bodies and beautiful souls, and thence sometimes to display thyself a little to the eyes and minds of those who are worthy to behold thee, methinks that now thy abode is here among us.

"Deign, then, O Lord, to hear our prayers, pour thyself upon our hearts, and with the splendour of thy most holy fire illumine our darkness and, like a trusted guide, in this blind labyrinth show us the true path. Correct the falseness of our senses, and after our long pursuit of vanities give us true and solid good; make us to inhale those spiritual odours that quicken the powers of the intellect, and to hear the celestial harmony with such accord that there may no longer be room in us for any discord of passion; fill us at that inexhaustible fountain of content which ever delights and never satiates, and gives a taste of true beatitude to all who drink of its living and limpid waters; with the beams of thy light purge our eyes of misty ignorance, to the end that they may no longer prize mortal beauty, and may know that the things which first they seemed to see, are not, and that those which they saw not, really are.

"Accept our souls, which are offered thee in sacrifice; burn them in that living flame which consumes all mortal dross, to the end that, being wholly separated from the body, they may unite with divine beauty by a perpetual and very sweet bond, and that we, being severed from ourselves, may, like true lovers, be able to transform ourselves into the beloved, and rising above the earth may be admitted to the angels' feast, where, fed on ambrosia and immortal nectar, we may at last die a most happy and living death, as died of old those ancient fathers whose souls thou, by the most glowing power of contemplation, didst ravish from the body and unite with God."

Having thus far spoken, with such vehemence that he almost seemed transported and beside himself, Bembo remained silent and motionless, keeping his eyes towards heaven, as if wrapped in ecstasy; when my lady Emilia, who with the others had been listening most attentively to his discourse, took him by the border of his robe, and shaking him a little, said:

"Have a care, messer Pietro, that with these thoughts your soul, also, does not forsake your body."

"My Lady," replied messer Pietro, "that would not be the first miracle that love has wrought upon me."

Then my lady Duchess and all the others again began urging Bembo to continue his discourse: and everyone seemed almost to feel in his mind a spark of that divine love which inspired the speaker, and all desired to hear more; but Bembo added:

"My Lords, I have said that which love's sacred phrensy dictated to me at the moment; now that it seems to inspire me no further, I should not know what to say: and I think love is not willing that its secrets should be further disclosed, or that the Courtier should pass beyond that stage which it has been pleased to have me show him; and therefore perhaps it is not permitted to speak more of this matter."

"Verily," said my lady Duchess, "if the unyouthful Courtier should prove able to follow the path that you have shown him, he ought in all reason to content himself with such great felicity, and to have no envy of the youthful Courtier."

Then messer Cesare Gonzaga said:

"The road which leads to this felicity seems to me so steep that I believe it is very hard to travel."

My lord Gaspar added:

"I believe it is hard for men to travel, but impossible for women."

My lady Emilia laughed, and said:

"My lord Gaspar, if you return to wronging us so often, I promise you that you will not be pardoned again."

My lord Gaspar replied:

"No wrong is done you by saying that women's souls are not so purged of passion as those of men, nor given to contemplation, as messer Pietro said those must be who would taste divine love. Thus we do not read that any woman has had this grace, but that many men have had it, like Plato, Socrates, and Plotinus, and many others; and so many of our holy Fathers, like St. Francis, upon whom an ardent spirit of love impressed the most holy seal of the five wounds: nor could aught but the power of love lift St. Paul to the vision of those mysteries whereof man is not allowed to speak; nor show St. Stephen the opened heavens."

Here the Magnifico Giuliano replied:

"In this, women will by no means be outdone by men; for Socrates himself confesses that all the mysteries of love which he knew were revealed to him by a woman, who was the famous Diotima; [4] and the angel who wounded St. Francis with the fire of love, has also made several women of our age worthy of the same seal. You must remember, too, that St. Mary Magdalen had many sins forgiven her because she loved much, and perhaps with no less grace than St. Paul was she many times lifted to the third heaven by angelic love; and so many others, who (as I narrated yesterday more at large) for the love of Christ's name took no heed of life, nor were afraid of torments or any manner of death however horrible and cruel it might be; and they were not old, as messer Pietro would have our Courtier, but tender and delicate girls, and of that age wherein he says that sensual love ought to be allowed in men."

My lord Gaspar began making ready to reply, but my lady Duchess said:

"Of this let messer Pietro Bembo be the judge, and let us abide by his decision whether or not women are as capable of divine love as men are. But as the controversy between you might be too long, it will be well to postpone it until tomorrow."

"Nay, until this evening," said messer Cesare Gonzaga.

"How until this evening?" said my lady Duchess.

Messer Cesare replied:

"Because it is already day;" and he showed her the light that was beginning to come in through the cracks at the windows.

Then everyone rose to his feet in great surprise, for the discussion did not seem to have lasted longer than usual; but by reason of having been begun much later, and by its pleasantness, it had so beguiled the company that they had not perceived the flight of hours; nor was there anyone who felt the heaviness of sleep upon his eyes, which nearly always happens when the accustomed hour of sleep is passed in watching. The windows having then been opened on that side of the palace which looks towards the lofty crest of Mount Catria,[5] they saw that a beautiful dawn of rosy hue was already born in the east, and that all the stars had vanished save Venus, sweet mistress of the sky, who holds the bonds of night and day; from which there seemed to breathe a gentle wind that filled the air with crisp coolness and began to waken sweet choruses of joyous birds in the murmuring forests of the hills hard by.

So, having reverently taken leave of my lady Duchess, they all started towards their chambers without light of torches, that of day being enough for them; and as they were about to quit the room, my lord Prefect turned to my lady Duchess, and said:

"My Lady, to finish the controversy between my lord Gaspar and my lord Magnifico, we will come with our judge this evening earlier than we did yesterday."

My lady Emilia replied:

"On condition that if my lord Gaspar wishes to accuse women and put some fresh imputation upon them, as is his wont, he shall also give bond to sustain his charge, for I account him a shifty disputant."

NOTES TO THE FOURTH BOOK OF THE COURTIER

1. Bembo was thirty-six years old at the date of the Courtier dialogues. See note 9, Book I.

2. In Book III of Bembo's *Gli Asolani* (1505), a hermit discourses to Lavinello on the beauty of mystical Christian love. Bembo had a villa called Lavinello, near Padua.

3. Much of the following disquisition seems to be drawn from Plato and from Bembo's *Gli Asolani*. As Bembo is known to have revised *The Courtier* before publication, we may assume that he was content with the form and substance of the discourse here attributed to him.

4. Diotima was a probably fictitious priestess of Mantinea in the Peloponnesus, reputed to have been the instructress of Socrates. Her supposed opinions as to the origin, nature and objects of life, form the subject of Plato's *Symposium*.

5. Mount Catria lies less than twenty miles to the southward of Urbino, between Pergola and Gubbio, and rises a little more than a mile above the sea level. . .

LUDOVICO ARIOSTO

(1474–1533)

No poet so completely gave expression to the height of the Renaissance in Italy as Ariosto. Courtier, diplomat, and poet at the brilliant court of the Estensi at Ferrara, he was educated in the humanist tradition, and inherited the chivalric synthesis of Boiardo's *Orlando Innamorato,* which had so successfully combined the legends of Charlemagne and of Arthur and which he was to continue and surpass.

He was born in 1474 in Reggio d'Emilia of an ancient Bolognese family. His father, Count Niccolò, at that time captain of the citadel of Reggio, held several positions of high responsibility under Ercole I, second Duke of Ferrara, becoming finally captain of the guard of Ferrara. The poet's youth was spent in the city at whose court the gracious Duchess Leonora of Aragon presided, at the time her famous daughters Isabella and Beatrice were in their girlhood. The ten years before the French invasion in 1494 were the most splendid period of culture in Italian courts, and most of the influences of the world of the Renaissance met in Ferrara.

Ariosto has himself given the most illuminating revelation we have of his life and personality in a series of seven *Satires,* or metrical epistles, in the manner of Horace. He was the oldest of ten children. It was his father's intention that he should study law and he was placed in the university at Ferrara for five years, which the poet considered wasted. At the age of twenty, however, he was permitted to follow his own interests. Classical studies had been long established in Ferrara, Guarino da Verona having been called there in the second quarter of the fifteenth century as a tutor to the young prince, Leonello d'Este. Gregorio da Spoleto was now the resident humanist, and Ludovico placed himself immediately in his charge and plunged into the study of Latin literature in the years following 1493. Then Pietro Bembo came in 1498. Thus the youth of Ariosto "was all Latin," as Carducci phrased it. To this period extending to 1503, his "fair years between April and May," belong his Latin poems written under the influence of Horace, Catullus, and Tibullus: odes, epigrams, hendecasyllabics, and elegies. Some were written to friends; others sing of his early loves, Philiroe, Lydia, Glycera, Lycoris, and extol a life of idyllic beauty and serenity.

In 1500, however, his father died, and an abrupt change came in his life. Abandoning his studies, he took charge of the family: his mother, four younger brothers, and five sisters, exchanging, as he said, "Homer for records of household expenses." At first the Duke Ercole appointed him captain of the Rocca of Canossa. Then, in 1503, he entered the service of the Cardinal Ippolito d'Este in which he was to remain for fifteen years. The Cardinal was an example of the irreverent, even licentious churchman of the time, a diplomatist, skilled in military matters, and fond of hunting. He turned Ariosto "from a poet to a post-horseman," sending him on confidential and delicate diplomatic missions to many parts of Italy. In 1507, he sent him to his sister, Isabella, then Marchioness of Mantua, to congratulate her on the birth of a son. Isabella took much pleasure in his visit and was delighted with the readings from the *Orlando Furioso* which he gave for her through two days. In 1510, he was sent several times to Rome to placate the wrath of Pope Julius II against the Cardinal; he seems to have spoken courageously and ably on his patron's behalf, but in the end the Pope threatened to have him thrown into the Tiber if he did not leave his presence. In 1512, when the Duke Alfonso, having failed to effect a reconciliation with the Pope, was fleeing from Rome in disguise, Ariosto was sent to accompany him in the long and hazardous feat of returning to Ferrara uncaptured.

In 1513, at the election of Pope Leo X, Ippolito hurried him again to Rome, with congratulations. Since Ariosto had known Leo well, he had high hopes of a post which would free him from the Cardinal's service, but he was disappointed. Returning northward sick at heart, he stopped at Florence on the occasion of the Festival of St. John. Here he met Alessandra Benucci. He has told of the experience in his finest lyric poem, the *canzone, Non so s'io potrò ben chiudere in rima.* She was Florentine by birth, wife of the Ferrarese Tito di Leonardo Strozzi, a widow by 1515. The poet's love for her became a passion through the rest of his life.

The Cardinal was not one to appreciate the poet's qualities. Nevertheless, the *Orlando* was begun in 1505 and the first edition was published in 1516; furthermore, Ippolito seems to have paid for its printing and to have allowed the poet to sell the copies for his own profit. It was dedicated to the Cardinal and in it the House of Este was made illustrious. However, when in 1517 Ippolito asked him to go with him to his diocese in Hungary, Ariosto on the plea of care for his family and his health refused, and the Cardinal dismissed him from his service. He never entered the Cardinal's presence again.

Ariosto was not able to live in independence, however, and in 1518 he entered the service of Alfonso I, third Duke of Ferrara, for the rest of his life. The third of the *Satires* indicates clearly his weariness of court life; and yet, before his final years of contentment, he was to undertake one more most uncongenial task. Since the poet was in financial need or possibly was planning for later freedom, Alfonso appointed him governor of the Garfagnana, a remote region in the Apennines, overrun by outlaws nearly to the point of anarchy. For three years, from 1522 to 1525, he attempted to establish order and maintain justice under conditions that made both seem impossible. These tasks he met with a nobility of bearing, an impartiality, and a loyalty which compel admiration. Finally he persuaded the Duke to recall him.

The last eight years of Ariosto's life, after 1525, were years of comparative contentment. Although he accompanied the Duke on his journeys and carried out one important and successful diplomatic mission, his chief duties were connected with the production of dramatic performances at court. Ariosto himself was among the first to introduce Italian comedy in Italy modeled after the plays of Plautus and Terence, and such comedies became very popular at the Ferrarese court. His own *Cassaria* was played in the carnival in 1508; his *Suppositi,* a year later. The *Negromante,* finished in 1520, was produced probably in the carnival of 1530. *La Lena* was produced in 1529. The peace which reigned at Ferrara during the early 1530's gave opportunity for a gay and colorful court life, with endless balls, banquets, pageants, tournaments, and dramatic productions. Ariosto directed the construction of a permanent stage and designed the scenery himself.

He now separated from his brothers and bought a little house and garden in the Contrada di Mirasole which may still be seen. In about 1527 or 1528, he married Alessandra secretly, perhaps because she wished to retain her life-interest in the estate of her first husband. He had had two natural sons; Virginio, the second, who has left us invaluable information about his father, was his favorite, whom he had kept to live with him. In 1531, he sent him to the university at Padua with a special letter of introduction to Pietro Bembo concerning his education. During these years, also, a group of young disciples had gathered about him. For sixteen years he worked over the *Orlando* until the final edition was printed in 1532. On the last night of that year, fire destroyed the theater in the court. The reaction from this aggravated the final illness from which he died on the 6th of July 1533. He is now buried in the public library in Ferrara.

In personality, Ariosto possessed a simplicity, a dignity, and a witty joviality, yet always with a reserve. The Italy of the cinquecento had become indifferent to the idealisms of morality, religion, and patriotism. The ideal of beauty and form in art remained, and in literature refuge was sought in the imaginative worlds of the pastoral and the chivalry of the past. In his romantic epic Ariosto recreated the world of chivalry in an artistic form of which only his fastidious taste was capable. Its atmosphere and colors are of a dream world of escape, but its predominant note is that of irony. Although an artist and a dreamer, he knew the actual world as it was too well to desert it entirely. Therefore, the Spirit of Comedy plays through his dream world disclosing the actual character of men and women as they then were and as they are.

SELECTED BIBLIOGRAPHY

EDITIONS

Orlando Furioso, ed. S. Debenedetti, 3 vols., Bari, Laterza, 1928; ed. N. Zingarelli, 4th edit., 1 vol., Milan, Hoepli, 1943; *Opere Minori in*

Verso e in Prosa, ed. F. L. Polidori, 2 vols., Florence, Le Monnier, 1857; *Lirica,* ed. G. Fatini, Bari, Laterza, 1924; *Le Satire,* ed. G. Tambara, Livorno, 1903; *Commedie,* ed. M. Catalano, 2nd edit., 2 vols., Bologna, Zanichelli, 1940; *Lettere,* ed. A. Cappelli, 3rd edit., Milan, 1887.

TRANSLATIONS

Orlando Furioso, trans. Sir John Harington, London, 1591; trans. John Hoole, London, 1783; trans. William Stewart Rose, 8 vols., London, Murray, 1823–31, 2 vols. Bohn Lib., Bell, London, 1858; *Tales from Ariosto,* J. S. Nicholson, London, Macmillan, 1913; trans. Allan H. Gilbert, 2 vols., New York, Vanni, 1954.

BIOGRAPHY AND CRITICISM

F. Torraca, "L. Ariosto," in *Enciclopedia Italiana,* IV, 314–21, 1929; Michele Catalano, *Vita di L. Ariosto,* 2 vols., Geneva, Olschki, 1930–31; Henri Hauvette, *L'Arioste et la Poésie Chevaleresque à Ferrare,* Paris, Champion, 2nd edit. 1933.

Edmund G. Gardner, *Dukes and Poets in Ferrara,* 1904, and *The King of Court Poets. Ariosto,* 1906, New York, Dutton; Benedetto Croce, *Ariosto, Shakespeare, and Corneille,* New York, Holt, 1920; Rev. E. W. Edwards, *The Orlando Furioso and Its Predecessor,* Camb. Univ. Press, 1924; A. J. Grant, "Ariosto," *History,* N.S. XX (1935), 18–28; J. W. Mackail, "Ariosto," in *Studies in Humanism,* London, Longmans, 1938; Giacomo Grillo, *Poets at the Court of Ferrara,* Boston, Excelsior Press, 1943; Jean H. Fragonard, *Drawings from Ariosto,* ed. E. Mongan, P. Hofer, and J. Seznec, New York, Pantheon, 1945.

SPECIAL STUDIES

R. E. N. Dodge, "Spenser's Imitations from Ariosto," *Pub. Mod. Lang. Assoc.,* XII (1897), 151–204: see also Gilbert, XXXIV (1919), 225–32; Susannah J. McMurphy, *Spenser's Use of Ariosto for Allegory,* Univ. of Washington Pub. in Lang. and Lit., II, 1924; Anon., "Ariosto," *Times Lit. Supplement,* London, No. 1636 (1933), 385–6; Freda L. Townsend, "Sidney and Ariosto," *Pub. Mod. Lang. Assoc.,* LXI (1946), 97–108; A. H. Gilbert, "The Qualities of the Renaissance Epic," *So. Atlant. Quar.,* LIII (1953), 372–78.

ORLANDO FURIOSO

Translated by William Stewart Rose

[Taken from *The Orlando Furioso of Ludovico Ariosto,* translated by William Stewart Rose, Bohn Library, G. Bell & Sons, London, 1858.]

[The *Orlando Furioso* is in narrative content, although not in spirit, a continuation of the *Orlando Innamorato* of Matteo Maria Boiardo. Three major narratives may be distinguished in its complex structure: (1) the background action, (2) the main narrative, (3) the title theme. Of these, the first two were begun by Boiardo; the third was Ariosto's own conception.

The background action of the entire poem consists of the great war waged by the powers of Pagandom under Agramant, Emperor of Africa, against the powers of Christendom under Charlemagne. Agramant secured as ally Marsilius, the Saracen king of Spain, and together they invaded France and even besieged Paris. In the end, Charles drives them back, carries the war into Africa, and it ends with a final combat, three against three, on the island of Lampedosa in the Mediterranean.

Against this background, Boiardo began the story of Rogero and Bradamant, which constitutes the continuous thread of narrative throughout Ariosto's poem. Rogero was a young knight ingeniously obtained by Agramant from the care of the magician Atlantes to accompany his army into France because of a prophecy that Rogero alone could aid the pagan host. Subsequently, in a romantic episode in southern France, Rogero generously gave assistance to an unknown Christian warrior fighting, as he considered, under conditions unethical in the code of chivalry. The unknown Christian warrior proved to be the maiden knight, Bradamant, sister to Rinaldo of Mont Albano. Scarcely had they learned the identity of each other in this, their first meeting, before they were suddenly attacked and separated. At the beginning of the *Furioso,* Bradamant is in quest of her beloved, Rogero. From their marriage in the end were to issue ultimately the members of the House of Este, two of whom were Ariosto's patrons at Ferrara.

Boiardo, combining the chivalric matter of France with the romantic matter of the Arthurian cycle, had caused Orlando (Roland) to fall in love. Ariosto causes his passion to become madness, thus providing the title theme of his poem. Angelica was an eastern princess of incredible beauty, the daughter of King Galafron of Cathay. Her father sent her in company with her brother to the camp of Charlemagne to deprive the Christian army of its greatest knights and thus to aid the pagan cause. One after another, Charlemagne's greatest warriors, including Orlando and his cousin Rinaldo, deserted the camp and followed her back to Cathay, where many adventurous happenings took place. At the opening of Ariosto's poem, they have returned in Charlemagne's dire need;

Orlando, with Angelica, is the last to arrive back. Charlemagne, becoming aware of the distractive power of Angelica, however, commits her to the care of the aged Duke Namus of Bavaria, decreeing that she shall be awarded to that knight who most distinguishes himself in the fighting. Namus, however, is captured by the enemy, and Angelica escapes, to undergo many more adventures.

In addition to these three major narratives, the *Furioso* contains many other shorter stories. All are skillfully integrated in the complex structure of the work, as the many-colored threads of a great tapestry. One story is carried to a climax, then dismissed, to be continued later, while another story is taken up to be handled in the same manner. In Ariosto's skillful art, every story is carried to completion sooner or later within the forty-six cantos of the poem. The selections given below are taken from the main narrative and the title theme; obviously, the background action continues or is understood to be taking place throughout the poem.]

CANTO I

ARGUMENT

Angelica, whom pressing danger frights,
Flies in disorder through the greenwood shade.
Rinaldo's horse escapes: he, following, fights
Ferrau, the Spaniard, in a forest glade.
A second oath the haughty paynim plights,
And keeps it better than the first he made.
King Sacripant regains his long-lost treasure;
But good Rinaldo mars his promised pleasure.

1.

Of LOVES and LADIES, KNIGHTS and ARMS, I sing,
Of COURTESIES, and many a DARING FEAT;
And from those ancient days my story bring,
When Moors from Afric passed in hostile fleet,
And ravaged France, with Agramant their king,
Flushed with his youthful rage and furious heat;
Who on king Charles', the Roman emperor's, head
Had vowed due vengeance for Troyano dead.

2.

In the same strain of Roland will I tell
Things unattempted yet in prose or rhyme,
On whom strange madness and rank fury fell,
A man esteemed so wise in former time;
If she,[1] who to like cruel pass has well
Nigh brought my feeble wit which fain would climb
And hourly wastes my sense, concede me skill
And strength my daring promise to fulfil.

1. Alessandra Benucci, whom the poet married.

3.

Good seed of Hercules,[2] give ear and deign,
Thou that this age's grace and splendour art,
Hippolitus, to smile upon his pain
Who tenders what he has with humble heart.
For though all hope to quit the score were vain,
My pen and page may pay the debt in part;
Then, with no jealous eye my offering scan,
Nor scorn my gift who give thee all I can.

4.

And me, amid the worthiest shalt thou hear,
Whom I with fitting praise prepare to grace,
Record the good Rogero, valiant peer,
The ancient root of thine illustrious race.
Of him, if thou wilt lend a willing ear,
The worth and warlike feats I shall retrace;
So thou thy graver cares some little time
Postponing, lend thy leisure to my rhyme.

5.

Roland, who long the lady of Catay,
Angelica, had loved, and with his brand
Raised countless trophies to that damsel gay,
In India, Median, and Tartarian land,
Westward with her had measured back his way;
Where, nigh the Pyrenees, with many a band
Of Germany and France, King Charlemagne
Had camped his faithful host upon the plain.

6.

To make king Agramant, for penance, smite
His cheek, and rash Marsilius rue the hour;
This, when all trained with lance and sword to fight,
He led from Africa to swell his power;
That other when he pushed, in fell despite,
Against the realm of France Spain's martial flower.
'Twas thus Orlando came where Charles was tented
In evil hour, and soon the deed repented.

7.

For here was seized his dame of peerless charms,
(How often human judgment wanders wide)!
Whom in long warfare he had kept from harms,
From western climes to eastern shores her guide
In his own land, 'mid friends and kindred arms,

2. The Cardinal Ippolito d'Este, son of Duke Ercole d'Este of Ferrara, and Ariosto's first patron.

Now without contest severed from his side.
Fearing the mischief kindled by her eyes,
From him the prudent emperor reft the prize.

8.

For bold Orlando and his cousin,[3] free
Rinaldo late contended for the maid,
Enamoured of that beauty rare; since she
Alike the glowing breast of either swayed.
But Charles, who little liked such rivalry,
And drew an omen thence of feebler aid,
To abate the cause of quarrel, seized the fair,
And placed her in Bavarian Namus' care.

9.

Vowing with her the warrior to content,
Who in that conflict, on that fatal day,
With his good hand most gainful succour lent,
And slew most paynims in the martial fray.
But counter to his hopes the battle went,
And his thinned squadrons fled in disarray;
Namus, with other Christian captains taken,
And his pavilion in the rout forsaken.

10.

There, lodged by Charles, that gentle bonnibel,
Ordained to be the valiant victor's meed,
Before the event had sprung into her sell,
And from the combat turned in time of need;
Presaging wisely Fortune would rebel
That fatal day against the Christian creed:
And, entering a thick wood, discovered near,
In a close path, a horseless cavalier,

11.

With shield upon his arm, in knightly wise,
Belted and mailed, his helmet on his head;
The knight more lightly through the forest hies
Than half-clothed churl to win the cloth of red.
But not from cruel snake more swiftly flies
The timid shepherdess, with startled tread,
Than poor Angelica the bridle turns
When she the approaching knight on foot discerns.[4]

3. Rinaldo, cousin to Orlando, eldest son of Amone of Mont Albano; in French, Renaud of Mont Auban, son of Aymon. He is a brother to Bradamant.

4. By drinking of the Fountain of Hate, Angelica became possessed with intense hatred of Rinaldo. At the same time, Rinaldo — by drinking of the Fountain of Love — was consumed with love for Angelica.

12.

This was that Paladin, good Aymon's seed,
Who Mount Albano had in his command;
And late Bayardo lost, his gallant steed,
Escaped by strange adventure from his hand.
As soon as seen, the maid who rode at speed
The warrior knew, and, while yet distant, scanned
The angelic features and the gentle air
Which long had held him fast in Cupid's snare.

13.

The affrighted damsel turns her palfrey round,
And shakes the floating bridle in the wind;
Nor in her panic seeks to choose her ground,
Nor open grove prefers to thicket blind.
But reckless, pale and trembling, and astound,
Leaves to her horse the devious way to find.
He up and down the forest bore the dame,
Till to a sylvan river's bank he came.

14.

Here stood the fierce Ferrau in grisly plight,
Begrimed with dust, and bathed with sweat and blood;
Who lately had withdrawn him from the fight,
To rest and drink at that refreshing flood:
But there had tarried in his own despite,
Since bending from the bank, in hasty mood,
He dropped his helmet in the crystal tide,
And vainly to regain the treasure tried.

15.

Thither at speed she drives, and evermore
In her wild panic utters fearful cries;
And at the voice, upleaping on the shore,
The Saracen her lovely visage spies.
And, pale as is her cheek, and troubled sore,
Arriving, quickly to the warrior's eyes
(Though many days no news of her had shown)
The beautiful Angelica is known.

16.

Courteous, and haply gifted with a breast,
As warm as either of the cousins two; [5]
As bold, as if his brows in steel were dressed,
The succour which she sought he lent, and drew
His faulchion, and against Rinaldo pressed,
Who saw with little fear the champion true.

5. Orlando and Rinaldo.

Not only each to each was known by sight,
But each had proved in arms his foeman's might.

17.

Thus, as they are, on foot the warriors vie
In cruel strife, and blade to blade oppose;
No marvel plate or brittle mail should fly,
When anvils had not stood the deafening blows.
It now behooves the palfrey swift to ply
His feet; for while the knights in combat close,
Him vexed to utmost speed, with goading spurs,
By waste or wood the frighted damsel stirs.

18.

After the two had struggled long to throw
Each other in the strife, and vainly still;
Since neither valiant warrior was below
His opposite in force and knightly skill:
The first to parley with his Spanish foe
Was the good master of Albano's hill
(As one within whose raging breast was pent
A reckless fire which struggled for a vent).

19.

"Thou think'st," he said, "to injure me alone,
"But know thou wilt thyself as much molest:
"For if we fight because yon rising sun
"This raging heat has kindled in thy breast,
"What were thy gain, and what the guerdon won,
"Though I should yield my life, or stoop my crest;
"If she shall never be thy glorious meed,
"Who flies, while vainly we in battle bleed?

20.

"Then how much better, since our stake's the same,
"Thou, loving like myself, should'st mount and stay
"To wait this battle's end, the lovely dame,
"Before she fly yet further on her way.
"The lady taken, we repeat our claim
"With naked faulchion to that peerless prey:
"Else by long toil I see not what we gain
"But simple loss and unrequited pain."

21.

The peer's proposal pleased the paynim well.
And so their hot contention was foregone;
And such fair truce replaced that discord fell,
So mutual wrongs forgot and mischief done;
That for departure seated in his sell,

On foot the Spaniard left not Aymon's son;
But him to mount his courser's crupper prayed;
And both united chased the royal maid.

22.

Oh! goodly truth in cavaliers of old!
Rivals they were, to different faith were bred.
Not yet the weary warriors' wounds were cold—
Still smarting from those strokes so fell and dread.
Yet they together ride by waste and wold,
And, unsuspecting, devious dingle thread.
Them, while four spurs infest his foaming sides,
Their courser brings to where the way divides.

23.

And now the warlike pair at fault, for they
Knew not by which she might her palfrey goad,
(Since both, without distinction, there survey
The recent print of hoofs on either road),
Commit the chase to fortune. By this way
The paynim pricked, by that Rinaldo strode.
But fierce Ferrau, bewildered in the wood,
Found himself once again where late he stood.

24.

Beside the water, where he stoop'd to drink,
And dropt the knightly helmet,—to his cost,
Sunk in the stream; and since he could not think
Her to retrieve, who late his hopes had crossed,
He, where the treasure fell, descends the brink
Of that swift stream, and seeks the morion lost.
But the casque lies so bedded in the sands,
'Twill ask no light endeavour at his hands.

25.

A bough he severs from a neighbouring tree,
And shreds and shapes the branch into a pole:
With this he sounds the stream, and anxiously
Fathoms, and rakes, and ransacks shelf and hole.
While angered sore at heart, and restless, he
So lingered, where the troubled waters roll,
Breast-high, from the mid river rose upright,
The apparition of an angry knight.

26.

Armed at all points he was, except his head,
And in his better hand a helmet bore;
The very casque, which in the river's bed
Ferrau sought vainly, toiling long and sore.

Upon the Spanish knight he frowned, and said:
"Thou traitor to thy word, thou perjured Moor,
"Why grieve the goodly helmet to resign,
"Which, due to me long since, is justly mine?

27.

"Remember, pagan, when thine arm laid low
"The brother of Angelica.[6] That knight
"Am I; — thy word was plighted then to throw
"After my other arms this helmet bright.
"If Fortune now compel thee to forego
"The prize, and do my will in thy despite,
"Grieve not at this, but rather grieve that thou
"Art found a perjured traitor to thy vow.

28.

"But if thou seek'st a helmet, be thy task
"To win and wear it more to thy renown.
"A noble prize were good Orlando's casque;
"Rinaldo's such, or yet a fairer crown;
"Almontes', or Mambrino's iron masque:
"Make one of these, by force of arms, thine own.
"And this good helm will fitly be bestowed
"Where (such thy promise) it has long been owed."

29.

Bristled the paynim's every hair at view
Of that grim shade, uprising from the tide,
And vanished was his fresh and healthful hue,
While on his lips the half-formed accents died.
Next hearing Argalia, whom he slew,
(So was the warrior hight) that stream beside,
Thus his unknightly breach of promise blame,
He burned all over, flushed with rage and shame.

30.

Nor having time his falsehood to excuse,
And knowing well how true the phantom's lore,
Stood speechless; such remorse the words infuse.
Then by Lanfusa's life the warrior swore,
Never in fight, or foray would he use
Helmet but that which good Orlando bore
From Aspramont, where bold Almontes paid
His life a forfeit to the Christian blade.

31.

And this new vow discharged more faithfully
Than the vain promise which was whilom plight;

6. This is Argalia, brother to Angelica, who had originally brought her to the camp of Charlemagne. The story is told in Boiardo.

And from the stream departing heavily,
Was many days sore vexed and grieved in sprite;
And still intent to seek Orlando, he
Roved wheresoe'er he hoped to find the knight.
A different lot befel Rinaldo; who
Had chanced another pathway to pursue.

32.

For far the warrior fared not, ere he spied,
Bounding across the path, his gallant steed,
And, "stay, Bayardo mine," Rinaldo cried,
"Too cruel care the loss of thee does breed."
The horse for this returned not to his side,
Deaf to his prayer, but flew with better speed.
Furious, in chase of him, Rinaldo hies.
But follow we Angelica, who flies.

33.

Through dreary woods and dark the damsel fled,
By rude unharboured heath and savage height,
While every leaf or spray that rustled, bred
(Of oak, or elm, or beech) such new affright,
She here and there her foaming palfrey sped
By strange and crooked paths with furious flight;
And at each shadow, seen in valley blind,
Or mountain, feared Rinaldo was behind.

34.

As a young roe or fawn of fallow deer,
Who, 'mid the shelter of its native glade,
Has seen a hungry pard or tiger tear
The bosom of its bleeding dam, dismayed,
Bounds, through the forest green in ceaseless fear
Of the destroying beast, from shade to shade,
And at each sapling touched, amid its pangs,
Believes itself between the monster's fangs,

35.

One day and night, and half the following day,
The damsel wanders wide, nor whither knows;
Then enters a deep wood, whose branches play,
Moved lightly by the freshening breeze which blows.
Through this two clear and murmuring rivers stray:
Upon their banks a fresher herbage grows;
While the twin streams their passage slowly clear,
Make music with the stones, and please the ear.

36.

Weening removed the way by which she wends,
A thousand miles from loathed Rinaldo's beat,

To rest herself a while the maid intends,
Wearied with that long flight and summer's heat.
She from her saddle 'mid spring flowers descends
And takes the bridle from her courser fleet;
And loose along the river lets him pass,
Roving the banks in search of lusty grass.

37.

Behold! at hand a thicket she surveys
Gay with the flowering thorn and vermeil rose;
The tuft reflected in the stream which strays
Beside it, overshadowing oaks enclose.
Hollow within, and safe from vulgar gaze,
It seemed a place constructed for repose;
With bows so interwoven, that the light
Pierced not the tangled screen, far less the sight.

38.

Within soft moss and herbage form a bed;
And to delay and rest the traveller woo.
'Twas there her limbs the weary damsel spread,
Her eye-balls bathed in slumber's balmy dew;
But little time had eased her drooping head,
Ere, as she weened, a courser's tramp she knew.
Softly she rises, and the river near,
Armed cap-à-piè, beholds a cavalier.

39.

If friend or foe, she nothing comprehends,
(So hope and fear her doubting bosom tear)
And that adventure's issue mute attends,
Nor even with a sigh disturbs the air.
The cavalier upon the bank descends;
And sits so motionless, so lost in care,
(His visage propt upon his arm) to sight
Changed into senseless stone appeared the knight.

40.

Pensive, above an hour, with drooping head,
He rested mute, ere he began his moan;
And then his piteous tale of sorrow said,
Lamenting in so soft and sweet a tone,
He in a tiger's breast had pity bred,
Or with his mournful wailings rent a stone.
And so he sighed and wept; like rivers flowed
His tears, his bosom like an Ætna glowed.

41.

"Thought which now makes me burn, now freeze with hate,
"Which gnaws my heart and rankles at its root!

"What's left to me," he said, "arrived too late,
"While one more favoured bears away the fruit?
"Bare words and looks scarce cheered my hopeless state,
"And the prime spoils reward another's suit.
"Then since for me nor fruit nor blossom hangs,
"Why should I longer pine in hopeless pangs?

42.

"The virgin has her image in the rose
"Sheltered in garden on its native stock,
"Which there in solitude and safe repose,
"Blooms unapproached by shepherd or by flock,
"For this earth teems, and freshening water flows,
"And breeze and dewy dawn their sweets unlock:
"With such the wishful youth his bosom dresses,
"With such the enamoured damsel braids her tresses.

43.

"But wanton hands no sooner this displace
"From the maternal stem, where it was grown,
"Than all is withered; whatsoever grace
"It found with man or heaven; bloom, beauty, gone.
"The damsel who should hold in higher place
"Than light or life the flower which is her own,
"Suffering the spoiler's hand to crop the prize,
"Forfeits her worth in every other's eyes.

44.

"And be she cheap with all except the wight
"On whom she did so large a boon bestow.
"Ah! false and cruel Fortune! foul despite!
"While others triumph, I am drown'd in woe.
"And can it be that I such treasure slight?
"And can I then my very life forego?
"No! let me die; 'twere happiness above
"A longer life, if I must cease to love."

45.

If any ask who made this sorrowing,
And pour'd into the stream so many tears,
I answer, it was fair Circassia's king,[7]
That Sacripant, oppressed with amorous cares.
Love is the source from which his troubles spring,
The sole occasion of his pains and fears;
And he to her a lover's service paid,
Now well remembered by the royal maid.

7. Sacripant, king of Circassia, had fought in defense of Albracca, capital of Cathay (in the great siege carried on by Agrican of Tartary to gain Angelica's hand), and had become Angelica's suitor.

46.

He for her sake from Orient's farthest reign
Roved thither, where the sun descends to rest;
For he was told in India, to his pain,
That she Orlando followed to the west.
He after learned in France that Charlemagne
Secluded from that champion and the rest,
As a fit guerdon, mewed her for the knight
Who should protect the lilies best in fight.

47.

The warrior in the field had been, and viewed,
Short time before, king Charlemagne's disgrace;
And vainly had Angelica pursued,
Nor of the damsel's footsteps found a trace.
And this is what the weeping monarch rued,
And this he so bewailed in doleful case:
Hence, into words his lamentations run,
Which might for pity stop the passing sun.

48.

While Sacripant laments him in this plight,
And makes a tepid fountain of his eyes;
And, what I deem not needful to recite,
Pours forth yet other plaints and piteous cries;
Propitious Fortune wills his lady bright
Should hear the youth lament him in such wise:
And thus a moment compassed what, without
Such chance, long ages had not brought about.

49.

With deep attention, while the warrior weeps,
She marks the fashion of the grief and tears
And words of him, whose passion never sleeps;
Nor this the first confession which she hears.
But with his plaint her heart no measure keeps,
Cold as the column which the builder rears.
Like haughty maid, who holds herself above
The world, and deems none worthy of her love.

50.

But her from harm amid those woods to keep,
The damsel weened she might his guidance need;
For the poor drowning caitiff, who, chin-deep,
Implores not help, is obstinate indeed.
Nor will she, if she let the occasion sleep,
Find escort that will stand her in such stead:
For she that king by long experience knew
Above all other lovers, kind and true.

51.

But not the more for this the maid intends
To heal the mischief which her charms had wrought.
And for past ills to furnish glad amends
In that full bliss by pining lover sought.
To keep the king in play are all her ends,
His help by some device or fiction bought,
And having to her purpose taxed his daring,
To reassume as wont her haughty bearing.

52.

An apparition bright and unforeseen,
She stood like Venus or Diana fair,
In solemn pageant, issuing on the scene
From out of shadowy wood or murky lair.
And "Peace be with you," cried the youthful queen,
"And God preserve my honour in his care,
"Nor suffer that you blindly entertain
"Opinion of my fame so false and vain!"

53.

Not with such wonderment a mother eyes,
With such excessive bliss the son she mourned
As dead, lamented still with tears and sighs,
Since the thinned files without her boy returned.
— Not such her rapture as the king's surprise
And ecstasy of joy when he discerned
The lofty presence, cheeks of heavenly hue,
And lovely form which broke upon his view.

54.

He, full of fond and eager passion, pressed
Towards his Lady, his Divinity;
And she now clasped the warrior to her breast,
Who in Catày had haply been less free.
And now again the maid her thoughts addressed
Towards her native land and empery:
And feels, with hope revived, her bosom beat
Shortly to repossess her sumptuous seat.

55.

Her chances all to him the damsel said,
Since he was eastward sent to Sericane
By her to seek the martial monarch's aid,
Who swayed the sceptre of that fair domain;
And told how oft Orlando's friendly blade
Had saved her from dishonour, death, and pain;
And how she so preserved her virgin flower
Pure as it blossomed in her natal hour.

56.

Haply the tale was true; yet will not seem
Likely to one of sober sense possessed:
But Sacripant, who waked from worser dream,
In all without a cavil acquiesced:
Since Love, who sees without one guiding gleam,
Spies in broad day but that which likes him best:
For one sign of the afflicted man's disease
Is to give ready faith to things which please.

57.

"If good Anglante's lord the prize forbore,
"Nor seized the fair occasion when he might,
"The loss be his, if Fortune never more
"Him to enjoy so fair a prize invite.
"To imitate that lord of little lore
"I think not," said, apart, Circassia's knight,
"To quit such proffered good, and, to my shame,
"Have but myself on after-thought to blame.

58.

"No! I will pluck the fresh and morning rose,
"Which, should I tarry, may be overblown.
"To woman, (this my own experience shows,)
"No deed more sweet or welcome can be done.
"Then, whatsoever scorn the damsel shows,
"Though she awhile may weep and make her moan,
"I will, unchecked by anger, false or true,
"Or sharp repulse, my bold design pursue."

59.

This said, he for the soft assault prepares,
When a loud noise within the greenwood shade
Beside him, rang in his astounded ears,
And sore against his will the monarch stayed.
He donned his helm (his other arms he wears),
Aye wont to rove in steel, with belted blade,
Replaced the bridle on his courser fleet,
Grappled his lance, and sprang into his seat.

60.

With the bold semblance of a valiant knight,
Behold a warrior threads the forest hoar.
The stranger's mantle was of snowy white,
And white alike the waving plume he wore.
Balked of his bliss, and full of fell despite,
The monarch ill the interruption bore,
And spurred his horse to meet him in mid space,
With hate and fury glowing in his face.

61.

Him he defies to fight, approaching nigh,
And weens to make him stoop his haughty crest:
The other knight, whose worth I rate as high,
His warlike prowess puts to present test;
Cuts short his haughty threats and angry cry,
And spurs, and lays his levelled lance in rest.
In tempest wheels Circassia's valiant peer,
And at his foeman's head each aims his spear.

62.

Not brindled bulls or tawny lions spring
To forest warfare with such deadly will
As those two knights, the stranger and the king.
Their spears alike the opposing bucklers thrill:
The solid ground, at their encountering,
Trembles from fruitful vale to naked hill:
And well it was the mail in which they dressed
Their bodies was of proof, and saved the breast.

63.

Nor swerved the chargers from their destined course;
Who met like rams, and butted head to head.
The warlike Saracen's ill-fated horse,
Well valued while alive, dropt short and dead:
The stranger's, too, fell senseless; but perforce
Was roused by rowel from his grassy bed.
That of the paynim king, extended straight,
Lay on his battered lord with all his weight.

64.

Upright upon his steed, the knight unknown,
Who at the encounter horse and rider threw,
Deeming enough was in the conflict done,
Cares not the worthless warfare to renew;
But endlong by the readiest path is gone,
And measures, pricking frith and forest through,
A mile, or little less, in furious heat,
Ere the foiled Saracen regains his feet.

65.

As the bewildered and astonished clown
Who held the plough (the thunder storm o'erpast)
There, where the deafening bolt had beat him down,
Nigh his death-stricken cattle, wakes aghast,
And sees the distant pine without its crown,
Which he saw clad in leafy honours last;
So rose the paynim knight with troubled face,
The maid spectatress of the cruel case.

66.

He sighs and groans, yet not for mischief sore
Endured in wounded arm or foot which bled;
But for mere shame, and never such before
Or after, dyed his cheek so deep a red,
And if he rued his fall, it grieved him more
His dame should lift him from his courser dead.
He speechless had remained, I ween, if she
Had not his prisoned tongue and voice set free.

67.

"Grieve not," she said, "sir monarch, for thy fall;
"But let the blame upon thy courser be!
"To whom more welcome had been forage, stall,
"And rest, than further joust and jeopardy;
"And well thy foe the loser may I call,
"(Who shall no glory gain) for such is he
"Who is the first to quit his ground, if aught
"Angelica of fighting fields be taught."

68.

While she so seeks the Saracen to cheer,
Behold a messenger with pouch and horn,
On panting hackney! — man and horse appear
With the long journey, weary and forlorn.
He questions Sacripant, approaching near,
Had he seen warrior pass, by whom were borne
A shield and crest of white; in search of whom
Through the wide forest pricked the weary groom.

69.

King Sacripant made answer, "As you see,
"He threw me here, and went but now his way:
"Then tell the warrior's name, that I may be
"Informed whose valour foiled me in the fray."
To him the groom, — "That which you ask of me
"I shall relate to you without delay:
"Know that you were in combat prostrate laid
"By the tried valour of a gentle maid.

70.

"Bold is the maid; but fairer yet than bold,
"Nor the redoubted virgin's name I veil:
" 'Twas Bradamant [8] who marred what praise of old
"Your prowess ever won with sword and mail."
This said, he spurred again, his story told,
And left him little gladdened by the tale.

8. The first appearance of Bradamant in Ariosto.

He recks not what he says or does, for shame,
And his flushed visage kindles into flame.

71.

After the woeful warrior long had thought
Upon his cruel case, and still in vain,
And found a woman his defeat had wrought,
For thinking but increased the monarch's pain,
He climbed the other horse, nor spake he aught;
But silently uplifted from the plain,
Upon the croup bestowed that damsel sweet,
Reserved to gladder use in safer seat.

72.

Two miles they had not rode before they hear
The sweeping woods which spread about them, sound
With such loud crash and trample, far and near,
The forest seemed to tremble all around;
And shortly after see a steed appear,
With housings wrought in gold and richly bound;
Who clears the bush and stream, with furious force
And whatsoever else impedes his course.

73.

"Unless the misty air," the damsel cries,
"And boughs deceive my sight, yon noble steed
"Is, sure, Bayardo, who before us flies,
"And parts the wood with such impetuous speed.
"—Yes, 'tis Bayardo's self I recognize.
"How well the courser understands our need!
"Two riders ill a foundered jade would bear,
"But hither speeds the horse to end that care."

74.

The bold Circassian lighted, and applied
His hand to seize him by the flowing rein,
Who, swiftly turning, with his heels replied,
For he like lightning wheeled upon the plain.
Woe to the king! but that he leaps aside,
For should he smite, he would not lash in vain.
Such are his bone and sinew, that the shock
Of his good heels had split a metal rock.

75.

Then to the maid he goes submissively,
With gentle blandishment and humble mood;
As the dog greets his lord with frolic glee,
Whom, some short season past, he had not viewed.
For good Bayardo had in memory

Albracca, where her hands prepared his food,[9]
What time the damsel loved Rinaldo bold;
Rinaldo, then ungrateful, stern, and cold.

76.

With her left hand she takes him by the bit,
And with the other pats his sides and chest:
While the good steed (so marvellous his wit),
Lamb-like, obeyed the damsel and caressed.
Meantime the king, who sees the moment fit,
Leapt up, and with his knees the courser pressed.
While on the palfrey, eased of half his weight,
The lady left the croup, and gained the seat.

77.

Then, as at hazard, she directs her sight,
Sounding in arms a man on foot espies,
And glows with sudden anger and despite;
For she in him the son of Aymon eyes.
Her more than life esteems the youthful knight,
While she from him, like crane from falcon, flies.
Time was the lady sighed, her passion slighted;
'Tis now Rinaldo loves, as ill requited.

78.

And this effect two different fountains wrought,
Whose wonderous waters different moods inspire.
Both spring in Arden, with rare virtue fraught:
This fills the heart with amorous desire:
Who taste that other fountain are untaught
Their love, and change for ice their former fire.
Rinaldo drank the first, and vainly sighs;
Angelica the last, and hates and flies.

79.

Mixed with such secret bane the waters glide,
Which amorous care convert to sudden hate;
The maid no sooner had Rinaldo spied,
Than on her laughing eyes deep darkness sate:
And with sad mien and trembling voice she cried
To Sacripant, and prayed him not to wait
The near approach of the detested knight,
But through the wood with her pursue his flight.

9. Angelica was at first in love with Rinaldo, having first drunk from the Fountain of Love, even as Rinaldo had first drunk from the Fountain of Hate; it was on their return trip to France that the situation became suddenly reversed. Rinaldo fought among Angelica's enemies at Albracca. Bayardo fell into Angelica's hands; she took care of him, and later returned him to his master.

80.

To her the Saracen, with anger hot:
"Is knightly worship sunk so low in me,
"That thou should'st hold my valour cheap, and not
"Sufficient to make yonder champion flee?
"Already are Albracca's fights forgot,
"And that dread night I singly stood for thee?
"That night when I, though naked, was thy shield
"Against King Agrican and all his field?"

81.

She answers not, and knows not in her fear
What 'tis she does; Rinaldo is too nigh:
And from afar that furious cavalier
Threats the bold Saracen with angry cry,
As soon as the known steed and damsel dear,
Whose charms such flame had kindled, meet his eye.
But what ensued between the haughty pair
I in another canto shall declare.

CANTO II

ARGUMENT

A hermit parts, by means of hollow sprite,
The two redoubted rivals' dangerous play;
Rinaldo goes where Love and Hope invite,
But is dispatched by Charles another way:
Bradamant, seeking her devoted knight,
The good Rogero, nigh becomes the prey
Of Pinabel, who drops the damsel brave
Into the dungeon of a living grave.

* * * * *

31.

I speak of that famed damsel,[1] by whose spear
O'erthrown, King Sacripant on earth was flung;
The worthy sister of the valiant peer,
From Beatrix and good Duke Aymon sprung.
By daring deeds and puissance no less dear
To Charlemagne and France: Since proved among
The first, her prowess, tried by many a test,
Equal to good Rinaldo's shone confessed.

32.

A cavalier was suitor to the dame,
Who out of Afric passed with Agramant;
Rogero was his valiant father's name,
His mother was the child of Agolant.

1. Bradamant.

And she, who not of bear or lion came,
Disdained not on the Child her love to plant,
Though cruel Fortune, ill their wishes meeting,
Had granted to the pair a single greeting.[2]

33.

Alone thenceforth she sought her lover (he
Was named of him to whom he owed his birth),
And roved as safe as if in company
Of thousands, trusting in her single worth.
She having made the king of Circassy
Salute the visage of old mother earth,
Traversed a wood, and that wood past, a mountain;
And stopt at length beside a lovely fountain.

34.

Through a delicious mead the fountain-rill,
By ancient trees o'ershaded, glides away;
And him whose ear its pleasing murmurs fill,
Invites to drink, and on its banks to stay;
On the left side a cultivated hill
Excludes the fervors of the middle day.
As first the damsel thither turns her eyes,
A youthful cavalier she seated spies;

35.

A cavalier, who underneath the shade,
Seems lost, as in a melancholy dream;
And on the bank, which gaudy flowers displayed,
Reposing, overhangs the crystal stream.
His horse beneath a spreading beech is laid,
And from a bough the shield and helmet gleam.
While his moist eyes, and sad and downcast air,
Speak him the broken victim of despair.

36.

Urged by the passion lodged in every breast,
A restless curiosity to know
Of others' cares, the gentle maid addressed
The knight, and sought the occasion of his woe.
And he to her his secret grief confessed,
Won by her gentle speech and courteous show,
And by that gallant bearing, which at sight,
Prepared who saw her for a nimble knight.

37.

"Fair sir, a band of horse and foot," he said,
"I brought to Charlemagne; and thither pressed,

2. The first and only preceding meeting of Bradamant and Rogero, in Boiardo.

"Where he an ambush for Marsilius spread,
"Descending from the Pyrenean crest;
"And in my company a damsel led,
"Whose charms with fervid love had fired my breast,
"When, as we journey by Rhone's current, I
"A rider on a winged courser spy.

38.

"The robber, whether he were man or shade,
"Or goblin damned to everlasting woe,
"As soon as he beheld my dear-loved maid,
"Like falcon, who, descending, aims its blow,
"Sank in a thought and rose; and soaring, laid
"Hands on his prize, and snatched her from below.
"So quick the rape, that all appeared a dream,
"Until I heard in air the damsel's scream.

39.

"The ravening kite so swoops and plunders, when
"Hovering above the sheltered yard, she spies
"A helpless chicken near unwatchful hen,
"Who vainly dins the thief with after cries.
"I cannot reach the mountain-robber's den,
"Compassed with cliffs, or follow one who flies.
"Besides, way-foundered is my weary steed,
"Who 'mid these rocks has wasted wind and speed.

40.

"But I, like one who from his bleeding side
"Would liefer far have seen his heart out-torn,
"Left my good squadrons masterless, to ride
"Along the cliffs, and passes least forlorn;
"And took the way (love served me for a guide)
"Where it appeared the ruthless thief had borne,
"Ascending to his den, the lovely prey,
"What time he snatched my hope and peace away.

41.

"Six days I rode, from morn to setting sun,
"By horrid cliff, by bottom dark and drear;
"And giddy precipice, where path was none,
"Nor sign, nor vestiges of man were near.
"At last a dark and barren vale I won,
"Where caverned mountains and rude cliffs appear:
"Where in the middle rose a rugged block,
"With a fair castle planted on the rock.

42.

"From far it shone like flame, and seemed not dight
"Of marble or of brick; and in my eye
"More wonderful the work, more fair to sight
"The walls appeared, as I approached more nigh.
"I, after, learned that it was built by sprite
"Whom potent fumes had raised and sorcery:
"Who on this rock its towers of steel did fix,
"Case-hardened in the stream and fire of Styx.

43.

"Each polished turret shines with such a ray
"That it defies the mouldering rust and rain:
"The robber scours the country night and day,
"And after harbours in this sure domain.
"Nothing is safe which he would bear away;
"Pursued with curses and with threats in vain.
"There (fruitless every hope to foil his art)
"The felon keeps my love, oh! say my heart.

44.

"Alas! what more is left me but to eye
"Her prison on that cliff's aërial crest?
"Like the she-fox, who hears her offspring cry,
"Standing beneath the ravening eagle's nest;
"And since she has not wings to rise and fly,
"Runs round the rugged rock with hopeless quest,
"So inaccessible the wild dominion
"To whatsoever has not plume and pinion.

45.

"While I so lingered where those rocks aspire,
"I saw a dwarf guide two of goodly strain;
"Whose coming added hope to my desire
"(Alas! desire and hope alike were vain)
"Both barons bold, and fearful in their ire:
"The one Gradasso, King of Sericane,
"The next, of youthful vigour, was a knight,
"Prized in the Moorish court, Rogero hight.

46.

"The dwarf exclaimed, 'These champions will assay
'Their force with him who dwells on yonder steep,
'And by such strange and unattempted way
'Spurs the winged courser from his mountain-keep.'
"And I to the approaching warriors say,
'Pity, fair sirs, the cruel loss I weep,
'And, as I trust, yon daring spoiler slain,
'Give my lost lady to my arms again.'

47.

"Then how my love was ravished I make known,
"Vouching with bitter tears my deep distress.
"They proffer aid, and down the path of stone
"Which winds about the craggy mountain, press.
"While I, upon the summit left alone,
"Look on, and pray to God for their success.
"Beneath the wily wizard's castle strong
"Extends a little plain, two bow-shots long.

48.

"Arrived beneath the craggy keep, the two
"Contend which warrior shall begin the fight.
"When, whether the first lot Gradasso drew,
"Or young Rogero held the honor light,
"The King of Sericane his bugle blew,
"And the rock rang and fortress on the height;
"And, lo! apparelled for the fearful course,
"The cavalier upon his winged horse!

49.

"Upwards, by little and by little, springs
"The winged courser, as the pilgrim crane
"Finds not at first his balance and his wings,
"Running and scarcely rising from the plain;
"But when the flock is launched and scattered, flings
"His pinions to the wind, and soars amain.
"So straight the necromancer's upward flight,
"The eagle scarce attempts so bold a height.

50.

"When it seems fit, he wheels his courser round,
"Who shuts his wings, and falling from the sky,
"Shoots like a well trained falcon to the ground,
"Who sees the quarry, duck or pigeon, fly:
"So, through the parting air, with whizzing sound,
"With rested lance, he darted from on high;
"And while Gradasso scarcely marks the foe
"He hears him swooping near, and feels the blow.

51.

"The wizard on Gradasso breaks his spear,
"He wounds the empty air, with fury vain.
"This in the feathered monster breeds no fear;
"Who to a distance shifts, and swoops again.
"While that encounter made the Alfana rear,
"Thrown back upon her haunches, on the plain.
"The Alfana that the Indian monarch rode,
"The fairest was that ever man bestrode.

52.

"Up to the starry sphere with swift ascent
"The wizard soars, then pounces from the sky,
"And strikes the young Rogero, who, intent
"Upon Gradasso, deems no danger nigh.
"Beneath the wizard's blow the warrior bent,
"Which made some deal his generous courser ply;
"And when to smite the shifting foe he turned,
"Him in the sky, and out of reach discerned.

53.

"His blows Rogero, now Gradasso, bruise
"On forehead, bosom, back, or flanks between;
"While he the warrior's empty blows eschews,
"Shifting so quickly that he scarce is seen.
"Now this, now that, the wizard seems to choose,
"The monster makes such spacious rings and clean,
"While the enchanter so deceives the knights,
"They view him not, and know not whence he smites.

54.

"Between the two on earth and him o' the sky,
"Until that hour the warfare lasted there,
"Which, spreading wide its veil of dusky dye,
"Throughout the world, discolours all things fair.
"What I beheld, I say; I add not, I,
"A tittle to the tale; yet scarcely dare
"To tell to other what I stood and saw;
"So strange it seems, so passing Nature's law.

55.

"Well covered in a goodly silken case,
"He, the celestial warrior, bore his shield;
"But why delayed the mantle to displace
"I know not, and its lucid orb concealed.
"Since this no sooner blazes in his face,
"Than his foe tumbles dazzled on the field;
"And while he, like a lifeless body, lies,
"Becomes the necromancer's helpless prize.

56.

"Like carbuncle, the magic buckler blazed,
"No glare was ever seen which shone so bright:
"Nor could the warriors choose but fall, amazed
"And blinded by the clear and dazzling light.
"I, too, that from a distant mountain gazed,
"Fell senseless; and when I regained my sight,
"After long time, saw neither knights nor page,
"Nor aught beside a dark and empty stage.

57.

"This while the fell enchanter, I supposed,
"Dragged both the warriors to his prison-cell;
"And by strange virtue of the shield disclosed,
"I from my hope and they from freedom fell:
"And thus I to the turrets, which enclosed
"My heart, departing, bade a last farewell.
"Now sum my griefs, and say if love combine
"Other distress or grief to match with mine."

58.

The knight relapsed into his first disease,
After his melancholy tale was done.
This was Count Pinabel, the Maganzese,
Anselmo d' Altaripa's faithless son.
He, where the blood ran foul through all degrees,
Disdained to be the only virtuous one;
Nor played a simple part among the base,
Passing in vice the villains of his race.

59.

With aspect changing still, the beauteous dame
Hears what the mournful Maganzese narrates;
And, at first mention of Rogero's name,
Her radiant face with eager joy dilates.
But, full of pity, kindles into flame
As Pinabel his cruel durance states.
Nor finds she, though twice told, the story stale;
But makes him oft repeat and piece his tale.

60.

And, after, when she deemed that all was clear,
Cried to the knight, "Repose upon my say.
"To thee may my arrival well be dear,
"And thou as fortunate account this day.
"Straight wend me to the keep, sir cavalier,
"Which holds a jewel of so rich a ray:
"Nor shalt thou grudge thy labour and thy care,
"If envious Fortune do but play me fair."

61.

The knight replied, "Then nought to me remains
"But that I yonder mountain-passes show;
"And sure 'tis little loss to lose my pains,
"Where every thing is lost I prize below.
"But you would climb yon cliffs, and for your gains
"Will find a prison-house; and be it so!
"Whate'er betide you, blame yourself alone;
"You go forewarned to meet a fate foreshown."

62.

So said, the cavalier remounts his horse,
And serves the gallant damsel as a guide;
Who is prepared Rogero's gaol to force,
Or to be slain, or in his prison stied.
When lo! a messenger, in furious course,
Called to the dame to stay, and rode and cried.
This was the post who told Circassia's lord
What valiant hand had stretched him on the sward.

63.

The courier, who so plied his restless heel,
News of Narbonne and of Montpelier bore:
How both had raised the standard of Castile,
All Acquamorta siding with the Moor;
And how Marseilles' disheartened men appeal
To her, who should protect her straightened shore;
And how, through him, her citizens demand
Counsel and comfort at their captain's hand.

64.

This goodly town, with many miles of plain,
Which lie 'twixt Var and Rhone, upon the sea,
To her was given by royal Charlemagne:
Such trust he placed in her fidelity.
Still wont with wonder on the tented plain
The prowess of that valiant maid to see.
And now the panting courier, as I said,
Rode from Marseilles to ask the lady's aid.

65.

Whether or not she should the call obey,
The youthful damsel doubts some little space;
Strong in one balance Fame and Duty weigh,
But softer thoughts both Fame and Duty chase:
And she, at length, resolved the emprize to assay,
And free Rogero from the enchanted place:
Or, should her valour in the adventure fail,
Would with the cherished lover share his jail.

66.

And did with such excuse that post appay,
He was contented on her will to wait:
Then turned the bridle to resume her way
With Pinabel, who seemed no whit elate.
Since of that line he knows the damsel gay,
Held in such open and such secret hate;
And future trouble to himself foresees,
Were he detected as a Maganzese.

67.

For 'twixt Maganza's and old Clermont's line
There was an ancient and a deadly feud:
And oft to blows the rival houses came,
And oft in civil blood their hands embrued.
And hence some treason to this gentle dame,
In his foul heart, the wicked County brewed;
Or, as the first occasion served, would stray
Out of the road, and leave her by the way.

68.

And so the traitor's troubled fancy rack
Fear, doubt, and his own native, rancorous mood,
That unawares he issued from the track,
And found himself within a gloomy wood:
Where a rough mountain reared its shaggy back,
Whose stony peak above the forest stood;
The daughter of Dordona's duke [3] behind,
Dogging his footsteps through the thicket blind.

69.

He, when he saw himself within the brake,
Thought to abandon his unweeting foe;
And to the dame — " 'Twere better that we make
"For shelter ere the gathering darkness grow;
"And, yonder mountain past, (save I mistake)
"A tower is seated in the vale below.
"Do you expect me then, while from the peak
"I measure the remembered place I seek."

70.

So said, he pushed his courser up the height
Of that lone mountain; in his evil mind
Revolving, as he went, some scheme or sleight
To rid him of the gentle dame behind.
When lo! a rocky cavern met his sight,
Amid those precipices dark and blind:
Its sides descended thirty yards and more,
Worked smooth, and at the bottom was a door.

71.

A void was at the bottom, where a wide
Portal conducted to an inner room:
From thence a light shone out on every side,
As of a torch illumining the gloom.
Fair Bradamant pursued her faithless guide,
Suspended there, and pondering on her doom:

3. Bradamant.

And came upon the felon where he stood,
Fearing lest she might lose him in the wood.

72.

When her approach the County's first intent
Made vain, the wily traitor sought to mend
His toils, and some new stratagem invent
To rid her thence, or bring her to her end.
And so to meet the approaching lady went,
And showed the cave, and prayed her to ascend;
And said that in its bottom he had seen
A gentle damsel of bewitching mien,

73.

Who, by her lovely semblance and rich vest,
Appeared a lady of no mean degree;
But melancholy, weeping, and distressed,
As one who pined there in captivity;
And that when he towards the entrance pressed,
To learn who that unhappy maid might be,
One on the melancholy damsel flew,
And her within that inner cavern drew.

74.

The beauteous Bradamant, who was more bold
Then wary, gave a ready ear; and, bent
To help the maid, imprisoned in that hold,
Sought but the means to try the deep descent.
Then, looking round, descried an elm-tree old,
Which furnished present means for her intent;
And from the tree, with boughs and foliage stored,
Lopt a long branch, and shaped it with her sword.

75.

The severed end she to the count commended,
Then, grasping it, hung down that entrance steep,
With her feet foremost, by her arms suspended:
When asking if she had the skill to leap,
The traitor, with a laugh, his hands extended,
And plunged his helpless prey into the deep.
"And thus," exclaimed the ruffian, "might I speed
"With thee each sucker of thy cursed seed!"

76.

But not, as was the will of Pinabel,
Such cruel lot fair Bradamant assayed;
For striking on the bottom of the cell,
The stout elm-bough so long her weight upstayed,
That, though it split and splintered where it fell,

It broke her fall, and saved the gentle maid.
Some while astounded there the lady lay,
As the ensuing canto will display.

CANTO III

ARGUMENT

Restored to sense, the beauteous Bradamant
Finds sage Melissa in the vaulted tomb,
And hears from her of many a famous plant
And warrior, who shall issue from her womb.
Next, to release Rogero from the haunt
Of old Atlantes, learns how from the groom,
Brunello hight, his virtuous ring to take;
And thus the knight's and others' fetters break.

[Bradamant discovers the cavern into which she was plunged by Pinabel to be the Cave of Merlin. She meets there the sage Melissa, who conducts her to Merlin's Tomb. The voice of Merlin speaks informing her that Fate has brought her there, that she is destined to marry Rogero, and that their issue is to become a line of celebrated rulers. Melissa then calls these spirits forth before their birth, and the rulers of the House of Este appear down to Ippolito and Alfonso, patrons of Ariosto. Melissa then instructs her how to find and free Rogero, who is held captive by the wizard Atlantes, and leads her on her way.]

64.

All night the maid reposes in the cave,
And the best part in talk with Merlin spends;
While with persuasive voice the wizard grave
To her Rogero's honest love commends;
Till from the vault goes forth that virgin brave,
As through the sky the rising sun ascends,
By path, long space obscure on either side,
The weïrd woman still her faithful guide.

65.

They gain a hidden glen, which heights inclose,
And mountains inaccessible to man:
And they all day toil on, without repose,
Where precipices frowned and torrents ran.
And (what may some diversion interpose)
Sweet subjects of discourse together scan,
In conference, which best might make appear
The rugged road less dismal and severe.

66.

Of these the greater portion served to guide
(Such the wise woman's scope) the warlike dame;
And teach by what device might be untied

Rogero's gyves, if stedfast were her flame.
"If thou wert Mars himself, or Pallas," cried
The sage Melissa; "though with thee there came
"More than King Charles or Agramant command,
"Against the wizard foe thou could'st not stand.

67.

"Besides that it is walled about with steel,
"And inexpugnable his tower, and high;
"Besides that his swift horse is taught to wheel,
"And caracol and gallop in mid sky,
"He bears a mortal shield of power to seal,
"As soon as 'tis exposed, the dazzled eye;
"And so invades each sense the splendour shed,
"That he who sees the blaze remains as dead.

68.

"And lest to shut thine eyes, thou should'st suppose
"Might serve, contending with the wizard knight;
"How would'st thou know, when both in combat close,
"When he strikes home, or when eschews the fight?
"But to escape the blaze which blinds his foes,
"And render vain each necromantic sleight,
"Have here a speedy mean which cannot miss;
"Nor can the world afford a way but this.

69.

"King Agramant of Africa a ring,
"Thieved from an Indian queen [1] by subtle guiles,
"Has to a baron of his following
"Consigned, who now precedes us by few miles;
"Brunello he. Who wears the gift shall bring
"To nought all sorceries and magic wiles.
"In thefts and cheats Brunello is as well
"Instructed, as the sage in charm and spell.

70.

"Brunello, he so practised and so sly
"As now I tell thee, by his king is sent,
"That he with aid of mother wit may try,
"And of this ring, well proved in like event,
"To take Rogero from the castle high;
"So has he boasted, by the wizard pent:
"And to his lord such promise did impart,
"Who has Rogero's presence most at heart.

1. This magic ring was the means by which King Agramant first obtained Rogero from Atlantes in Africa. Brunello, a dwarf and expert thief, was commissioned by Agramant to steal it for this purpose from Angelica, who first possessed it. Angelica regains it later.

71.

"That his escape to thee alone may owe,
"Not to the king, the youthful cavalier,
"How to release Rogero from his foe
"And his enchanted cage, prepare to hear.
"Three days along the shingle shalt thou go,
"Beside the sea, whose waves will soon appear
"Thee the third day shall to a hostel bring,
"Where he shall come who bears the virtuous ring.

72.

"That thou may'st recognise the man, in height
"Less than six palms, observe one at this inn
"Of black and curly hair the dwarfish wight!
"Beard overgrown about the cheek and chin;
"With shaggy brow, swoln eyes, and cloudy sight,
"A nose close flattened, and a sallow skin;
"To this, that I may make my sketch complete,
"Succinctly clad, like courier, goes the cheat.

73.

"Thy conversation with this man shall turn
"Upon enchantment, spell, and mystic pact:
"And thou shalt, in thy talk, appear to yearn
"To prove the wizard's strength, as is the fact.
"But, lady, let him not thy knowledge learn
"Of his good ring, which mars all magic act:
"He shall propose to bring thee as a guide
"To the tall castle, whither thou would'st ride.

74.

"Follow him close, and viewing (for a sign),
"Now near, the fortress of the enchanter hoar;
"Let no false pity there thy mind incline
"To stay the execution of my lore.
"Give him his death; but let him not divine
"Thy thought, nor grant him respite; for before
"Thine eyes, concealed by it, the caitiff slips
"If once he place the ring between his lips."

75.

Discoursing thus, they came upon the sea
Where Garonne near fair Bordeaux meets the tide;
Here, fellow travellers no more to be,
Some natural tears they drop and then divide.
Duke Aymon's child, who slumbers not till she
Release her knight, holds on till even-tide:
'Twas then the damsel at a hostel rested,
Where Sir Brunello was already guested.

76.

The maid Brunello knows as soon as found
(So was his image on her mind impressed),
And asks him whence he came, and whither bound;
And he replies and lies, as he is pressed.
The dame, who is forewarned, and knows her ground,
Feigns too as well as he, and lies her best:
And changes sex and sect, and name and land,
And her quick eye oft glances at his hand;

77.

Oft glances at his restless hand, in fear
That he might undetected make some prize;
Nor ever lets the knave approach too near,
Well knowing his condition: In this guise
The couple stand together, when they hear
A sudden sound: but what that sound implies
I, sir, shall tell hereafter with its cause;
But first shall break my song with fitting pause.

CANTO IV

ARGUMENT

The old Atlantes suffers fatal wreck,
Foiled by the ring, and young Rogero freed,
Who soars in air till he appears a speck,
Mounted upon the wizard's winged steed.
Obedient to the royal Charles's beck,
He who had followed Love's imperious lead,
Rinaldo, disembarks on British land,
And saves Geneura, doomed to stake and brand.

1.

Though an ill mind appear in simulation,
And, for the most, such quality offends;
'Tis plain that this in many a situation
Is found to further beneficial ends,
And save from blame, and danger, and vexation;
Since we converse not always with our friends,
In this, less clear than clouded, mortal life,
Beset with snares, and full of envious strife.

2.

If after painful proof we scarcely find
A real friend, through various chances sought,
To whom we may communicate our mind,
Keeping no watch upon our wandering thought;
What should the young Rogero's lady kind
Do with Brunello, not sincere, but fraught

With treasons manifold, and false and tainted,
As by the good enchantress truly painted?

3.

She feigns as well with that deceitful scout;
(Fitting with him the father of all lies)
Watches his thievish hands in fear and doubt;
And follows every motion with her eyes.
When lo! a mighty noise is heard without!
"O mighty mother! king of heaven!" she cries,
"What thing is this I hear?" and quickly springs
Towards the place from whence the larum rings,

4.

And sees the host and all his family,
Where, one to door, and one to window slips,
With eyes upturned and gazing at the sky,
As if to witness comet or eclipse.
And there the lady views, with wondering eye,
What she had scarce believed from other's lips
A feathered courser, sailing through the rack,
Who bore an armed knight upon his back.

5.

Broad were his pinions, and of various hue;
Seated between, a knight the saddle pressed,
Clad in steel arms, which wide their radiance threw,
His wonderous course directed to the west:
There dropt among the mountains lost to view.
And this was, as that host informed his guest,
(And true the tale) a sorcerer, who made
Now farther, now more near, his frequent raid.

6.

"He, sometimes towering, soars into the skies;
"Then seems, descending, but to skim the ground:
"And of all beauteous women makes a prize,
"Who, to their mischief, in these parts are found.
"Hence, whether in their own or others' eyes,
"Esteemed as fair, the wretched damsels round,
"(And all in fact the felon plunders) hide;
"As fearing of the sun to be descried.

7.

"A castle on the Pyrenean height
"The necromancer keeps, the work of spell,"
(The host relates) "of steel, so fair and bright,
"All nature cannot match the wonderous shell.
"There many cavaliers, to prove their might,

"Have gone, but none returned the tale to tell.
"So that I doubt, fair sir, the thief enthralls
"Or slays whoever in the encounter falls."

8.

The watchful maid attends to every thing,
Glad at her heart, and trusting to complete
(What she shall compass by the virtuous ring)
The downfall of the enchanter and his seat.
Then to the host — "A guide I pray thee bring;
"Who better knows than me the thief's retreat.
"So burns my heart, (nor can I choose but go)
"To strive in battle with this wizard foe."

9.

"It shall not need," exclaimed the dwarfish Moor,
"For I, myself, will serve you as a guide;
"Who have the road set down, with other lore,
"So that you shall rejoice with me to ride."
He meant the ring, but further hint forbore;
Lest dearly he the avowal should abide.
And she to him — "Your guidance gives me pleasure."
Meaning by this she hoped to win his treasure.

10.

What useful was to say, she said, and what
Might hurt her with the Saracen, concealed.
Well suited to her ends, the host had got
A palfrey, fitting for the road or field.
She bought the steed, and as Aurora shot
Her rosy rays, rode forth with spear and shield:
And maid and courier through a valley wind,
Brunello now before and now behind.

11.

From wood to wood, from mount to mountain hoar,
They clomb a summit, which in cloudless sky
Discovers France and Spain, and either shore.
As from a peak of Apennine the eye
May Tuscan and Sclavonian sea explore,
There, whence we journey to Camaldoli.
Then through a rugged path and painful wended,
Which thence into a lowly vale descended.

12.

A rock from that deep valley's centre springs;
Bright walls of steel about its summit go:
And this as high that airy summit flings,
As it leaves all the neighbouring cliffs below.

He may not scale the height who has not wings
And vainly would each painful toil bestow.
"Lo! where his prisoners!" Sir Brunello cries,
"Ladies and cavaliers, the enchanter sties."

13.

Scarped smooth upon four parts, the mountain bare
Seemed fashioned with the plumb, by builder's skill
Nor upon any side was path or stair,
Which furnished man the means to climb the hill.
The castle seemed the very nest and lair
Of animal, supplied with plume and quill.
And here the damsel knows 'tis time to slay
The wily dwarf, and take the ring away.

14.

But deems it foul, with blood of man to stain
Unarmed and of so base a sort, her brand;
For well, without his death, she may obtain
The costly ring; and so suspends her hand.
Brunello, off his guard, with little pain,
She seized, and strongly bound with girding band
Then to a lofty fir made fast the string;
But from his finger first withdrew the ring.

15.

Neither by tears, nor groans, nor sound of woe,
To move the stedfast maid the dwarf had power:
She down the rugged hill descended slow,
Until she reached the plain beneath the tower.
Then gave her bugle breath, the keep below,
To call the castled wizard to the stower:
And when the sound was finished, threatening cried,
And called him to the combat and defied.

16.

Not long within his gate the enchanter stayed,
After he heard the voice and bugle ring.
Against the foe, who seemed a man, arrayed
In arms, with him the horse is on the wing.
But his appearance well consoled the maid,
Who, with small cause for fear, beheld him bring
Nor mace, nor rested lance, nor biting sword,
Wherewith the corselet might be bruised or gored.

17.

In his left arm alone his shield he took,
Covered all o'er with silk of crimson hue;
In his right-hand he held an open book,

Whence, as the enchanter read, strange wonder grew:
For often times, to sight, the lance he shook;
And flinching eyelids could not bide the view;
With tuck or mace he seemed to smite the foe:
But sate aloof and had not struck a blow.

18.

No empty fiction wrought by magic lore,
But natural was the steed the wizard pressed:
For him a filly to a griffin bore;
Hight hippogryph. In wings and beak and crest,
Formed like his sire, as in the feet before;
But like the mare, his dam, in all the rest.
Such on Riphaean hills, though rarely found,
Are bred, beyond the frozen ocean's bound.

19.

Drawn by enchantment from his distant lair,
The wizard thought but how to tame the foal;
And, in a month, instructed him to bear
Saddle and bit, and gallop to the goal;
And execute on earth or in mid air,
All shifts of manege, course and caracole;
He with such labour wrought. This only real,
Where all the rest was hollow and ideal.

20.

This truth by him with fictions was combined,
Whose sleight passed red for yellow, black for white:
But all his vain enchantments could not blind
The maid, whose virtuous ring assured her sight:
Yet she her blows discharges at the wind;
And spurring here and there prolongs the fight.
So drove or wheeled her steed, and smote at nought,
And practised all she had before been taught.

21.

When she sometime had fought upon her horse,
She from the courser on her feet descends:
To compass and more freely put in force,
As by the enchantress schooled, her wily ends.
The wizard, to display his last resource,
Unweeting the defence, towards her wends.
He bares the shield, secure to blind his foe,
And by the magic light, astonished, throw.

22.

The shield might have been shown at first, nor he
Needed to keep the cavaliers at bay;

But that he loved some master-stroke to see,
Achieved by lance or sword in single fray.
As with the captive mouse, in sportive glee,
The wily cat is sometimes seen to play;
Till waxing wroth, or weary of her prize,
She bites, and at a snap the prisoner dies.

23.

To cat and mouse, in battles fought before,
I liken the magician and his foes;
But the comparison holds good no more:
For, with the ring, the maid against him goes;
Firm and attentive still, and watching sore,
Lest upon her the wizard should impose:
And as she sees him bare the wondrous shield,
Closes her eyes and falls upon the field.

24.

Not that the shining metal could offend,
As wont those others, from its cover freed;
But so the damsel did, to make descend
The vain enchanter from his wonderous steed.
Nor was in ought defeated of her end;
For she no sooner on the grassy mead
Had laid her head, than wheeling widely round,
The flying courser pitched upon the ground.

25.

Already cased again, the shield was hung,
By the magician, at his saddle bow.
He lights and seeks her, who like wolf among
The bushes, couched in thicket, waits the roe;
She without more delay from ambush sprung,
As he drew near, and grappled fast the foe.
That wretched man, the volume by whose aid
He all his battles fought, on earth had laid:

26.

And ran to bind her with a chain, which he,
Girt round about him for such purpose, wore;
Because he deemed she was no less to be
Mastered and bound than those subdued before.
Him hath the dame already flung; by me
Excused with reason, if he strove not more.
For fearful were the odds between that bold
And puissant maid, and warrior weak and old!

27.

Intending to behead the fallen foe,
She lifts her conquering hand; but in mid space,
When she beholds his visage, stops the blow,
As if disdaining a revenge so base.
She sees in him, her prowess has laid low,
A venerable sire, with sorrowing face;
Whose hair and wrinkles speak him, to her guess,
Of years six score and ten, or little less.

28.

"Kill me, for love of God!" (afflicted sore,
The old enchanter full of wrath did cry)
But the victorious damsel was not more
Averse to kill, than he was bent to die.
To know who was the necromancer hoar
The gentle lady had desire, and why
The tower he in that savage place designed,
Doing such outrage foul to all mankind.

29.

"Nor I, by malice moved, alas! poor wight,"
(The weeping necromancer answer made,)
"Built the fair castle on the rocky height,
"Nor yet for rapine ply the robber's trade;
"But only to redeem a gentle knight
"From danger sore and death, by love was swayed;
"Who, as the skies foreshow, in little season,
"Is doomed to die a Christian, and by treason.

30.

"The sun beholds not 'twixt the poles, a Child
"So excellent as him, and passing fair;
"Who from his infancy, Rogero styled,
"(Atlantes I) was tutored by my care.
"By love of fame and evil stars beguiled,
"He follows into France Troyano's heir.[1]
"Him, in my eyes, than son esteemed more dear,
"I seek to snatch from France and peril near.

31.

"I only built the beauteous keep to be
"Rogero's dungeon, safely harboured there;
"Who whilom was subdued in fight by me,
"As I to-day had hoped thyself to snare,
"And dames and knights, and more of high degree,
"Have to this tower conveyed, his lot to share,

1. Agramant.

"That with such partners of his prison pent,
"He might the loss of freedom less lament.

32.

"Save they should seek to break their dungeon's bound,
"I grant my inmates every other pleasure.
"For whatsoever in the world is found,
"Search its four quarters, in this keep I treasure;
"(Whatever heart can wish or tongue can sound)
"Cates, brave attire, game, sport, or mirthful measure.
"My field well sown, I well had reaped my grain,
"But that thy coming makes my labour vain.

33.

"Ah! then unless thy heart less beauteous be
"Than thy sweet face, mar not my pious care;
"Take my steel buckler, this I give to thee,
"And take that horse, which flies so fast in air,
"Nor meddle with my castle more; or free
"One or two captive friends, the rest forbear —
"Or (for I crave but this) release them all,
"So that Rogero but remain my thrall.

34.

"Or if disposed to take him from my sight,
"Before the youth be into France conveyed,
"Be pleased to free my miserable sprite
"From its now rotted bark, long since decayed."
"Prate as thou wilt, I shall restore the knight
"To liberty," replied the martial maid,
"Nor offer shield and courser to resign,
"Which are not in thy gift, — already mine.

35.

"Nor were they thine to take or to bestow,
"Would it appear that such exchange were wise;
"Thou sayest to save him from what stars foreshow,
"And cheat an evil influence of the skies
"Rogero is confined. Thou canst not know,
"Or knowing, canst not change his destinies:
"For, if unknown an ill so near to thee,
"Far less mayest thou another's fate foresee.

36.

"Seek not thy death from me; for the petition
"Is made in vain; but if for death thou sigh,
"Though the whole world refused the requisition,
"A soul resolved would find the means to die.
"But ope thy gates to give thy guests dismission

"Before thine hand the knot of life untie."
So spake the scornful dame with angry mock,
Speeding her captive still towards the rock.

37.

Bound by the conqueror with the chain he bore,
Atlantes walked, the damsel following nigh,
Who trusted not to the magician hoar,
Although he seemed subdued in port and eye.
Nor many paces went the pair, before
They at the mountain's foot the cleft espy,
With steps by which the rugged hill to round;
And climb, till to the castle-gate they wound:

38.

Atlantes from the threshold, graved by skill,
With characters and wondrous signs, upturned
A virtuous stone, where, underneath the sill,
Pots, with perpetual fire and secret, burned.
The enchanter breaks them; and at once the hill
To an inhospitable rock is turned.
Nor wall nor tower on any side is seen,
As if no castle there had ever been.

39.

Then from the lady's toils the wizard clears
His limbs, as thrush escapes the fowler's snare;
With him as well his castle disappears,
And leaves the prisoned troop in open air;
From their gay lodgings, dames and cavaliers,
Unhoused upon that desert, bleak and bare.
And many at the freedom felt annoy,
Which dispossessed them of such life of joy.

40.

There is Gradasso, there is Sacripant,
There is Prasildo, noble cavalier,
Who with Rinaldo came from the Levant;
Iroldo, too, Prasildo's friend sincere.
And there, at last, the lovely Bradamant
Discerns Rogero, long desired and dear;
Who, when assured it was that lady, flew
With joyful cheer to greet the damsel true; [2]

41.

As her he prized before his eyes, his heart,
His life; from that day cherished when she stood
Uncasqued for him, and from the fight apart;

2. This is the first meeting of the lovers in Ariosto's poem; they had met once before, in Boiardo.

And hence an arrow drank her virgin blood,
'Twere long to tell who launched the cruel dart,
And how the lovers wandered in the wood:
Now guided by the sun, and now benighted,
Here first since that encounter reunited.

42.

Now that the stripling sees her here, and knows
Alone she freed him from the wizard's nest,
He deems, his bosom with such joy overflows,
That he is singly fortunate and blest.
Thither, where late the damsel conquered, goes
The band, descending from the mountain's crest;
And finds the hippogryph, who bore the shield,
But in its case of crimson silk concealed.

43.

To take him by the rein the lady there
Approached, and he stood fast till she was nigh,
Then spread his pinions to the liquid air,
And at short distance lit, half-mountain high:
And, as she follows him with fruitless care,
Nor longer flight nor shorter will he try.
'Tis thus the raven, on some sandy beach,
Lures on the dog, and flits beyond his reach.

44.

Gradasso, Sacripant, Rogero, who
With all those other knights below were met,
Where'er they hope he may return, pursue
The beast, and up and down, each pass beset.
He having led those others, as he flew,
Often to rocky height, and bottom wet,
Among the rocks of the moist valley dropt,
And at short distance from Rogero stopt.

45.

This was Atlantes the enchanter's deed,
Whose pious wishes still directed were,
To see Rogero from his peril freed:
This was his only thought, his only care;
Who for such end dispatched the winged steed,
Him out of Europe by this sleight to bear.
Rogero took his bridle, but in vain;
For he was restive to the guiding rein.

46.

Now the bold youth from his Frontino flings
(Frontino was his gentle courser hight)

Then leaps on him who towers in air, and stings
And goads his haughty heart with rowels bright.
He runs a short career; then upward springs,
And through mid ether soars a fairer flight
Than hawk, from which the falconer plucks away
In time the blinding hood, and points her prey.

47.

When her Rogero the fair dame discerned,
In fearful peril, soar so high a strain,
She stood long space amazed, ere she returned
To her right judgement, and sound wits again:
And what she erst of Ganymede had learned,
Snatched up to heaven from his paternal reign,
Feared might befall the stripling, born through air,
As gentle as young Ganymede and fair.

48.

She on Rogero looks with steadfast eyes
As long as feeble sight can serve her use;
And in her mind next tracks him through the skies,
When sight in vain the cherished youth pursues.
And still renewing tears, and groans, and sighs,
Will not afford her sorrow peace or truce.
After the knight had vanished from her view,
Her eyes she on the good Frontino threw:

49.

And lest the courser should become the prey
Of the first traveller, who passed the glen,
Him will not leave; but thence to bear away
Resolves, in trust to see his lord again.
The griffin soars, nor can Rogero stay
The flying courser; while, beneath his ken,
Each peak and promontory sinks in guise,
That he discerns not flat from mountain-rise.

50.

After the hippogryph has won such height,
That he is lessened to a point, he bends
His course for where the sun, with sinking light,
When he goes round the heavenly crab, descends;
And shoots through air, like well-greased bark and light,
Which through the sea a wind propitious sends.
Him leave we on his way, who well shall speed,
And turn we to Rinaldo in his need.

* * * * *

CANTO XIX

ARGUMENT

Medoro, by Angelica's quaint hand,
Is healed, and weds, and bears her to Catay.
At length Marphisa, with the chosen band,
After long suffering, makes Laiazzi's bay.
Guido the savage, bondsman in the land,
Which impious women rule with evil sway,
With bold Marphisa strives in single fight,
And lodges her and hers at fall of night.

[This selection is taken from the title theme. In the preceding cantos, Angelica has experienced several dramatic adventures. Orlando has travelled widely in quest of her. Meanwhile, in the war, Paris is besieged, and Charlemagne wins a great battle which leaves the fields outside strewn with the slaughtered pagans. On the night after, two obscure Moorish youths resolve to search among the dead for the body of their king, to give it burial. They are discovered by the Christians and supposedly killed. One of them, Medoro, however, is still alive when Angelica, in her wanderings chances upon him. She, for whom the world's great — Christians and pagans alike — had contended, now feels her heart touched for the first time by this unknown youth.]

18.

Angelica, when she had won again
The ring Brunello had from her conveyed,
So waxed in stubborn pride and haught disdain,
She seemed to scorn this ample world, and strayed
Alone, and held as cheap each living swain,
Although, amid the best, by Fame arrayed:
Nor brooked she to remember a galant
In Count Orlando or king Sacripant;

19.

And above every other deed repented,
That good Rinaldo she had loved of yore;
And that to look so low she had consented,
(As by such choice dishonoured) grieved her sore.
Love, hearing this, such arrogance resented,
And would the damsel's pride endure no more.
Where young Medoro lay he took his stand,
And waited her, with bow and shaft in hand.

20.

When fair Angelica the stripling spies,
Nigh hurt to death in that disastrous fray,
Who for his king, that there unsheltered lies,
More sad than for his own misfortune lay,
She feels new pity in her bosom rise,

Which makes its entry in unwonted way.
Touched was her haughty heart, once hard and curst,
And more when he his piteous tale rehearsed.

21.

And calling back to memory her art,
For she in Ind had learned chirurgery,
(Since it appears such studies in that part
Worthy of praise and fame are held to be,
And, as an heirloom, sires to sons impart,
With little aid of books, the mystery)
Disposed herself to work with simples' juice,
Till she in him should healthier life produce;

22.

And recollects a herb had caught her sight
In passing hither, on a pleasant plain.
What (whether dittany or pancy hight)
I know not; fraught with virtue to restrain
The crimson blood forth-welling, and of might
To sheathe each perilous and piercing pain,
She found it near, and having pulled the weed,
Returned to seek Medoro on the mead.

23.

Returning, she upon a swain did light,
Who was on horseback passing through the wood.
Strayed from the lowing herd, the rustic wight
A heifer, missing for two days, pursued.
Him she with her conducted, where the might
Of the faint youth was ebbing with his blood:
Which had the ground about so deeply dyed,
Life was nigh wasted with the gushing tide.

24.

Angelica alights upon the ground,
And he her rustic comrade, at her hest.
She hastened 'twixt two stones the herb to pound,
Then took it, and the healing juice exprest:
With this did she foment the stripling's wound,
And, even to the hips, his waist and breast;
And (with such virtue was the salve endued)
It stanched his life-blood, and his strength renewed;

25.

And into him infused such force again,
That he could mount the horse the swain conveyed:
But good Medoro would not leave the plain
Till he in earth had seen his master laid.

He, with the monarch, buried Cloridane,
And after followed whither pleased the maid,
Who was to stay with him, by pity led,
Beneath the courteous shepherd's humble shed.

26.

Nor would the damsel quit the lowly pile
(So she esteemed the youth) till he was sound;
Such pity first she felt, when him erewhile
She saw outstretched and bleeding on the ground.
Touched by his mien and manners next, a file
She felt corrode her heart with secret wound;
She felt corrode her heart, and with desire,
By little and by little warmed, took fire.

27.

The shepherd dwelt, between two mountains hoar,
In goodly cabin, in the greenwood-shade,
With wife and children; in short time before,
The brent-new shed had builded in the glade.
Here of his griesly wound the youthful Moor
Was briefly healed by the Catayan maid;
But who in briefer space, a sorer smart
Than young Medoro's, suffered at her heart.

28.

A wound far wider and which deeper lies,
Now in her heart she feels, from viewless bow;
Which from the boy's fair hair and beauteous eyes
Had the winged archer dealt: a sudden glow
She feels, and still the flames increasing rise;
Yet less she heeds her own than other's woe:
— Heeds not herself, and only to content
The author of her cruel ill is bent.

29.

Her ill but festered and increased the more
The stripling's wounds were seen to heal and close:
The youth grew lusty, while she suffered sore,
And, with new fever parched, now burnt, now froze:
From day to day in beauty waxed Medore:
She miserably wasted; like the snow's
Unseasonable flake, which melts away
Exposed, in sunny place, to scorching ray.

30.

She, if of vain desire she will not die,
Must help herself, nor yet delay the aid.
And she in truth, her will to satisfy,

Deemed 'twas no time to wait till she was prayed.
And next of shame renouncing every tie,
With tongue as bold as eyes, petition made,
And begged him, haply an unwitting foe,
To sheathe the suffering of that cruel blow.

31.

O Count Orlando, O king of Circassy,
Say what your valour has availed to you!
Say what your honour boots, what goodly fee
Remunerates ye both, for service true!
Sirs, show me but a single courtesy,
With which she ever graced ye,—old or new,—
As some poor recompense, desert, or guerdon,
For having born so long so sore a burden!

32.

Oh! couldst thou yet again to life return,
How hard would this appear, O Agricane! [1]
In that she whilom thee was wont to spurn,
With sharp repulse and insolent disdain.
O Ferrau, O ye thousand more, forlorn,
Unsung, who wrought a thousand feats in vain
For this ungrateful fair, what pain 'twould be
Could you within his arms the damsel see!

33.

To pluck, as yet untouched, the virgin rose,
Angelica permits the young Medore.
Was none so blest as in that garden's close
Yet to have set his venturous foot before.
They holy ceremonies interpose,
Somedeal to veil—to gild—the matter o'er.
Young Love was bridesman there the tie to bless,
And for brideswoman stood the shepherdess.

34.

In the low shed, with all solemnities,
The couple made their wedding as they might;
And there above a month, in tranquil guise,
The happy lovers rested in delight.
Save for the youth the lady has no eyes,
Nor with his looks can satisfy her sight.
Nor yet of hanging on his neck can tire,
Or feel she can content her fond desire.

1. Agrican, King of Tartary, had been promised the hand of Angelica by her father, King Galafron. When the promise was not fulfilled, he raised a mighty army and besieged Albracca, Galafron's capital city.

35.

The beauteous boy is with her, night and day
Does she untent herself, or keep the shed.
Morning or eve they to some meadow stray,
Now to this bank, and to that other led:
Haply, in cavern harboured, at mid-day,
Grateful as that to which Aeneas fled
With Dido, when the tempest raged above,
The faithful witness to their secret love.

36.

Amid such pleasures, where, with tree o'ergrown,
Ran stream, or bubbling fountain's wave did spin,
On bark or rock, if yielding were the stone,
The knife was straight at work or ready pin.
And there, without, in thousand places lone,
And in as many places graved, within,
MEDORO and ANGELICA were traced,
In divers cyphers quaintly interlaced.

37.

When she believed they had prolonged their stay
More than enow, the damsel made design
In India to revisit her Catày,
And with its crown Medoro's head entwine.
She had upon her wrist an armlet, gay
With costly gems, in witness and in sign
Of love to her by Count Orlando borne,
And which the damsel for long time had worn.

38.

On Ziliantes, hid beneath the wave,
This Morgue bestowed; and from captivity
The youth (restored to Monodante's grave,
His ancient sire, through Roland's chivalry)
To Roland in return the bracelet gave:
Roland, a lover, deigned the gorgeous fee
To wear, with the intention to convey
The present to his queen, of whom I say.

39.

No love which to the paladin she bears,
But that it costly is and wrought with care,
This to Angelica so much endears,
That never more esteemed was matter rare:
This she was suffered, in THE ISLE OF TEARS,
I know not by what privilege, to wear,
When, naked, to the whale exposed for food
By that inhospitable race and rude.[2]

40.

She, not possessing wherewithal to pay
The kindly couple's hospitality,
Served by them in their cabin, from the day
She there was lodged, with such fidelity,
Unfastened from her arm the bracelet gay,
And bade them keep it for her memory.
Departing hence the lovers climb the side
Of hills, which fertile France from Spain divide.

41.

Within Valencia or Barcelona's town
The couple thought a little to remain,
Until some goodly ship should make her boun
To loose for the Levant: as so the twain
Journey, beneath Gerona, — coming down
Those mountains — they behold the subject main;
And keeping on their left the beach below,
By beaten track to Barcelona go.

42.

But, ere they there arrive, a crazed wight
They find, extended on the outer shore;
Who is bedaubed like swine, in filthy plight,
And smeared with mud, face, reins, and bosom o'er;
He comes upon them, as a dog in spite
Swiftly assails the stranger at the door;
And is about to do the lovers scorn.
But to the bold Marphisa I return —

CANTO XXIII

ARGUMENT

Astolpho soars in air. Upon account
Of Pinnabel is prisoned Scotland's heir:
By Roland freed. Frontino Rodomont
Takes from Hippalca, trusted to her care.
With Mandricardo strives Aglantes' count:
Who, next, offended by his lady fair,
Into the fury falls, so strange and fell,
Which in the world has not a parallel.

[Meanwhile, Orlando comes by chance into the place of sojourn from which Angelica and Medoro have recently departed, and where they have left behind so many reminders of their happy experience.]

2. Angelica had been exposed on the island of Ebuda as a human sacrifice to the hideous sea monster called the "orc," from which she was rescued by Rogero. See Cantos VIII, X, not given in these selections.

100.

The course in pathless woods, which, without rein,
The Tartar's charger had pursued astray,
Made Roland for two days, with fruitless pain,
Follow him, without tidings of his way.
Orlando reached a rill of crystal vein,
On either bank of which a meadow lay;
Which, stained with native hues and rich, he sees,
And dotted o'er with fair and many trees.

101.

The mid-day fervour made the shelter sweet
To hardy herd as well as naked swain;
So that Orlando, well beneath the heat
Some deal might wince, opprest with plate and chain.
He entered, for repose, the cool retreat,
And found it the abode of grief and pain;
And place of sojourn more accursed and fell,
On that unhappy day, than tongue can tell.

102.

Turning him round, he there, on many a tree,
Beheld engraved, upon the woody shore,
What as the writing of his deity
He knew, as soon as he had marked the lore.
This was a place of those described by me,
Whither ofttimes, attended by Medore,
From the near shepherd's cot had wont to stray
The beauteous lady, sovereign of Catày.

103.

In a hundred knots, amid those green abodes,
In a hundred parts, their cyphered names are dight;
Whose many letters are so many goads,
Which Love has in his bleeding heart-core pight.
He would discredit in a thousand modes,
That which he credits in his own despite;
And would parforce persuade himself, *that* rhind
Other Angelica than his had signed.

104.

"And yet I know these characters," he cried,
"Of which I have so many read and seen;
"By her may this Medoro be belied,
"And me, she, figured in the name, may mean."
Feeding on such like phantasies, beside
The real truth, did sad Orlando lean
Upon the empty hope, though ill contented,
Which he by self-illusions had fomented.

105.

But stirred and aye rekindled it, the more
That he to quench the ill suspicion wrought,
Like the incautious bird, by fowler's lore,
Hampered in net or lime; which, in the thought
To free its tangled pinions and to soar,
By struggling, is but more securely caught.
Orlando passes thither, where a mountain
O'erhangs in guise of arch the crystal fountain.

106.

Splay-footed ivy, with its mantling spray,
And gadding vine, the cavern's entry case:
Where often in the hottest noon of day
The pair had rested, locked in fond embrace.
Within the grotto, and without it, they
Had oftener than in any other place
With charcoal or with chalk their names pourtrayed,
Or flourished with the knife's indenting blade.

107.

Here from his horse the sorrowing County lit,
And at the entrance of the grot surveyed
A cloud of words, which seemed but newly writ,
And which the young Medoro's hand had made.
On the great pleasure he had known in it,
This sentence he in verses had arrayed;
Which in his tongue, I deem, might make pretence
To polished phrase; and such in ours the sense.

108.

"Gay plants, green herbage, rill of limpid vein,
"And, grateful with cool shade, thou gloomy cave,
"Where oft, by many wooed with fruitless pain,
"Beauteous Angelica, the child of grave
"King Galaphron, within my arms has lain;
"For the convenient harbourage you gave,
"I, poor Medoro, can but in my lays,
"As recompence, for ever sing your praise.

109.

"And any loving lord devoutly pray,
"Damsel and cavalier, and every one,
"Whom choice or fortune hither shall convey,
"Stranger or native,—to this crystal run,
"Shade, caverned rock, and grass, and plants, to say,
"Benignant be to you the fostering sun
"And moon, and may the choir of nymphs provide,
"That never swain his flock may hither guide!"

110.

In Arabic was writ the blessing said,
Known to Orlando like the Latin tongue,
Who, versed in many languages, best read
Was in this speech; which oftentimes from wrong,
And injury, and shame, had saved his head,
What time he roved the Saracens among.
But let him boast not of its former boot,
O'erbalanced by the present bitter fruit.

111.

Three times, and four, and six, the lines imprest
Upon the stone that wretch perused, in vain
Seeking another sense than was exprest,
And ever saw the thing more clear and plain;
And all the while, within his troubled breast,
He felt an icy hand his heart-core strain.
With mind and eyes close fastened on the block,
At length he stood, not differing from the rock.

112.

Then well-nigh lost all feeling; so a prey
Wholly was he to that o'ermastering woe.
This is a pang, believe the experienced say
Of him who speaks, which does all griefs outgo.
His pride had from his forehead passed away,
His chin had fallen upon his breast below;
Nor found he, so grief barred each natural vent,
Moisture for tears, or utterance for lament.

113.

Stifled within, the impetuous sorrow stays,
Which would too quickly issue; so to abide
Water is seen, imprisoned in the vase,
Whose neck is narrow and whose swell is wide;
What time, when one turns up the inverted base,
Towards the mouth, so hastes the hurrying tide,
And in the streight encounters such a stop,
It scarcely works a passage, drop by drop.

114.

He somewhat to himself returned, and thought
How possibly the thing might be untrue:
That some one (so he hoped, desired, and sought
To think) his lady would with shame pursue;
Or with such weight of jealousy had wrought
To whelm *his* reason, as should him undo;
And that he, whosoe'er the thing had planned,
Had counterfeited passing well her hand.

115.

With such vain hope he sought himself to cheat,
And manned some deal his spirits and awoke;
Then prest the faithful Brigliadoro's seat,
As on the sun's retreat his sister broke.
Nor far the warrior had pursued his beat,
Ere eddying from a roof he saw the smoke;
Heard noise of dog and kine, a farm espied,
And thitherward in quest of lodging hied.

116.

Languid, he lit, and left his Brigliador
To a discreet attendant: one undrest
His limbs, one doffed the golden spurs he wore,
And one bore off, to clean, his iron vest.
This was the homestead where the young Medore
Lay wounded, and was here supremely blest.
Orlando here, with other food unfed,
Having supt full of sorrow, sought his bed.

117.

The more the wretched sufferer seeks for ease,
He finds but so much more distress and pain;
Who every where the loathed hand-writing sees,
On wall, and door, and window: he would fain
Question his host of this, but holds his peace,
Because, in sooth, he dreads too clear, too plain
To make the thing, and this would rather shroud,
That it may less offend him, with a cloud.

118.

Little availed the count his self-deceit;
For there was one who spake of it unsought;
The shepherd-swain, who to allay the heat,
With which he saw his guest so troubled, thought:
The tale which he was wonted to repeat
— Of the two lovers — to each listener taught,
A history which many loved to hear,
He now, without reserve, 'gan tell the peer.

119.

'How at Angelica's persuasive prayer,
'He to his farm had carried young Medore,
'Grievously wounded with an arrow; where,
'In little space she healed the angry sore.
'But while she exercised this pious care,
'Love in her heart the lady wounded more,
'And kindled from small spark so fierce a fire,
'She burnt all over, restless with desire:

120.

"Nor thinking she of mightiest king was born,
'Who ruled in the east, nor of her heritage,
'Forced by too puissant love, had thought no scorn
'To be the consort of a poor foot-page.'
— His story done, to them in proof was borne
The gem, which, in reward for harbourage,
To her extended in that kind abode,
Angelica, at parting, had bestowed.

121.

A deadly axe was this unhappy close,
Which, at a single stroke, lopt off the head;
When, satiate with innumerable blows,
That cruel hangman Love his hate had fed.
Orlando studied to conceal his woes;
And yet the mischief gathered force and spread,
And would break out parforce in tears and sighs,
Would he, or would he not, from mouth and eyes.

122.

When he can give the rein to raging woe,
Alone, by other's presence unreprest,
From his full eyes the tears descending flow,
In a wide stream, and flood his troubled breast.
'Mid sob and groan, he tosses to and fro
About his weary bed, in search of rest;
And vainly shifting, harder than a rock
And sharper than a nettle found its flock.

123.

Amid the pressure of such cruel pain,
It past into the wretched sufferer's head,
That oft the ungrateful lady must have lain,
Together with her leman, on that bed:
Nor less he loathed the couch in his disdain,
Nor from the down upstarted with less dread,
Than churl, who, when about to close his eyes,
Springs from the turf, if he a serpent spies.

124.

In him, forthwith, such deadly hatred breed
That bed, that house, that swain, he will not stay
Till the morn break, or till the dawn succeed,
Whose twilight goes before approaching day.
In haste, Orlando takes his arms and steed,
And to the deepest greenwood wends his way.
And, when assured that he is there alone,
Gives utterance to his grief in shriek and groan.

125.

Never from tears, never from sorrowing,
He paused; nor found he peace by night or day:
He fled from town, in forest harbouring,
And in the open air on hard earth lay.
He marvelled at himself, how such a spring
Of water from his eyes could stream away,
And breath was for so many sobs supplied;
And thus ofttimes, amid his mourning, cried:

126.

"These are no longer real tears which rise,
"And which I scatter from so full a vein.
"Of tears my ceaseless sorrow lacked supplies;
"They stopt when to mid-height scarce rose my pain.
"The vital moisture rushing to my eyes,
"Driven by the fire within me, now would gain
"A vent; and it is this which I expend,
"And which my sorrows and my life will end.

127.

"No; these, which are the index of my woes,
"These are not sighs, nor sighs are such; they fail
"At times, and have their season of repose:
"I feel, my breast can never less exhale
"Its sorrow: Love, who with his pinions blows
"The fire about my heart, creates this gale.
"Love, by what miracle dost thou contrive,
"It wastes not in the fire thou keep'st alive?

128.

"I am not — am not what I seem to sight:
"What Roland was is dead and under ground,
"Slain by that most ungrateful lady's spite,
"Whose faithlessness inflicted such a wound.
"Divided from the flesh, I am his sprite,
"Which in this hell, tormented, walks its round,
"To be, but in its shadow left above,
"A warning to all such as trust in love."

129.

All night about the forest roved the count,
And, at the break of daily light, was brought
By his unhappy fortune to the fount,
Where his inscription young Medoro wrought.
To see his wrongs inscribed upon that mount,
Inflamed his fury so, in him was nought
But turned to hatred, frenzy, rage, and spite;
Nor paused he more, but bared his faulchion bright;

130.

Cleft through the writing; and the solid block,
Into the sky, in tiny fragments sped.
Wo worth each sapling and that caverned rock,
Where Medore and Angelica were read!
So scathed, that they to shepherd or to flock
Thenceforth shall never furnish shade or bed.
And that sweet fountain, late so clear and pure,
From such tempestuous wrath was ill secure.

131.

For he turf, stone, and trunk, and shoot, and lop
Cast without cease into the beauteous source;
Till, turbid from the bottom to the top,
Never again was clear the troubled course.
At length, for lack of breath, compelled to stop,
(When he is bathed in sweat, and wasted force,
Serves not his fury more) he falls, and lies
Upon the mead, and, gazing upward, sighs.

132.

Wearied and woe-begone, he fell to ground,
And turned his eyes toward heaven; nor spake he aught,
Nor ate, nor slept, till in his daily round
The golden sun had broken thrice, and sought
His rest anew; nor ever ceased his wound
To rankle, till it marred his sober thought.
At length, impelled by frenzy, the fourth day,
He from his limbs tore plate and mail away.

133.

Here was his helmet, there his shield bestowed;
His arms far off, and, farther than the rest,
His cuirass; through the greenwood wide was strowed
All his good gear, in fine; and next his vest
He rent; and, in his fury, naked showed
His shaggy paunch, and all his back and breast.
And 'gan that frenzy act, so passing dread,
Of stranger folly never shall be said.

134.

So fierce his rage, so fierce his fury grew,
That all obscured remained the warrior's sprite;
Nor, for forgetfulness, his sword he drew,
Or wonderous deeds, I trow, had wrought the knight:
But neither this, nor bill, nor axe to hew,
Was needed by Orlando's peerless might.
He of his prowess gave high proofs and full,
Who a tall pine uprooted at a pull.

135.

He many others, with as little let
As fennel, wall-wort-stem, or dill, up-tore;
And ilex, knotted oak, and fir upset,
And beech, and mountain ash, and elm-tree hoar.
He did what fowler, ere he spreads his net,
Does, to prepare the champaigne for his lore,
By stubble, rush, and nettle-stalk; and broke,
Like these, old sturdy trees and stems of oak.

136.

The shepherd swains, who hear the tumult nigh,
Leaving their flocks beneath the greenwood tree,
Some here, some there, across the forest hie,
And hurry thither, all, the cause to see.
— But I have reached such point, my history,
If I o'erpass this bound, may irksome be;
And I my story will delay to end,
Rather than by my tediousness offend.

CANTO XXIX

ARGUMENT

Isabel makes the paynim take her head,
Rather than he his wicked will should gain;
Who, having his unhappy error read,
Seeks to appease his wounded spirit in vain.
He builds a bridge, and strips those thither led;
But falls from it with Roland the insane;
Who thence, of him regardless, endlong speeds,
And by the road achieves prodigious deeds.

[Orlando enters upon his mad career. He puts a band of shepherds to flight, plucks off the head of one as easily as one might pick an apple from a tree, and swinging the body by one leg wields it as a mace upon the others. All take refuge on the house tops, since trees are useless for refuge before his strength, as he proceeds to slay horses and oxen. The alarm spreads throughout the villages, and armies gather from the mountains and valleys to war against him. After he has slaughtered twice ten peasants, the rest learn to stand aloof and the army retreats, for no one can wound him since God has made him invulnerable to protect His Holy Faith. He overthrows bear and boar with naked hand, and swallows them, hide and hair and all.]

50.

'Twere frenzy of his every frantic feat
To promise the relation, one by one!
So many and many, — should I these repeat,
I know not when my story would be done.

Yet some of his notorious deeds, and meet
For mention in my song, will I make known:
Nor will I not that wondrous one recount,
Near Thoulouse, on the Pyrenaean Mount.

51.

Much country had been traversed by the knight,
Urged by the furious rage which him misguides:
At last he reached the hill whose boundary height
Arragonese and neighbouring Frank divides.
Thither directing aye his course outright,
Where the descending sun his visage hides,
He reached a path upon the rugged steep,
Which overhung a valley dark and deep.

52.

Here he by chance encountered in mid road
Two youths, that woodmen were, and drove before
An ass along that pathway, with a load
Of logs; they, marking well what scanty store
Of brain in poor Orlando's head was stowed,
Called to the approaching knight, and threatened sore
Bidding him stand aside, or else go back,
Nor to their hindrance block the common track.

53.

To this address Orlando answered nought,
Save that his foot he to their beast applied,
Smote in mid-breast, which, with that vigour fraught,
— That force exceeding every force beside —
Tost him so high, that the beholders thought
It was a bird in air which they descried.
The ass upon a mountain-summit fell,
Which rose above a mile beyond that dell.

54.

Upon those youths next sprang the furious knight.
With better luck than wit, one woodman shear
From that tall cliff, twice thirty yards in height,
Cast himself headlong downward in his fear:
Him a moist patch of brambles, in his flight,
Received; and, amid grass and bushes, here,
From other mischief safe, the stripling lit,
And for some scratches in his face was quit.

55.

That other to a jutting fragment clung
Who so to gain the higher steep would strive;
Because he hopes, if once those crags among,

To keep him from that fool he may contrive;
But by the feet Orlando, ere he sprung,
Seized him, who will not leave the wretch alive;
And stretching them as wide as he could strain,
So stretched his arms, he rent his prey in twain.

56.

Even in such mode as often we descry
Falconer by heron or by pullet do;
Whose entrails he plucks out, to satisfy
Merlin or falcon that the game pursue.
How happy was that other not to die!
Who risked his neck in that deep bottom, who
Rehearsed the tale so often, Turpin heard,
And handed down to us the wondrous word.

57.

These and more marvels does the count, who bends
His steps across that mountain to the plain;
And, seeking long a path, at length descends
Towards the south, upon the land of Spain.
His way along the beach he after wends,
Near Arragon, beside the tumbling main,
And, ever prompted by his frenzy rank,
Will make himself a dwelling on the bank,

58.

Where he somedeal may shun the noontide ray,
With dry and powdery sea-sand covered o'er;
And here, while so employed, upon their way
Arrives Angelica with her Medore,
Who, as you have been told in former lay,
Had from the hills descended on that shore.
Within a yard or less approached the fair,
Ere yet she of his presence was aware.

59.

So different from himself was he to sight,
Nought of Orlando she in him surveyed:
For, from the time that rage possest his sprite,
He had gone naked forth in sun and shade.
Had he been born on hot Syene's site,
Or sands where worship is to Ammon paid,
Or nigh those hills, whence Nile's full waters spin,
Orlando had not borne a dingier skin.

60.

Nigh buried in their sockets are his eyes,
Spare in his visage, and as dry as bone:

70.

Next, for he felt that weight too irksome grow,
He put her down, to lead her by the rein:
Who followed him with limping gait and slow.
"Come on," Orlando cried, and cried in vain;
And, could the palfrey at a gallop go,
This ill would satisfy his mood insane.
The halter from her head he last unloosed,
Wherewith her hind off-foot the madman noosed.

71.

'Tis thus he comforts and drags on that mare,
That she may follow with more ease, so led;
Who whiles despoiled of flesh, and whiles of hair,
Is scathed by stones which that ill road o'erspread.
At length the misused beast, with wear and tear
Of the rude rocks, and suffering sore, lies dead.
Orlando nought the slaughtered mare regards,
Nor anywise his headlong course retards.

72.

To drag that palfrey ceased he not, though dead,
Continuing still his course towards the west,
And all this while sacked hamlet, farm, and stead,
Whenever he by hunger was distrest;
And aye to glut himself with meat, and bread,
And fruit, he every one by force opprest.
One by his hand was slain, one foully shent;
Seldom he stopt, and ever onward went.

73.

As much, or little less, would do the knight
By his own love, did not that damsel hide;
Because the wretch discerns not black from white,
And harms where he would help. A curse betide
The wonder-working ring, and eke the wight
Who gave it to that lady, full of pride!
Since Roland, but for this, would venge the scorn
He and a thousand more from her had borne.

74.

Would that of her Orlando were possest,
And of all women that are above ground!
For one and all are ingrates at the best,
Nor is in all an ounce of goodness found.
But it is meet I let my hearer rest
Ere my strained chords return a faltering sound,
And that he may less tedious deem the rhyme,
Defer my story till another time.

CANTO XXX

ARGUMENT

Great feats achieves Orlando by the way.
The Tartar king is by Rogero slain;
For whom fair Bradamant, his spouse, does stay,
And, him expecting, suffers cruel pain.
But Fate forbade, that he who wounded lay
To her his plighted promise should maintain.
He after boldly with the brethren made,
Their lord Rinaldo in his need to aid.

1.

When Reason, giving way to heat of blood,
Herself from hasty choler ill defends,
And, hurried on by blind and furious mood,
We with the tongue or hand molest our friends,
Though the offence is, after, wept and rued,
The penance which we pay is poor amends.
Alas! I sorrow and lament in vain
For what I said in other angry strain.

2.

But like sick man am I, who, sore bested,
Suffering with patience many and many a day,
When against pain he can no more make head,
Yields to his rage, and curses; pain gives way,
And with it the impetuous wrath is fled,
Which moved his ready tongue such ill to say;
And he is left his wilful rage to rue,
But cannot that which he has done undo.

3.

Well hope I, from your sovereign courtesy,
Your pardon, since I crave it, ladies bright;
You will excuse, if moved by madness, I
Rave in my passion; let your censure light
On foe, who treats me so despiteously,
I could not be reduced to worser plight;
Who prompts what sore repents me: Heaven above
Knows how she wrongs me, knows how well I love.

4.

No less beside myself than Brava's peer
Am I, nor less my pardon should obtain,
He, who by mead or mountain, far or near,
Had scowered large portion of the land of Spain,
Dragging that jennet in his wild career,

Dead as she was, behind him by the rein;
But, where a river joined the sea, parforce
Abandoned on the bank her mangled corse.

5.

And he, who could like any otter swim,
Leapt in, and rose upon the further side.
Behold! a mounted shepherd at the brim
Arrived, his horse to water in the tide:
Now when he saw Orlando coming, him
Eschewed, whom naked and alone he spied.
— "My jennet for thy hackney were I fain
"To barter," cried the madman to the swain:

6.

"Her will I show thee, if thou wilt; who dead
"Upon the river's other margin fell;
"At leisure may'st thou have her cured," (he said)
"And of no other fault have I to tell.
"Give me thy hackney, with some boot instead:
"Prythee, dismount thee, for he likes me well."
The peasant, laughing, answered not a word,
But left the fool and pricked towards the ford.

7.

"Hearest thou not? hola! I want thy steed,"
(Cried Roland) and advanced with wrathful cheer.
A solid staff and knotted, for his need,
That shepherd had, wherewith he smote the peer;
Whose violence and ire all bounds exceed,
Who seems withal to wax more fierce than e'er:
A cuff he levels at that rustic's head,
And splits the solid bone, and lays him dead.

8.

Then leaping on his horse, by different way
The country scowers, to make more spoil and wrack:
That palfrey never more tastes corn or hay;
So that few days exhaust the famished hack.
But not afoot does fierce Orlando stray,
Who will not, while he lives, conveyance lack.
As many as he finds, so many steeds
— Their masters slain — he presses for his needs.

9.

He came at last to Malaga, and here
Did mightier scathe than he had done elsewhere;
For now — besides that the infuriate peer
Of all its people left the country bare,

Nor (such the ravage) could another year
The desperate havoc of the fool repair—
So many houses burnt he, or cast down,
Sacked was a third of that unhappy town.

10.

Departing thence, insane Orlando flees
To Zizera, a seaward town, whose site
Is in Gibraltar's bay, or (if you please)
Say Gibletàr's; for either way 'tis hight;
Here, loosening from the land, a boat he sees
Filled with a party: and for pleasure dight:
Which, for their solace, to the morning gale,
Upon that summer sea, had spread their sail.

11.

"Hoah! the boat! put back!" the count 'gan cry,
Who was in mind to go aboard their barge:
But vainly on their ears his clamours die:
For of such freight none willingly take charge.
As swiftly as a swallow cleaves the sky,
Furrowing the foamy wave the boat goes large.
Orlando urges on, with straightening knee,
And whip and spur, his horse towards the sea.

12.

He plunged into the waves, at last, parforce;
For vainly would he shun the waters green.
Bathed are knees, paunch, and croup, till of that horse
Scarcely the head above the wave is seen:
Let him not hope to measure back his course,
While smitten with the whip his ears between.
Woe worth him! he must founder by the way
Or into Africa his load convey.

13.

Nor poops nor prows does Roland more descry,
For all have launched their shallops, which are wide
Of that dry shore; while from his level eye
Their hulls the tall and shifting surges hide.
He spurs his horse amid the billows high,
Wholly resolved to reach the farther side.
The courser ends his swim and life in fine,
Drained of his strength, and drenched brimfull of brine.

14.

He sinks, and would with him draw down his load
But that himself the madman's arms upbear:
With sinewy arms and either palm he rowed,

And puffed and blew the brine before; the air
Breathed softly, and the water gently flowed;
And well was needed weather more than fair:
For if the waters yet a little rise,
Whelmed by the waxing tide Orlando dies.

15.

But Fortune, that of madmen is the guide,
Him from the water drew near Ceuta's shore,
Upon that beach, and of those walls as wide
As twice an archer's hand could shoot at score.
For many days along the bank he hied,
At hazard, ever westward hurrying sore,
Until he came where on the sea-beat strand
Encamped a host of blacks, a countless band.

16.

Leave we the paladin at will to stray!
To speak of him occasion will come round.
—Sir, what befel the lady of Catày,
Who scaped, in time, from him of wit unsound,
And afterwards, upon her homeward way,
Was with good bark and better weather bound;
And how she made Medoro, India's king; [1]
Perchance some voice in happier verse may sing.

[The selections are here taken again from the main narrative of Rogero and Bradamant. Since Canto IV, the lovers have been united a third time, and again separated. Bradamant finally returns to her home at Mount Albano, and sends her damsel Hippalca as messenger to Rogero.]

76.

Bradamant's torment have I to recount,
While for the courier damsel she did stay:
With tidings of her love to Alban's Mount,
To her Hippalca measured back her way:
She of Frontino first and Rodomont,[2]
And next of good Rogero had to say;
'How to the fount anew he had addrest
'His way, with Richardetto and the rest;

77.

'And how the Child, in rescue of the steed,
'Had gone with her to find the paynim rude;
'And weened to have chastised his foul misdeed,
'That from a woman took Frontino good.
'And how the youth's design did ill succeed,

1. This is the last we hear of Angelica.
2. Bradamant had sent with Hippalca to Rogero his horse, Frontino, but Rodomont had taken it from her on the way.

'Because the king had other way pursued.
'The reason too why to Mount Alban's hold
'Rogero had not come,[3] at full she told;

78.

'And fully she to Bradamant exprest
'What to excuse himself Rogero said:'
She after drew the letter from her breast,
Wherewith entrusted she had thither sped:
With visage which more care than hope confest,
The paper Bradamant received and read;
Which, but that she expected to have seen
Rogero's self, more welcome would have been.

79.

To find herself with written scroll appaid
In good Rogero's place, whom she attends,
Marred her fair visage; which such fear pourtrayed,
Despite and sorrow at her bosom rends.
Ten times the page she kisses, while the maid
As oft to him who writes her heart commends:
The tears alone which trickle from her eyes
Keep it from kindling at her burning sighs.

80.

Four times, nay six, she that epistle read,
And willed moreover that as many more
The message by that damsel should be said,
Who word and letter to Mount Alban bore.
This while unceasing tears the lady shed,
Nor, I believe, would ever have given o'er,
Save by the hope consoled, that she anew
Should briefly her beloved Rogero view.

81.

Rogero's word was pledged for his return
When fifteen days or twenty were gone by
So had he after to Hippalca sworn,
Bidding her boldly on his faith rely.
"From accidents that chance at every turn"
(Cried Bradamant) "what warranty have I,
"Alas! — and such are commonest in war —
"That none the knight's return for ever bar?

82.

"Alas! alas! Rogero, that above
"Myself hast evermore been prized by me,

3. While Rogero was occupied in numerous adventures, Agramant had sent to request his immediate presence in the army.

"Who would have thought thou more than me could'st love
"Any, and most thy mortal enemy?
"Thou helpest where to punish would behove,
"And harm'st where thou should'st help; nor do I see
"If thou as worthy praise or blame regard
"Such tardiness to punish and reward.

83.

"I know not if thou knowest — the stones know —
"How by Troyano was thy father slain;
"And yet Troyano's son, against his foe,
"Thou would'st defend,[4] and keep from harm or stain.
"Such vengeance upon him do'st thou bestow?
"And do his vengers, as their meed obtain,
"That I, descended of this stock, should be
"The martyr of thy mortal cruelty?"

84.

To her Rogero, in his absence, said
The lady these sad words, and more beside,
Lamenting aye; while her attendant maid
Not once alone, but often, certified
'The stripling would observe his faith, and prayed
'Her — who could do no better — to abide
'The Child's arrival till the time came round
'When he by promise to return was bound.'

85.

The comfort that Hippalca's words convey,
And Hope, companion of the loving train,
Bradamant's fear and sorrow so allay,
That she enjoys some respite from her pain:
This moves her in Mount Alban's keep to stay;
Nor ever thence that lady stirred again
Until the day, that day the youthful knight
Had fixt, who ill observed his promise plight.

86.

But in that he his promise ill-maintained,
No blame upon Rogero should be cast;
Him one or other cause so long detained,
The appointed time parforce he overpast:
On a sick bed, long time, he, sorely pained,
Was laid, wherein a month or more he past
In doubt of death; so deeply him had gored
Erewhile in fight the Tartar monarch's sword.

4. The history of Rogero's parents will be disclosed later. His father had been killed by Troyano, the father of Agramant, and yet he is now fighting in Agramant's war.

87.

Him on the day prefixed the maid attended,
Nor other tidings of the youth had read,
But those he through Hippalca had commended,
And that which after Richardetto said:
Who told, 'how him Rogero had defended,
'And freed the captive pair to prison led.'
The tidings, overjoyed, she hears repeat;
Yet blended with some bitter is the sweet.

88.

For she had heard as well in that discourse,
For might and beauty voiced, Marphisa's praise;
Heard, how Rogero thither bends his course,
Together with that lady, as he says,
Where in weak post and with unequal force
King Agramant the Christian army stays.
Such fair companionship the lady lauds,
But neither likes that union, nor applauds.

89.

Nor light suspicion has she of that queen;
For, were Marphisa beauteous, as was said,
And they together till that time had been,
'T were marvel but Rogero loved the maid:
Yet would she not believe; but hung between
Her hopes and fears, and in Mount Alban stayed;
And close and anxious there, until the day
Which was to bring her joy or sorrow, lay.

90.

This while Mount Alban's prince and castellain,
Rinaldo, first of that fair brotherhood,
— I say in honour, not in age, for twain
In right of birth before the warrior stood,
Who — as the sun illumes the starry train
Had by his deeds ennobled Aymon's blood,
One day at noon, with none beside a page
To serve him, reached that famous fortilage.

91.

Hither had good Rinaldo now repaired;
Because returning Paris-ward again,
From Brava, (whither had he often fared,
As said, to seek Angelica in vain)
He of that pair those evil news had heard,
His Malagigi and his Viviane,
How they were to Maganza to be sent;
And hence to Agrismont his way had bent.

92.

There, hearing of the safety of that pair,
And of their enemies' defeat and fall:
And how Rogero and Marphisa were
The authors of their ruin: and how all
His valiant brethren and his cousins are
Returned, and harboured in Mount Alban's hall,
Until he there embrace the friendly throng
Each hour appears to him a twelvemonth long.

93.

His course to Mont Albano has he ta'en;
And, there embracing wife and children dear,
Mother and brethren and the cousins twain,
(They who were captives to their foe whilere)
A parent swallow seems, amid that train,
Which, with full beak, its fasting young doth cheer.
With them a day or more the warrior stayed,
Then issued forth and others thence conveyed.

94.

Guichard, Duke Aymon's eldest born, and they,
Richard, Alardo, and Richardet' combined,
Vivian and Malagigi, wend their way
In arms, the martial paladin behind.
Bradamant, waiting the appointed day,
Which she, in her desire, too slow opined,
Feigned herself ailing to the brethren true,
Nor would she join in arms the banded crew;

95.

And, saying that she ailed, most truly said;
Yet 'twas not corporal pain or fever sore,
It was Desire that on her spirit preyed,
Diseased with Love's disastrous fit; [5] no more
Rinaldo in Mount Alban's castle stayed:
With him his kinsman's flower the warrior bore.
How he for Paris journeyed, and how well
He succoured Charles, shall other canto tell.

CANTO XXXII

ARGUMENT

To her that does for her Rogero stay,
Tidings are brought which irk the damsel sore,
That fair Marphisa caused the youth's delay.
She bent to slay her, grieving evermore,

5. Rogero was with the Moorish army which, defeated at Paris, had turned southward and halted at Arles. When she learned this, Bradamant turned south and went to the pagan encampment.

Departs, and overtakes, upon the way,
Ullania with the three kings who rode before.
These she o'ercomes, and had o'ercome that maid,
But that an evil law she disobeyed.

* * * * *

10.

This while does good duke Aymon's daughter mourn,
Because those twenty days so slowly trail:
— Which term elapsed — Rogero should return,
And be received into her church's pale.
Time halts not more with him to foreign bourne
Exiled, with prisoner pent in noisome jail;
Pines the poor wretch for liberty and light,
Or his loved land, desired and gladsome sight!

11.

Aye sick with hope deferred, the expecting maid,
That Phoebus' steed were foundered onewhile deemed;
Then that his wheels were out of frame, so stayed,
Beyond the wonted term, his chariot seemed.
Yet longer than *that* day when Faith delayed
The sun, which on the righteous Hebrew beamed,
Or than *that* night Alcides was conceived,
She every day and every night believed.

12.

How oft of dormouse, badger, or of bear,
The heavy slumber would she fain partake!
For she that time in sleep would waste and wear;
Nor such prolonged repose desired to break;
Nor wished the damsel any sound to hear,
Until Rogero's voice should her awake:
But not alone is this beyond her power;
She cannot close her eyes one single hour.

13.

She here and there, throughout the livelong night,
Tosses and turns, nor ever finds repose;
And still, impatient for the dawn of light,
From time to time she to her window goes,
To see if Tithon's spouse the lily white
Yet scatters mingled with the crimson rose.
Nor less desires the damsel, when 'tis morn,
To see the golden stars the heavens adorn.

14.

When, saving some four days, the term was ended,
Appointed for the youthful warrior's stay,

She, full of hope, the messenger attended
From hour to hour, that should arrive, and say,
"Behold Rogero comes;" and oft ascended
A turret, from whose top she might survey
Gay champaign, wood, and, mid the wide expanse,
A portion of the road, that led to France.

15.

When shining arms at distance she perceives,
Or any thing that speaks a cavalier,
'Tis her desired Rogero, she believes;
And her fair eyes and brows are seen to clear.
If footman, or unarmed, the maid conceives,
It is a courier from the youthful peer;
And, though fallacious every hope she feeds,
Another and another aye succeeds.

16.

And then she arms, and will the warrior meet;
And from the hill descends into the plain:
She finds him not, and to Montalban's seat
Hopes he by other road his way has ta'en.
In the design, wherewith she moved her feet
From thence, she to her fort returns in vain;
Nor finds him here nor there; meanwhile expired
The period whose approach she so desired.

17.

— The period so prefixt o'erpast by one,
By two, three, six, by eight, by twenty days —
She seeing not her spouse, and tidings none
Receiving of the youth, laments 'gan raise,
Which had from snake-haired Furies pity won,
In those dark realms that Rhadamanthus sways.
She smote her eyes divine, and bosom fair;
She rent the tresses of her golden hair.

18.

"Can it be true?" — (she cried) — "Shall I be fain
"To follow one, that strives to hide and fly?
"Esteem a man that has me in disdain?
"Pray him that never hears my suppliant cry?
"Suffer who hates me o'er my heart to reign?
"One that his lofty virtues holds so high,
" 'Twere need some heaven-born goddess should descend
"From realms above, his stubborn heart to bend?

19.

"Proud youth! he knows my worship and my love,
"Nor me will have for lover or for slave.
"The cruel stripling knows what pangs I prove,
"Yet will not aid me till I am in my grave.
"Nor let me tell my sorrows, lest they move
"Him his perverse and evil will to wave;
"Shunning me like malignant asp, that fears
"To change his mood, if he the charmer hears.

20.

"Ah! Love, arrest this wight who runs so free,
"Outstripping my slow feet, or me instal
"In the condition whence thou tookest me,
"Such as I was, ere thine or other's thrall.
"—Alas! how vain the hope! that thou shouldst be
"Ever to pity moved by suppliant call,
"Who sport, yea feed and live, in streams that rise
"From the distracted lover's brimming eyes.

21.

"But, woe is me, alas! and, what can I
"Save my irrational desire lament?
"Which makes me soar a pitch so passing high,
"I reach a region, where my plumes are brent;
"Then, unsustained, fall headlong from the sky;
"Nor ends my woe; on other flight intent,
"Again I imp my wings, again I soar;
"To flame and fall, tormented evermore.

22.

"Yea; rather of myself should I complain,
"Than the desire, to which I bared my breast
"Whereby was Reason hunted from her reign,
"And all my powers by stronger force opprest.
"Thus borne from bad to worse, without a rein,
"I cannot the unbridled beast arrest;
"Who makes me see I to destruction haste,
"That I more bitterness in death may taste.

23.

"Yet, ah! why blame myself? Wherein have I
"Ever offended, save in loving thee?
"What wonder was it then that suddenly
"A woman's feeble sense opprest should be?
"Why fence and guard myself, lest bearing high,
"Wise words, and beauty rare should pleasure me?
"Most wretched is the mortal that would shun
"To look upon the visage of the sun.

24.

"Besides that me my destiny entrained,
"Words, worthy credence, moved me much, that drew
"A picture of rare happiness, ordained
"As meed of this fair union to ensue.
"If these persuasive words were false and feigned,
"If famous Merlin's counsel was untrue,
"Wrath at the wizard may I well profess;
"But cannot therefore love Rogero less.

25.

"Both Merlin and Melissa have I need
"To blame, and shall for ever blame the twain,
"That, to exhibit suckers of my seed,
"Conjured up spirits from infernal reign,
"Who with this empty hope my fancy feed,
"Me in perpetual bondage to detain.
"Nor other cause for this can I suppose,
"Save that they grudge me safe and sweet repose."

26.

Sorrow the maid so wholly occupies,
Room has she none for comfort or for rest.
Yet, maugre her affliction, Hope will rise,
And form a lodgement in her harassed breast;
And to the damsel's memory still supplies
Rogero's parting words to her addrest;
So makes her, in all seeming facts, despite,
Await from hour to hour the youthful knight.

27.

For a month's space beyond those twenty days
This hope affords fair Bradamant content:
Hence sorrow not on her so heavy weighs
As it would else her harassed soul have shent.
She, one day that along the road she strays,
By which she oft to meet Rogero went,
Hears tidings, that of Hope — last comfort left —
(Like every other good) her breast bereft.

28.

Bound homeward from the hostile camp, where lay
King Agramant, she met a Gascon knight,
A prisoner to those paynims, from the day
That fought nigh Paris was the famous fight.
The damsel prest him all he knew to say:
Then to the point she covets led the knight:
Asks of Rogero, on that theme abides,
Listens to that, nor aught inquires besides.

29.

Of him a full account did he afford,
As well acquainted with the court; he said,
'How, matched with Mandricardo, strove that lord,
'And layed the martial king in combat dead.
'And how, sore wounded by the Tartar's sword,
'Above a month the stripling kept his bed:'
And had the stranger here but closed his news,
Well might his tale the missing knight excuse.

30.

But then subjoins the Gascon cavalier,
'How in the Moorish camp a damsel lies,
'By name Marphisa hight, of beauteous cheer,
'Bold and as skilled in arms of every guise,
'Who loves Rogero and to him is dear;
'And them the host so rarely sundered spies,
'That every one, throughout the paynim train,
'Deems that betrothed in wedlock are the twain;

31.

'And hope, when healed shall be the youthful knight,
'The marriage of those lovers will succeed;
'(For sure) with pleasure and sincere delight,
'Those tidings paynim prince and monarch read:
'Since, knowing either's superhuman might,
'They augur, from their loins will spring a breed,
'In little season, which shall pass in worth
'The mightiest race that ever was on earth.'

32.

What he rehearsed, the Gascon knight believed,
Nor without cause believed the news he bore,
A rumour universally received
And bruited through the squadrons of the Moor;
Who had that notion of their love conceived
From signs of kindness witnessed evermore.
For — good or bad — though from one mouth it flows,
Fame to a boundless torrent quickly grows.

33.

That she with him had brought the Paynim aid,
And ne'er was seen without the cavalier,
The first foundation of the rumour layed:
But what confirmed that fame in every ear,
Was, that she, having from the camp conveyed
The thief Brunello (as I sang whilere)
As if alone to see Rogero brought,
Had to the camp returned, uncalled, unsought.

34.

She solely to the camp had ta'en her way,
To visit him that on a sick-bed smarted;
Nor once alone; but often all the day
There passed that maid, and but at eve departed:
Who gave yet greater cause of her to say,
That — known as one so haughty and hard-hearted,
Who all the world despised — she now was grown
Benign and humble to the Child alone.

35.

When Bradamant the Gascon's story heard,
That lady suffered such tormentitng pain,
Such cruel woe her inmost bosom stirred,
From falling she preserved herself with pain.
She turned her courser round, without a word,
Inflamed with jealousy and fierce disdain:
From her all hope the wretched damsel spurns,
And to her chamber breathing wrath returns.

36.

Turned on her face, her body on the bed,
Armed as she is, the grieving damsel throws,
And that the sad lament by sorrow bred,
May be unheard of any, bites the clothes;
And so, repeating what the stranger said,
To such a pitch her smothered anguish grows,
Her plaints no longer able to restrain,
So vents the maid parforce her piteous pain:

37.

"Who ever can be trusted? woe is me!
"All false and cruel well may be esteemed,
"If thou, Rogero, false and cruel be,
"That I so pious and so faithful deemed.
"What foul and felon act, what treachery,
"Was ever yet by tragic poet dreamed,
"But will fall short of thine, if thou wilt set
"The sum of my desert against thy debt?

38.

"Wherefore, Rogero, since no cavalier
"Mates thee in beauteous form and daring feat,
"Since thou in matchless valour hast no peer,
"And none with thee in gentleness compete,
"Why cannot we, 'mid godlike gifts and clear,
"Allow thee truth, thy graces to complete?
"The praise of spotless truth to thee allow,
"To which all other virtues yield and bow?

39.

"Knowest thou not, without it, worthless are
"All gentle bearing and all martial might?
"As there is nothing, howsoever fair,
"That can be seen without the aid of light.
"Easily mightest thou a maid ensnare,
"Lord as thou wast, and idol in her sight.
"Her with thy honied words thou might'st have won,
"To deem that cold and darksome was the sun.

40.

"Cruel what sin can trouble thee, if thou
"Do'st not her murder who loved *thee* repent?
"If held so lightly be a breach of vow —
"Beneath what burden will thy heart be bent?
"What treatment will thine adversary know,
"If one who loves like me thou so torment?
"Justice is none in heaven, I well may say,
"If Heaven its vengeance for my wrongs delay.

41.

"If of all human sins of deepest dye
"Be fell ingratitude; if doomed to smart
"For this, the fairest angel of the sky
"Was banished into foul and darksome part;
"If mighty sins for mighty vengeance cry,
"Where due atonement cleanses not the heart;
"Beware lest thou beneath such vengeance groan,
"Ingrate! that wouldst not thy sin atone.

42.

"Cruel Rogero, I of theft, beside
"All other sins, may justly thee arraign.
"That thou my heart hast ravished from my side,
" — Of this offence I will not, I, complain —
"But, having made it mine, that thou defied
"All right, and took away thy gift again.
"Restore it; well thou know'st what pains requite
"His sin, who keeps what is another's right.

43.

"Thou hast left *me,* Rogero; *thee* to leave,
"Alas! I neither will nor power possess.
"But will and power have I my life to reave,
"To scape from this o'erwhelming wretchedness.
"To die at strife with thee alone I grieve:
"For, had the gods so pleased my lot to bless,
"As to require my life, when loved of thee,
"Never so welcome had been death to me."

44.

Resolved to die, 'twas so the damsel cried;
And starting from her bed, by passion warmed,
To her left breast her naked sword applied;
Then recollected she was wholly armed.
Meanwhile her better Spirit, at her side,
With these persuasive words her fury charmed:
"O lady, born to such illustrious name!
"Would'st thou conclude thy life with such foul shame?

45.

"Were it not better to the field to go,
"Where aye thy breath with glory may be spent?
"There, should Rogero chance to lay thee low,
"He to have slain thee haply may repent;
"But, should his faulchion deal the mortal blow,
"What death could ever yield thee more content?
"Reason it were thou should'st by him be slain,
"Who dooms thee living to such passing pain.

46.

"Haply of that Marphisa, too, before
"Thou die, thou yet may deadly vengeance take,
"Who with dishonest love and treacherous lore
"Did thy beloved Rogero's fealty shake."
This seemed to please the mournful lady more
Than her first thought; and she forthwith bade make
A mantle for her arms, which should imply
Her desperation and desire to die.

47.

The vest is of that colour which is spied
In leaf, when gray and yellow are at strife;
When it is gathered from the branch, or dried
Is the green blood, that was its parent's life.
Embroidered is the surcoat's outer side
With stems of cypress which disdain the knife;
Which shoot not, when by biting steel laid low.
A habit well according with her woe.

48.

She took the courser that was wont to bear
Astolpho, and with him the lance of gold,
By whose sole touch unhorsed all champions were.
Needless anew I deem it to unfold
Why by Astolpho given, and when and where,
Or how that spear obtained the warrior bold.
The lady took the lance, but nothing guessed
Of the stupendous virtue it possessed.

49.

Without attendants, without squire, alone,
The hill descending by the nearest way,
Towards Paris is the mournful damsel gone,
Where camped erewhile the Moorish forces lay;
For yet to her the tidings were unknown,
That good Rinaldo and his bold array
Had raised, with Charles' and Maligigi's aid,
The siege the paynims had to Paris laid.

* * * * *

CANTO XXXIV

ARGUMENT

In the infernal pit Astolpho hears
Of Lydia's woe, by smoke well nigh opprest.
He mounts anew, and him his courser bears
To the terrestrial paradise addrest.
By John advised in all, to heaven he steers;
Of some of his lost sense here repossest,
Orlando's wasted wit as well he takes,
Sees the Fates spin their threads, and earthward makes.

[This selection resumes the title theme. Astolpho, the English duke, had obtained the flying horse of Atlantes', and had resolved to journey around the world on it. In his journeyings he flies to the top of a high mountain and finds himself in the Earthly Paradise. Here he learns of the true cause of Orlando's madness and that he has himself been chosen to restore Orlando's wits to him.]

48.

Then backed the griffin-horse, and soared a flight
Whereby to reach that mountain's top he schemes;
Which little distant, with its haughty height,
From the moon's circle good Astolpho deems;
And, such desire to see it warms the knight,
That he aspires to heaven, nor earth esteems.
Through air so more and more the warrior strains,
That he at last the mountain-summit gains.

49.

Here sapphire, ruby, gold, and topaz glow,
Pearl, jacinth, chrysolite and diamond lie,
Which well might pass for natural flowers which blow,
Catching their colour from that kindly sky.
So green the grass! could we have such below,
We should prefer it to our emerald's dye.
As fair the foliage of those pleasant bowers!
Whose trees are ever filled with fruit and flowers.

50.

Warble the wanton birds in verdant brake,
Azure, and red, and yellow, green and white.
The quavering rivulet and quiet lake
In limpid hue surpass the crystal bright.
A breeze, which with one breath appears to shake,
Aye, without fill or fall, the foliage light,
To the quick air such lively motion lends,
That Day's oppressive noon in nought offends;

51.

And this, mid fruit and flower and verdure there,
Ever more stealing divers odours, went;
And made of those mixt sweets a medley rare,
Which filled the spirit with a calm content.
In the mid plain arose a palace fair,
Which seemed as if with living flames it brent.
Such passing splendour and such glorious light
Shot from those walls, beyond all usage bright.

52.

Thither where those transparent walls appear,
Which cover more than thirty miles in measure,
At ease and slowly moved the cavalier,
And viewed the lovely region at his leisure;
And deemed — compared with this — that sad and drear,
And seen by heaven and nature with displeasure,
Was the foul world, wherein we dwell below:
So jocund this, so sweet and fair in show!

53.

Astound with wonder, paused the adventurous knight,
When to that shining palace he was nigh,
For, than the carbuncle more crimson bright,
It seemed one polished stone of sanguine dye.
O mighty wonder! O Daedalian sleight!
What fabric upon earth with this can vie?
Let them henceforth be silent, that in story
Exalt the world's seven wonders to such glory!

54.

An elder, in the shining entrance-hall
Of that glad house, towards Astolpho prest;
Crimson his waistcoat was, and white his pall;
Vermillion seemed the mantle, milk the vest:
White was that ancient's hair, and white withal
The bushy beard descending to his breast;
And from his reverend face such glory beamed,
Of the elect of Paradise he seemed.

55.

He, with glad visage, to the paladine,
  Who humbly from his sell had lighted, cries:
  "O gentle baron, that by will divine
  "Have soared to this terrestrial paradise!
  "Albeit nor you the cause of your design,
  "Nor you the scope of your desire surmise,
  "Believe, you not without high mystery steer
  "Hitherward, from your arctic hemisphere.

56.

"You for instruction, how to furnish aid
  "To Charles and to the Church in utmost need,
  "With me to counsel, hither are conveyed,
  "Who without counsel from such distance speed.
  "But, son, ascribe not you the journey made
  "To wit or worth; nor through your winged steed,
  "Nor through your virtuous bugle had ye thriven,
  "But that such helping grace from God was given.

57.

"We will discourse at better leisure more,
  "And you what must be done shall after hear;
  "But you, that, through long fast, must hunger sore,
  "First brace your strength with us, with genial cheer."
  Continuing his discourse, that elder hoar
  Raised mighty wonder in the cavalier,
  When he avouched, as he his name disclosed,
  That he THE HOLY GOSPEL had composed;

58.

He of our Lord so loved, the blessed John;
  Of whom a speech among the brethren went,
  'He never should see death,' and hence the Son
  Of God with this rebuke St. Peter shent;
  In saying, "What is it to thee, if one
  "Tarry on earth, till I anew be sent?"
  Albeit he said not that he should not die,
  That so he meant to say we plain descry.

59.

Translated thither, he found company,
  The patriarch Enoch, and the mighty seer
  Elias; nor as yet those sainted three
  Have seen corruption, but in garden, clear
  Of earth's foul air, will joy eternity
  Of spring, till they angelic trumpets hear,
  Sounding through heaven and earth, proclaim aloud
  Christ's second advent on the silvery cloud.

60.

The holy ancients to a chamber lead,
With welcome kind, the adventurous cavalier;
And in another then his flying steed
Sufficiently with goodly forage cheer.
Astolpho they with fruits of Eden feed,
So rich, that in his judgment 'twould appear,
In some sort might our parents be excused
If, for such fruits, obedience they refused.

61.

When with that daily payment which man owes,
Nature had been contented by the peer,
As well of due refreshment as repose,
(For all and every comfort found he here)
And now Aurora left her ancient spouse,
Not for his many years to her less dear,
Rising from bed, Astolpho at his side
The apostle, so beloved of God, espied.

62.

Much that not lawfully could here be shown,
Taking him by the hand, to him he read.
"To you, though come from France, may be unknown
"What there hath happened," next the apostle said;
"Learn, your Orlando, for he hath foregone
"The way wherein he was enjoined to tread,
"Is visited of God, that never shends
"Him whom he loveth best, when he offends:

63.

"He, your Orlando, at his birth endowed
"With sovereign daring and with sovereign might,
"On whom, beyond all usage, God bestowed
"The grace, that weapon him should vainly smite,
"Because he was selected from the crowd
"To be defender of his Church's right.
"As he elected Sampson, called whilere
"The Jew against the Philistine to cheer;

64.

"He, your Orlando, for such gifts has made
"Unto his heavenly Lord an ill return:
"Who left his people, when most needing aid,
"Then most abandoned to the heathens' scorn.
"Incestuous love for a fair paynim maid
"Has blinded so that knight, of grace forlorn,
"That twice and more in fell and impious strife
"The count has sought his faithful cousin's life.

65.

"Hence God hath made him mad, and, in this vein,
"Belly, and breast, and naked flank expose;
"And so diseased and troubled is his brain,
"That none, and least himself, the champion knows.
"Nebuchadnezzar whilom to such pain
"God in his vengeance doomed, as story shows;
"Sent, for seven years, of savage fury full,
"To feed on grass and hay, like slavering bull.

66.

"But yet, because the Christian paladine
"Has sinned against his heavenly Maker less,
"He only for three months, by will divine,
"Is doomed to cleanse himself of his excess.
"Nor yet with other scope did your design
"Of wending hither the Redeemer bless,
"But that through us the mode you should explore,
"Orlando's missing senses to restore.

67.

" 'Tis true to journey further ye will need,
"And wholly must you leave this nether sphere;
"To the moon's circle you I have to lead,
"Of all the planets to our world most near.
"Because the medicine, that is fit to speed
"Insane Orlando's cure, is treasured here.
"This night will we away, when over head
"Her downward rays the silver moon shall shed."

68.

In talk the blest apostle is diffuse
On this and that, until the day is worn:
But when the sun is sunk i' the salt sea ooze,
And overhead the moon uplifts her horn,
A chariot is prepared, erewhile in use
To scour the heavens, wherein of old was borne
From Jewry's misty mountains to the sky,
Sainted Elias, rapt from mortal eye.

69.

Four goodly coursers next, and redder far
Than flame, to that fair chariot yokes the sire;
Who, when the knight and he well seated are,
Collects the reins; and heavenward they aspire,
In airy circles swiftly rose the car,
And reached the region of eternal fire;
Whose heat the saint by miracle suspends,
While through the parted air the pair ascends.

70.

The chariot, towering, threads the fiery sphere,
And rises thence into the lunar reign.
This, in its larger part they find as clear
As polished steel, when undefiled by stain;
And such it seems, or little less, when near,
As what the limits of our earth contain:
Such as our earth, the last of globes below,
Including seas, which round about it flow.

71.

Here doubly waxed the paladin's surprise,
To see that place so large, when viewed at hand;
Resembling but a little hoop in size,
When from the globe surveyed whereon we stand,
And that he both his eyes behoved to strain,
If he would view Earth's circling seas and land;
In that, by reason of the lack of light,
Their images attained to little height.

72.

Here other river, lake, and rich champaign
Are seen, than those which are below descried;
Here other valley, other hill and plain,
With towns and cities of their own supplied;
Which mansions of such mighty size contain,
Such never he before or after spied.
Here spacious holt and lonely forest lay,
Where nymphs for ever chased the panting prey.

73.

He, that with other scope had thither soared,
Pauses not all these wonders to peruse:
But led by the disciple of our Lord,
His way towards a spacious vale pursues;
A place wherein is wonderfully stored
Whatever on our earth below we lose.
Collected there are all things whatsoe'er,
Lost through time, chance, or our own folly, here.

74.

Nor here alone of realm and wealthy dower,
O'er which aye turns the restless wheel, I say:
I speak of what it is not in the power
Of Fortune to bestow, or take away.
Much fame is here, whereon Time and the Hour,
Like wasting moth, in this our planet prey,
Here countless vows, here prayers unnumbered lie,
Made by us sinful men to God on high.

75.

The lover's tears and sighs; what time in pleasure
And play we here unprofitably spend;
To this; of ignorant men the eternal leisure,
And vain designs, aye frustrate of their end.
Empty desires so far exceed all measure,
They o'er that valley's better part extend.
There wilt thou find, if thou wilt thither post,
Whatever thou on earth beneath hast lost.

76.

He, passing by those heaps, on either hand,
Of this and now of that the meaning sought;
Formed of swollen bladders here a hill did stand,
Whence he heard cries and tumults, as he thought.
These were old crowns of the Assyrian land
And Lydian — as that paladin was taught —
Grecian and Persian, all of ancient fame;
And now, alas! well-nigh without a name.

77.

Golden and silver hooks to sight succeed,
Heaped in a mass, the gifts which courtiers bear,
— Hoping thereby to purchase future meed —
To greedy prince and patron; many a snare,
Concealed in garlands, did the warrior heed,
Who heard, these signs of adulation were;
And in cicalas, which their lungs had burst,
Saw fulsome lays by venal poets versed.

78.

Loves of unhappy end in imagery
Of gold or jewelled bands he saw exprest.
Then eagles' talons, the authority
With which great lords their delegates invest:
Bellows filled every nook, the fume and fee
Wherein the favourites of kings are blest:
Given to those Ganymedes that have their hour,
And reft, when faded is their vernal flower.

79.

O'erturned, here ruined town and castle lies,
With all their wealth: "The symbols" (said his guide)
"Of treaties and of those conspiracies,
"Which their conductors seemed so ill to hide."
Serpents with female faces, felonies
Of coiners and of robbers, he descried;
Next broken bottles saw of many sorts,
The types of servitude in sorry courts.

80.

He marks a mighty pool of porridge spilled,
And asks what in that symbol should be read,
And hears 'twas charity, by sick men willed
For distribution, after they were dead.
He passed a heap of flowers, that erst distilled
Sweet savours, and now noisome odours shed;
The gift (if it may lawfully be said)
Which Constantine to good Sylvester made.

81.

A large provision, next, of twigs and lime
— Your witcheries, O women! — he explored.
The things he witnessed, to recount in rhyme
Too tedious were; were myriads on record,
To sum the remnant ill should I have time.
'Tis here that all infirmities are stored,
Save only Madness, seen not here at all,
Which dwells below, nor leaves this earthly ball.

82.

He turns him back, upon some days and deeds
To look again, which he had lost of yore;
But, save the interpreter the lesson reads,
Would know them not, such different form they wore.
He next saw that which man so little needs,
As it appears — none pray to Heaven for more;
I speak of sense; whereof a lofty mount
Alone surpast all else which I recount.

83.

It was as 'twere a liquor soft and thin,
Which, save well corked, would from the vase have drained;
Laid up, and treasured various flasks within,
Larger or lesser, to that use ordained.
That largest was which of the paladin,
Anglantes' lord, the mighty sense contained;
And from those others was discerned, since writ
Upon the vessel was ORLANDO'S WIT.

84.

The names of those whose wits therein were pent
He thus on all those other flasks espied.
Much of his own, but with more wonderment,
The sense of many others he descried,
Who, he believed, no dram of theirs had spent;
But here, by tokens clear was satisfied,
That scantily therewith were they purveyed;
So large the quantity he here surveyed.

85.

Some waste on love, some seeking honour, lose
  Their wits, some, scouring seas, for merchandise,
  Some, that on wealthy lords their hope repose,
  And some, befooled by silly sorceries;
  These upon pictures, upon jewels those;
  These on whatever else they highest prize.
  Astrologers' and sophists' wits mid these,
  And many a poet's too, Astolpho sees.

86.

Since his consent the apostle signified
  Who wrote the obscure Apocalypse, his own
  He took, and only to his nose applied,
  When (it appeared) it to its place was gone;
  And henceforth, has Sir Turpin certified,
  That long time sagely lived king Otho's son;
  Till other error (as he says) again
  Deprived the gentle baron of his brain.

87.

The fullest vessel and of amplest round
  Which held the wit Orlando erst possessed,
  Astolpho took; nor this so light he found,
  As it appeared, when piled among the rest.
  Before, from those bright spheres, now earthward bound,
  His course is to our lower orb addressed,
  Him to a spacious palace, by whose side
  A river ran, conducts his holy guide.

* * * * *

CANTO XXXV

ARGUMENT

The apostle praises authors to the peer.
  Duke Aymon's martial daughter in affray,
  Conquers the giant monarch of Argièr,
  And of the good Frontino makes a prey.
  She next from Arles defies her cavalier,
  And, while he marvels who would him assay,
  Grandonio and Ferrau she with her hand
  And Serpentine unhorses on the strand.

[This selection resumes the main narrative. Bradamant, with Flordelice, sets out for Arles to find Rogero.]

57.

When she in other writing had displayed
How she had freed that passage from the foe,
To mournful Flordelice the martial maid,
She that still held her weeping visage low,
Turned her, and courteously that lady prayed
To tell her whither she designed to go.
To her afflicted Flordelice replied:
"To Arles, where camp the paynims, would I ride.

58.

"Which bark (I hope) and fitting company,
"To carry me to Africk may afford;
"Nor will I halt upon my way, till I
"Once more rejoin my husband and my lord;
"All means and measures there resolved to try,
"That may release him from his jailer's ward;
"And should the Saracen deceitful prove,
"Others, and others yet, I mean to move."

59.

"My company (replied the martial fair)
"For some part of the road, I offer thee,
"Till we have sight of Arles; then to repair
"Thither, will pray you, for the love of me,
"To find King Agramant's Rogero there,
"Whose glorious name is spread o'er land and sea,
"And render to that knight this goodly horse,
"Whence the proud Moor was flung in martial course.

60.

"Say thus, from point to point, 'A cavalier
'That would in combat prove his chivalry,
'And to the world at large would fain make clear
'Thy breach of faith with him, that thou may'st be
'Ready and well prepared for the career,
'Gave me this horse, that I might give it thee.
'He bids thee promptly mail and corslet dight,
'And wait him, who with thee will wage the fight.'

61.

"Say this and nought beside, and would he hear
"My name, declare that 'tis to thee unknown."
With wonted kindness cried that dame, "I ne'er
"In spending life itself, not words alone,
"Should weary in your service; since whilere
"You would in my behalf as much have done."
Her Aymon's daughter thanked in courteous strain,
And to her hand consigned Frontino's rein.

62.

Through long days' journeys, by that river-shore,
Together go the lovely pilgrim pair,
Till they see Arles, and hear the hollow roar
Of billows breaking on the sea-beach bare.
Almost without the suburbs, and before
The furthest barrier, stops the martial fair;
To furnish Flordelice what time might need
For the conveyance of Rogero's steed.

63.

She forward rode, within the enclosure sped,
And o'er the bridge and through the gateway wended,
And (furnished with a guide, who thither led)
To young Rogero's inn; and there descended.
She to the Child, as bid, her message said,
And gave the courser, to her care commended:
Then (for she waits not for an answer) speeds
In haste to execute her proper needs.

64.

Rogero stands confused; he finds no end
To his perplexing thoughts, and cannot see
Who should defy him, who that message send,
To speak him ill, and do him courtesy,
Who thus as faithless him should reprehend,
Or any reprehend, whoe'er it be,
Nor knows he nor imagines; least of all
On Bradamant the knight's suspicions fall.

65.

To think 'twas Rodomont the youthful peer
Was more inclined than any other wight;
And wherefore even from him he this should hear,
Muses, nor can the cause divine aright;
Save him, in all the world the cavalier
Knows not of one, that has him at despite.
Meanwhile Dordona's lady craved the field;
And loud that martial damsel's bugle pealed.

66.

To Agramant and King Marsilius flew
The news, that one craved battle on the plain.
Serpentine stood by chance before the two,
And gained their leave to don his plate and chain,
And vowed to take that haughty man; the crew
Of people over wall and rampart strain;
Nor child nor elder was there, but he pressed
To see which champion should bestir him best.

67.

In beauteous arms and costly surcoat drest,
Serpentine of the star to combat sped;
The ground he at the first encounter prest;
As if equipt with wings, his courser fled.
The damsel flew his charger to arrest,
And by the bridle to that paynim led,
Exclaiming; "Mount, and bid your monarch send
"A knight that better can with me contend."

68.

The Moorish king, that on the rampart's height
Stood, with a mighty following, next the plain,
Marking the joust, much marvelled at the sight
Of the foe's courtesy to him of Spain.
"He takes him not, although he may of right,"
He cries i' the hearing of the paynim train.
Serpentine comes, and, as the maid commands,
A better warrior of that king demands.

69.

Grandonio de Volterna, fierce of mood,
And in all Spain the proudest cavalier,
The second for that fell encounter stood,
Such favour had his suit obtained whilere.
"To thee thy courtesy shall do no good,"
He threats, "for if unhorsed in the career,
"A prisoner to my lord shalt thou be led;
"But, if I fight as wonted, thou art dead."

70.

She cries, "I would not thy discourtesy
"Should make me so forget my courteous vein,
"But that aforehand I should caution thee
"Back to thy fortress to return again,
"Ere on hard earth thy bones shall battered be.
"Go tell thy king no champion of thy grain
"I seek, but hither come to crave the fight
"With warrior that is worthy of my might."

71.

Bradamant's sharp and stinging answer stirred
The paynim's fury to a mighty flame;
So that, without the power to speak a word,
He wheeled his courser, filled with rage and shame;
Wheeling as well, at that proud paynim spurred
Her horse with levelled lance the warlike dame.
As the charmed weapon smites Grandonio's shield,
With heels in air, he tumbles on the field.

72.

To him the high-minded damsel gave his horse,
And said, "Yet was this fate to thee foreshown,
"Instead of craving thus the knightly course,
"Better mine embassy wouldst thou have done,
"Some other knight, that equals me in force,
"I pray thee bid the Moorish king send down,
"Nor weary me, by forcing me to meet
"Champions like thee, untried in martial feat."

73.

They on the walls, that know not who the peer
That in the joust so well maintains his seat,
Name many a warrior, famous in career,
That often make them shake in fiercest heat.
Brandimart many deem the cavalier;
More guesses in renowned Rinaldo meet:
Many would deem Orlando was the knight,
But that they knew his pitiable plight.

74.

The third encounter craved Lanfusa's son,
And cried, "Not that I better hope to fare,
"But that to warriors who this course have run,
"My fall may furnish an excuse more fair."
Next, with all arms that martial jousters don,
Clothed him, and of a hundred steeds that were
Ready for service, kept in lordly stall,
For speed and action chose the best of all.

75.

He bowned him for the tournay, on his side,
But first saluted her and she the knight.
"If 'tis allowed to ask," (the lady cried),
"Tell me in courtesy how ye are hight."
In this Ferrau the damsel satisfied,
Who rarely hid himself from living wight.
"Ye will I not refuse," (subjoined the dame),
"Albeit I to meet another came."

76.

—"And who?" the Spaniard said:—the maid replied,
"Rogero;" and pronounced the word with pain.
And, in so saying, her fair face was dyed
All over with the rose's crimson grain.
She after added, "Hither have I hied,
"To prove how justly famed his might and main.
"No other care have I, no other call,
"But with that gentle youth to try a fall."

77.

She spoke the word in all simplicity,
Which some already may in malice wrest.
Ferrau replied, "Assured I first must be
"Which of us two is schooled in warfare best,
"If what has chanced to many, falls on me,
"Hither, when I return, shall be addrest,
"To mend my fault, that gentle cavalier,
"With whom you so desire to break a spear."

78.

Discoursing all this while, the martial maid
Spake with her beavor up, without disguise:
Ferrau, as that fair visage he surveyed,
Perceived he was half vanquished by its eyes.
And to himself, in under tone, he said,
"He seems an angel sent from Paradise;
"And, though he should not harm me with his lance,
"I am already quelled by that sweet glance."

79.

They take their ground, and to the encounter ride,
And, like those others, Ferrau goes to ground;
His courser Bradamant retained, and cried,
"Return, and keep thy word with me as bound."
Shamed, he returned, and by his monarch's side,
Among his peers, the young Rogero found;
And let the stripling know the stranger knight,
Without the walls, defied him to the fight.

80.

Rogero (for not yet that warrior knows
What champion him in duel would assail)
Nigh sure of victory, with transport glows,
And bids his followers bring his plate and mail;
Nor having seen beneath those heavy blows
The rest dismounted, makes his spirit quail.
But how he armed, how sallied, what befel
That knight, in other canto will I tell.

CANTO XXXVI

ARGUMENT

While with the fierce Marphisa at despite
Duke Aymon's daughter wages fierce affray,
One and the other host engage in fight,
With Bradamant Rogero wends his way.
With other war disturbs their great delight

Marphisa bold; but when that martial may
Has for her brother recognized the peer,
They end their every strife with joyous cheer.

* * * * *

12.

Rogero heard the call in joyous vein,
And bade his arms be brought; now while in view
Of Agramant he donned the plate and chain,
Those lords the former question moved anew;
'Who was the knight, that on the martial plain
'The manage of the lance so quaintly knew?'
And of Ferrau, who spake with him whilere,
Craved, if to him was known that cavalier.

13.

"Be ye assured," to them Ferrau replied,
"He is not one of those I hear you cite
"To me (for I his open face descried).
"Rinaldo's youthful brother seemed the knight.
"But since his doughty valour I have tried,
"And wot not such is Richardetto's might,
"I ween it is his sister, who, I hear,
"Resembles much in mien that martial peer.

14.

"The damsel equals well, so Rumour tells,
"Rinaldo, and every paladin in fray:
"But brother she and cousin [1] both excels,
"Measured by that which I have seen to-day."
Hearing him, while upon her praise he dwells,
As the sky reddens with the morning ray,
Rogero's face is flushed with crimson hue,
And his heart throbs, nor knows he what to do.

15.

Stung, at these tidings, by the amorous dart—
Within, new fire inflames the cavalier;
And straight, together with the burning smart,
Shoots through his bones a chill, produced by fear;
Fear, that new wrath had stifled in her heart
That mighty love, wherewith she burned whilere.
Confused he stands, irresolute and slow,
And undecided if to stay or go.

16.

Now fierce Marphisa, who was there, and prest
By huge desire to meet the stranger wight,

1. Rinaldo and Orlando.

And armed withal (for, save in iron vest,
Her seldom would you find by day or night),
Hearing Rogero is in armour drest,
Fearing to lose the honour of the fight,
If first that champion with the stranger vies;
Thinks to prevent the youth and win the prize.

17.

She leapt upon her horse, and thither hied
Where Aymon's daughter on the listed plain,
With palpitating heart, upon her side,
Waited Rogero; whom the damsel fain
Would make her prisoner, and but schemed to guide
Her lance in mode the stripling least to pain.
Marphisa from the city portal fares,
And on her gallant helm a phoenix wears.

18.

Whether the maid would publish, in her pride,
That she was single in the world, for might;
Or whether by that symbol signified,
That she would live, exempt from bridal rite.
Her closely Aymon's martial daughter eyed;
When seeing not those features, her delight,
She craves the damsel's name before they move,
And hears that it is she who joys her love:

19.

Or rather she, that gentle lady thought,
Had joyed her love; and whom she hated so,
Her to Death's door her anger would have brought,
Unless she venged her sorrow on the foe.
She wheeled her courser round, with fury fraught,
Less with desire to lay her rival low,
Than with the lance to pierce her in mid breast,
And put her every jealousy at rest.

20.

Parforce to ground must go the royal maid,
To prove if hard or soft the listed plain,
And be with such unwonted scorn appaid,
That she is nearly maddened by disdain.
Scarce was she thrown, before her trenchant blade
She bared, and hurried to avenge the stain.
Cried Aymon's daughter, no less proud of heart,
"What art thou doing? Thou my prisoner art."

21.

"Though I have courtesy for others, none"
(She said) "from me, Marphisa, shalt thou find.
"Since evermore I hear of thee, as one
"To pride and every churlishness inclined."
Marphisa, at these words, was heard to groan,
As roars in some sea-rock the prisoned wind.
She screamed an answer; but its sense was drowned
(Such rage confused that damsel) in the sound.

22.

She whirls this while her faulchion, and would fain
Wound horse or rider in the paunch or breast;
But Aymon's watchful daughter turns the rein;
And on one side her courser leaps; possest
With furious anger and with fierce disdain,
She at her opposite her lance addrest;
And hardly touched the damsel, ere, astound,
Marphisa fell, reversed upon the ground.

23.

Scarce down, Marphisa started from the plain,
Intent fell mischief with her sword to do,
Bradamant couched her golden spear again,
And yet again the damsel overthrew.
Yet Bradamant, though blest with might and main,
Was not so much the stronger of the two
As to have flung the maid in every just,
But that such power was in the lance's thrust.

24.

This while some knights (some knights upon our side,
I say) forth issuing from the city, go
Towards the field of strife, which did divide
The squadrons, here and there, of either foe
— Not half a league of one another wide —
Seeing their knight such mighty prowess show:
Their knight, but whom no otherwise they knew
Than as a warrior of the Christian crew.

25.

Troyano's generous son, who had espied
This band approaching to the city-wall,
For due defence would every means provide,
And every peril, every case forestall:
And orders many to take arms, who ride
Forth from the ramparts, at the monarch's call.
With them Rogero goes, in armour cased,
Balked of the battle by Marphisa's haste.

26.

The enamoured youth, with beating heart, intent,
Stood by, the issue of the just to view.
For his dear consort fearing the event,
In that he well Marphisa's valour knew
— At the beginning I would say — when, bent
On mischief, fiercely closed the furious two:
But when that duel's turn the stripling eyes,
He stands amazed and stupid with surprise;

27.

And when he saw unfinished was the fight,
At the first onset, like the justs whilere,
Misdoubting some strange accident, in sprite,
Sore vexed, this while remained the cavalier.
To either maid wished well that youthful knight;
For both were loved, but not alike were dear.
For *this* the stripling's love was fury, fire;
For *that* 'twas rather fondness than desire.

28.

If so Rogero could with honour do,
He willingly the warriors would divide;
But his companions, in the fear to view
Victory with King Charles's knight abide,
Esteeming him the better of the two,
Break in between and turn their arms aside;
Upon the other part, the Christian foes
Advance, and both divisions come to blows.

29.

On this side and that other, rings the alarm,
Which in those camps is sounded every day.
Bidding the unmounted mount, the unarmed arm,
And all their standards seek, without delay,
Where, under separate flags, the squadrons swarm,
More than one shrilling trump is heard to bray;
And as their rattling notes the riders call,
Rousing the foot, beat drum and ataball.

30.

As fierce as thought could think, 'twixt either host
Kindled the fell and sanguinary fray.
The daring damsel, fair Dordona's boast,
Sore vexed and troubled, that in the affray
She cannot compass what she covets most,
— Marphisa with avenging steel to slay, —
Now here, now there, amid the medley flies,
Hoping to see the youth for whom she sighs.

31.

By the eagle argent on the shield of blue [2]
She recognized Rogero, mid the rest.
With eyes and thought intent, she stops to view
The warrior's manly shoulders and his breast,
Fair face and movements full of graceful shew;
And then the maid, with mickle spite possest,
Thinking another joys the stripling's love,
Thus speaks, as sovereign rage and fury move.

32.

"Shall then another kiss those lips so bright
"And sweet, if those fair lips are lost to me?
"Ah! never other shall in thee delight;
"For if not mine, no other's shalt thou be.
"Rather than die alone and of despite,
"I with this hand will slay myself and thee,
"That if I lose thee here, at least in hell
"With thee I to eternity may dwell.

33.

"If thou slay'st me, there is good reason, I
"The comfort too of vengeance should obtain;
"In that all edicts and all equity
"The death of him that causes death ordain;
"Nor, since you justly, I unjustly, die,
"Deem I that thine is equal to my pain.
"I him who seeks my life, alas! shall spill,
"Thou her that loves and worships thee wouldst kill.

34.

"My hand, why hast thou not the hardiment
"To rive with steel the bosom of my foe,
"That me so many times to death has shent,
"Under the faith of love, in peaceful show;
"Him, who to take my life can now consent,
"Nor even have pity of my cruel woe?
"Dare, valiant heart, this impious man to slay,
"And let his death my thousand deaths appay!"

35.

So said, she spurred at him amid the throng;
But, first — "Defend thee, false Rogero!" — cried.
"No more, if I have power, in spoil and wrong,
"Done to a virgin heart, shalt thou take pride."
Hearing that voice the hostile ranks among,
He deems — and truly deems — he hears his bride;

2. The coat-of-arms of the House of Este.

Whose voice the youth remembers in such wise,
That mid a thousand would he recognize.

36.

Her further meaning well did he divine,
Weening that him she in that speech would blame,
For having broke their pact; and — with design,
The occasion of his failure to proclaim, —
Of his desire for parley made a sign:
But she, with vizor closed, already came,
Raging and grieved, intent, with vengeful hand,
To fling the youth; nor haply upon sand.

37.

Rogero, when he saw her so offended,
Fixed himself firmly in his arms and seat.
He rests his lance, but holds the stave suspended,
So that it shall not harm her when they meet.
She that to smite and pierce the Child intended,
Pitiless, and inflamed with furious heat,
Has not the courage, when she sees him near,
To fling, or do him outrage with the spear.

38.

Void of effect, 'tis thus their lances go;
And it is well; since Love with burning dart,
Tilting this while at one and the other foe,
Has lanced the enamoured warriors in mid-heart.
Unable at the Child to aim her blow,
The lady spent her rage in other part,
And mighty deeds achieved, which fame will earn
While overhead the circling heavens shall turn.

39.

Above three hundred men in that affray
In little space by her dismounted lie.
Alone that warlike damsel wins the day;
From her alone the Moorish people fly.
To her Rogero, circling, threads his way,
And says; "Unless I speak with you I die.
"Hear me, for love of heaven! — what have I done,
"Alas! that ever mine approach ye shun?"

40.

As when soft southern breezes are unpent,
Which with a tepid breath from seaward blow,
The snows dissolve, and torrents find a vent,
And ice, so hard erewhile, is seen to flow;
At those entreaties, at that brief lament,

Rinaldo's sister's heart is softened so;
Forthwith compassionate and pious grown;
Which anger fain had made more hard than stone.

41.

Would she not, could she not, she nought replied,
But spurred aslant the ready Rabicane,
And, signing to Rogero, rode as wide
As she could wend from that embattled train;
Then to a sheltered valley turned aside,
Wherein embosomed was a little plain.
In the mid lawn a wood of cypress grew,
Whose saplings of one stamp appeared to view.

42.

Within that thicket, of white marble wrought,
Is a proud monument, and newly made;
And he that makes enquiry, here is taught
In few brief verses who therein is laid.
But of those lines, methinks, took little thought,
Fair Bradamant, arriving in the glade.
Rogero spurred his courser, and pursued
And overtook that damsel in the wood.

43.

But turn we to Marphisa, that anew
During this space was seated on her steed,
And sought again the valiant champion, who
At the first onset cast her on the mead;
And saw, how from the mingling host withdrew
Rogero, after that strange knight to speed;
Nor deemed the youth pursued in love; she thought
He but to end their strife and quarrel sought.

44.

She pricks her horse behind the two, and gains,
Well nigh as soon as they, that valley; how
Her coming thither either lover pains,
Who lives and loves, untaught by me, may know:
But sorest vext sad Bradamant remains;
Beholding her whence all her sorrows flow.
Who shall persuade the damsel but that love
For young Rogero brings her to that grove?

45.

And him perfidious she anew did name.
—"Perfidious, was it not enough (she said)
"That I should know thy perfidy from fame,
"But must the witness of thy guilt be made?

"I wot, to drive me from thee is thine aim;
"And I, that thy desires may be appaid,
"Will die; but strive, in yielding up my breath,
"She too shall die, the occasion of my death."

46.

Angrier than venomed viper, with a bound,
So saying, she upon Marphisa flies;
And plants so well the spear, that she, astound,
Fell backward on the champaigne in such guise,
Nigh half her helm was buried in the ground:
Nor was the damsel taken by surprise:
Nay, did her best the encounter to withstand;
Yet with her helmed head she smote the sand.

47.

Bradamant who will die, or in that just
Will put to death Marphisa, rages so,
She has no mind again with lance to thrust,
Again that martial maid to overthrow:
But thinks her head to sever from the bust,
Where it half buried lies, with murderous blow:
Away the enchanted lance that damsel flings,
Unsheathes the sword, and from her courser springs.

48.

But is too slow withal; for on her feet
She finds Marphisa, with such fierce disdain
Inflamed, at being in that second heat
So easily reversed upon the plain,
She hears in vain exclaim, in vain entreat,
Rogero, who beholds their strife with pain.
So blinded are the pair with spite and rage,
That they with desperate fury battle wage.

49.

At half-sword's length engage the struggling foes;
And — such their stubborn mood — with shortened brand
They still approach, and now so fiercely close,
They cannot choose but grapple, hand to hand.
Her sword, no longer needful, each foregoes;
And either now new means of mischief planned.
Rogero both implores with earnest suit;
But supplicates the twain with little fruit.

50.

When he entreaties unavailing found,
The youth prepared by force to part the two:
Their poniards snatched away, and on the ground,

Beneath a cypress-tree, the daggers threw.
When they no weapons have wherewith to wound,
With prayer and threat, he interferes anew:
But vainly; for, since better weapons lack,
Each other they with fists and feet attack.

51.

Rogero ceased not from his task; he caught,
By hand or arm, the fiercely struggling pair,
Till to the utmost pitch of fury wrought
The fell Marphisa's angry passions were.
She, that this ample world esteemed at nought,
Of the Child's friendship had no further care.
Plucked from the foe, she ran to seize her sword,
And fastened next upon that youthful lord.

52.

"Like a discourteous man and churl ye do,
"Rogero to disturb another's fight;
"A deed (she cried) this hand shall make ye rue,
"Which, I intend, shall vanquish both." The knight
Sought fierce Marphisa's fury to subdue
With gentle speech; but full of such despite
He found her, and inflamed with such disdain,
All parley was a waste of time and pain.

53.

At last his faulchion young Rogero drew;
For ire as well had flushed that cavalier:
Nor it is my belief, that ever shew
Athens or Rome, or city whatsoe'er
Witnessed, which ever so rejoiced the view,
As this rejoices, as this sight is dear
To Bradamant, when, through their strife displaced,
Every suspicion from her breast is chased.

54.

Bradamant took her sword, and to descry
The duel of those champions stood apart.
The god of war, descended from the sky,
She deemed Rogero, for his strength and art:
If he seemed Mars, Marphisa to the eye
Seemed an infernal Fury, on her part.
'Tis true, that for a while the youthful knight
Against that damsel put not forth his might.

55.

He knew the virtues of that weapon well,
Such proof thereof the knight erewhile had made.

Where'er it falls parforce is every spell
Annulled, or by its stronger virtue stayed.
Hence so Rogero smote, it never fell
Upon its edge or point, but still the blade
Descended flat: he long this rule observes;
Yet once he from his patient purpose swerves.

56.

In that, a mighty stroke Marphisa sped,
Meaning to cleave the brainpan of her foe:
He raised the buckler to defend his head,
And the sword smote upon its bird of snow,
Nor broke nor bruised the shield, by spell bested;
But his arm rang astounded by the blow;
Nor aught but Hector's mail the sword had stopt,
Whose furious blow would his left arm have lopt;

57.

And had upon his head descended shear,
Whereat designed to strike the savage fair.
Scarce his left arm can good Rogero rear;
Can scarce the shield and blazoned bird upbear.
All pity he casts off, and 'twould appear
As in his eyes a lighted torch did glare.
As hard as he can smite, he smites; and woe
To thee, Marphisa, if he plants the blow!

58.

I cannot tell you truly in what wise
That faulchion swerves against a cypress-stock,
In such close-serried ranks the saplings rise,
Buried above a palm within the block.
At this the mountain and the plain that lies
Beneath it, with a furious earthquake rock;
And from that marble monument proceeds
A voice, that every mortal voice exceeds.

59.

The horrid voice exclaims, "Your quarrel leave;
"For 'twere a deed unjust and inhumane,
"That brother should of life his sister reave,
"Or sister by her brother's hand be slain.
"Rogero and Marphisa mine, believe!
"The tale which I deliver is not vain.
"Seed of one father, in one womb ye lay;
"And first together saw the light of day.

60.

"Galaciëlla's children are ye, whom
"She to Rogero, hight the second, bare.
"Whose brothers, having, by unrighteous doom,
"Of your unhappy sire deprived that fair,
"Not heeding that she carried in her womb
"Ye, who yet suckers of their lineage are,
"Her in a rotten carcase of a boat,
"To founder in mid ocean, set afloat.

61.

"But Fortune, that had destined you whilere,
"And yet unborn, to many a fair emprize,
"Your mother to that lonely shore did steer,
"Which overright the sandy Syrtes lies.
"Where, having given you birth, that spirit dear
"Forthwith ascended into Paradise.
"A witness of the piteous case was I,
"So heaven had willed, and such your destiny!

62.

"I to the dame as decent burial gave
"As could be given upon that desert sand.
"Ye, well enveloped in my vest, I save,
"And bear to Mount Carena[3] from the strand;
"And make a lioness leave whelps and cave,
"And issue from the wood, with semblance bland.
"Ye, twice ten months, with mickle fondness bred,
"And from her paps the milky mother fed.

63.

"Needing to quit my home upon a day,
"And journey through the country, (as you can
"Haply remember ye) we on our way
"Were overtaken by an Arab clan.
"Those robbers thee, Marphisa, bore away;
"While young Rogero 'scaped, who better ran.
"Bereaved of thee, thy woeful loss I wept,
"And with more watchful care thy brother kept.

64.

"Rogero, if Atlantes watched thee well,
"While yet he was alive, thou best dost know.
"I the fixed stars had heard of thee foretell,
"That thou shouldst perish by a treacherous foe
"In Christian land; and till their influence fell
"Was ended, laboured to avert the blow;

It was from Mount Carena in Africa that Agramant first obtained Rogero from A...ntes by the magic power of the ring stolen from Angelica.

"Nor having power in fine thy will to guide,
"I sickened sore, and of my sorrow died.

65.

"But here, before my death, for in this glade
"I knew thou should'st with bold Marphisa fight,
"I with huge stones, amassed by hellish aid,
"Had this fair monument of marble dight;
"And I to Charon with loud outcries said;
'I would not he should hence convey my sprite,
'Till here, prepared in deadly fray to strive,
'Rogero and his sister should arrive.'

66.

"Thus has my spirit for this many a day
"Waited thy coming in these beauteous groves;
"So be no more to jealous fears a prey,
"O Bradamant, because Rogero loves.
"But me to quit the cheerful realms of day,
"And seek the darksome cloisters it behoves."
Here ceased the voice; which in the Child amazed
And those two damsels mighty marvel raised.

67.

Gladly a sister in the martial queen
Rogero, she in him a brother knows;
Who now embrace, nor move her jealous spleen,
That with the love of young Rogero glows;
And citing what, and when, and where had been
Their childish deeds, as they to memory rose,
In summing up past time, more sure they hold
The things whereof the wizard's spirit told.

68.

Rogero from Marphisa does not hide,
How Bradamant to him at heart is dear;
And by what obligations he is tied
In moving words relates the cavalier;
Nor ceases till he has, on either side,
Turned to firm love the hate they bore whilere.
When, as a sign of peace, and discord chased,
They, at his bidding, tenderly embraced.

69.

Marphisa to Rogero makes request
'To say what sire was theirs, and what their strain;
'And how he died; by banded foes opprest,
'Or at close barriers, was the warrior slain?
'And who it was had issued the behest

'To drown their mother in the stormy main?
'For of the tale, if ever heard before,
'Little or nothing she in memory bore.'

70.

"Of Trojan ancestors are we the seed,
"Through famous Hector's line," (Rogero said)
"For after young Astyanax was freed,
"From fierce Ulysses and the toils he spread,
"Leaving another stripling in his stead,
"Of his own age, he out of Phrygia fled.
"Who, after long and wide sea-wandering, gained
"Sicily's shore, and in Messina reigned.

71.

"Part of Calabria within Faro held
"The warrior's heirs, who after a long run
"Of successors, departed thence and dwelled
"In Mars' imperial city: more than one
"Famed king and emperor, who that list have swelled,
"In Rome and other part has filled the throne:
"And from Constantius and good Constantine,
"Stretched to the son of Pepin, is their line.

72.

"Rogero, Gambaron, Buovo hence succeed;
"And that Rogero, second of the name,
"Who filled our fruitful mother with his seed;
"As thou Atlantes may'st have heard proclaim.
"Of our fair lineage many a noble deed
"Shalt thou hear blazed abroad by sounding Fame."
'Of Agolant's inroad next the stripling told,
'With Agramant and with Almontes bold;

73.

'And how a lovely daughter, who excelled
'In feats of arms, that king accompanied;
'So stout she many paladins had quelled;
'And how, in fine, she for Rogero sighed;
'And for his love against her sire rebelled;
'And was baptized, and was Rogero's bride;
'And how a traitor loved (him Bertram name)
'His brother's wife with an incestuous flame;

74.

'And country, sire, and brethren two betrayed,
'Hoping he so the lady should have won;
'How Risa open to the foe he laid,
'By whom all scathe was on those kinsmen done;

'How Agolant's two furious sons conveyed
'Their mother, great with child, and six months gone,
'Aboard a helmless boat, and with its charge,
'In wildest winter, turned adrift the barge.'

75.

Valiant Marphisa, with a tranquil face,
Heard young Rogero thus his tail pursue,
And joyed to be descended of a race
Which from so fair a font its waters drew:
Whence Clermont, whence renowned Mongrana trace
Their noble line, the martial damsel knew;
Blazoned through years and centuries by Fame,
Unrivalled, both, in men of mighty name.

76.

When afterwards she from her brother knew
Agramant's uncle, sire, and grandsire fell,
In treacherous wise, the first Rogero slew
And brought to cruel pass Galaciëlle,
Marphisa could not hear the story through:
To him she cries, "With pardon, what you tell,
"Brother, convicts you of too foul a wrong,
"In leaving thus our sire unvenged so long.

77.

"Could'st thou not in Almontes and Troyane,
"As dead whilere, your thirsty faulchion plant,
"By you those monarch's children might be slain.
"Are you alive, and lives King Agramant?
"Never will you efface the shameful stain,
"That ye, so often wronged, not only grant
"Life to that king, but as your lord obey;
"Lodge in his court, and serve him for his pay?

78.

"Here heartily in face of Heaven I vow,
"*That* Christ my father worshipped, to adore;
"And till I venge my parents on the foe
"To wear this armour; and I will deplore
"Your deed, Rogero, and deplore even now,
"That you should swell the squadrons of the Moor,
"Or other follower of the Moslem faith,
"Save sword in hand, and to the paynim's scathe."

79.

Ah! how fair Bradamant uplifts again
Her visage at that speech, rejoiced in sprite!
Rogero she exhorts in earnest vein

To do as his Marphisa counsels right;
And bids him seek the camp of Charlemagne,
And have himself acknowledged in his sight,
Who so reveres and lauds his father's worth,
He even deems him one unmatched on earth.

80.

'In the beginning so he should have done,'
(Warily young Rogero answer made,)
'But, for the tale was not so fully known,
'As since, the deed had been too long delayed.
'Now, seeing it was fierce Troyano's son
'That had begirt him with the knightly blade,
'He, as a traitor, well might be abhorred,
'If he slew one, accepted as his lord.'

81.

But, as to Bradamant whilere, he cries,
'He will all measures and all means assay,
'Whereby some fair occasion may arise
'To leave the king; and had there been delay,
'And he whilere had done in otherwise,
'She on the Tartar king the fault must lay:
'How sorely handled that redoubted foe
'Had left him in their battle, she must know;

82.

'And she, that every day had sought his bed,
'Must of this truth the fittest witness be.'
Much upon this was answered, much was said,
Between those damsels, who at last agree;
And as their last resolve, last counsel read,
He should rejoin the paynim's ensignry,
Till he found fair occasion to resort
From Agramant's to Charles's royal court.

83.

To Bradamant the bold Marphisa cries:
"Let him begone, nor doubt but I, before
"Many days pass, will manage in such wise,
"That Agramant shall be his lord no more."
So says the martial damsel, nor implies
The secret purpose which she has in store.
Making his congees to the friendly twain,
To join his king Rogero turns the rein.[4]

4. The last three cantos of the poem are devoted to the completion of the story of Bradamant and Rogero. In the end, Bradamant's ambitious parents resolve to marry their daughter to Leo, son of the Emperor of Constantinople. Rogero goes east in quest of Leo. Dramatic adventures continue with movingly ironic situations before the marriage of Bradamant and Rogero with all its festivities is celebrated.

CANTO XXXIX

ARGUMENT

Agramant breaks the pact, is overthrown,
And forced fair France for Afric to forego.
Meanwhile Astolpho in Biserta's town
Having with numerous host besieged the foe,
By hazard there arrives bold Milo's son,
To whom the duke, instructed how to do,
Restores his wits. At sea does Dudon meet
King Agramant, and sore annoys his fleet.

[This selection continues the title theme. The mad Orlando was racing along the African shore when he came to where Astolpho was laying siege to the city of Biserta. It is here that Orlando's wits are restored. In the end, Orlando, cured and ennobled, fights and wins the final great battle, three against three, on the island of Lampedosa, which concludes the great war between pagan and Christian.]

44.

He stretched his arms, and would embrace the knight
And — wherefore he was come — would bid him say:
But was prevented by the sudden flight
Of the scared host, which fled in disarray,
Before the club of that mad, naked wight,
Who with the brandished sapling cleared his way.
Flordelice viewed the furious man in front;
And cried to Brandimart, "Behold the count!"

45.

At the same time, withal, Astolpho bold
That this was good Orlando plainly knew,
By signs, whereof those ancient saints had told,
In the earthly paradise, as tokens true.
None of those others, who the knight behold,
The courteous baron in the madman view;
That from long self-neglect, while wild he ran,
Had in his visage more of beast than man.

46.

With breast and heart transfixed with pity, cried
Valiant Astolpho — bathed with many a tear —
Turning to Danish Dudon, at this side,
And afterwards to valiant Olivier;
"Behold Orlando!" Him awhile they eyed,
Straining their eyes and lids; then knew the peer;
And, seeing him in such a piteous plight,
Were filled with grief and wonder at the sight.

47.

So grieve and so lament the greater part
 Of those good warriors, that their eyes o'erflow.
 " 'Tis time" (Astolpho cried) "to find some art
 "To heal him, not indulge in useless woe;"
 And from his courser sprang: bold Brandimart,
 Olivier, Sansonet and Dudon so
 All leap to ground, and all together make
 At Roland, whom the warriors fain would take.

48.

Seeing the circle round about him grow,
 Levels his club that furious paladin,
 And makes fierce Dudon feel (who — couched below
 His buckler — on the madman would break in)
 How grievous is that staff's descending blow;
 And but that Olivier, Orlando's kin,
 Broke in some sort its force, that stake accurst
 Had shield and helmet, head and body burst.

49.

It only burst the shield, and in such thunder
 Broke on the casque, that Dudon prest the shore:
 With that, Sir Sansonet cut clean asunder
 The sapling, shorn of two cloth-yards and more,
 So vigorous was that warrior's stroke, while under
 His bosom, Brandimart girt Roland sore
 With sinewy arms about his body flung;
 And to the champion's legs Astolpho clung.

50.

Orlando shook himself, and England's knight,
 Ten paces off, reversed upon the ground;
 Yet loosed not Brandimart, who with more might
 And better hold had clasped the madman round.
 To Olivier, too forward in that fight,
 He dealt so furious and so fell a wound,
 With his clenched fist, that pale the marquis fell;
 And purple streams from eyes and nostrils well;

51.

And save his morion had been more than good,
 Bold Olivier had breathed his last, who lies,
 So battered with his fall, it seemed he would
 Bequeath his parting soul to paradise.
 Astolpho and Dudon, that again upstood
 (Albeit swoln were Dudon's face and eyes)
 And Sansonet, who plied so well his sword,
 All made together at Anglantes' lord.

52.

Dudon Orlando from behind embraced,
And with his foot the furious peer would throw:
Astolpho and others seize his arms; but waste
Their strength in all attempts to hold the foe.
He who has seen a bull, by mastiffs chased
That gore his bleeding ears, in fury lowe,
Dragging the dogs that bait him there and here,
Yet from their tusks unable to get clear;

53.

Let him imagine, so Orlando drew
Astolpho and those banded knights along.
Meanwhile upstarted Oliviero, who
By that fell fistycuff on earth was flung;
And, seeing they could ill by Roland do
That sought by good Astolpho and his throng,
He meditates, and compasses, a way
The frantic paladin on earth to lay.

54.

He many a hawser made them thither bring,
And running knots in them he quickly tied;
Which on the count's waist, arms, and legs, they fling:
And then, among themselves, the ends divide,
Conveyed to this or that amid the ring,
Compassing Roland upon every side.
The warriors thus Orlando flung parforce,
As farrier throws the struggling ox or horse.

55.

As soon as down, they all upon him are,
And hands and feet more tightly they constrain:
He shakes himself, and plunges here and there;
But all his efforts for relief are vain.
Astolpho bade them hence the prisoner bear;
'For he would heal (he said) the warrior's brain.'
Shouldered by sturdy Dudon is the load,
And on the beach's furthest brink bestowed.

56.

Seven times Astolpho makes them wash the knight;
And seven times plunged beneath the brine he goes.
So that they cleanse away the scurf and blight,
Which to his stupid limbs and visage grows.
This done, with herbs, for that occasion dight,
They stop his mouth, wherewith he puffs and blows,
For, save his nostrils, would Astolpho leave
No passage whence the count might air receive.

57.

Valiant Astolpho had prepared the vase,
Wherein Orlando's senses were contained,
And to his nostrils in such mode conveys,
That, drawing-in his breath, the county drained
The mystic cup withal. Oh wondrous case!
The unsettled mind its ancient seat regained;
And, in its glorious reasonings, yet more clear
And lucid waxed his wisdom than whilere.

58.

As one, that seems in troubled sleep to see
Abominable shapes, a horrid crew;
Monsters which are not, and which cannot be;
Or seems some strange, unlawful thing to do,
Yet marvels at himself, from slumber free,
When his recovered senses play him true;
So good Orlando, when he is made sound,
Remains yet full of wonder, and astound.

59.

Aldabelle's brother, Monodantes' son,
And him that on his brain such cure had wrought,
He wondering marked, but word he spake to none;
And when and how he was brought thither, thought.
He turned his restless eyes now up now down,
Nor where he was withal, imagined aught,
Marvelling why he there was naked cast,
And wherefore tethered, neck and heels, so fast.

60.

Then said, as erst Silenus said — when seen,
And taken sleeping in the cave of yore —
SOLVITE ME, with visage so serene,
With look so much less wayward than before,
That him they from his bonds delivered clean,
And raiment to the naked warrior bore;
All comforting their friend, with grief opprest
For that delusion which had him possest.

61.

When to his former self he was restored,
Of wiser and of manlier mind than e'er,
From love as well was freed the enamoured lord;
And she, so gentle deemed, so fair whilere,
And by renowned Orlando so adored,
Did but to him a worthless thing appear.
What he through love had lost, to reacquire
Was his whole study, was his whole desire.

DESIDERIUS ERASMUS

(1469–1536)

Erasmus was the prince of humanists. International in outlook and experience, he was the most universal scholar of his time, writing and speaking Latin as a living language. He lived through the crisis of the Reformation, and all of Europe looked to him as arbiter in the theological warfare that tore the Church asunder. Even though he did not accept the part, his intellectual influence permeated every country of western Europe.

He was born at Rotterdam, in the delta of the Rhine, in 1469, the younger of two brothers. His mother's name was Margaret; she was the daughter of a physician. His father, whose name was Gerard, went to Rome, earned a living by copying manuscripts, and later became a priest. His parents were never married. Charles Reade has told their story in his fine novel, *The Cloister and the Hearth.*

The story of Erasmus' education reveals a successful struggle to burst the mold of monastic confinement. Although it began at Gouda when he was five years old, in 1475, at the age of six, he entered the church school at Deventer, established by the founder of the Brethren of the Common Life. Both parents were dead by 1484. The two brothers were left in charge of guardians; they asked to be sent to a university but were urged to enter monastic life. Erasmus entered the religious school at Hertogenbosch, and two years later the priory of Emmaus at Steyn, of the order of Augustinian Canons, being ordained as priest in 1492. The opportunity for freedom came, however, with the offer to become Latin secretary to the Bishop of Cambrai, Henry of Bergen, leading prelate at the Burgundian court. It was through him that Erasmus was enabled to enter the university at Paris in 1495. He matriculated at the College of Montaigu, although he later lived in private lodgings where he received pupils. He became Bachelor of Theology in 1498. In Paris he wrote the first of his *Colloquies.* Later he was at the university in Louvain, where he wrote the *Handbook of the Christian Knight* in 1503.

It was in the company of one of his pupils, Lord Mountjoy, that Erasmus first went to England in 1499. He was to return five times later, and his English experience and friends became of permanent significance in his life. On his first visit, at Mountjoy's country house at Greenwich, he met Thomas More — student of the humanities, then practicing law in London, twenty-one years of age; at Eltham Place near by, he was presented to the children of Henry VII, including the nine-year-old Prince Henry. At Oxford he was introduced to John Colet, student of primitive texts and lecturer on St. Paul's Epistles, later to be Dean of St. Paul's in London. On his second visit in 1505–6, he met John Fisher, Bishop of Rochester, Chancellor of Cambridge University, and William Warham, Archbishop of Canterbury. His third visit proved to be the longest: from October 1509 to July 1514. During a part of this time, through Fisher's influence, he became lecturer in Greek at Cambridge and accepted the chair in Divinity founded by Lady Margaret Tudor, residing at Queen's College. Warham conferred upon him the benefice of Aldington in Kent. One's imagination likes to linger over Erasmus' life at Cambridge and his friendships with More and Colet. "When I hear my Colet I seem to be listening to Plato himself . . . What has nature ever created more gentle, sweet, or happy than the genius of Thomas More?" he wrote enthusiastically in one of his letters. In More's house, after his Italian trip in 1509, he wrote *The Praise of Folly*. It was at Cambridge that he completed his work on the *Greek New Testament*.

He left England after his second visit in 1506 to go to Italy. The opportunity had come with the offer to act as tutor to the sons of the Italian physician of Henry VII. Erasmus was too cosmopolitan to remain in any one place permanently. He wished to visit the sacred places and libraries of Italy and to know the learned beyond the Alps. At Turin he took the degree of Doctor in Theology. He studied at the university in Bologna. He spent a year in Venice, much of the time a guest of the humanist printer Aldo Manuzio, who brought out a handsome edition of his *Adages*. He was at Padua, Ferrara, Florence, Siena. At Rome he was honored by the society of eminent prelates. "There one enjoys sweet liberty, rich libraries, the charming friendship of writers and scholars, and the sight of antique monuments," he later wrote. He left in 1509 at the accession of Henry VIII of England, induced to return by his English friends with expectation of preferment.

After his third and longest sojourn in England, in 1514, Erasmus — now famous — returned to the banks of the Rhine, which were to be the center of his activity for the rest of his life. Although he was frequently elsewhere — at Louvain from 1517 to 1521, at Constance, at Besançon, at Freiburg in the Breisgau — he lived chiefly in the Swiss town of Basel: from 1514 to 1516, again from 1521 to 1529, and during the last year of his life. Basel was a pleasant and cultured town located on the upper Rhine, the home of writers and artists, the seat of a university, and famous most of all for the press of the eminent printer John Froben. With Froben Erasmus formed a warm friendship; Froben brought out his *Greek New Testament* in 1516, and Erasmus became general editor and literary adviser to the press. It was in Basel that the German artist, Hans Holbein, made the famous portraits of Erasmus.

In October 1517, Martin Luther posted his *Ninety-five Theses* on indulgences on the doors of the church in Wittenberg. Thereafter Erasmus, against his will, was drawn inevitably into the conflicts of the Reformation. In 1519, Ulrich Zwingli entered upon the reform of the city of Zurich, which became the Swiss center of revolt from Rome. The history of Erasmus' attitude toward the Reformers reveals the essential relationship between the Renaissance and the Reformation. As he said himself, in his battle to change the pagan humanism of Italy into an European Christian humanism, at that point when success seemed in prospect, Luther arose and threw the apple of discord into the world.

"I think we should rather strive to instil Christ into the minds of men than to fight with Christians," Erasmus wrote. He sought to dissociate the religious conflict from the cause of "sound learning." At first he tended to exert his influence to obtain for Luther a fair hearing and to protect him from unjust persecution; it was his plan to submit the controversy to a committee of arbitration of impartial and learned judges. In the end, however, he was alienated both by the violence of Luther's dogmatism and partisanship and the obscurantism and conduct of his Catholic opponents. He sought to maintain a neutral position, but ended by bringing upon himself the antagonism of both sides. "O Erasmus of Rotterdam," Albrecht Dürer wrote in his diary, "where wilt thou abide? O thou Knight of Christ, seize the martyr's crown." But the scholarly mind of Erasmus saw clearly the good and evil of both parties; he was a scholar, but not a dogmatist; and he hated revolution.

When the Swiss Reformers abolished the Mass and pulled down the images in the church at Basel, Erasmus left in 1529 and took up his residence at Freiburg in the Breisgau, a beautiful city in the Black Forest of southwestern Germany. He was now sixty years of age, and weary of the war of sects. With the university here he was on intimate terms; his fame brought visits and letters from friends and admirers from all of western Christendom. He continued to work with absorption to the end. Here, however, came the tragic news from England of the execution of Fisher, Bishop of Rochester, and Sir Thomas More. Erasmus returned to Basel in the summer of 1535. He died there in July 1536. "He was borne on the shoulders of students to the cathedral," wrote Beatus Rhenanus, "and there near the steps which lead up to the choir, on the left side of the church, by the chapel of the Blessed Virgin, was honorably laid to rest. In the funeral procession walked the chief magistrate and many members of the council. Of the professors and students of the University not one was absent."

It was Erasmus' life purpose to return to the original sources of both the pagan and the Christian traditions, to determine the original truth of both, and to apply their knowledge and wisdom to the problems of his own age. He believed that, if men should know the truth, it would set them free. His text of the *Greek New Testament,* first printed by Froben in 1516, was the first to be put in print. It revealed the true character of the Vulgate and became the foundation for the new translations into the vernacular languages of Europe which were to follow. He then published a new Latin translation of the *New Testament,* and paraphrases of most of its books. He edited a large number of the Church Fathers both Latin and Greek, and a large number of the Latin and Greek classics.

As social critic and man of letters, Erasmus won international fame with *The Praise of Folly,* first published in Paris in 1511. The *Familiar Colloquies,* first published at Basel in 1518, but in many enlarged editions later, although first intended as a Latin textbook, spread the author's liberal ideas throughout western Europe with immense popularity. About 3000 of Erasmus' letters are preserved; the expression of his personality and the record of Europe during the age of the Reformation which they give make them of enduring value. They were published in various collections during his lifetime, the largest being the *Opus Epistolarum,* published by Froben in 1529.

Of his many other writings, mention here should be made of the *Adages, Familiar Quotations from the Classics,* first published in Paris in 1500; the *Enchiridion Militis Christiani,* or the *Handbook of the Christian Knight,* first published at Antwerp in 1503; the *Institution of a Christian Prince,* written for Charles V and published by Froben in 1516; the dialogue called the *Ciceronian,* a satire upon the literary idolatry of late humanists, published in 1528; and the *Apothegms,* written at Freiburg, and published by Froben in 1531.

No portrait is perhaps seen more frequently on the walls of the modern scholar's study than one by Holbein of Erasmus. In personal appearance, he was slight, frequently of infirm health, with blue eyes and light brown hair. In Sir Richard Jebb's analysis, the face has "two chief characteristics, — quiet, watchful sagacity, — and humour, half playful, half sarcastic. The eyes are calm, critical, steadily observant, with a half-latent twinkle in them; . . . the rippling curves of the large mouth indicate a certain energetic vivacity of temperament, and tenacity of purpose . . ." The features speak of "insight and refinement; of a worldly yet very gentle shrewdness . . . of a mind which has its weapons ready at every instant."

No other scholar of the Renaissance achieved the position of Erasmus. A list of his friends and correspondents would include the foremost figures as well as the choice spirits of his day in England, Germany, Italy, France, and Spain — kings and queens and princes, churchmen, scholars, men of genius in affairs. There was nothing more dreaded by those who still held to the superstitions and dogmas of the past than the rapier of his wit and ridicule. The rich synthesis he wrought of both the pagan and Christian traditions resulted in his teaching "the philosophy of Christ." He learned that there was an inward relation between all the noble truths of the past, both Christian and pagan, and that the true worship of Christ was an imitation of His life. Having recognized in reason the final judge, he forever stands as one who was loyal to the end to the truth as he found it, and the freedom and integrity of the intellectual life.

SELECTED BIBLIOGRAPHY

EDITIONS

Opera Omnia, ed. Johannes Clericus, Leyden, 1703–6, 10 vols. *Opus Epistolarum,* ed. P. S. Allen and H. M. Allen, and later H. W. Garrod, Oxford, Clarendon Press, 1906–47, 11 vols.

TRANSLATIONS

The Epistles of Erasmus, trans. Francis M. Nichols, London, Longmans, 1901–18, 3 vols. *Twenty Select Colloquies,* trans. Sir Roger L'Estrange (1680), Boston, Small Maynard, n.d.; *The Colloquies,* trans. Nathan Bailey, ed. Rev. E. Johnson, London, Gibbings & Co., 1900, 3 vols. *The Praise of Folly,* trans. John Wilson (1668), ed. Mrs. P. S. Allen, Oxford, Clarendon Press, 1913; trans. Hoyt H. Hudson, Princeton Univ. Press, 1941; trans. Leonard F. Dean, Chicago, Packard, 1947. *The Apophthegmes,* trans. Nicholas Udall (1564), ed. Robert Roberts, Boston, Lincolnshire, R. Roberts, 1877. *A Book Called in Latin Enchiridion Militis Christiani and in English The Manual of the Christian Knight,* London, Methuen, 1905; *The Education of the Christian Prince,* trans. Lester K. Born, Columbia Univ. Press, 1936. *Erasmus against War,* introd. J. W. Mackail, Boston, Humanists' Lib., Updike, 1907; *The Complaint of Peace,* introd. W. J. Hirten, New York, Scholars' Facsimiles & Reprints, 1946. *Ciceronianus,* trans. Izora Scott, Columbia Univ. Press, 1908.

BIOGRAPHY AND CRITICISM

Frederic Seebohm, *The Oxford Reformers. Colet, Erasmus and More,* London, Longmans, 1867, also in Everyman's Lib.; Sir Richard C. Jebb, *Erasmus,* Cambridge Univ. Press, 1890; J. A. Froude, *Life and Letters of Erasmus,* New York, Scribners, 1894; Ephraim Emerton, *D. Erasmus of Rotterdam* (Heroes of the Reformation), New York, Putnam, 1899; W. H. Woodward, *D. Erasmus Concerning the Aim and Method of Education,* Cambridge Univ. Press, 1904; P. S. Allen, *The Age of Erasmus,* Oxford Univ. Press, 1914; Preserved Smith, *Erasmus. A Study of His Life, Ideals and Place in History,* New York, Harpers, 1923; Joseph Mangan, *The Life, Character, and Influence of D. Erasmus,* New York, 1926, valuable for letters; Albert Hyma, *The Youth of Erasmus,* Univ. of Michigan Press, 1930; Christopher Hollis, *Erasmus,* London, Eyre & Spottiswoode, 1933; P. S. Allen, *Erasmus Lectures and Wayfaring Sketches,* Oxford Univ. Press, 1934; Stefan Zweig, *Erasmus of Rotterdam,* New York, Viking Press, 1934; J. Huizinga, *Erasmus of Rotterdam; with a Selection from the Letters of Erasmus,* London, Phaidon, 1952.

SPECIAL STUDIES

Preserved Smith, *A Key to the Colloquies of Erasmus,* Harvard Univ. Press, 1927; Rachel Giese: "Erasmus' Greek Studies," *Class. Jour.,* XXIX (1934), 517–26; "Erasmus and the Fine Arts," *Jour. of Mod. Hist.,* VII (1935), 257–79; "Erasmus' Knowledge and Estimate of the Vernacular Languages," *Romanic Rev.,* XXVIII (1937), 3–18; Preserved Smith, "Erasmus, Enemy of Pedantry," *Am. Scholar,* VI (1937), 85–92; Rudolph Schevill, "Erasmus and the Fate of a Liberalistic Movement Prior to the Counter Reformation," *Hispanic Rev.,* V (1937), 103–23, and "Erasmus and Spain," *ibid.,* VII (1939), 93–116; Margaret M. Phillips, "Erasmus and Propaganda. A Study of the Translations of Erasmus in English and French," *Mod. Lang. Rev.,* XXXVII (1942), 1–17; R. P. Adams, "Designs by More and Erasmus for a New Social Order," *Stud. in Philol.,* XLII (1945), 131–45; Rachel Giese, "Erasmus in Effigy," *So. Atlantic Quar.,* XLIV (1945), 195–201; Fritz Caspari, "Erasmus on the Social Functions of Christian Humanism," *Jour. Hist. Ideas,* VIII (1947), 78–106; H. W. Garrod, "Erasmus and his English Patrons," *The Library,* IV (1950), 1–13; E. F. Rice, Jr., "Erasmus and the Religious Tradition, 1495–1499," *Jour. Hist. Idcas,* XI (1950), 387–411; W. Schenk, "The Erasmian Idea," *Hibbert Jour.,* XLVIII (1950), 257–65.

FAMILIAR COLLOQUIES

Translated by NATHAN BAILEY

[First published in 1725; the most recent edition is *The Colloquies of Desiderius Erasmus,* translated by N. Bailey, edited by the Rev. E. Johnson, 3 vols., Gibbings & Co., London, 1900.]

DIVERSORIA OR THE INNS

Bertulph and William

Bert. I wonder what is the fancy of a great many for staying two or three days at Lyons? When I have once set out on a journey I am not at rest till I come to my journey's end. *Will.* Nay, I wonder as much that anybody can get away from thence. *Bert.* But why so? *Will.* Because that is a place the companions of Ulysses could not have got away from. There are syrens. Nobody is better entertained at his own house than he is there at an inn. *Bert.* What is done there?

Will. There is a woman always waiting at table, which makes the entertainment pleasant with railleries and pleasant jests; and the women are very handsome there. First, the mistress of the house came and bade us welcome, and to accept kindly what fare we should have; after her comes her daughter, a very fine woman, of so handsome a carriage and so pleasant in discourse that she would make even Cato himself merry were he there. And they don't talk to you as if you were perfect strangers, but as those they have been a long time acquainted with, and familiar friends. *Bert.* Oh, I know the French way of civility very well. *Will.* And because they cannot be always with you, by reason of the other affairs of the house, and the welcoming of other guests, there comes a lass that supplies the place of the daughter till she is at leisure to return again. This lass is so well instructed in the knack of repartees, that she has a word ready for everybody, and no conceit comes amiss to her. The mother, you must know, was somewhat in years. *Bert.* But what was your table furnished with, for stories fill no bellies? *Will.* Truly, so splendid that I was amazed that they could afford to entertain their guests so for so small a price. And then, after dinner they entertain a man with such facetious discourse, that one cannot be tired, that I seemed to be at my own house, and not in a strange place. *Bert.* And how went matters in your chambers?

Will. Why, there was everywhere some pretty lass or other giggling and playing wanton tricks. They asked us if we had any foul linen to wash, which they wash and bring to us again. In a word, we saw nothing there but young lasses and women, except in the stables, and they would every now and then run in there too. When you go away they embrace you, and part with you with as much affection as if you were their own brothers or near kinsfolk.

Bert. This mode, perhaps, may become the French, but methinks the way of the Germans pleases me better, which is more manly. *Will.* I never have seen Germany; therefore, pray don't think much to tell how they entertain a traveller. *Bert.* I cannot tell whether the method of entertaining be the same everywhere; but I will tell you what I saw there. Nobody bids a guest welcome, lest he should seem to court his guests to come to him, for that they look upon to be sordid and mean, and not becoming the German gravity. When you have called a good while at the gate, at length one puts his head out of the stove window (for they commonly live in stoves till midsummer) like a tortoise from under his shell. Him you must ask if you can have any lodging there; if he does not say no, you may take it for granted that there is room for you. When you ask where the stable is he points to it; there you may curry your horse as you please yourself, for there is no servant will put a hand to it. If it be a noted inn, there is a servant shews you the stable and a place for your horse, but incommodious enough, for they keep the best places for those that shall come afterwards, especially for noblemen. If you find fault with anything, they tell you presently, if you don't like, look for another inn. In their cities they allow hay, but very unwillingly and sparingly, and that is almost as dear as oats. When you have taken care of your horse, you come whole into the stove, boots, baggage, dirt, and all, for that is a common room for all comers. *Will.* In France they appoint you a separate chamber, where you may change your clothes, clean and warm yourself, or take rest, if you have a mind to it.

Bert. There is nothing of that here. In the stove you pull off your boots, put on your shoes, and, if you will, change your shirt, hang up your wet clothes near the stove iron, and get near it to dry yourself. There is water provided for you to wash your hands if you will; but as for the cleanness of it, it is for the most part such that you will want another water to wash that off. *Will.* I commend this sort of people that have nothing of effeminacy in them. *Bert.* If you come in at four o'clock in the afternoon, you must not go to supper till nine, and sometimes not till ten. *Will.* Why so? *Bert.* They never make anything ready till they see all their company together, that one trouble may serve for all. *Will.* They are for taking the shortest way.

Bert. You are right; so that oftentimes there come all together into the same stove eighty or ninety footmen, horsemen, merchants, mariners, waggoners, husbandmen, children, women, sick and sound. *Will.* This is having all things in common. *Bert.* There one combs his head, another wipes off his sweat, another cleans his spatterdashes or boots, another belches garlic, and, in short, there is as great a confusion of tongues and persons as there was at the building the tower of Babel. And if they see any person of another country, who by his habit looks like a man of quality, they all stare at him so wistfully as if he was a sort of strange animal brought out of Africa. And when they are set at table, and he behind them, they will be still looking back at him, and be staring him in the face, till they have forgot their suppers. *Will.* At Rome, Paris, or Venice there is no person thinks anything strange.

Bert. In the meantime, it is a crime for you to call for anything. When it is grown pretty late, and they don't expect any more guests, out comes an old grey-bearded servant, with his hair cut short, and a crabbed look and a slovenly dress. *Will.* Such fellows ought to be cup-bearers to the cardinals at Rome. *Bert.* He having cast his eyes about, counts to himself how many there are in the stove; the more he sees there the more fire he makes in the stove, although it be at a time when the very heat of the sun would be troublesome; and this with them is accounted a principal part of good entertainment to make them all sweat till they drop again. If any one who is not used to the steam shall presume to open the window never so little that he be not stifled, presently they cry out to shut it again. If you answer you are not able to bear it, you will presently hear, get you another inn then. *Will.* But, in my opinion, nothing is more dangerous than for so many to draw in the same vapour, especially when their bodies are opened with the heat; and to eat in the same place, and to stay there so many hours, not to mention the belching of garlic, the stinking breaths — for many have secret distempers, and every distemper has its contagion; and, without doubt, many have the Spanish, or, as it is called, the French pox, although it is common to all nations. And it is my opinion there is as much danger from such persons as there is from those that have the leprosy. Tell me, now, what is this short of a pestilence? *Bert.* They are persons of a strong constitution, and laugh at and disregard those niceties. *Will.* But, in the meantime, they are bold at the perils of other men. *Bert.* What would you do in this case? It is what they have been used to, and it is a part of a constant mind not to depart from a custom. *Will.* And yet, within these five and twenty years nothing was more in vogue in Brabant than hot baths, but now they are everywhere grown out of use; but the new scabbado has taught us to lay them down.

Bert. Well, but hear the rest. By and by in comes our bearded Ganymede again, and lays on the table as many napkins as there are guests. But, good God! not damask ones, but such as you would take to have been made out of old sails. There are at least eight guests allotted to every table. Now those that know the way of the country take their places, every one as he pleases, for there is no difference between poor and rich, between the master and the servant. *Will.* This was that ancient equality which now the tyrant custom has driven quite out of the world. I suppose Christ lived after this manner with His disciples. *Bert.* After they are all placed, out comes the sour-looked Ganymede again, and counts his company over again; by and by he comes in again and brings every man a wooden dish and a spoon of the same silver, and then a glass, and then, a little after, he brings bread which the guests may chip every one for themselves at leisure, while the porridge is boiling. For sometimes they sit thus for near an hour. *Will.* Do none of the guests call for meat in the meantime? *Bert.* None who knows the way of the country.

At last the wine is set upon the table: good God! how far from being tasteless! So thin and sharp that sophists ought to drink no other. And if any of the guests should privately offer a piece of money to get a little better wine somewhere else, at first they will say nothing to you, but give you a look, as if they were going to murder you; and if you press it further, they answer you there have been so many counts and marquises that have lodged here, and none of them ever found fault with this wine. If you do not like it, get you another inn. They account only the noblemen of their own nation to be men, and wherever you come they are shewing you their arms. By this time comes a morsel to pacify a barking stomach. And by and by follow the dishes in great pomp; commonly the first has sippits of bread in flesh broth, or, if it be a fish day, in a soup of pulse. After that comes in another soup, and then a service of butcher's meat that has been twice boiled, or salt meats warmed again, and then pulse again, and by and by something of more solid food, until their stomachs being pretty well staid, they bring roast meat or stewed fish, which is not to be at all contemned; but this they are sparing of, and take it away again quickly. This is the manner they order the entertainment, as comedians do, who intermingle dances among their scenes, so do they their chops and soups by turns. But they take care that the last act shall be the best. *Will.* This is the part of a good poet.

Bert. And it would be a heinous offence if, in the meantime, anybody should say, take away this dish, there is nobody eats. You must sit your time appointed, which I think they measure by the hour-glass. At length out comes that bearded fellow, or the landlord himself, in a habit but little differing from his servants, and asks how cheer you? And by and by some better wine is brought. And they like those best that drink most, though he that drinks most pays no more than he that drinks least. *Will.* A strange temper of the nation! *Bert.* There are some of them that drink twice as much wine as they pay for their ordinary. But before I leave this entertainment, it is wonderful what a noise and chattering there is when once they come to be warm with wine. In short, it deafens a man. They oftentimes bring in a mixture of mimics, which these people very much delight in, though they are a detestable sort of men. There is such a singing, prating, bawling, jumping, and knocking, that you would think the stove were falling upon your head, and that one man cannot hear another speak. And this they think is a pleasant way of living, and there you must sit in spite of your heart till near midnight.

Will. Make an end of your meal now, for I myself am tired with such a tedious one. *Bert.* Well, I will. At length the cheese is taken away, which scarcely pleases them, except it be rotten and full of maggots. Then the old bearded fellow comes again with a trencher and many circles and semi-circles drawn upon it with chalk; this he lays down upon the table with a grim countenance and without speaking. You would say he was some Charon. They that understand the meaning of this lay down their money one after another till the trencher is filled. Having taken notice of those who lay down, he reckons it up himself, and if all is paid he gives you a nod. *Will.* But what if there should be anything over and above? *Bert.* Perhaps he will give it you again, and they oftentimes do so. *Will.* Does nobody find fault with the reckoning? *Bert.* Nobody that is wise. For they will say, what sort of a fellow are you? you pay no more than the rest. *Will.* This is a frank sort of men you are speaking of.

Bert. If any one is weary with his journey, and desires to go to bed as soon as he has supped, he is bid to stay till the rest go too. *Will.* This seems to me to be Plato's city. *Bert.* Then every one is shewn to his chamber, and truly it is nothing else but a chamber; there is only a bed there, and nothing else that you can either make use of or steal. *Will.* Are things very clean there? *Bert.* As clean as they were at the table. Sheets washed perhaps six months ago. *Will.* What becomes of your horses all this while? *Bert.* They are treated after the manner that the men are. *Will.* But is there the same treatment everywhere? *Bert.* It is a little more civil in some places and worse in others than I have told you, but in general it is thus. *Will.* What if I should now tell you how they treat their guests in that part of Italy called Lombardy, and in Spain, and in England, and in Wales, for the English have the manners both of the French and the Germans, being a mixture of those two nations. The Welsh boast themselves to be the original English. *Bert.* Pray relate it. I never had the opportunity of travelling in them. *Will.* I have not leisure now, and the master of the ship bid me be on board by three o'clock, unless I would lose my passage. Another time we shall have an opportunity of prating our bellyful.

THE EXORCISM OR THE APPARITION

Thomas and Anselm

Tho. What good news have you had that you laugh to yourself thus, as if you had found a treasure? *Ans.* Nay, you are not far from the matter. *Tho.* But will you not impart it to your companion, what good thing soever it is? *Ans.* Yes, I will, for I have been wishing a good while for somebody to communicate my merriment to. *Tho.* Come on then, let us have it. *Ans.* I was just now told the pleasantest story, which you would swear was a sham if I did not know the place, the persons, and whole matter as well as you know me. *Tho.* I am with child to hear it.

Ans. Do you know Polus, Faunus's son-in-law? *Tho.* Perfectly well. *Ans.* He is both the contriver and actor of this play. *Tho.* I am apt enough to believe that, for he can act any part to the life. *Ans.* He can so. I suppose, too, you know that he has a farm not far from London. *Tho.* Phoo, very well. He and I have drank together many a time there. *Ans.* Then you know there is a way between two straight rows of trees. *Tho.* Upon the left hand, about two flight-shot from the house? *Ans.* You have it. On one side of the way there is a dry ditch overgrown with thorns and brambles, and then there is a way that leads into an open field from a little bridge. *Tho.* I remember it. *Ans.* There went a report for a long time among the country people of a spirit that walked near that bridge, and of hideous howlings that were every now and then heard there. They concluded it was the soul of somebody that was miserably tormented. *Tho.* Who was it that raised this report? *Ans.* Who but Polus, that made this the prologue to his comedy. *Tho.* What did he mean by inventing such a flam? *Ans.* I know nothing, but that it is the humour of the man. He takes delight to make himself sport, by playing upon the simplicity of people by such fictions as these.

I will tell you what he did lately of the same kind. We were a good many of us riding to Richmond, and some of the company were such that you would say were men of judgment. It was a wonderful clear day, and not so much as a cloud to be seen there. Polus, looking wistfully up into the air, signed his face and breast with the sign of the cross, and having composed his countenance to an air of amazement, says to himself, O immortal God, what do I see! They that rode next to him asking him what it was that he saw, he fell again to signing himself with a greater cross. May the most merciful God, says he, deliver me from this prodigy. They having urged him, desiring to know what was the matter, he fixing his eyes up to heaven, and pointing with his finger to a certain quarter of it, Do you not see, says he, that monstrous dragon armed with fiery horns, and its tail turned up in a circle? And they denying they saw it, he bid them look earnestly, every now and then pointing to the place. At last one of them, that he might not seem to be bad-sighted, affirmed that he saw it. And in imitation of him, first one, and then another, for they were ashamed that they could not see what was so plain to be seen. And in short, in three days' time the rumour of this portentous apparition had spread all over England. And it is wonderful to think how popular fame had amplified the story, and some pretended seriously to expound to what this portent did predict, and he that was the contriver of the fiction took a mighty pleasure in the folly of these people. *Tho.* I know the humour of the man well enough. But to the story of the apparition.

Ans. In the meantime one Faunus, a priest (of those which in Latin they call regulars, but that is not enough, unless they add the same in Greek too, who was parson of a neighbouring parish, this man thought himself wiser than is common, especially in holy matters), came very opportunely to pay a visit to Polus. *Tho.* I understand the matter. There is one found out to be an actor in this play. *Ans.* At supper a discourse was raised of the report of this apparition, and when Polus perceived that Faunus had not only heard of the report, but believed it, he began to entreat the man, that as he was a holy and a learned person, he would afford some relief to a poor soul that was in such dreadful torment. And, says he, if you are in any doubt as to the truth of it, examine into the matter, and do but walk near that bridge about ten o'clock, and you shall hear miserable cries; take who you will for a companion along with you, and so you will hear both more safely and better. *Tho.* Well, what then?

Ans. After supper was over, Polus, as his custom was, goes a hunting or fowling. And when it grew duskish, the darkness having taken away all opportunity of making any certain judgment of anything, Faunus walks about, and at last hears miserable howlings. Polus having hid himself in a bramble hedge hard by, had very artfully made these howlings by speaking through an earthen pot; the voice coming through the hollow of it gave it a most mournful sound. *Tho.* This story, as far as I see, outdoes Menander's Phasma. *Ans.* You will say more if you shall hear it out. Faunus goes home, being impatient to tell what he had heard. Polus, taking a shorter way, had got home before him. Faunus up and tells Polus all that passed, and added something of his own to it, to make the matter more wonderful. *Tho.* Could Polus keep his countenance in the meantime? *Ans.* He kept his countenance! He has his countenance in his hand; you would have said that a serious affair was transacted.

In the end Faunus, upon the pressing importunity of Polus, undertakes the business of exorcism, and slept not one wink all that night, in contriving by what means he might go about the matter with safety, for he was wretchedly afraid. In the first place he got together the most powerful exorcisms that he could get, and added some new ones to them, as the bowels of the Virgin Mary and the bones of St. Winifred. After that he makes choice of a place in the plain field, near the bramble bushes from whence the voice came. He draws a very large circle with a great many crosses in it, and a variety of characters. And all this was performed in a set form of words; there was also there a great vessel full of holy water, and about his neck he had a holy stole (as they called it), upon which hung the beginning of the Gospel of St. John. He had in his pocket a little piece of wax, which the bishop of Rome used to consecrate once a year, which is commonly called *Agnus Dei.* With these arms in times past they were wont to defend themselves against evil spirits, before the cowl of St. Francis was found to be so formidable. All these things were provided, lest if it should be an evil spirit, it should fall foul upon the exorcist; nor did he for all this dare to trust himself in the circle alone, but he determined to take some other priest along with him. Upon this Polus being afraid, that if he took some sharper fellow than himself along with him, the whole plot might come to be discovered, he got a parish priest thereabout, whom he acquainted beforehand with the whole design; and, indeed, it was necessary for the carrying on the adventure, and he was a man fit for such a purpose.

The day following, all things being prepared and in good order, about ten o'clock Faunus and the parish priest enter the circle. Polus had got thither before them, and made a miserable howling out of the hedge; Faunus begins his exorcism, and Polus steals away in the dark to the next village, and brings from thence another person, for the play could not be acted without a great many of them. *Tho.* Well, what do they do? *Ans.* They mount themselves upon black horses, and privately carry fire along with them; when they come pretty near to the circle they shew the fire to affright Faunus out of the circle. *Tho.* What a deal of pains did this Polus take to put a cheat upon people? *Ans.* His fancy lies that way. But this matter had like to have been mischievous to them. *Tho.* How so? *Ans.* For the horses were so startled at the sudden flashing of the fire that they had like to have thrown their riders. Here is an end of the first act of this comedy.

When they were returned and entered into discourse, Polus, as though he had known nothing of the matter, inquires what was done. Faunus tells him that two hideous Cacodemons appeared to him on black horses, their eyes sparkling with fire, and breathing fire out of their nostrils, making an attempt to break into the circle, but that they were driven away with a vengeance by the power and efficacy of his words. This encounter having put courage into Faunus, the next day he goes into his circle again with great solemnity, and after he had provoked the spirit a long time with the vehemence of his words, Polus and his companion appear again at a pretty distance, with their black horses, with a most outrageous noise, making a feint as if they would break into the circle. *Tho.* Had they no fire then? *Ans.* No, none at all; for that had liked to have fallen out very unluckily to them. But hear another device: they threw a long rope over the ground, and then hurrying from one place to another, as though they were beat off by the exorcisms of Faunus, they threw down both the priest and holy water-pot all together. *Tho.* This reward the parish priest had for playing his part? *Ans.* Yes, he had; and for all that he had rather suffer this than quit the design. After this encounter, when they came to talk over the matter again, Faunus tells a mighty story to Polus, what great danger he had been in, and how courageously he had driven both the evil spirits away with his charms, and now he had arrived at a firm persuasion that there was no demon, let him be ever so mischievous or impudent, that could possibly break into this circle. *Tho.* This Faunus was not far from being a fool.

Ans. You have heard nothing yet. The comedy being thus far advanced, Polus's son-in-law comes in very good time, for he had married Polus's eldest daughter; he is a wonderful merry droll, you know. *Tho.* Know him! ay, I know him, that he has no aversion for such tricks as these. *Ans.* No aversion, do you say? nay, he would leave the most urgent affair in the world if such a comedy were either to be seen or acted. His father-in-law tells him the whole story, and gives him his part — that was to act the ghost. He puts on a dress, and wraps himself up in a shroud, and carrying a live coal in a shell, it appeared through his shroud as if something were burning. About night he goes to the place where this play was acted; there were heard most doleful moans. Faunus lets fly all his exorcisms. At length the ghost appears a good way off in the bushes, every now and then shewing the fire and making a rueful groaning.

While Faunus was adjuring the ghost to declare who he was, Polus of a sudden leaps out of the thicket, dressed like a devil, and making a roaring, answers him, You have nothing to do with this soul, it is mine; and every now and then runs to the very edge of the circle as if he would set upon the exorcist, and then retired back again as if he was beaten back by the words of the exorcism and the power of the holy water, which he threw upon him in great abundance. At last when this guardian devil was chased away, Faunus enters into a dialogue with the soul. After he had been interrogated and adjured, he answers, that he was the soul of a Christian man, and being asked his name, he answered Faunus. Faunus! replies the other, that is my name. So then they being namesakes, he laid the matter more to heart, that Faunus might deliver Faunus. Faunus asking a multitude of questions, lest a long discourse should discover the fraud, the ghost retires, saying it was not permitted to stay to talk any longer, because its time was come that it must go whither its devil pleased to carry it, but yet promised to come again the next day at what hour it could be permitted. They meet together again at Polus's house, who was the master of the show. There the exorcist relates what was done, and though he added some lies to the story, yet he believed them to be true himself — he was so heartily affected with the matter in hand.

At last it appeared manifestly that it was the soul of a Christian who was vexed with the dreadful torments of an unmerciful devil. Now all the endeavours are bent this way. There happened a ridiculous passage in the next exorcism. *Tho.* Prithee, what was that? *Ans.* When Faunus had called up the ghost, Polus, that acted the devil, leaped directly at him, as if he would, without any more to do, break into the circle; and Faunus he resisted stoutly with his exorcisms, and had thrown a power of holy water, the devil at last cries out that he did not value all this of a rush; you have had to do with a wench, and you are my own yourself. And though he had told Polus so in jest, it seemed that he had spoken truth; for the exorcist being touched with this word, presently retreated to the very centre of the circle and whispered something in the priest's ear. Polus seeing that, retires, that he might not hear what it was not fit for him to hear. *Tho.* In truth, Polus was a very modest, religious devil. *Ans.* He was so, otherwise he might have been blamed for not observing a decorum, but yet he heard the priest's voice appointing him satisfaction. *Tho.* What was that? *Ans.* That he should say the glorious 78th psalm three times over, by which he conjectured he had had to do with her three times that night. *Tho.* He was an irregular regular. *Ans.* They are but men, and this is but human frailty. *Tho.* Well, proceed: What was done after this?

Ans. Now Faunus more courageously advances to the very edge of the circle and challenges the devil of his own accord; but the devil's heart failed him, and he fled back. You have deceived me, says he, if I had been wise I had not given you that caution. Many are of opinion, that what you have once confessed is immediately struck out of the devil's memory, that he can never be able to twit you in the teeth for it. *Tho.* What a ridiculous conceit do you tell me of?

Ans. But to draw towards a conclusion of the matter. This dialogue with the ghost held for some days; at last it came to this issue: The exorcist asking the soul if there was any way by which it might possibly be delivered from its torments? It answered it might, if the money that it had left behind, being got by cheating, should be restored. Then, says Faunus, what if it were put into the hands of good people to be disposed of to pious uses? The spirit replied, That might do. The exorcist was rejoiced at this; he inquires particularly what sum there was of it? The spirit replied that it was a vast sum, and might prove very good and commodious. It told the place too where the treasure was hid, but it was a long way off; and it ordered what uses it should be put to. *Tho.* What were they? *Ans.* That three persons were to undertake a pilgrimage — one to the threshold of St. Peter, another to salute St. James at Compostella, and the third should kiss Jesus's comb at Tryers; and after that a vast number of services and masses should be performed in several great monasteries, and as to the overplus, he should dispose of it as he pleased. Now Faunus's mind was fixed upon the treasure; he had, in a manner, swallowed it in his mind. *Tho.* That is a common disease, but more peculiarly thrown in the priest's dish upon all occasions.

Ans. After nothing had been omitted that related to the affair of the money, the exorcist being put upon it by Polus, began to put questions to the spirit about several arts, as alchemy and magic. To these things the spirit gave answers, putting off the resolution of these questions for the present, promising it would make larger discoveries as soon as ever, by his assistance, it should get out of the clutches of its keeper, the devil; and, if you please, you may let this be the third act of this play.

As to the fourth act, Faunus began in good earnest everywhere to talk high, and to talk of nothing else in all companies and at the table, and to promise glorious things to monasteries, and talked of nothing that was low and mean. He goes to the place and finds the tokens, but did not dare to dig for the treasure, because the spirit had thrown this caution in the way, that it would be extremely dangerous to touch the treasure before the masses had been performed. By this time a great many of the wiser sort had smelt out the plot, while Faunus at the same time was everywhere proclaiming his folly; though he was privately cautioned by his friends, and especially his abbot, that he who had hitherto had the reputation of a prudent man should not give the world a specimen of his being quite contrary. But the imagination of the thing had so entirely possessed his mind that all that could be said of him had no influence upon him, to make him doubt of the matter, and he dreamt of nothing but spectres and devils. The very habit of his mind was got into his face, that he was so pale, and meagre, and dejected, that you would say he was rather a sprite than a man. And, in short, he was not far from being stark mad, and would have been so had it not been timely prevented.

Tho. Well, let this be the last act of the play. *Ans.* Well, you shall have it. Polus and his son-in-law hammered out this piece betwixt them. They counterfeited an epistle written in a strange antique character, and not upon common paper, but such as gold-beaters put their leaf-gold in, a reddish paper, you know. The form of the epistle was thus:

Faunus, long a captive, but now free. To Faunus, his gracious deliverer, sends eternal health. There is no need, my dear Faunus, that thou shouldest macerate thyself any longer in this affair. God has respected the pious intention of thy mind, and by the merit of it has delivered me from torments, and I now live happily among the angels. Thou hast a place provided for thee with St. Austin, which is next to the choir of the apostles: when thou comest to us I will give thee public thanks. In the meantime see that thou live merrily.

From the Imperial Heaven, the
Ides of September, Anno 1498.
Under the seal of my own ring.

This epistle was laid privately under the altar where Faunus was to perform divine service. This being done there was one appointed to advertise him of it, as if he had found it by chance. And now he carries the letter about him, and shews it as a very sacred thing, and believes nothing more firmly than that it was brought from heaven by an angel. *Tho.* This is not delivering the man from his madness, but changing the sort of it. *Ans.* Why truly, so it is, only he is now more pleasantly mad than before. *Tho.* I never was wont to give much credit to stories of apparitions in common, but for the time to come I shall give much less; for I believe that many things that have been printed and published as true relations were only by artifice and imposture impositions upon credulous persons and such as Faunus. *Ans.* And I also believe that a great many of them are of the same kind.

THE RELIGIOUS PILGRIMAGE

Menedemus, Ogygius

Me. What novelty is this? Don't I see my old neighbour Ogygius, that nobody has set their eyes on this six months? There was a report he was dead. It is he, or I am mightily mistaken. I will go up to him, and give him his welcome. Welcome, Ogygius. *Og.* And well met, Menedemus. *Me.* From what part of the world came you? for here was a melancholy report that you had taken a voyage to the Stygian shades. *Og.* Nay, I thank God, I never was better in all my life than I have been ever since I saw you last. *Me.* And may you live always to confute such vain reports. But what strange dress is this? It is all over set off with shells scolloped, full of images of lead and tin, and chains of straw-work, and the cuffs are adorned with snakes' eggs, instead of bracelets. *Og.* I have been to pay a visit to St. James at Compostella, and after that to the famous virgin on the other side the water in England; and this was rather a re-visit, for I had been to see her three years before. *Me.* What! out of curiosity, I suppose? *Og.* Nay, upon the score of religion. *Me.* That religion, I suppose, the Greek tongue taught you.

Og. My wife's mother had bound herself by a vow, that if her daughter should be delivered of a live male child, I should go to present my respects to St. James in person, and thank him for it. *Me.* And did you salute the saint only in your own and your mother-in-law's name? *Og.* Nay, in the name of the whole family. *Me.* Truly I am persuaded your family would have been every whit as well if you had never complimented him at all. But, prithee, what answer did he make you when you thanked him? *Og.* None at all, but upon tendering my present he seemed to smile, and gave me a gentle nod, with this same scollop shell. *Me.* But why does he rather give those than anything else? *Og.* Because he has plenty of them, the neighbouring sea furnishing him with them. *Me.* O gracious saint, that is both a midwife to women in labour and hospitable to travellers too!

But what new fashion of making vows is this, that one who does nothing himself shall make a vow that another man shall work? Put the case that you should tie yourself up by a vow that I should fast twice a week if you should succeed in such and such an affair, do you think I would perform what you had vowed? *Og.* I believe you would not, although you had made the vow yourself, for you make a joke of fobbing the saints off. But it was my mother-in-law that made the vow, and it was my duty to be obedient. You know the temper of women, and also my own interest lay at stake. *Me.* If you had not performed the vow what risk had you run? *Og.* I do not believe the saint could have laid an action at law against me, but he might for the future have stopped his ears at my petitions, or slily have brought some mischief or other upon my family; you know the humour of great persons.

Me. Prithee, tell me how does the good man St. James do, and what was he doing? *Og.* Why, truly, not so well as by far he used to be. *Me.* What is the matter; is he grown old? *Og.* Trifler, you know saints never grow old. No, but it is this new opinion that has been spread abroad through the world is the occasion that he has not so many visits paid to him as he used to have, and those that do come give him a bare salute, and either nothing at all, or little or nothing else; they say they can bestow their money to better purpose upon those that want it. *Me.* An impious opinion. *Og.* And this is the cause that this great apostle, that used to glitter with gold and jewels, now is brought to the very block that he is made of, and has scarce a tallow candle. *Me.* If this be true the rest of the saints are in danger of coming to the same pass.

Og. Nay, I can assure you that there is a letter handed about which the Virgin Mary herself has written about this matter. *Me.* What Mary? *Og.* She that is called Maria a Lapide. *Me.* That is up towards Basil, if I am not mistaken. *Og.* The very same. *Me.* You talk of a very stony saint. But who did she write it to? *Og.* The letter tells you the name. *Me.* Who did she send it by? *Og.* An angel, no doubt, who laid it down in the pulpit, where the preacher to whom it was sent took it up; and to put the matter out of all doubt, you shall see the original letter. *Me.* Do you know the angel's hand that is secretary to the Virgin Mary? *Og.* Well enough. *Me.* By what token? *Og.* I have read St. Bede's epitaph that was engraven by the same angel, and the shape of the letters are exactly the same; and I have read the discharge sent to St. Ægidius, and they agree exactly. Do not these prove the matter plain enough? *Me.* May a person see it? *Og.* You may, if you will damn your soul to the pit of hell if ever you speak about it. *Me.* It is as safe as if you spoke it to a stone. *Og.* But there are some stones that are infamous for this, that they cannot keep a secret. *Me.* If you cannot trust to a stone, speak to a mute then. *Og.* Upon that condition I will recite it to you; but prick up both your ears. *Me.* I have done so.

Og. Mary, the mother of Jesus, to Glaucoplutus sendeth greeting. This is to let you know that I take it in good part, and you have much obliged me in that you have so strenuously followed Luther, and convinced the world that it is a thing altogether needless to invoke saints. For before this time I was even wearied out of my life with the wicked importunities of mortals. Everything was asked of me, as if my Son was always a child, because He is painted so, and at my breast, and therefore they take it for granted I have Him still at my beck, and that He dares not deny me anything I ask of Him, for fear I should deny Him the bubby when He is thirsty. Nay, and they ask such things from me, a virgin, that a modest young man would scarce dare to ask of a bawd, and which I am ashamed to commit to writing.

A merchant that is going a voyage to Spain to get pelf recommends to me the chastity of his kept mistress; and a professed nun, having thrown away her veil in order to make her escape, recommends to me the care of her reputation, which she at the same time intends to prostitute. The wicked soldier, who butchers men for money, bawls out to me with these words, O blessed Virgin, send me rich plunder. The gamester calls out to me to give him good luck, and promises I shall go snips with him in what he shall win; and if the dice do not favour, I am railed at and cursed because I would not be a confederate in his wickedness. The usurer prays, Help me to large interest for my money, and if I deny them anything they cry out I am no mother of mercy.

And there is another sort of people whose prayers are not properly so wicked as they are foolish. The maid prays, Mary, give me a handsome, rich husband; the wife cries, Give me fine children; and the woman with child, Give me a good delivery. The old woman prays to live long without a cough and thirst; and the doting old man, Send that I may grow young again. The philosopher says, Give me the faculty of starting difficulties never to be resolved; the priest says, Give me a fat benefice; the bishop cries out for the saving of his diocese, and the mariner for a prosperous voyage; the magistrate cries out, Shew me thy Son before I die; the courtier, that he may make an effectual confession when at the point of death; the husbandman calls on me for seasonable rain, and a farmer's wife to preserve her sheep and cattle. If I refuse them anything, then presently I am hard-hearted. If I refer them to my Son they cry, If you will but say the word, I am sure He will do it. How is it possible for me a lone body, a woman, and a virgin, to assist sailors, soldiers, merchants, gamesters, brides and bridegrooms, women in travail, princes, kings, and peasants? And what I have mentioned is the least part of what I suffer.

But I am much less troubled with these concerns now than I have been, for which I would give you my hearty thanks, if this conveniency did not bring a greater inconveniency along with it. I have indeed more leisure, but less honour and less money. Before I was saluted queen of the heavens and lady of the world, but now there are very few from whom I hear an Ave Mary. Formerly I was adorned with jewels and gold, and had abundance of changes of apparel: I had presents made me of gold and jewels; but now I have scarce half a vest to cover me, and that is mouse-eaten too. And my yearly revenue is scarce enough to keep alive my poor sexton, who lights me up a little wax or tallow candle.

But all these things might be borne with, if you did not tell us that there were greater things going forward. They say you aim at this, to strip the altars and temples of the saints everywhere. I advise you again and again to have a care what you do, for other saints do not want power to avenge themselves for the wrong done to them. Peter, being turned out of his church, can shut the gate of the kingdom of heaven against you; Paul has a sword, and St. Bartholomew a knife. The monk William has a coat of mail under his habit, and a heavy lance too. And how will you encounter St. George on horseback, in his cuirassier's arms, his sword, and his whinyard? Nor is Anthony without his weapon; he has his sacred fire. And the rest of them have either their arms or their mischiefs, that they can send out against whom they please. And as for myself, although I wear no weapons, you shall not turn me out unless you turn out my Son too, whom I hold in my arms. I will not be pulled away from Him; you shall either throw us both out or leave us both, unless you have a mind to have a church without a Christ. These things I would have you know, and consider what answer to give me, for I have the matter much at heart.

From our Stone House, the Calends of
August, the Year of my Son's Passion,
1524. I, the Stony Virgin, have subscribed this with my own hand.

Me. In truth, this is a very terrible threatening letter, and I believe Glaucoplutus will take care what he does. *Og.* He will, if he is wise. *Me.* But why did not honest James write to him about this matter? *Og.* Truly I cannot tell, except it is because he is a great way off, and now-a-days all letters are intercepted. *Me.* But what wind carried you to England? *Og.* A very favourable wind, and I had made half a promise to the beyond-sea she-saint to pay her another visit within two or three years. *Me.* What did you go to ask for of her? *Og.* Nothing new but those common matters, the health of my family, the increase of my fortune, a long and a happy life in this world, and eternal happiness in the next. *Me.* But could not our Virgin Mary have done as much for you here? She has at Antwerp a temple much more magnificent than that beyond sea. *Og.* I will not deny that she is able, but one thing is bestowed in one place and another thing in another; whether this be her pleasure merely, or whether she being of a kind disposition, accommodates herself in this to our affections.

Me. I have often heard of James, but, prithee, give me some account of the beyond-sea lady. *Og.* I will do it as briefly as I can. Her name is very famous all over England, and you shall scarce find anybody in that island who thinks his affairs can be prosperous unless he every year makes some present to that lady, greater or smaller, according as his circumstances are in the world. *Me.* Whereabouts does she dwell? *Og.* Near the coast, upon the furthest part between the west and the north, about three miles from the sea; it is a town that depends chiefly upon the resort of strangers. There is a college of canons there, to which the Latins have added the name of Regulars, which are of a middle sort between monks and those canons that are called Seculars. *Me.* You tell me of amphibious creatures, such as the beavers are. *Og.* Nay, so are crocodiles too. But trifling apart, I will tell you in three words: in odious cases they are canons, in favourable cases they are monks. *Me.* You have hitherto been telling me riddles. *Og.* Why, then, I will give you a mathematical demonstration. If the pope of Rome should throw a thunderbolt at all monks, then they will be all canons; and if he will allow all monks to marry, then they will be all monks. *Me.* These are new favours; I wish they would take mine for one.

Og. But to return to the matter in hand. This college has little else to maintain it but the liberality of the Virgin, for all presents of value are laid up; but as for anything of money or lesser value, that goes to the support of the flock and the head of it, which they call the prior. *Me.* Are they men of good lives? *Og.* Not much amiss. They are richer in piety than in revenue. There is a clever neat church, but the Virgin does not dwell in it herself, but upon point of honour has given it to her Son. Her church is on the right hand of her Son's. *Me.* Upon His right hand! which way then does her Son look? *Og.* That is well taken notice of. When He looks toward the west He has His mother on the right, and when He looks toward the east she is on His left hand. And she does not dwell there neither, for the building is not finished; the doors and windows are all open, and the wind blows through it; and not far off is a place where Oceanus the father of the winds resides. *Me.* That is a hard case; where does she dwell then? *Og.* In that unfinished church that I spoke of, there is a little boarded chapel with a little door on each side to receive visitors. There is but little light to it but what comes from the tapers; but the scent is very grateful. *Me.* All these things conduce to religion. *Og.* Nay, Menedemus, if you saw the inside of it you would say it was the seat of the saints, it is all so glittering with jewels, gold, and silver. *Me.* You set me agog to go thither too. *Og.* If you do you will never repent of your journey.

Me. Is there any holy oil there? *Og.* Simpleton, that oil is only the sweat of saints in their sepulchres, as of Andrew, Catherine, &c. Mary was never buried. *Me.* I confess I was under a mistake; but make an end of your story. *Og.* That religion may spread itself the more widely, some things are shewn at one place and some at another. *Me.* And it may be that the donations may be larger, according to the old saying, Many hands will carry off much plunder. *Og.* And there are always some at hand to shew you what you have a mind to see. *Me.* What, of the canons? *Og.* No, no, they are not permitted, lest under the colour ot religion they should prove irreligious, and while they are serving the Virgin lose their own virginity. Only in the inner chapel, which I call the chamber of the holy Virgin, a certain canon stands at the altar. *Me.* What does he stand there for? *Og.* To receive and keep that which is given. *Me.* Must people give whether they will or no? *Og.* No;

but a certain religious modesty makes some give, when anybody stands by, who would not give a farthing if there were no witness of it, or give more than otherwise they would give. *Me.* You set forth human nature as I have experienced in myself. *Og.* There are some so devoted to the human nature, that while they pretend to lay one gift on the altar, by a wonderful sleight of hand they steal what another has laid down. *Me.* But put the case, if nobody were by, would the Virgin thunder at them? *Og.* Why should the Virgin do that any more than God himself does, whom they are not afraid to strip of His ornaments, and to break through the walls of the church to come at them? *Me.* I cannot well tell which I admire at most, the impious confidence of those wretches or God's patience.

Og. At the north side there is a certain gate, not of a church, don't mistake me, but of the wall that encloses the churchyard, that has a very little wicket, as in the great gates of noblemen, that he that has a mind to get in must first venture the breaking of his shins and afterwards stoop his head too. *Me.* In truth, it would not be safe for a man to enter in at such a little door. *Og.* You are in the right of it. But yet the verger told me that some time since a knight on horseback, having escaped out of the hands of his enemy, who followed him at the heels, got in through this wicket. The poor man at the last pinch, by a sudden turn of thought, recommended himself to the holy Virgin that was the nearest to him, for he resolved to take sanctuary at her altar, if the gate had been open. When, behold, which is such a thing as was never heard of, both man and horse were on a sudden taken into the churchyard and his enemy left on the outside of it stark mad at his disappointment.

Me. And did he give you reason to believe so wonderful a relation? *Og.* Without doubt. *Me.* That was no easy matter to a man of your philosophy. *Og.* He shewed me a plate of copper nailed on the door, that had the very image of this knight that was thus saved, and in the very habit which was then in fashion among the English, which is the same we see in old pictures, which, if they are drawn truly, the barbers and dyers and weavers in those days had but a bad time of it. *Me.* Why so? *Og.* Why, he had a beard like a goat, and there was not a wrinkle in any of his clothes — they were made so strait to his body that the very straitness of them made his body the more slender. There was also another plate that was an exact description of the chapel and the size of it. *Me.* Then there was no doubt to be made of it. *Og.* Under the little wicket there was an iron grate, no bigger than what a man on foot could just get in at; for it was not fit that any horse afterwards should tread upon that place which the former knight had consecrated to the Virgin. *Me.* And very good reason.

Og. From hence towards the east, there is another chapel full of wonders; thither I went. Another verger received me. There we prayed a little; and there was shewn us the middle joint of a man's finger. I kissed it, and asked whose relic it was? He told me it was St. Peter's. What, said I, the Apostle? He said it was. I then took notice of the bigness of the joint, which was large enough to be taken for that of a giant. Upon which, said I, Peter must needs have been a very lusty man. At this, one of the company fell a laughing. I was very much vexed at it; for if he had held his tongue the verger would have shewn us all the relics. However, we pacified him pretty well, by giving him a few groats.

Before this little chapel stood a house, which he told us, in the winter time, when all things were buried in snow, was brought there on a sudden from some place a great way off. Under this house there were two pits brimful, that were fed by a fountain consecrated to the holy Virgin. The water was wonderful cold, and of great virtue in curing pains in the head and stomach. *Me.* If cold water will cure pains in the head and stomach, in time oil will quench fire. *Og.* But, my good friend, you are hearing that which is miraculous; for what miracle is there in cold water quenching thirst? *Me.* That shift goes a great way in this story. *Og.* It was positively affirmed that this spring burst out of the ground on a sudden at the command of the holy Virgin.

I, observing everything very diligently, asked him how many years it was since that little house was brought thither? He said it had been there for some ages. But, said I, methinks the walls don't seem to carry any marks of antiquity in them. He did not much deny it. Nor these pillars, said I. He did not deny but those had been set up lately; and the thing shewed itself plainly. Then, said I, that straw and reeds, the whole thatch of it seems not to have been so long laid. He allowed it. Nor do these cross beams and rafters that bear up the roof seem to have been laid many years ago. He confessed they were not. And there being no part of that cottage remaining, said I to him, How then does it appear that this is the very cottage that was brought so far through the air? *Me.* Prithee, how did the sexton extricate himself out of this difficulty? *Og.* He presently shewed us an old bear's skin tacked there to a piece of timber, and almost laughed at us to our very faces for not having eyes to perceive a thing that was so plain. Therefore, seeming to be satisfied, and excusing our dulness of apprehension, we turned ourselves to the heavenly milk of the blessed Virgin.

Me. O mother like her Son! for as He has left us so much of His blood upon earth, so she has left us so much of her milk, that it is scarce credible that a woman who never had but one child should have so much, although her child had never sucked a drop. *Og.* And they tell us the same stories about our Lord's cross, that is shewn up and down both publicly and privately in so many places, that if all the fragments were gathered together, they would seem to be sufficient loading for a good large ship; and yet our Lord himself carried the whole cross upon his shoulders. *Me.* And don't you think this is wonderful? *Og.* It may be said to be an extraordinary thing, but not a wonderful one, since the Lord, who increases these things according to His own pleasure, is omnipotent.

Me. You put a very pious construction upon it, but I am afraid that a great many such things are forged for the sake of getting money. *Og.* I cannot think God would suffer any one to put these mockeries upon Him. *Me.* Nay, when both the mother and Son, Father and Spirit are robbed by sacrilegious persons, they don't seem to be moved the least in the world, so as to deter wicked persons, so much as by a nod or a stamp, so great is the lenity of the divine being.

Og. This is true, but hear me out. That milk is kept upon the high altar in which Christ is in the middle, and his mother, for respect sake, at his right hand; for the milk represents the mother. *Me.* Why, is it plain to be seen then? *Og.* It is preserved in a crystal glass. *Me.* Is it liquid then? *Og.* What do you talk of being liquid, when it has been put in above 1500 years ago. It is so concreted, you would take it for beaten chalk tempered with the white of an egg. *Me.* But why don't they shew it open? *Og.* Lest the milk of the Virgin should be defiled by the kisses of men. *Me.* You say very well, for I believe there are some who put lips to it, that are neither pure nor virgin ones. *Og.* As soon as the officer sees us, he runs presently and puts on a surplice and a stole about his neck, and falls down very devoutly and worships, and by and by gives us the holy milk to kiss. Then we prostrated ourselves at the lowest step of the altar, and having first paid our adoration to Christ, we applied ourselves to the Virgin in the following prayer, which we had framed beforehand for this very purpose:—

"Virgin Mother, who hast merited to give suck to the Lord of heaven and earth, thy Son Jesus, from thy virgin breasts, we desire that, being purified by His blood, we may arrive at that happy infant state of dove-like innocence which, being void of malice, fraud, and deceit, we may continually desire the milk of the evangelical doctrine, until it grows up to a perfect man, and to the measure of the fulness of Christ, whose blessed society thou wilt enjoy for evermore, with the Father and the Holy Spirit. Amen."

Me. Truly, a devout prayer. But what answer did she make? *Og.* If my eyes did not deceive me, they were both pleased, for the holy milk seemed to give a leap, and the eucharist seemed to look somewhat bigger than usual. In the meantime the shower of the relics came to us, without speaking a word, holding out such a kind of table as they in Germany that take toll on the bridges hold out to you. *Me.* In truth, I have oftentimes cursed those craving tables when I travelled in Germany. *Og.* We laid down some pieces of money, which he presented to the Virgin.

After this, by our interpreter (if I remember right), one Robert Aldridge, a well-spoken young man, and a great master of the English tongue, I inquired as civilly as I could, what assurance he had that this was really the Virgin's milk. And truly I desired to be satisfied of this with a pious intention, that I might stop the mouths of some impious persons who are used to scoff at all these things. The officer first contracted his brow without speaking a word; thereupon I pressed the interpreter to put the same question to him again, but in the fairest manner that could be, and he did it in so obliging a manner that if he had addressed himself to the mother herself in these terms, when she had but newly lain in, she would not have taken it amiss. But the officer, as if he had been inspired with some enthusiasm, looking upon us with astonished eyes, and with a sort of horror, cursing our blasphemous expression, said, What need is there for your putting this question, when you have an authentic record? and had turned us out of doors for heretics, had not a few pence pacified his rage.

Me. But how did you behave yourselves in the interim? *Og.* Just as if we had been stunned with a cudgel, or struck with thunder; we sneaked away, humbly begging his pardon for our boldness; for so a man ought to do in holy matters. Thence we went to the little chapel, the dwelling of the Virgin Saint. In our way thither an expounder of sacred things, one of the minors, offers himself; he stares upon us as if he had a mind to draw our pictures; and having gone a little farther, another meets us, staring upon us after the same manner; and after him a third. *Me.* It may be they had a mind to have drawn your picture. *Og.* But I suspected far otherwise. *Me.* What did you imagine then? *Og.* That some sacrilegious person had stolen some of the Virgin's vestments, and that I was suspected as the thief. Therefore, having entered the chapel, I addressed myself to the Virgin mother with this short prayer:—

"O thou who only of all women art a mother and a virgin, the most happy of mothers and the purest of virgins, we that are impure do now come to visit and address ourselves to thee that art pure, and reverence thee with our poor offerings, such as they are. Oh that thy son would enable us to imitate thy most holy life, that we may deserve, by the grace of the Holy Spirit, to conceive the Lord Jesus in the most inward bowels of our minds, and having once conceived him, never to lose him. Amen."

So I kissed the altar, laid down some money, and withdrew.

Me. What, did the Virgin hear? Did she give you no nod as a token that she had heard your prayer? *Og.* As I told you before, it was but an uncertain light, and she stood in the dark at the right side of the altar. And the check of the former officer had made me so dejected that I did not dare to lift up my eyes again. *Me.* Then this adventure had not a very happy conclusion? *Og.* Nay, the happiest of all. *Me.* Nay, now you put me in courage again; for, as your Homer says, my heart was even sunk into my breeches. *Og.* After dinner we go to church again. *Me.* How did you dare to do that, being suspected of sacrilege? *Og.* It may be I was; but I did not suspect myself. A clear conscience fears nothing. I had a great mind to see the record that the shower of the relics had referred us to. Having hunted a great while for it, we found it at last; but it was hung up so high that he must have good eyes that could read it; and mine are none of the best, nor none of the worst. Therefore, not being willing wholly to trust to him in a matter of such moment, I went along with Aldrisius as he read it.

Me. Well! and were all your doubts removed? *Og.* I was ashamed of myself that I should doubt of a matter that there was made so plain before one's eyes, the name, the place, the order of the proceeding—in one word, there was nothing omitted. There was one William of Paris, a man of general piety, but more especially religious in getting together the relics of saints all over the earth, he having travelled over a great many countries, and having everywhere diligently searched monasteries and churches, at last arrived at Constantinople (for this William's brother was a bishop there). When he was preparing to return home, the bishop acquainted him that there was a certain nun that had the Virgin's milk, and that he would be the happiest man in the world if he could possibly get any of it, either for love or money, or by any other means, for that all the relics he had hitherto collected were nothing compared to that sacred milk. Upon this William never was at rest till he had obtained one-half of this milk, and having gotten this treasure, thought himself richer than Croesus. *Me.* And very well he might. It was a thing so unexpected too.

Og. He goes straight homeward, but falls sick by the way. *Me.* Oh, how little trust is to be put in human felicity that it shall be either perfect or long-lived! *Og.* Finding himself in danger he sends for a Frenchman, a faithful fellow-traveller, and makes him swear secrecy, and then delivers the milk to him upon this condition, "That if he got home safe he should deposit that treasure on the altar of the holy Virgin that is worshipped at Paris in that noble church that has the river Seine on each side of it, as if itself gave place in reverence to the divinity of the Virgin. To sum up the matter in few words, William was buried; the other rides post, but he falls sick by the way, and thinking himself past recovery, he delivers the milk to an Englishman that was his fellow-traveller, making him take a solemn oath that he would perform that which he himself was to have done. The one dies, the other takes it and puts it upon the altar in the presence of all the canons of the place, those that at that time were called regulars, as they are yet at St. Genoveve. He obtained half this milk of them and carried it into England, and made a present of it to this beyond-sea place, his mind being moved thereunto by a divine impulse. *Me.* Truly this story hangs very handsomely together.

Og. Nay, further, that there might not be left the least room to doubt, the very names of the bishops were set down that were authorised to grant releases and indulgences to such as should come to see the milk according to the power to them given, but not without some donation or another. *Me.* And how far did that power extend? *Og.* To forty days. *Me.* But are there days in purgatory? *Og.* For certain there is time there. *Me.* But when they have disposed of this stock of forty days have they no more to bestow? *Og.* No; for there ever and anon arises something for them to bestow, and it is in this quite otherwise than it is with the tub of the Danaides; for though that is continually filling, it is always empty; but in this, though you are continually drawing out, there is never the less in the vessel. *Me.* But if the remission of forty days were given to a hundred thousand men would every one have so much? *Og.* Yes, so much. *Me.* And suppose that they that have received forty days in the morning should ask for forty days more at night, would they have wherewithal to give them? *Og.* Yes, ten times over in an hour. *Me.* I wish I had such a cabinet at home. I would not wish for above three groats if they might be doubled and tripled after that manner. *Og.* You might as well have wished to be all turned into gold yourself, and as soon have had what you wished for.

But to return to my story, there was one argument added by a man of great piety and candour, which is, that though the Virgin's milk, which is shewn in many other places, is indeed venerable enough in that it was scraped off from stones, yet this was more venerable than all the rest, because this was saved as it flowed from the Virgin's breast without touching the ground. *Me.* But how does that appear? *Og.* Oh, the nun at Constantinople that gave it said so. *Me.* It may be she had it of St. Bernard. *Og.* I believe she had. *Me.* He, when he was very old, had the happiness to taste milk from the same nipple which the child Jesus sucked, whence I wonder he was not rather called Lactifluous than Mellifluous. But how is that called the Virgin's milk that did not flow from her breasts? *Og.* That did flow from her breasts, but dropping upon the stone she sat upon while she was giving suck it concreted, and was afterwards by Providence so multiplied. *Me.* Right. Go on.

Og. These things being over, we were just upon the point of going away, but walking about and looking round us to see if there was anything worth taking notice of, the chapel officers come to us again, leering at us. Pointing at us with their fingers, they advance to us, retreat, run backward and forward, nod as if they would fain have said something to us, if they had had courage enough to have done it. *Me.* And was not you afraid then? *Og.* No, not at all; but I looked them full in the face very cheerfully, as who should say speak and welcome. At length one of them comes up to me and asked my name. I told it him. He asked me if I was the person that a matter of two years ago set up a votive table in Hebrew letters? I told him I was. *Me.* Can you write Hebrew then? *Og.* No; but they call everything Hebrew that they cannot understand. But by and by, upon calling, as I suppose, came the πρῶτος ὕστερος of the college.

Me. What title of dignity is that? Have they not an abbot? *Og.* No. *Me.* Why so? *Og.* Because they do not understand Hebrew. *Me.* Have they no bishop? *Og.* None at all. *Me.* Why so? *Og.* Because the Virgin is so poor that she has not wherewith to buy a staff and mitre. *Me.* Have they not so much as a president? *Og.* No, nor that neither. *Me.* What hinders? *Og.* Because a president is a name of dignity and not of holiness, and therefore the colleges of canons reject the name of an abbot, but they willingly allow the name of a president. *Me.* But this πρῶτος ὕστερος is what I never heard of before. *Og.* In truth you are but an indifferent grammarian then. *Me.* I know what ὑστερόπρωτον is in rhetoric. *Og.* Why, that is it. He that is next the prior is posterior-prior. You mean a sub-prior.

Og. He saluted me very courteously. He told me what great pains had been taken to read those verses; what wiping of spectacles there had been to no purpose; how often one grave doctor of divinity, and another of law, had been brought thither to expound the table. One said the letters were Arabic, another said they were fictitious ones; but at last they found one that made a shift to read the title. It was written in Latin words and Latin capitals. The verses were Greek in Greek capitals, which at first sight looked like Roman capitals. Being requested, I turned the verses into Latin, word for word. They would have given me a reward for this small service, but I positively refused it, affirming that there was nothing so difficult that I would not, with all the readiness in the world, undertake for the sake of the holy Virgin, even if she should command me to carry a letter for her from thence to Jerusalem. *Me.* What occasion can she have for you to be her letter-carrier that has so many angels for her secretaries and pages?

Og. He pulled out of his pouch a little piece of wood, cut off from the beam on which the Virgin mother stood. The admirable fragrancy of it shewed it to be a thing that was highly sacred. I having received this present in the lowest posture of humility and bare headed, and having kissed it over and over, put it in my pocket. *Me.* May a person see it? *Og.* I will let you see it if you will. But if you have eaten or drank to-day, or have had to do with your wife last night, I would not advise you to look upon it. *Me.* Let me see it; there is no danger. *Og.* Here it is for you. *Me.* O happy man art thou that hast such a present! *Og.* Whether you know it or no, I would not exchange this little fragment for all the gold in Tagus. I will set it in gold, and put it in a crystal case so that it may be seen through it.

When this hysteroprotos saw me so religiously transported with that small present, thinking I deserved to have things of greater moment imparted to me, he asked me if I had seen the Virgin's secrets. That word startled me a little, but I durst not ask him what he meant by the Virgin's secrets, for in matters so sacred there is danger in a slip of the tongue. I told him I had not seen them, but I had a very great desire to see them. Then I am conducted in as one in an ecstasy. A wax taper or two was lighted, and a little image was shewn me that made no extraordinary figure, neither for magnitude, matter, nor workmanship, but of extraordinary virtue. *Me.* Bulk has no great matter in it as to the doing of miracles. I have seen St. Christopher at Paris, not him of a cartload or of the size of a colossus, but rather of a large mountain; but I never heard he was famous for doing miracles. *Og.* At the feet of the Virgin there is a jewel that neither the Latins nor Greeks have yet given a name to. The French have given it a name from a toad, because it has the resemblance of a toad in it so lively that no art can match it. And that which is the more miraculous is that it is a very small stone, and the image does not stand out of it, but is included in the very body of the stone, and may be seen through it.

Me. Perhaps they may fancy they see the likeness of a toad cut in it, as some fancy they see that of an eagle in the stalk of a brake or fern; and as boys, who see everything in the clouds, as dragons breathing out fire, burning mountains, and armed men fighting. *Og.* Nay, that you may be thoroughly satisfied in the matter, no living toad ever shewed itself more plainly than that is expressed there. *Me.* I have been hearing your stories all this while, but I would have you find out somebody else to give credit to your story of the toad. *Og.* I do not at all wonder, Menedemus, that you are so incredulous; I should not have believed it myself if the whole tribe of divines had asserted it, unless I had seen it with these eyes—I say beheld it with these very eyes, and had experienced the truth of it. But methinks you seem not to be curious enough upon these natural rarities. *Me.* Why so? what, because I will not believe that asses fly.

Og. But do you not observe how nature sports herself in imitating the shapes and colours of everything in other things, but especially in precious stones? And also what admirable virtues it has planted in them, which are altogether incredible if common experience did not force us to a belief of them? Prithee, tell me, would you ever have believed without seeing it with your eyes that steel could have been drawn by the loadstone without touching it, or be driven away from it without being touched by it? *Me.* No, indeed, I never should, although ten Aristotles had taken their oaths of the truth of it.

Og. Well, then, do not say everything is a fable that has not fallen within the compass of your experience. We find the figure of a bolt in a thunder-stone, fire in the carbuncle, the figure of hail and the coldness of it in the hail-stone, nay, even though you throw it into the midst of the fire; the deep and transparent waves of the sea in the emerald; the carcinias imitates the figure of a sea-crab, the echites of a viper, the scarites of a gilt head, the theracites of a hawk, the geranites shews you the figured neck of a crane, the aegophthalmus shews the eye of a goat, and some shew that of a hog, and another three human eyes together; the lycophthalmus paints you out the eye of a wolf in four colours, fiery and bloody, and in the middle black encompassed with white. If you open the black cyamea you will find a bean in the middle; the dryites represents the trunk of a tree, and burns like wood; the cissites and narcissites represent ivy, the astrapias darts forth rays of lightning out of the midst of white or blue, the phlegontites shews a flame within that does not come out; in the anthracitis you may see certain sparks running to and fro; the crocias represents the colour of saffron, the rhodites that of a rose, the chalcites of brass, the aietites the figure of an eagle with a white tail, the taos represents a peacock, the chelidonia an asp, the mermecites has the image of a creeping pismire growing within it; the cantharias shews a perfect beetle, and the scorpites admirably deciphers a scorpion. But why should I proceed to recount that which is innumerable, when there is no part of nature, either in elements, animals, or plants, which nature, as it were to sport herself, does not give us some resemblance of in stones? And do you then admire that the form of a toad is represented in the bufonites? *Me.* I wonder that nature has so much spare time as to divert herself in drawing the pictures of everything. *Og.* It has a mind to exercise the curiosity of mankind, and by that means to keep us from being idle. And yet, as though we were at a loss to know how to pass away our time, we run a madding after buffoons, dice, and jugglers. *Me.* You say true.

Og. And some persons of credit add, that if you put this toadstone into vinegar it will move its legs and swim. *Me.* But why is this dedicated to the Virgin? *Og.* Because she has overcome, trampled upon, and extinguished all uncleanness, malice, pride, avarice, and all manner of earthly desires. *Me.* Woe to us, then, who carry so much of the toad still in our hearts! *Og.* But we shall be pure if we worship the Virgin as we ought. *Me.* How would she have us worship her? *Og.* You will perform most acceptable service to her if you imitate her. *Me.* That is soon said, but not so easily performed. *Og.* It is hard indeed, but then it is very well worth the pains. *Me.* Come on, go forwards in what you have begun. *Og.* Afterwards he shewed me statues of gold and silver. This, says he, is solid gold, and this is only silver gilt. He told me the weight of every one, the price, and the name of the donor.

I being full of admiration at everything, and congratulating the Virgin being mistress of so much wealth, says the officer to me, Inasmuch as I perceive you are so pious a spectator, I think I should not do fairly by you if I should conceal anything from you, therefore you shall see the greatest privacies the Virgin has. And presently he takes out of a drawer from under the altar a world of admirable things, the particulars of which, if I should proceed to mention, the day would not be long enough; so that thus far the journey succeeded to my wish. I satisfied my curiosity abundantly with fine sights, and brought home with me this inestimable present, a pledge of the Virgin's love, given me by herself.

Me. Did you ever make trial of the virtues of this piece of wood? *Og.* I have. Three or four days ago I, being in an house of entertainment, found a man stark mad, whom they were just going to put into chains; I put this piece of wood privately under his bolster, and he fell into a sound sleep and slept a long time, and when he rose in the morning he was as sober as ever. *Me.* Perhaps he was not distracted but drunk, and sleep commonly cures that distemper. *Og.* Menedemus, since you love to use raillery, take another subject. It is neither pious nor safe to make sport with saints; nay, the man himself told me that there was a woman appeared to him in his sleep of an incomparable beauty, that held forth a cup to him to drink. *Me.* Hellebore, I believe. *Og.* That is uncertain; but this is certain, that the man recovered his reason.

Me. Did you pass by Thomas, Archbishop of Canterbury? *Og.* No, I think I did not. It is one of the most religious pilgrimages in the world. *Me.* I long to hear it, if it will not be too much trouble to you. *Og.* It is so far from that, that you will oblige me in hearing of it. That part of England that looks towards Flanders and France is called Kent; the metropolis of it is Canterbury. There are two monasteries in it that are almost contiguous, and they are both of Benedictines. That which bears the name of Augustine is the ancienter of the two; that which is now called by the name of St. Thomas seems to have been the seat of St. Thomas the archbishop, where he had led his life with a few monks whom he chose for his companions, as now-a-days deans have their palaces near the church, though separate from the houses of other canons. For, in old time, both bishops and canons were monks, as appears by the manifest vestigia of things.

But the church that is dedicated to St. Thomas raises itself up towards heaven with that majesty that it strikes those that behold it at a great distance with an awe of religion, and now with its splendour makes the light of the neighbouring palaces look dim, and as it were obscures the place that was anciently the most celebrated for religion. There are two lofty turrets which stand as it were bidding visitants welcome from afar off, and a ring of bells that make the adjacent country echo far and wide with their rolling sound. In the south porch of the church stand three stone statues of men in armour, who with wicked hands murdered the holy man, with the names of their countries—Tusci, Fusci, and Betri. *Me.* Why have such wicked men so much honour done them? *Og.* They have the same honour done to them that is done to Judas, Pilate, Caiaphas, and the band of wicked soldiers whose images you may see carved upon stately altars; and their names are added that none after them might arrogate to themselves the glory of the fact. They are set there in open sight to be a warning to wicked courtiers, that no one may hereafter presume to lay his hand on either bishops or the possessions of the church. For these three ruffians ran mad with horror of the fact they had committed; nor had they come to themselves again, had not holy Thomas been implored in favour of them. *Me.* Oh, the perpetual clemency of martyrs!

Og. When you are entered in, a certain spacious majesty of place opens itself to you, which is free to every one. *Me.* Is there nothing to be seen there? *Og.* Nothing but the bulk of the structure, and some books chained to the pillars, containing the gospel of Nicodemus and the sepulchre of I cannot tell who. *Me.* And what else? *Og.* Iron grates enclose the place called the choir, so that there is no entrance, but so that the view is still open from one end of the church to the other. You ascend to this by a great many steps, under which there is a certain vault that opens a passage to the north side. There they shew a wooden altar consecrated to the holy Virgin; it is a very small one, and remarkable for nothing except as a monument of antiquity, reproaching the luxury of the present times. In that place the good man is reported to have taken his last leave of the Virgin, when he was at the point of death. Upon the altar is the point of the sword with which the top of the head of that good prelate was wounded, and some of his brains that were beaten out, to make sure work of it. We most religiously kissed the sacred rust of this weapon out of love to the martyr.

Leaving this place, we went down into a vault underground; to that there belong two showers of relics. The first thing they shew you is the skull of the martyr, as it was bored through; the upper part is left open to be kissed, all the rest is covered over with silver. There also is shewn you a leaden plate with this inscription, Thomas Acrensis. And there hang up in a great place the shirts of haircloth, the girdles, and breeches with which this prelate used to mortify his flesh, the very sight of which is enough to strike one with horror, and to reproach the effeminacy and delicacy of our age. *Me.* Nay, perhaps of the monks themselves. *Og.* That I can neither affirm nor deny, nor does it signify much to me. *Me.* You say right.

Og. From hence we return to the choir. On the north side they open a private place. It is incredible what a world of bones they brought out of it, skulls, chins, teeth, hands, fingers, whole arms, all which we having first adored, kissed; nor had there been any end of it had it not been for one of my fellow-travellers, who indiscreetly interrupted the officer that was shewing them. *Me.* Who was he? *Og.* He was an Englishman, his name was Gratian Pullus, a man of learning and piety, but not so well affected to this part of religion as I could wish he were. *Me.* I fancy he was a Wickliffite. *Og.* No, I believe he was not, though he had read his books; but I do not know where he had them. *Me.* Did he make the officer angry? *Og.* He took out an arm having yet some bloody flesh upon it; he shewed a reluctance to the kissing it, and a sort of uneasiness in his countenance: and presently the officer shut up all his relics again.

After this we viewed the table of the altar, and the ornaments; and after that those things that were laid up under the altar: all was very rich; you would have said Midas and Croesus were beggars compared to them, if you beheld the great quantities of gold and silver. *Me.* And was there no kissing here? *Og.* No, but my mind was touched with other sorts of wishes. *Me.* What were they? *Og.* It made me sigh to think I had no such relics in my own house. *Me.* A sacrilegious wish! *Og.* I confess it, and I humbly begged pardon of the saint before I set my foot out of the church.

After this we were carried into the vestry. Good God! what a pomp of silk vestments was there, of golden candlesticks! There we saw also St. Thomas's foot. It looked like a reed painted over with silver; it hath but little of weight, and nothing of workmanship, and was longer than up to one's girdle. *Me.* Was there never a cross? *Og.* I saw none. There was a gown shewn; it was silk, indeed, but coarse and without embroidery or jewels, and a handkerchief, still having plain marks of sweat and blood from the saint's neck. We readily kissed these monuments of ancient frugality. *Me.* Are these shewn to everybody? *Og.* No, certainly, my good friend. *Me.* How then did you come to have such credit with them, that none of their secrets were concealed from you? *Og.* I had some acquaintance with the reverend prelate, William Warham, the archbishop, and he recommended me. *Me.* I have heard he was a man of great humanity. *Og.* Nay, if you knew the man, you would take him for humanity itself. He was a man of that learning, that candour of manners, and that piety of life, that there was nothing wanting in him to make him a most accomplished prelate.

From hence we were conducted up higher; for behind the high altar there is another ascent as into another church. In a certain new chapel there was shewn to us the whole face of the good man set in gold, and adorned with jewels; and here a certain unexpected chance had near interrupted all our felicity. *Me.* I want sadly to hear what mischievous matter this was. *Og.* My friend Gratian lost himself here extremely. After a short prayer, he says to the assistant of him that shewed us the relics, Good father, is it true, as I have heard, that Thomas, while he lived, was very charitable to the poor? Very true, replies he, and began to relate a great many instances of his charity. Then, answers Gratian, I do not believe that good inclination in him is changed, unless it be for the better. The officer assented. Then, says he again, if this holy man was so liberal to the poor when he was a poor man himself, and stood in need of charity for the support of his own body, do you not think he would take it well now, when he is grown so rich and wants nothing, if some poor woman having a family of children at home ready to starve, or daughters in danger of being under a necessity to prostitute themselves for want of portions, or a husband sick in bed, and destitute of all comforts; if such a woman should ask him leave to make bold with some small portion of these vast riches for the relief of her family, taking it either as by consent, or by gift, or by way of borrowing?

The assistant making no answer to this, Gratian being a warm man, I am fully persuaded, says he, that the good man would be glad at his heart, that when he is dead he could be able to relieve the necessities of the poor with his wealth. Upon this the shower of the relics began to frown, and to pout out his lips, and to look upon us as if he would have eaten us up; and I do not doubt but he would have spit in our faces, and have turned us out of the church by the neck and shoulders, but that we had the archbishop's recommendation. Indeed I did in some measure pacify him with good words, telling him that Gratian did not speak this from his heart, but had a droll way with him, and also laid down a little money.

Me. Indeed, I exceedingly approve of your piety. But I sometimes seriously think of it, how they can possibly excuse themselves from being guilty of a fault who consume such vast sums in building, beautifying, and enriching churches, setting no bound to their expenses. I allow that there ought to be a dignity in the sacred vestments, the vessels of a church, agreeable to the solemn service, and would have the structure of it to have a certain air of majesty; but to what purpose are so many golden fonts, so many candlesticks, and so many images? To what purpose is such a profusion of expense upon organs, as they call them? Nor are we, indeed, content with one pair. What signify those concerts of music, hired at so great an expense; when in the meantime our brothers and sisters, Christ's living temples, are ready to perish for hunger and thirst!

Og. There is no man, either of piety or wisdom, but would wish for a moderation in these matters; but since this error proceeds from a certain extreme of piety, it deserves some favour, especially when we reflect, on the other hand, on the contrary errors of others, who rob churches rather than build them up. They are commonly endowed by great men and monarchs, who would employ the money worse in gaming or war. And, moreover, if you take anything away from the church, in the first place it is accounted sacrilege; and in the second place, it shuts up the hands of those who had an inclination to give; and besides, it is a temptation to rapine. The churchmen are rather guardians of these things than masters of them. And lastly, I had rather see a church luxuriant with sacred furniture, than as some of them are, naked and sordid, more like stables than churches. *Me*. But we read the the bishops of old were commended for selling the sacred vessels and relieving the poor with the money. *Og*. And so they are commended at this day; but they are only commended; for I am of the mind, they neither have the power nor the will to follow the example.

Me. But I hinder your narration; I now expect to hear the conclusion of your story. *Og*. Well, you shall have it, and I will be very brief. Upon this, out comes the head of the college. *Me*. Who was he, the abbot of the place? *Og*. He wears a mitre, and has the revenue of an abbot—he wants nothing but the name; he is called the prior, because the archbishop is in the place of an abbot; for in old time every one that was an archbishop of that diocese was a monk. *Me*. It did not matter if I was called a camel, if I had but the revenue of an abbot. *Og*. He seemed to me to be a godly and prudent man, and not unacquainted with the Scotch divinity. He opened us the box in which the remainder of the holy man's body is said to rest. *Me*. Did you see the bones? *Og*. That is not permitted, nor can it be done without a ladder. But a wooden box covers a golden one, and that being craned up with ropes, discovers an inestimable treasure. *Me.* What say you? *Og.* Gold was the basest part. Everything sparkled and shined with very large and scarce jewels, some of them bigger than a goose's egg. There some monks stood about with the greatest veneration. The cover being taken off, we all worshipped. The prior, with a white wand, touched every stone one by one, telling us the name in French, the value of it, and who was the donor of it. The principal of them were the presents of kings. *Me.* He had need to have a good memory. *Og.* You guess right, and yet practice goes a great way, for he does this frequently.

Hence he carried us back into a vault. There the Virgin Mary has her residence; it is something dark; it is doubly railed in and encompassed about with iron bars. *Me.* What is she afraid of? *Og.* Nothing, I suppose, but thieves. And I never in my life saw anything more laden with riches. *Me.* You tell me of riches in the dark. *Og.* Candles being brought in we saw more than a royal sight. *Me.* What, does it go beyond the Parathalassian virgin in wealth? *Og.* It goes far beyond in appearance. What is concealed she knows best. These things are shewn to none but great persons or peculiar friends. In the end we were carried back into the vestry. There was pulled out a chest covered with black leather; it was set upon the table and opened. They all fell down on their knees and worshipped. *Me.* What was in it? *Og.* Pieces of linen rags, a great many of them retaining still the marks of the snot. These were those, they say, that the holy man used to wipe the sweat off from his face and neck with, the snot out of his nose, or any other such sort of filth which human bodies are not free from.

Here again my Gratian behaved himself in none of the most obliging manners; for the gentle prior offered to him, being an Englishman, an acquaintance, and a man of considerable authority, one of the rags for a present, thinking he had presented him with a very acceptable gift; but Gratian unthankfully took it squeamishly in his fingers, and laid it down with an air of contempt, making up his mouth at it as if he would have smacked it. For this was his custom, if anything came in his way that he would express his contempt to. I was both ashamed and afraid. Nevertheless the good prior, though not insensible of the affront, seemed to take no notice of it; and after he had civilly entertained us with a glass of wine, dismissed us, and we went back to London.

Me. What need was there for that when you were not far from your own shore? *Og.* I was not, but I industriously shunned that shore, it being more infamous for cheats and rapines than any rocks are for shipwrecks. I will tell you what I saw in my last passage that way. There was a pretty many of us upon the shore of Calais, who were carried thence in a chaloupe to a large ship. Among the rest there was a young Frenchman that was poor and ragged, and they demanded twopence for his passage, for so much they will have if they carry you but a boat's length. He pleaded poverty. They in a frolic would needs search him, and having pulled off his shoes they find ten or twelve pieces of silver between the soles. They took the money, laughed at him to his face, and bantered the Frenchman as a cheat into the bargain. *Me.* What did the fellow do then? *Og.* What should he do but lament his misfortune?

Me. Do they do these things by authority? *Og.* By the same authority that they steal the baggage of a guest in his inn, or take his purse upon the road, if they find an opportunity. *Me.* It is very strange that they dare to commit such villainy before so many witnesses. *Og.* They are so used to it that they think they do well in it. There were many in the great ship who looked on, and some English merchants in the boat who grumbled at it, but to no purpose. They boasted of it as a piece of wit in catching the Frenchman in his roguery. *Me.* I would hang up those coast thieves, and laugh at them, and banter them at the gallows. *Og.* Nay, both shores abound with such fellows. Hence I make this improvement, If the little thieves dare to do thus, what will their masters do? So that I had rather for the future go ever so far about than that shortest way. And besides, as the descent to hell is easy but the return is difficult, so the entrance of this shore is not very easy, and the getting out of it very difficult.

There were at London some skippers belonging to Antwerp, so I determined to take passage with them. *Me.* Are the skippers of that country any better than others? *Og.* I confess, as an ape will always be an ape, so a skipper will always be a skipper; but if you compare them to those that live upon the catch, they are angels. *Me.* I shall remember it, if I ever have a mind to visit that island. But go on again, I have led you out of the way.

Og. In our journey to London, not far from Canterbury there is a narrow, hollow, steep way, and a cragged, steep bank on either side, so that you cannot escape it, for there is no other way to go. Upon the left hand of that way there is a little cottage of old mendicants. As soon as they espy a man on horseback coming, one of them runs out and sprinkles him with holy water, and then offers him the upper leather of a shoe, with a brass ring to it, in which is a glass, as if it were some gem. Having kissed it, you give a small piece of money. *Me.* In such a way I had rather meet with a cottage of old mendicants than a gang of lusty footpads.

Og. Gratian rode on my left hand, next to this cottage; he was sprinkled with holy water, and took it pretty well; but upon presenting the shoe he asked what was meant by that? This, says the poor man, was St. Thomas's shoe. Gratian fell into a passion, and turning to me said, What would these brutes have? Will they make us kiss the shoes of all that have been good men? Why do they not as well give us their spittle and the other excrements of their bodies to kiss? I pitied the poor old man, and comforted him, being sorrowful, by giving him a little money. *Me.* In my opinion Gratian was not angry altogether without a cause. If these shoes and slippers were preserved as an argument of moderation in living I should not dislike it, but I think it a piece of impudence to thrust slippers, and shoes, and stockings upon any one to be kissed. If any one shall do it of their own free choice, from a great affection to piety, I think they deserve to be left to their own liberty.

Og. Not to dissemble, I think those things had better be let alone; but in those matters that cannot be mended on a sudden, it is my way to make the best of them. In the meantime my mind was delighted with this contemplation, that a good man was like a sheep and a wicked man like a hurtful beast. A viper, indeed, cannot bite when it is dead, yet it is infectious by its stink and corruption. A sheep, while it lives, nourishes us with its milk, clothes us with its wool, and enriches us by its increase; when it is dead it supplies us with leather, and is every part of it fit to be eaten. In like manner, men that are furious and devoted to this world while they live are troublesome to all persons, and when they are dead are a disturbance to those that are alive, with the noise of the bells and a pompous funeral, and sometimes to their successors at their entering upon their possessions, by causing new exactions. But good men make themselves profitable in all respects to the whole world. As this saint, while he was alive, by his example, his doctrine, and admonitions invited to piety, comforted the friendless, succoured the needy, so now he is dead he is in some sort more useful. He built this magnificent church, and advanced the authority of the priesthood all over England; and now, after all, this fragment of his shoe maintains a conventicle of poor men.

Me. That, indeed, is a very pious contemplation; but I wonder, since you are of this mind, that you never went to see St. Patrick's den, of which the people say so many prodigious things that I can scarce think likely to be true. *Og.* Nay, there is no report of it can be so prodigious but that the thing itself exceeds it. *Me.* Why, then, did you ever enter into it? *Og.* Yes, I have ferried over a lake truly Stygian, and descended into the very jaws of Avernus, and seen all that is done in hell. *Me.* You will bless me if you shall not think much to relate it. *Og.* I think this preface of our discourse has been prolix enough. I am going home to give order to get supper ready, for I have not dined yet.

Me. Why have you had no dinner? Is it upon a religious account? *Og.* No, but out of spite. *Me.* What, do you spite your belly? *Og.* No, but unconscionable victuallers who, although they serve you with what is not fit to be eaten, make no scruple of demanding for it an unreasonable price. This is the way that I revenge myself on them. If I am in hope of a good supper, either at an acquaintance's or at an eating-house, that is anything tolerable, my stomach fails me at dinner. If fortune throws in my way a dinner such as I like, then my stomach fails me at supper-time. *Me.* And are you not ashamed to be so stingy and sneaking? *Og.* Believe me, Menedemus, in such cases as this those that make use of their modesty employ it to a wrong use. I have learned to keep my bashfulness for other purposes.

Me. I do even long for the remainder of your story, and therefore expect me at supper, and there you may tell it more at leisure. *Og.* In truth, I give you thanks for taking the freedom to invite yourself, when many who are invited with earnestness will not accept of it; but I will thank you over and over if you shall sup at home to-night, for my time will be taken up in congratulating my family. But I have advice to give you that will be more commodious for us both. Do you provide a dinner at your house for me and my wife to-morrow, and I will proceed in my story till supper-time, till you shall say you have your bellyfull; and if you are contented so, we will not leave you at supper neither. What, do you scratch your head? Do you but make provision, and I will give you my word we will come without fail.

Me. I like stories best gratis. However, come, I will provide a dinner for you, but it shall be an unsavoury one if you do not make it relishing with your stories. *Og.* But hark ye, have not I set you a-gog to go on pilgrimages? *Me.* Perhaps you may by that time you have finished your relation, but as I find myself at present I have enough to do to travel my Roman stations. *Og.* Roman ones, you who never saw Rome? *Me.* I will tell you after that manner I walk about my house, I go to my study, and take care of my daughter's chastity; thence I go into my shop and see what my servants are doing, then into the kitchen and see if anything be amiss there; and so from one place to another, what my wife and what my children are doing, taking care that every one be at his business. These are my Roman stations. *Og.* But St. James would take care of these things for you. *Me.* The Holy Scriptures enjoin me to look after them myself, but I do not find any text to leave them to the saints.

THE PRAISE OF FOLLY

Translated by John Wilson, 1668,
and edited by Mrs. P. S. Allen

[Taken from *The Praise of Folly,* by Erasmus, 1509, translated by John Wilson, 1668, edited by Mrs. P. S. Allen, Oxford, at the Clarendon Press, 1913.]

Erasmus of Rotterdam
To his Friend
Thomas More, Health:

As I was coming a while since out of Italy for England, that I might not waste all that time I was to sit on Horsback in foolish and illiterate Fables, I chose rather one while to revolve with my self something of our common Studies, and other while to enjoy the remembrance of my Friends, of whom I left here some no lesse learned than pleasant. Amongst these you, my More, came first in my mind, whose memory, though absent your self, gives me such delight in my absence, as when present with you I ever found in your company; than which, let me perish if in all my life I ever met with any thing more delectable. And therefore, being satisfy'd that something was to be done, and that that time was no wise proper for any serious matter, I resolv'd to make some sport with The Praise of Folly. But who the Devil put that in thy head? you'l say. The first thing was your sirname of More, which comes so near the word *Moriae* (Folly) as you are far from the thing. And that you are so, all the world will clear you. In the next place, I conceiv'd this exercise of wit would not be least approv'd by you; inasmuch as you are wont to be delighted with such kind of mirth, that is to say, neither unlearned, if I am not mistaken, nor altogether insipid, and in the whole course of your life have play'd the part of a Democritus. And though such is the excellence of your Judgement that 'twas ever contrary to that of the people's, yet such is your incredible affability and sweetness of temper that you both can and delight to carry your self to all men a man of all hours. Wherefore you will not only with good will accept this small Declamation, but take upon you the defence of 't, forasmuch as being dedicated to you, it is now no longer mine but yours. But perhaps there will not be wanting some wranglers that may cavil and charge me, partly that these toyes are lighter than may become a Divine, and partly more biting than may beseem the modesty of a Christian, and consequently exclaim that I resemble the Ancient Comedy, or another Lucian, and snarle at every thing. But I would have them whom the lightness or foolery of the Argument may offend, to consider that mine is not the first of this kind, but the same thing that has been often practis'd even by great Authors: when Homer, so many Ages since, did the like with the battel of Frogs and Mice; Virgil, with the Gnat, and Puddings; Ovid, with the Nut; when Polycrates, and his Corrector Isocrates, extol'd Tyranny; Glauco, Injustice; Favorinus, Deformity, and the quartan Ague; Synescius, Baldness; Lucian, the Fly, and Flattery; when Seneca made such sport with Claudius's Canonizations; Plutarch, with his Dialogue between Ulysses and Gryllus; Lucian and Apuleius, with the Asse; and some other, I know not who, with the Hog that made his last Will and Testament, of which also, even S. Jerome makes mention. And therefore if they please, let 'em suppose I play'd at Tables for my diversion, or if they had rather have it so, that I rod on a Hobby-horse. For what injustice is it, that when we allow every course of life its Recreation, that Study only should have none? especially when such toyes are not without their serious matter, and foolery is so handled that the Reader that is not altogether thick-skull'd may reap more benefit from 't than from some men's crabbish and specious Arguments. As when one, with long study and great pains, patches many pieces together on the praise of Rhetorick or Philosophy; another makes a Panegyrick to a Prince; another encourages him to a War against the Turks; another tells you what will become of the world after himself is dead; and another finds out some new device for the better ordering of Goat's-wooll: for as nothing is more trifling than to treat of serious matters triflingly, so nothing carries a better grace, than so to discourse of trifles as a man may seem to have intended them least. For my own part, let other men judge of what I have written; though yet, unlesse an overweening opinion of my self may have made me blind in my own cause, I have prais'd Folly, but not altogether foolishly. And now to say somewhat to that other cavil, of biting. This liberty was ever permitted to all men's wits, to make their smart witty reflections on the common errors of mankind, and that too without offence, as long as this liberty does not run into licentiousness; which makes me the more admire the tender ears of the men of this age, that can away with solemn Titles. Nay, you'l meet with some so preposterously religious, that they will sooner endure the broadest scoffs even against Christ himself, than hear the Pope or a Prince be toucht in the least, especially if it be any thing that concerns their profit; whereas he that so taxes the lives of men, without naming any one in particular, whither, I pray, may he be said to bite, or rather to teach and admonish? Or otherwise, I beseech ye, under how many notions do I tax my self? Besides, he that spares no sort of men cannot be said to be angry with any one in particular, but the vices of all. And therefore, if there shall happen to be any one that shall say he is hit, he will but discover either his guilt or fear. Saint Jerome sported in this kind with more freedome and greater sharpnesse, not sparing sometimes men's very name. But I, besides that I have wholly avoided it, I have so moderated my stile, that the understanding Reader will easily perceive my endeavours herein were rather to make mirth than bite. Nor have I, after the Example of Juvenal, raked up that forgotten sink of filth and ribaldry, but laid before you things rather ridiculous than dishonest. And now, if there be any one that is yet dissatisfied, let him at least remember that it is no dishonour to be discommended by Folly; and having brought her in speaking, it was but fit that I kept up the character of the person. But why do I run over these things to you, a person so excellent an Advocate that no man better defends his Client, though the cause many times be none of the best? Farewell, my best disputant More, and stoutly defend your Moriae.

From the Country,
the 5th of the Ides of June.

AN ORATION, OF FEIGNED MATTER, SPOKEN BY FOLLY IN HER OWN PERSON

At what rate soever the World talks of me (for I am not ignorant what an ill report Folly hath got, even amongst the most Foolish), yet that I am that She, that onely She, whose Deity recreates both gods and men, even this is a sufficient Argument, that I no sooner stept up to speak to this full Assembly, than all your faces put on a kind of new and unwonted pleasantness. So suddenly have you clear'd your brows, and with so frolique and hearty a laughter given me your applause, that in troth, as many of you as I behold on every side of me, seem to me no less than Homer's gods drunk with Nectar and Nepenthe; whereas before, ye sat as lumpish and pensive as if ye had come from consulting an Oracle. And as it usually happens when the Sun begins to shew his Beams, or when after a sharp Winter the Spring breathes afresh on the Earth, all things immediately get a new face, new colour, and recover as it were a certain kind of youth again: in like manner, by but beholding me, ye have in an instant gotten another kind of Countenance; and so what the otherwise great Rhetoricians with their tedious and long-studied Orations can hardly effect, to wit, to remove the trouble of the Mind, I have done it at once, with my single look.

But if ye ask me why I appear before you in this strange dress, be pleas'd to lend me your ears, and I'le tell you; not those ears, I mean, ye carry to Church, but abroad with ye, such as ye are wont to prick up to Jugglers, Fools and Buffons, and such as our Friend Midas once gave to Pan. For I am dispos'd awhile to play the Sophister with ye; not of their sort who nowadays buzle Young-men's heads with certain empty notions and curious trifles, yet teach them nothing but a more than Womanish obstinacy of scolding: but I'le imitate those Antients, who, that they might the better avoid that infamous appellation of *Sophi* or *Wise,* chose rather to be call'd

Sophisters. Their business was to celebrate the Praises of the gods and valiant men. And the like Encomium shall ye hear from me, but neither of Hercules nor Solon, but mine own dear Self, that is to say, Folly. Nor do I esteem those Wise-men a rush, that call it a foolish and insolent thing to praise one's self. Be it as foolish as they would make it, so they confess it proper: and what can be more, than that Folly be her own Trumpet? For who can set me out better than my self, unless perhaps I could be better known to another than to my self? Though yet I think it somewhat more modest than the general practice of our Nobles and Wise men, who, throwing away all shame, hire some flattering Orator or Lying Poet, from whose mouth they may hear their praises, that is to say meer lyes; and yet, composing themselves with a seeming modesty, spread out their Peacock's plumes and erect their Crests, whilst this impudent Flatterer equals a man of nothing to the gods, and proposes him as an absolute pattern of all Virtue that's wholly a stranger to 't, sets out a pittiful Jay in other's Feathers, washes the Blackmoor white, and lastly swells a Gnat to an Elephant. In short, I will follow that old Proverb that says, 'He may lawfully praise himself that lives far from Neighbours.' Though, by the way, I cannot but wonder at the ingratitude, shall I say, or negligence of Men, who, notwithstanding they honour me in the first place and are willing enough to confess my bounty, yet not one of them for these so many ages has there been, who in some thankful Oration has set out the praises of Folly; when yet there has not wanted them, whose elaborate endeavours have extol'd Tyrants, Agues, Flyes, Baldness and such other Pests of Nature, to their own loss of both time and sleep. And now ye shall hear from me a plain extemporary speech, but so much the truer. Nor would I have ye think it like the rest of Orators, made for the Ostentation of Wit; for these, as ye know, when they have been beating their heads some thirty years about an Oration, and at last perhaps produce somewhat that was never their own, shall yet swear they compos'd it in three dayes, and that too for diversion: whereas I ever lik't it best to speak whatever came first out.

But let none of ye expect from me, that after the manner of Rhetoricians I should go about to Define what I am, much less use any Division; for I hold it equally unlucky to circumscribe her whose Diety is universal, or make the least Division in that Worship about which every thing is so generally agree'd. Or to what purpose, think ye, should I describe my self, when I am here present before ye, and ye behold me speaking? For I am, as ye see, that true and onely giver of wealth, whom the Greeks call Μωρία, the Latines *Stultitia,* and our plain English *Folly*. Or what need was there to have said so much, as if my very looks were not sufficient to inform ye who I am? Or as if any man, mistaking me for Wisedome, could not at first sight convince himself by my face, the true index of my mind? I am no Counterfeit, nor do I carry one thing in my looks and another in my breast. No, I am in every respect so like my self, that neither can they dissemble me, who arrogate to themselves the appearance and title of Wisemen, and walk like Asses in Scarlet-hoods; though after all their hypocrisie Midas's ears will discover their Master. A most ingrateful generation of men, that, when they are wholly given up to my Party, are yet publickly asham'd of the name, as taking it for a reproach; for which cause, since in truth they are Μωρότατοι, Fools, and yet would appear to the World to be Wisemen and Thales's, wee'll ev'n call 'em Μωροσόφους, Wise-fools.

Nor will it be amiss also to imitate the Rhetoricians of our times, who think themselves in a manner Gods, if like Horse-leeches they can but appear to be double-tongu'd; and believe they have done a mighty act if in their Latin Orations they can but shuffle-in some ends of Greek, like Mosaick-work, though altogether by head and shoulders and less to the purpose. And if they want hard words, they run over some Worm-eaten Manuscript, and pick out half a Dozen of the most old and absolete to confound their Reader, believing, no doubt, that they that understand their meaning will like it the better, and they that do not, will admire it the more by how much the lesse they understand it. Nor is this way of ours of admiring what seems most Forreign without it's particular grace; for if there happen to be any more ambitious than others, they may give their applause with a smile, and, like the Asse, shake their ears, that they may be thought to understand more than the rest of their neighbours.

But to come to the purpose: I have giv'n ye my name; but what Epithet shall I adde? What but that of the most Foolish? For by what properer name can so great a goddess as Folly be known to her Disciples? And because it is not alike known to all from what stock I am sprung, with the Muses' good leave I'le do my endeavour to satisfie you. But yet neither the first Chaos, Orcus, Saturn, or Japhet, nor any of those thred-bare, musty Gods, were my Father, but Plutus, Riches; that only he, that is, in spight of Hesiod, Homer, nay and Jupiter himself, *Divum Pater atque Hominum Rex,* the Father of Gods and Men; at whose single beck, as heretofore, so at present, all things Sacred and Prophane are turn'd topsie turvy. According to whose Pleasure War, Peace, Empire, Counsels, Judgements, Assemblies, Wedlocks, Bargains, Leagues, Laws, Arts, all things Light or Serious — I want breath — in short, all the publick and private business of mankind, is govern'd; without whose help all that Herd of Gods of the Poets' making, and those few of the better sort of the rest, either would not be at all, or if they were, they would be but such as live at home and keep a poor house to themselves. And to whomsoever hee's an Enemy, 'tis not Pallas her self that can befriend him: as on the contrary he whom he favours may lead Jupiter and his Thunder in a string. This is my father and in him I glory. Nor did he produce me from his brain, as Jupiter that sowre and ill-look'd Pallas; but of that lovely Nymph call'd Youth, the most beautiful and galliard of all the rest. Nor was I, like that limping Black-smith, begot in the sad and irksome bonds of Matrimony. Yet, mistake me not, 'twas not that blind and decrepit Plutus in Aristophanes that got me, but such as he was in his full strength and pride of youth; and not that onely, but at such a time when he had been well heated with Nectar, of which he had, at one of the Banquets of the Gods, taken a dose extraordinary.

And as to the place of my birth, forasmuch as nowadays that is look'd upon as a main point of Nobility, it was neither, like Apollo's, in the floating Delos, nor Venus-like on the rolling Sea, nor in any of blind Homer's as blind Caves: but in the fortunate Islands, where all things grew without plowing or sowing; where neither Labour, nor Old-age, nor Disease, was ever heard of; and in whose field neither Daffadil, Mallows, Onyons, Beans, and such contemptible things would ever grow; but, on the contrary, Rue, Angelica, Buglosse, Marjoram, Trefoiles, Roses, Violets, Lillies, and all the Gardens of Adonis, invite both your sight and your smelling. And being thus born, I did not begin the world, as other Children are wont, with crying; but streight perch'd up and smil'd on my mother. Nor do I envy to the great Jupiter the Goat, his Nurse, forasmuch as I was suckled by two jolly Nymphs, to wit, Drunkenness, the daughter of Bacchus, and Ignorance, of Pan. And as for such my companions and followers as ye perceive about me, if you have a mind to know who they are, ye are not like to be the wiser for me, unlesse it be in Greek: This here, which you observe with that proud cast of her eye, is Φιλαυτία, Self-love; She with the smiling countenance, that is ever and anon clapping her hands, is Κολακία, Flattery; She that looks as if she were half asleep, is Λήθη, Oblivion; She that sits leaning on both Elbows with her hands clutch'd together, is Μισοπονία, Laziness; She with the Garland on her head, and that smells so strong of perfumes, is Ἡδονὴ, Pleasure; She with those staring eyes, moving here and there, is Ἀνοία, Madness; She with the smooth Skin and full pamper'd body is Τρυφὴ, Wantonness; and, as to the two Gods that ye see with them, the one is Κῶμος, Intemperance, the other Νήγρετος ὕπνος, Dead Sleep. These, I say, are my household Servants, and by their faithful Counsels I have subjected all things to my Dominion, and erected an empire over Emperors themselves. Thus have ye had my Lineage, Education, and Companions.

And now, lest I may seem to have taken upon me the name of Goddess without cause, you shall in the next place understand how far my Deity extends, and what advantage by 't I have brought both to Gods and Men. For, if it was not unwisely said by some body, that this only is to be a God, To help Men; and if they are deservedly enroll'd among the Gods that first brought in Corn and Wine and such other things as are for the common good of mankind, why am not I of right the ἄλφα, or first, of all the gods? who being but one, yet bestow all things on all men. For first, What is more sweet or more precious than Life? And yet from whom can it more properly be said to come than from me? For neither the Crab-favour'd Pallas's spear, nor the Cloud-gathering Jupiter's Shield, either beget, or propagate mankind; But even he himself, the Father of Gods, and King of Men at whose very beck the Heavens shake, must lay-by his forked thunder, and those looks wherewith he conquer'd the Gyants, and with which at pleasure he frights the rest of the Gods, and like a Common Stage-player put on a Disguise, as often as he goes about that, which now and then he do's, that is to say the getting of children: And the Stoicks too, that conceive themselves next to the Gods, yet shew me one of them, nay the veryest Bygot of the Sect, and if he do not put off his beard, the badge of Wisdom, though yet it be no more than what is common with him and Goats; yet at least he must lay-by his supercilious Gravity, smooth his forehead, shake off his rigid Principles, and for some time commit an act of folly and dotage. In fine, that Wiseman who ever he be, if he intends to have Children must have recourse to me. But tell me, I beseech ye, What Man is that would submit his neck to the Noose of Wedlock, if as Wisemen should, he did but first truly weigh the inconvenience of the thing? Or what Woman is there would ever go to 't did she seriously consider either the peril of Child-bearing, or the trouble of bringing them up? So then, if ye owe your beings to Wedlock, ye owe that Wedlock to this my follower, Madness; and what ye owe to me I have already told ye. Again, she that has but once try'd what it is, would she, do ye think, make a second venture, if it were not for my other Companion, Oblivion? Nay, even Venus her self, notwithstanding what ever Lucretius has said, would not deny but that all her vertue were lame and fruitless without the help of my Deity. For out of that little, odd, ridiculous May-game came the supercilious Philosophers, in whose room have succeeded a kind of people the world calls Monks, Cardinals, Priests, and the most holy Popes. And Lastly, all that Rabble of the Poets'-Gods, with which Heaven is so thwack't and throng'd, that though it be of so vast an extent, they are hardly able to croud one by another.

But I think it a small matter that ye thus owe your beginning of life to me, unless I also shew you that whatever benefit you receive in the progress of it is of my gift likewise. For what other is this? Can that be call'd life where ye take away pleasure? Oh! Do ye like what I say? I knew none of you could have so little Wit, or so much folly, or Wisdom rather, as to be of any other opinion. For even the Stoicks themselves, that so severely cry'd down pleasure, did but handsomly dissemble, and rail'd against it to the common People, to no other end but that having discourag'd them from it, they might the more plentifully enjoy it themselves. But tell me, by Jupiter, what part of man's life is that that is not sad, crabbed, unpleasant, insipid, troublesome, unless it be seasoned with Pleasure, that is to say, Folly? For the proof of which the never-sufficiently prais'd Sophocles, in that his happy Elogy of us 'To know nothing is the onely happiness', might be Authority enough, but that I intend to take every particular by it's self.

And first, Who knows not but a man's Infancy is the merriest part of life to himself, and most acceptable to others? For what is that in them which we kiss, embrace, cherish, nay Enemies succour, but this witchcraft of Folly, which wise Nature did of purpose give them into the world with them, that they might the more pleasantly passe-over the toil of Education, and as it were flatter the care and diligence of their Nurses. And then for Youth, which is in such reputation everywhere, how do all men favour it, study to advance it and lend it their helping hand? And whence, I pray, all this Grace? Whence but from me? by whose kindness, as it understands as little as may be, it is also for that reason the higher priviledged from exceptions; and I am mistaken if, when it is grown up and by experience and discipline brought to savour something like Man, if in the same instant that beauty does not fade, it's liveliness decay, it's pleasantness grow flat, and it's briskness fail. And by how much the further it runs from me, by so much the less it lives, till it comes to the burthen of Old age, not onely hateful to others, but to it self also. Which also were altogether insupportable did not I pitty it's condition, in being present with it, and, as the Poets'-gods were wont to assist such as were dying with some pleasant Metamorphωsis, help their decrepitness as much as in me lies by bringing them back to a second childhood, from whence they are not improperly called Twice-Children. Which, if ye ask me how I do it, I shall not be shy in the point. I bring them to our River Lethe (for it's spring-head rises in the Fortunate Islands, and that other of Hell is but a Brook in comparison), from which, as soon as they have drunk down a long forgetfulness, they wash away by degrees the perplexity of their minds, and so wax young again.

But perhaps you'll say, They are foolish and doting. Admit it; 'tis the very essence of Child-hood; as if to be such were not to be a fool, or that that condition had any thing pleasant in it, but that it understood nothing. For who would not look upon that Child as a Prodigy that should have as much Wisdome as a Man? — according to that common Proverb, 'I do not like a Child that is a Man too soon.' Or who would endure a Converse or Friendship with that Old-man, who to so large an experience of things, had joyn'd an equal strength of mind and sharpness of judgement? And therefore for this reason it is that Old-age dotes; and that it does so, it is beholding to me. Yet, not withstanding, is this dotard exempt from all those cares that distract a Wise man; he is not the less pot-Companion, nor is he sensible of that burden of life, which the more manly Age finds enough to do to stand upright under 't. And sometimes too, like Plautus's Old-man, he returns to his three Letters, A.M.O., the most unhappy of all things living, if he rightly understood what he did in 't. And yet, so much do I befriend him, that I make him well receiv'd of his friends, and no unpleasant Companion; for as much as, according to Homer, Nestor's discourse was pleasanter than Honey, whereas Achilles's was both bitter and malicious; and that of Old-men, as he has it in another place, florid. In which respect, also, they have this advantage of children, in that they want the onely pleasure of t' others life, we'll suppose it pratling. Adde to this that old men are more eagerly delighted with children, and they, again, with Old-men. 'Like to like', quoth the Divel to the Collier. For what difference between them, but that the one has more wrinckles and years upon his head than the other? Otherwise, the brightness of their hair, toothless mouth, weakness of body, love of Milk, broken speech, chatting, toying, forgetfulness, inadvertency, and briefly, all other their actions, agree in every thing. And by how much the nearer they approach to this Old-age, by so much they grow backward into the likeness of Children, until like them they pass from life to death, without any weariness of the one, or sense of t' other.

And now, let him that will compare the benefits they receive by me, with the Metamorphoses of the Gods; of whom, I shall not mention what they have done in their pettish humours, but where they have been most favourable: turning one into a Tree, another into a Bird, a third into a Grashopper, Serpent, or the like. As if there were any difference between perishing, and being another thing! But I restore the same man to the best and happiest part of his life. And if Men would but refrain from all commerce with Wisdom, and give up themselves to be govern'd by me, they should never know what it were to be old, but solace themselves with a perpetual youth. Do but observe our grim Philosophers that are perpetually beating their brains on knotty Subjects, and for the most part you'll find 'em grown old before they are scarce young. And whence is it, but that their continual and restless thoughts insensibly prey upon their spirits, and dry up their Radical Moisture? Whereas, on the contrary, my fat fools are as plump and round as a Westphalian Hogg, and never sensible of old age, unless perhaps, as sometimes it rarely happens, they come to be infected with Wisdom; so hard a thing it is for a man to be happy in all things. And to this purpose is that no small testimony of the Proverb, that sayes, 'Folly is the onely thing that keeps Youth at a stay, and Old age afar off;' as it is verifi'd in the Brabanders, of whom there goes this common saying, 'That Age, which is wont to render other Men wiser, makes them the greater Fools.' And yet there is scarce any Nation of a more jocund converse, or that is less sensible of the misery of Old age, than they are. And to these, as in scituation, so for manner of living, come nearest my friends the Hollanders. And why should I not call them mine, since they are so diligent observers of me that they are commonly call'd by my name? — of which they are so far from being asham'd, they rather pride themselves in 't. Let the foolish world then be packing and seek out Medeas, Circes, Venuses, Auroras and I know not what other Fountains of restoring Youth. I am sure I am the onely person that both can, and have made it good. 'Tis I alone that have that wonderful Juice with which Memnon's daughter prolong'd the youth of her Grandfather Tithon. I am that Venus by whose favour Phaon became so young again that Sappho fell in love with him. Mine are those Herbs, if yet there be any such, mine those Charms, and mine that Fountain, that not onely restores departed Youth but, which is more desirable, preserves it perpetual. And if ye all subscribe to this Opinion, that nothing is better than Youth, or more execrable than Age, I conceive you cannot but see how much ye are indebted to me, that have retain'd so great a good, and shut out so great an evil.

But why do I altogether spend my breath in speaking of Mortals? View Heaven round, and let him that will, reproach me with my name, if he find any one of the Gods that were not stinking and contemptible, were he not made acceptable by my Diety. Whence is it that Bacchus is always a Stripling, and bushy-hair'd? but because he is mad, and drunk, and spends his life in Drinking, Dancing, Revels, and May-games, not having so much as the least society with Pallas. And lastly, he is so far from desiring to be accounted wise, that he delights to be worshipp'd with Sports and Gambals; nor is he displeas'd with the Proverb that gave him the sirname of Fool, 'A greater Fool than Bacchus'; which name of his was chang'd to Morychus, for that sitting before the gates of his Temple, the wanton Countrey people were wont to bedaub him with new Wine and Figgs. And of scoffs, what not, hath not the antient Comedies thrown on him? O foolish God, say they, and worthy to be born as thou wert of thy Father's thigh! And yet, who had not rather be thy Fool and Sot, alwayes merry, ever young, and making sport for other people, than either Homer's Jupiter, with his crooked Councels, terrible to every one; or old Pan with his Hubbubs; or smutty Vulcan half-cover'd with Cinders; or even Pallas her self, so dreadful with her Gorgon's Head and Spear and a Countenance like Bulbeef? Why is Cupid always Pourtrai'd like a Boy, but because he is a very Wagg, and can neither do nor so much as think of any thing sober? Why Venus ever in her prime, but because of her affinity with me? Witness that colour of her Hair, so resembling my Father, from whence she is call'd the golden Venus; and lastly, ever laughing, if ye give any credit to the Poets, or their followers the Statuaries. What Diety did the Romans ever more religiously adore than that of Flora, the foundress of all pleasure? Nay, if ye should but diligently search the lives of the most sowre and morose of the Gods out of Homer and the rest of the Poets, you would find 'em all but so many pieces of Folly. And to what purpose should I run over any of the other gods' tricks when ye know enough of Jupiter's loose Loves? when that chast Diana shall so far forget her Sexe as to be ever hunting and ready to perish for Endymion? But I had rather they should hear these things from Momus, from whom heretofore they were wont to have their shares, till in one of their angry humours they tumbled him, together with Ate, Goddess of Mischief, down headlong to the Earth, because his wisdom, forsooth, unseasonably disturb'd their happiness. Nor since that dares any mortal give him harbour, though I must confess there wanted little but that he had been receiv'd into the Courts of Princes, had not my companion Flattery reign'd in chief there, with whom and t' other there is no more correspondence than between Lambs and Wolves. From whence it is that the Gods play the fool with the greater liberty and more content to themselves, 'doing all things carelessly,' as says Father Homer, that is to say, without any one to correct them. For what ridiculous stuff is there which that stump of the Fig-tree Priapus does not afford 'em? what Tricks and Legerdemains with which Mercury does not cloak his thefts? what buffonry that Vulcan is not guilty of, while one while with his poltfoot, another with his smutcht muzzle, another with his impertinencies, he makes sport for the rest of the Gods? As also that old Silenus with his Countrey-dances, Polyphemus footing time to his Cyclops hammers, the Nymphs with their Jiggs, and Satyrs with their Anticks; whilst Pan makes 'em all twitter with some coarse Ballad, which yet they had rather hear than the Muses themselves, and chiefly when they are well whitled with Nectar. Besides, what should I mention what these Gods do when they are half drunk? Now by my troth, so foolish that I my self can hardly refrain laughter. But in these matters 'twere better we remember'd Harpocrates, lest some Evesdropping God or other take us whispering that which Momus onely has the priviledge of speaking at length.

And therefore, according to Homer's example, I think it high time to leave the Gods to themselves, and look down a little on the Earth; wherein likewise you'll find nothing frolick or fortunate, that it ows not to me. So provident has that great Parent of Mankind, Nature, been, that there should not be any thing without it's mixture, and as it were seasoning of Folly. For since according to the definition of the Stoicks, Wisdom is nothing else than to be govern'd by reason; and on the contrary Folly, to be giv'n up to the will of our Passions; that the life of man might not be altogether disconsolate and hard to away with, of how much more Passion than Reason has Jupiter compos'd us? putting in, as one would say, 'scarce half an ounce to a pound'. Besides, he has confin'd Reason to a narrow corner of the brain, and left all the rest of the body to our Passions; as also set up, against this one, two as it were, masterless Tyrants — Anger, that possesseth the region of the heart, and consequently the very Fountain of life, the Heart it self; and Lust, that stretcheth its Empire every where. Against which double force how powerful Reason is, let common experience declare, inasmuch as she, which yet is all she can do, may call out to us till she be hoarse again, and tell us the Rules of Honesty and Vertue; while they give up the Reins to their Governour, and make a hideous clamour, till at last being wearied, he suffer himself to be carried whither they please to hurry him.

But forasmuch as such as are born to the business of the world have some little sprinklings of Reason more than the rest, yet that they may the better manage it, even in this as well as in other things, they call me to counsel; and I give 'em such as is worthy of my self, to wit That they take to 'em a wife — a silly thing, God wot, and foolish, yet wanton and pleasant, by which means the roughness of the Masculine temper is season'd and sweeten'd by her folly. For in that Plato seems to doubt under which Genus he should put woman, to wit that of rational Creatures or Brutes, he intended no other in it than to shew the apparent folly of the Sexe. For if perhaps any of them goes about to be thought wiser than the rest, what else does she do but play the fool twice, as if a man should 'teach a Cow to dance', 'a thing quite against the hair'. For as it doubles the crime if any one should put a disguise upon Nature, or endeavour to bring her to that she will in no wise bear, according to that Proverb of the Greeks, 'An Ape is an Ape, though clad in Scarlet'; so a woman is a woman still, that is to say foolish, let her put on what ever Vizard she please.

But, by the way, I hope that Sexe is not so foolish as to take offence at this, that I my self, being a woman, and Folly too, have attributed Folly to them. For if they weigh it right, they needs must acknowledg that they owe it to Folly that they are more fortunate than men. As first their Beauty, which, and that not without cause, they prefer before every thing, since by its means they exercise a Tyranny even upon Tyrants themselves; otherwise, whence proceeds that sowre look, rough skin, bushy beard and such other things as speak plain Old age in a man, but from that Disease of Wisdom? whereas women's Cheeks are ever plump and smooth, their Voice small, their Skin soft, as if they imitated a certain kind of perpetual Youth. Again, what greater thing do they wish in their whole lives, than that they may please the Men? For to what other purpose are all those Dresses, Washes, Baths, Curlings, Slops, Perfumes, and those several little tricks of setting their Faces, painting their Eye-brows, and smoothing their Skins? And now tell me, what higher Letters of Recommendation have they to men than this Folly? For what is it they do not permit 'em to do? and to what other purpose than that of pleasure? wherein yet their folly is not the least thing that pleaseth; which how true it is, I think no one will deny, that does but consider with himself, what foolish Discourse and odd Gambals pass between a man and his woman, as oft as he has a mind to be gamesome? And so I have shown ye whence the first and chiefest delight of man's life springs.

But there are some, you'll say, and those too none of the youngest, that have a greater kindness for the Pot than the Petticoat, and place their chiefest pleasure in good fellowship. If there can be any great entertainment without a woman at it, let others look to 't. This I am sure, there was never any pleasant which Folly gave not the relish to. Insomuch that if they find no occasion of Laughter, they send for 'one that may make it', or hire some Buffon flatterer, whose ridiculous discourse may put by the Gravity of the company. For to what purpose were it to clogg our Stomacks with Dainties, Junkets and the like Stuff, unless our Eyes and Ears, nay whole Mind, were likewise entertain'd with Jests, Merriments and Laughter? But of these kind of second Courses I am the onely Cook; though yet those ordinary practises of our Feasts, as choosing a

King, throwing Dice, drinking Healths, trouling it Round, dancing the Cushion and the like, were not invented by the seven Wise Men but my Self, and that too for the common pleasure of Mankind. The nature of all which things is such, that the more of Folly they have, the more they conduce to Humane Life, which, if it were unpleasant, did not deserve the name of Life; and other than such it could not well be, did not these kind of Diversions wype away tediousnesse, nexte cosyn to the other.

But perhaps there are some that neglect this way of pleasure, and rest satisfi'd in the enjoyment of their Friends, calling friendship the most desirable of all things; more necessary than either air, fire, or water; so delectable, that he that shall take it out of the World had as good put out the Sun; and lastly so commendable, if yet that make any thing to the matter, that neither the Philosophers themselves doubted to reckon it among their chiefest good. But what if I shew you that I am both the beginning and end of this so great good also? Nor shall I go about to prove it by Fallacies, Sorites, Dilemmas, or other the like subtilties of Logicians, but after my blunt way, point out the thing as clearly as 'twere with my finger.

And now tell me, if to wink, slip over, be blind at, or deceiv'd in, the vices of our friends, nay, to admire and esteem them for Virtues, be not at least the next degree to folly? What is it when one kisses his Mistresses freckle Neck, another the Wart on her Nose? When a Father shall swear his squint-ey'd Child is more lovely than Venus? What is this, I say, but meer folly? And so, perhaps you'l cry, it is; and yet 'tis this onely that joyns friends together, and continues them so joyn'd. I speak of ordinary men, of whom none are born without their imperfections, and happy is he that is prest with the least: for among wise Princes there is either no friendship at all, or if ther be, 'tis unpleasant and reserv'd, and that too but amongst a very few, 'twere a crime to say none. For that the greatest part of mankind are fools, nay there is not any one that dotes not in many things; and friendship, you know, is seldome made but amongst equalls. And yet if it should so happen that there were a mutual good-will between them, it is in no wise firm nor very long liv'd; that is to say, among such as are morose and more circumspect than needs, as being Eagle-sighted into his friends' faults, but so blear-ey'd to their own that they take not the least notice of the Wallet that hangs behind their own Shoulders. Since then the nature of Man is such that there is scarce any one to be found that is not subject to many errors, add to this the great diversity of minds and studies, so many slips, oversights and chances of humane life, and how is it possible there should be any true friendship between those Argus's, so much as one hour, were it not for that which the Greeks excellently call εὐήθειαν? and you may render by Folly or good Nature, chuse you whether. But what? Is not the Author and Parent of all our Love, Cupid, as blind as a beetle? and as with him all colours agree, so from him is it that every one likes his own Sweeter-kin best, though never so ugly, and 'that an old man dotes on his old wife, and a boy on his girle'. These things are not onely done every where but laught at too, yet as ridiculous as they are, they make society pleasant, and, as it were, glew it together.

And what has been said of Friendship may more reasonably be presum'd of Matrimony, which in truth is no other than an inseparable conjunction of life. Good God! What Divorces, or what not worse than that, would daily happen, were not the converse between a man and his wife supported and cherished by flattery, apishnesse, gentlenesse, ignorance, dissembling, certain Retainers of mine also! Whoop holiday! how few marriages should we have, if the Husband should but through-examin how many tricks his pretty little Mop of Modesty has plaid before she was marry'd! And how fewer of them would hold together, did not most of the Wife's actions escape the Husband's knowledg through his neglect or sottishness! And for this also ye are beholding to me, by whose means it is that the Husband is pleasant to his Wife, the Wife to her Husband, and the house kept in quiet. A man is laught at, when seeing his Wife weeping he licks up her tears. But how much happier is it to be thus deceiv'd than by being troubled with jealousie, not onely to torment himself, but set all things in a hub-bub!

In fine, I am so necessary to the making of all society and manner of life both delightful and lasting, that neither would the people long endure their Governors, nor the Servant his Master, nor the Master his Footman, nor the Scholar his Tutor, nor one friend another, nor the Wife her Husband, nor the Userer the Borrower, nor a Souldier his Commander, nor one Companion another, unlesse all of them had their interchangeable failings, one while flattering, other while prudently conniving, and generally sweetning one another with some small relish of Folly.

And now you'd think I had said all, but ye shall hear yet greater things. Will he, I pray, love any one that hates himself? Or ever agree with another who is not at peace with himself? Or beget pleasure in another that is troublesome to himself? I think no one will say it that is not more foolish than Folly. And yet, if ye should exclude me, there 's no man but would be so far from enduring another that he would stink in his own nostrils, be nauseated with his own actions, and himself become odious to himself; forasmuch as Nature, in too many things rather a Stepdame than a Parent to us, has imprinted that evil in men, especially such as have least judgment, that every one repents him of his own condition and admires that of others. Whence it comes to pass that all her gifts, elegancy and graces corrupt and perish. For what benefit is Beauty, the greatest blessing of Heaven, if it be mixt with affectation? What Youth, if corrupted with the severity of old Age? Lastly, what is that in the whole business of a man's life he can do with any grace to himself or others — for it is not so much a thing of Art, as the very life of every Action, that it be done with a good meen — unlesse this my friend and companion, Self-love, be present with it? Nor does she without cause supply me the place of a Sister, since her whole endeavours are to act my part every where. For what is more foolish than for a man to study nothing else than how to please himself? To make himself the object of his own admiration? And yet, what is there that is either delightful or taking, nay rather what not the contrary, that a man does against the hair? Take away this Salt of life, and the Orator may ev'n sit still with his Action, the Musitian with all his division will be able to please no man, the Player be hist off the Stage, the Poet and all his Muses ridiculous, the Painter with his Art contemptible, and the Physitian with all his Slip-slops go a begging. Lastly, thou wilt be taken for an Ugly fellow instead of a Beautiful, for Old and Decrepit instead of Youthful, and a Beast instead of a Wise man, a Child instead of Eloquent, and instead of a well-bred man, a clown. So necessary a thing it is that every one flatter himself, and commend himself to himself before he can be commended by others.

Lastly, since it is the chiefest point of happinesse 'that a man is willing to be what he is', you have further abridg'd in this my Self-love, that no man's asham'd of his own face, no man of his own wit, no man of his own parentage, no man of his own house, no man of his manner of living, nor any man of his own Country; so that a Highlander has no desire to change with an Italian, a Thracian with an Athenian, nor a Scythian for the fortunate Islands. O the singular care of Nature, that in so great a variety of things has made all equal! Where she has been sometime sparing of her gifts she has recompenc'd it with the more of self-Love; though here, I must confess, I speak foolishly, it being the greatest of all other her Gifts: to say nothing that no great action was ever attempted without my Motion, or Art brought to perfection without my help.

* * * * *

And now, having vindicated to my self the praise of Fortitude and Industry, what think ye if I do the same by that of Prudence? But some will say, You may as well joyn Fire and Water. It may be so. But yet I doubt not but to succeed even in this also, if, as ye have done hitherto, ye will but favour me with your attention. And first, if Prudence depends upon Experience, to whom is the honour of that name more proper? To the Wiseman, who partly out of modesty and partly distrust of himself, attempts nothing; or the Fool, whom neither Modesty which he never had, nor Danger which he never considers, can discourage from any thing? The Wiseman has recourse to the Books of the Antients, and from thence picks nothing but subtilties of words. The Fool, in undertaking and venturing on the business of the world, gathers, if I mistake not, the true Prudence, such as Homer though blind may be said to have seen, when he said 'The burnt child dreads the fire'. For there are two main obstacles to the knowledge of things, Modesty that casts a mist before the understanding, and Fear that, having fanci'd a danger, disswades us from the attempt. But from these Folly sufficiently frees us, and few there are that rightly understand of what great advantage it is to blush at nothing and attempt every thing.

But if ye had rather take Prudence for that that consists in the judgment of things, hear me, I beseech ye, how far they are from it that yet crack of the name. For first 'tis evident that all Humane things, like Alcibiades's Sileni or rural Gods, carry a double face; but not the least alike; so that what at first sight seems to be death, if you view it narrowly may prove to be life; and so the contrary. What appears beautiful may chance to be deform'd; what wealthy, a very begger; what infamous, praiseworthy; what learned, a dunce; what lusty, feeble; what jocund, sad; what noble, base; what lucky, unfortunate; what friendly, an enemy; and what healthful, noisome. In short, view the inside of these Sileni, and you'll find them quite other than what they appear; which, if perhaps it shall not seem so Philosophically spoken, I'll make it plain to you 'after my blunt way'. Who would not conceive a Prince a great Lord and abundant in every thing? But yet being so ill furnisht with the gifts of the mind, and ever thinking he shall never have enough, he's the poorest of all men. And then for his mind so giv'n up to Vice, 'tis a shame how it inslaves him. I might in like manner Philosophy of the rest; but let this one, for example's sake, be enough.

Yet why this? will some one say. Have patience, and I'll shew ye what I drive at. If any one seeing a Player acting his Part on a Stage, should go about to strip him of his disguise, and shew him to the people in his true Native Form, would he not, think ye, not onely spoil the whole design of the Play, but deserve himself to be pelted off with stones as a Phantastical Fool, and one out of his wits? But nothing is more common with them than such changes; the same person one while personating a Woman, and another while a Man; now a Youngster, and by and by a grim Seigniour; now a King, and presently a Peasant; now a God, and in a trice agen an ordinary Fellow. But to discover this were to spoil all, it being the onely thing that entertains the Eyes of the Spectators. And what is all this Life but a kind of Comedy, wherein men walk up and down in one another's Disguises, and Act their respective Parts, till the property-man brings 'em back to the Tyring House. And yet he often orders a different Dress, and makes him that came but just now off in the Robes of a King, put on the Raggs of a Begger. Thus are all things represented by Counterfeit, and yet without this there were no living.

And here if any wise man, as it were dropt from Heaven, should start up and cry, This great thing, whom the World looks upon for a God and I know not what, is not so much as a Man, for that like a Beast he is led by his Passions, but the worst of Slaves, inasmuch as he gives himself up willingly to so many and such detestable Masters. Again if he should bid a man that were bewailing the death of his Father to laugh, for that he now began to live by having got an Estate, without which Life is but a kind of Death; or call another that were boasting of his Family, ill begotten or base, because he is so far remov'd from Vertue that is the only Fountain of Nobility; and so of the rest: what else would he get by 't but be thought himself Mad and Frantick? For as nothing is more foolish than preposterous Wisdome, so nothing is more unadvised than a froward unseasonable Prudence. And such is his that does not comply with the present time 'and order himself as the Market goes', but forgetting that Law of Feasts, 'either drink or begon,' undertakes to disprove a common receiv'd Opinion. Whereas on the contrary 'tis the part of a truly Prudent man not to be wise beyond his Condition, but either to take no notice of what the world does, or run with it for company. But this is foolish, you'll say; nor shall I deny it, provided always ye be so civil on t' other side as to confess that this is to Act a Part in that World.

But, O ye Gods, 'shall I speak or hold my tongue?' But why should I be silent in a thing that is more true than truth it self? However it might not be amiss perhaps in so great an Affair, to call forth the Muses from Helicon, since the Poets so often invoke 'em upon every foolish occasion. Be present then awhile, and assist me, ye Daughters of Jupiter, while I make it out that there is no way to that so much Fam'd Wisdome, nor access to that Fortress as they call it of Happiness, but under the Banner of Folly. And first 'tis agreed of all hands that our passions belong to Folly; inasmuch as we judge a wise Man from a Fool by this, that the one is order'd by them, the other by Reason; and therefore the Stoicks remove from a wise man all disturbances of Mind as so many Diseases. But these Passions do not onely the Office of a Tutor to such as are making towards the Port of Wisdome, but are in every exercise of Vertue as it were Spurs and Incentives, nay and Encouragers to well doing: which though that great Stoick Seneca most strongly denys, and takes from a wise man all affections whatever, yet in doing that he leaves him not so much as a Man, but rather a new kind of God, that was never yet, nor ever like to be. Nay, to speak plainer, he sets up a stony Semblance of a Man, void of all Sense and common feeling of Humanity. And much good to them with this Wise Man of theirs; let them enjoy him to themselves, love him without Competitors, and live with him in Plato's Common-wealth, the Countrey of Ideas, or Tantalus's Orchards. For who would not shun and startle at such a man, as at some unnatural accident or Spirit? A man dead to all sense of Nature and common affections, and no more mov'd with Love or Pity than if he were a Flint or Rock; whose censure nothing escapes; that commits no errors himself, but has a Lynx's eyes upon others; measures every thing by an exact Line, and forgives nothing; pleases himself with himself onely; the onely Rich, the onely Wise, the onely Free Man, and onely King; in brief, the onely man that is every thing, but in his own single judgment onely; that cares not for the Friendship of any man, being himself a friend to no man; makes no doubt to make the Gods stoop to him, and condemns and laughs at the whole

Actions of our Life? And yet such a Beast is this their perfect Wise Man. But tell me pray, if the thing were to be carri'd by most voices, what City would chuse him for its Governour, or what Army desire him for their General? What Woman would have such a Husband, what Good-fellow such a Guest, or what Servant would either wish or endure such a Master? Nay, who had not rather have one of the middle sort of Fools, who, being a Fool himself, may the better know how to command or obey Fools; and who though he please his like, 'tis yet the greater number; one that is kind to his Wife, merry among his Friends, a Boon Companion, and easie to be liv'd with; and lastly one that thinks nothing of Humanity should be a stranger to him? But I am weary of this Wise Man, and therefore I'll proceed to some other advantages.

Go to then. Suppose a man in some lofty high Tower, and that he could look round him, as the Poets say Jupiter was now and then wont. To how many misfortunes would he find the life of man subject? How miserable, to say no worse, our Birth, how difficult our Education; to how many wrongs our Childhood expos'd, to what pains our Youth; how unsupportable our Old-age, and grievous our unavoidable Death? as also what Troups of Diseases beset us, how many Casualties hang over our Heads, how many Troubles invade us, and how little there is that is not steept in Gall? to say nothing of those evils one man brings upon another, as Poverty, Imprisonment, Infamy, Dishonesty, Racks, Snares, Treachery, Reproaches, Actions, Deceipts—But I'm got into as endless a work as numbring the Sands—For what offences Mankind have deserv'd these things, or what angry God compell'd 'em to be born into such miseries, is not my present business. Yet he that shall diligently examine it with himself, would he not, think ye, approve the example of the Milesian Virgins, and kill himself? But who are they that for no other reason but that they were weary of life, have hastned their own Fate? were they not the next Neighbours to Wisdom? amongst whom, to say nothing of Diogenes, Xenocrates, Cato, Cassius, Brutus, that Wise Man Chiron, being offer'd Immortality, chose rather to dye than be troubled with the same thing always.

And now I think ye see what would become of the World if all men should be wise; to wit 'twere necessary we got another kind of Clay and some better Potter. But I, partly through ignorance, partly unadvisedness, and sometimes through forgetfulness of evil, do now and then so sprinkle pleasure with the hopes of good, and sweeten men up in their greatest misfortunes, that they are not willing to leave this life, even then when according to the account of the Destinys this life has left them; and by how much the less reason they have to live, by so much the more they desire it; so far are they from being sensible of the least wearisomness of life. Of my gift it is, that ye have so many old Nestors every where, that have scarce left 'em so much as the shape of a Man; Stutterers, Dotards, Toothless, Gray-hair'd, Bald; or rather, to use the words of Aristophanes, 'Nasty,

Crumpt, Miserable, Shrivel'd, Bald, Toothless, and wanting their Baubles': yet so delighted with life and to be thought young, that one dies his gray hairs; another covers his baldness with a Periwigg; another gets a set of new Teeth; another falls desperately in love with a young Wench, and keeps more flickering about her than a young man would have been asham'd of. For to see such an old crooked piece, with one foot in the grave, to marrie a plump young Wench, and that too without a portion, is so common that men almost expect to be commended for 't. But the best sport of all is to see our old Women, even dead with age, and such skeletons one would think they had stoln out of their graves, and ever mumbling in their mouths, 'Life is sweet'; and as old as they are, still catter-wawling, daily plaistering their face, scarce ever from the glasse, gossipping, dancing, and writing Love-letters. These things are laught at as foolish, as indeed they are; yet they please themselves, live merrily, swimme in pleasure, and in a word are happy, by my courtesie. But I would have them to whom these things seem ridiculous, to consider with themselves whether it be not better to live so pleasant a life, in such kind of follies, than, as the Proverb goes, 'To take a Halter and hang themselves'. Besides though these things may be subject to censure, it concerns not my fools in the least, in as much as they take no notice of it, or if they do, they easily neglect it. If a stone fall upon a man's head, that's evil indeed; but dishonesty, infamy, villany, ill reports, carrie no more hurt in them than a man is sensible of; and if a man have no sense of them, they are no longer evils. What art thou the worse if the people hisse at thee, so thou applaud thy self? And that a man be able to do so, he must ow it only to Folly.

But methinks I hear the Philosophers opposing it, and saying 'tis a miserable thing for a man to be foolish, to erre, mistake, and know nothing truly. Nay rather, this is to be a man. And why they should call it miserable, I see no reason; forasmuch as we are so born, so bred, so instructed, nay, such is the common condition of us all. And nothing can be call'd miserable that suits with its kind, unless perhaps you'l think a man such because he can neither flie with Birds, nor walk on all four with Beasts, and is not arm'd with Horns as a Bull.

* * * *

And now, by the immortal Gods! I think nothing more happy than that generation of men we commonly call fools, ideots, lack-wits and dolts; splendid Titles too, as I conceive 'em. I'le tell ye a thing, which at first perhaps may seem foolish and absurd, yet nothing more true. And first they are not afraid of death; no small evil, by Jupiter! They are not tormented with the conscience of evil acts; not terrify'd with the fables of Ghosts, nor frighted with Spirits and Goblins. They are not distracted with the fear of evils to come, nor the hopes of future good. In short they are not disturb'd with those thousand of cares to which this life is subject. They are neither modest, nor fearful, nor ambitious, nor envious, nor love they any man. And lastly if they should come nearer even to the very ignorance of Brutes, they could not sin, for so hold the Divines. And now tell me, thou wise fool, with how many troublesome cares thy mind is continually perplext; heap together all the discommodities of thy life, and then thou'lt be sensible from how many evils I have delivered my Fools. Add to this that they are not onely merry, play, sing, and laugh themselves, but make mirth where ever they come, a special priviledge it seems the Gods have given 'em to refresh the pensiveness of life. Whence it is, that whereas the world is so differently affected one towards another,—that all men indifferently admit them as their companions, desire, feed, cherish, embrace them, take their parts upon all occasions, and permit 'em without offence to do or say what they list. And so little doth every thing desire to hurt them, that even the very Beasts, by a kind of natural instinct of their innocence no doubt, pass by their injuries. For of them it may be truly said that they are consecrate to the Gods, and therefore and not without cause do men have 'em in such esteem. Whence is it else that they are in so great request with Princes, that they can neither eat nor drink, go any whither, or be an hour without them? Nay, and in some degree they prefer these Fools before their crabbish Wise-men, whom yet they keep about them for State-sake. Nor do I conceive the reason so difficult, or that it should seem strange why they are prefer'd before t' others, for that these wise men speak to Princes about nothing but grave, serious matters, and trusting to their own parts and learning do not fear sometimes 'to grate their tender ears with smart truths'; but fools fit 'em with that they most delight in, as jeasts, laughter, abuses of other men, wanton pastimes, and the like.

Again, take notice of this no contemptible blessing which Nature hath giv'n fools, that they are the only plain, honest men and such as speak truth. And what is more commendable than truth? for though that Proverb of Alcibiades in Plato attributes Truth to Drunkards and Children, yet the praise of it is particularly mine, even from the testimony of Euripides; amongst whose other things there is extant that his honourable saying concerning us, 'A fool speaks foolish things'. For whatever a fool has in his heart, he both shews it in his looks and expresses it in his discourse; while the wise men's are those two Tongues which the same Euripides mentions, whereof the one speaks truth, the other what they judge most seasonable for the occasion. These are they 'that turn black into white', blow hot and cold with the same breath, and carry a far different meaning in their Breast from what they feign with their Tongue. Yet in the midst of all their prosperity, Princes in this respect seem to me most unfortunate, because, having no one to tell them truth, they are forc't to receive flatterers for friends.

But, some one may say, the ears of Princes are strangers to truth, and for this reason they avoid those Wise men, because they fear lest some one more frank than the rest should dare to speak to them things rather true than pleasant; for so the matter is, that they don't much care for truth. And yet this is found by experience among my Fools, that not onely Truths but even open reproaches are heard with pleasure; so that the same thing which, if it came from a wise man's mouth might prove a Capital Crime, spoken by a Fool is receiv'd with delight. For Truth carries with it a certain peculiar Power of pleasing, if no Accident fall in to give occasion of offence; which faculty the Gods have given onely to Fools. And for the same reasons is it that Women are so earnestly delighted with this kind of Men, as being more propense by Nature to Pleasure and Toyes. And whatsoever they may happen to do with them, although sometimes it be of the seriousest, yet they turn it to Jest and Laughter; as that Sexe was ever quick-witted, especially to colour their own faults.

But to return to the happiness of Fools, who when they have past over this life with a great deal of Pleasantness, and without so much as the least fear or sense of Death, they go straight forth into the Elysian Field, to recreate their Pious and Careless Souls with such Sports as they us'd here. Let's proceed then, and compare the condition of any of your Wise Men with that of this Fool. Fancy to me now some example of Wisdome you'd set up against him; one that had spent his Childhood and Youth in learning the Sciences; and lost the sweetest part of his life in Watchings, Cares, Studies; and for the remaining part of it never so much as tasted the least of pleasure; ever sparing, poor, sad, sowre, unjust and rigorous to himself, and troublesome and hateful to others; broken with Paleness, Leanness, Crasiness, sore Eyes, and an Old-age and Death contracted before their time (though yet, what matter is it, when he dye that never liv'd?); and such is the Picture of this great Wise Man.

* * * * *

For whereas among the many praises of Bacchus they reckon this the chief, that he washeth away cares, and that too in an instant; do but sleep off his weak spirits, and they come on agen, as we say, on horseback. But how much larger and more present is the benefit ye receive by me, since, as it were with a perpetual drunkenness, I fill your minds with Mirth, Fancies and Jollities, and that too without any trouble? Nor is there any man living whom I let be without it; whereas the gifts of the Gods are scrambled, some to one and some to another. The sprightly delicious Wine that drives away cares and leaves such a Flavour behind it, grows not every where. Beauty, the gift of Venus, happens to few; and to fewer gives Mercury Eloquence. Hercules makes not every one rich. Homer's Jupiter bestows not Empire on all men. Mars oftentimes favours neither side. Many return sad from Apollo's Oracle. Phoebus sometimes shoots a Plague amongst us. Neptune drowns more than he saves: to say nothing of those mischievous Gods, Plutoes, Ates, Punishments, Feavours and the like, not Gods but Executioners. I am that only Folly that so readily and indifferently bestow my benefits on all. Nor do I look to be entreated, or am I subject to take pett, and require an expiatory sacrifice if some Ceremony be omitted. Nor do I beat heaven and earth together, if, when the rest of the Gods are invited, I am past by or not admitted to the steam of their Sacrifices. For the rest of the Gods are so curious in this point, that such an omission may chance to spoil a man's business; and therefore one had as good ev'n let 'em alone as worship 'em: just like some men, who are so hard to please, and withall so ready to do mischief, that 'tis better be a stranger than have any familiarity with 'em.

But no man, you'll say, ever sacrific'd to Folly, or built me a Temple. And troth, as I said before, I cannot but wonder at the ingratitude; yet because I am easie to be entreated, I take this also in good part, though truelie I can scarce request it. For why should I require Incense, Wafers, a Goat or Sow, when all men pay me that worship every where, which is so much approv'd even by our very Divines? Unless perhaps I should envy Diana, that her Sacrifices are mingled with Humane blood. Then do I conceive my self most religiouslie worshipp'd, when every where, as 'tis generally done, men embrace me in their Minds, express me in their Manners, and represent me in their Lives; which worship of the Saints is not so ordinary among Christians. How many are there that burn Candles to the Virgin Mother, and that too at noon day, when there's no need of 'em! But how few are there that studie to imitate her in pureness of Life, Humility and love of Heavenlie things, which is the true worship and most acceptable to Heaven! Besides why should I desire a Temple, when the whole world is my Temple, and I'm deceiv'd or 'tis a goodly one? Nor can I want Priests, but in a Land where there are no men. Nor am I yet so foolish as to require Statues or painted Images, which do often obstruct my Worship, since among the stupid and gross multitude those Figures are worshipt for the Saints themselves. And so it would fare with me, as it doth with them that are turn'd out of doors by their Substitutes. No, I have Statues enough, and as many as there are Men; every one bearing my lively Resemblance in his Face, how unwilling so ever he be to the contrary. And therefore there is no reason why I should envie the rest of the Gods, if in particular places they have their particular worship, and that too on set-days — as Phoebus at Rhodes; at Cyprus, Venus; at Argos, Juno; at Athens, Minerva; in Olympus, Jupiter; at Tarentum, Neptune; and near the Hellespont, Priapus — ; as long as the World in general performs me every day much better Sacrifices.

Wherein notwithstanding if I shall seem to any one to have spoken more boldlie than trulie, let us, if ye please, look a little into the lives of men, and it will easily appear not onely how much they owe to me, but how much they esteem me even from the highest to the lowest. And yet we will not run over the lives of everie one, for that would be too long; but onelie some few of the great ones, from whence we shall easilie conjecture the rest. For to what purpose is it to say anything of the common people, who without dispute are whollie mine? For they abound every where with so many several sorts of Folly, and are everie day so busie in inventing new, that a thousand Democriti are too few for so general a laughter, though there were another Democritus to laugh at them too. 'Tis almost incredible what Sport and Pastime they dailie make the Gods; for though they set aside their sober forenoon hours to dispatch business and receive prayers, yet when they begin to be well whitled with Nectar, and cannot think of anything that's serious, they get 'em up into some part of Heaven that has better prospect than other, and thence look down upon the actions of men. Nor is there anie thing that pleases 'em better. Good, good! what an excellent sight 'tis! How many several Hurlie-burlies of Fools! for I my self sometimes sit among those Poetical Gods.

Here's one desperatelie in love with a young Wench, and the more she sleights him the more outragiouslie he loves her. Another marries a woman's money, not her self. Another's jealousie keeps more eyes on her than Argos. Another becomes a Mourner, and how foolishlie he carries it! nay, hires others to bear him companie, to make it more ridiculous. Another weeps over his Mother in Law's Grave. Another spends all he can rap and run on his Bellie, to be the more hungry after it. Another thinks there is no happiness but in sleep and idleness. Another turmoils himself about other men's business, and neglects his own. Another thinks himself rich in taking up moneys and changing Securities, as we say borrowing of Peter to pay Paul, and in a short time becomes bankrupt. Another starves himself to enrich his Heir. Another for a small and incertain gain exposes his life to the casualties of Seas and Winds, which yet no money can restore. Another had rather get Riches by War than live peaceably at home. And some there are that think them easiest attain'd by courting old childless men with Presents; and others again by making rich old women believe they love 'm; both which afford the Gods most excellent pastime, to see them cheated by those persons they thought to have over-cach't. But the most foolish and basest of all others are our Merchants, to wit such as venture on every thing be it never so dishonest, and manage it no better; who though they lie by no allowance, swear and forswear, steal, cozen, and cheat, yet shufle themselves into the first rank, and all because they have Gold Rings on their Fingers. Nor are they without their flattering Friers that admire them and give 'em openly the title of Honourable, in hopes, no doubt, to get some small snip of 't themselves.

* * * * *

But perhaps I had better pass over our Divines in silence and not stir this Pool, or touch this fair but unsavoury Plant; as a kind of men that are supercilious beyond comparison, and to that too, implacable; lest setting 'em about my ears, they attaque me by Troops, and force me to a Recantation-Sermon, which if I refuse, they streight pronounce me an Heretick. For this is the Thunder-bolt with which they fright those whom they are resolv'd not to favour. And truly, though there are few others that less willingly acknowledge the kindnesses I have done them, yet even these too stand fast bound to me upon no ordinary accounts; whil'st being happy in their own Opinion, and as if they dwelt in the third Heaven, they look with Haughtiness on all others as poor creeping things, and could almost find in their hearts to pitie 'em; whilst hedg'd in with so many Magisterial Definitions, Conclusions, Corollaries, Propositions Explicit and Implicit, they abound with so many starting-holes, that Vulcan's Net cannot hold 'em so fast, but they'll slip through with their distinctions; with which they so easily cut all knots asunder that a Hatchet could not have done it better, so plentiful are they in their new-found Words and prodigious Terms. Besides, whil'st they explicate the most hidden Mysteries according to their own fancie: — as, how the World was first made; how Original Sin is deriv'd to Posterity; in what manner, how much room, and how long time, Christ lay in the Virgin's Womb; how Accidents subsist in the Eucharist without their Subject.

But these are common and threadbare; these are worthy of our great and illuminated Divines, as the world calls 'em! At these, if ever they fall a thwart 'em, they prick up: — as, whether there was any instant of time in the generation of the Second Person; whether there be more than one Filiation in Christ; whether it be a possible Proposition that God the Father hates the Son; or whether it was possible that Christ could have taken upon Him the likeness of a Woman, or of the Devil, or of an Ass, or of a Stone, or of a Gourd; and then how that Gourd should have Preach't, wrought Miracles, or been hung on the Cross; and, what Peter had Consecrated, if he had administred the Sacrament at what time the Body of Christ hung upon the Cross; or whether at the same time he might be said to be Man; whether after the Resurrection there will be any eating and drinking, since we are so much afraid of hunger and thirst in this world. There are infinite of these subtile Trifles, and others more subtile than these; of Notions, Relations, Instants, Formalities, Quiddities, Ecceities, which no one can perceive without a Lynceus his eyes, that could look through a stone-wall, and discover those things through the thickest darkness that never were.

Add to this those their other Determinations, and those too so contrary to common Opinion that those Oracles of the Stoicks, which they call Paradoxes, seem in comparison of these but blockish and idle: — as, 'tis a lesser crime to kill a thousand men than to set a stitch on a poor man's shooe on the Sabbath-day; and that a man should rather chuse that the whole world with all Food and Raiment, as they say, should perish, than tell a lye, though never so inconsiderable. And these most subtile subtilties are rendred yet more subtile by the several Methods of so many Schoolmen, that one might sooner wind himself out of a Labyrinth than the entanglements of the Realists, Nominalists, Thomists, Albertists, Occamists,

Scotists. Nor have I nam'd all the several Sects, but onely some of the chief; in all which there is so much Doctrine and so much difficultie, that I may well conceive the Apostles, had they been to deal with these new kind of Divines, had needed to have pray'd in aid of some other Spirit.

Paul knew what Faith was, and yet when he saith, 'Faith is the Substance of things hop'd for, and the Evidence of things not seen', he did not define it Doctor-like. And as he understood Charity well himself, so he did as Illogically divide and define it to others in his first Epistle to the Corinthians, Chapter the thirteenth. And devoutly, no doubt, did the Apostles consecrate the Eucharist; yet, had they been askt the question touching the 'Terminus a quo' and the 'Terminus ad quem' of Transubstantiation; of the manner how the same body can be in several places at one and the same time; of the difference the body of Christ has in Heaven from that of the Cross, or this in the Sacrament; in what punct of time Transubstantiation is, whereas Prayer, by means of which it is, as being a discrete quantity, is transient; they would not, I conceive, have answer'd with the same subtilty as the Scotists Dispute and Define it. They knew the Mother of Jesus; but which of them has so Philosophically demonstrated how she was preserv'd from Original sin, as have done our Divines? Peter receiv'd the Keyes, and from Him too that would not have trusted them with a person unworthy; yet whether he had understanding or no, I know not, for certainly he never attain'd to that subtilty to determine how he could have the Key of knowledge that had no knowledge himself. They Baptized far and near, and yet taught no where what was the Formal, Material, Efficient, and final cause of Baptisme; nor made the least mention of delible and indelible Characters. They worshipt, 'tis true, but in Spirit, following herein no other than that of the Gospel, 'God is a Spirit, and they that worship, must worship him in Spirit and Truth'; yet it does not appear it was at that time reveal'd to them that an Image sketcht on the Wall with a Cole, was to be worshipt with the same worship as Christ Himself, if at least the two 'fore fingers be stretcht out, the hair long and uncut, and have three Rayes about the Crown of the Head. For who can conceive these things, unless he has spent at least six and thirty years in the Philosophical and Supercoelestial Whims of Aristotle and the Schoolmen?

In like manner, the Apostles press to us Grace; but which of them distinguisheth between free grace and grace that makes a man acceptable? They exhort us to good works, and yet determine not what is the working, and what a resting in the work done. They incite us to Charity, and yet make no difference between Charity infus'd and Charity wrought in us by our own endeavours. Nor do they declare whether it be an Accident or a Substance, a thing Created or Uncreated. They detest and abominate sin, but let me not live if they could define according to Art what that is which we call Sin, unless perhaps they were inspir'd by the spirit of the

Scotists. Nor can I be brought to believe that Paul, by whose learning you may judge the rest, would have so often condemn'd Questions, Disputes, Genealogies, and, as himself calls 'em, 'Strifes of words', if he had throughly understood those subtilties; especially when all the Debates and Controversies of those times were rude and blockish, in comparison of the more than Chrysippean subtilties of our Masters. Although yet the Gentlemen are so modest, that if they meet with any thing written by the Apostles not so smooth and even as might be expected from a Master, they do not presently condemn it, but handsomly bend it to their own purpose; so great Respect and Honour do they give, partly to Antiquity and partly to the name of Apostle. And truly 'twere a kind of injustice to require so great things of them that never heard the least word from their Masters concerning it. And so if the like happen in Chrysostome, Basil, Jerome, they think it enough to say, They are not oblig'd by 't.

The Apostles also confuted the Heathen Philosophers and Jews, a people than whom none more obstinate; but rather by their good Lives and Miracles than Syllogisms: and yet there was scarce one amongst 'em that was capable of understanding the least 'Quodlibet' of the Scotists. But now, where is that Heathen or Heretick that must not presently stoop to such Wire-drawn subtilties, unless he be so thick-skul'd that he can't apprehend 'em, or so impudent as to hiss 'em down, or, being furnisht with the same Tricks, be able to make his party good with 'em? As if a man should set a Conjurer on work against a Conjurer, or fight with one hallowed Sword against another, which would prove no other than a work to no purpose. For my own part I conceive the Christians would do much better, if instead of those dull Troops and Companies of Souldiers, with which they have manag'd their War with such doubtful success, they would send the bauling Scotists, the most obstinate Occamists, and invincible Albertists to war against the Turks and Saracens; and they would see, I guess, a most pleasant Combate, and such a Victory as was never before. For who is so faint whom their devices will not enliven? who so stupid whom such spurrs can't quicken? or who so quick-sighted, before whose eyes they can't cast a mist?

But you'l say, I jest. Nor are ye without cause, since even amongst Divines themselves there are some that have learnt better, and are ready to turn their stomacks at those foolish subtilties of t' others. There are some that detest 'em as a kind of Sacriledge, and count it the height of Impiety to speak so irreverently of such hidden things, rather to be ador'd than explicated; to dispute of 'em with such profane and Heathenish niceties; to define 'em so arrogantly, and pollute the majestie of Divinity with such pithless and sordid terms and opinions. Mean time the others please, nay hug themselves in their happiness, and are so taken up with these pleasant trifles, that they have not so much leisure as to cast the least eye on the Gospel or S. Paul's Epistles. And while they play the fool at this rate in their Schools, they make account the Universal Church would otherwise perish, unless, as the Poets fancy'd of Atlas that he supported Heaven with his shoulders, they underpropt t' other with their Syllogistical Buttresses. And how great a happiness is this, think ye? while, as if holy Writ were a Nose of Wax, they fashion and refashion it according to their pleasure; while they require that their own Conclusions, subscrib'd by two or three Schoolmen, be accounted greater than Solon's Laws, and prefer'd before the Papal Decretals; while, as Censors of the world, they force every one to a Recantation, that differs but a hair's bredth from the least of their Explicit or Implicit Determinations. And those too they pronounce like Oracles. This Proposition is scandalous; this Irreverent; this has a smatch of Heresie; this no very good sound: so that neither Baptisme, nor the Gospel, nor Paul, nor Peter, nor St. Jerome, nor St. Augustine, no nor most Aristotelitotical Thomas himself, can make a man a Christian, without these Batchelours too be pleas'd to give him his grace. And the like is their subtilty in judging; for who would think he were no Christian that should say these two Speeches 'Matula Putes' and 'matula Putet', or 'Ollae fervere' and 'ollam fervere' were not both good Latine, unless their wisdomes had taught us the contrary? who had deliver'd the Church from such Mists of Errour, which yet no one e're met with, had they not come out with some University Seal for 't? And are they not most happy while they do these things?

Then for what concerns Hell, how exactly they describe every thing, as if they had been conversant in that Common-wealth most part of their time! Again, how do they frame in their fancy new Orbes, adding to those we have already an eighth! a goodly one, no doubt, and spatious enough, lest perhaps their happy Souls might lack room to walk in, entertain their friends, and now and then play at Foot-ball. And with these and a thousand the like fopperies their heads are so full stufft and stretcht, that I believe Jupiter's brain was not near so bigg when, being in labour with Pallas, he was beholding to the Midwifery of Vulcan's Axe. And therefore ye must not wonder if in their publique Disputes they are so bound about the head, lest otherwise perhaps their brains might leap out. Nay, I have sometimes laught my self, to see 'em so towre in their own opinion when they speak most barbarously; and when they Humh and Hawh so pitifully that none but one of their own Tribe can understand 'em, they call it heights which the Vulgar can't reach; for they say 'tis beneath the dignity of Divine Mysteries to be crampt and ty'd up to the narrow Rules of Grammarians: from whence we may conjecture the great Prerogative of Divines, if they onely have the priviledge of speaking corruptly, in which yet every Cobler thinks himself concern'd for his share. Lastly, they look upon themselves as somewhat more than Men, as often as they are devoutly saluted by the name of 'Our Masters', in which they fancy there lyes as much as in the Jews' 'Jehovah'; and therefore they reckon it a crime if 'Magister noster' be written other than in Capital Letters; and if any one should preposterously say 'Noster magister', he has at once overturn'd the whole body of Divinity.

And next these come those that commonly call themselves the Religious and Monks; most false in both Titles, when both a great part of 'em are farthest from Religion, and no men swarm thicker in all places than themselves. Nor can I think of any thing that could be more miserable, did not I support 'em so many several wayes. For whereas all men detest 'em to that height, that they take it for ill luck to meet one of 'em by chance, yet such is their happiness that they flatter themselves. For first, they reckon it one of the main Points of Piety if they are so illiterate that they can't so much as read. And then when they run over their Offices, which they carry about 'em, rather by tale than understanding, they believe the Gods more than ordinarily pleas'd with their braying. And some there are among 'em that put off their trumperies at vast rates, yet roave up and down for the bread they eat; nay, there is scarce an Inne, Waggon, or Ship into which they intrude not, to the no small damage of the Common-wealth of Beggars. And yet, like pleasant fellows, with all this Vileness, Ignorance, Rudeness and Impudence, they represent to us, for so they call it, the lives of the Apostles. Yet what is more pleasant than that they do all things by Rule and, as it were, a kind of Mathematicks, the least swerving from which were a crime beyond forgiveness:—as, how many knots their shooes must be ti'd with, of what colour every thing is, what distinction of habits, of what stuffe made, how many straws broad their Girdles and of what fashion, how many bushels wide their Cowle, how many fingers long their Hair, and how many hours sleep; which exact equality, how disproportionable it is, among such variety of bodies and tempers, who is there that does not perceive it? And yet by reason of these fooleries they not onely set slight by others, but each different Order, men otherwise professing Apostolical Charity, despise one another, and for the different wearing of a habit, or that 'tis of darker colour, they put all things in combustion. And amongst these there are some so rigidly Religious that their upper Garment is hair-Cloth, their inner of the finest Linnen; and, on the contrary, others wear Linnen without, and hair next their skins. Others, agen, are as affraid to touch mony as poyson, and yet neither forbear Wine nor dallying with Women. In a word, 'tis their onely care that none of 'em come near one another in their manner of living, nor do they endeavour how they may be like Christ, but how they may differ among themselves.

And another great happiness they conceive in their Names, while they call themselves Cordiliers, and among these too, some are Colletes, some Minors, some Minims, some Crossed; and agen, these are Benedictines, those Bernardines; these Carmelites, those Augustines; these Williamites, and those Jacobines; as if it were not worth the while to be call'd Christians. And of these, a great part build so much on their Ceremonies and petty Traditions of Men, that they think one Heaven is too poor a reward for so great merit; little dreaming that the time will come when Christ, not regarding any of these trifles, will call 'em to account for His precept of Charity. One shall shew ye a large Trough full of all kinds of Fish; another tumble ye out so many bushels of Prayers; another reckon ye so many myriads of Fasts, and fetch 'em up agen in one dinner by eating till he cracks agen; another produces more bundles of Ceremonies than seven of the stoutest Ships would be able to carry; another brags he has not toucht a penny these three score Years without two pair of Gloves at least upon his hands; another wears a Cowl so lin'd with grease that the poorest Tarpaulin would not stoop to take it up; another will tell ye he has liv'd these fifty five Years like a Spunge, continually fastned to the same place; another is grown hoarse with his daily chanting; another has contracted a Lethargy by his solitary living; and another the Palsie in his Tongue for want of speaking. But Christ, interrupting them in their vanities, which otherwise were endless, will ask 'em, 'Whence this new kind of Jews? I acknowledge one Commandment, which is truly mine, of which alone I hear nothing. I promist, 'tis true, my Father's heritage, and that without Parables, not to Cowls, odd Prayers, and Fastings, but to the duties of Faith and Charity. Nor can I acknowledge them that least acknowledg their faults. They that would seem holier than my self, let 'em if they list possess to themselves those three hundred sixty five Heavens of Basilides the Heretick's invention, or command them whose foolish Traditions they have prefer'd before my Preceps, to erect them a new one'. When they shall hear these things, and see common ordinary persons perferr'd before 'em, with what countenance, think ye, will they behold one another? In the meantime they are happy in their hopes, and for this also they are beholding to me.

And yet these kind of people, though they are as it were of another Common-wealth, no man dares despise; especially those begging Friars, because they are privie to all men's secrets by means of Confessions, as they call 'em. Which yet were no less than treason to discover, unless, being got drunk, they have a mind to be pleasant, and then all comes out, that is to say by hints and conjectures, but suppressing the names. But if any one should anger these Wasps, they'll sufficiently revenge themselves in their publique Sermons, and so point out their enemy by circumlocutions that there's no one but understands whom 'tis they mean, unless he understand nothing at all; nor will they give over their barking till you throw the Dogs a bone. And now tell me, what Jugler or Mountebank you had rather behold than hear them rhetorically play the fool in their Preachments, and yet most sweetly imitating what Rhetoricians have written touching the Art of good speaking? Good God! what several postures they have! How they shift their voice, sing out their words, skip up and down, and are ever and anon making such new faces, that they confound all things with noise! and yet this Knack of theirs is no less than a Mystery that runs in succession from one brother to another; which though it be not lawful for me to know, however I'll venture at it by conjectures. And first they invoke what ever they have scrapt from the Poets; and in the next place, if they are to discourse of Charity, they take their rise from the river Nilus; or to set out the Mystery of the Cross, from Bell and the Dragon; or to dispute of Fasting, from the twelve signs of the Zodiack; or, being to preach of Faith, ground their matter on the square of a Circle.

I have heard my self one, and he no small fool,—I was mistaken, I would have said Scholar,—that being in a Famous Assembly explaining the Mystery of the Trinity, that he might both let 'em see his Learning was not ordinary, and withal satisfie some Theological ears, he took a new way, to wit from the Letters, Syllables, and the Word it self; then from the Cohærence of the Nominative Case and the Verb, and the Adjective and Substantive: and while most of the Auditory wonder'd, and some of 'em mutter'd that of Horace, 'what does all this Trumpery drive at?' at last he brought the matter to this head, that he would demonstrate that the Mystery of the Trinity was so clearly exprest in the very Rudiments of Grammar, that the best Mathematician could not chalk 't out more plainly. And in this Discourse did this most Superlative Theologue beat his brains for eight whole moneths, that at this hour he's as blind as a Beetle, to wit, all the sight of his eyes being run into the sharpness of his wit. But for all that he nothing forthinketh his blindness, rather taking the same for too cheap a price of such a glory as he wan thereby.

And besides him I met with another, some eighty years of age, and such a Divine that you'd have sworn Scotus himself was reviv'd in him. He, being upon the point of unfolding the Mystery of the name Jesus, did with wonderful subtilty demonstrate that there lay hidden in those Letters what ever could be said of him; for that it was only declin'd with three Cases, he said, it was a manifest token of the Divine Trinity; and then, that the first ended in S, the second in M, the third in U, there was in it an ineffable Mystery, to wit, those three Letters declaring to us that he was the Beginning, Middle, and End of all. Nay, the Mystery was yet more abstruse; for he so Mathematically split the word Jesus into two equal parts, that he left the middle letter by it self, and then told us that that letter in Hebrew was (שׁ) *Schin* or *Sin,* and that *Sin* in the Scotch tongue, as he remember'd, signifi'd as much as Sin; from whence he gather'd that it was Jesus that took away the sins of the world. At which new Exposition the Auditory were so wonderfully intent and struck with admiration, especially the Theologues, that there wanted little but that Niobe-like they had been turn'd to stones; whereas the like had almost happen'd to me, as befell the Priapus in Horace. And not without cause, for when were the Grecian Demosthenes or Roman Cicero e're guilty of the like? They thought that Introduction faulty that was wide of the

Matter, as if it were not the way of Carters and Swinheards, that have no more wit than God sent 'em. But these learned men think their Preamble, for so they call it, then chiefly Rhetorical when it has least Coherence with the rest of the Argument, that the admiring Auditory may in the mean while whisper to themselves, 'What will he be at now'? In the third place, they bring in instead of Narration some Texts of Scripture, but handle 'em cursorily, and as it were by the bye, when yet it is the onely thing they should have insisted on. And fourthly, as it were changing a Part in the Play, they bolt out with some question in Divinity, and many times relating neither to Earth nor Heaven, and this they look upon as a piece of Art. Here they erect their Theological Crests, and beat into the people's ears those Magnifical Titles of Illustrious Doctors, Subtile Doctors, most Subtile Doctors, Seraphick Doctors, Cherubin-Doctors, Holy Doctors, Unquestionable Doctors, and the like; and then throw abroad among the ignorant people Syllogisms, Majors, Minors, Conclusions, Corollaries, Suppositions, and those so weak and foolish that they are below Pedantry. There remaines yet the fifth Act, in which one would think they should shew their Mastery. And here they bring in some foolish insipid Fable out of *Speculum Historiale* or *Gesta Romanorum,* and Expound it Allegorically, Tropologically, and Anagogically. And after this manner do they end their Chimæra, and such as Horace despair'd of compassing, when he writ 'Humano capiti,' &c.

But they have heard from some body, I know not whom, that the beginning of a Speech should be Sober and Grave, and least given to noise. And therefore they begin theirs at that rate they can scarce hear themselves, as if it were no matter whether any one understood 'em. They have learnt some where that to move the affections a lowder voice is requisite. Whereupon they that otherwise would speak like a Mouse in a Cheese, start out of a suddain into a downright fury, even there too, where there's the least need of it. A man would swear they were past the power of Hellebor, so little do they consider where 'tis they run out. Again, because they have heard that as a Speech comes up to something, a man should press it more earnestly, they, how ever they begin, use a strange contention of voice in every part, though the Matter it self be never so flat, and end in that manner as if they'd run themselves out of breath. Lastly, they have learnt that among Rhetoricians there is some mention of Laughter, and therefore they study to prick in a jest here and there; but, O Venus! so void of wit and so little to the purpose, that it may be truly call'd an Asses playing on the Harp. And sometimes also they use somewhat of a sting, but so nevertheless that they rather tickle than wound; nor do they ever more truly flatter than when they would seem to use the greatest freedom of speech. Lastly, such is their whole action that a man would swear they had learnt it from our common Tumblers, though yet they come short of 'em in every respect. However, they are both so like, that no man will dispute but that either these learnt their Rhetorick from them, or they theirs from these. And yet they light on some that, when they hear 'em, conceive they hear very Demosthenes and Ciceroes: of which sort chiefly are our Merchants and Women, whose Ears onely they endeavour to please, because as to the first, if they stroake 'em handsomely, some part or other of their ill-gotten goods is wont to fall to their share. And the Women, though for many other things they favour this Order, this is not the least, that they commit to their breasts what ever discontents they have against their Husbands. And now, I conceive me, ye see how much this kind of people are beholding to me, that with their Petty Ceremonies, Ridiculous Trifles, and Noise, exercise a kind of Tyranny among mankind, believing themselves very Pauls and Anthonies.

But I willingly give over these Stage-players, that are such ingrateful dissemblers of the courtesies I have done 'em, and such impudent pretenders to Religion which they ha' n't. And now I have a mind to give some small touches of Princes and Courts, of whom I am had in reverence, above-board and, as it becomes Gentlemen, frankly. And truly, if they had the least proportion of sound judgment, what life were more unpleasant than theirs, or so much to be avoided? For who ever did but truly weigh with himself how great a burthen lies upon his shoulders that would truly discharge the duty of a Prince, he would not think it worth his while to make his way to a Crown by Perjury and Parricide. He would consider that he that takes a Scepter in his hand should manage the Publick, not his Private Interest; study nothing but the common good; and not in the least go contrary to those Laws whereof himself is both the Author and Exactor: that he is to take an account of the good or evil administration of all his magistrates and subordinate Officers; that, though he is but one, all men's Eyes are upon him, and in his power it is, either like a good Planet to give life and safety to mankind by his harmless influence, or like a fatal Comet to send mischief and destruction: that the vices of other men are not alike felt, nor so generally communicated; and that a Prince stands in that place that his least deviation from the Rule of Honesty and Honour reaches farther than himself, and opens a gap to many men's ruine. Besides, that the fortune of Princes has many things attending it that are but too apt to train 'em out of the way, as Pleasure, Liberty, Flattery, Excess; for which cause he should the more diligently endeavour and set a watch o're himself, lest perhaps he be led aside and fail in his duty. Lastly, to say nothing of Treasons, ill will and such other Mischiefs he's in jeopardy of, that that True King is over his head, who in a short time will cal him to account for every the least trespass, and that so much the more severely, by how much more mighty was the Empire committed to his charge. These and the like if a Prince should duly weigh, and weigh it he would if he were wise, he would neither be able to sleep nor take any hearty repast.

But now by my courtesie they leave all this care to the Gods, and are onely taken up with themselves, not admitting any one to their eare but such as know how to speak pleasant things, and not trouble 'em with business. They believe they have discharg'd all the duty of a Prince if they Hunt every day, keep a Stable of fine Horses, sell Dignities and Commanderies, and invent new wayes of draining the Citizens' Purses and bringing it into their own Exchequer; but under such dainty new-found names, that though the thing be most injust in it self, it carries yet some face of equity; adding to this some little sweetnings, that what ever happens, they may be secure of the common people. And now suppose some one, such as they sometimes are, a man ignorant of Laws, little less than an enemy to the publique good, and minding nothing but his own, given up to Pleasure, a hater of Learning, Liberty, and Justice, studying nothing less than the publique safety, but measuring every thing by his own will and profit; and then put on him a golden Chain, that declares the accord of all Vertues linkt one to another; a Crown set with Diamonds, that should put him in mind how he ought to excell all others in Heroick Vertues; besides a Scepter, the Emblem of Justice and an untainted heart; and lastly, a Purple Robe, a Badge of that Charity he owes the Common-wealth. All which if a Prince should compare 'em with his own life, he would I believe be clearly asham'd of his bravery, and be afraid lest some or other gibing Expounder turn all this Tragical Furniture into a ridiculous Laughing-stock.

And as to the Court-Lords, what should I mention them? than most of whom though there be nothing more indebted, more servile, more witless, more contemptible, yet they would seem as they were the most excellent of all others. And yet in this only thing no men more modest, in that they are contented to wear about 'em Gold, Jewels, Purple, and those other marks of Vertue and Wisdome, but for the study of the things themselves, they remit it to others; thinking it happiness enough for them that they can call the King Master, have learnt the cringe *à la mode,* know when and where to use those Titles of Your Grace, My Lord, Your Magnificence; in a word that they are past all shame and can flatter pleasantly. For these are the Arts that speak a man truly Noble and an exact Courtier. But if ye look into their manner of life you'll find 'em meer Sots, as debaucht as Penelope's Wooers; you know the other part of the verse, which the Echo will better tell ye than I can. They sleep till noon, and have their mercenary Levite come to their bed side, where he chops over his Mattins before they are half up. Then to Break-fast, which is scarce done but Dinner staies for 'em. From thence they go to Dice, Tables, Cards, or entertain themselves with Jesters, Fools, Gambolls, and Horse-tricks. In the mean time they have one or two Bevers, and then Supper, and after that a Banquet, and 'twere well, by Jupiter, there were no more than one. And in this manner do their Hours, Dayes, Moneths, Years, Age slide away without the least irksomeness. Nay, I have sometimes gone away many Inches fatter, to see 'em speak bigg words; whiles each of the Ladies believes her self so much nearer to the Gods, by how much the longer train she trails after her; whiles one Nobleman edges out another, that he may get the nearer to Jupiter himself; and every one of 'em pleases himself the more by how massier is the Chain he swaggs on his shoulders, as if he meant to shew his strength as well as his wealth.

Nor are Princes by themselves in their manner of life, since Popes, Cardinals, and Bishops have so diligently follow'd their steps, that they've almost got the start of 'em. For if any of 'em would consider what their Albe should put 'em in mind of, to wit a blameless life; what is meant by their forked Miters, whose each point is held in by the same knot, wee'll suppose it a perfect knowledge of the Old and New Testaments; what those Gloves on their Hands, but a sincere administration of the Sacraments, and free from all touch of worldly business; what their Crosier, but a careful looking after the Flock committed to their charge; what the Cross born before 'em, but victory over all earthly affections: — these, I say, and many of the like kind should any one truly consider, would he not live a sad and troublesome life? Whereas now they do well enough while they feed themselves onely; and for the care of their Flock, either put it over to Christ or lay it all on their Suffragans, as they call 'em, or some poor Vicars. Nor do they so much as remember their name, or what the word Bishop signifies; to wit, Labour, Care and Trouble. But in racking to gather moneys they truly act the part of Bishops, and herein acquit themselves to be no blind Seers.

In like manner Cardinals, if they thought themselves the successours of the Apostles, they would likewise imagine that the same things the other did are requir'd of them, and that they are not Lords, but Dispensers of Spiritual things, of which they must shortly give an exact account. But if they also would a little Philosophize on their Habit, and think with themselves what's the meaning of their Linen Rochet; is it not a remarkable and singular integrity of life? what that inner Purple; is it not an earnest and fervent love of God? or what that outward, whose loose Plaits and Long Train fall round his Reverence's Mule, and are large enough to cover a Camel; is it not Charity, that spreads it self so wide to the succour of all men? that is, to Instruct, Exhort, Comfort, Reprehend, Admonish, compose Wars, resist wicked Princes, and willingly expend, not onely their Wealth but their very Lives for the Flock of Christ: though yet what need at all of wealth to them that supply the room of the poor Apostles? — These things, I say, did they but duely consider, they would not be so ambitious of that Dignity; or, if they were, they would willingly leave it and live a laborious, careful life, such as was that of the antient Apostles.

And for Popes, that supply the place of Christ, if they should endeavour to imitate His Life, to wit His Poverty, Labour, Doctrine, Cross, and contempt of Life, or should they consider what the name Pope, that is Father, or Holiness, imports, who would live more disconsolate than themselves? or who would purchase that Chair with all his substance? or defend it so purchast, with Swords, Poisons, and all force imaginable? so great a profit would the access of Wisdom deprive him of; — Wisdom did I say? nay, the least corn of that Salt which Christ speaks of: so much Wealth, so much Honour, so much Riches, so many Victories, so many Offices, so many Dispensations, so much Tribute, so many Pardons; such Horses, such Mules, such Guards, and so much Pleasure would it lose them. You see how much I have comprehended in a little: instead of which it would bring in Watchings, Fastings, Tears, Prayers, Sermons, good Endeavours, Sighs, and a thousand the like troublesome Exercises. Nor is this least considerable: so many Scribes, so many Copying Clerks, so many Notaries, so many Advocates, so many Promooters, so many Secretaries, so many Muletters, so many Grooms, so many Bankers: in short, that vast multitude of men that overcharge the Roman See — I mistook, I meant honour —, might beg their bread.

A most inhumane and abominable thing, and more to be execrated, that those great Princes of the Church and true Lights of the World should be reduc'd to a Staff and a Wallet. Whereas now, if there be any thing that requires their pains, they leave that to Peter and Paul that have leisure enough; but if there be any thing of Honour or Pleasure, they take that to themselves. By which means it is, yet by my courtesie, that scarce any kind of men live more voluptuously or with less trouble; as believing that Christ will be well enough pleas'd, if in their Mystical and almost mimical Pontificalibus, Ceremonies, Titles of Holiness and the like, and Blessing and Cursing, they play the parts of Bishops. To work Miracles is old and antiquated, and not in fashion now; to instruct the people, troublesome; to interpret the Scripture, Pedantick; to pray, a sign one has little else to do; to shed tears, silly and womanish; to be poor, base; to be vanquisht, dishonourable, and little becoming him that scarce admits even Kings to kiss his Slipper; and lastly, to dye, uncouth; and to be stretcht on a Cross, infamous.

Theirs are only those Weapons and sweet Blessings, which Paul mentions, and of these truly they are bountiful enough: as Interdictions, Hangings, Heavy Burthens, Reproofs, Anathemas, Executions in Effigie, and that terrible Thunder-bolt of Excommunication, with the very sight of which they sink men's Souls beneath the bottom of Hell: which yet these most holy Fathers in Christ and his Vicars hurl with more fierceness against none than against such as, by the instigation of the Devil, attempt to lessen or rob 'em of Peter's Patrimony. When, though those words in the Gospel, 'We have left all, and follow'd Thee,' were his, yet they call his Patrimony Lands, Cities, Tribute, imposts, Riches; for which, being enflam'd with the love of Christ, they contend with Fire and Sword, and not without losse of much Christian blood, and believe they have then most Apostolically defended the Church, the Spouse of Christ, when the enemy, as they call 'em, are valiantly routed. As if the Church had any deadlier enemies than wicked Prelates, who not onely suffer Christ to run out of request for want of preaching him, but hinder his spreading by their multitudes of Laws, meerly contriv'd for their own profit, corrupt him by their forc'd Expositions, and murder him by the evil example of their pestilent life.

Nay, further, whereas the Church of Christ was founded in blood, confirm'd by blood, and augmented by blood, now, as if Christ, who after his wonted manner defends his people, were lost, they govern all by the Sword. And whereas War is so Savage a thing that it rather befits Beasts than Men, so outragious that the very Poets feign'd it came from the Furies, so pestilent that it corrupts all men's manners, so injust that it is best executed by the worst of men, so wicked that it has no agreement with Christ; and yet, omitting all the other, they make this their onely business. Here you'll see decrepit old fellows acting the parts of young men, neither troubled at their costs nor weari'd with their labours, nor discourag'd at any thing, so they may have the liberty of turning Laws, Religion, Peace and all things else quite topsie turvie. Nor are they destitute of their learned Flatterers that call that palpable Madness Zeal, Piety, and Valour, having found out a new way by which a man may kill his brother without the least breach of that Charity which, by the command of Christ, one Christian owes another. And here, in troth, I'm a little at a stand whether the Ecclesiastical German Electors gave 'em this example, or rather took it from 'em; who, laying aside their Habit, Benedictions and all the like Ceremonies, so act the part of Commanders that they think it a mean thing, and least beseeming a Bishop, to shew the least courage to God-ward unless it be in a battle.

And as to the common Heard of Priests, they account it a crime to degenerate from the Sanctity of their Prelates. Heidah! how Souldier-like they bussle about the *jus divinum* of Titles, and how quick-sighted they are to pick the least thing out of the Writings of the Antients, wherewith they may fright the common people, and convince 'em, if possible, that more than a Tenth is due! Yet in the mean-time it least comes in their heads how many things are every where extant concerning that duty which they owe the people. Nor does their shorn Crown in the least admonish 'em that a Priest should be free from all worldly desires, and think of nothing but heavenly things. Whereas on the contrary, these jolly fellows say they have sufficiently discharg'd their Office if they but any-how mumble over a few odd Prayers, which, so help me, Hercules! I wonder if any God either hear or understand, since they do neither themselves; especially when they thunder 'em out in that manner they are wont. But this they have in common with those of the Heathens, that they are vigilant enough to the harvest of their profit, nor is there any of 'em that is not better read in those Laws than the Scripture. Whereas if there be any thing burthensome, they prudently lay that on other men's shoulders, and shift it from one to t'other, as men toss a Ball from hand to hand; following herein the example of Lay Princes, who commit the Government of their Kingdoms to their Grand Ministers, and they again to others, and leave all study of Piety to the common people. In like manner the common people put it over to those they call Ecclesiasticks, as if themselves were no part of the Church, or that their vow in Baptism had lost its obligation. Again, the Priests that call themselves Secular, as if they were initiated to the world, not to Christ, lay the burthen on the Regulars; the Regulars on the Monks; the Monks that have more liberty, on those that have less; and all of 'em on the Mendicants; the Mendicants on the Carthusians, amongst whom, if any where, this Piety lies buried, but yet so close that scarce any one can perceive it. In like manner the Popes, the most diligent of all others in gathering in the Harvest of mony, refer all their Apostolical work to the Bishops; the Bishops to the Parsons; the Parsons to the Vicars; the Vicars to their brother Mendicants; and they again throw back the care of the Flock on those that take the Wooll.

* * * * *

But not to run too far in that which is infinite. To speak briefly, all Christian Religion seems to have a kind of allyance with folly, and in no respect to have any accord with wisedom. Of which if ye expect proofs, consider first that boyes, old men, women and fools are more delighted with religious and sacred things than others, and to that purpose are ever next the Altars; and this they do by meer impulse of Nature. And in the next place, you see that those first founders of it were plain, simple persons, and most bitter enemies of Learning. Lastly there are no sort of fools seem more out of the way than are these whom the zeal of Christian Religion has once swallow'd up; so that they waste their estates, neglect injuries, suffer themselves to be cheated, put no difference between friends and enemies, abhor pleasure, are cram'd with poverty, watchings, tears, labours, reproaches, loathe life, and wish death above all things; in short, they seem senseless to common understanding, as if their minds liv'd elsewhere and not in their own bodies, which, what else is it than to be mad? For which reason you must not think it so strange if the Apostles seem'd to be drunk with new wine, and if Paul appear'd to Festus to be mad.

But now, having once gotten on the Lion's skin, go to, and I'll shew ye that this happinesse of Christians, which they pursue with so much toil, is nothing else but a kind of madnesse and folly; far be it that my words should give any offence, rather consider my matter. And first, the Christians and Platonicks do as good as agree in this, that the Soul is plung'd and fetter'd in the prison of the body, by the grossnesse of which it is so ty'd up and hinder'd, that it cannot take a view of or enjoy things as they truly are; and for that cause their master defines Philosophy to be a contemplation of death, because it takes off the mind from visible and corporeal objects, than which death does no more. And therefore, as long as the Soul useth the Organs of the Body in that right manner it ought, so long it is said to be in good state and condition; but when, having broke its fetters, it endeavours to get loose, and assayes, as it were, a flight out of that prison that holds it in, they call it madness; and if this happen through any distemper, or indisposition of the organs, then, by the common consent of every man, 'tis down-right madnesse. And yet we see such kind of men foretell things to come, understand Tongues and Letters they never learnt before, and seem, as it were, big with a kind of Divinity. Nor is it to be doubted but that it proceeds from hence, that the mind, being somewhat at liberty from the infection of the body, begins to put forth it self in its native vigour. And I conceive 'tis from the same cause that the like often happens to sick men a little before their death, that they discourse in strain above mortality, as if they were inspir'd. Agen, if this happens upon the score of Religion, though perhaps it may not be the same kind of madness, yet 'tis so near it that a great many men would judge it no better, especially when a few inconsiderable people shall differ from the rest of the world in the whole course of their life. And therefore it fares with them, as, according to the Fiction of Plato, happens to those that being coopt up in a cave stand gaping with admiration at the shadows of things; and that fugitive who, having broke from 'em and returning to 'em agen, told 'em he had seen things truly as they were, and that they were the most mistaken in believing there was nothing but pitiful shadows. For as this wise man pitty'd and bewail'd their palpable madness that were possest with so grosse an error, so they in return laught at him as a doating fool, and cast him out of their company. In like manner the common sort of men chiefly admire those things that are most corporeal, and almost believe there is nothing beyond 'em. Whereas on the contrary, these devout persons, by how much the nearer any thing concerns the body, by so much the more they neglect it, and are wholly hurry'd away with the contemplation of things invisible. For the one give the first place to riches, the next to their corporal pleasures, leaving the last place to their soul; which yet most of 'em do scarce believe, because they can't see it with their eyes. On the contrary, the others first rely wholly on God, the most unchangeable of all things; and next him, yet on this that comes nearest him, they bestow the second on their soul; and lastly, for their body, they neglect that care, and contemn and fly monies as superfluity that may be well spar'd; or if they are forc't to meddle with any of these things, they do it carelesly and much against their wills, having as if they had it not, and possessing as if they possessed it not.

There are also in each several things several degrees wherein they disagree among themselves. And first as to the senses, though all of 'em have more or lesse affinity with the body, yet of these some are more gross and blockish, as tasting, hearing, seeing, smelling, touching; some more remov'd from the body, as memory, intellect, and the will. And therefore to which of these the mind applies it self, in that lyes its force. But holy men, because the whole bent of their minds is taken up with those things that are most repugnant to these grosser senses, they seem brutish and stupid in the common use of them. Whereas on the contrary, the ordinary sort of people are best at these, and can do least at to'ther; from whence it is, as we have heard, that some of these holy men have by mistake drunk oil for wine. Agen, in the affections of the mind, some have a greater commerce with the body than others, as lust, desire of meat and sleep, anger, pride, envy; with which holy men are at irreconcilable enmity, and contrary, the common people think there's no living without 'em. And lastly there are certain middle kind of affections, and as it were natural to every man, as the love of one's Country, Children, Parents, Friends, and to which the common people attribute no small matter; whereas to'ther strive to pluck 'em out of their mind: unlesse insomuch as they arrive to that highest part of the soul, that they love their Parents not as Parents — for what did they get but the body? though yet we owe it to God, not them — but as good men or women, and in whom shines the Image of that highest wisdom, which alone they call the chiefest good, and out of which, they say, there is nothing to be belov'd or desir'd.

And by the same rule do they measure all things else, so that they make lesse account of whatever is visible, unlesse it be altogether contemptible, than of those things which they cannot see. But they say that in Sacraments and other religious Duties there is both body and Spirit. As in fasting they count it not enough for a man to abstain from eating, which the common people take for an absolute Fast, unlesse there be also a lessening of his deprav'd affections: as that he be lesse angry, less proud, than he was wont, that the Spirit, being less clog'd with its bodily weight, may be the more intent upon heavenly things. In like manner, in the Eucharist, though, say they, it is not to be esteem'd the less that 'tis administer'd with Ceremonies, yet of its self 'tis of little effect, if not hurtful, unless that which is spiritual be added to it, to wit, that which is represented under those visible signes. Now the death of Christ is represented by it, which all men, vanquishing, abolishing and, as it were, burying their carnal affections, ought to express in their lives and conversations, that they may grow up to a newness of life, and be one with him, and the same one amongst another. This a holy man does, and in this is his only meditation. Whereas on the contrary, the common people think there's no more in that Sacrifice than to be present at the Altar, and crow'd next it, to have a noise of words and look upon the Ceremonies. Nor in this alone, which we onely propos'd by way of example, but in all his life, and without hypocrisie, does a holy man fly those things that have any alliance with the body, and is wholly ravisht with things Eternal, Invisible, and Spiritual. For which cause there's so great contrariety of opinion between 'em, and that too in every thing, that each party thinks the other out of their wits; though that character, in my judgment, better agrees with those holy men than the common people: which yet will be more clear if, as I promis'd, I briefly shew ye that that great reward they so much fancy is nothing else but a kind of madness.

And therefore suppose that Plato dreamt of somewhat like it when he call'd the madness of Lovers the most happy condition of all others. For he that's violently in Love lives not in his own body, but in the thing he loves; and by how much the farther he runs from himself into another, by so much the greater is his pleasure. And then, when the mind strives to rove from its body, and does not rightly use its own organs, without doubt you may say 'tis down-right madnesse and not be mistaken, or otherwise what's the meaning of those common sayings, 'He does not dwell at home', 'Come to your self', 'He's his own man again'? Besides, the more perfect and true his love is, the more pleasant is his madness. And therefore, what is that life hereafter, after which these holy minds so pantingly breathe, like to be? To wit, the Spirit shall swallow up the Body, as conqueror and more durable; and this it shall do with the greater ease because heretofore, in its life-time, it had cleans'd and thinn'd it into such another nothing as its self. And then the Spirit agen shall be wonderfully swallow'd up by that highest mind, as being more powerful than infinite parts; so that the whole man is to be out of himself, nor to be otherwise happy in any respect, but that being stript of himself, he shall participate of somewhat ineffable from that chiefest good that draws all things into its self. And this happiness though 'tis only then perfected when souls being joyn'd to their former bodies shall be made immortal, yet forasmuch as the life of holy men is nothing but a continu'd meditation and, as it were, shadow of that life, it so happens that at length they have some taste or relish of it; which, though it be but as the smallest drop in comparison of that fountain of eternal happiness, yet it far surpasses all worldly delight, though all the pleasures of all mankind were all joyn'd together. So much better are things spiritual than things corporal, and things invisible than things visible; which doubtless is that which the Prophet promiseth: 'The eye hath not seen, nor the ear heard, nor has it entred into the heart of man to consider what God has provided for them that love Him'. And this is that Mary's better part, which is not taken away by change of life, but perfected.

And therefore they that are sensible of it, and few there are to whom this happens, suffer a kind of somewhat little differing from madness; for they utter many things that do not hang together, and that too not after the manner of men, but make a kind of sound which they neither heed themselves, nor is it understood by others, and change the whole figure of their countenance, one while jocund, another while dejected, now weeping, then laughing, and agen sighing. And when they come to themselves, tell ye they know not where they have been, whether in the body or out of the body, or sleeping; nor do they remember what they have heard, seen, spoken or done, and only know this, as it were in a mist or dream, that they were the most happy while they were so out of their wits. And therefore they are sorry they are come to themselves agen, and desire nothing more than this kind of madnesse, to be perpetually mad. And this is a small taste of that future happiness.

But I forget my self and run beyond my bounds. Though yet, if I shall seem to have spoken any thing more boldly or impertinently than I ought, be pleas'd to consider that not only Folly but a Woman said it; remembring in the mean time that Greek Proverb, 'Sometimes a fool may speak a word in season', unlesse perhaps you'll say this concerns not Women. I see you expect an Epilogue, but give me leave to tell ye you are much mistaken if you think I remember any thing of what I have said, having foolishly bolted out such a hodg podg of words. 'Tis an old Proverb, 'I hate one that remembers what's done over the Cup'. This is a new one of my own making: I hate a man that remembers what he hears. Wherefore farewell, clap your hands, live, and drink lustick, my most excellent Disciples of Folly.

FRANÇOIS RABELAIS

(1494–1553)

In 1903, in Paris, under the leadership of M. Abel Lefranc, was founded the *Société des Etudes Rabelaisiennes*. The investigations carried on by the distinguished French scholars in this society have long since dispelled the erroneous legends and inaccurate conceptions gathered about Rabelais. The documents their skillful researches have brought to light have enabled us to know about his career and to interpret his personality and writings with an accuracy based upon historical evidence. It is now seen that he was a humanist who had training in theology, law, and medicine, and that he became finally one of the most famous physicians of France. His friends and patrons were the enlightened churchmen, scholars, and professional men of the day, and included Francis I and his famous sister, Marguerite, Queen of Navarre.

Rabelais belonged to the country of the Touraine. His father, Antoine Rabelais, was a practicing lawyer, a "licentiate in law, counsellor and advocate in the court of Chinon," a town about thirty miles southwest of Tours. His mother came from Angers. They had three sons and one daughter. The family belonged to the bourgeois or middle class and had acquired several properties in and about Chinon. François was born at their country place, La Devinière, about four miles southwest of the town, probably in 1494.

According to a local tradition, the young Rabelais received his first schooling at the Benedictine Abbey of Saint-Pierre de Seuilly near his birthplace. His youth seems to have associations also with Angers, and it was stated in the seventeenth century that he was a novice there in the Franciscan monastery of La Baumette. The first document we possess, however, is a letter which he wrote to the famous humanist, Guillaume Budé, in 1521. It was written from the Puy-Saint-Martin, a Franciscan monastery at Fontenay-le-Comte, in Bas-Poitou. He had entered this institution the preceding year at the age of twenty-six. Apparently he had become a Friar Minor and wished to become a priest because of the opportunity such a life afforded for study. His interests took him beyond theology, however, to the profane knowledge of "philosophy" and "good letters." With a brother friar, Pierre Amy, he studied Greek literature, a study then new in France, to be undertaken only by the most ardent. Moreover, the two frequented the discussions of a group of humanist lawyers at Fontenay-le-Comte, headed by the advocate André Tiraqueau. In correspondence with Budé, and in association with this learned group, they established contacts with the humanist world of their time. In 1523, their superiors at the monastery confiscated their Greek books.

Apparently fearing for his future, Rabelais obtained authorization from Clement VII to transfer to the near-by monastery of Saint-Pierre-de-Maillezais, of the more enlightened Benedictine Order. The abbot of this monastery was Geoffroy d'Estissac, bishop of the diocese of Maillezais, and also prior of Ligugé. It was perhaps through his support that Rabelais was enabled to make the transfer. Geoffroy lived chiefly at the priory at Ligugé, not far from Poitiers. For most of the period from 1524 to 1527, Rabelais became an intimate member of Geoffroy's household, as secretary, perhaps also as tutor to the bishop's nephew. He signs a letter to a friend "at Ligugé, in my little room"; he must have carried on his studies here. Geoffroy surrounded himself with cultured and learned men. Not far away, at the Abbey of Fontaine-le-Comte, there gathered another learned company about its abbot. We know that Rabelais lived in both of these circles, where discussions of the larger world of Italy, of the religious reformers of the North, took place. Furthermore, he accompanied Geoffroy on his constant travels throughout the length and breadth of Poitou. His writings indicate that he mixed widely and intimately with the people of the province. Poitiers, near by, was — after Paris — one of the greatest towns of France; because of its distinguished Faculty of Law, its university ranked second in the country. Probably Rabelais studied law at Poitiers and associated with its legists and officers of justice; his writings show a close knowledge of the works of law and jurisprudence. It is apparent that, under the patronage of Geoffroy d'Estissac, Rabelais' life was pleasant and soon widened to the new horizons of a larger world.

In 1527, however, we lose sight of Rabelais for about three years. The indications we possess make it probable that he assumed the habit of a secular priest and became a wandering scholar at the universities of France — at Bordeaux, Toulouse, Bourges, Orléans, and finally at Paris. The intimate knowledge of these places and the acquaintance with their residents shown later in his writings and correspondence may well have been obtained at this time. The sojourn at Paris was the longest: here he lived in the midst of that colorful and motley life of students, monks, and professors that went on about the Hill of Sainte-Geneviève. It was the time when the Faculty of Theology of the Sorbonne, caught by the Greek scholarship of the Hellenists which they themselves did not possess, arose against the humanists and reformers. Then came the establishment of the Royal Lectors, later to be called the Collège de France.

By September 1530, however, there was no longer any uncertainty whither Rabelais' life was tending; at this time he matriculated at Montpellier to study with the most famous Faculty of Medicine in France. Indeed he must have already entered upon these studies, for he was admitted as Bachelor of Medicine on the following 1st of November. The required course of lectures he gave in the following year was unique: he selected for his subject the Greek medical works of Hippocrates and Galen, expounded them from the Greek texts themselves, and sought to clear away the later false interpretations of the Arabians. We catch a glimpse of the lighter side of his university life. He tells us of the production of a farce in which he names himself as having acted a part, and which he may even have written himself. There is already clear indication of the value placed upon fun and laughter by medical scholars in their hours and moods of relaxation.

Rabelais' professional establishment came in 1532. On November 1st of that year he was appointed as physician to the Great Hospital of the town of Lyons, an institution of ancient and important standing. Lyons had become one of the foremost commercial and intellectual centers of France, noted for its printers and booksellers, and for the quarterly fairs which attracted buyers from much of Europe. Here the German, Sebastian Gryphius, had established himself to print ancient texts and learned works. Earlier in the same year, he had brought out learned works for Rabelais: the *Medical Letters of Jean Manardi,* a physician of Ferrara, and the *Aphorisms* of Hippocrates. As lawyers had sought to restore their profession by returning to the purity of ancient texts, so Rabelais sought to renovate medicine by presenting the Greek texts cleared of the errors of medieval glosses. His position as physician, apparently his first as practitioner, made him virtually head of the Great Hospital. That he was successful seems certain, for a modern scholar has shown that, during the time he was there, the death rate decreased by 2 to 3 per cent. In the autumn of 1532, there appeared for sale in Lyons a book entitled *The Horrible and Frightful Acts and Prowesses of the Very Renowned Pantagruel, King of the Dipsodes, Son of the Great Giant Gargantua, Composed Newly by Master Alcofrybas Nasier.* This author's name was the anagram of François Rabelais, and this volume was the one now arranged as second in his works.

Rabelais' professional reputation, and no doubt the qualities of his companionship, soon won further recognition. The Bishop of Paris, Jean du Bellay, high in the confidence of Francis I as an able diplomat, on his way to Rome early in 1534, requested Rabelais to accompany him as his personal physician. This was the journey dear to the heart of every humanist. Rabelais planned to confer with Italian scholars, to examine new plants and drugs beyond the Alps, and to study the city of ancient Rome. They spent the months of February and March in the Eternal City. The Sorbonne had condemned the *Pantagruel* by Alcofrybas Nasier, but François Rabelais had now gained the protection of the churchman who was long to remain loyal to him. In the autumn of 1534, Rabelais being again in attendance at the Great Hospital, there appeared in Lyons another volume by Master Alcofrybas Nasier, entitled *The Very Horrific Life of the Great Gargantua, Father of Pantagruel.* This is the volume now placed first in Rabelais' works.

In October 1534, the Affair of the Placards temporarily gave supremacy to the Sorbonne in its persecution of the humanists, with even the approval of Francis I. In February of 1535, Rabelais suddenly left the hospital in Lyons without notice, and a successor was eventually appointed. We have no trace of him for several months. In July, however, Jean du Bellay set out again for Rome, this time to receive the cardinal's hat; Rabelais again accompanied him and was there for seven months. On this occasion he sought and obtained absolution from Paul III for the act of "apostasy" committed when, without authorization, he had discarded the habit of a Benedictine and entered the world as a secular priest. Upon his return in 1536, the Cardinal du Bellay appointed him canon at the Benedictine Monastery of St. Maur-les-Fossés near Paris, a monastery secularized in that same year. Although he did not remain there, Rabelais thus became freed from his monastic vows.

During the following years, in the documents we possess, Rabelais appears in many parts of France. In February 1537, he was present at a banquet in Paris, given by eminent scholars and humanists in honor of Etienne Dolet. In May, he was admitted to the Doctorate in Medicine at Montpellier and later delivered a course of lectures on the *Prognostics* of Hippocrates, expounding them from the Greek text. In the summer, he was practicing in Lyons and instructing by the new method of dissection. In the summer of 1538, we find him for the first time in the entourage of Francis I, at Aigues-Mort. Early in 1540, he was at Turin in Piedmont with Guillaume du Bellay, Seigneur de Langey, brother to the Cardinal, now appointed Governor of Turin. Langey was a soldier and administrator of high rank; Rabelais was in his service and enjoyed his confidence and intimacy until his death in 1543. By this year Rabelais had been named Master of the King's Requests, an appointment which must have given him accession to the king. In 1545, he obtained a royal "privilege" for the printing of the continuation of his writings. Early in 1546 the *Third Book* appeared. The title page bore his own name, and the work was dedicated to Marguerite, Queen of Navarre.

The *Third Book* was condemned by the Sorbonne, however, and by March 1546 Rabelais saw fit to leave France for the town of Metz in the Empire. He entered the service of this municipality for about two years. In 1548, he went for the third time to Rome for several months, again as physician to Cardinal Jean du Bellay. In 1551, Jean appointed him to the two curacies of Saint-Martin-de-Meudon and Saint-Christophe-de-Jambet, in the Sarthe, although it is not known that he ever did personal duty as curate in either. Meanwhile, the Cardinal de Châtillon, Odet de Coligny, had obtained for him royal "privilege" from Henry II for further printing of his works. The *Fourth Book* appeared in 1552.

In March 1552, the Council of Parliament, censured by the Faculty of Theology of the Sorbonne, decreed that booksellers should not sell the *Fourth Book*. Thereafter, we have very little evidence concerning Rabelais' life. He resigned the benefices of Saint-Martin-de-Meudon and Saint-Christophe-de-Jambet in January 1553. It is not certain exactly when he died, but it was probably late in 1553. According to one statement, he died in the Rue des Jardins in Paris and was buried in the Cemetery of St. Paul's; according to another, he was buried in the nave of the church itself. After his death, what is known as the *Fifth Book* was published, a part in 1562, and complete in 1564. This is not considered by scholars to be authentic; it may include fragments written by Rabelais, but probably additions and modifications by another hand.

Rabelais remains as supremely expressive of the age of Francis I. His personal development parallels the growth of humanism in France. Entering the cloister for the opportunity of study, he left its confines for the broader experience of the universities, to know the world and men. He arose to distinction in his profession; he took his position among the noble spirits of rank and learning of his time. His writings are seen as the product of a scholarly mind during non-professional hours which loved a good story and knew well the value of laughter as a therapeutic as well as a social corrective. They convey the enthusiasm of a many-sided curiosity, the high spirits, gaiety, and joy of one who would drink life to the lees. Essentially they are the product of abounding health in body and in mind. The philosophy of Pantagruelism he described as "a certain gaiety of mind made up in scorn of accidents of fortune." This seems to have been characteristic of his abiding temper and outlook. One finally discerns there wisdom and serenity. George Meredith's Spirit of Comedy plays through his pages. There is abundant knowledge of men as they are, but also freedom from pettiness and prejudice, freedom from regimentation, as well as from chance or circumstance.

SELECTED BIBLIOGRAPHY

EDITIONS

Oeuvres. Edition Critique, ed. A. Lefranc, J. Boulenger, H. Clouzot, P. Dorveaux, J. Plattard, and L. Sainéan, Paris, Champion, 1912–47, 6 vols., as yet incomplete; *Oeuvres Complètes,* ed. J. Plattard, Paris, Roches, 1929, 5 vols.

TRANSLATIONS

Works, trans. T. Urquhart and P. le Motteux (1653–94), Tudor Translations, London, Nutt, 1900, 3 vols.; one-vol. edit., London, Chatto & Windus, 1928; ed. A. J. Nock and C. R. Wilson, New York, Harcourt Brace, 1931, 2 vols.; also in Everyman's Lib., and World's Classics. *The Five Books,* trans. W. F. Smith, London, 1893, 2 vols., 2nd edit. Vol. 1, Camb. Univ. Press, 1934. *Works,* trans. S. Putnam, New York, Covici-Friede, 1929, 3 vols.; also by same translator, *The Portable Rabelais,* New York, Viking Press, 1946. *Works,* trans. J. LeClercq, New York, Limited Editions Club, 1936, 5 vols.; also in Modern Lib. Giant Edit.

BIOGRAPHY AND CRITICISM

Jean Plattard, *L'Oeuvre de Rabelais,* Paris, Champion, 1910, also "F. Rabelais," in *Hist. de la Litt. Française Illustrée,* I, 151–64, ed. J. Bédier and P. Hazard, Paris, Larousse, 1923; Pierre Villey, *Rabelais et Marot,* Paris,

Champion, 1923, for Rabelais' evolution as a writer; Georges Lote, *La Vie et l'Oeuvre de F. Rabelais,* Paris, Droz, 1938.

Arthur Tilley, *François Rabelais,* Philadelphia, Lippincott, 1907; A. F. Chappell, *The Enigma of Rabelais,* Camb. Univ. Press, 1924; J. Plattard, *The Life of Rabelais* (1928), trans. L. P. Roche, London, Routledge, 1930; Anatole France, *François Rabelais,* trans. E. Boyd, New York, Holt, 1929; A. J. Nock and C. R. Wilson, *F. Rabelais: The Man and His Work,* New York, Harpers, 1929; Samuel Putnam, *Rabelais, Man of the Renaissance,* New York, Cape and Smith, 1930; Francis Watson, *Laughter for Pluto. A Book about Rabelais,* London, Dickson, 1933; A. J. Nock, *A Journey into Rabelais's France,* New York, Morrow, 1934; Huntington Brown, *Rabelais in English Literature,* Harvard Univ. Press, 1934.

SPECIAL STUDIES

A. Tilley, "Rabelais and Geographical Discovery," *Mod. Lang. Rev.,* II (1907), 316–26, III (1908), 209–17, V (1910), 68–77; R. H. Armitage, "Is *Gargantua* a Reworking of *Pantagruel* I?" *Pub. Mod. Lang. Assoc.,* LIX (1944), 944–51; G. O. Seiver, "Cicero's *De Oratore* and Rabelais," *Pub. Mod. Lang. Assoc.,* LIX (1944), 655–71; A. Haslam, "The Religion of Rabelais," *Contemp. Rev.,* CLXVII (1945), 38–41; R. Lebègue, "Rabelais, the Last of the French Erasmians," *Jour. of Warburg and Courtauld Inst.,* XII (1949), 91–100; A. C. Keller, "The Idea of Progress in Rabelais," *Pub. Mod. Lang. Assoc.,* LXVI (1951), 235–43; M. A. Screech, "Rabelais, de Billon and Erasmus: A Reexamination of Rabelais' Attitude to Women," *Bibl. d'Humanisme et Renaissance,* XIII (1951), 241–65; C. A. Mayer, "The Genesis of a Rabelaisian Character: Menippus and Frère Jean," *French Studies,* VI (1952), 219–29; G. Cohen, "A Rabelais Anniversary," *Times Lit. Supplement,* London, No. 2671 (1953), 240; Nan Cooke Carpenter, *Rabelais and Music,* Univ. of N. Carolina Press, 1954.

THE LIVES, HEROIC DEEDS AND SAYINGS OF GARGANTUA AND HIS SON PANTAGRUEL

Translated by Sir Thomas Urquhart
and edited with notes by Albert Jay Nock *and* Catherine Rose Wilson

[Taken from *The Urquhart–Le Motteux Translation of the Works of Francis Rabelais,* edited by Albert Jay Nock and Catherine Rose Wilson, 2 vols., Harcourt, Brace & Co., New York, 1931.]

THE FIRST BOOK: GARGANTUA

TO THE READER

Good friends, my readers, who peruse this book,
Be not offended whilst on it you look.
Denude yourselves of all depraved affection,
For it contains no badness, nor infection.
'Tis true that it brings forth to you no birth
Of any value, but in point of mirth;
Thinking therefore how sorrow might your mind
Consume, I could no apter subject find.
One inch of joy surmounts of grief a span,
Because to laugh is proper to the man.

THE AUTHOR'S PROLOGUE

Most noble and illustrious drinkers, and you thrice-precious pockified blades (for to you and none else do I dedicate my writings), Alcibiades, in that dialogue of Plato's which is entitled *The Banquet,* whilst he was setting forth the praises of his schoolmaster, Socrates (without all question the prince of philosophers), amongst other discourses to that purpose said that he resembled the Sileni. Sileni of old [1] were little boxes, like those we now may see in the shops of apothecaries, painted on the outside with wanton toyish figures, as harpies, satyrs, bridled geese, horned hares, saddled ducks, flying goats, thiller harts, and other such-like counterfeited pictures, at pleasure, to excite people unto laughter, as Silenus himself, who was the foster-father of good Bacchus, was wont to do; but within those capricious caskets called Sileni were carefully preserved and kept many rich and fine drugs, such as balm, ambergris, amomum, musk, civet, with several kinds of precious stones, and other things of great price. Just such another thing was Socrates; for to have eyed his outside and esteemed of him by his exterior appearance, you would not have given the peel of an onion for him, so deformed he was in body and ridiculous in his gesture. He had a sharp-pointed nose, with the look of a bull, and countenance of a fool; he was in his carriage simple, boorish in his apparel, in fortune poor, unhappy in his wives, unfit for all offices in the commonwealth, always laughing, tippling and merry, carousing to every one, with continual jibes and jeers, the better by those means to conceal his divine knowledge. But opening this box, you would have found within it a heavenly and inestimable drug, a more than human understanding, an admirable virtue, matchless learning, invincible courage, inimitable sobriety, certain contentment of mind, perfect assurance, and an incredible disregard of all that for which men commonly do so much watch, run, sail, fight, travel, toil and turmoil themselves.

Whereunto, think ye, doth this little flourish of a preamble tend? For so much as you, my good disciples, and some other jolly fools of ease and leisure, reading the pleasant titles of some books of our invention, as *Gargantua, Pantagruel, Whippot, The Dignity of Codpieces, Of Pease and Bacon, with a Commentary,*[2] etc., are too ready to judge that there is nothing in them but jests, mockeries, lascivious discourse, and recreative lies; because the outside (which is the title) is usually, without any farther inquiry, entertained with scoffing and derision. But truly, it is very unbeseeming to make so slight account of the works of men, seeing yourselves avouch that it is not the habit makes the monk, many being monasterially accoutred who inwardly are nothing less than monachal, and that there are of those that wear Spanish cloaks who have but little of the valour of Spaniards in them. Therefore is it, that you must open the book and seriously consider of the matter treated in it. Then shall you find that it containeth things of far higher value than the box did promise; that is to say, that the subject thereof is not so foolish as by the title, at the first sight, it would appear to be.

And put the case, that in the literal sense you meet with matters that are light and ludicrous, and suitable enough to their inscriptions; yet must not you stop there, as at the melody of the charming sirens, but endeavour to interpret that in a sublimer sense, which possibly you might think was spoken in the jollity of heart.

Did you ever pick the lock of a cupboard to steal a bottle of wine out of it? Tell me truly, and if you did, call to mind the countenance which then you had. Or, did you ever see a dog with a marrow-bone in his mouth (the beast of all others, says Plato, *lib. ii. de republica,* the most philosophical)? If you have seen him, you might have remarked with what caution and circumspectness he wards and watcheth it, with what care he keeps it, how fervently he holds it, how prudently he gobbets it, with what affection he breaks it, and with what diligence he sucks it. To what end all this? What moveth him to take all these pains? What are the hopes of his labour? What doth he expect to reap thereby?

Nothing but a little marrow. True it is, that this little is more savoury and delicious than the great quantities of other sorts of meat, because the marrow, as Galen testifieth, *iii Facult. nat. et xi de usu partium,* is a nourishment most perfectly elaboured by nature.

In imitation of this dog, it becomes you to be wise, to smell, feel, and have in estimation these fair, goodly books, stuffed with high conceptions that seem easy and superficial, but are not so readily fathomed; and then, like him, you must by a sedulous lecture and frequent meditation, break the bone and suck out the substantial marrow — that is, my allegorical sense, or the things I to myself propose to be signified by these Pythagorical symbols [3] — with assured hope that in so doing, you will at last attain to be both very wise and very brave; for in the perusal of this treatise, you shall find another kind of taste, and a doctrine of a more profound and abstruse consideration, which will disclose unto you the most glorious doctrine and dreadful mysteries, as well in what concerneth your religion, as matters of the public state and life economical.

Do you believe, upon your conscience, that Homer, whilst he was couching his Iliads and Odysseys, had any thought upon those allegories which Plutarch, Heraclides Ponticus, Eustathius, Cornutus, squeezed out of him, and which Politian filched again from them? If that is your faith, you shall never be of my church, who hold that those mysteries were as little dreamed of by Homer as the Gospel sacraments were by Ovid, in his *Metamorphoses;* though a certain gulligut friar,[4] and true bacon-eater, would have undertaken to prove it, if perhaps he had met with as very fools as himself, and, as the proverb says, "a lid worthy of such a kettle."

If you give any credit to him, why are you not as kind to these jovial new chronicles of mine? — albeit, when I did dictate them, I thought thereof no more than you, who possibly are drinking the whilst, as I was; for in the composing of this masterly book, I never lost nor bestowed any more, nor any other time, than what was appointed to serve me for taking of my bodily refection, that is, whilst I was eating and drinking. And indeed, that is the fittest and most proper hour wherein to write these high matters and deep sciences, as Homer knew very well, the paragon of all philologues, and Ennius, the father of the Latin poets, as Horace calls him, although a certain sneaking jobbernowl objected that his verses savoured more of the wine than of the oil.

A certain addle-headed coxcomb saith the same of my books; but a turd for him! The fragrant odour of the wine — oh, how much more sparkling, warming, charming, celestial, and delicious it is, than of oil! And I will glory as much when it is said of me, that I have spent more on wine than oil, as did Demosthenes, when it was told him that his expense on oil was greater than on wine. I truly hold it for an honour to be called and reputed a good fellow, a pleasant companion, or merry-Andrew, for under this name am I welcome in all choice companies of Pantagruelists. It was upbraided to Demosthenes by an envious, surly knave, that his *Orations* did smell like the sarpler, or clout, that had stopped a musty oil vessel. Therefore, I pray, interpret you all my deeds and sayings in the perfectest sense; reverence the cheese-like brain that feeds you with all these jolly maggots, and do what lies in you to keep me always merry.

Be frolic now, my lads, cheer up your hearts, and joyfully read the rest, with all the ease of your body and comfort to your reins. But hearken, joltheads—oh, dickens take ye!—off with your bumper, I will do you reason. Pull away, supernaculum.

NOTES TO THE AUTHOR'S PROLOGUE

1. "Sileni of old" contained the image of a god, as the passage referred to in the *Banquet* states; but Rabelais combines the characteristics of the ancient Sileni with those of the sixteenth-century apothecaries' boxes. The comparison of Socrates with the Sileni was a favourite one among the humanists.

2. This mention of the *Pantagruel* clearly intimates that the Second Book was written before the First. By the *Gargantua* is meant the anonymous booklet, *Les Grandes Chronicques de Gargantua,* which inspired the writing of the *Pantagruel.* The other titles seem to be purely imaginary.

3. The precepts of Pythagoras were supposed both by the ancients and by the Renaissance humanists to hide their philosophical import under a symbol or allegory. When Rabelais playfully leads his readers on to expect abstruse and profound doctrines hidden beneath his words, he is following the tradition of the Italian mock-epics, which use this device to pique the reader's curiosity. Thus he has misled whole centuries of commentators . . .

4. Allegorical interpretations of Ovid's *Metamorphoses* as symbolical of the Christian religion were much in vogue during the Middle Ages, but in thorough discredit with the Renaissance humanists. . .

[The first chapters deal with the genealogy of Gargantua, his father Grangousier and his mother Gargamelle, and with his birth.]

CHAPTER VII

After what manner Gargantua had his name given him; and how he tippled, bibbed, and curried the can

The good man Grangousier, drinking and making merry with the rest, heard the horrible noise which his son had made as he entered into the light of this world, when he cried out, "Drink! drink! drink!" Whereupon he said in French, "QUE GRAND TU AS *et souple le gousier!"* [1] (that is to say, "How great and nimble a throat thou hast"); which the company hearing, said that verily the child ought to be called Gargantua, because it was the first word that after his birth, his father had spoke, in imitation and at the example of the ancient Hebrews; whereunto he condescended, and his mother was very well pleased therewith. In the meanwhile, to quiet the child they gave him to drink *à tirelarigot,* that is, till his throat was like to crack with it; then was he carried to the font, and there baptized, according to the manner of good Christians.

Immediately thereafter were appointed for him seventeen thousand nine hundred and thirteen cows, of the towns of Pontille and Bréhémont, to furnish him with milk in ordinary; for it was impossible to find a nurse sufficient for him in all the country, considering the great quantity of milk that was requisite for his nourishment; although there were not wanting some doctors of the opinion of Scotus,[2] who affirmed that his own mother gave him suck, and that she could draw out of her breasts one thousand four hundred two pipes and nine pails of milk at every time: which, indeed, is not probable; and this point hath been found duggishly scandalous and offensive to tender ears, for that it savoured a little of heresy.

Thus was he handled for one year and ten months; after which time, by the advice of physicians, they began to carry him abroad; and then was made for him a fine little cart, drawn with oxen, of the invention of Jan Denio, wherein they led him hither and thither with great joy. And he was worth the seeing, for he was a fine boy, had a burly physiognomy, and almost ten chins; he cried very little, but beshit himself every hour; for, to speak truly of him, he was wonderfully phlegmatic in his posteriors, both by reason of his natural complexion, and the accidental disposition which had befallen him by his too much quaffing of the Septembral juice. Yet without a cause did not he sip one drop; for if he happened to be vexed, angry, displeased or sorry; if he did fret, if he did weep, if he did cry, and what grievous quarter soever he kept; bring him some drink, he would be instantly pacified, come to his own temper, be in a good humour again, and as still and quiet as ever.

One of his governesses told me (swearing by her fig) how he was so accustomed to this kind of way, that at the sound of pints and flagons he would on a sudden fall into an ecstasy, as if he had then tasted of the joys of Paradise; so that they, upon consideration of this his divine complexion, would every morning, to cheer him up, play with a knife upon the glasses, on the bottles with their stopples, and on the pottle-pots with their lids and covers; at the sound whereof he became gay, would leap for joy, would loll and rock himself in the cradle, then nod with his head, monochordizing with his fingers, and barytonizing with his tail.

NOTES TO CHAPTER VII

1. This derivation of the name Gargantua playfully follows the etymological absurdities of the time. In point of fact, Gargantua is a name of popular origin, meaning, like Grangousier, "great throat."

2. Followers of John Duns Scotus, called also Erigena, the renowned scholastic of the thirteenth century. Rabelais more than once mocks his obscurantism, crediting him with various ridiculous assertions, on the order of this one. Our modern word *dunce* is derived from his name, and reflects the general contempt of the Renaissance toward him.

[An account is given of the liveries of the youthful Gargantua. Grangousier converses with him and his governesses about his cleanliness, whereupon Gargantua enters upon a discourse on this subject.]

CHAPTER XIV

How Gargantua was taught Latin by a sophister[1]

The good man Grangousier, having heard this discourse, was ravished with admiration, considering the high reach and marvellous understanding of his son Gargantua, and said to his governesses: "Philip, king of Macedon, knew the great wit of his son Alexander by his skilful managing of a horse; for his horse Bucephalus was so fierce and unruly that none durst adventure to ride him, after that he had given to his riders such devilish falls, breaking the neck of this man, the other man's leg, braining one, and cracking another's jaw-bone. This by Alexander being considered, one day in the hippodrome (which was a place appointed for the breaking and managing of great horses), he perceived that the fury of the horse proceeded merely from the fear he had of his own shadow; whereupon getting on his back, he ran him against the sun, so that the shadow fell behind, and by that means tamed the horse, and brought him to his hand. Whereby his father, perceiving his marvellous capacity and divine insight, caused him most carefully to be instructed by Aristotle, who at that time was highly renowned above all the philosophers of Greece. After the same manner, I tell you that by this only discourse, which now I have here had before you with my son Gargantua, I know that his understanding doth participate of some divinity; and that if he be well taught, and have that education which is fitting, he will attain to a supreme degree of wisdom. Therefore will I commit him to some learned man, to have him indoctrinated according to his capacity, and will spare no cost."

Presently they appointed him a great sophister-doctor, called master Tubal Holofernes, who taught him his A B C so well that he could say it by heart backwards; and about this he was five years and three months.

Then read he to him *Donat,* the *Facet, Theodolet,* and Alanus *in Parabolis*. About this he was thirteen years, six months and two weeks. But you must remark, that in the meantime he did learn to write in Gothic characters, and that he wrote all his books; for the art of printing was not then in use.

And did ordinarily carry a great pen and ink-horn, weighing above seven thousand quintals, the pen-case whereof was as big and as long as the great pillar of Enay; and the horn was hanged to it in great iron chains, it being of the wideness to hold a ton of merchandise.

After that was read unto him the book *de modis significandi,* with the commentaries of Hurtbise, of Fasquin, of Tropditeux, of Gualehault, of John Calf, of Billonio, of Brelinguandus, and a rabble of others; and herein he spent more than eighteen years and eleven months, and was so well versed therein, that to try masteries in school-disputes with his condisciples, he would recite it by heart backwards; and did sometimes prove on his fingers' ends to his mother, that *de modis significandi non erat scientia.* Then was read to him the *Compost,* on which he spent sixteen years and two months. And at that very time, which was in the year 1420, his said preceptor died of the pox.

Afterwards he got an old coughing fellow to teach him, named master Jobelin Bridé, who read unto him Hugutio, Hebrard's *Grecism,* the *Doctrinal,* the *Pars,* the *Quid est,* the *Supplementum,* Marmotretus, *de moribus in mensa servandis,* Seneca *de quatuor virtutibus cardinalibus,* Passaventus *cum commento,* and *Dormi secure* for the holidays, and other such-like stuff; by reading whereof he became as wise as any we ever since baked in an oven.

NOTE TO CHAPTER XIV

1. Gargantua's text-books are those of medieval scholasticism . . . As Gargantua's childhood is placed in pre-Renaissance times, he has to master the old Gothic characters, discarded by the humanists for the new Italian script; and what books he has are those that he copies out in manuscript for himself. . . His new tutor, master Jobelin Bridé, whose name signifies a half-wit, puts him at work on Hugutio of Pisa's Latin vocabulary, written in the thirteenth century, and regarded by the Renaissance humanists as a monument of barbarism . . .

All these text-books were famous at the beginning of the sixteenth century, when the old ways of thought were only just breaking up. . .

CHAPTER XV

How Gargantua was put under other schoolmasters

At the last his father perceived that indeed he studied hard, and that although he spent all his time therein, yet for all that did he profit nothing; but, which is worse, grew thereby a fool, a sot, a dolt and blockhead; whereof making a heavy complaint to don Philip of Marais, viceroy of Papeligosse, he found that it were better for his son to learn nothing at all than to be taught such-like books, under such schoolmasters, because their knowledge was nothing but all trifle, and their wisdom foppery, serving only to bastardize good and noble spirits, and to corrupt the whole flower of youth.

"That it is so, take," said he, "any young boy of this time, who hath only studied two years. If he have not a better judgment, a better discourse, and that expressed in better terms than your son, with a completer carriage and civility to all manner of persons, account me forever hereafter a very clounch and bacon-slicer of Brenne." This pleased Grangousier very well, and he commanded that it should be done.

At night, at supper, the said don Philip brought in a young page of his, of Villegongis, called Eudemon,[1] so neat, so trim, so handsome in his apparel, so spruce, with his hair in so good order, and so sweet and comely in his behaviour, that he had the resemblance of a little angel more than of a human creature. Then he said to Grangousier, "Do you see this young boy? He is not as yet full twelve years old; let us try (if it like you) what difference there is betwixt the knowledge of the dunces mateologian [2] of old time and the young lads that are now."

The trial pleased Grangousier, and he commanded the page to begin. Then Eudemon, asking leave of the viceroy his master so to do, with his cap in his hand, a clear and open countenance, beautiful and ruddy lips, his eyes steady, and his looks fixed upon Gargantua with a youthful modesty, standing up straight on his feet, began to commend him, first for his virtue and good manners; secondly, for his knowledge; thirdly, for his nobility; fourthly, for his bodily accomplishments; and in the fifth place, most sweetly exhorted him to reverence his father with all due observancy, who was so careful to have him well brought up; in the end, he prayed him that he would vouchsafe to admit of him amongst the least of his servants; for other favour at that time desired he none of heaven, but that he might do him some grateful and acceptable service. All this was by him delivered with such proper gestures, such distinct pronunciation, so pleasant a delivery, in such exquisite fine terms and so good Latin, that he seemed rather a Gracchus, a Cicero, an Æmilius of the time past, than a youth of this age.

But all the countenance that Gargantua kept was that he fell to crying like a cow, and cast down his face, hiding it with his cap; nor could they possibly draw one word from him, no more than a fart from a dead ass. Whereat his father was so grievously vexed that he would have killed master Jobelin, but the said don Philip withheld him from it by fair persuasions, so that at length he pacified his wrath. Then Grangousier commanded he should be paid his wages, that they should whittle him up soundly, sophister-like, and then give him to all the devils in hell. "At least," said he, "today, shall it not cost him much to his host if by chance he should die as drunk as an Englishman."

Master Jobelin being gone out of the house, Grangousier consulted with the viceroy what schoolmaster they should choose for him, and it was betwixt them resolved that Ponocrates,[3] the tutor of Eudemon, should have the charge, and that they should go all together to Paris, to know what was the study of the young men of France at that time.

NOTES TO CHAPTER XV

1. Eudemon, "fortunate, happy," a name full of Renaissance feeling, in contrast with the mediaeval flavour of the preceding chapter.

2. Mateologian, "teller of silly tales," is a term, like *sophist, sophistical,* which would be immediately understood as referring to the scholastic theologians, particularly to the Sorbonne (the Faculty of Theology in the University of Paris).

3. Name forged from two Greek words, meaning "vigorous."

CHAPTER XXI

The study of Gargantua, according to the discipline of his schoolmasters the sophisters [1]

The first day being thus spent, and the bells put up again in their own place, the citizens of Paris, in acknowledgment of this courtesy, offered to maintain and feed his mare as long as he pleased, which Gargantua took in good part; and they sent her to graze in the forest of Bière. I think she is not there now.

This done, he with all his heart submitted his study to the discretion of Ponocrates; who first of all appointed that he should do as he was accustomed, to the end it might be understood by what means, in so long time, his old masters had made him such a sot and puppy.

He disposed therefore of his time in such fashion that ordinarily he did awake betwixt eight or nine o'clock, whether it was day or night; for so had his ancient governors ordained, alleging that which David saith: *Vanum est vobis ante lucem surgere.* Then did he tumble and toss, wag his legs, and wallow in the bed some time, the better to stir up and rouse his vital spirits; and apparelled himself according to the season, but willingly he would wear a great long gown of thick frieze, furred with fox skins. Afterwards he combed his head with a comb *de Almain,*[2] which is the four fingers and the thumb, for his preceptors had said that to comb himself otherways, to wash and make himself neat, was to lose time in this world. Then he dunged, pissed, spued, belched, cracked, yawned, spitted, coughed, hawked, sneezed and snotted himself like an archdeacon; and to fortify against the fog and bad air, went to breakfast, having some good fried tripes, fair rashers on the coals, good gammons of bacon, store of good minced meat, and a great deal of sippet-brewis, made up of the fat of the beef-pot laid upon bread, cheese and chopped parsley strewed together.

Ponocrates showed him that he ought not to eat so soon after rising out of his bed, unless he had performed some exercise beforehand. Gargantua answered, "What! have not I sufficiently well exercised myself? I have wallowed and rolled myself six or seven turns in my bed, before I rose; is not that enough? Pope Alexander did so, by the advice of a Jew his physician, and lived till his dying day in despite of his enemies. My first masters have used me to it, saying that to eat breakfast made a good memory; and therefore they drank first. I am very well after it, and dine but the better. And master Tubal (who was the first licentiate at Paris) told me that it was not enough to run apace, but to set forth betimes. So the total welfare of our humanity doth not depend upon drinking switter-swatter like ducks, but in being at it early in the morning; *unde versus:*

> To rise betimes is good for nothing,
> To drink betimes is meat and clothing."

After a good breakfast he went to church, and they carried to him in a great basket a huge breviary, weighing, what in grease, clasps, parchment and cover, little more or less than eleven hundred and six pounds. There he heard six-and-twenty or thirty masses. This while, to the same place came his matin-mumbler, muffled up about the chin, round as a hoop, and his breath pretty well antidoted with the vine-tree syrup. With him he mumbled all his kyriels, which he so curiously thumbed and fingered that there fell not so much as one bead of them to the ground.

As he went from the church, they brought him, upon a dray drawn with oxen, a confused heap of paternosters of Saint-Claude, every one of the bigness of a hat-block; and sauntering along through the cloisters, galleries or garden, he riddled over more of them than sixteen hermits would have done.

Then did he study some paltry half-hour with his eyes fixed upon his book; but (as the comedy has it) his mind was in the kitchen. Pissing then a whole potful, he sat down at table; and because he was naturally phlegmatic, he began his meal with some dozens of gammons, dried neats' tongues, botargos, sausages, and such other forerunners of wine; in the meanwhile, four of his folks did cast into his mouth, one after another continually, mustard by the whole shovels full. Immediately after that, he drank a horrible draught of white wine for the comfort of his kidneys. When that was done, he ate, according to the season, meat agreeable to his appetite; and then left off eating when his belly was like to crack for fulness. As for his drinking, he had in that neither end nor rule; for he was wont to say that the limits and bounds of drinking were that a man might drink till the cork of his shoes swells up half a foot high.

NOTES TO CHAPTER XXI

1. This chapter continues the persiflage against the Sorbonne. The implication that the theologians were dirty and lazy follows the criticism of such humanists as Erasmus; and the relation between asceticism and squalor soon became traditional.

2. Jacques Almain was a theologian at the University of Paris in the beginning of the sixteenth century. There is a play on words here (Almain, à la main, "by hand").

CHAPTER XXII

The games of Gargantua

Then with a starched phiz mumbling over some scraps of a scurvy grace, he washed his hands in fresh wine, picked his teeth with the foot of a hog, and talked merrily with his people; then the carpet being spread, they brought plenty of cards, many dice, with great store and abundance of checkers and chess-boards.

There he played,

At flusse.
At primero.
At the beast.
At the rifle.
At trump.
At the prick and spare not.
At the hundred.
At the peenie.
At the unfortunate woman.
At the fib.
At the pass ten.
At one and thirty.
At post and pair, or even and sequence.
At three hundred.
At the unlucky man.
At the last couple in hell.
At the hock.
At the surly.
At the lansquenet.
At the cuckoo.
At puff, or let him speak that hath it.
At take nothing and throw out.
At the marriage.
At the frolic, or jackdaw.
At the opinion.
At who doth the one doth the other.
At the sequences.
At the ivory bundles.
At the tarots.
At losing load him.
At he's gulled and *esto*.
At the torture.
At the handruff.
At the click.
At honours.
At love.
At the chess.
At Reynard the fox.
At the squares.
At the cows.
At the lottery.
At the chance or mumchance.
At three dice, or maniest bleaks.
At the tables.
At nivinivinack.
At the lurch.
At doublets, or queen's game.
At the failie.
At the French trictrac.
At the long tables, or ferkeering.
At felldown.
At tods body.
At needs must.
At the dames, or draughts.
At bob and mow.
At *primus secundus*.
At mark-knife.
At the keys.
At span-counter.
At even and odd.
At cross or pile.
At ball and huckle-bone.
At ivory balls.
At the billiards.
At bob and hit.
At the owl.
At the charming of the hare.
At pull yet a little.
At trudge-pig.
At the magpies.
At the horn.
At the flower over Shrovetide ox.
At the madge-owlet.
At pinch without laughing.
At prickle me tickle me.
At the unshoeing of the ass.
At the cocksess.
At hari hohi.
At I set me down.
At earl beardie.
At the old mode.
At draw the spit.
At put out.
At gossip, lend me your sack.
At ramcod ball.
At thrust out the harlot.
At Marseilles figs.
At nicknamery.
At stick and hole.
At boke or him, or flaying the fox.

At the branching it.
At trill madam, or grapple my lady.
At the cat selling.
At blow the coal.
At the re-wedding.
At the quick and dead judge.
At unoven the iron.
At the false clown.
At the flints, or at the nine stones.
At to the crutch, hulchback.
At the saint is found.
At hinch, pinch, and laugh not.
At the leek.
At bumdockdousse.
At the loose gig.
At the hoop.
At the sow.
At belly to belly.
At the dales or straths.
At the twigs.
At the quoits.
At I'm for that.
At tilt at Weekie.
At ninepins.
At the cock quintain.
At tip and hurl.
At the flat bowls.
At the veer and turn.
At rogue and ruffian.
At bumbatch touch.
At the mysterious trough.
At the short bowls.
At the dapple grey.
At cock and crank it.
At break pot.
At my desire.
At twirly whirlytrill.
At the rush bundles.
At the short staff.
At the whirligig.
At hide and seek, or are you all hid.
At the picket.
At the blank.
At the pilferers.
At the caveson.
At prison bars.
At have at the nuts.
At cherry pit.
At rub and rice.
At whip top.
At the casting top.
At the hobgoblin.
At the O wonderful.
At soilie smutchie.
At the fast and loose.
At sutch-breech.
At the broom-besom.
At St. Cosme, I come to adore thee.
At the lusty brown boy.
At I take you napping.
At fair and softly passeth Lent.
At the forked oak.
At truss.
At the wolf's tail.
At bum to buss, or nose in breech.
At Geordy, give me my lance.
At swaggy, waggy, or shoggy-shou.
At stook and rook, shear and threave.
At the birch.
At the musse.
At the dilly dilly darling.
At ox moudy.
At purpose in purpose.
At nine less.
At blind-man buff.
At the fallen bridges.
At bridle Nick.
At the white at butts.
At thwack swinge him.
At apple, pear, plum.
At mumgi.
At the toad.
At cricket.
At the pounding stick.
At jack and the box.
At the queens.
At the trades.
At heads and points.
At the vine-tree hug.
At black be thy fall.
At ho! the distaff.
At Joan Tomson.
At the boulting cloth.

At the oats' seed.
At greedy glutton.
At the moorish dance.
At feeby.
At the whole frisk and gambol.
At battabum, or riding of the wild mare.
At Hind the plowman.
At the good mawkin.
At the dead beast.
At climb the ladder, Billy.
At the dying hog.
At the salt doup.
At the pretty pigeon.
At barley break.
At the bavin.
At the bush leap.
At crossing.
At the hardit arsepursy.
At the harrowers' nest.
At forward hey.
At the fig.
At gunshot crack.
At mustard peel.
At the gome.
At the relapse.
At jog breech, or prickle him forward.
At knock-pate.
At the Cornish chough.
At the crane dance.
At slash and cut.
At bobbing, or the flirt on the nose.
At the larks.
At filipping.

After he had thus well played, shuffled, clogged, and thrown away his time, it was thought fit to drink a little, and that was every man eleven bumpers; and afterwards make much of himself, and stretch upon a fair bench, or a good large bed, and there sleep for two or three hours together, without thinking or speaking any hurt. After he was awakened, he would shake his ears a little, and then they brought him fresh wine, and he drank better than ever.

Ponocrates showed him that it was an ill diet to drink after sleeping. "It is," answered Gargantua, "the very life of the patriarchs and holy fathers. For naturally I sleep; salt and sleep to me is so many gammons."

Then began he to study a little, and out came the paternosters, which the more formally to dispatch, he got upon an old mule which had served nine kings; and so mumbling with his mouth, nodding and doddling his head, would go and see a cony ferreted or caught in a gin.

At his return he went into the kitchen, to know what roast meat was on the spit, and supped very well, upon my conscience; and commonly did invite some of his neighbours that were good drinkers, with whom, carousing merrily, they told stories of all sorts, from the old to the new. Among others, he had for domestics the lords of Fou, of Gourville, of Grignault, and of Marigny.

After supper were brought into the room the fair wooden gospels, and the books of the four kings, that is to say, the tables and cards, with a deal of cockalls, mumblety-pegs, and wheels of fortune; or else they went to see the wenches thereabouts with their wakes, their junketings and little collations; then to sleep without unbridling till eight o'clock the next morning.

CHAPTER XXIII

How Gargantua was instructed by Ponocrates, and in such sort disciplinated that he lost not one hour of the day[1]

When Ponocrates knew Gargantua's vicious manner of living, he resolved to bring him up in another-gates way; but for a while bore with him, considering that nature cannot endure a sudden change without great violence. Therefore, to begin his work the better he requested a learned physician of that time, called master Theodore, seriously to perpend, if it were possible, how to bring Gargantua unto a better course. The said physician purged him canonically with Anticyrian hellebore, by which medicine he cleansed all that foulness and perverse habit of his brain. By this means, also, Ponocrates made him forget all that he had learned under his ancient preceptors, as Timotheus did to his scholars who had been instructed under other musicians. To do this the better, they brought him into the company of learned men, which stirred in him an emulation and desire to whet his wit and improve his parts, and to bend his study another way; so as that the world might have a value for him. And afterwards he put himself into such a road that he lost not any one hour in the day, but employed all his time in learning and honest knowledge.

Gargantua awaked about four o'clock in the morning. Whilst they were in rubbing of him, there was read unto him some chapter of the Holy Scripture aloud and clearly, with a pronunciation fit for the matter; and hereunto was appointed a young page, born in Basché, named Anagnostes. According to the purpose and argument of that lesson, he oftentimes gave himself to worship, adore, pray, and send up his supplications to that good God, whose Word did show His majesty and marvellous judgment.

Then went he unto the secret places to make excretion of his natural digestions; there his master repeated what had been read, expounding unto him the most obscure and difficult points. In returning, they considered the face of the sky, if it were such as they had observed it the night before, and into what signs the sun was entering, as also the moon for that day.

This done, he was apparelled, combed, curled, trimmed and perfumed, during which time they repeated to him the lessons of the day before. He himself said them by heart, and upon them would ground some practical cases concerning the estate of man, which he would prosecute sometimes two or three hours, but ordinarily they ceased as soon as he was fully clothed.

Then for three good hours he had a lecture read unto him. This done, they went forth, still conferring on the substance of the lecture, either unto a field near the university, called the Bracque, or unto the meadows, where they played at the ball, tennis, and at the *piletrigone,* most gallantly exercising their bodies, as before they had done their minds. All their play was but in liberty, for they left off when they pleased, and that was commonly when they did sweat over all their body, or were otherwise weary. Then were they very well wiped and rubbed, shifted their shirts, and walking soberly, went to see if dinner was ready. Whilst they stayed for that, they did clearly and eloquently pronounce some sentences that they had retained of the lecture.

In the meantime master Appetite came, and then very orderly sat they down at table. At the beginning of the meal there was read some pleasant history of the warlike actions of former times, until he had taken a glass of wine. Then (if they thought good) they continued reading, or began to discourse merrily together; speaking first of the virtue, propriety, efficacy and nature of all that was served in at the table: of bread, of wine, of water, of salt, of fleshes, fishes, fruits, herbs, roots, and of their dressing; by means whereof he learned, in a little time, all the passages competent for this that were to be found in Pliny, Athenaeus, Dioscorides, Julius Pollux, Galen, Porphyry, Oppian, Polybius, Heliodorus, Aristotle, Ælian, and others. Whilst they talked of these things, many times, to be more certain, they caused the very books to be brought to the table. And so well and perfectly did he in his memory retain the things above said, that in those days there was not a physician that knew half so much as he did.

Afterwards they conferred of the lessons read in the morning, and ending their repast with some conserve, or marmalade of quinces, he picked his teeth with mastic tooth-pickers, washed his hands and eyes with fair fresh water, and gave thanks unto God in some neat hymn, made in the praise of the divine bounty and munificence.

This done, they brought in cards, not to play, but to learn a thousand pretty tricks and new inventions, which were all grounded upon arithmetic. By this means he fell in love with that numerical science, and every day after dinner and supper he passed his time in it as pleasantly as he was wont to do at cards and dice; so that at last he understood so well both the theory and practical part thereof, that Tunstal, the Englishman, who had written very largely to that purpose, confessed that verily, in comparison of him, he understood no more High Dutch. And not only in that, but in the other mathematical sciences, as geometry, astronomy, and music. For, in waiting on the concoction and attending the digestion of his food, they made a thousand pretty instruments and geometrical figures, and did in some measure practise the astronomical canons.

After this they recreated themselves with singing musically, in four or five parts, or upon a set theme or ground, at random, as it best pleased them. In matter of musical instruments he learned to play upon the lute, the virginals, the harp, the Allman flute with nine holes, the viol, and the sackbut.

This hour thus spent, and digestion finished, he did purge his body of natural excrements; then betook himself to his principal study for three hours together or more, as well to repeat his morning lectures as to proceed in the book he had in hand, as also to write handsomely, to draw and form the antique and Roman letters.

This being done, they went abroad, and with them a young gentleman of Touraine, named the esquire Gymnast, who taught him the art of riding. Changing then his clothes, he rode a Naples courser, a Dutch *roussin,* a Spanish jennet, a barded or trapped steed, then a light fleet horse, unto whom he gave a hundred careers, made him go the high saults, bounding in the air, free the ditch with a skip, leap over a stile or pale, turn short in a ring both to the right and left hand. There he broke not his lance; for it is the greatest foolery in the world to say, "I have broken ten lances at tilt, or in fight"—a carpenter can do even as much—but it is a glorious and praiseworthy action, with one lance to break and overthrow ten enemies. Therefore with a sharp, stiff, strong and well-steeled lance would he usually force up a door, pierce a harness, beat down a tree, carry away the ring, lift up a cuirassier saddle, with the mail-coat and gauntlet; all this he did in complete armour from head to foot.

As for the prancing flourishes and smacking poppisms, for the better cherishing of the horse commonly used in riding, none did them better than he. The great vaulter of Ferrara was but as an ape compared to him. He was singularly skilful in leaping nimbly from one horse to another, without putting foot to ground, and these horses were called desultories; he could likewise, from either side, with a lance in his hand, leap on horseback without stirrups, and rule the horse at his pleasure without a bridle, for such things are useful in military engagements.

Another day he exercised the battle-axe, which he so dextrously wielded both in the nimble, strong and smooth management of that weapon, and that in all the feats practisable by it, that he passed knight of arms in the field, and at all essays.

Then tossed he the pike, played with the two-handed sword, with the back-sword, with the Spanish tuck, the dagger, poniard, armed or unarmed, with a buckler, with a cloak, with a target.

Then would he hunt the hart, the roebuck, the bear, the fallow deer, the wild boar, the hare, the pheasant, the partridge and the bustard. He played at the balloon, and made it bound in the air, both with fist and foot.

He wrestled, ran, jumped, not at three steps and a leap, nor at the hare's leap, nor yet at the *Alemant*—"for," said Gymnast, "these jumps are for the wars altogether unprofitable, and of no use"—but at one leap he would skip over a ditch, spring over a hedge, mount six paces upon a wall, ramp and grapple after this fashion up against a window, of the full height of a lance.

He did swim in deep waters on his belly, on his back, sideways, with all his body, with his feet only, with one hand in the air, wherein he held a book, crossing thus the breadth of the river Seine without wetting it, and dragged along his cloak with his teeth, as did Julius Caesar. Then with the help of one hand he entered forcibly into a boat, from whence he cast himself again headlong into the water, sounded the depths, hollowed the rocks, and plunged into the pits and gulfs. Then turned he the boat about, governed it, led it swiftly or slowly with the stream and against the stream, stopped it in its course, guided it with one hand and with the other laid hard about him with a huge great oar, hoisted the sail, hied up along the mast by the shrouds, ran upon the edge of the decks, set the compass in order, tackled the bowlines, and steered the helm.

Coming out of the water, he ran furiously up against a hill, and with the same alacrity and swiftness ran down again, he climbed up trees like a cat, and leaped from one to the other like a squirrel; he did pull down the great boughs and branches like another Milo. Then with two sharp, well-steeled daggers, and two tried bodkins, would he run up by the wall to the very top of a house, like a rat; then suddenly came down from the top to the bottom, with such an even composition of members, that by the fall he would catch no harm.

He did cast the dart, throw the bar, put the stone, practise the javelin, the boar-spear or partisan, and the halbert; he broke the strongest bows in drawing, bended against his breast the greatest cross-bows of steel, took his aim by the eye with the hand-gun, and shot well, traversed and planted the cannon, shot at butt marks, at the papgay, from below upwards, from above downwards, then before him, sideways, and behind him, like the Parthians.

They tied a cable rope to the top of a high tower, by one end whereof hanging near the ground he wrought himself with his hands to the very top; then upon the same track came down so sturdily and firm that you could not, on a plain meadow, have run with more assurance. They set up a great pole, fixed upon two trees. There would he hang by his hands, and with them alone, his feet touching at nothing, would go back and fore along the aforesaid rope, with so great swiftness that hardly could one overtake him with running; and then, to exercise his breast and lungs, he would shout like all the devils in hell. I heard him once call Eudemon, from St. Victor's gate to Montmartre; Stentor had never such a voice at the siege of Troy.

Then, for the strengthening of his nerves or sinews, they made him two great sows of lead, each of them weighing eight thousand and seven hundred quintals, which they called *alteres;* those he took up from the ground, in each hand one, then lifted them up over his head, and held them so without stirring, three-quarters of an hour or more, which was an inimitable force.

He fought at barriers with the stoutest and most vigorous champions; and when it came to the cope, he stood so sturdily on his feet that he abandoned himself unto the strongest, in case they could remove him from his place, as Milo was wont to do of old; in whose imitation likewise he held a pomegranate in his hand, to give it unto him that could take it from him.

The time being thus bestowed, and himself rubbed, cleansed, wiped and refreshed with other clothes, he returned fair and softly, and passing through certain meadows or other grassy places, beheld the trees and plants, comparing them with what is written of them in the books of the ancients, such as Theophrast, Dioscorides, Marinus, Pliny, Nicander, Macer and Galen; and carried home to the house great handfuls of them, whereof a young page, called Rhizotomos, had charge, together with little mattocks, pick-axes, grubbing hooks, cabbies, pruning knives, and other instruments requisite for gardening.

Being come to their lodging, whilst supper was making ready, they repeated certain passages of that which had been read, and then sat down at table. Here remark, that his dinner was sober and thrifty, for he did then eat only to prevent the gnawings of his stomach; but his supper was copious and large, for he took then as much as was fit to maintain and nourish him: which, indeed, is the true diet prescribed by the art of good and sound physic, although a rabble of loggerheaded physicians, nuzzled in the brabbling shop of sophisters, counsel the contrary. During that repast was continued the lesson read at dinner, as long as they thought good; the rest was spent in good discourse, learned and profitable.

After they had given thanks, he set himself to sing vocally and play upon harmonious instruments, or otherwise passed his time at some pretty sports, made with cards or dice, or in practising the feats of legerdemain with cups and balls. There they stayed some nights in frolicking thus, and making themselves merry till it was time to go to bed; and on other nights they would go make visits unto learned men, or to such as had been travellers in strange and remote countries.

When it was full night, before they retired themselves, they went unto the most open place of the house to see the face of the sky, and there beheld the comets, if any were, as likewise the figures, situations, aspects, oppositions and conjunctions, of both fixed stars and planets.

Then with his master did he briefly recapitulate, after the manner of the Pythagoreans, that which he had read, seen, learned, done and understood, in the whole course of that day. Then prayed they unto God the Creator, in falling down before Him, and strengthening their faith towards Him, and glorifying Him for His boundless bounty; and giving thanks to Him for the time that was past, they recommended themselves to His divine clemency for the future; which being done they went to bed, and betook themselves to their repose.

NOTE TO CHAPTER XXIII

1. This new régime of Ponocrates, with its balance of physical and mental development, and its emphasis on the importance of *interest* in learning, is not unlike the latest tendencies in pedagogy; barring, of course, the intensive cultivation of the memory, necessary in a day of few books. It must be remembered that Gargantua was both a giant and a prince, and it is not surprising that his daily round of work would stagger an ordinary mortal.

CHAPTER XXIV

How Gargantua spent his time in rainy weather

If it happened that the weather was anything cloudy, foul and rainy, all the forenoon was employed as before specified, according to custom, with this difference only, that they had a good clear fire lighted, to correct the distempers of the air; but after dinner, instead of their wonted exercitations, they did abide within, and by way of apotherapy, did recreate themselves in bottling of hay, in cleaving and sawing of wood, and in threshing sheaves of corn at the barn. Then they studied the art of painting or carving, or brought into use the antique play of Tables, as Leonicus hath written of it, and as our good friend Lascaris playeth at it. In playing, they examined the passages of ancient authors wherein the said play is mentioned, or any metaphor drawn from it.

They went likewise to see the drawing of metals, or the casting of great ordnance; how the lapidaries did work, as also the goldsmiths and cutters of precious stones. Nor did they omit to visit the alchemists, money-coiners, upholsterers, weavers, velvet-workers, watch-makers, looking-glass framers, printers, organists, dyers, and other-such kind of artificers; and everywhere giving them somewhat to drink, did learn and consider the industry and invention of the trades.

They went also to hear the public lectures, the solemn commencements, the repetitions, the acclamations, the pleadings of the lawyers, and sermons of evangelical preachers.

He went through the halls and places appointed for fencing, and there played against the masters themselves at all weapons, and showed them by experience that he knew as much in it as, yea, more than they. And instead of simpling, they visited the shops of druggists, herbalists and apothecaries, and diligently considered the fruits, roots, leaves, gums, seeds, the grease and ointments of some foreign parts, as also how they did adulterate them.

He went to see the jugglers, tumblers, mountebanks and quacksalvers; and considered their cunning, their shifts, their somersaults, and smooth tongue, especially of those of Chauny in Picardy, who are naturally great praters, and will banter and lie as fast as a dog can trot.

Being returned home, they did eat at supper more soberly than at other times, and meats more desiccative and extenuating; to the end that the intemperate moisture of the air, communicated to the body by a necessary confinity, might by this means be corrected, and that they might not receive any prejudice for want of their ordinary bodily exercise.

Thus was Gargantua governed, and kept on in this course of education from day to day, profiting, as you understand such a young man of his age and good sense, so kept to his exercise, may well do; which, although at the beginning it seemed difficult, became a little after so sweet, so easy, and so delightful, that it seemed rather the recreation of a king, than the study of a scholar. Nevertheless, Ponocrates, to divert him from this vehement intension of the spirits, thought fit, once in a month, upon some fair and clear day, to go out in the city betimes in the morning, either towards Gentilly or Boulogne, or to Montrouge, or Charenton bridge, or to Vanves, or St.-Cloud,[1] and there spend all the day long in making the greatest cheer that could be devised, sporting, making merry, drinking healths, playing, singing, dancing, tumbling in some fair meadow, unnestling of sparrows, taking of quails, and fishing for frogs and crabs.

But although that day was passed without books or lecture, yet was it not spent without profit; for in the said meadows they usually repeated certain pleasant verses of Virgil's *Agriculture,* of Hesiod, and of Politian's *Husbandry,* would set abroach some witty Latin epigrams, then immediately turned them into roundelays and songs in the French language. In their feasting, they would sometimes separate the water from the wine that was therewith mixed (as Cato teacheth, *de re rustica,* and Pliny) with an ivy cup; would wash the wine in a basin full of water, then take it out again with a funnel as pure as ever. They made the water go from one glass to another, and contrived a thousand little automatory engines; that is to say, moving of themselves.

NOTE TO CHAPTER XXIV

1. To these places round about Paris the university students used to go for recreation. Montrouge is on the Paris-Orléans road; the town of Pont-du-Charenton is on the right bank of the Marne; and Vanves is a league to the west of Paris.

CHAPTER XXV

How there was great strife and debate raised betwixt the cake-bakers of Lerné and those of Gargantua's country, whereupon were waged great wars

At that time — which was the season of vintage, in the beginning of harvest, when the country shepherds were set to keep the vines and hinder the starlings from eating up the grapes — as some cake-bakers of Lerné [1] happened to pass along the broad highway, driving unto the city ten or twelve horses loaded with cakes, the said shepherds courteously entreated them to give them some for their money, as the price then ruled in the market. For here it is to be remarked that it is a celestial food to eat for breakfast hot fresh cakes with grapes, especially the frail clusters, the great red grapes, muscadine, the verjuice grape, and the luskard for those that are costive in their belly; because it will make them gush out, and squirt the length of a hunter's staff, like the very tap of a barrel, and oftentimes thinking to let a squib, they did all-to-besquatter and conshite themselves, whereupon they are commonly called the "vintage thinkers."

The cake-bakers were in nothing inclinable to their request; but which was worse, did injure them most outrageously, calling them prating gabblers, lickerish gluttons, freckled bittors, mangy rascals, shite-a-bed scoundrels, drunken roisterers, sly knaves, drowsy loiterers, slapsauce fellows, slabber-degullion druggles, lubberly louts, cozening foxes, ruffian rogues, paltry customers, sycophant varlets, drawlatch hoydens, flouting milk-sops, jeering companions, staring clowns, forlorn snakes, ninny lobcocks, scurvy sneaksbies, fondling fops, base loons, saucy coxcombs, idle lusks, scoffing braggarts, noddy meacocks, blockish grutnols, doddypoll joltheads, jobbernowl goosecaps, foolish loggerheads, slutch calf-lollies, grout-head gnatsnappers, lobdotterels, gaping changelings, codshead loobies, woodcock slangams, ninny-hammer flycatchers, noddypeak simpletons, turdy gut, shitten shepherds, and other such defamatory epithets; saying further that it was not for them to eat of these dainty cakes, but might very well content themselves with the coarse unranged bread, or to eat of the great brown household loaf.

To which provoking words, one amongst them called Forgier (an honest fellow of his person, and a notable springal) made answer very calmly thus: "How long is it since you have got horns,[2] that you are become so proud? Indeed, formerly you were wont to give us some freely, and will you not now let us have some for our money? This is not the part of good neighbours, neither do we serve you thus when you come hither to buy our good corn, whereof you make your cakes and buns. Besides that, we should have given you to the bargain some of our grapes, but by his zounds, you may chance to repent it, and possibly have need of us another time, when we shall use you after the like manner; and therefore remember it."

Then Marquet, a prime man in the confraternity of the cake-bakers, said unto him, "Yea, sir, thou art pretty well crest-risen this morning; thou didst eat yesternight too much millet and bullimong.[3] Come hither, sirrah, come hither, I will give thee some cakes."

Whereupon Forgier, dreading no harm, in all simplicity went towards him, and drew a sixpence out of his leather satchel, thinking that Marquet would have sold him some of his cakes; but instead of cakes, he gave him with his whip such a rude lash overthwart his legs, that the marks remained; then would have fled away, but Forgier cried out as loud as he could, "Oh, murder, murder, help, help, help, help!" and in the meantime threw a great cudgel after him which he carried under his arm, wherewith he hit him in the coronal joint of his head, upon the crotophic artery of the right side thereof, so forcibly that Marquet fell down from his mare, more like a dead than a living man.

Meanwhile the farmers and country swains that were watching their walnuts near to that place, came running with their great poles and long staves, and laid such load on these cake-bakers, as if they had been to thresh upon green rye. The other shepherds and shepherdesses, hearing the lamentable shout of Forgier, came with their slings and slackies, following them and throwing great stones at them as thick as hail. At last these overtook them, and took from them about four or five dozen of their cakes. Nevertheless, they paid for them the ordinary price, and gave them over and above one hundred eggs, and three baskets full of mulberries. Then did the cake-bakers help to get Marquet mounted upon his mare again, who was most shrewdly wounded; and forthwith they returned to Lerné, changing the resolution they had to go to Parilly, threatening very sharp and boisterously the cowherds, shepherds and farmers of Seuilly and Cinais.

This done, the shepherds and shepherdesses made merry with these cakes and fine grapes, and sported themselves together at the sound of the pretty small pipe, scoffing and laughing at those vainglorious cake-bakers, who had that day met with mischief for want of crossing themselves with a good hand in the morning. Nor did they forget to apply to Forgier's leg some fair, great, red, and medicinal grapes, and so handsomely dressed it and bound it up that it was quickly cured.

NOTES TO CHAPTER XXV

1. Lerné, a kilometer west of la Devinière, was famous for its cakes (*fouaces*) throughout the region of the Chinonais. . . Noteworthy in the minds of Rabelais's readers was the fact that Gaucher de Ste.-Marthe, physician to the abbess of Fontevrault, held lease of the seigniory of Lerné from her, and was called by courtesy the "lord" of Lerné. Rabelais's father, Antoine Rabelais, was at one time seneschal of Lerné on his behalf. Thus the cake-bakers were Ste.-Marthe's feudal subjects, as the peasants of la Devinière were Antoine Rabelais's. The traditional identification of Picrochole (Greek, "Bitterbile") with Gaucher de Ste.-Marthe, and of Grangousier with Antoine Rabelais, would seem plausible.

2. I.e., "How long is it since you grew up from the calf you were, into a bull?"

3. A mixture of several kinds of grain for feeding cattle.

[The cake-bakers return to Lerné and report to their king, Picrochole. The furious Picrochole immediately summons his army, which marches into Grangousier's country devastating and making havoc of all wherever it goes.]

CHAPTER XXVII

How a monk of Seuilly saved the close of the abbey from being ravaged by the enemy

So much they did, and so far they went pillaging and stealing that at last they came to Seuilly, where they robbed both men and women, and took all they could catch: nothing was either too hot or too heavy for them. Although the plague was there in the most part of all the houses, they nevertheless entered everywhere; then plundered and carried away all that was within, and yet for all this, not one of them took any hurt, which is a most wonderful case. For the curates, vicars, preachers, physicians, chirurgeons and apothecaries who went to visit, to dress, to cure, to heal, to preach unto, and admonish those that were sick, were all dead of the infection; and these devilish robbers and murderers caught never any harm at all. Whence comes this to pass, my masters? I beseech you think upon it.

The town being thus pillaged, they went unto the abbey with a horrible noise and tumult, but they found it shut and made fast against them; whereupon the body of the army marched forward towards a ford called Gué de Vède, except seven companies of foot and two hundred lancers who staying there, broke down the walls of the close to waste, spoil and make havoc of all the vines and vintage within that place.

The monks, poor devils! knew not in that extremity to which of all their saints they should vow themselves; nevertheless, at all adventures they rang the bells *ad capitulum capitulantes.*[1] There it was decreed that they should make a fair procession, stuffed with good lectures, prayers and litanies *contra hostium insidias,* and jolly responses *pro pace.*

There was then in the abbey a claustral monk called Friar John of the Funnels,[2] young, gallant, frisk, lusty, nimble, quick, active, bold, adventurous, resolute, tall, lean, wide-mouthed, long-nosed, a rare mumbler of matins, unbridler of masses, and runner-over of vigils; and to conclude summarily in a word, a right monk, if ever there were any, since the monking world monked a monkery. For the rest, a clerk, even to the teeth, in matter of breviary.

This monk, hearing the noise that the enemy made within the enclosure of the vineyard, went out to see what they were doing, and perceiving that they were cutting and gathering the grapes whereon was grounded the foundation of all their next year's wine, returned unto the choir of the church where the other monks were, all amazed and astonished like so many bell-melters, whom when he heard sing, *ini, nim, pe, ne, ne, ne, ne, ne, ne, tum, ne, num, num, ini, i, mi, i, mi, co, o, ne, no, o, o, ne, no, ne, no, no, no, rum, ne, num, num:* "This is," said he, "*bien chié chanté* well shit, well sung. By the virtue of God, why do you not sing—

Panniers farewell, vintage is done.

The devil snatch me if they be not already within the middle of our close and cut so well both vines and grapes, that by cods body, there will not be found for these four years to come so much as a gleaning in it. By the belly of Saint James, what shall we poor devils drink the while? Lord God! *da mihi potum.*"

Then said the prior of the convent, "What should this drunken fellow do here? Let him be carried to prison for troubling the divine service."

"Nay," said the monk, "the wine service. Let us behave ourselves so that it be not troubled; for you yourself, my lord prior, love to drink of the best, and so doth every honest man. Never yet did a man of worth dislike good wine; it is a monastical apophthegm. But these responses that you chant here, by God, are not in season.

"Wherefore is it that our devotions were instituted to be short in the time of harvest and vintage, and long in the Advent and all the winter? The late friar Messepelosse, of good memory, a true zealous man (or the devil take me) of our religion, told me, and I remember it well, how the reason was that in this season we might press and make the wine, and in the winter whiff it up.

"Hark you, my masters, you that love the wine: cops body, follow me, for Saint Anthony burn me as freely as a faggot, if they taste one drop of the liquor, that will not now come and fight in defence of the vine! Hog's belly, the goods of the church! Ha, no, no! What the devil! Saint Thomas of England was well content to die for them. If I die, shall not I be a saint likewise? Yet will not I die for all this, but send others a-packing."

As he spake this, he threw off his great monk's habit and laid hold upon the staff of the cross, which was made of the heart of a sorb-apple tree; it being of the length of a lance, round, of a full gripe, and a little powdered with flower-de-luces, almost all defaced and worn out. Thus went he out in a fair long-skirted jacket, putting his frock scarfways athwart his breast, and with his staff of the cross laid on so lustily upon his enemies, who without any order, or ensign, or trumpet, or drums, were busied in gathering the grapes of the vineyard — for the cornets, guidons and ensign-bearers had laid down their standards, banners and colours by the wall-sides; the drummers had knocked out the heads of their drums on one end, to fill them with grapes; the trumpeters were loaded with great bundles of bunches and huge knots of clusters; in sum, every one of them was out of array, and all in disorder.

He hurried therefore upon them so rudely, without crying *gare,* or beware, that he overthrew them like hogs, tumbled them over like swine, striking athwart and alongst, and by one means or other laid so about him, after the old fashion of fencing, that to some he beat out their brains, to others he crushed their arms, battered their legs, and bethwacked their sides till their ribs cracked with it. To others again, he unjointed the spondyles of the neck, disfigured their chaps, gashed their faces, made their cheeks hang flapping over their chin, and so swinged and belammed them that they fell down before him like hay before a mower. To some others he spoiled the frame of their kidneys, marred their backs, broke their thigh-bones, pushed in their noses, poached out their eyes, cleft their mandibles, tore their jaws, dashed their teeth into their throat, shook asunder their omoplates, or shoulder-blades, sphacelated their shins, mortified their shanks, inflamed their ankles, heaved off of the hinges their ishies, their sciatica or hip-gout, dislocated the joints of their knees, squattered into pieces the boughs or pestles of their thighs; and so thumped, mauled and belaboured them everywhere, that never was corn so thick and threefold threshed upon by ploughmen's flails, as were the pitifully disjointed members of their mangled bodies under the merciless baton of the cross.

If any offered to hide himself amongst the thickest of the vines, he laid him squat as a flounder, bruised the ridge of his back, and dashed his reins like a dog. If any thought by flight to escape, he made his head to fly in pieces by the lambdoidal commissure. If any one did scramble up into a tree, thinking there to be safe, he rent up his perineum, and impaled him in at the fundament.

If any one of his old acquaintance happened to cry out, "Ha, Friar John, my friend! Friar John, quarter, quarter! I yield myself to you, to you I render myself."

"So thou shalt," said he, "perforce, and thy soul to all the devils in hell"; then suddenly gave him *dronos*.

If any was so rash and full of temerity as to resist him to his face, then was it he did show the strength of his muscles; for without more ado he did transpierce him by running him in at the breast through the mediastinum and the heart. Others again he so quashed and bebumped, that with a sound bounce under the hollow of their short ribs he overturned their stomachs, so that they died immediately. To some, with a smart souse on the epigaster, he would make their midriff swag; then redoubling the blow, gave them such a home push on the navel that he made their puddings to gush out. To others, through their ballocks he pierced their bum-gut, and left not bowel, tripe nor entrail in their body that had not felt the impetuosity, fierceness and fury of his violence. Believe that it was the most horrible spectacle that ever one saw.

Some cried unto Saint Barbe, others to St. George.

"O the holy Lady Nytouch," said one, "the good sanctess!"

"O our Lady of Succours," said another, "help, help!"

Others cried, "Our Lady of Cunault! of Loretta! of Good Tidings! on the other side of the water St. Mary-over!"

Some vowed a pilgrimage to St. James, and others to the Holy Handkerchief at Chambéry, which three months after that burnt so well in the fire that they could not get one thread of it saved.

Others sent up their vows to St. Cadouin, others to St. John of Angély, and to St. Eutropius of Saintes.

Others again invoked St. Mexme of Chinon, St. Martin of Canades, St. Cloud of Cinais, the holy relics of Javarzay, with a thousand other jolly little sancts and santrels.

Some died without speaking, others spoke without dying; some died in speaking, others spoke in dying. Others shouted aloud, "Confession! Confession! *Confiteor! Miserere! In manus!*"

So great was the cry of the wounded that the prior of the abbey with all his monks came forth, who, when they saw these poor wretches so slain amongst the vines and wounded to death, confessed some of them. But whilst the priests were busy in confessing them, the little monkies ran all to the place where Friar John was, and asked him wherein he would be pleased to require their assistance. To which he answered, that they should cut the throats of those he had thrown down upon the ground. They, presently leaving their outer habits and cowls upon the rails, began to throttle and make an end of those whom he had already crushed. Can you tell with what instruments they did it? With fair gullicks, which are little hulched-backed demi-knives wherewith the little boys in our country cut ripe walnuts in two.

In the meantime, Friar John, with his formidable baton of the cross, got to the breach which the enemies had made, and there stood to snatch up those that endeavoured to escape. Some of the *monkitos* carried the standards, banners, ensigns, guidons and colours into their cells and chambers, to make garters of them. But when those that had been shriven would have gone out at the gap of the said breach, the sturdy monk quashed and felled them down with blows, saying, "These men have had confession and are penitent souls, they have got their absolution, and gained the pardons; they go into Paradise as straight as a sickle, or as the way is to Faye" (like Crooked-lane at Eastcheap).

Thus by his prowess and valour were discomfited all those of the army that entered into the close of the abbey, unto the number of thirteen thousand six hundred twenty and two, besides the women and little children, which is always to be understood. Never did Maugis the hermit bear himself more valiantly with his pilgrim's staff against the Saracens, of whom it is written in the acts of the Four Sons of Aymon, than did this monk against his enemies with the staff of the cross.

NOTES TO CHAPTER XXVII

1. "To the chapter-house, those who have votes!"; the signal for a general assembly.

2. The translators were at a loss how to deal with the name *Frère Jean des Entommeures,* nor have the critics until recently decided the exact meaning of the word *entommeures* (*entamûres*). Urquhart translated the name in this passage by the paraphrase, "Friar John of the funnels and gobbets, in French, *des entoumeures,*" then subsequently throughout the First and Second Books, sometimes "Friar John of the Funnels," sometimes "Friar John des Entoumeures." The Frenchman le Motteux, in his revision of Urquhart wrote here "Friar John des Entoumeures," and made an effort to be consistent throughout, without quite succeeding. We have kept to the variant which has the sanction of universal acceptance; this great character is known to the whole English-speaking world only, though incorrectly, as Friar John of the Funnels. Urquhart's collateral reading "gobbets," or hashed-up morsels, is fairly accurate. . .

[Grangousier writes to recall Gargantua from Paris to help defend his country. He sends an ambassador to reason with Picrochole, but in vain.]

CHAPTER XXXIII

How some ministers of Picrochole by hairbrained counsel put him in extreme danger [1]

The carts being unloaded, and the money and cakes secured, there came before Picrochole the duke of Smalltrash, the earl Swashbuckler, and Captain Durtaille, who said unto him, "Sir, this day we make you the happiest, the most warlike and chivalrous prince that ever was since the death of Alexander of Macedonia."

"Be covered, be covered," said Picrochole.

"Cry you mercy," said they, "we do but our duty. The matter is thus: You shall leave some captain here to have the charge of this garrison, with a party competent for keeping of the place, which, besides its natural strength, is made stronger by the rampiers and fortresses of your devising. Your army you are to divide into two parts, as you know very well how to do. One part thereof shall fall upon Grangousier and his forces. By it shall he be easily at the very first shock, routed, and then shall you get money by heaps; for the clown hath store of ready coin. Clown we call him, because a noble and generous prince hath never a penny, and that to hoard up treasure is the part of a clown. The other part of the army, in the meantime, shall draw towards Onys, Saintonge, Angoumois, and Gascony; then march to Périgord, Médoc, and the Landes, taking, wherever you come, without resistance towns, castles and forts. Afterwards to Bayonne, St.-Jean-de-Luz, to Fontarabia, where you shall seize upon all the ships, and coasting along Galicia and Portugal, shall pillage all the maritime places even unto Lisbon, where you shall be supplied with all necessaries befitting a conqueror. By copsodi, Spain will yield, for they are but a race of loobies! Then are you to pass the Straits of Gibraltar, where you shall erect two pillars more stately than those of Hercules, to the perpetual memory of your name; and the narrow entrance there shall be called the Picrocholinal Sea. Having passed the Picrocholinal Sea, behold, Barbarossa yields himself your slave . . ."

"I will," said Picrochole, "give him fair quarter."

"Yea," said they, "so that he be content to be christened. And you shall conquer the kingdoms of Tunis, of Hippos, Algeria, Bomine, Corona, yea, all Barbary. Furthermore, you shall take into your hands Majorca, Minorca, Sardinia, Corsica, with the other islands of the Ligustic and Balearian Seas. Going along on the left hand, you shall subdue all Gallia Narbonensis, Provence, the Allobrogians, Genoa, Florence, Lucca, and then God b' w' ye, Rome! [2] Our poor monsieur the pope dies now for fear."

"By my faith," said Picrochole, "I will not then kiss his pantoffle."

"Italy being thus taken, behold Naples, Calabria, Apulia and Sicily all ransacked, and Malta too. I wish those jovial quondam knights of Rhodes would but come to resist you, that we might see their urine." [3]

"I would," said Picrochole, "very willingly go to Loretta."

"No, no," said they, "that shall be at our return. From thence we will sail eastwards, and take Candia, Cyprus, Rhodes and the Cyclades Islands, and set upon the Morea. It is ours, by St. Trenian. The Lord preserve Jerusalem! for the great Soldan is not comparable to you in power."

"I will then," said he, "cause Solomon's Temple to be built."

"No," said they, "not yet; have a little patience. Stay awhile. Be never too sudden in your enterprises. Can you tell what Octavian Augustus said? *Festina lente.* It is requisite that you first have the Lesser Asia, Caria, Lycia, Pamphylia, Cilicia, Lydia, Phrygia, Mysia, Bithynia, Carazia, Satalia, Samagaria, Kastamuni, Luga. Sabasteia, even unto Euphrates."

"Shall we see," said Picrochole, "Babylon and Mount Sinai?"

"There is no need," said they, "at this time. Have we not hurried up and down, travelled and toiled enough, in having transfretted and passed over the Hyrcanian Sea, marched along the two Armenias and the three Arabias?"

"By my faith," said he, "we have played the fools, and are undone. Ha, poor souls!"

"What's the matter?" said they.

"What shall we have," said he, "to drink in these deserts? For Julian Augustus, with his whole army, died there for thirst, as they say."

"We have already," said they, "given order for that. In the Syriac Sea, you have nine thousand and fourteen great ships laden with the best wines in the world; they arrived at Port Joppa. There you shall find two-and-twenty thousand camels and sixteen hundred elephants, which you shall find at one hunting about Sigelmes, when you enter into Libya; and besides this, you will have all the Mecca caravan. Will not they furnish you sufficiently with wine?"

"Yes, but," said he, "we shall not drink it fresh."

"That," said they, "is for a little fish; but a mighty man, a pretender, one that aspires to the monarchy of the world, cannot always have his ease. God be thanked that you and your men are come safe and sound unto the banks of the river Tigris."

"But," said he, "what doth that part of our army, in the meantime, which overthrows that unworthy swill-pot Grangousier?"

"They are not idle," said they; "we shall meet with them by-and-by. They shall have won you Brittany, Normandy, Flanders, Hainault, Brabant, Artois, Holland, Zeeland. They have passed the Rhine, over the bellies of the Switzers and lansquenets, and a party of them hath subdued Luxemburg, Lorraine, Champagne and Savoy, even to Lyons, in which place they have met with your forces returning from the naval conquests of the Mediterranean Sea; and have rallied again in Bohemia, after they had plundered and sacked Swabia, Wittemberg, Bavaria, Austria, Moravia and Styria. Then they set fiercely together upon Lübeck, Norway, Swedeland, Rie, Denmark, Guitland, Greenland, the Sterlins, even unto the Frozen Sea. This done, they conquered the Isles of Orkney, and subdued Scotland, England and Ireland. From thence sailing through the Sandy Sea and by the Sarmates, they have vanquished and overcome Prussia, Poland, Lithuania, Russia, Wallachia, Transylvania, Hungaria, Bulgaria, Turkeyland, and are now at Constantinople."

"Come," said Picrochole, "let us go join them quickly; for I will be emperor of Trebizond also. Shall we not kill all these dogs, Turks and Mahometans?"

"What a devil should we do else?" said they. "And you shall give their goods and lands to such as shall have served you honestly."

"Reason," said he, "will have it so; that is but just. I give unto you Carmania, Syria, and all Palestine."

"Ah, sir," said they, "it is your goodness. Gramercy, God grant you may always prosper."

There was present at the time an old gentleman well experienced in the wars, a stern soldier, and who had been in many great hazards, named Echephron,[4] who hearing this discourse, said: "I do heartily doubt that all this enterprise will be like the tale of the pitcher full of milk, wherewith a shoemaker made himself rich in conceit; but when the pitcher was broken, he had not whereupon to dine. What do you pretend by these large conquests? What shall be the end of so many labours and crosses?"

"Thus it shall be," said Picrochole, "that when we return we shall sit down, rest, and be merry."

"But," said Echephron, "if by chance you should never come back, for the voyage is long and dangerous, were it not better for us to take our rest now, than unnecessarily to expose ourselves to so many dangers?"

"Oh," said Swashbuckler, "by God, here is a good dotard! Come, let us go hide ourselves in the corner of a chimney, and there spend the whole time of our life amongst ladies, in threading of pearls, or spinning like Sardanapalus. 'He that nothing ventures hath neither horse nor mule,' said Solomon."

" 'He who adventureth too much,' " said Echephron, " 'loseth both horse and mule,' as Malchon answered." [5]

"Enough," said Picrochole, "go forward. I fear nothing but that these devilish legions of Grangousier, whilst we are in Mesopotamia, will come on our backs and charge upon our rear. What remedy then?"

"A very good one," said Durtaille. "Send a pretty round commission to the Muscovites, and they will bring instantly into the field for you four hundred and fifty thousand choice fighting men. Oh, that you would but make me your lieutenant-general, how I should truss up the rogues with discipline! I fret, I charge, I strike, I take, I kill, I slay, I play the devil!"

"On, on," said Picrochole, "he that loves me, follow me."

NOTES TO CHAPTER XXXIII

1. This lively chapter was suggested to Rabelais from two sources: a conversation between Pyrrhus and Cineas in Plutarch's *Life of Pyrrhus,* and, more especially, Lucian's dialogue called *The Ship, or the Wishes.* The latter, in which a character is invited to make a wish, and, wishing himself king, goes on to dream aloud of voyages and conquests, has many points of similarity — the method of conquest and victualling, the granting rewards of conquest to listening friends, the splendid sweep of imagination which brushes suggested obstacles lightly aside. But though indebted to so fine a writer, Rabelais stamps the episode with his own genius, and it is solely for the light it throws on his creative methods that it is necessary to mention the debt at all.

2. I.e., good-bye Rome!

3. That we might see what stuff they are made of.
4. I.e., "prudence."
5. *The Dialogues of Solomon and Marcoul* were very popular in the Middle Ages. They opposed to the wisdom of Solomon the reflections of the popular character Marcoul (Malchon), who epitomizes the common sense of the people.

[Gargantua returns with his companions from Paris.]

CHAPTER XXXIX

How the monk was feasted by Gargantua, and of the jovial discourse they had at supper

When Gargantua was set down at table, and all of them had somewhat stayed their stomachs, Grangousier began to relate the source and cause of the war raised between him and Picrochole, and came to tell how Friar John of the Funnels had triumphed at the defence of the close of the abbey, and extolled him for his valour above Camillus, Scipio, Pompey, Caesar and Themistocles. Then Gargantua desired that he might be presently sent for, to the end that with him they might consult of what was to be done; whereupon, by a joint consent, his steward went for him, and brought him along merrily with his staff of the cross, upon Grangousier's mule.

When he was come, a thousand huggings, a thousand embracements, a thousand good-days were given: "Ha, Friar John, my friend, Friar John, my brave cousin, Friar John from the devil, let me clip thee about the neck! Let me have thee in my arms! I must gripe thee, my cod, till thy back crack!" And Friar John, the gladdest man in the world, never was man made welcomer, never was any more courteously and graciously received than Friar John.

"Come, come," said Gargantua, "a stool here close by me at this end."

"With all my heart," said the monk, "seeing you will have it so. Some water, page! Fill, my boy, fill; it is to refresh my liver. Give me some, child, to gargle my throat withal."

"Deposita cappa," [1] said Gymnast, "let us pull off this frock."

"Ho, by God, gentlemen," said the monk, "there is a chapter in *Statutis ordinis,* which opposeth my laying it down."

"Pish," said Gymnast, "a fig for your chapter! This frock breaks both your shoulders; put it off."

"My friend," said the monk, "let me alone with it, for by God I'll drink the better that it is on, it makes all my body jocund. If I should lay it aside, the waggish pages would cut to themselves garters out of it, as I was once served at Coulaines; and, which is worse, I should lose my appetite. But if in this habit I sit down at table, I will drink, by God, both to thee and to thy horse, and so courage, frolic, God save the company! I have already supped, yet I will eat never a whit the less for that, for I have a paved stomach as hollow as St. Benêt's boots, always open like a lawyer's pouch. Of all fishes but the tench, take the wing of a partridge, or the thigh of a nun. Doth not he die like a good fellow that dies with a stiff *cazzo?* Our prior loves exceedingly the white of a capon."

"In that," said Gymnast," he doth not resemble the foxes; for of the capons, hens and pullets which they carry away, they never eat the white."

"Why?" said the monk.

"Because," said Gymnast, "they have no cooks to dress them, and if they be not competently made ready, they remain red and not white, the redness of meats being a token that they have not got enough of the fire, except the shrimps, lobsters, crabs and crayfishes, which are cardinalized with boiling."

"God's fish," said the monk, "the porter of our abbey then hath not his head well-boiled, for his eyes are as red as a mazer made of an alder tree. . . . The thigh of this leveret is good for those that have the gout. Some natural philosophy: ha, ha, what is the reason that the thighs of a gentlewoman are always fresh and cool?"

"This problem," said Gargantua, "is neither in Aristotle, in Alexander Aphrodiseus, nor in Plutarch."

"There are three causes," said the monk, "by which that place is naturally refreshed. *Primo,* because the water runs all along it. *Secundo,* because it is a shady place, obscure and dark, upon which the sun never shines. And thirdly, because it is continually blown upon and aired by a reverberation from the back-door, by the fan of the smock, and flip-flap of the codpiece. And lusty my lads, some bousing liquor, page! . . . So crack, crack, crack! . . . Oh, what a good God have we, that gives us this excellent juice! I call Him to witness, if I had been in the time of Jesus Christ, I would have kept Him from being taken by the Jews in the Garden of Olivet; and the devil fail me, if I should have failed to cut off the hams of these gentlemen apostles who ran away so basely after they had well supped, and left their good master in the lurch. I hate that man worse than poison that offers to run away, when he should fight and lay stoutly about him. Oh, that I were but king of France for fourscore or a hundred years! By God, I should whip like curtailed dogs these runaways of Pavia.[2] A plague take them, why did they not choose rather to die there than to leave their good prince in that pinch and necessity? Is it not better and more honourable to perish in fighting valiantly, than to live in disgrace by a cowardly running away? We are like to eat no great store of goslings this year; therefore, friend, reach me some of that roasted pig there.

"*Diavolo,* is there no more must? No more sweet wine? *Germinavit radix Jesse.* I renounce my life, I die for thirst. This wine is none of the worst. What wine drank you at Paris? I give myself to the devil, if I did not once keep open house at Paris for all comers six months together. Do you know Friar Claude of the High Kilderkins? Oh, the good fellow that he is! But what fly hath stung him of late, he is become so hard a student? For my part, I study not at all. In our abbey we never study, for fear of the mumps. Our late abbot was wont to say that it is a monstrous thing to see a learned monk. By God, master my friend, *magis magnos clericos non sunt magis magnos sapientes.*[3] . . . You never saw so many hares as there are this year. I could not anywhere come by a goshawk, nor tassel of falcon; my lord Bellonnière promised me a lanner, but he wrote to me not long ago that he was become pursy. The partridges will so multiply henceforth that they will go near to eat up our ears. I take no delight in the stalking-horse, for I catch such cold that I am like to founder myself at that sport; if I do not run, toil, travel and trot about, I am not well at ease. True it is, that in leaping over hedges and bushes my frock leaves always some of its wool behind it. I have recovered a dainty greyhound; I give him to the devil if he suffer a hare to escape him. A groom was leading him to my lord Huntlittle, and I robbed him of him; did I ill?"

"No, Friar John," said Gymnast, "no, by all the devils that are, no."

"So," said the monk, "do I attest these same devils so long as they last! Virtue God, what could that gouty limpard have done with so fine a dog? By the body of God, he is better pleased when one presents him with a good yoke of oxen."

"How now," said Ponocrates, "you swear, Friar John?"

"It is only," said the monk, "but to grace and adorn my speech; they are colours of a Ciceronian rhetoric."

NOTES TO CHAPTER XXXIX

1. From the rituals, which indicate the moment for the officiant to remove his cope.

2. Referring to the defeat of the French at Pavia in 1525, when Francis I was taken prisoner.

3. "The biggest clerks are not the cleverest." Friar John, who boasts of his lack of learning, has at his tongue's end a good many phrases of kitchen-Latin.

CHAPTER XL

Why monks are the outcasts of the world, and wherefore some have bigger noses than others

"By the faith of a Christian," said Eudemon, "I am highly transported when I consider what an honest fellow this monk is, for he makes us all merry. How is it then that they exclude the monks from all good companies, calling them feast-troublers, as the bees drive away the drones from their hives? *'Ignavum fucos pecus,'* said Maro, *'a præsepibus arcent.'* "

Hereunto answered Gargantua, "There is nothing so true as that the frock and cowl draw to them the opprobries, injuries and maledictions of the world, just as the wind called Cecias attracts the clouds. The peremptory reason is because they eat the turd of the world, that is to say, they feed upon the sins of the people; and as a noisome thing, they are cast into the privies, that is, the convents and abbeys, separated from civil conversation as the privies and retreats of a house are. But if you conceive how an ape in a family is always mocked and provokingly incensed, you shall easily apprehend how monks are shunned of all men, both young and old. The ape keeps not the house as a dog doth; he draws not in the plough as the ox; he yields neither milk nor wool as the sheep; he carrieth no burden as a horse doth. That which he doth is only to conskit, spoil and defile all, which is the cause wherefore he hath of all men mocks, frumperies and bastinadoes. After the same manner a monk (I mean those little, idle, lazy monks) doth not labour and work as do the peasant and artificer, doth not ward and defend the country as doth the soldier, cureth not the sick and diseased as the physician doth, doth neither preach nor teach as do the evangelical doctors and schoolmasters, doth not import commodities and things necessary for the commonwealth as the merchant doth; therefore is it that by and of all men they are hooted at, hated and abhorred."

"Yea, but," said Grangousier, "they pray to God for us."

"Nothing less," answered Gargantua. "True it is, with a tingle-tangle jangling of bells they trouble and disquiet all their neighbours about them."

"Right," said the monk, "a mass, a matin, a vesper well rung is half said."

"They mumble out great store of legends and psalms, by them not at all understood; they say many paternosters, interlarded with Ave Marias, without thinking upon or apprehending the meaning of what it is they say, which truly I call mocking of God, and not prayers. But so help them God as they pray for us, and not for being afraid to lose their victuals, their manchets and good fat pottage! All true Christians, of all estates and conditions, in all places and at all times, send up their prayers to God, and the spirit prayeth and intercedeth for them, and God is gracious to them. Now such a one is our good Friar John; therefore every man desireth to have him in his company. He is no bigot; he is not for division; he is an honest heart, plain, resolute, good fellow; he travails, he labours, he defends the oppressed, comforts the afflicted, helps the needy, and keeps the close of the abbey."

"Nay," said the monk, "I do a great deal more than that; for whilst we are dispatching our matins and anniversaries in the choir, I make withal some cross-bow strings, polish glass bottles and bolts, I twist lines and weave purse-nets, wherein to catch conies. I am never idle. But hola! fill, fill, some drink, some drink, here! Bring the fruit; these chestnuts are of the wood of Estrocz, and with good new wine, will make you a composer of bum-sonnets. You are not yet well liquored. By God, I drink at all fords like a promoter's horse."

"Friar John," said Gymnast, "take away the snot that hangs at your nose."

"Ha, ha," said the monk, "am not I in danger of drowning, seeing I am in water even to the nose? No, no! *Quare? Quia,* though it comes out thence abundantly, yet there never goes in any; for it is well antidoted with syrup of the vine. O my friend, he that hath winter boots made of such leather, may boldly fish for oysters, for they will never take water."

"What is the cause," said Gargantua, "that Friar John hath such a goodly nose?"

"Because," said Grangousier, "that God would have it so, who frameth us in such form, and for such end as is most agreeable to His divine will, even as a potter fashioneth his vessels."

"Because," said Ponocrates, "he came with the first to the Fair of Noses, and therefore made choice of the fairest and the greatest."

"Pish," said the monk, "that is not the reason of it, but according to the true monastical philosophy, it is because my nurse had soft teats; by virtue whereof whilst she gave me suck, my nose did sink in, as in so much butter. The hard breasts of nurses make children short-nosed. But hey dey, *ad formam nasi cognoscitur ad-te-levavi*. . . . I am for no sweet stuff with my tipple, boy. *Item,* rather some toasts!"

[In the intervening chapters, Gargantua utterly defeats Picrochole and his army. Grangousier then rewards the victorious members of his own army led by Gargantua.]

CHAPTER LII

How Gargantua caused to be built for the monk the abbey of Theleme

There was left only the monk to provide for, whom Gargantua would have made abbot of Seuilly, but he refused it. He would have given him the abbey of Bourgueil or of Saint-Florent,[1] which was better, or both if it pleased him. But the monk gave him a very peremptory answer, that he would never take upon him the charge nor government of monks. "For how shall I be able," said he, "to rule over others, that have not full power and command of myself? If you think I have done you, or may hereafter do you any acceptable service, give me leave to found an abbey after my own mind and fancy."

The notion pleased Gargantua very well, who thereupon offered him all the country of Theleme by the river of Loire, till within two leagues of the great forest of Port-Huault.[2] The monk then requested Gargantua to institute his religious order contrary to all others.

"First then," said Gargantua, "you must not build a wall about your convent, for all other abbeys are strongly walled and mured about."

"See," said the monk, "and not without cause; where there is *mur* [3] before and *mur* behind, there is store of *murmur,* envy, and mutual conspiracy."

Moreover, seeing there are certain convents in the world whereof the custom is, if any women come in (I mean chaste and honest women) they immediately sweep the ground which they have trod upon; therefore was it ordained that if any man or woman, entered into religious orders, should by chance come within this new abbey, all the rooms should be thoroughly washed and cleansed through which they had passed. And because in all other monasteries and nunneries all is compassed, limited and regulated by hours, it was decreed that in this new structure there should be neither clock nor dial, but that according to the opportunities and incident occasions all their hours should be disposed of. "For," said Gargantua, "the greatest loss of time that I know, is to count the hours. What good comes of it? Nor can there be any greater dotage in the world than for one to guide and direct his courses by the sound of a bell, and not by his own judgment and discretion."

Item, because at that time they put no women into nunneries but such as were either purblind, blinkards, lame, crooked, ill-favoured, misshapen, fools, senseless, spoiled or corrupt; nor encloistered any men but those that were either sickly, subject to defluxions, ill-bred louts, simple sots, or peevish trouble-houses—"But to the purpose," said the monk, "a woman that is neither fair nor good, to what use serves she?"

"To make a nun of," said Gargantua.

"Yea," said the monk, "and to make shirts and smocks."[4]

Therefore was it ordained that into this religious order should be admitted no women that were not fair, well-featured, and of a sweet disposition; nor men that were not comely, personable and well-conditioned.

Item, because in the convents of women men come not but underhand, privily and by stealth, it was therefore enacted that in this house there shall be no women in case there be not men, nor men in case there be not women.

Item, because both men and women that are received into religious orders, after the expiring of their novitiate, or probation year, were constrained and forced perpetually to stay there all the days of their life, it was therefore ordered that all whatever, men or women, admitted within this abbey, should have full leave to depart with peace and contentment, whensoever it should seem good to them so to do.

Item, for that the religious men and women did ordinarily make three vows, to wit, those of chastity, poverty and obedience, it was therefore constituted and appointed that in this convent they might be honourably married, that they might be rich, and live at liberty. In regard of the legitimate time of the persons to be initiated, and years under and above which they were not capable of reception, the women were to be admitted from ten till fifteen, and the men from twelve to eighteen.

NOTES TO CHAPTER LII

1. These Benedictine abbeys were at that time among the richest of the region.

2. Theleme means in Greek "the will." This then is to be the abbey of free will. The abbey's situation is given with some exactitude: it is

in the fertile region watered by the Indre, the old course of the Cher, and the Loire, near Port-Huault.

3. In French, a wall.

4. The pun is lost in English. Friar John says, "Of what use is *toile*" (cloth, pronounced in the current Parisian fashion *tèle,* as *telle,* such a one). Gargantua understands the latter meaning, "such a one"; Friar John replies that *toile* is used to make shirts and smocks.

CHAPTER LIII

How the abbey of the Thelemites was built and endowed

For the fabric and furniture of the abbey Gargantua caused to be delivered out, in ready money, seven-and-twenty hundred thousand, eight hundred and one-and-thirty of those golden rams of Berry, which have a sheep stamped on the one side, and a flowered cross on the other. And for every year until the whole work were completed, he allotted threescore and nine thousand crowns of the sun, and as many of the seven stars, to be charged all upon the receipt of the custom. For the foundation and maintenance thereof forever, he settled a perpetual fee-farm rent of three-and-twenty hundred, threescore and nine thousand, five hundred and fourteen rose nobles, exempt from all homage, fealty, service or burden whatsoever, and payable every year at the gate of the abbey; and of this, by letters patent, passed a very good grant.

The architecture was in a figure hexagonal, and in such a fashion that in every one of the six corners there was built a great round tower of threescore feet in diameter, and were all of a like form and bigness. Upon the north side ran along the river Loire, on the bank whereof was situated the tower called Arctic. Going towards the east, there was another called Calaer; the next following, Anatole; the next, Mesembrine; the next, Hesperia; and the last, Crière.[1] Every tower was distant from the other the space of three hundred and twelve paces. The whole edifice was everywhere six stories high, reckoning the cellars underground for one. The second was arched after the fashion of a basket-handle. The rest were ceiled with pure wainscot, flourished with Flanders fret-work in the form of the foot of a lamp; and covered above with fine slates, with an endorsement of lead carrying the antique figures of little puppets and animals of all sorts, notably well suited to one another, and gilt, together with the gutters, which, jetting without the walls from betwixt the cross-bars in a diagonal figure, painted with gold and azure, reached to the very ground, where they ended into great conduit-pipes which carried all away unto the river from under the house.

This same building was a hundred times more sumptuous and magnificent than ever was Bonnivet, Chambord, or Chantilly.[2] For there were in it nine thousand, three hundred, and two-and-thirty chambers; every one whereof had a withdrawing-room, a handsome closet, a wardrobe, an oratory, and neat passage leading into a great and spacious hall. Between every tower, in the midst of the said body of building, there was a pair of winding stairs, whereof the steps were part of porphyry, part of Numidian stone, and part of serpentine marble; each of those steps being two-and-twenty feet in length, and three fingers thick, and the just number of twelve betwixt every rest or landing-place. In every resting-place were two fair antique arches, where the light came in, and by those they went into a cabinet made even with, and of the breadth of the said winding;[3] and the re-ascending above the roofs of the house ended conically in a pavilion. By that vize, or winding, they entered on every side into a great hall, and from the halls into the chambers.

From the Arctic tower unto the Crière were the fair great libraries in Greek, Latin, Hebrew, French, Italian and Spanish, respectively distributed in their several cantons,[4] according to the diversity of these languages.[5] In the midst there was a wonderful winding stair, the entry whereof was without the house, in a vault or arch six fathoms broad. It was made in such symmetry and largeness that six men-at-arms, with their lances in their rests, might together in a breast ride all up to the very top of all the palace.[6]

From the tower Anatole to the Mesembrine were spacious galleries, all coloured over and painted with the ancient prowesses, histories and descriptions of the world. In the midst thereof there was likewise such another ascent and gate, as we said there was on the river side. . .

NOTES TO CHAPTER LIII

1. The names of the seven towers are from the Greek: Arctic, northern; Calaer, situated in fine air; Anatole, oriental, or eastern; Mesembrine, southern; Hesperia, occidental; and Crière, glacial.

2. The château of Bonnivet, built during Rabelais's stay in the Poitou, for Guillaume Gouffier, the admiral killed at Pavia, was no doubt the first structure of the kind that Rabelais saw, and probably served as model for Theleme. It was destroyed in 1788, but plans of it indicate a rectangular building with symmetrical towers at the corners, staircases in the walls, well lighted by windows and round arches. The names of Chambord and Chantilly appear only in the later editions. Chambord was in process of construction at the time, and Chantilly was just about finished; both must have struck the imaginations of contemporaries with their magnificence. Chambord alone survives today to give us an idea of the grandiose character of Theleme.

3. These "cabinets" into which the antique or round archways led, were open loggias. The stairways of the Renaissance châteaux were often the most carefully and elaborately conceived detail of the whole building, as at Chambord.

4. Sections.

5. Note that the abbey was intended for men and women not only of physical perfection, but of a high degree of intelligence and humanist culture. Perhaps no dream was dearer to the humanist of the Renaissance than "fair great libraries in Greek, Latin and Hebrew"; Greek and Hebrew books being then a great rarity and hard to come at, in a day when books of all sorts were scarce. The growing interest in the vernacular literatures is also evidenced.

6. Such a winding ramp for cavaliers is to be seen today at the château of Amboise, which Rabelais may have visited.

CHAPTER LV

What manner of dwelling the Thelemites had

In the middle of the lower court there was a stately fountain of fair alabaster; upon the top thereof stood the three Graces with their cornucopias, and did jet out the water at their breasts, mouth, ears, eyes and other open passages of the body. The inside of the buildings in this lower court stood upon great pillars of chalcedony stone and porphyry marble, made arch-ways, after a goodly antique fashion. Within those were spacious galleries, long and large, adorned with curious pictures, the horns of bucks and unicorns, with rhinoceroses, water-horses called hippopotami, the teeth and tusks of elephants, and other things well worth the beholding. The lodging of the ladies took up all from the tower Arctic unto the gate Mesembrine. The men possessed the rest. Before the said lodging of the ladies, that they might have their recreation between the two first towers, on the outside were placed the tilt-yard, the theatre and natatory, with most admirable baths in three stages, situated above one another, well furnished with all necessary accommodations and store of myrtle water.

By the riverside was a fine pleasure-garden, and in the midst of that a labyrinth. Between the two other towers were the courts for tennis and the balloon. Towards the tower Crière stood the orchard, full of all fruit-trees, set and ranged in a quincuncial order. At the end of that was the great park, abounding with all sorts of venison. Betwixt the third couple of towers were the butts and marks for shooting with a snap-work gun, an ordinary bow for common archery, or with a cross-bow. The office-houses were without the tower Hesperia, of one story high. The stables were beyond the offices, and before them stood the falconry, managed by ostrich-keepers and falconers, very expert in the art. And it was yearly supplied and furnished by the Candians, Venetians and Sarmates with all sorts of most excellent hawks, eagles, gerfalcons, goshawks, sacres, lanners, falcons, sparhawks, merlins,[1] and all other kinds of them, so gentle and perfectly well manned, that flying of themselves sometimes from the castle for their own disport, they would not fail to catch whatever they encountered. The venery, where the beagles and hounds were kept, was a little farther off, drawing towards the park.

All the halls, chambers and closets, or cabinets, were richly hung with tapestry and hangings of divers sorts, according to the variety of the seasons of the year. All the pavements and floors were covered with green cloth; the beds were all embroidered. In every back chamber or withdrawing-room, there was a looking-glass of pure crystal, set in a frame of fine gold, garnished all about with pearls, and was of such greatness that it would represent to the full the whole lineaments and proportion of the person that stood before it.[2] At the going-out of the halls which belong to the ladies' lodgings, were the perfumers and trimmers, through whose hands the gallants passed when they were to visit the ladies. Those sweet artificers did every morning furnish the ladies' chambers with the spirit of roses, orange-flower water and angelica; and to each of them gave a little precious casket, vapouring forth the most odoriferous exhalations of the choicest aromatical scents.

NOTES TO CHAPTER LV

1. The eagle was used for hunting hares, foxes and cranes; the *sacre,* or saker-falcon, hunted the wild geese, herons and bitterns; the lanners, sparhawks and merlins were used for hunting smaller birds, such as larks and partridges. No man of Renaissance times but took an interest in the intricacies of falconry, the sport of princes.

2. The first mirrors of artificial crystal were imported into France from Venice in 1520, as a great luxury, and they were of small dimensions. One large enough to reflect the whole figure was an index of great magnificence.

CHAPTER LVI

How the men and women of the Religious Order of Theleme were apparelled

The ladies at the foundation of this order were apparelled after their own pleasure and liking; but since that, of their own accord and free-will they have reformed themselves. Their accoutrements were in manner as followeth: They wore stockings of scarlet crimson, or ingrained purple dye, which reached just three inches above the knee, having a list beautified with exquisite embroideries and rare incisions of the cutter's art. Their garters were of the colour of their bracelets, and circled the knee a little, both over and under. Their shoes, pumps and slippers were either of red, violet, or crimson velvet, pinked and jagged like lobsters' wattles.

Next to their smock they put on the pretty kirtle or vasquin of pure silk camlet. Above that went the taffeta or tabby farthingale, of white, red, tawny, grey, or of any other colour. Above this taffeta petticoat they had another of cloth, of tissue or brocade, embroidered with fine gold and interlaced with needlework; or as they thought good, and according to the temperature and disposition of the weather, had their upper coats of satin, damask or velvet, and those either orange, tawny, green, ash-coloured, blue, yellow, bright red, crimson or white, and so forth; or had them of cloth of gold, cloth of silver, or some other choice stuff, enriched with purple, or embroidered according to the dignity of the festival days and times wherein they wore them.

Their gowns, being still correspondent to the season, were either of cloth of gold, frizzled with a silver-raised work, of red satin, covered with gold purple, of tabby or taffeta, white, blue, black, tawny, etc., of silk serge, silk camlet, velvet, cloth of silver, silver tissue, cloth of gold, gold wire, figured velvet, or figured satin, tinselled and overcast with golden threads, in divers variously purfled draughts.

In summer some days, instead of gowns, they wore light handsome mantles, made either of the stuff of the aforesaid attire, or like Moresco rugs, of violet velvet frizzled with a raised work of gold upon silver purl, or with a knotted cord-work of gold embroidery, everywhere garnished with little Indian pearls. They always carried a fair panache or plume of feathers of the colour of their muff, bravely adorned and tricked out with glistering spangles of gold. In the winter time they had their taffeta gowns of all colours, as above-named, and those lined with the rich furrings of hindwolves or speckled lynxes, black-spotted weasels, marten-skins of Calabria, sables and other costly furs of inestimable value.

Their beads, rings, bracelets, collars, carcanets and neck-chains were all of precious stones, such as carbuncles, rubies, balas, diamonds, sapphires, emeralds, turquoises, garnets, agates, beryls, and excellent margarites.

Their head-dressing also varied with the season of the year according to which they decked themselves. In winter it was of the French fashion; in the spring, of the Spanish; in summer, of the fashion of Tuscany, except only upon the holidays and Sundays, at which time they were accoutred in the French mode, because they accounted it more honourable, and better befitting the garb of a matronal pudicity.[1]

The men were apparelled after their fashion. Their stockings were of tamin or of cloth serge, of white, black, scarlet, or some other ingrained colour. Their breeches were of velvet, of the same colour with their stockings, or very near, embroidered and cut according to their fancy. Their doublet was of cloth of gold, cloth of silver, of velvet, satin, damask, taffetas, etc., of the same colours, cut, embroidered and suitably trimmed up in perfection. The points were of silk of the same colours; the tags were of gold well enamelled. Their coats and jerkins were of cloth of gold, cloth of silver, gold tissue, or velvet embroidered, as they thought fit. Their gowns were every whit as costly as those of the ladies. Their girdles were of silk, of the colour of their doublets. Every one had a gallant sword by his side, the hilt and handle whereof were gilt, and the scabbard of velvet of the colour of his breeches, with a chape of gold and pure goldsmiths' work. The dagger was of the same. Their caps or bonnets were of black velvet, adorned with jewels and buttons of gold; upon that they wore a white plume, most prettily and mignon-like parted by so many rows of gold spangles, at the end whereof hung dangling in a more sparkling resplendency, fair rubies, emeralds, diamonds, etc.

But there was such a sympathy betwixt the gallants and the ladies, that every day they were apparelled in the same livery. And that they might not miss, there were certain gentlemen appointed to tell the youths every morning what vestments the ladies would on that day wear; for all was done according to the pleasure of the ladies.

In these so handsome clothes and habiliments so rich, think not that either one or the other of either sex did waste any time at all; for the masters of the wardrobes had all their raiments and apparels so ready for every morning, and the chamber-ladies were so well skilled, that in a trice they would be dressed and completely in their clothes from head to foot. And to have those accoutrements with the more conveniency, there was about the wood of Theleme a row of houses of the extent of half a league, very neat and cleanly, wherein dwelt the goldsmiths, lapidaries, jewellers, embroiderers, tailors, gold-drawers, velvet-weavers, tapestry-makers and upholsterers, who wrought there every one in his own trade, and all for the aforesaid jolly friars and nuns of the new stamp. They were furnished with matter and stuff from the hands of the lord Nausiclete, who every year brought them seven ships from the Perlas and Cannibal islands laden with ingots of gold, with raw silk, with pearls and precious stones. And if any unions began to grow old and lose somewhat of their natural whiteness and lustre, those by their art they did renew by tendering them to eat to some pretty cocks, as they use to give casting unto hawks.

NOTE TO CHAPTER LVI

1. The French coiffure was in fact the most severe, a cap coming down over the temples, covered by a velvet hood with hanging tail; while the Spanish headdress consisted of laces and veils, and the luxurious Tuscan mode was such as one sees in Italian Renaissance portraits, the hair elaborately twisted and entwined with gold chains and jewels.

CHAPTER LVII

How the Thelemites were governed, and of their manner of living

All their life was spent not in laws, statutes, or rules, but according to their own free will and pleasure. They rose out of their beds when they thought good; they did eat, drink, labour, sleep, when they had a mind to it and were disposed for it. None did awake them, none did offer to constrain them to eat, drink, nor do any other thing; for so had Gargantua established it. In all their rule and strictest tie of their order, there was but this one clause to be observed:

DO WHAT THOU WILT

Because men that are free, well-born, well-bred, and conversant in honest companies, have naturally an instinct and spur that prompteth them unto virtuous actions and withdraws them from vice, which is called honour. Those same men, when by base subjection and constraint they are brought under and kept down, turn aside from that noble disposition by which they formerly were inclined to virtue, to shake off that bond of servitude wherein they are so tyrannously enslaved; for it is agreeable to the nature of man to long after things forbidden, and to desire what is denied us.

By this liberty they entered into a very laudable emulation to do, all of them, what they saw did please one. If any of the gallants or ladies should say, "Let us drink," they would all drink. If any one of them said, "Let us play," they all played. If one said, "Let us go a-walking into the fields," they went all. If it were to go a-hawking or a-hunting, the ladies, mounted upon dainty well-paced nags, seated in a stately palfrey saddle, carried on their lovely fists miniardly begloved every one of them, either a sparhawk, or a lanneret, or a merlin, and the young gallants carried the other kinds of hawks.

So nobly were they taught that there was neither he nor she amongst them but could read, write, sing, play upon several musical instruments, speak five or six several languages, and compose in them all very quaintly, both in verse and prose. Never were seen so valiant knights, so noble and worthy, so dextrous and skilful both on foot and horseback, more brisk and lively, more nimble and quick, or better handling all manner of weapons, than were there. Never were seen ladies so proper and handsome, so miniard and dainty, less froward, or more ready with their hand and with their needle, in every honest and free action belonging to that sex, than were there.

For this reason, when the time came that any man of the said abbey, either at the request of his parents or for some other cause, had a mind to go out of it, he carried along with him one of the ladies, namely her whom he had before that chosen for his mistress, and they were married together. And if they had formerly in Theleme lived in good devotion and amity, they did continue therein and increase it to a greater height in their state of matrimony; and did entertain that mutual love till the very last day of their life, in no less vigour and fervency than at the very day of their wedding. . .

THE SECOND BOOK: PANTAGRUEL

THE AUTHOR'S PROLOGUE

Most illustrious and thrice valorous champions, gentlemen and others who willingly apply your minds to the high flights and harmless sallies of wit: you have not long ago seen, read, and understood the *Great and Inestimable Chronicles of the Huge Giant Gargantua;* and like true men of faith, have firmly believed all that is contained in them, and have very often passed your time amongst honourable ladies and gentlewomen, telling them fair long stories, when you are out of all other talk, for which you are worthy of great praise and sempiternal memory. And I do heartily wish that every man would lay aside his own business, meddle no more with his profession nor trade, and throw all affairs concerning himself behind his back, to attend this wholly, without distracting or troubling his mind with anything else, until he have learned them without book; that if by chance the art of printing should cease, or in case that in time to come, all books should perish, every man might truly teach them to his children, and deliver them over to his successors and survivors, from hand to hand, as a religious cabala; for there is in it more profit than a rabble of great pocky loggerheads are able to discern, who surely understand far less in these little merriments, then Raclet did in the *Institutes*.

I have known great and mighty lords, and those not a few, who going a-deer-hunting or a-hawking after wild ducks, when the chase [1] had not encountered with the blinks [2] that were cast in her way to retard her course, or that the hawk did but plain and smoothly fly without moving her wings, perceiving the prey by force of flight to have gained bounds of her, have been much chafed and vexed, as you understand well enough; but the comfort unto which they had refuge, and that they might not take cold, was to relate the inestimable deeds of the said Gargantua.

There are others in the world (these are no flimflam stories) who being much troubled with the toothache, after they had spent their goods upon physicians without receiving at all any ease of their pain, have found no more ready remedy than to put the said *Chronicles* betwixt two pieces of linen cloth, made very hot, and so apply them to the place that smarteth, synapizing them with a little powder of projection, otherwise called doribus.

But what shall I say of those poor men that are plagued with the pox and the gout? Oh, how often have we seen them, even immediately after they were anointed and thoroughly greased till their faces did glister like the key-hole of a powdering-tub, their teeth dance like the jacks of a pair of little organs or virginals, when they are played upon, and that they foamed from their very throats like a boar which the mongrel mastiff-hounds have driven in and overthrown amongst the toils! What did they then? All their consolation was to have some page of the said jolly book read unto them. And we have seen those who have given themselves to a hundred puncheons of old devils, in case that they did not feel a manifest ease and assuagement of pain at the hearing the said book read, even when they were kept in a purgatory of torment; no more nor less than women in travail use to find their sorrow abated when the life of St. Marguerite is read unto them.

Is this nothing? Find me a book in any language, in any faculty or science whatsoever, that hath such virtues, properties and prerogatives, and I will be content to pay you a chopin of tripes. No, my masters, no. It is peerless, incomparable, and not to be matched; and this am I resolved forever to maintain, even unto the fire exclusive.[3] And those that will pertinaciously hold the contrary opinion, let them be accounted abusers, predestinators, impostors and seducers of the people. It is very true, that there are found in some noble and famous books certain occult and hidden properties, in the number of which are reckoned *Whippot, Orlando Furioso, Robert the Devil, Fierabras, William without Fear, Huon of Bordeaux, Mandeville* and *Matabrune;* but they are not comparable to that which we speak of. And the world hath well known by infallible experience the great emolument and utility which it hath received by this Gargantuan chronicle; for the printers have sold more of them in two months' time, than there will be bought of Bibles in nine years.

I therefore, your humble slave, being very willing to increase your solace and recreations yet a little more, do offer you for a present another book of the same stamp, only that it is a little more reasonable and worthy of credit than the other was. For think not, unless you wilfully will err against your knowledge, that I speak of it as the Jews do of the Law. I was not born under such a planet, neither did it ever befall me to lie, or affirm a thing for true that was not. I speak of it like a jolly onocrotary—I should say crotenotary—of the martyrized lovers, and croquenotary of love. *Quod vidimus testamur.* It is of the horrible and dreadful feats and prowesses of Pantagruel, whose menial servant I have been ever since I was a page, till this hour that by his leave I am permitted to visit my cow-country,[4] and to know if any of my kindred there be alive.

And therefore, to make an end of this prologue, even as I give myself fairly to a hundred thousand panniers full of devils, body and soul, tripes and guts, in case that I lie so much as one single word in this whole history; just so St. Anthony's fire burn you, Mawmet's disease whirl you, the squinance choke you, botches, crinkums sink you plumb down to Peg Trantum's, plagues of Sodom and Gomorrah cram your pocky arse with sorrow, fire, brimstone and pits bottomless swallow you all alive, in case you do not firmly believe all that I shall relate unto you in this present chronicle!

NOTES TO THE AUTHOR'S PROLOGUE

1. Quarry.
2. Boughs thrown to turn aside deer from their course.
3. I.e., up to any test short of the trial by fire or burning at the stake.
4. It seems evident from this passage that in 1532 Rabelais returned to Chinon and la Devinière for a visit, probably in the autumn when the newly-vintaged "Septembral juice" of chapter XXXIV was being sampled.

CHAPTER II

Of the nativity of the most dread and redoubted Pantagruel

Gargantua, at the age of four hundred fourscore forty and four years, begat his son Pantagruel upon his wife named Badebec, daughter to the king of the Amaurots in Utopia,[1] who died in childbirth; for he was so wonderfully great and lumpish that he could not possibly come forth into the light of the world without thus suffocating his mother.

But that we may fully understand the cause and reason of the name of Pantagruel, which at his baptism was given him, you are to remark that in that year there was so great a drought [2] over all the country of Afric, that there passed thirty and six months, three weeks, four days, thirteen hours, and a little more, without rain, but with a heat so vehement that the whole earth was parched and withered by it; neither was it more scorched and dried up with heat in the days of Elijah than it was at that time, for there was not a tree to be seen that had either leaf or bloom upon it. The grass was without verdure or greenness, the rivers were drained, the fountains dried up, the poor fishes abandoned and forsaken by their proper element, wandering and crying upon the ground most horribly; the birds did fall down from the air for want of moisture and dew wherewith to refresh them; the wolves, foxes, harts, wild boars, fallow-deer, hares, conies, weasels, brocks, badgers and other-such beasts were found dead in the fields, with their mouths open.

In respect of men, there was the pity! You should have seen them lay out their tongues like greyhounds that had run six hours. Many did throw themselves into the wells; others entered within a cow's belly to be in the shade—those Homer calls *Alibantes*. All the country was at a stand, and nothing could be done. It was a most lamentable case, to have seen the labour of mortals in defending themselves from the vehemency of this horrific drought, for they had work enough to do to save the holy water in the churches from being wasted; but there was such order taken by the counsel of my lords the cardinals, and of our holy father, that none did dare to take above one lick. Yet when any one came into the church, you should have seen above twenty poor thirsty fellows hang upon him that was the distributor of the water, and that with a wide open throat, gaping for some little drop, like the rich glutton in St. Luke, that might fall by, lest anything should be lost. Oh, how happy was he that year who had a cool cellar under ground, well plenished with fresh wine!

The Philosopher reports in moving the questions, wherefore is it that the sea-water is salt, that at the time when Phœbus gave the government of his resplendent chariot to his son Phaeton, the said Phaeton, unskilful in the art and not knowing how to keep the ecliptic line betwixt the two tropics of the latitude of the sun's course, strayed out of his way and came so near the earth that he dried up all the countries that were under it, burning a great part of the heaven, which the philosophers call *Via lactea,* and the huff-snuffs, St. James's Way, although the most lofty and high-crested poets affirm that to be the place where Juno's milk fell when she gave suck to Hercules. The earth at that time was so excessively heated that it fell into an enormous sweat, yea, such a one that made it sweat out the sea, which is therefore salt, because all sweat is salt; and this you cannot but confess to be true, if you will taste of your own, or of those that have the pox, when they are put into a sweating; it is all one to me.

Just such another case fell out this same year; for on a certain Friday, when the whole people were bent upon their devotions, and had made goodly processions, with store of litanies and fair preachings, and beseechings of God Almighty to look down with His eye of mercy upon their miserable and disconsolate condition, there was even then visibly seen issue out of the ground great drops of water, such as fall from a man in a top sweat; and the poor hoydens began to rejoice, as if it had been a thing very profitable unto them.

For some said that there was not one drop of moisture in the air, whence they might have any rain, and that the earth did supply the default of that. Other learned men said that it was a shower of the Antipodes, as Seneca saith in his fourth book *Quæstionum naturalium,* speaking of the source and spring of Nilus. But they were deceived; for the procession being ended, when every one went about to gather of this dew and to drink of it with full bowls, they found it was nothing but pickle, and the very brine of salt, more brackish in taste than the saltest water of the sea.

And because in that very day Pantagruel was born, his father gave him that name; for *Panta* in Greek is as much as to say *all,* and *Gruel* in the Hagarene language [3] doth signify *thirsty;* inferring hereby, that at his birth the whole world was a-dry and thirsty; as likewise foreseeing that he would be some day supreme lord and sovereign of the thirsty companions, which was shown to him at that very same hour by a more evident sign. For when his mother Badebec was in the bringing of him forth, and that the midwives did wait to receive him, there came first out of her belly threescore and eight sellers of salt, every one of them leading in a halter a mule heavy loaded with salt; after whom issued forth nine dromedaries, with great loads of gammons of bacon, and dried neats' tongues on their backs; then followed seven camels loaded with links and chitterlings, hog's puddings and sausages; after them came out five great wains full of leeks, garlic, onions and chibols, drawn with five-and-thirty strong cart-horses, which was six for every one, besides the thiller. At the sight hereof the midwives were much amazed; yet some of them said, "Lo, here is good provision, and indeed we need it, for we drink but lazily, as if our tongues walked on crutches. Truly this is a good sign; there is nothing here but what is fit for us, these are the spurs of wine that set it going."

As they were tattling thus together, after their own manner of chat, behold! out comes Pantagruel, all hairy like a bear; whereupon one of them, inspired with a prophetical spirit, said, "This will be a terrible fellow. He is born with all his hair, he is undoubtedly to do wonderful things; and if he live, he will be of age."

NOTES TO CHAPTER II

1. In Sir Thomas More's *Utopia,* published in 1516, the principal city is named Amaurote, from a Greek word meaning "dimly seen," hence "imaginary."

2. Critics have pointed out that the summer of 1532, the year in which the Second Book was published, was marked by unheard-of heat and drought. . .

3. I.e., the Moorish language, the Saracens being the reputed descendants of Hagar. This etymology is purely fanciful.

CHAPTER IV

Of the infancy of Pantagruel

I find by the ancient historiographers and poets, that divers have been born in this world after very strange manners, which would be too long to repeat; read therefore the seventh book of Pliny, if you have so much leisure. Yet have you never heard of any so wonderful as that of Pantagruel; for it is a very difficult matter to believe how, in the little time he was in his mother's belly, he grew both in body and strength. That which Hercules did was nothing, when in his cradle he slew two serpents, for those serpents were but little and weak; but Pantagruel, being yet in his cradle, did far more admirable things, and more to be amazed at.

I pass by here the relation of how at every one of his meals he supped up the milk of four thousand and six hundred cows; and how to make him a skillet to boil his milk in, there were set a-work all the braziers of Saumur in Anjou, of Villedieu in Normandy, and of Bramont in Lorraine. And they served-in this whitepot-meat to him in a huge great bell, which is yet to be seen in the city of Bourges in Berry, near the palace; [1] but his teeth were already so well grown and so strengthened in vigour, that of the said bell he bit off a great morsel, as very plainly doth appear till this hour.

One day in the morning, when they would have made him suck one of his cows (for he never had any other nurse, as the history tells us), he got one of his arms loose from the swaddling bands wherewith he was kept fast in the cradle, laid hold on the said cow under the left fore-ham, and grasping her to him, ate up her udder and half her paunch, with the liver and the kidneys, and had devoured all up, if she had not cried out most horribly, as if the wolves had held her by the legs; at which noise company came in, and took away the said cow from Pantagruel. Yet could they not so well do it but that the quarter whereby he caught her was left in his hand, of which quarter he gulped up the flesh in a trice, even with as much ease as you would eat a sausage; and that so greedily, with desire of more, that when they would have taken away the bone from him, he swallowed it down whole, as a cormorant would do a little fish, and afterwards began fumblingly to say, "Good, good, good!" for he could not yet speak plain, giving them to understand thereby that he had found it very good, and that he did lack but so much more. Which when they saw that attended him, they bound him with great cable-ropes, like those that are made at Tain for the carriage of salt to Lyons, or such as those are whereby the great French ship rides at anchor in the road of Newhaven in Normandy. But on a certain time a great bear which his father had bred got loose, came towards him, began to lick his face (for his nurses had not thoroughly wiped his chaps); at which unexpected approach being on a sudden offended, he as lightly rid himself of those great cables as Samson did of the hawser ropes wherewith the Philistines had tied him, and, by your leave, takes up monsieur the bear and tears him in pieces like a pullet, which served him for a gorgeful, or good warm bit for that meal.

Whereupon Gargantua, fearing lest the child should hurt himself, caused four great chains of iron to be made to bind him, and so many strong wooden arches unto his cradle, most firmly stocked and mortised in huge frames. Of those chains you have one at la Rochelle, which they draw up at night betwixt the two great towers of the haven; another is at Lyons, a third at Angers,[2] and the fourth was carried away by the devils to bind Lucifer, who broke his chains in those days by reason of a colic that did extraordinarily torment him, taken with eating a sergeant's soul fricasseed for his breakfast. And therefore you may believe that which Nicolas de Lyra saith upon that place of the Psalter, where it is written, *"et Og regem Basan,"* that the said Og, being yet little, was so strong and robustious that they were fain to bind him with chains of iron in his cradle. Thus continued Pantagruel for a while very calm and quiet, for he was not able so easily to break those chains, especially having no room in the cradle to give a swing with his arms.

But see what happened once upon a great holiday, that his father Gargantua made a sumptuous banquet to all the princes of his court! I am apt to believe that the menial officers of the house were so imbusied in waiting each on his proper service at the feast, that nobody took care of poor Pantagruel, who was left *a reculorum,* behindhand all alone, and as forsaken. What did he? Hark what he did, good people! He strove and essayed to break the chains of the cradle with his arms, but could not, for they were too strong for him; then did he keep with his feet such a stamping stir, and so long, that at last he beat out the lower end of his cradle, which notwithstanding was made of a great beam five foot in square; and as soon as he had gotten out his feet, he slid down as well as he could, till he had got his soles to the ground. And then with a mighty force he rose up, carrying his cradle upon his back, bound to him like a tortoise that crawls up against a wall; and to have seen him, you would have thought it had been a great carrack of five hundred ton upon one end.

In this manner he entered into the great hall where they were banqueting, and that very boldly, which did much affright the company. Yet because his arms were tied in, he could not reach anything to eat, but with great pain stooped now and then a little, to take with the whole flat of his tongue, some lick, good bit, or morsel. Which when his father saw, he knew well enough that they had left him without giving him anything to eat, and therefore commanded that he should be loosed from the said chains, by the counsel of the princes and lords there present; besides that also the physicians of Gargantua said that if they did thus keep him in the cradle, he would be all his lifetime subject to the stone. When he was unchained they made him to sit down, where, after he had fed very well, he took his cradle and broke it into more than five hundred thousand pieces with one blow of his fist that he struck in the midst of it, swearing that he would never come into it again.

NOTES TO CHAPTER IV

1. The translator has it wrong; it should be "huge great cup." There used to stand in front of the palace of the duke of Berry, in Bourges, a great stone vat, which was filled once a year with wine for distribution to the poor. It was popularly called "the Giant's Bowl," and Rabelais appropriates it for Pantagruel's cup.

2. The great chain of la Rochelle which was hung at night between the towers of the Chaîne and of St.-Nicholas (both still standing), to close the harbour, may still be seen in the garden of the little Rochelle museum. At Lyons the chains are stretched across the Saône River between the abbey of Ainay and the Porte St.-Georges. At Angers an enormous chain barred the course of the Maine, for the control of navigation.

CHAPTER V

Of the acts of the noble Pantagruel in his youthful age

Thus grew Pantagruel from day to day, and to every one's eye waxed more and more in all his dimensions, which made his father to rejoice by a natural affection. Therefore caused he to be made for him, whilst he was yet little, a pretty cross-bow wherewith to shoot at small birds, which now they call the great cross-bow at Chantelle.

Then he sent him to school to learn, and to spend his youth in virtue. In the prosecution of which design he came first to Poitiers, where as he studied and profited very much, he saw that the scholars were oftentimes idle and knew not how to bestow their time, which moved him to take such compassion on them, that one day he took from a long ledge of rocks (called there Passelourdin) a huge great stone, of about twelve fathom square and fourteen handfuls thick, and with great ease set it upon four pillars, in the midst of a field; to no other end but that the said scholars, when they had nothing else to do, might pass their time in getting up on that stone, and feast it with store of gammons, pasties and flagons, and carve their names upon it with a knife; in token of which deed, till this hour, the stone is called the Lifted Stone. And in remembrance hereof, there is none entered into the register and matricular book of the said university of Poitiers, or accounted capable of taking any degrees therein, till he have first drunk in the caballine fountain of Croûtelle, passed at Passelourdin, and got up upon the Lifted Stone.[1]

Afterwards reading the delectable chronicles of his ancestors, he found that Geoffrey of Lusignan, called Geoffrey with the Great Tooth, grandfather to the cousin-in-law of the eldest sister of the aunt of the son-in-law of the uncle of the good daughter of his stepmother, was interred at Maillezais. Therefore he took a play-day to pay his respects to him in a visit; and going from Poitiers with some of his companions, they passed by Ligugé, visiting the noble abbot Ardillon, then by Lusignan, by Sanxay, by Celles, by Coulonges, by Fontenay-le-Comte, saluting the learned Tiraqueau; and from thence arrived at Maillezais, where he went to see the sepulchre of the said Geoffrey with the Great Tooth; which made him somewhat afraid, looking upon the portraiture representing a man in an extreme fury, drawing his great malchus falchion half-way out of his scabbard.[2] When the reason hereof was demanded, the canons of the said place told him that there was no other cause of it, but that *pictoribus atque poetis, etc.,* that is to say, that painters and poets have liberty to paint and devise what they list after their own fancy; but he was not satisfied with their answers, and said, "He is not thus painted without a cause; and I suspect that at his death there was some wrong done him, whereof he requireth his kindred to take revenge. I will inquire further into it, and then do what shall be reasonable."

Then he returned not to Poitiers, but would take a view of the other universities of France. Therefore going to la Rochelle, he took shipping and arrived at Bordeaux, where he found no great diversion, only now and then he would see some mariners and lightermen a-wrestling on the quay or strand, by the river-side.[3] From thence he came to Toulouse, where he learned to dance very well, and to play with the two-handed sword, as the fashion of the scholars of the said university is. But he stayed not long there when he saw that they stuck not to burn their regents alive like red herrings, saying, "Now, God forbid that I should die this death, for I am by nature sufficiently dry already, without being heated any further."

He went then to Montpellier, where he met with the good wines of Mirevaux, and good jovial company withal, and thought to have set himself to the study of physic; but he considered that that calling was too troublesome and melancholy, and that physicians did smell of glisters like old devils. Therefore he resolved he would study the laws; but seeing that there were but three scalled, and one bald-pated legist in that place,[4] he departed from thence, and in his way made the Pont de Gard and the amphitheatre of Nîmes in less than three hours, which nevertheless seems to be more than mortal man could do. After that he came to Avignon, where he was not above three days before he fell in love; for the women there take great delight in playing at the close-buttock game, because it is papal ground. Which his tutor Epistemon[5] perceiving, he drew him out of that place and brought him to Valence in the Dauphiny,[6] where he saw no great matter of recreation, only that the lubbers of the town did beat the scholars; which so incensed him with anger that when, upon a certain very fair Sunday, the people being at their public dancing in the streets, and one of the scholars offering to put himself into the ring, the bumpkins would not let him; whereupon Pantagruel taking the scholar's part, so belaboured them with blows and laid such load upon them, that he drove them all before him even to the brink of the river Rhône, and would have there drowned them, but that they did squat into the ground like moles, and there lay close a full half-league under the river. The hole is to be seen there yet.

After that, he departed from thence, and in three strides and a leap came to Angers, where he found himself very well, and would have continued there some space, but that the plague drove them away.[7] So from thence he came to Bourges,[8] where he studied a good long time, and profited very much in the faculty of the laws; and would sometimes say that law books were like a wonderful rich cloth of gold edged with sir-reverence, for in the world are no goodlier books to be seen, more ornate, nor more eloquent than the texts of the Pandects; but the bordering of them, that is to say, the gloss of Accursius, is so vile, mean and scandalous, that it is nothing but dirt and excrement.[9]

Going from Bourges he came to Orléans, where he found store of sparkish scholars that made him great entertainment at his coming,[10] and with whom he learned to play at tennis so well that he was a master at that game; for the students there are excellent at it. And sometimes they carried him unto Cupid's Gardens, there to recreate his person at the *poussavant,* or in-and-in. As for breaking his head with over-much study, he had an especial care not to do it in any case, for fear of spoiling his eyes; which he the rather observed, for that one of the regents there had often in his lectures maintained that nothing could be so hurtful to the sight as to have sore eyes. So one day, when a scholar of his acquaintance who had of learning not much more than his brethren, though instead of that, he could dance very well, and play at tennis, was made a licentiate in law, he blazoned the licentiates of that university in this manner:

In his hand is always a racket,
Or his tennis-ball in a placket;
In a dance he neatly can trip it;
And for law, it is all in his tippet.

NOTES TO CHAPTER V

1. The University of Poitiers had then about four thousand students and was reputed the second in France. Rabelais may have attended lectures there while he was with Geoffroy d'Estissac at Ligugé. The caves of Passelourdin, approximately three miles south-east of Poitiers, are reached by a path about two feet wide along a ledge midway of the cliffs, which now is guarded by an iron rail. Rabelais must often have seen crowds of students wandering through the pleasant meadows which lie between Ligugé and Passelourdin. The dolmen called *Pierre Levée,* the "Lifted Stone," still stands in a suburb of Poitiers, though it is now broken in two pieces, one of its supports having given way. The charming spring of Croûtelle is just off the road from Poitiers to la Fontaine, where the "noble abbot Ardillon" extended his hospitality to Rabelais and other humanists.

2. Geoffrey of Lusignan, lord of Vouvant and Mervent, was a fine example of the thirteenth-century buccaneering nobleman. He ravaged

and burned the countryside, destroying the monastery of Maillezais; but later on was constrained to rebuild it, and reconciled himself so well with the monks that after his death they erected a cenotaph to him in their church. In 1834, excavations in the church choir turned up the stone head of a warrior whose fiece expression identified it as that described by Rabelais, though the "great tooth" was missing. This stone head is now in the museum of Niort, and a replica of it is on the railway station at Lusignan. The route Pantagruel took to reach Maillezais is by no means direct, but it is the one on which Rabelais doubtless often travelled with Geoffroy d'Estissac, for almost all the localities named were lands or benefices of the bishop of Maillezais.

3. The University of Bordeaux was of small repute in the sixteenth century.

4. Montpellier was in fact famous for its Faculty of Medicine, and negligible in point of its Faculty of Law.

5. The name means, the knowing, or learned one.

6. The University of Valence, founded in 1454 by Louis XI while Dauphin, was very flourishing in Rabelais's time.

7. There were several outbreaks of the plague in Angers about this time, in 1518–1519, 1530 and 1532. Rabelais may have studied there himself if the tradition of his novitiate at la Baumette, near by, be true. The University of Angers was famous at this time.

8. The University of Bourges was celebrated for its Faculty of Law. The great Alciat taught there from 1529 on.

9. The humanist legists of the sixteenth century, including Budé, Alciat, Tiraqueau, expressed the same admiration for the Roman law as set forth in the Pandects, and the same contempt for the mediaeval commentators, of whom Accursius is the type. These commentaries were printed in the margins, surrounding the text and often dwarfing it.

10. The University of Orléans, like that of Bourges, was noted for its instruction in law, having in 1512 five doctors in civil law and three in canon law. Students came there from Paris, where only canon law was taught. . .

[Pantagruel finally goes with his retinue to Paris and enters upon his studies there.]

CHAPTER VIII

How Pantagruel, being at Paris, received letters from his father Gargantua, and the copy of them [1]

Pantagruel studied very hard, as you may well conceive, and profited accordingly; for he had an excellent understanding and notable wit, together with a capacity in point of memory equal to the measure of twelve oil budgets, or butts of olives. And as he was there abiding, one day he received a letter from his father, in manner as followeth:

"Most Dear Son,

"Amongst the gifts, graces and prerogatives, with which the Sovereign Plasmator, God Almighty, hath endowed and adorned human nature from the beginning, that seems to me most singular and excellent by which we may in a mortal estate attain to a kind of immortality, and in the course of this transitory life perpetuate our name and seed, which is done by a progeny issued from us in the lawful bonds of matrimony; whereby, that in some measure is restored unto us, which was taken from us by the sin of our first parents; to whom it was said, that because they had not obeyed the commandment of God their Creator, they should die, and by death should be brought to nought that so stately frame and plasmature wherein the man at first had been created. But by this means of seminal propagation, there continueth in the children what was lost in the parents, and in the grandchildren that which perished in their fathers, and so successively until the day of the Last Judgment, when Jesus Christ shall have rendered up to God the Father His kingdom in a peaceable condition, out of all danger and contamination of sin. For then shall cease all generations and corruptions, and the elements leave off their continual transmutations; seeing the so much desired peace shall be attained unto and enjoyed, and that all things shall be brought to their end and period.

"And therefore, not without just and reasonable cause do I give thanks to God my Saviour and Preserver, for that He hath enabled me to see my bald old age reflourish in thy youth: for when at His good pleasure, who rules and governs all things, my soul shall leave this mortal habitation, I shall not account myself wholly to die, but to pass from one place unto another; considering that in and by thee I continue in my visible image living in the world, visiting and conversing with people of honour, and other my good friends, as I was wont to do. Which conversation of mine, although it was not without sin (because we are all of us trespassers, and therefore ought continually to beseech His Divine Majesty to blot our transgressions out of His memory), yet was it, by the help and grace of God, without all manner of reproach before men.

"Wherefore if those qualities of the mind but shine in thee, wherewith I am endowed, as in thee remaineth the perfect image of my body, thou wilt be esteemed by all men to be the perfect guardian and treasure of the immortality of our name; but if otherwise, I shall truly take but small pleasure to see it, considering that the lesser part of me, which is the body, would abide in thee, and the best (to wit, that which is the soul, and by which our name continues blessed amongst men) would be degenerate and bastardized. This I do not speak out of any distrust that I have of thy virtue, which I have heretofore already tried, but to encourage thee yet more earnestly to proceed from good to better. And that which I now write unto thee, is not so much that thou shouldest live in this virtuous course, as that thou shouldest rejoice in so living, and having lived, cheer up thyself with the like resolution in time to come. To the prosecution and accomplishment of which enterprise and generous undertaking, thou mayest easily remember how that I have spared nothing, but have so helped thee as if I had had no other treasure in this world but to see thee once in my life completely well-bred and accomplished, as well in virtue, honesty and valour, as in all liberal knowledge and civility; and so to leave thee after my death as a mirror representing the person of me thy father; and if not so excellent, and such indeed as I do wish thee, yet such in desire.

"But although my deceased father, of happy memory, Grangousier, had bent his best endeavours to make me profit in all perfection and political knowledge, and that my labour and study was fully correspondent to, yea, went beyond his desire; nevertheless, as thou mayest well understand, the time then was not so proper and fit for learning as it is at present, neither had I plenty of such good masters as thou hast had. For that time was darksome, obscured with clouds of ignorance, and savouring a little of the infelicity and calamity of the Goths, who had, wherever they set footing, destroyed all good literature, which in my age hath by the divine goodness been restored unto its former light and dignity, and that with such amendment and increase of knowledge that now hardly should I be admitted unto the first form of the little grammar-school boys; I say, I, who in my youthful days was (and that justly) reputed the most learned of that age. Which I do not speak in vainboasting, although I might lawfully do it in writing unto thee, by the authority of Marcus Tullius, in his book of *Old Age,* and the sentence of Plutarch, in the book entitled, *How a Man may Praise Himself without Envy;* but to give thee an emulous encouragement to strive yet farther.

"Now is it that the minds of men are qualified with all manner of discipline, and the old sciences revived, which for many ages were extinct. Now it is that the learned languages are to their pristine purity restored—viz., Greek (without which a man may be ashamed to account himself a scholar), Hebrew, Arabic, Chaldean and Latin. Printing likewise is now in use, so elegant and so correct that better cannot be imagined, although it was found out but in my time by divine inspiration; as by a diabolical suggestion, on the other side, was the invention of ordnance. All the world is full of knowing men, of most learned schoolmasters, and vast libraries; and it appears to me as a truth that neither in Plato's time, nor Cicero's, nor Papinian's, there was ever such conveniency for studying as we see at this day there is. Nor must any adventure henceforward to come in public, or represent himself in company, that hath not been pretty well polished in the shop of Minerva. I see robbers, hangmen, freebooters, tapsters, ostlers, and such-like, of the very rubbish of the people, more learned now than the doctors and preachers were in my time.

"What shall I say? The very women and children have aspired to this praise and celestial manna of good learning. Yet so it is, that at the age I am now of, I have been constrained to learn the Greek tongue, which I contemned not like Cato, but had not the leisure in my younger years to attend the study of it. And I take much delight in the reading of Plutarch's *Morals,* the pleasant *Dialogues* of Plato, the *Monuments* of Pausanias, and the *Antiquities* of Athenæus, whilst I wait the hour wherein God my Creator shall call me, and command me to depart from this earth and transitory pilgrimage.

"Wherefore, my son, I admonish thee to employ thy youth to profit as well as thou canst, both in thy studies and in virtue. Thou art at Paris, where the laudable examples of many brave men may stir up thy mind to many gallant actions; and hast likewise for thy tutor the learned Epistemon, who by his lively and vocal documents may instruct thee in the arts and sciences.

"I intend, and will have it so, that thou learn the languages perfectly. First of all, the Greek, as Quintilian will have it; secondly, the Latin; and then the Hebrew, for the Holy Scripture's sake; and then the Chaldee and Arabic likewise; and that thou frame thy style in Greek, in imitation of Plato; and for the Latin, after Cicero. Let there be no history which thou shalt not have ready in thy memory; and to help thee therein, the books of cosmography will be very conducible. Of the liberal arts of geometry, arithmetic and music, I gave thee some taste when thou wert yet little, and not above five or six years old; proceed further in them, and learn the remainder if thou canst. As for astronomy, study all the rules thereof; let pass nevertheless the divining and judicial astrology, and the art of Lullius, as being nothing else but plain cheats and vanities. As for the civil law, of that I would have thee to know the texts by heart, and then to confer them with philosophy.

"Now in matter of the knowledge of the works of nature, I would have thee to study that exactly; so that there be no sea, river or fountain of which thou dost not know the fishes, all the fowls of the air, all the several kinds of shrubs and trees, whether in forest or orchard, all the sorts of herbs and flowers that grow upon the ground, all the various metals that are hid within the bowels of the earth, together with all the diversity of precious stones that are to be seen in the orient and south parts of the world; let nothing of all these be hidden from thee. Then fail not most carefully to peruse the books of the Greek, Arabian and Latin physicians; not despising the Talmudists and Cabalists; and by frequent anatomies [2] get thee the perfect knowledge of the microcosm, which is man. And at some hours of the day apply thy mind to the study of the Holy Scriptures: first in Greek, the New Testament with the Epistles of the Apostles; and then the Old Testament in Hebrew. In brief, let me see thee an abyss and bottomless pit of knowledge. For from henceforward, as thou growest great and becomest a man, thou must part from this tranquillity and rest of study; thou must learn chivalry, warfare and the exercise of the field, the better thereby to defend my house and our friends, and to succour and protect them at all their needs against the invasion and assaults of evil-doers.

"Furthermore, I will that very shortly thou try how much thou hast profited, which thou canst not better do than by maintaining publicly theses and conclusions in all arts, against all persons whatsoever, and by haunting the company of learned men, both at Paris and otherwhere. But because, as the wise man Solomon saith, wisdom entereth not into a malicious mind, and that science without conscience is but the ruin of the soul; it behoveth thee to serve, to love, to fear God, and on Him to cast all thy thoughts and all thy hope, and by faith formed in charity, to cleave unto Him, so that thou mayest never be separated from Him by thy sins. Suspect the abuses of the world; set not thy heart upon vanity, for this life is transitory, but the word of the Lord endureth forever. Be serviceable to all thy neighbours, and love them as thyself. Reverence thy preceptors; shun the conversation of those whom thou desirest not to resemble, and receive not in vain the graces which God hath bestowed upon thee. And when thou shalt see that thou hast attained to all the knowledge that is to be acquired in that part, return unto me, that I may see thee and give thee my blessing before I die.

"My son, the peace and grace of our Lord be with thee. Amen.

"From Utopia, the 17th day
of the month of March.

Thy father,
GARGANTUA"

These letters being received and read, Pantagruel plucked up his heart, took a fresh courage to him, and was inflamed with a desire to profit in his studies more than ever; so that if you had seen him, how he took pains and how he advanced in learning, you would have said that the vivacity of his spirit amidst the books was like a great fire amongst dry wood, so active it was, vigorous and indefatigable.

NOTES TO CHAPTER VIII

1. The letter of Gargantua to Pantagruel shows the Renaissance enthusiasm for the newly opened reaches of learning. It is such a letter as Budé or Erasmus might have written, and often did write. Gargantua's religious conviction was likewise shared by the humanists in the brief period when "humanist" and "Protestant" were practically synonymous, and when both seemed to be working for a common end.

2. That is, by dissection, an innovation in Rabelais's day.

CHAPTER IX

How Pantagruel found Panurge, whom he loved all his lifetime

One day as Pantagruel was taking a walk without the city towards St. Anthony's abbey, discoursing and philosophating with his own servants and some other scholars, he met with a young man of a very comely stature, and surpassing handsome in all the lineaments of his body, but in several parts thereof most pitifully wounded; in such bad equipage in matter of his apparel, which was but tatters and rags, and every way so far out of order, that he seemed to have been fighting with mastiff-dogs, from whose fury he had made an escape; or to say better, he looked in the condition wherein he then was, like an apple-gatherer of the country of Perche.

As far off as Pantagruel saw him, he said to those that stood by, "Do you see that man there who is coming hither upon the road from Charenton bridge? By my faith, he is only poor in fortune;

for I may assure you that by his physiognomy it appeareth that Nature hath extracted him from some rich and noble race, and that too much curiosity hath thrown him upon adventures which possibly have reduced him to this indigence, want and penury."

Now as he was just among them, Pantagruel said unto him, "Let me entreat you, friend, to stop here a little, and answer me to that which I shall ask you, and I am confident you will not think your time ill bestowed; for I have an extreme desire, according to my ability to give you some supply in this distress wherein I see you are, because I do very much commiserate your case, which truly moves me to great pity. Therefore, my friend, tell me who you are, whence you come, whither you go, what you desire, and what your name is."

The companion answered him in the German tongue thus: *"Junker, Gott gib euch Glück und Heil. Zuvor, lieber Junker, ich las euch wissen das da ihr mich von fragt, ist ein arm und erbärmlich Ding, und wer viel davon zu sagen, welches euch verdrüsslich zu hœren, und mir zu erzelen wer, wiewol die Poeten und Oratoren vorzeiten haben gesagt in ihren Sprüchen und Sentenzen das die Gedechtniss des Ellendz und Armuth vorlängst erlitten ist ein grosse Lust."* [1]

"My friend," said Pantagruel, "I have no skill in that gibberish of yours; therefore, if you would have us to understand you, speak to us in some other language."

Then did the drole answer him thus: *"Al barildim gotfano dech min brin alabo dordin falbroth ringuam albaras. Nin porth zadikin almucathim milko prin al elmin enthoth dal heben ensouim: kuth im al dum alkatim nim broth dechoth porth min michais im endoth, pruch dal maisoulum hol moth dansrilrim lupaldas im voldemoth. Nin hur diavosth mnarbotim dal gousch palfrapin duch im scoth pruch galeth dal Chinon, min foulchrich al conin butathen doth dal prim."* [2]

"Do you understand none of this?" said Pantagruel to the company.

"I believe," said Epistemon, "that this is the language of the Antipodes, and such a hard one that the devil himself knows not what to make of it."

Then said Pantagruel, "Gossip, I know not if the walls do comprehend the meaning of your words; but none of us here doth so much as understand one syllable of them."

Then said my blade again, *"Signor mio, voi vedete per essempio che la cornamusa non suona mai, s'ella non ha il ventre pieno; cosi io parimente non vi saprei contare le mie fortune, se prima il tribulato ventre non ha la solita refectione. Al quale è adviso che le mani e li denti abbiano perso il loro ordine naturale e del tutto annichillati."* [3]

To which Epistemon answered, "As much of the one as of the other, and nothing of either."

Then said Panurge, "My lord, if the generosity of your mind be suitable to your body, you would naturally have pity of me. For nature made us equal; but fortune has exalted some, and other-some has depressed. Nevertheless, though virtue is despised, and worthy men depressed; yet till the end none can be pronounced happy."[4]

"Yet less do I understand of this," said Pantagruel.

Then said Panurge, *"Jona andie, guaussa goussyetan behar da erremedio, beharde, versela ysser landa. Anbates, otoyyes nausu, eyn essassu gourr ay proposian ordine den. Non yssena bayta fascheria egabe, genherassy badia sadassu noura assia. Aran hondovan gualde eydassu nay dassuna. Estou oussyc eguinan soury hin, er darstura eguy harm, Genicoa plasar vadu."*[5]

"Are you there," said Eudemon, "Genicoa?"

To this said Carpalim, "St. Trinian's rammer unstitch your bum, for I had almost understood it."

Then answered Panurge, *"Prug frest frinst sorgdmand strochdt drhds pag brledand Gravot Chavigny Pomardiere rusth pkallhdracg Deviniere pres Nays. Bouille kalmuch monach drupp delmeupplistrincq dlrnd dodelb up drent loch minc stzrinquald de vins ders cordelis hur jocststzampenards."*[6]

"Do you speak Christian," said Epistemon, "or the gypsy language?"

"Nay, it is Lantern language," said another.

Then said Panurge, *"Heere, ik en spreck anders gheen taele dan kersten taele; my dunkt nogtans, al en seg ik u niet een woord, mynen noot verklaert genoegh wat ik begeere; geeft my uyt bermhertigheyt yets waar van ik gevoet mag syn."*[7]

To which answered Pantagruel, "As much of that."

Then said Panurge, *"Sennor, de tanto hablar yo soy cansado. Porque supplico à vuestra reverencia que mire a los precettos evangelicos, para que ellos muevan vuestra excellencia a lo que es de consciencia, y, si ellos non bastaren para mover vuestra reverencia a piedad, supplico que mire a la piedad natural, laqual yo creo que le movera, como es de razon; y con esso non digo mas."*[8]

"Truly, my friend," said Pantagruel, "I doubt not but you can speak divers languages; but tell us that which you would have us to do for you in some tongue which you conceive we may understand."

Then said the companion, *"Myn herre, endog ıeg med ıngen tunge talede, ligesom boern, oc uskellige creature! Mine klaedebon, oc mit legoms magerhed udviser alligevel klarlig hvad ting mig best behof gioris, som er sandelig mad oc dricke: hvorfor forbarme dig ofver mig, oc befal at give mig nuoget, af huilcket jeg kand styre min gioendis mage, ligerviis som mand Cerbero en suppe forsetter. Saa skalt du lefve lœnge oc lyksalig."*[9]

"I think, really," said Eusthenes, "that the Goths spoke thus of old; and that if it pleased God, we should all of us speak so with our tails."

Then again said Panurge, *"Adoni, scholom lecha: im ischar harob hal habdeca bemeherah thithen li kikar lehem, chancath ub: laah al Adonai cho nen ral."*[10]

To which answered Epistemon, "At this time have I understood him very well; for it is the Hebrew tongue most rhetorically pronounced."

Then again said the merry fellow, *"Despota tinyn panagathe, diati si mi ouk artodotis? Horas gar limo analiscomenon eme athlion. Ke en to metaxy me ouk eleis oudamos, zetis de par emou ha ou chre, ke homos philologi pantes homologousi tote logous te ke remata peritta hyparchin, opote pragma afto pasi delon esti. Entha gar anankei monon logi isin, hina pragmata (hon peri amphisbetoumen) me prosphoros epiphenete."* [11]

"What!" said Carpalim, Pantagruel's footman, "it is Greek, I have understood him. And how? Hast thou dwelt any while in Greece?"

Then said the drole again, *"Agonou dont oussys vou denaguez algarou, nou den farou zamist vous mariston ulbrou, fousquez vou brol, tam bredaguez moupreton den goul houst, daguez daguez nou croupys fost bardounnoflist nou grou. Agou paston tol nalprissys hourtou los ecbatonous, prou dhouquys brol panygou den bascrou noudous caguons goulfren goul oust troppassou?"* [12]

"Methinks I understand him," said Pantagruel; "for either it is the language of my country of Utopia, or sounds very like it." And as he was about to have begun some argument, the companion said:

"Jam toties vos per sacra, perque deos deasque omnes obtestatus sum ut, si qua vos pietas permovet, egestatem meam solaremini, nec hilum proficio clamans et ejulans. Sinite, quæso, sinite, viri impii, quo me fata vocant abire, nec ultra vanis vestris interpellationibus obtundatis, memores veteris illius adagii, quo venter famelicus auriculis carere dicitur." [13]

"Well, my friend," said Pantagruel, "but cannot you speak French?"

"That I can do, sir, very well," said the companion, "God be thanked. It is my natural language and mother-tongue; for I was born and bred in my younger years in the garden of France, to wit, Touraine."

Then said Pantagruel, "Tell us what is your name, and from whence you are come; for, by my faith, I have already stamped in my mind such a deep impression of love towards you, that if you will condescend unto my will, you shall not depart out of my company, and you and I shall make up another couple of friends such as Æneas and Achates were."

"Sir," said the companion, "my true and proper Christian name is Panurge; and I am just come out of Turkey, to which country I was carried away prisoner at that time when they went to Mytilene with a mischief. And willingly would I relate unto you my fortunes, which are more wonderful than those of Ulysses were; but seeing that it pleaseth you to retain me with you, I most heartily accept of the offer, protesting never to leave you, should you go to all the devils in hell. We shall have therefore more leisure at another time, and a fitter opportunity wherein to report them; for at this present I am in a very urgent necessity to feed. My teeth are sharp, my belly empty, my throat dry, and my stomach fierce and burning; all is ready, if you will but set me to work. It will be as good as a balsam for sore eyes, to see me gulch and raven it; for God's sake give order for it."

Then Pantagruel commanded that they should carry him home and provide him good store of victuals; which being done, he ate very well that evening, and capon-like, went early to bed; then slept until dinner-time the next day, so that he made but three steps and one leap from the bed to the board.

NOTES TO CHAPTER IX

1. Rabelais probably drew on some German student for this specimen of literary German: "Young sir, before all, may God give you happiness and prosperity. Dear young gentleman, know that what you ask me is sad and piteous, and there might be said on this subject many things painful for you to hear and for me to relate, although the poets and orators of ancient times have stated in their adages and sentences that the remembrance of sorrows and poverty is a great joy."

2. Jargon in which one may distinguish a few proper names.

3. In Italian: "My lord, you see for example that the bagpipe never sounds without a full belly. I, in the same way, couldn't tell you my fortunes, if first my troubled stomach hadn't his usual refreshment. It seems to him that the hands and teeth have lost their normal function and are totally annihilated."

4. In the first French editions, this trifle of English is in the Scotch dialect. English or Scotch would be incomprehensible to these French scholars.

5. This bit of Basque was perhaps cadged from some Basque lackey such as Gargantua employed: "Great lord, in all ills a remedy is necessary; to be *comme il faut* is the difficulty. I have begged you so much! Bring order into our discourse; that will be, without offence, when you bring about my surfeit. After that, ask me what you will. It will not be amiss in you even to pay the bill for two, if it please God." *Genoica* is the Basque word for God.

6. Fantastic jargon in which one makes out the names *Gravot, Chavigny, Pomardière, Devinière near Cinais,* all properties of the Rabelais family.

7. Here Panurge speaks Dutch: "Lord, I do not speak a tongue that is not Christian: it seems to me nevertheless that without my saying a single word to you, my rags reveal to you well enough what I wish. Be charitable enough to give me somewhat to restore me."

8. Spanish, this time: "My lord, I am tired from so much speaking, so I beg your Reverence to consider the Evangelical precepts, in order that you may be moved by them to the demands of conscience: if they are not sufficient to move your Reverence to pity, I beg you to consider natural pity, which, I believe, will touch you as it should; upon this, I say no more."

9. This Danish may have been picked up from a student of that nationality: "Sir, even supposing that, like infants and the brutes, I spoke no language, my garments and the thinness of my body would show clearly what

I need, that is, to eat and to drink: have pity on me then, and cause them to give me the wherewithal to master my baying stomach, even as one throws a sop to Cerberus. Thus you will live long and happily."

10. Hebrew: "Sir, peace be upon you. If you wish to do good to your servitor, give me on the instant a loaf of bread, even as it is written: 'He that hath pity upon the poor lendeth unto the Lord.'"

11. Panurge falls into classical Greek, which the humanist would understand, transcribed according to the modern Eastern pronunciation. "Excellent master, why do you not give me bread? You see me miserable, perishing of hunger, and yet you have no pity on me, and ask me irrelevant things, notwithstanding all friends of letters are in agreement that discourse and words are superfluous when the facts are evident to all. Discourse is necessary only when the facts which we discuss are not self-evident."

12. This language of Utopia is mere jargon.

13. Panurge's Latin was understood at once, and from Latin he passed to French.

CHAPTER XIV

How Panurge related the manner how he escaped out of the hands of the Turks

The great wit and judgment of Pantagruel was immediately after this made known to all the world by setting forth his praises in print, and putting upon record this late wonderful proof he had given thereof amongst the rolls of the crown and registers of the Palace; in such sort that everybody began to say that Solomon, who by a probable guess only, without any further certainty, caused the child to be delivered to his own mother, showed never in his time such a masterpiece of wisdom as the good Pantagruel had done; happy are we therefore that have him in our country!

And indeed they would have made him thereupon master of the requests, and president in the court; but he refused all, very graciously thanking them for their offer; "for," said he, "there is too much slavery in these offices, and very hardly can they be saved that do exercise them, considering the great corruption that is amongst men; which makes me believe, if the empty seats of angels be not filled with other kind of people than those, we shall not have the final judgment these seven thousand sixty and seven jubilees yet to come; and so Cusanus will be deceived in his conjecture. Remember that I have told you of it, and given you fair advertisement in time and place convenient. But if you have any hogsheads of good wine, I willingly will accept of a present of that."

Which they very heartily did do, in sending him of the best that was in the city; and he drank reasonably well. But poor Panurge bibbed and boused of it most villainously; for he was as dry as a red herring, as lean as a rake, and like a poor lank slender cat, walked gingerly as if he had trod upon eggs. So that by some one being admonished, in the midst of his draught of a large deep bowlful of excellent claret, with these words, "Fair and softly, gossip, you suck up as if you were mad"; "I give thee to the devil," said he. "Thou hast not found here thy little tippling sippers of Paris that drink no more than the chaffinch, and never take in their beak full of liquor, till they be bobbed on the tails after the manner of the sparrows. O companion, if I could mount up as well as I can get down, I had been long ere this above the sphere of the moon with Empedocles. But I cannot tell what a devil this means. This wine is so good and delicious that the more I drink thereof, the more I am athirst. I believe the shadow of my master Pantagruel maketh men a-thirsty, as the moon makes the catarrhs and defluxions."

At which word the company began to laugh; which Pantagruel perceiving, said, "Panurge, what is that which moves you to laugh so?"

"Sir," said he, "I was telling them that those devilish Turks are very unhappy, in that they never drink one drop of wine; and that though there were no other harm in all Mahomet's Alcoran, yet for this one base point of abstinence from wine which therein is commanded, I would not submit myself unto their law."

"But now tell me," said Pantagruel, "how you escaped out of their hands."

"By God, sir," said Panurge, "I will not lie to you in one word:

"The rascally Turks had broached me upon a spit, all larded like a rabbit, for I was so dry and meagre that otherwise of my flesh they would have made but very bad meat; and in this manner began to roast me alive. As they were thus roasting me, I recommended myself unto the divine grace, having in mind the good St. Lawrence, and always hoped in God that He would deliver me out of this torment; which came to pass, and that very strangely; for as I did commit myself with all my heart to God, crying, 'Lord God, help me! Lord God, save me! Lord God, take me out of this pain and hellish torture, wherein these traitorous dogs detain me for my sincerity in the maintenance of Thy law!' the turnspit fell asleep by the divine will, or else by the virtue of some good Mercury, who cunningly brought Argus into a sleep, for all his hundred eyes. When I saw that he did no longer turn me in roasting, I looked upon him and perceived that he was fast asleep. Then took I up in my teeth a firebrand by the end where it was not burnt, and cast it into the lap of my roaster; and another did I throw as well as I could under a field-bed that was placed near to the chimney, wherein was the straw bed of my master turnspit.

"Presently the fire took hold in the straw, and from the straw to the bed, and from the bed to the loft which was planked and ceiled with fir, after the fashion of the foot of a lamp. But the best was that the fire which I had cast into the lap of my paltry roaster, burnt all his groin, and was beginning to seize upon his cullions when he became sensible of the danger; for his smelling was not so bad but that he felt it sooner than he could have seen daylight. Then suddenly getting up, and in great amazement running to the window, he cried out to the streets as high as he could, *'Dal baroth! dal baroth! dal baroth!'* which is as much as to say, 'Fire! fire! fire!'

"Incontinently turning about, he came straight towards me to throw me quite into the fire; and to that effect had already cut the ropes wherewith my hands were tied, and was undoing the cords from off my feet, when the master of the house hearing him cry Fire! and smelling the smoke from the very street where he was walking with some other bashaws and mustaphas, ran with all the speed he had, to save what he could, and to carry away his jewels. Yet such was his rage, before he could well resolve how to go about it, that he caught the broach whereon I was spitted and therewith killed my roaster stark dead, of which wound he died there for want of regimen, or otherwise; for he ran him in with the spit a little above the navel, towards the right flank, till he pierced the third lappet of his liver, and the blow slanting upwards from the diaphragm, through which it had made penetration, the spit passed athwart the pericardium and came out above at his shoulders, betwixt the spondyls and the left homoplate.

"True it is, for I will not lie, that in drawing the spit out of my body, I fell to the ground near unto the andirons, and so by the fall took some hurt; which indeed had been greater but that the lardons, or little slices of bacon wherewith I was stuck, kept off the blow.

"My bashaw then seeing the case to be desperate, his house burnt without remission, and all his goods lost, gave himself over unto all the devils in hell, calling upon some of them by their names, Grilgoth, Astarot, Rapallus and Gribouillis, nine several times; which when I saw, I had above five pennyworth of fear, dreading that the devils would come even then to carry away this fool, and seeing me so near him would perhaps snatch me up too. I am already, thought I, half roasted, and my lardons will be the cause of my mischief, for these devils are very lickerish of lardons, according to the authority which you have of the philosopher Jamblicus and Murmault, in the apology of Bossutis, adulterated *pro magistros nostros*. But for my better security I made the sign of the cross, crying, '*Hagios athanatos, ho Theos!*' and none came. At which my rogue bashaw being very much aggrieved, would in transpiercing his heart with my spit have killed himself; and to that purpose had set it against his breast, but it could not enter because it was not sharp enough.

"Whereupon I, perceiving that he was not like to work upon his body the effect which he intended, although he did not spare all the force he had to thrust it forward, came up to him and said, 'Master Bugrino, thou dost here but trifle away thy time, for thou wilt never kill thyself thus as thou doest. Well thou mayest hurt or bruise somewhat within thee, so as to make thee languish all thy lifetime most pitifully amongst the hands of the chirurgeons; but if thou wilt be counselled by me, I will kill thee clear outright, so that thou shalt not so much as feel it; and trust me, for I have killed a great many others, who never have complained afterwards.'

"'Ha, my friend,' said he, 'I prithee do so, and for thy pains I will give thee my codpiece. Take, here it is. There are six hundred seraphs in it, and some fine diamonds and most excellent rubies.'"

"And where are they?" said Epistemon.

"By St. John!" said Panurge, "they are a good way hence, if they always keep going. But where is the last year's snow? This was the greatest care that Villon the Parisian poet took."

"Make an end," said Pantagruel, "that we may know how thou didst dress thy bashaw."

"By the faith of an honest man," said Panurge, "I do not lie in one word. I swaddled him in a scurvy swathel-binding which I found lying there half-burnt, and with my cords tied him roisterer-like both hand and foot, in such sort that he was not able to wince; then passed my spit through his throat and hanged him thereon, fastening the end thereof at two great hooks or cramp-irons upon which they did hang their halberds; and then kindling a fire under him, did flame you up my milord, as they use to dry herrings in a chimney. With this, taking his budget and a little javelin that was upon the foresaid hooks, I ran away a fair gallop-rake, and God He knows how I did smell my shoulder of mutton.

"When I was come down into the street, I found everybody come to put out the fire with store of water, and seeing me so half-roasted, they did naturally pity my case and threw all their water upon me, which by a most joyful refreshing of me, did me very much good. Then did they present me with some victuals; but I could not eat much, because they gave me nothing to drink but water, after their fashion. Other hurt they did me none, only one little villainous Turkey knob-breasted rogue came to snatch away some of my lardons; but I gave him such a sturdy thump and sound rap on the fingers with all the weight of my javelin, that he came no more the second time. Shortly after this, there came towards me a pretty young Corinthian wench, who brought me a box full of conserves, of round Myrobalan plums called emblics, and looked upon my poor Roger with an eye of great compassion, as it was flea-bitten and pinked with the sparkles of the fire from whence it came; for it reached no further in length, believe me, than my knees. But note, that this roasting cured me entirely of a sciatica where unto I had been subject above seven years before, upon that side which my roaster by falling asleep suffered to be burnt.

"Now whilst they were thus busy about me, the fire triumphed, never ask how; for it took hold on above two thousand houses; which one of them espying, cried out, saying, 'By Mahoum's belly, all the city is on fire, and we do nevertheless stand gazing here without offering to bring any relief.' Upon this, every one ran to save his own.

"For my part, I took my way towards the gate. When I was got upon the knap of a little hillock not far off, I turned me about as did Lot's wife, and looking back, saw all the city burning in a fair fire; whereat I was so glad that I had almost beshit myself for joy, but God punished me well for it."

"How?" said Pantagruel.

"Thus," said Panurge; "for when with pleasure I beheld this jolly fire, jesting with myself and saying, 'Ha! poor fleas, ha! poor mice, you will have a bad winter of it this year; the fire is in your ricks, it is in your bed-straw!' out came more than six, yea, more than thirteen hundred and eleven dogs, great and small, all together out of the town, flying away from the fire. At the first approach they ran all upon me, being carried on by the scent of my lecherous half-roasted flesh, and had even then devoured me in a trice, if my good angel had not then inspired me with the instruction of a remedy, very sovereign against the pain of the teeth."

"And wherefore," said Pantagruel, "wert thou afraid of the pain of the teeth? Wert thou not cured of thy rheums?"

"By Palm Sunday," said Panurge, "is there any greater pain of the teeth than when the dogs have you by the legs? But on a sudden, as my good angel directed me, I thought upon my lardons, and threw them into the midst of the field amongst them. Then did the dogs run and fight with one another at fair teeth, which should have the lardons. By this means they left me, and I left them also bustling with, and haring one another. Thus did I escape, frolic and lively, gramercy roast meat and cookery."

CHAPTER XVI

Of the qualities and conditions of Panurge

Panurge was of a middle stature, not too high nor too low, and had somewhat an aquiline nose, made like the handle of a razor. He was at that time five-and-thirty years old, or thereabouts, fine to gild like a leaden dagger; for he was a very gallant man of his person, only that he was a little lewd, and naturally subject to a kind of disease which at that time they called lack of money, a malady of nonpareil. Yet notwithstanding, he had threescore and three tricks to help himself at his need, of which the most honourable and most ordinary was by the way of filching; for he was a quarrelsome fellow, a sharper, drinker, roisterer, scowerer, and a very dissolute and debauched fellow, if there were any in Paris; otherwise, and in all matters else, the best man in the world. And he was still contriving some plot, and devising mischief against the sergeants and the watch.

At one time he assembled three or four especial good hacksters and roaring boys, made them in the evening drink like Templars, afterwards led them till they came above Ste.-Geneviève, or about the college of Navarre; [1] and at the hour that the watch was coming up that way, which he knew by putting his sword upon the pavement, and his ear by it (and when he heard his sword shake, it was an infallible sign that the watch was near), at that instant he and his companions took a tumbrel or dung-cart and gave it the brangle,[2] hurling it with all their force down the hill, and so overthrew all the poor watchmen like pigs, and then ran away upon the other side;

for, in less than two days, he knew all the streets, lanes and turnings in Paris as well as his *Deus det.*

At another time he laid in some fair place where the said watch was to pass, a train of gunpowder, and at the very instant that they went along, set fire to it, and then made himself sport to see what good grace they had in running away, thinking that St. Anthony's fire had caught them by the legs.

As for the poor masters of arts and theologues, he did persecute them above all others. When he met with any of them upon the street, he would never fail to put some trick or other upon them; sometimes putting a fried turd in their graduate hoods; at other times pinning on little fox-tails or hares-ears behind them, or some such other roguish prank.

One day that they were appointed all to meet in the Fodder Street,[3] he made a barbonnesa tart, made of store of garlic, galbanum, assafœtida, castoreum, dogs' turds very warm; which he steeped, tempered and liquefied in the corrupt matter of pocky biles and pestiferous botches; and very early in the morning therewith anointed all the pavement in such sort that the devil could not have endured it. Which made all these good people there to give up their gorges, and vomit what was upon their stomachs before all the world, as if they had flayed the fox. And ten or twelve of them died of the plague, fourteen became lepers, eighteen grew lousy, and above seven-and-twenty had the pox; but he did not care a button for it.

He commonly carried a whip under his gown, wherewith he whipped without remission the pages whom he found carrying wine to their masters, to make them mend their pace. In his coat he had above six-and-twenty little fobs and pockets always full, one with some lead-water, and a little knife as sharp as a glover's needle, wherewith he used to cut purses; another with some kind of bitter stuff, which he threw into the eyes of those he met; another with clotburs, penned with little geese or capon's feathers, which he cast upon the gowns and caps of honest people, and often made them fair horns which they wore about all the city, sometimes all their life. Very often also upon the women's hoods would he stick, in the hind-part, somewhat made in the shape of a man's member. In another he had a great many little horns full of fleas and lice which he borrowed from the beggars of St.-Innocent, and cast them with small canes or quills to write with, into the necks of the daintiest gentlewomen that he could find, yea even in the church; for he never seated himself above in the choir, but always sat in the body of the church amongst the women, both at mass, at vespers and at sermon. In another he used to have good store of hooks and buckles, wherewithal he would couple men and women together, that sat in company close to one another, but especially those that wore gowns of crimson taffetas; that when they were about to go away, they might rend all their gowns. In another he had a squib furnished with tinder, matches, stones to strike fire, and all other tackling necessary for it. In another, two or three burning-glasses, wherewith he made both men and women sometimes mad, and in the church put them quite out of countenance; for he said that there was but an antistrophe between a woman *folle à la messe,* and *molle à la fesse.*

In another he had a good deal of needles and thread, wherewith he did a thousand little devilish pranks. One time, at the entry of the Palace unto the great hall,[4] where a Cordelier was to say mass to the counsellors, he did help to apparel him and put on his vestments; but in the accoutring of him, he sewed on his alb, surplice, or stole, to his gown and shirt, and then withdrew himself when the said lords of the court, or counsellors, came to hear the said mass. But when it came to the *Ite, missa est,* that the poor frater would have laid by his stole or surplice, he plucked off withal both his frock and shirt, which were well sewed together, and thereby stripping himself up to the very shoulders, showed his what-d'ye-call-'em to all the world; which was no small one, as you may imagine. And the friar still kept haling, but so much the more did he discover himself and lay open his backparts; till one of the lords of the court said, "How now, what is the matter? Will this good father make us here an offering of his tail to kiss it? Nay, St. Anthony's fire kiss it for us!" From thenceforth was made an ordinance that the poor fathers should never disrobe themselves any more before the world, but in their vestry-room, especially in the presence of women, lest it should tempt them to the sin of longing, and disordinate desire.

The people then asked why it was the friars had so long and large genitories. The said Panurge resolved the problem very neatly, saying, "That which makes asses to have such great ears is that their dams did put no biggins on their heads, as d'Alliaco mentioneth in his *Suppositions.* By the like reason, that which makes the generation-tools of those fair fraters so long is for that they wear no bottomed breeches, and therefore their jolly member, having no impediment, hangeth dangling at liberty as far as it can reach, with a wiggle-waggle down to their knees, as women carry their paternoster beads. And the cause wherefore they have it so correspondently great is that in this constant wig-wagging the humours of the body descend into the said member; for according to the legists, agitation and continual motion is cause of attraction."

Item, he had another pocket full of itching powder, called stone-alum, whereof he would cast some into the backs of those women whom he judged to be most beautiful and stately; which did so ticklishly gall them that some would strip themselves in the open view of the world, and others dance like a cock upon hot embers, or a drum-stick on a tabor. Others again ran about the streets, and he would run after them. To such as were in the stripping-vein, he would very civilly come to offer his attendance and cover them with his cloak, like a courteous and very gracious man.

Item, in another he had a little leather bottle full of old oil, wherewith when he saw any man or woman in a rich new handsome suit, he would grease, smutch and spoil all the best parts of it, under colour and pretence of touching them, saying, "This is good cloth, this is good satin, good taffetas, madam; God give you all that your noble heart desireth. You have a new suit, pretty sir; and you a new gown, sweet mistress; God give you joy of it, and maintain you in all prosperity." And with this would lay his hand upon their shoulders; at which touch such a villainous spot was left behind, so enormously engraven to perpetuity in the very soul, body and reputation, that the devil himself could never have taken it away. Then upon his departing, he would say, "Madam, take heed you do not fall, for there is a filthy great hole before you."

Another he had all full of euphorbium, very finely pulverized. In that powder did he lay a fair handkerchief curiously wrought which he had stolen from a pretty seamstress of the Palace, in taking away a louse from off her bosom, which he had put there himself. And when he came into the company of some good ladies, he would trifle them into a discourse of some fine workmanship of bone-lace; then immediately put his hand into their bosom, asking them, "And this work, is it of Flanders, or of Hainault?" And then drew out his handkerchief, and said, "Hold, hold, look what work here is! It is of Frontignan, or of Fontarabia"; and shaking it hard at their nose, made them sneeze for four hours without ceasing. In the meanwhile he would fart like a horse, and the women would laugh, and say, "How now, do you fart, Panurge?"

"No, no, madam," said he, "I do but tune my tail to the plain-song of the music which you make with your nose."

In another he had a picklock, a pelican, a cramp-iron, a crook, and some other iron tools, wherewith there was no door nor coffer which he would not pick open. He had another full of little cups, wherewith he played very artificially; for he had his fingers made to his hand, like those of Minerva or Arachne, and had heretofore cried treacle. And when he changed a teston, cardecu, or any other piece of money, the changer had been more subtle than a fox, if Panurge had not at every time made five or six sols vanish away visibly, openly and manifestly, without making any hurt or lesion, whereof the changer should have felt nothing but the wind.

NOTES TO CHAPTER XVI

1. The rue de la Montagne Ste.-Geneviève is a steeply inclined street between the rue St.-Étienne-du-Mont and the Place Maubert on the Left Bank. The College of Navarre, founded by the queen Jeanne of Navarre in 1309, stood where is now the École Polytechnique.

2. Tumble, end over end.

3. Meeting-place of the Faculty of Arts. The early French editions before 1542 had instead: "One day that the theologians were appointed all to meet in the Sorbonne to examine the articles of faith"; and instead of anointing the pavement, it was originally, "the lattices and grates of the Sorbonne," a trellised gallery along the Hall of Records (*Salle des Actes*).

4. The Grand' Salle of the Palais, with its beautiful timbered vaulting

and famous marble table, was used for great judicial ceremonies. Every day a mass opened the proceedings of Parlement, and it was this mass at which the Cordelier was officiating.

CHAPTER XVII

How Panurge gained the pardons . . .

One day I [1] found Panurge very much out of countenance, melancholic and silent, which made me suspect that he had no money; whereupon I said unto him, "Panurge, you are sick, as I do very well perceive by your physiognomy; and I know the disease, you have a flux in your purse. But take no care, I have yet sevenpence halfpenny that never saw father nor mother, which shall not be wanting no more than the pox in your necessity."

Whereunto he answered me, "Well, well, for money, one day I shall have but too much; for I have a philosopher's stone which attracts money out of men's purses as the loadstone doth iron. But will you go with me to gain the pardons?" [2] said he.

"By my faith," said I, "I am no great pardon-taker in this world; if I shall be any such in the other, I cannot tell. Yet let us go in God's name, it is but one farthing more or less."

"But," said he, "lend me then a farthing upon interest."

"No, no," said I, "I will give it you freely, and from my heart."

"Grates vobis dominos," said he.

So we went along, beginning at St.-Gervais, and I got the pardons at the first box only; for in those matters very little contenteth me. Then did I say my small suffrages, and the prayers of St. Brigid. But he gained them at all the boxes, and always gave money to every one of the pardoners.[3] From thence we went to Our Lady's church, to St. John's, to St. Anthony's, and so to the other churches where there was a bank of pardons. For my part, I gained no more of them. But he at all the boxes kissed the relics, and gave at every one. To be brief, when we were returned, he brought me to drink at the Castle Tavern, and there showed me ten or twelve of his little bags full of money; at which I blessed myself, and made the sign of the cross, saying, "Where have you recovered so much money in so little time?"

Unto which he answered me, that he had taken it out of the basins of the pardons. "For in giving them the first farthing," said he, "I put it in with such sleight of hand, and so dextrously, that it appeared to be a threepence; thus with one hand I took threepence, ninepence, or sixpence at the least, and with the other as much, and so through all the churches where we have been."

"Yea, but," said I, "you damn yourself like a snake, and are withal a thief and sacrilegious person."

"True," said he, "in your opinion; but I am not of that mind. For the pardoners do give me it, when they say unto me in presenting the relics to kiss, *centuplum accipies;* that is, that for one penny I should take a hundred. For *accipies* is spoken according to the manner of the Hebrews, who use the future tense instead of the imperative, as you have in the law, *Diliges Dominum,* that is, *dilige.* Even so when the pardon-bearer says to me, *centuplum accipies,* his meaning is, *centuplum accipe;* and so doth Rabbi Kimi and Rabbi Aben Ezra expound it, and all the massoretes, *et ibi Bartolus.* Moreover, Pope Sixtus gave me fifteen hundred francs of yearly pension upon his ecclesiastical revenues and treasure, for having cured him of a cankerous botch, which did so torment him that he thought to have been a cripple by it all his life. Thus do I pay myself at my own hand (for otherwise I get nothing) upon the said ecclesiastical treasure. Ho, my friend!" said he, "if thou didst know how well I feathered my nest by the pope's bull of the crusade, thou wouldest wonder exceedingly. It was worth to me above six thousand florins."

* * * * *

NOTES TO CHAPTER XVII

1. Rabelais's abrupt introduction of narrative in the first person is characteristically informal.
2. I.e., the indulgences that were to be had by visiting certain sanctuaries and leaving alms there.
3. The pardoners were the officials who stood with a plate to receive the "alms" offered in exchange for indulgences. Rabelais goes on to call their station the "bank [or cashier's desk] of pardons."

CHAPTER XXIII

How Pantagruel departed from Paris, hearing the news that the Dipsodes had invaded the land of the Amaurots . . .

A little while after, Pantagruel heard news that his father Gargantua had been translated into the land of the fairies by Morgan,[1] as heretofore were Ogier and Arthur; and that, the report of his translation being spread abroad, the Dipsodes[2] had issued out beyond their borders, with inroads had wasted a great part of Utopia, and at that very time had besieged the great city of the Amaurots. Whereupon departing from Paris without bidding any man farewell, for the business required diligence, he came to Rouen.

* * * * *

Parting from Rouen, they arrived at Honfleur, and there took shipping, Pantagruel, Panurge, Epistemon, Eusthenes and Carpalim. . .

NOTES TO CHAPTER XXIII

1. Morgan the Fay appears frequently in the Arthurian cycle of romance, always beneficent towards the heroes Arthur, Ogier, etc. It is characteristic of Rabelais's disregard of consistency that he later forgets all about this translation of Gargantua to the land of the fairies, and brings him into the narrative again without explanation or comment.
2. "Thirsty ones."

CHAPTER XXIV

* * * * *

And indeed within an hour after that, the wind arose at the north-north-west, wherewith they hoisted sail and put out, even into the main sea; so that within few days, passing by Porto Santo and by the Madeiras, they went ashore in the Canary islands. Parting from thence, they passed by Capo Bianco, by Senegal, by Capo Verde, by Gambia, by Sagres, by Melli, by the Cap di Buona Speranza, and set ashore again in the kingdom of Melinda.[1] Parting from thence, they sailed away with a tramontane or northerly wind, passing by Meden, by Uti, by Uden, by Gelasim, by the isles of the Fairies, and along the kingdom of Achory, till at last they arrived at the port of Utopia, distant from the city of the Amaurots three leagues and somewhat more.

When they were ashore and pretty well refreshed, Pantagruel said, "Gentlemen, the city is not far from hence. Therefore were it not amiss, before we set forward, to advise well what is to be done, that we be not like the Athenians, who never took counsel until after the fact. Are you resolved to live and die with me?"

"Yes, sir," said they all, "and be as confident of us, as of your own fingers."

"Well," said he, "there is but one thing that keeps my mind in great doubt and suspense, which is this: that I know not in what order, nor of what number the enemy is, that layeth siege to the city; for if I were certain of that, I should go forward and set on with the better assurance. Let us therefore consult together, and bethink ourselves by what means we may come to this intelligence."

Whereunto they all said, "Let us go thither and see, and stay you here for us; for this very day, without further respite, do we make account to bring you a certain report thereof."

"Myself," said Panurge, "will undertake to enter into their camp within the very midst of their guards, unespied by their watch, and merrily feast and lecher it at their cost without being known of any, to see the artillery and the tents of all the captains, and thrust myself in with a grave and magnific carriage amongst all their troops and companies, without being discovered. The devil would not be able to pick me out with all his circumventions; for I am of the race of Zopyrus."

"And I," said Epistemon, "know all the plots and stratagems of the valiant captains and warlike champions of former ages, together with all the tricks and subtleties of the art of war. I will go; and though I be detected and revealed, I will escape, by making them believe of you whatever I please; for I am of the race of Sinon."

"I," said Eusthenes, "will enter and set upon them in their trenches, in spite of their sentries, and all their guards. For I will tread upon their bellies, and break their legs and arms, yea, though they were every whit as strong as the devil himself; for I am of the race of Hercules."

"And I," said Carpalim, "will get in there, if the birds can enter. For I am so nimble of body, and light withal, that I shall have leaped over their trenches and run clean through all their camp, before that they perceive me. Neither do I fear shot, nor arrow, nor horse, how swift soever, were he the Pegasus of Perseus, or Pacolet; being assured that I shall be able to make a safe and sound escape before them all without any hurt. I will undertake to walk upon the ears of corn, or grass in the meadows, without making either of them do so much as bow under me; for I am of the race of Camilla the Amazon.[2]

NOTES TO CHAPTER XXIV

1. Up to this point Pantagruel follows the regular route of the Spanish traders to India, as given in the work of Simon Grynaeus, *Novis Orbis,* 1532. Porto Sancto is in the archipelago of Madeira; Capo Bianco, a promontory on the west coast of Africa; Gambia, the Gambia River; Sagres, a cape on the coast of Liberia; Melli, a country in the same region; Cap di Buona Speranza, the Cape of Good Hope; and Melinda, a city of Zanzibar, where Vasco da Gama made his first stop after rounding the cape in 1498. Then in order to reach the mythical Utopia, the heroes set off by a route through imaginary countries — Meden, Uti, Uden (from Greek words signifying "nothing"), Gelasim (meaning "laughable"), and Achory ("without country"), a name borrowed from Sir Thomas More's *Utopia.*

2. The names of Pantagruel's companions, like those of the heroes of Pulci's *Morgante* and Folengo's *Macaronics,* represent each a special attribute: Panurge, craftiness; Epistemon, learning; Eusthenes, muscular vigour; Carpalim, swiftness.

[Pantagruel and his companions enter the city of the Amaurots where the Dipsodes are encamped and proceed to despoil the camp.]

CHAPTER XXIX

How Pantagruel discomfited the three hundred giants armed with freestone, and Loupgarou their captain

The giants, seeing all their camp drowned, carried away their king Anarchus upon their backs, as well as they could, out of the fort, as Æneas did his father Anchises, in the time of the conflagration of Troy.

When Panurge perceived them, he said to Pantagruel, "Sir, yonder are the giants coming forth against you. Lay on them with your mast gallantly, like an old fencer; for now is the time that you must show yourself a brave and an honest man. And for our part, we will not fail you. I myself will kill ye a good many gallantly enough; for why, David killed Goliath very easily. And then this great lecher Eusthenes, who is stronger than four oxen, will not spare himself. Be of good courage, therefore, and valiant; charge amongst them with point and edge, and by all manner of means."

"Well," said Pantagruel, "of courage I have more than for fifty Franks; but let us be wise, for Hercules never undertook against two."

"That is well cacked, well scummered," said Panurge. "Do you compare yourself with Hercules? You have by God, more strength in your teeth, and more scent in your bum, than ever Hercules had in all his body and soul. So much is a man worth as he esteems himself."

Whilst they spake those words, behold, Loupgarou was come with all his giants, who seeing Pantagruel in a manner alone, was carried away with temerity and presumption, for hopes that he had to kill the good man. Whereupon he said to his companions the giants, "You wenchers of the low-country, by Mahoum, if any of you undertake to fight against these men here, I will put you cruelly to death. It is my will that you let me fight single; in the meantime you shall have good sport to look upon us."

Then all the other giants retired with their king to the place where the flagons stood, and Panurge and his comrades with them, who counterfeited those that have had the pox; for he writhed about his mouth, shrunk up his fingers, and with a harsh and hoarse voice said unto them, "I forsake God, fellow soldiers, if I would have it to be believed that we make any war at all. Give us somewhat to eat with you, whilst our masters fight against one another." To this the king and giants jointly condescended, and accordingly made them to banquet with them.

In the meantime Panurge told them the fables of Turpin, the examples of St. Nicholas, and the Tale of a Tub. Loupgarou then set forward toward Pantagruel with a mace all of steel, and that of the best sort, weighing nine thousand seven hundred quintals and two quarterons, at the end whereof were thirteen pointed diamonds, the least whereof was as big as the greatest bell of Our Lady's church at Paris (there might want perhaps the thickness of a nail, or at most, that I may not lie, of the back of those knives which they call cutlugs; but for a little off or on, more or less, it is no matter); and it was enchanted in such sort that it could never break, but contrarily all that it did touch did break immediately. Thus then as he approached with great fierceness and pride of heart, Pantagruel, casting up his eyes to heaven, recommended himself to God with all his soul, making such a vow as followeth:

"O thou Lord God, who has always been my protector and my saviour, Thou seest the distress wherein I am at this time. Nothing brings me hither but a natural zeal, which Thou hast permitted unto mortals, to keep and defend themselves, their wives and children, country and family, in case Thy own proper cause were not in question, which is the Faith. For in such a business Thou wilt have no coadjutors, only a catholic confession and service of Thy word, and hast forbidden us all arming and defence; for Thou art the Almighty, who in Thine own cause, and where Thine own business is taken to heart, canst defend it far beyond all that we can conceive, Thou who hast thousand thousands of hundreds of millions of legions of angels, the least of which is able to kill all mortal men and turn about the heavens and earth at his pleasure, as heretofore it very plainly appeared in the army of Sennacherib. If it may please Thee therefore at this time to assist me, as my whole trust and confidence is in Thee alone, I vow unto Thee, that in all countries whatsoever wherein I shall have any power or authority, whether in this of Utopia, or elsewhere, I will cause Thy holy gospel to be purely, simply and entirely preached; so that the abuses of a rabble of hypocrites and false prophets, who by human constitutions and depraved inventions have empoisoned all the world, shall be quite exterminated from about me."

This vow was no sooner made, but there was heard a voice from heaven, saying, *"Hoc fac, et vinces";* that is to say, "Do this, and thou shalt overcome."

Then Pantagruel, seeing that Loupgarou with his mouth wide open was drawing near to him, went against him boldly, and cried out as loud as he was able, "Thou diest, villain, thou diest!" purposing by his horrible cry to make him afraid, according to the discipline of the Lacedæmonians. Withal, he immediately cast at him, out of his barque which he wore at his girdle, eighteen cags and four bushels of salt, wherewith he filled both his mouth, throat, nose and eyes. At this Loupgarou was so highly incensed that, most fiercely setting upon him, he thought even then with a blow of his mace to have beat out his brains. But Pantagruel was very nimble, and had always a quick foot and a quick eye, and therefore with his left foot did he step back one pace; yet not so nimbly, but that the blow, falling upon the barque, broke it in four thousand fourscore and six pieces, and threw all the rest of the salt about the ground. Pantagruel, seeing that, most gallantly displayed the vigour of his arms, and according to the art of the axe, gave him with the great end of his mast a home thrust a little above the breast; then bringing along the blow to the left side with a slash, struck him between the neck and shoulders. After that, advancing his right foot, he gave him a push upon the *couillons* with the upper end of his said mast; wherewith breaking the scuttle on the top thereof, he spilt three or four puncheons of wine that were left therein. Upon that, Loupgarou thought that he had pierced his bladder, and that the wine that came forth had been urine. Pantagruel, being not content with this, would have doubled it by a side-blow, but Loupgarou lifting up his mace, advanced one step upon him, and with all his force would have dashed it upon Pantagruel; wherein (to speak the truth) he so sprightfully carried himself, that if God had not succored the good Pantagruel, he had been cloven from the top of his head to the bottom of his milt; but the blow glanced to the right side by the brisk nimbleness of Pantagruel, and his mace sank into the ground above threescore and thirteen feet through a huge rock, out of which the fire did issue greater than nine thousand and six tuns.

Pantagruel seeing him busy about plucking out his mace, which stuck in the ground between the rocks, ran upon him and would have clean cut off his head, if by mischance his mast had not touched a little against the stock of Loupgarou's mace, which was enchanted, as we have said before. By this means his mast broke off about three handfuls above his hands; whereat he stood amazed like a bell-founder, and cried out, "Ah, Panurge, where art thou?"

Panurge, seeing that, said to the king and the giants, "By God, they will hurt one another if they be not parted." But the giants were as merry as if they had been at a wedding.

Then Carpalim would have risen from thence to help his master, but one of the giants said to him, "By Golfarin, the nephew of Mahoum, if thou stir hence I will put thee in the bottom of my breeches instead of a suppository, which cannot choose but do me good; for in my belly I am very costive, and cannot well cagar without gnashing my teeth and making many filthy faces."

Then Pantagruel, thus destitute of a staff, took up the end of his mast, striking athwart and alongst upon the giant; but he did him no more hurt than you would do with a fillip upon a smith's anvil. In the meantime Loupgarou was drawing his mace out of the ground and, having already plucked it out, was ready therewith to have struck Pantagruel, who, being very quick in turning, avoided all his blows in taking only the defensive part in hand; until on a sudden he saw that Loupgarou did threaten him with these words, saying, "Now, villain! will not I fail to chop thee as small as minced meat, and keep thee henceforth from ever making any more poor men athirst."

Then without any more ado, Pantagruel struck him such a blow with his foot against the belly that he made him fall backwards, his heels over his head, and dragged him thus along at flay-buttock above a flight-shot. Then Loupgarou cried out, bleeding at the throat, "Mahoum! Mahoum! Mahoum!" at which noise all the giants arose to succour him; but Panurge said unto them, "Gentlemen, do not go, if you will believe me; for our master is mad, and strikes athwart and alongst, he cares not where. He will do you a mischief." But the giants made no account of it, seeing that Pantagruel had never a staff.

And when Pantagruel saw those giants approach very near unto him, he took Loupgarou by the two feet and lifted up his body like a pike in the air, wherewith, it being harnessed with anvils, he laid such heavy load amongst those giants armed with freestone, that striking them down as a mason doth little knobs of stones, there was not one of them that stood before him whom he threw not flat to the ground; and by the breaking of this stony armour, there was made such a horrible rumble as put me in mind of the fall of the butter-tower of St. Stephen's at Bourges, when it melted before the sun.

Panurge, with Carpalim and Eusthenes, did cut in the meantime the throats of those that were struck down, in such sort that there escaped not one. Pantagruel to any man's sight was like a mower, who with his scythe, which was Loupgarou, cut down the meadow-grass, to wit, the giants. But with this fencing of Pantagruel's, Loupgarou lost his head, which happened when Pantagruel struck down one whose name was Riflandouille, who was armed cap-à-pie with grison stones, one chip whereof splintering abroad cut off Epistemon's neck clean and fair; for otherwise the most part of them were but lightly armed with a kind of sandy brittle stone, and the rest with slates.

At last, when he saw that they were all dead, he threw the body of Loupgarou as hard as he could against the city, where, falling like a frog upon his belly in the great piazza, he with the fall killed a singed he-cat, a wet she-cat, a farting duck, and a bridled goose.

CHAPTER XXXII

How Pantagruel with his tongue covered a whole army, and what the author saw in his mouth

Thus as Pantagruel with all his army had entered into the country of the Dipsodes, every one was glad of it, and incontinently rendered themselves unto him, bringing him out of their own good wills the keys of all the cities where he went, the Almirods only excepted; who, being resolved to hold out against him, made answer to his heralds that they would not yield but upon very honourable and good conditions.

"What!" said Pantagruel, "do they ask any better terms than the hand at the pot, and the glass in their fist? Come, let us go sack them, and put them all to the sword."

Then did they put themselves in good order, as being fully determined to give an assault. But by the way, passing through a large field, they were overtaken by a great shower of rain, whereat they began to shiver and tremble, to crowd, press and thrust close to one another. When Pantagruel saw that, he made their captains tell them that it was nothing, and that he saw well above the clouds that it would be nothing but a little dew; but howsoever, that they should put themselves in order, and he would cover them. Then did they put themselves in a close order, and stood as near to each other as they could; and Pantagruel drew out his tongue only half way, and covered them all as a hen doth her chickens.

In the meantime I, who relate to you these so veritable stories, hid myself under a burdock leaf which was not much less in largeness than the arch of the bridge of Montrible; but when I saw them thus covered, I went towards them to shelter myself likewise, which I could not do, for that (as the saying is) at the yard's end there is no cloth left. Then as well as I could, I got upon it and went forwards full two leagues upon his tongue; and so long marched, that at last I came into his mouth. But, O gods and goddesses! what did I see there? Jupiter confound me with his trisulk lightning if I lie! I walked there as they do in Sophia at Constantinople, and saw there great rocks like the mountains in Denmark; I believe that those were his teeth. I saw also fair meadows, large forests, great and strong cities, not a jot less than Lyons or Poitiers.

The first man I met with there was a good honest fellow planting coleworts; [1] whereat being very much amazed, I asked him, "My friend, what art thou doing here?"

"I am planting coleworts," said he.

"But how, and wherewith?" said I.

"Ha, sir," said he, "every one cannot have his baws as heavy as a mortar; neither can we be all rich. Thus do I get my poor living, and carry them to the market to sell in the city, which is here behind."

"Jesus!" said I, "is there here a new world?"

"Sure," said he, "it is never a jot new; but it is commonly reported that without this there is an earth, whereof the inhabitants enjoy the light of a sun and a moon, and that it is full of, and replenished with, very good commodities; but yet, this is more ancient than that."

"Yea, but," said I, "my friend, what is the name of that city whither thou carriest thy coleworts to sell?"

"It is called Aspharage," said he, "and all the indwellers are Christians, very honest men, and will make you good cheer."

To be brief, I resolved to go thither. Now, in my way, I met with a fellow that was lying in wait to catch pigeons, of whom I asked, "My friend, from whence come these pigeons?"

"Sir," said he, "they come from the other world." Then I thought that when Pantagruel yawned the pigeons went into his mouth in whole flocks, thinking that it had been a pigeon-house.

Then I went into the city, which I found fair, very strong, and seated in a good air; but at my entry, the guard demanded of me my pass or ticket, wherat I was much astonished, and asked them, "My masters, is there any danger of the plague here?"

"O Lord!" said they, "they die hard by here so fast, that the cart runs about the streets."

"Good God!" said I, "and where?"

Whereunto they answered that it was in Larynx and Pharynx, which are two great cities, such as Rouen and Nantes, rich, and of great trading, and the cause of the plague was by a stinking and infectious exhalation which lately vapoured out of the abysms, whereof there have died above two-and-twenty hundred and three-score thousand and sixteen persons within this seven-night. Then I considered, calculated and found that it was a rank and unsavoury breathing which came out of Pantagruel's stomach when he did eat so much garlic, as we have aforesaid.

Parting from thence, I passed amongst the rocks, which were his teeth, and never left walking till I got upon one of them; and there I found the pleasantest places in the world, great large tennis-courts, fair galleries, sweet meadows, store of vines, and an infinite number of banqueting summer-outhouses in the fields, after the Italian fashion, full of pleasure and delight; where I stayed full four months, and never made better cheer in my life than at that time. After that, I went down by the hinder teeth to come to the chaps; but in the way I was robbed by thieves in a great forest, that is in the territory towards the ears.

Then after a little further travelling, I fell upon a pretty village (truly I have forgot the name of it) where I was yet merrier than ever, and got some certain money to live by. Can you tell how? By sleeping; [2] for there they hire men by the day to sleep, and they get by it sixpence a day; but they that can snore hard, get at least ninepence. How I had been robbed in the valley I informed the senators, who told me that in very truth the people of that side were bad livers, and naturally thievish; whereby I perceived well, that as we have with us the countries Cisalpine and Transalpine, so have they there the countries Cidentine and Tradentine, that is, behither and beyond the teeth; but it is far better living on this side, and the air is purer.

There I began to think that it is very true which is commonly said, that the one half of the world knoweth not how the other half liveth. Seeing none before myself had ever written of that country, wherein are above five-and-twenty kingdoms inhabited, besides deserts and a great arm of the sea, I have composed a great book entitled, *The History of the Gorgians,* because they dwell in the gorge of my master Pantagruel.

At last I was willing to return, and passing by his beard, I cast myself upon his shoulders, and from thence slid down to the ground and fell before him. As soon as I was perceived by him, he asked me, "Whence comest thou, Alcofribas?"

I answered him, "Out of your mouth, my lord."

"And how long hast thou been there?" said he.

"Since the time," said I, "that you went against the Almirods."

"That is about six months ago," said he. "And wherewith didst thou live? What didst thou drink?"

I answered, "My lord, of the same that you did, and of the daintiest morsels that passed through your throat I took toll."

"Yea, but," said he, "where didst thou shite?"

"In your throat, my lord," said I.

"Ha, ha! thou art a merry fellow," said he. "We have, with the help of God, conquered all the land of the Dipsodes; I will give thee the chatelainy of Salmigondin."

"Gramercy, my lord," said I, "you gratify me beyond all that I have deserved of you."

NOTES TO CHAPTER XXXII

1. I.e., cabbages. Another debt to Lucian. In his *True History,* I, 30–40, Lucian shows the hero of his imaginary voyage discovering a new country in the jaws of an enormous cetacean, and an old man and a young one at work there in a garden. But Rabelais developed the idea freely, and in quite another vein of realism and robust humour.

2. This is a reminiscence of the legendary land of Cockaigne, where "the more one sleeps, the more one gains."

CHAPTER XXXIV

The conclusion of this present book, and the excuse of the author

Now, my masters, you have heard a beginning of the horrific history of my lord and master Pantagruel. Here will I make an end of the first book.[1] My head aches a little, and I perceive that the registers of my brain are somewhat jumbled and disordered with the Septembral juice.

You shall have the rest of the history at Frankfort mart[2] next coming, and there shall you see how Panurge was married, and made a cuckold within a month after his wedding; how Pantagruel found out the philosopher's stone,[3] the manner how he found it, and the way how to use it; how he passed over the Caspian Mountains, and how he sailed through the Atlantic Sea, defeated the cannibals and conquered the isles of Perlas; how he married the daughter of the king of India, called Presthan; how he fought against the devil and burnt up five chambers of hell, ransacked the great black chamber, threw Proserpine into the fire, broke four teeth of Lucifer, and the horn that was in his arse; how he visited the regions of the moon, to know whether indeed the moon were not entire and whole, or if the women had three quarters of it in their heads; and a thousand other little merriments, all veritable.[4] These are brave things truly.

Good night, gentlemen. *Perdonate mi,* and think not so much upon my faults that you forget your own. If you say to me, "Master, it would seem that you were not very wise in writing to us these flimflam stories and pleasant fooleries," I answer you, that you are not much wiser to spend your time in reading them.

Nevertheless, if you read them to make yourselves merry, as in manner of pastime I wrote them, you and I both are far more worthy of pardon than a great rabble of squint-minded fellows, counterfeit saints, demure lookers, hypocrites, zealots, tough friars, buskin-monks, and other-such sects of men, who disguise themselves like maskers to deceive the world. For, whilst they give the common people to understand that they are busied about nothing but contemplation and devotion in fastings and maceration of their sensuality, and that only to sustain and aliment the small frailty of their humanity, it is so far otherwise that, on the contrary, God knows what cheer they make,

Et Curios simulant, sed bacchanalia vivunt.

You may read it in great letters in the colouring of their red snouts, and gulching bellies as big as a tun, unless it be when they perfume themselves with sulphur. As for their study, it is wholly taken up in reading of Pantagrueline books; not so much to pass the time merrily, as to hurt some one or other mischievously, to wit, in articling, sole-articling, wry-neckifying, buttock-stirring, ballocking and diabliculating, that is, calumniating. Wherein they are like unto the poor rogues of a village, that are busy in stirring up and scraping in the ordure and filth of little children, in the season of cherries and guinds, and that only to find the kernels, that they may sell them to the druggists to make thereof pomander oil.

Fly from these men, abhor and hate them as much as I do, and upon my faith you will find yourselves the better for it. And if you desire to be good Pantagruelists, that is to say, to live in peace, joy, health, making yourselves always merry, never trust those men that always peep out at one hole.[5]

NOTES TO CHAPTER XXXIV

1. The first in order of writing.
2. The spring and fall fairs held at Frankfort-on-the-Main were important book markets.
3. The philosophers' stone had long been vainly sought by alchemists.
4. In these promises which are strung along in the conventional manner of the tale, Rabelais appears to have had no idea of laying out a plan for further books, but only of making a pleasant ending for this one.
5. I.e., through the opening of the monachal hood.

[Additional selected readings: *The Third Book*, Prologue, Chapters 2–4, 9–10, 30, 32; *The Fourth Book*, Chapters 1, 5–8, 18–24, 48–53.]

PIERRE DE RONSARD

(1524–1585)

Ronsard was the greatest poet of the French Renaissance. The leader of The Pléiade, who won the acceptance of the new poetry which was the beginning of modern French literature, he was praised and imitated throughout Europe. His own countrymen acknowledged him Prince of Poets. A friend to the Valois kings — Francis I, his son, and three grandsons — his poetry gave expression to the romantic and glamorous society of the Louvre and Fontainebleau and the châteaux and gardens of the Touraine country.

In spite of his life at court, however, Ronsard belongs to the country of the Vendômois, a hundred miles southwest of Paris. He was born on the 11th of September 1524 in his ancestral manor, La Poissonnière, near the village of Couture on the river Le Loir, just below the edge of the forest of Gastine. His ancestors had been established in this region at least since the year 1000, and since the fifteenth century had been Keepers of the ancient forest. His father, Loys or Louis de Ronsard, was a distinguished Italian campaigner under Louis XII, and under Francis I became Maître d'Hotel to the two princes, accompanying them as royal hostages in Spain. His mother, Jeanne de Chaudrier, came from an ancient family of Poitou of noble connections. The poet was the youngest of four surviving children, having two brothers and a sister.

From his earliest years he loved to wander in his native country. At the age of nine he was sent for a semester to the Collège de Navarre in Paris where he studied Latin literature, and forever after his woods and meadows and caves were haunted by Pan, and fauns, satyrs, and dryads. He was not to be permitted the literary solitude of a dreamer, however. His father urged the law, medicine, or the career of the soldier and the courtier. Consequently, at the age of twelve, he became page to the Dauphin, Charles, duc d'Orléans. In the following year, 1537, when James V of Scotland came to marry the Princess Madeleine, the young Ronsard returned to Scotland as page to the queen. He was also to have several months in England. In 1540, back in France, Charles appointed him to his Royal Stables, a "seminary of all good and virtuous exercises," especially those of horsemanship. In May, he accompanied Lazare de Baïf, eminent diplomat and scholar, on a mission to the meeting of the German Protestant princes at Hagenau in Alsace. By August he was back at La Possonnière; an illness contracted on this journey had left him partly deaf. He was now sixteen years of age.

In March 1543, Pierre and his father attended the funeral of Guillaume du Bellay (patron of François Rabelais, who was also present) at Le Mans. At this time, Pierre received from the Bishop of Le Mans the tonsure of Minor Orders which would enable him to hold an ecclesiastical benefice. He also conversed with the bishop's secretary, Jacques Peletier, poet, scholar, and humanist; he advised young Ronsard to leave composition in Latin to the pedants and to write his poetry in French. Ronsard's future career began to open to him.

His father died in 1544. In that year, in the house of Lazare de Baïf in the Rue des Fossés-St. Victor in Paris, Ronsard joined De Baïf's son as a pupil in Greek and Latin to the eminent teacher Jean Dorat. Three years later, Dorat became Master of the Collège de Coqueret, and for five years Ronsard reveled in the Greek classics. The life and passion of Dorat's students bespeak the humanistic revival of letters on the Hill of Ste. Geneviève. Ronsard's earliest biographer, Binet, wrote: "With what desire and noble emulation did they toil together! . . . Ronsard, who had spent his youth in courts, being accustomed to watch late, studied until two or three o'clock past midnight; and then going to his bed, woke Baïf, who rose and took the candle, and did not let the place grow cold." From these pupils came the group of seven which was later to be called The Pléiade. In 1547, at an inn on the road from Poitiers to Paris, Ronsard met a young law student by the name of Joachim du Bellay. As a result of their conversations on poetry, Du Bellay joined the group at the Collège de Coqueret. In 1549, Du Bellay published *La Deffence et Illustration de la Langue Françoyse,* which set forth the principles of the new French poetry now being written by these young poets. In 1550 appeared the first four books of Ronsard's *Odes* which proceeded to carry out the program of the new school; they were followed two years later by *Le Cinquiesme Livre des Odes.*

Jacques Peletier had recommended the study of Petrarch, and the sonnets to Laura became much in vogue. One April day in 1546, Ronsard—then twenty-one years of age—bid fair to repeat Petrarch's experience. It was a spring day, and the court was in the château at Blois. The daughters of the noble châtelaines of the Touraine were in attendance. One with dark eyes and hair played on her lute and sang a *branle de Bourgogne.* She was Cassandre Salviati, of Italian blood. Her father was a wealthy Florentine banker allied with the Medici, who had become banker to Francis I, had married a French wife, and had acquired the château at Talcy. As Ronsard phrased it in Greek around his own portrait, he saw her, and went mad. She became his first love, the first inspiration in the youth of his genius. To be sure, he sang of her in the Petrarchan strain, but his passion breaks through the convention and the Cassandre of his youth never faded from his mind. A year later, she married Jean de Peigné, Seigneur de Pray, and went to live in the manor in the country between Blois and Vendôme. She never returned his love, even though there were many meetings in the manors and châteaux of the Loir. In 1552 appeared *Les Amours,* containing 182 sonnets addressed to her.

In April 1555, Ronsard was at Bourgueil, a village in Anjou between Tours and Saumur. On the banks of the Loire outside the village, he saw Marie Dupin and her two sisters. She was a farmer's daughter, fifteen years of age, with chestnut brown hair, in the freshness and gaiety of her youth. She became the poet's second love. He sought to abandon his learning and literary style and to enter her own simple life and ways. His new style appears in the sonnets written for her, *La Continuation des Amours* of 1555, and the *Nouvelle Continuation des Amours* of 1556. He wooed her in the summers of 1555 and 1556; she had to him the spirit of the youth which was already beginning to leave him behind. He overwhelmed her with his wooing. In the end she wearied and married another.

Meanwhile, at the court of Henry II and Catherine de Médicis, Ronsard's poetry and his personality had made him famous as Prince of Poets. His athletic figure and handsome bearing fitted him for royal patronage; Henry appointed him "Councilor and Almoner," a post he was to retain to the end of his life. At the same time he was given several benefices by his ecclesiastical patrons. In 1559, Mary Stuart of Scotland became Queen of France to Francis II. Admiration and understanding were inevitable between this romantic, beautiful maiden and the poet who had lived in her country and served her mother as a page. "She delighted in poetry and poets," Brantôme wrote, "and most of all in M. de Ronsard, M. du Bellay, and M. de Maisonfleur, who have made such fine poems and elegies for her . . . which I have often seen her read to herself in France and in Scotland, with tears in her eyes and sighs from her heart." Ronsard worshipped her. She sent him costly gifts, among them a vase engraved with the inscription, "To Ronsard, Apollo of the Muses' Fountain."

In 1560, Charles IX came to the throne as a boy of ten. He had a taste for poetry; Ronsard became a favorite, and during his reign of fourteen years Ronsard's court career was at its height. He enjoyed the personal friendship of the king, accompanied the court wherever it went, and provided and produced masques for its endless festivities. Meanwhile the issues between Huguenots and Catholics flared into open warfare. Ronsard, who entered action himself at one time in the Vendômois, adhered to the king's party and to the Catholic cause, although he was outspoken in his criticism. During the 1560's there were more adventures of the heart. In the summer of 1561, he first saw Genèvre dancing on the bank of the Seine while he was swimming. There was the witty and audacious Isabeau de la Tour, cousin and maid of honor to the Queen Mother, superior to the poet in rank. There was Françoise d'Estrée, Ronsard's Astrée, also maid of honor, who first fascinated him as she played in a masque in the festivities at Fontainebleau.

The final woman to appear in Ronsard's poetry, however, was the inspiration for many of his finest sonnets. She was Hélène de Surgères, of Franco-Spanish blood. By the early 1570's a new poetry crept into vogue at court, the Italianate *mignardises,* dainty, precious, imbued with the Platonic idea of love, with which a young poet, Philippe Desportes, was attracting attention. Hélène de Surgères, member of the Queen Mother's company of maids, pale, dark, and precociously learned, was spiritually and physically a devotee of Platonic doctrines. Ronsard was now approaching fifty; she was still in her teens. He seems first to have wooed her in the spring of 1572. The love he sought was of the poets of Greece and Rome. Perhaps Hélène's love was basically centered upon herself; her replies were fashioned by the neo-Platonists of Italy. For nearly seven years he continued under her spell. His love for her was perhaps the noblest of his life. It was expressed in the *Sonnets pour Hélène,* which first appeared in 1578. But at the memorial service held in his honor at Paris, although she lived long after his death, she was not present.

Henry III came to the throne in 1574. Already there was abundant evidence that Ronsard had wearied of court life. Yet he endeavored loyally to play his part for the new king. At the reorganization of the academy to be known as the *Académie du Palais* at the Louvre, he gave the inaugural speech. But the character and atmosphere of Henry's court became increasingly alien to him. He returned more and more frequently to his priories in the Vendômois and Touraine and to the country he had always loved. His favorites were Croixval, secluded in the forest of Gastine, St. Gilles-de-Montoire on Le Loir, and St. Cosme-lez-Tours, located on an island by the city on La Loire. He was fond of gardening, of fishing, of birds and flowers, of the slow pageant of the seasons as they passed. Afflicted with the gout, he spent the last years of his life between these priories and visits to Paris. In Paris it was then his practice to lodge with his friend Jean Galland, Master of the Collège de Boncourt. He spent many winter weeks in the spacious cloisters and congenial company of this college. In 1578, he prepared an edition of his complete works in seven volumes. In 1583, he prepared the splendid one volume folio edition.

He died at St. Cosme-lez-Tours on the 27th of December 1585. He was buried there near the high altar of the church. In the following February, at a memorial service in his honor, a special Requiem Mass was sung in the chapel at the Collège de Boncourt; it was followed by the eloquent oration given by his friend Davy du Perron. In March 1586 appeared his first biography, written by his secretary and friend, Claude Binet, *Discours de la Vie de Pierre de Ronsard, Gentilhomme Vandômois.* As time went by, the exact location of his grave was forgotten, and eventually the priory of St. Cosme was sold for a farm. Only in 1932 were its ruins purchased by the Society of the *Sauvegarde de l'Art Français;* in 1933, excavations were made for Ronsard's skeleton, and it was found and identified.

In 1924, the four hundredth anniversary of his birth was widely celebrated. During the present century eminent French scholars have disclosed the facts of his life and published many critical studies of his work. Chief of all is M. Paul Laumonier, of the University of Bordeaux, who has brought out the masterly critical edition of the *Oeuvres Complétès* for *La Société de Textes Français Modernes,* which began in 1932.

Carrying out the theories of The Pléiade, Ronsard sought to reproduce creatively in French most of the forms of the classical literatures. Influenced especially by Virgil, Horace, Pindar, and the Anacreontic poets, as well as by Petrarch, his works include, in addition to the sonnets and odes already mentioned, the *Hymnes* (mythological and philosophical) of 1555 and 1556; political writings such as the *Discours de Miseres de ce Temps* of 1562 and *Remonstrance au Peuple de France* of 1563; the elegiac and pastoral poetry of the *Trois Livres du Recueil de Nouvelles Poësies* (1563), the *Elégies, Mascarades et Bergerie* (1565), and the *Sixiesme et Septiesme Livre des Poëmes* (1569); the prose manual *L'Abbrégé de l'Art Poétique François* of 1565; and the unfinished and unsuccessful epic *La Franciade* published in 1572.

He lives pre-eminently as a lyric poet — the greatest in France before the Romantic poets of the nineteenth century. His music comes from a mastery of form achieved through a long assimilation of the spirit of Greek and Roman poetry. It is expressive of the highly civilized urbanity and artistic discipline of his race. Above all, like the English Herrick, he is the poet of youth, of the spring, of love, and of the Muses. Confronted by the transiency of the fair forms of life, his utterance catches at times that unique pathos of the Greek anthology and the lyrics of Elizabeth's age. Through his poems we are able to live again in the courtly and colorful society of the Valois kings, and to realize much of the gracious and beautiful that has vanished from our own.

SELECTED BIBLIOGRAPHY

EDITIONS

Oeuvres Complètes, ed. Paul Laumonier, Paris, Lemerre, 1914–19, 8 vols.; *Oeuvres Complètes. Edition Critique,* ed. Paul Laumonier (Société des Textes Français Modernes), Paris, Droz and later Didier, 1932– , 16 vols. now published; *Oeuvres Complètes,* ed. Gustave Cohen, Paris, La Pléiade, 1938, 2 vols., for general use.

TRANSLATIONS

Ballads and Lyrics of Old France, trans. Andrew Lang, London, Longmans, 1872; *Ronsard and La Pléiade,* trans. George Wyndham, London, Macmillan, 1906; *Songs and Sonnets of P. de Ronsard,* trans. Curtis Hidden Page, Boston, Houghton Mifflin, 1924; *The Defence and Illustration of the French Language* by Joachim du Bellay, trans. Gladys M. Turquet, London, Dent, 1939; *Sonnets pour Hélène,* trans. Humbert Wolfe, New York, Macmillan, 1934; *Ronsard, Lyrics,* trans. William Stirling, London, Wingate, 1946.

BIOGRAPHY AND CRITICISM

Paul Laumonier, *Ronsard, Poète Lyrique. Etude Historique et Littéraire* (1909), 2nd edit., Paris, Hachette, 1923; P. Laumonier, *La Vie de P. de Ronsard de Claude Binet* (1586), Paris, Hachette, 1910; Henri Longnon, *Pierre de Ronsard. Essai de Biographie, les Ancêstres, la Jeunesse,* Paris, Champion, 1912; J. J. Jusserand, *Ronsard,* (Les Grands Ecrivains Français), Paris, Hachette, 1913; Pierre de Nolhac, *Ronsard et l'Humanisme,* Paris, Champion, 1921; Gustave Cohen, *Ronsard. Sa Vie et Son Oeuvre* (1924), 2nd edit., Paris, Boivin, 1933; Pierre Champion, *Ronsard et Son Temps,* Paris, Champion, 1925; Henri Chamard, *Histoire de la Pléiade,* Paris, Didier, 1939–40, 4 vols.

Walter Pater, *Gaston de Latour,* London, Macmillan, 1896; J. J. Jusserand, "Ronsard and His Vendômois," in *The School for Ambassadors,* 155–214, New York, Putnam, 1925; F. L. Lucas, "The Prince of Court-Poets," in *Studies French and English,* 76–114, London, Cassell, 1934; Morris Bishop, *Ronsard. Prince of Poets,* New York, Oxford Univ. Press, 1940; Robert J. Clements, *Critical Theory and Practice of the Pléiade,* Harvard Univ. Press, 1942; D. B. Wyndham Lewis, *Ronsard,* London, Sheed & Ward, 1944.

SPECIAL STUDIES

N. H. Clement, "Nature and the Country in Sixteenth and Seventeenth Century French Poetry," *Pub. Mod. Lang. Assoc.,* XLIV (1929), 1005–47; P. M. Jones, "The Approach to Ronsard," *Criterion,* XII (1933), 571–84; William B. Cornelia, *The Classical Sources of the Nature References in Ronsard's Poetry,* Columbia Univ. Press, 1934; A. Tilley, "Ronsard's Poetic Growth," *Mod. Lang. Rev.,* XXIX (1934), 32–51, XXX (1935), 460–71, XXXI (1936), 161–75; Isidore Silver, *The Pindaric Odes of Ronsard,* Paris, 1937; J. Hutton, "Ronsard and the Greek Anthology," *Stud. in Philol.,* XL (1943), 103–27; M. G. Davis, "Colour in Ronsard's Poetry," *Mod. Lang. Rev.,* XL (1945), 95–103; Isidore Silver, "Ronsard's Early Philosophy," *Stud. in Philol.,* XLV (1948), 119–33; I. Silver, "Ronsard Studies (1936–1950)," *Bibl. d'Humanisme et Renaissance,* XII (1950), 332–64; also "A Flame among the Fagots: Ronsard on His Education as a Hellenist," in *Mélanges offerts a H. Chamard,* 81–90, Paris, Nizet, 1951; H. Hatzfeld, "Christian, Pagan, and Devout Humanism in Sixteenth-Century France," *Mod. Lang. Quar.,* XII (1951), 337–52; also "The Role of Mythology in Poetry during the French Renaissance," *Mod. Lang. Quar.,* XIII (1952), 392–404; I. Silver, "Ronsard Comparatist Studies: Achievements and Perspectives," *Compar. Lit.,* VI (1954), 148–73; R. E. Hallowell, *Ronsard and the Conventional Roman Elegy,* Univ. of Illinois Press, 1954.

LES AMOURS

Translated by CURTIS HIDDEN PAGE,
HUMBERT WOLFE, *and* ANDREW LANG

[Taken from: *Songs & Sonnets of Pierre de Ronsard,* translated by Curtis Hidden Page, Houghton Mifflin Co., Boston, 1924; *Pierre de Ronsard: Sonnets pour Hélène,* English renderings by Humbert Wolfe, Eyre & Spottiswoode, London, 1934, The Macmillan Co., New York, 1934; *Ballads & Lyrics of Old France,* by Andrew Lang, Longmans, Green & Co., London, 1872.]

I. AMOURS DE CASSANDRE

Nature ornant Cassandre qui devoit

When Nature formed Cassandra, who should move
The hardest hearts with love's soft passionings,
She made her of a thousand beauteous things
That she had hoarded like a treasure-trove

For centuries. And Love too interwove
All He was dearly nesting neath His wings
Of gentle, to make honey-sweet the stings
Of her fair eyes, that even the Gods must love.

And when from Heaven she was newly come
And first I saw her, my poor heart, struck dumb,
Was lost in love; and love, her minister,

So poured her charm into my very veins
That now I have no pleasure but my pains,
No aim or knowledge but the thought of her.

[CURTIS HIDDEN PAGE]

Une beauté de quinze ans enfantine

Maid of fifteen, in childlike beauty dight,
Fair head with crinkled ringlets golden-tressed,
Rose-petalled forehead, cheeks like amethyst,
Laughter that lifts the soul to Heaven's delight;

And neck like snow, and throat than milk more white,
  And heart full-blossomed neath a budding breast —
  Beauty divine in human form expressed,
And virtue worthy of that beauty bright —

An eye whose light can change the night to day,
  A gentle hand that smooths away my care,
  Yet holds my life caught in its fingers' snare;

Withal a voice that's ever fain to sing,
  Still stopped by smiles, or sweet sighs languishing —
  These are the spells that charmed my wits away.

[Curtis Hidden Page]

Cent et cent fois penser un penser mesme

To think one thought a hundred hundred ways,
  'Neath two loved eyes to lay your heart quite bare,
  To drink the bitter liquor of despair
And eat forever ashes of lost days —

In spirit and flesh to know youth's bloom decays,
  To die of pain, yet swear no pain is there,
  The more you sue, to move the less your fair,
Yet make her wish, the law your life obeys —

Anger that passes, faith that cannot move;
  Far dearer than yourself your foe to love;
  To build a thousand vain imaginings,

To long to plead, yet fear to voice a breath,
  In ruin of all hope to hope all things —
  These are the signs of love — love even to death.

[Curtis Hidden Page]

Avant qu' Amour du Chaos ocieux

Ere Love from barren Chaos drew the skies,
  Piercing its womb that hid the light of day,
  Beneath primaeval earth's and water's sway
The shapeless Heavens lay whelmed, in dark disguise.

Even so my sluggish soul, too dull to rise,
  Within this body's gross and heavy clay
  Without or form or feature shapeless lay
Until Love's arrow pierced it from your eyes.

Love brought me life and power and truth and light,
  Made pure my inmost heart through his control,
  And shaped my being to a perfect whole.

He warms my veins, he lights my thought, his flight
  Snatches me upward, till in Heaven's height
  I find the ordered pathway of my soul.

[CURTIS HIDDEN PAGE]

Comme un Chevreuil, quand le printemps détruit

As the young stag, when lusty Spring supreme
  O'er Winter's biting cold at last prevails,
  To crop the honeyed leafage seeks new trails
And leaves his dear retreat at dawn's first gleam;

Alone, secure, afar (as he may deem)
  From bay of hounds, or hunters' echoing hails,
  Now on the mountain-slopes, now in the vales.
Now by the waters of a secret stream,

He wantons freely, at his own sweet will,
  Knowing no fear of net or bow, until,
  Pierced with one dart, he lies dead in his pride —

Even so I wandered, with no thought of woe,
  In my life's April — when one quick-drawn bow
  Planted a thousand arrows in my side.

[CURTIS HIDDEN PAGE]

Pren ceste rose aimable comme toy

Take thou this rose, sweet even as thou art,
  Thou rose of roses rarest, loveliest,
  Thou flower of freshest flowers, whose fragrance blest
Enwraps me, ravished from myself apart.

Take thou this rose, and with it take my heart,
  My heart that hath no wings, unto thy breast,
  So constant that its faith stands manifest,
Though wounded sore with many a cruel dart.

The rose and I are diverse in one thing:
  Each morning's rose at eve lies perishing,
  While countless mornings see my love new-born

But never night shall see its life decay. . . .
Ah! would that love, new-blossomed in the morn,
Even as a flower had lasted but a day.
[Curtis Hidden Page]

Morne de corps, et plus morne d'espris

I dragged my life along with sullen sighs
In heaviness of body and of soul,
Knowing not yet the Muse's high control
And honor that she brings her votaries,

Until the hour I loved you. Then your eyes
Became my guide to lead to virtue's goal,
Where I might win that knowledge fair and whole
Which by true loving makes men nobly wise.

O love, my all, if aught of good I do,
If worthily of your dear eyes I write,
You are the cause, yours is the potency.

My perfect grace comes ever but from you,
You are my spirit! If I work aright,
'Tis you that do it, you that work in me.
[Curtis Hidden Page]

Voicy le bois, que ma sainte Angelette

This is the wood my holy angel-child
Made joyous with her song, that day in Spring;
These are the flowers her touch was gladdening
While here she dreamed apart, and dreaming smiled;

This is the little woodland meadow wild
Whose green young life seemed neath her feet to spring
As step by step she wandered, pillaging
Flowers sweet as she was, fresh and undefiled.

This is the spot where first I saw her smile
With eyes that rapt my soul away the while;
Here I have seen her weep, there heard her sing,

'Twas here I saw her dance, there sit aloof. . . .
Of such vague thoughts, with shuttle wandering,
Love weaves my web of life, both warp and woof.
[Curtis Hidden Page]

Page suy moy: par l'herbe plus espesse

Come, boy, and where the grass is thickest pied,
With robber hand cut the green season's bloom,
Then flinging open armfuls strew the room
With flowers that April bears in her young pride.

Then set my lyre, song's handmaid, by my side —
For if I may, I'll charm away the gloom
That like a poison worketh to consume
My life, through power of beauty undefied.

Then bring me ink and countless papers white —
White paper shall bear witness to my woe,
Whereon the record of this love I'll write.

White paper, that endures when diamond stone
Is worn away, shall bid the ages know
How for love's sake I suffer and make moan.
[CURTIS HIDDEN PAGE]

II. AMOURS DE MARIE

Marie levez-vous ma jeune paresseuse

Marie, arise, my indolent sweet saint!
Long since the skylark sang his morning stave,
Long since the nightingale, love's gentle slave,
Carolled upon the thorn his love-complaint.

Arise! come see the tender grass besprent
With dew-pearls, and your rose with blossoms brave.
Come see the dainty pinks to which you gave
Last eve their water with a care so quaint.

Last eve you swore and pledged your shining eyes
Sooner than I this morning you would rise,
But dawn's soft beauty-sleep, with sweet disguising,

Still gently seals those eyes — that now I kiss
And now again — and now this breast, and this,
A hundred times, to teach you early rising!
[CURTIS HIDDEN PAGE]

Cache pour ceste nuit ta corne, bonne Lune

Hide this one night thy crescent, kindly Moon;
So shall Endymion faithful prove, and rest
Loving and unawakened on thy breast;
So shall no foul enchanter importune
Thy quiet course; for now the night is boon,
And through the friendly night unseen I fare,
Who dread the face of foemen unaware,
And watch of hostile spies in the bright noon.
Thou knowest, Moon, the bitter power of Love;
'Tis told how shepherd Pan found ways to move,
For little price, thy heart; and of your grace,
Sweet stars, be kind to this not alien fire,
Because on earth ye did not scorn desire,
Bethink ye, now ye hold your heavenly place.

[ANDREW LANG]

Fleur Angevine de quinze ans

Fair flower of fifteen springs, that still
Art scarcely blossomed from the bud,
Yet hast such store of evil will,
A heart so full of hardihood,
Seeking to hide in friendly wise
The mischief of your mocking eyes.

If you have pity, child, give o'er;
Give back the heart you stole from me,
Pirate, setting so little store
On this your captive from Love's sea,
Holding his misery for gain,
And making pleasure of his pain.

Another, not so fair of face,
But far more pitiful than you,
Would take my heart, if of his grace,
My heart would give her of Love's due;
And she shall have it, since I find
That you are cruel and unkind.

Nay, I would rather that it died,
Within your white hands prisoning,
Would rather that it still abide
In your ungentle comforting,
Than change its faith, and seek to her
That is more kind, but not so fair.

[ANDREW LANG]

Quand ce beau Printemps je voy

When the beauteous Spring I see,
Glad and free,
Making young the sea and earth,
Then the light of day above
And our love
Seem but newly brought to birth.

When the sky of deeper blue
Lights anew
Lands more beautiful and green,
Love, with witching looks for darts,
Wars on hearts,
Winning them for his demesne.

Scattering his arrows dire
Tipped with fire,
He doth bring beneath his sway
Men and birds and beasts for slaves—
And the waves
To his power obeisance pay. . . .

Nature, for Love's triumphing,
In the Spring
Thrills my heart at every breath
By new beauties everywhere
Which her care
From my Lady borroweth:

When I see the woodland bowers
Bright with flowers,
And the banks with flowers bedight,
Then methinks I see the grace
Of her face
Fair with blended red and white;

When I see elm-branches bound
Close around
Where the loving ivies wind,
Then I feel encompassing
Arms that cling
Fast about my neck entwined;

When I hear thee in the vale,
Nightingale,
Uttering thy sweetest voice,
Then methinks her voice I hear,
Low and clear,
Making all my soul rejoice;

When the soft wind comes anon
    Murmuring on
Through the many-branchéd grove,
Then I hear the murmured word
    That I heard
Once alone beside my love;

When I see a new-blown flower's
    Earliest hours
By the morning sun caressed,
Then its beauty I compare
    To the rare
Budding beauty of her breast;

When the sun in Orient skies
    'Gins to rise,
Flaunting free his yellow hair,
Then methinks my sweet I see
    Fronting me,
Binding up her tresses fair;

When I see the meadows studded
    With new-budded
Flowers that overflow the earth,
Then my senses half believe
    They receive
Honeyed fragrance from her breath.

So it proveth, howsoe'er
    I compare
Spring-time with my chosen one.
Spring gives life to every flower —
    Life and power
Come to me from her alone.

Would 'twere mine, where streamlets flow
    Whispering low,
To unbind that wealth of hair,
Then to wind as many a curl
    As there purl
Running rippling wavelets there.

Would 'twere mine to be the god
    Of this wood,
So to seize and hold my love,
Kissing her as oft again
    As there ben
Greening leaves in all the grove. . . .

Ah, my sweet, my martyrdom,
    Hither come,
See the flowers how they fare.
They to pity me are fain—
    Of my pain
Thou alone hast not a care.

See the gentle mating dove
    And his love,
How they win the joy we seek,
How they love as Nature bade
    Unafraid,
How they kiss with wings and beak,

While we, following honor's shade,
    Have betrayed
Joy, through fear and coward shame.
Ah! the birds are happier far
    Than we are,
Loving without let or blame.

Time is hasting to destroy
    All our joy,
Snatching it with harpy claws.
Sweetheart, let us live and love
    Like the dove,
Heeding not men's rigorous laws.

Kiss me, ere the moment slips,
    On my lips,
O my love, and yet again
Kiss me, ere our youth's brief day
    Fleet away,
Making all our passion vain.

[Curtis Hidden Page]

Comme on voit sur la branche au mois de May la rose

As in the gardens, all through May, the rose,
  Lovely, and young, and fair apparelled,
  Makes sunrise jealous of her rosy red,
When dawn upon the dew of dawning glows;
Graces and Loves within her breast repose,
  The woods are faint with the sweet odour shed,
  Till rains and heavy suns have smitten dead
The languid flower, and the loose leaves unclose,—

So this, the perfect beauty of our days,
When earth and heaven were vocal of her praise,
The fates have slain, and her sweet soul reposes;
And tears I bring, and sighs, and on her tomb
Pour milk, and scatter buds of many a bloom,
That dead, as living, she may be with roses.

[Andrew Lang]

Deux puissans ennemis me combatoient alors

Twain that were foes, while Mary lived, are fled;
One laurel-crowned abides in heaven, and one
Beneath the earth has fared, a fallen sun,
A light of love among the loveless dead.
The first is Chastity, that vanquished
The archer Love, that held joint empery
With the sweet beauty that made war on me,
When laughter of lips with laughing eyes was wed.

Their strife the Fates have closed, with stern control,
The earth holds her fair body, and her soul
An angel with glad angels triumpheth;
Love has no more that he can do; desire
Is buried, and my heart a faded fire,
And for Death's sake, I am in love with Death.

[Andrew Lang]

SONNETS POUR HÉLÈNE

I. Le siecle où tu nasquis ne te cognoist Hélène

Helen, this age, by your exceeding worth
and sceptred grace bedazzled or made blind,
does not acclaim the empress of mankind,
whose majesty should have fulfilled the earth.
Alas! with greed besotted, in its dearth
it spurns the virtue which transcends the mind,
leaving your poet in your voice to find
echoes beyond the world that have their birth.
You needed but to speak, and love, that listened,
granted my ear immortal understanding,
and to your miracle unsealed my eyes.
I hold love's fief from hands divinely christened,
vassal by right, who first saw God attending
upon the lordship of your Paradise.

[Humbert Wolfe]

Nous promenant tous seuls, vous me distes, Maistresse

Madam, when we two walked, the rest unheeding,
"I wish," you said, "for poems where lovers use
to tell of ladies that they love and lose,
with lamentable voice and woe exceeding.
And therefore when in solitude I'm reading,
it is your saddest sonnets that I choose
to lead my willing feet down avenues,
where chiefly grows the blossom love-lies-bleeding."
Tis a sweet fashion, madam, but you lie.
For were it true, would not your tears beguile
the heart your beauty pierces with a knife?
You read my sonnets with a subtle eye
that weeps, like the Egyptian crocodile,
to further your designs upon my life.

[HUMBERT WOLFE]

Je liay d'un filet de soye cramoisie

Only your arm, and nothing more, I found,
nor heart, nor fancy, with my silken tether
was shackled, howsoe'er the scarf I wound
about you when we lately spoke together.
Ah beauty that I chose, and served, and crowned,
my luckless doom has made me wonder whether
I am not mad to be so straitly bound,
when you wear love so lightly as a feather.
O to have speech with some old sorcerer
who might have changed your heart and set it beating
with the same lovely griefs, so that they were
not (lady) like all other magic fleeting.
But no, youth, riches and a glozing tongue
can still outmagic all that I have sung.

[HUMBERT WOLFE]

Vous me distes, Maistresse, estant à la fenestre

Out of her lattice gazing on the leas
of green Montmartre my pensive lady cried:
"It is the still, sequestered countryside
and not the crowded Court hath power to please."
It happened that by prayers and penances
love for the moment had been mortified,

and, though the vampire sucked, I could abide
and overcome his malice at my ease.
Therefore said I, "Madam, it were as idle
to seek from love in cloisters sanctuary
as to believe no ash can hide a fire.
Love in the desert, as in towns, is tidal,
and since in heaven itself his will doth carry,
what prayer or fasting can subdue desire?"
[Humbert Wolfe]

D'autre torche mon coeur ne pouvoit s'allumer

No other torch save what my dreams discover
at your bright eyes could have restored the light
to one who had renounced the name of lover
as his brief day yielded to gradual night.
For, if I wooed, 'twas only to recover
my practised soul that, stooping in its flight
now here, now there, did nothing more than hover,
and would not stay to be ensnared outright.
But caught at last, like the old men, I cry on
Helen, "Beside your beauty little matter
ten years of war or Ilion's towers that tumble.
Yet to your prey be gentle as the lion,
since 'tis the peak, not grass, that lightnings shatter,
and love, a god, would have his captains humble."
[Humbert Wolfe]

Bien que l'esprit humain s'enfle par la doctrine

What though the spirit of man, by Plato taught,
claims springs in heaven and immortal sources,
without the body all the rest were naught,
and vain to praise the blood's celestial courses.
For all our virtues — hearing, sight, and thought
are bodily; and the wise sense endorses
our actions only to perfection brought
by matter working through the natural forces.
But you adore the spirit and profess,
mistaking for the truth the shape of error,
to find in bodily passion nothing less
than love's pollution and the devil's mirror.
That is to sin like Ixion, who vowed
to feast upon the wind, and loved a cloud.
[Humbert Wolfe]

II. *A fin qu' à tout jamais de siecle en siecle vive*

That century to century may tell
The perfect love Ronsard once bore to you,
How he was reason-reft for love of you
And thought it freedom in your chains to dwell;

That age on age posterity full well
May know my veins were filled with beauty of you
And that my heart's one wish was only you,
I bring for gift to you this immortelle.

Long will it live in freshness of its prime.
And you shall live, through me, long after death —
So can the well-skilled lover conquer Time,

Who loving you all virtue followeth.
Like Laura, you shall live the cynosure
Of earth, so long as pens and books endure.

[CURTIS HIDDEN PAGE]

Amour, qui as ton regne en ce monde si ample

See love, whose kingdom as the world is ample,
how in that garden strays your dear and mine,
and brighter than the sconces in your temple
her starry eyes see in their place divine.
And all the body, the likeness and example
of loveliness, that doth the dawn outshine,
see! and her fatal brow that no clouds dimple —
a heavenly glass for nature's perfect line.
Pensive she walks, oh see! herself suborning
binding you, love, with flowers, while the grasses
swoon into life where she in triumph goes,
and spring at her bright eyes herself adorning
see! and how earth grows richer where she passes,
and how the sky in her is all a rose.

[HUMBERT WOLFE]

Tandis que vous dancez et ballez à vostre aise

Dance, lovely lady, dance and mask your face
as you have masked your heart; and then remember
how I must walk in love's uneven pace,
cold as the snow, or hot as fallen ember.

Carnival pleases you: 'tis my disgrace
  whose heart is but a pain that will not slumber,
a cry against time's unrequited race
  and you the symbol of my love's November.
Lady, believe my tears, that must upbraid you,
  my lamentations and my long despair
  that only death, nor even he, can mend.
But if my brow and eyes do not persuade you,
  listen to words that die upon the air,
  when heart and voice in the same silence end.

[HUMBERT WOLFE]

Je ne veux comparer tes beautez à la Lune

Shall I your beauties with the moon compare?
  She's faithless, you a single purpose own.
Or to the general sun, who everywhere
  goes common with his light; you walk alone?
And you are such that envy must despair
  of finding in my praise aught to condone,
who have no likeness since there's naught as fair,
  yourself your god, your star, Fate's overtone.
Those mad or rash, who make some other woman
  your rival, hurt themselves when they would hurt you,
  so far your excellence their dearth outpaces.
Either your body shields some noble demon,
  or mortal you image immortal virtue,
  or Pallas you or first among the Graces.

[HUMBERT WOLFE]

III. Ces longues nuicts d'hyver, où la Lune ocieuse

In these long winter nights when moon doth steer
  her lazy car through heaven with what pale charms,
when dawn comes late with later Chanticleer,
  and anxious hearts endure a year's alarms,
I should have died of weariness and fear
  had not thy phantom form, of all love's harms
sweet remedy and salve, as ghost as dear,
  glided all naked to her lover's arms.
Thou art so proud that only in a dream
  can I be private with thee and believe
  that I at last am pillowed at thy breast.
There all is given. There with joys that seem

doth gentle sleep my amorous pain deceive,
and, where naught else avails, deception's best.

[HUMBERT WOLFE]

Quand vous serez bien vieille, au soir à la chandelle

When you are very old, by the hearth's glare,
  At candle-time, spinning and winding thread,
  You'll sing my lines, and say, astonishéd:
Ronsard made these for me, when I was fair.

Then not a servant even, with toil and care
  Almost out-worn, hearing what you have said,
  Shall fail to start awake and lift her head
And bless your name with deathless praise fore'er.

My bones shall lie in earth, and my poor ghost
  Take its long rest where Love's dark myrtles thrive.
  You, crouching by the fire, old, shrunken, grey,

Shall rue your proud disdain and my love lost. . . .
  Nay, hear me, love! Wait not to-morrow! Live,
  And pluck life's roses, oh! to-day, to-day.

[CURTIS HIDDEN PAGE]

Le soir qu'Amour vous fist en la salle descendre

That evening when love bad you take the floor
  to tread his brilliant ballet of Things Tender,
your eyes, though it was night, did day restore,
  those stars that took the ballroom with their splendour.
O what a proud pavane, now less, now more,
  breaking, rejoining, now in circled wonder
first mixing, then dividing, till I swore
  no dance it was but the bent stream Meander.
Now the ring formed, dissolved, now it was narrow,
  now in a pointed triangle it lifted
  sharp as the migrant squadron of the crane.
I lie. You did not dance. Your foot—an arrow—
  flew over earth, while your light body drifted,
  assuming for the night the god again.

[HUMBERT WOLFE]

Je ne serois marry si tu contois ma peine

Count me the stairs I climbed to your retreat
in the king's palace that outtop with ease
Olympus' peak, and, counting them, repeat
my pains as sharp and many in their degrees.
My breath I lost, my pulses missed a beat,
my brow was beaded, and I knocked my knees
hearing your voice before I heard it, sweet,
with proud disdain and with denial freeze.
You as a goddess are enthroned above,
but I, no god to reach you when you brood,
from earth below can only send these sighs
soaring to that high heaven of your love,
as men with prayer besiege the solitude
of Jupiter transcendent in the skies.

[Humbert Wolfe]

Il ne faut s'esbahir, disoient ces bons vieillars

"Who," cried the elders on the Trojan wall,
when Helen passed, "dare of the ills complain
which by that beauty have no weight at all,
whose single glance outbids a world of pain?
And yet the wrath of Ares to forestall
were it not better to yield her up again
than see the port besieged, the ramparts fall,
and all of Troas bloody with the slain?"
But that was old man's rede. King Menelaus
asked rightly her return whom rightly Paris
withheld, since both well knew it was the duty
of young and old alike, although it slay us,
to offer and to waste — if all miscarries —
country and goods and life itself for beauty.

[Humbert Wolfe]

A fin que ton honneur coule parmy la plaine

I consecrate this fountain Helen's, praying
the favour of the gods, and pouring wine,
so that its water may that name be spraying,
which climbs to heaven graven on a pine.
Shepherds, let not your flocks come hither straying
though cotton-white. But let the eglantine
and blooms that dawn uncrumples flourish, saying,
"Let this flow on for ever fresh and thine."

Here let the passer-by in summer slumber,
  or on the sward under the shade compose
a thousand songs for Helen, and remember
  Ronsard, and drink and burn, like him, with those.
And may they at their hearts the flame discover
which sealed him first a poet but most a lover.

[HUMBERT WOLFE]

Adieu, cruelle adieu, je te suis ennuyeux

Cruel, farewell, since I do but annoy thee,
  and love in song grows tedious unrequited.
I go, and let who will or can enjoy thee,
  though never will he match the love you slighted.
In fifteen months love taught me tricks and fashion,
  planting within my brain the seeds of verse.
Now reason schools the lunacies of passion
  and brings me to her side and makes me hers.
Feed not this child, who gnaws upon the heart,
  the angler catching fools upon the string,
the comedy, the perfect liar's art,
  a hundred pains and one joy vanishing.
Nay, let's be sure, however things may seem,
that man is doomed who sups upon a dream.

[HUMBERT WOLFE]

LES AMOURS DIVERSES

A Tres-Vertueux Seigneur N. de Neufville, Seigneur de Villeroy, Secretaire d'Estat de sa Majesté

Ja du prochain hyver je prevoy la tempeste

Another Winter comes. The last comes soon, I know.
For six and fifty years have blanched my head with snow.
The time is here to say, Farewell, to love and song,
And take my leave of life's best days, for oh! how long! . . .

Yet I have lived. So much stands safe beyond recall.
I grudge not life its joys. I have tasted one and all,
Nor e'er refrained my hand from pleasures within reach,
Save but as Reason set due measure unto each.
The part assigned me I have played on this life's stage
In costume fitted to the times and to my age.

I've seen the morning dawn, and evening come again.
I've seen the storm, the lightning-flash, the hail, the rain.
Peoples I've seen, and kings! — For twenty years now past
I've seen each day rise upon France as though her last.

Wars I have seen, and strife of words, and terms of truce
First made and then unmade again, then made by ruse
To break and make again! . . . I've seen that neath the moon
All was but change and chance, and danced to Fortune's tune.
Though man seek Prudence out for guide, it boots him naught;
Fate ineluctable doth hold him chained and caught,
Bound hand and foot, in prison; and all he may propose
Fortune and Fate, wisely mayhap, themselves dispose.

Full-feasted of the world, even as a wedding-guest
Goes from the banquet-hall, I go to my long rest;
As from a king's great feast, I go not with ill grace
Though after me one come, and take the abandoned place.

[CURTIS HIDDEN PAGE]

Plus estroit que la Vigne à l'Ormeau se marie

More closely than the clinging vine
About the wedded tree,
Clasp thou thine arms, ah, mistress mine!
About the heart of me.
Or seem to sleep, and stoop your face
Soft on my sleeping eyes,
Breathe in your life, your heart, your grace,
Through me, in kissing wise.
Bow down, bow down your face, I pray,
To me that swoon to death,
Breathe back the life you kissed away,
Breathe back your kissing breath.
So by your eyes I swear and say,
My mighty oath and sure,
From your kind arms no maiden may
My loving heart allure.
I'll bear your yoke, that's light enough,
And to the Elysian plain,
When we are dead of love, my love,
One boat shall bear us twain.
They'll flock around you, fleet and fair,
All true loves that have been,
And you of all the shadows there,
Shall be the shadow queen.

Ah shadow-loves, and shadow-lips!
Ah, while 'tis called to-day,
Love me, my love, for summer slips,
And August ebbs away.

[Andrew Lang]

OTHER POEMS

Translated by Curtis Hidden Page

[Taken from *Songs & Sonnets of Pierre de Ronsard,* translated by Curtis Hidden Page, Houghton Mifflin Co., Boston, 1924.]

GAYETEZ

L'Alouette. Hé Dieu que je porte d'envie

Skylark, how I envy you
Your gentle pleasures ever new,
Warbling at the break of day
Of love, sweet love, sweet love alway,
And shaking free your beating wings
Of dew that to each feather clings!

Ere Apollo risen hath,
You lift your body from its bath,
Darting up with little leaps
To dry it where the cloud-flock sleeps,
Fluttering free each tiny wing
And "tirra-lirra" carolling
Sweet, so sweet, that every swain,
Knowing Spring has come again,
Thinketh on his love anew
And longs to be a bird like you.

Then, when you have scaled the sky,
You drop — as swift, as suddenly,
As the spool a maid lets fall
When, caught at eve in slumber's thrall,
Distaff forgot, she nods so much
Her cheek and bosom almost touch;
Or as by day when she doth spin
And he that seeks her love to win
Cometh near her unbeknown —
Abashed she casts her glances down,
And quick the slender thin-wound spool
From her hand afar doth roll. . . .
So you drop, my lark, my lover,
Dainty minion, darling rover,

Lark I love more tenderly
Than all the other birds that fly,
More than even the nightingale
Whose notes through copse and grove prevail.

Innocent of every harm,
You never rob the toilsome farm
Like those birds that steal the wheat
And spoil the harvest — thieves that eat
Growing grain in stalk and leaf
Or shell it from the standing sheaf.
Greening furrows are your haunts,
Where the little worms and ants,
Or the flies and grubs, you seek,
To fill your children's straining beak,
While they wait, with wings ungrown,
Clothed in clinging golden down.

Wrongly have the poets told
That you, the larks, in days of old
Dared your father to betray
And cut his royal locks away
Wherein his fated power lay.
Out! alas! not you alone
The wrongs of poets' tongues have known.
Hear the nightingale complain
And from her bower their tales arraign.
Swallows sing the self-same plea
The while they chirp "cossi, cossi."
None the less, then, I entreat,
Your "tirra-lirra" still repeat —
Make them burst with very spite,
These poets, for the lies they write!

None the less, for what they say,
Live ye joyously alway!
Seek at each return of Spring
Your long-accustomed pleasuring.
Never may the pilfering raid
Of quaintly dainty shepherd-maid
Toward your furrows turn her quest
To spy your new-born cheeping nest
And steal it in her gown away
The while you sing in Heaven your lay.
Live, then, birdlings, live fore'er,
And lift aloft through highest air
Warbled song and soaring wing
To herald each return of Spring.

[Curtis Hidden Page]

LES ODES

I, 17. *A sa Maistresse. Mignonne, allons voir si la rose*

Sweet-heart, come see if the rose
Which at morning began to unclose
Its damask gown to the sun
Has not lost, now the day is done,
The folds of its damasked gown
And its colors so like your own.

Ah, see, in how brief a space,
Sweet-heart, it strewed the place,
Alas, with its beauties' fall! . . .
O step-dame Nature! — if all
Of life you will grant such a flower
Is from morning to evening hour!

Then hear me and heed, sweet-heart:
Swiftly the years depart!
Harvest, oh! harvest your hour
While life is a-bloom with youth!
For age with bitter ruth
Will fade your beauty's flower.
[CURTIS HIDDEN PAGE]

II, 13. *Des-Autels, qui redore'*

My des Autels, whose true,
  Pure utterance
Transforms to gold anew
  The speech of France,

List while I celebrate
  My dear Vendôme.
O land thrice fortunate,
  The Muses' home,

For thee ungrudging Heaven
  Has emptied free
The horn of plenty, and given
  All grace to thee.

Two ridges, circling, long,
  With summits bold
Shut out the South-winds strong,
  The North-winds cold;

On one, my loved Gastine,
  The sacred wood,
Lifts high its head of green,
  Holy, and proud;

Along the other's side
  Spring countless vines,
That almost match the pride
  Of Anjou wines;

In winding meadow-ways
  The Loir soft-flowing
With its own wavelets plays,
  Nor hastes its going.

Though none from distant lands,
  By hope cajoled,
Come seeking 'mongst thy sands
  The toilsome gold,

Though gems of Orient price
  Hide not in thee
To tempt man's avarice
  Across the sea,

Afric, nor boastful Ind
  Can thee outvie,
Honored, by Gods more kind,
  With gifts more high.

For Justice, fled from earth
  And dispossessed,
Left thee, to mark thy worth,
  Her footprints blest;

And while no more we see
  The golden age,
Virtue has chosen thee
  For hermitage.

The nymphs, that tune their voice
  To notes of streams
Have made of thee their choice
  To list high themes,

Singing with happy grace
  And sweet accords
Praise to the Heaven-born race,
  Our Bourbon lords.

The Muses, whom I woo,
  Worship, and fear,
The golden Graces too,
  Inhabit here.

Though ever back and forth
  My steps may roam,
This little plot of earth
  Alone is home.

Hence may my fated end,
  When time is full,
Me into exile send
  Perdurable.

And here you'll come to weep
  From lands afar,
While dust and darkness keep
  Your friend, RONSARD.

[CURTIS HIDDEN PAGE]

II, 18. · *J'ay l'esprit tout ennuyé*

Oh! but my mind is weary!
Long I have conned the dreary
  Tomes of Aratus.
Surely 'tis time to play now!
Ho! to the fields away now!
Shall we not live to-day now?
  What though dull fools berate us!

What is the use of learning,
When it but brings new yearning
  Problems to tease us?
When, or at eve or morning,
Soon, but without a warning,
Pleadings and pity scorning,
  Orcus the dark shall seize us.

Corydon, lead the way, and
Find where good wine's to pay, and
  Cool me a flagon!
Then in vine-trellised bowers,
Bedded on thick-strewn flowers,
Hours upon idle hours
  Sweetly shall haste or lag on.

Artichokes bring me, mellow
Apricots, melons yellow,
  Cream, and strawberries.
These have the sweetest savor
Eaten in forest cave, or
Lying by brooks that rave or
  Streamlet that singing tarries.

Now in my youth's fresh buoyance
Laughter shall wait on joyance,
  Wine shall flow fast now;
Lest, when my life grows colder,
Sickness, by age made bolder,
Say, as he taps my shoulder:
  "Come, friend — you've drunk your last now."

[Curtis Hidden Page]

III, 20. *A Antoine de Chasteigner, de la Roche de Posé*
Ne s'effroyer de chose qui arrive

Calmly to wait whatever Chance may give
  By Fate's decree
Alone brings happiness, and makes man live
  Fearless and free.

The things of this world, owning Time's control,
  Move neath His sway;
But Time is swift, and swift the seasons roll
  Briefly away.

Once knowledge dwelt beside the Nile, then passed
  To Greece alone;
Then Rome had joy of it, that now at last
  Paris doth own.

Cities and kingdoms perish and make room
  For others new
That live awhile in glory of their bloom,
  Then perish too.

So arm thyself in firm Philosophy
  Gainst Fate's control;
Be nobly brave, and with her precepts high
  Gird up thy soul.

Then whatsoever change may meet thine eyes
  Fear not at all,

Though the abyss should rise and be the skies
  And the skies fall.
[Curtis Hidden Page]

IV, 4. *De l'election de son sepulchre*
Antres, et vous fontaines

O caves, and you, O springs
The lofty mountain flings
  Downward along his sides
    With leaps and glides,

O woods, and sun-shot gleams
Of wandering meadow-streams,
  And banks with flowers gay,
    List what I say—

When Fate and Heaven decree
My hour is come to be
  Snatched from the light away
    Of common day,

Let none bring granite stones
To build above my bones
  A tomb of noble height
    In Time's despite—

Not marble, but a tree
Set to cast over me
  Shadows of billowy sheen,
    Forever green,

And from my earth let spring
An ivy, garlanding
  The grave, and round it wind
    Twisted and twined.

There shepherds with their sheep
Coming each year to keep
  My festival, shall pay
    Their rites, and say:

"Fair isle, great is thy grace,
To be his resting-place,
  While all the universe
    Repeats his verse.

"He taught the Muses' pride
To love our country-side,

And dance our flowers among,
To songs he sung.

"He struck his lyre on high
Fore'er to glorify
Our mountains, crofts, and wealds,
And blosmy fields.

"Let gentle manna fall
Alway, above his pall,
And dew that soft and still
Spring nights distil.

"And let us keep his name,
And glorying in his fame
Each year bring him again
Praise, as to Pan."

Thus shall the shepherd-troop
Speak, and from many a cup
Pour wine and milk for food
And young lambs' blood

Above me, who shall then
Be dwelling far from men,
Where happy spirits blest
Take their long rest,

Where Zephyr breathes his love
O'er field and myrtle-grove
And meadows at all hours
New-decked with flowers,

Where care comes not, nor hate,
Nor envy spurs the great
To spread fell sorrow's dower
For lust of power;

In brotherly good-will
All join, and follow still
The crafts they used to love
On earth above.

Ah, God! to think, mine ear
Alcæus' lyre shall hear,
And Sappho's, over all
Most musical!

See how the happy throngs
Press near to hear their songs

Till souls in woe rejoice
Listing their voice,

Till Sisyphus forget
His rock-worn toil and sweat,
Till Tantalus obtain
Surcease of pain. . . .

The sweet-toned lyre alone
Can comfort hearts that moan
And charm away all cares
Of whoso hears.
[Curtis Hidden Page]

IV, 21. *Dieu vous gard messagers fidelles*

God guard you, and greet you well,
Messengers of Spring:
Nightingale and cuckoo,
Turtle-dove and hoopoe,
Swallow swift, and all wild birds
That with a hundred varied words
Rouse and make to ring
Every greening glade and fell.

God guard you, and greet you fain,
Dainty flowerets, too:
Daisies, lilies, roses,
Poppies — and the posies
Sprung where ancient heroes fell,
Hyacinth and asphodel —
Mint and thyme and rue:
All be welcome back again!

God guard you, and greet you true,
Butterflies and bees,
In your motley dresses
Wooing the sweet grasses,
Flitting free on rainbow-wing,
Coaxing, kissing, cozening
Flowers of all degrees,
Red or yellow, white or blue.

A thousand thousand times I greet
Thy return again,

Sweet and beauteous season;
In sooth I love with reason
Better far thy sunny gleams
And thy gently prattling streams
Than Winter's wind and rain
That shut me close in my retreat.
[Curtis Hidden Page]

IV, 22. *Bel Aubepin fleurissant*

Hawthorn fair, whose burgeoning
Blossoms spring
Where these banks wind beauteously,
Down along thine arms there clings,
Waves, and swings,
Trailing wild-vine drapery.

Rival camps of scurrying ants
Have their haunts
Fortified, at thy roots' head.
In thy hollow-eaten bole's
Countless holes
Tiny bees find board and bed.

Nightingale the chorister
Dwelleth here
Where in flush of youth he made
Love, and still each year again
Shall obtain
Solace in thy leafy shade.

In thy top he hath his nest
Built, and dressed —
Woven of wool, with silks made gay;
Whence his young so soon as hatched,
Must be snatched,
For my hands a gentle prey.

Live, then, dainty hawthorn fair,
Live fore'er,
Live secure from every foe!
May nor axe nor lightning harm;
Wind, nor storm,
E'er avail to lay thee low.
[Curtis Hidden Page]

IV, 38. *Verson ces roses pres ce vin*

Pour we roses into wine!
  In this good wine these roses
Pour, and quaff the drink divine
  Till sorrow's hold uncloses
From our hearts, both mine and thine.

Kings and clowns from diverse ways
  At Charon's boat are meeting.
None escape their fated days. . . .
  Ah! friend, while time is fleeting
Let us sing the rose's praise.

Roses are the chief of all
  The flowers in garden closes,
Flowers of joy, and therewithal
  Of love — and so the roses
"Venus' violets" I call.

Roses are Love's own bouquet
  And joyance of the Graces.
Dawn doth give them pearls alway
  Whose white their red enlaces
Dipped in dew at break of day.

Roses are the Gods' delight,
  And maidens' best adorning,
Maidens deck their bosoms white
  With crimson roses, scorning
Gold and gems, though ne'er so bright.

What is fair without the rose?
  Beauty is born of roses.
Venus' skin is all one rose,
  Aurora's touch is roses,
Rising suns have brows of rose.

Be my brows with roses crowned
  In place of laurel's glory.
Call the twice-born God renowned,
  Our father hale and hoary;
Spread him roses all around;

Bacchus loves the beauty sweet
  Of crimson-petalled roses.
Roses fill his vine-retreat
  Where care-free he reposes
Drinking mid the Summer's heat.

[Curtis Hidden Page]

V, 16. *Nous ne tenons en nostre main*

We hold not in our power
The coming morrows' time;
Life has no certain dower.
Kings' favors we desire,
And waiting them, expire
Ere hope has passed its prime.

The man whom Death has ta'en
Eats not, and drinks no more,
Though barns be full of grain
And vaults have wine in store
On Earth, that he has bought.
They reach not even his thought.

Then what shall care bestead?
Go, Corydon, prepare
A couch with roses spread;
To banish cark and care
I'll lie outstretched for hours
Mid pots and heaped-up flowers.

And bring D'Aurat to me
And all that company
The Muses love so well,
Forgetting not Jodelle.
From eve to morn we'll feast
With fivescore cups at least!

Pour wine, and pour again!
In this great goblet golden
I'll drink to Estienne
Who saved from Lethe's treasures
The sweet, sweet Teian measures
Of that lost singer olden,

Anacreon the wine-king,
To whom the drinker's pleasure
Is due, and Bacchus' treasure
His flasks, and Love, and Venus,
And tipsy old Silenus
In vine-clad bowers drinking!

[CURTIS HIDDEN PAGE]

LES ELEGIES

Quiconque aura premier la main embesongnée

Stay, woodsman, stay thy hand awhile, and hark—
It is not trees that thou art laying low!
Dost thou not see the dripping life-blood flow
From Nymphs that lived beneath the rigid bark?
Unholy murderer of our Goddesses,
If for some petty theft a varlet hangs,
What deaths hast thou deserved, what bitter pangs,
What brandings, burnings, tortures, dire distress!

O lofty wood, grove-dwelling birds' retreat,
No more shall stag and doe, with light-foot tread,
Feed in thy shadow, for thy leafy head
No more shall break the sun's midsummer heat.
The loving shepherd on his four-holed flute
Piping the praises of his fair Janette,
His mastiff near, his crook beside him set,
No more shall sing of love, but all be mute.
Silence shall fall where Echo spoke of yore,
And where soft-waving lay uncertain shade,
Coulter and plough shall pass with cutting blade
And frighted Pans and Satyrs come no more.

Farewell, thou ancient forest, Zephyr's toy!
Where first I taught my seven-tongued lyre to sing,
Where first I heard Apollo's arrows ring
Against my heart, and strike it through with joy;
Where first I worshipped fair Calliope
And loved her noble company of nine
Who showered their roses on this brow of mine;
Where with her milk Euterpe nurtured me.

Farewell, ye ancient oaks, ye sacred heads,
With images and flower-gifts worshipped erst,
But now the scorn of passers-by athirst,
Who, parched with heat the gleaming ether sheds
And robbed of your cool verdure at their need,
Accuse your murderers, and speak them scathe. . . .
Farewell, ye oaks, the valiant patriot's wreath,
Ye trees of Jove himself, Dodona's seed.

'Twas you, great oaks that gave their earliest food
To men, ungrateful and degenerate race,
Forgetful of your favors, recreant, base,
And quick to shed their foster-fathers' blood!

Wretched is he who sets his trust upon
The world! — how truly speaks philosophy,
Saying that each thing in the end must die,
Must change its form and take another on.
Fair Tempé's vale shall be in hills uptossed,
And Athos' peak become a level plain;
Old Neptune's fields shall some day wave with grain.
Matter abides forever, form is lost.

[CURTIS HIDDEN PAGE]

LES POEMES

Dedié à tresillustre et vertueuse Princess Marie Stuart, Royne d'Escosse

Encores que la mer de bien loin nous separe

Though by wide seas and Time we sundered are,
Sweet Queen, the light-flash of that beauteous sun,
Your eyes, whose like the whole world holdeth none,
Ne'er from my heart can wander long or far.

Thou other Queen, that under prison bar
Holdest so rare a queen, bid wrath begone
And change thy rede. From dawn to evening star
The sun sees not so base an action done!

Peoples, you shame your birth, sluggards at arms!
Your forbears Roland, Renault, Lancelot,
Fought with glad hearts for noble ladies' charms,

Warded, and saved them. While you, FRENCHMEN, dare
Not don your armor! — nay, have touched it not
To free from slavery a queen so fair!

[CURTIS HIDDEN PAGE]

Discours. A elle-mesme

Le jour que vostre voile aux Zephyrs se courba

When that your sail bent to the ocean-swell
And from our weeping eyes bore you away,
The self-same sail bore far from France that day
The Muses, who were wont with us to dwell
While happy Fortune stayed you in our land
And the French sceptre lay within your hand. . . .

The Muses weeping left our countryside.
  What should the nine fair comrades sing of more,
Since you, their beauteous subject and their guide,
  On unreturning ways have left our shore,
    Since you, that gave them power to speak and sing,
    Cut short their words and left them sorrowing.

Your lips, where Nature set a garden-growth
  Of pinks that sweet Persuasion watereth
With nectar and with honey; and your mouth
  Made all of rubies, pearls, and gentle breath—

Your starry eyes, two fires that Love controls,
  That make the darkest night like day to shine,
And pierce men's hearts with flame, and teach men's souls
  To know the virtue of their light divine—

The alabaster of your brow, the gold
  Of curls whose slightest ringlet might have bound
A Scythian's heart, and made a warrior bold
  Let fall his sword in battle to the ground—

The white of ivory that rounds your breast,
  Your hand, so long and slender, and so pure;
Your perfect body, Nature's finished best
  And Heaven's ideal in earth-drawn portraiture—

All these, alas! are gone. . . . What wonder then
  (Since all the grace that lavish Heaven could pour,
Revealing beauty once for all to men,
  Hath left fair France) if France can sing no more?
    How should sweet songs to lips of poets come,
    When for your loss the Muses' selves are dumb?

All that is beautiful is transient too . . .
Lilies and roses live brief days and few.
  Even so your beauty, brilliant as the sun,
    In one brief day for France has risen and set;
  Bright as the lightning, 'twas as quickly gone,
    And left us only longing and regret.

[Curtis Hidden Page]

PIECES RETRANCHEES PAR RONSARD LUI-MEME

Continuation des Amours

Hé que me sert, Pasquier, ceste belle verdure

What boots it me to see this verdure fair
That laughs along the fields — to hear the call
Of birdlings, and the purling waterfall,
And Spring-time winds that woo the murmurous air,

When she that woundeth me, yet hath no care
Of how my pains increase, comes not at all
And hides the brightness of her eyes withal,
Twin stars, that fed my heart with heavenly fare.

I had far rather keep old Winter's cold;
For Winter doth less aptly aid Love's charms
Than Spring-time months, that are Love's Summoners

Yet make me hate myself, who cannot hold
In this fair month of April in my arms
Her who doth hold my life and death in hers.

[Curtis Hidden Page]

Je vous envoye un bouquet, que ma main

I send to you a nosegay that but now
I chose among the full-blown blossoms gay.
Had one not gathered them at eve to-day
The morrow morn had found them fallen low.

Let this ensample speak to you, and show
That even your beauties, in their flower-array,
Ere little time must fade and fall away
And like the flowers in one swift moment go.

Time passes swift, my love, ah! swift it flies!
Yet no — Time passes not, but we — we pass,
And soon shall lie outstretched beneath a stone.

And for this love we talk of — Death replies
Forever not one word of it, alas! . . .
Then love me, while thou'rt fair, ere youth is gone!

[Curtis Hidden Page]

Je veux lire en trois jours l'Iliade d'Homere

I want three days to read the Iliad through!
So, Corydon, close fast my chamber door.
If anything should bother me before
I've done, I swear you'll have somewhat to rue!

No! not the servant, nor your mate, nor you
Shall come to make the bed or clean the floor.
I must have three good quiet days — or four.
Then I'll make merry for a week or two.

Ah! but — if any one should come from HER,
Admit him quickly! Be no loiterer,
But come and make me brave for his receiving.

But no one else! — not friends or nearest kin!
Though an Olympian God should seek me, leaving
His Heaven, shut fast the door! Don't let him in!
[CURTIS HIDDEN PAGE]

MICHEL DE MONTAIGNE

(1533–1592)

The present château of Montaigne stands on the right bank of the Dordogne some thirty-five miles east of Bordeaux near the village of La Mothe-Montravel in ancient Périgord. Here Michel de Montaigne, essayist, moral philosopher, and distinguished Gascon gentleman, was born on the 28th of February 1533.

He came from a family of wealthy wine merchants of Bordeaux, which had arisen to the rank of nobility. The property had been acquired by his great grandfather, Ramon Eyquem. His father, Pierre Eyquem, had entered military service in the Italian wars of Francis I, and had thereby qualified himself for nobility. The essayist was the first to abandon the family name of Eyquem and to assume the name of his seigneurial property.

His father had brought back from Italy a love of culture and a respect for learning. Frequently living at the town house of the family, he became a distinguished citizen of Bordeaux, a holder of several public offices, and finally mayor. He was reverenced by his son. Montaigne's mother, Antoinette de Louppes, was the daughter of a wealthy merchant of Toulouse, of a family of Spanish Jews which had accepted Christianity and was living in exile. Thus the Gascon, Jewish, and Spanish strains mingled in the blood of the essayist. Furthermore, with a Catholic father and a Protestant mother, he was early accustomed to an atmosphere of toleration. Of the several brothers and sisters of the family, he was himself the oldest that lived.

Pierre Eyquem had learned in Italy of the new ideas in education. In order to accustom his son to a life of simplicity and sympathy with the poor, he sent him as an infant to be nursed by a peasant on his estate. A German physician was brought to teach him Latin as his first language; he was not permitted to hear French even from the servants. We are told that the child was awakened from his sleep by musical instruments. The desire for knowledge was fostered as a spontaneous growth in gentleness and liberty.

At the age of six, he was sent to the Collège de Guyenne in Bordeaux, one of the notable schools of France. Here, at the age of seven or eight, he first became interested in literature. He tells us that his tutor contrived to ignore his neglect of regular tasks when he discovered that he was reading Ovid, Virgil, and the plays of Terence and Plautus on his own initiative. He tells us further that he completed his course at the age of thirteen. There is some reason to believe that he may have continued two years longer for the advanced course. We have no information about the years which followed or where he obtained his legal training. It would have been most natural for him to study at the famous law school at Toulouse.

In 1554, however, at the age of twenty-one, Montaigne became a councillor in the new-established Cour des Aides at Périgeux, very probably succeeding his father in the position. In 1557, this court was abolished and incorporated with the similar one at Bordeaux. Thus, for thirteen years, until his resignation in July 1570, Montaigne was a councillor in the Parliament of Bordeaux. This judicial and administrative body included men of dignity and learning, but it cannot be said that Montaigne was especially fitted for it either by temperament or intellect. Accumulating evidence indicates that he felt at this time the attractions of the court at Paris and was frequently absent from the Parliament, at one time for nearly a year and a half. He was on one occasion with Francis II at Bar-le-Duc; on another, with Charles IX at the seige of Rouen. It is not known what objectives or what ambitions he may have entertained, but he confesses that he loved Paris, and one's imagination likes to ponder what part he played in its brilliant and colorful life.

The sole experience which opened for Montaigne the potentialities and meaning of life came during the years from 1557 to 1563. This was his friendship with Etienne de la Boétie, which is dealt with in the essay *On Friendship*. La Boétie was a fellow magistrate in the Parliament of Bordeaux, scholar, humanist, and poet, with a character of elevation and commanding esteem. The friendship was of mutual inspiration and ardor; Montaigne declared it to have been "so absolute and perfect that surely the like has seldom been read of, and among the men of our day no trace is seen of any such." It seemed to rank with the classical friendships of antiquity. Montaigne had first known of him by reading his treatise *La Servitude Volontaire*. They sought each other before their first meeting came at some great city gathering. The experience seemed to partake of mystic qualities. It was inconceivable to one who had never experienced it. "In the friendship of which I speak [the minds] are blended and melted one into another in a commingling so entire that they lose sight of that which first united them and can not again find it. If I am urged to say why I loved him, I feel that it can not be expressed save by replying: 'Because it was he, because it was I.' There is, beyond all my reasoning and beyond all that I can say in detail about it, I know not what inexplicable and inevitable force that brought about this union." When La Boétie died in 1563, Montaigne remained by his bedside to the end. He had known him for six years. The experience influenced profoundly the remainder of his life.

Two years later, in 1565, Montaigne married Françoise de la Chassaigne, the daughter of a colleague of the Parliament of Bordeaux. In 1568, his father died, and the estate came into his hands. After La Boétie, his father was the next person to enter most deeply into his life. In marriage he distinguished between passion and one's natural integration with society. So far as is known, his marriage was successful; Madame de Montaigne apparently played her part ably in the life and management of his estate.

In 1569, he published his translation of *The Natural Theology of Raimond Sebond,* a theological writing of the fifteenth century. His father had asked him to translate this volume, which sought to show how man can know God through human reason. From Montaigne's own essay, *Apology for Raimond Sebond,* we learn of its effect upon Montaigne's thinking; here we have the clearest statement of his attitude toward religion and his "scepticism." In 1570, he was in Paris for the purpose of seeing the writings of La Boétie through the press.

The major change in Montaigne's life came in 1570. In July he resigned his position in the Parliament of Bordeaux, and by the next year—at the age of thirty-eight—had retired to the life of his château. No doubt there were various reasons for this move. He was weary of public service. He wished to carry on his father's estate and live the life of the *châtelain*. He craved a life of freedom, tranquillity, and leisure. La Boétie had bequeathed his books to him; he now possessed as many as a thousand volumes. He could devote himself to reading and reflection.

The original château of Montaigne was destroyed by fire in the nineteenth century; the present structure follows the earlier design. But the original round tower at the gate to the courtyard still remains today. This contains the sanctuary famed to all lovers of the *Essays*. On the ground floor, one enters a chapel with the arms of Montaigne there displayed. A spiral staircase leads to the bedchamber on the floor above. Above that, on what the essayist called the third story, is the large circular room with adjoining "cabinet" he used for his library and study; there the *Essays* were written. On the ceiling beams of this room he inscribed fifty-four quotations from pagan and Christian antiquity that sound the keynote of his writings: "Be not wise in your own conceit." "There is no reason which is not opposed by an equal reason." "Rejoice in those things that are present; all else is beyond thee." "I determine nothing, I do not comprehend things, I suspend judgment, I examine." "Men are tormented by their opinions of things, not by the things themselves." The first edition of the *Essays* appeared in Bordeaux in 1580, divided into Books I and II. They were written here in the years between 1571 and 1580.

During these same years honors were bestowed upon him, honors which he had himself sought far more in his youth. In 1571, Charles IX elected him to be one of the Knights of the Order of St. Michael. Henry III made him a Gentleman of the King's Chamber. The same honor was given to him by King Henry of Navarre in 1577. Meanwhile the civil wars between Huguenot and Catholic ravaged the country about him. Some indications lead one to believe he knew the life of a soldier himself, but we have no real information about this phase of his life if he did. He remained a Catholic and royalist to the end. We know that six daughters were born; of these only Léonor, born in 1571, lived.

After the publication of the *Essays,* Montaigne launched out on a tour of travel. He left Montaigne in June 1580 and did not return until November 1581. His stated purpose was to obtain relief at foreign baths from the malady of the stone, apparently inherited from his father. With him went a brother, two or three other companions, and servants, all traveling on horseback. They went into Switzerland, Bavaria, the Tyrol, then through the cities of Italy to Rome. In the eighteenth century, the journal he kept was discovered in a chest at Montaigne, written partly by a servant, partly by himself, now in French, now in Italian; it was published in Rome in 1774. It shows clearly the untiring enthusiasm he took in the experience. Every new day brought him in contact with new people, new characters, opinions, institutions, ways of life. In the ardor of his intellectual curiosity he seems almost to have become indifferent to his physical suffering. He discussed Protestantism with Protestants; his favorite classical authors, with scholars in Rome. He visited the poet Tasso in his confinement in Sant'Anna in Ferrara. At Rome, Roman citizenship was conferred upon him. At the shrine of Our Lady of Loretto, he affixed silver images of his own family. Finally, at Bagni della Villa, on the 7th of September 1581, the notification reached him that he had been elected mayor of Bordeaux. It was not until October 15th that he set out from Rome on his return, after he had received further letters from the Bordeaux councillors.

Montaigne's election as mayor came at a time when the hostile parties of France seemed tending toward peace, and Bordeaux was an important city. The position required a man of tact, integrity, and detachment. Only after pressure from Henry III does Montaigne seem to have accepted the office. The appointment was for two years, and it was without financial compensation. At the end of his first term, he was re-elected for two years more. During the entire four years, the situation made no demands which were beyond his powers. Nineteenth-century critics felt that his failure to return to the city in time of plague indicated weakness in meeting his obligations; according to the best evidence we have, his contemporaries never took this attitude, there was no real necessity for his return, and the criticism seems entirely unjust. Looking back upon his service, he felt he never omitted any exertion his duty really demanded from him, and that he had succeeded in accomplishing more than he had promised, even though he did not reach his own satisfaction. He had retained the confidence of both Henry III and the Protestant Henry of Navarre. Indeed the latter, who was later to become Henry IV of France, with his distinguished entourage, was his guest at Montaigne for several days.

Montaigne's second retirement came by 1586. He then wrote the third book of his *Essays* and made many changes and additions in the first two; the new edition, including the three books, appeared in Paris in 1588. In 1586, he entertained at the château a new friend and disciple, Pierre Charron. In 1588, while he was in Paris, there came from her home in Picardy the young intellectual, Marie le Jars de Gournay, twenty-three years of age, reader and admirer of his writings, to seek his acquaintance and friendship. At the age of fifty-five he responded, visited her and her widowed mother in their home, and made her his *"fille d'alliance."* After his death, she edited the posthumous edition of the *Essays* which came out in 1595, and later visited Madame de Montaigne and her daughter in the château. In 1589, Henry of Navarre became king of France. Montaigne's relations with him were clearly such that, had it not been too late, Montaigne would have rendered him valuable service.

He died at Montaigne on the 13th of September 1592. He was buried in the church of the religious order of the Feuillants in Bordeaux, which he had patronized. His widow erected a tomb with his recumbent statue, clad in armor, upon it. The Church of the Feuillants has vanished, but in the last century the tomb and statue were placed in the Faculty of Letters of Bordeaux.

During his last years, Montaigne left on the margins of a copy of the 1588 edition many final corrections and additions to his essays. This priceless copy, long lost, is now in the municipal library of the city of Bordeaux. Mlle. de Gournay's edition of 1595 differs from this Bordeaux copy. What is now usually accepted as the most authentic text of Montaigne's writings, the *Municipal Edition,* is based upon this copy. It was edited by M. Fortunat Strowski and M. Pierre Villey and was published from 1906–33.

Montaigne's *Essays* constitute one of the major contributions to the world's literature. In spite of their seeming casualness and informality, they are the result of the disciplined evolution of a mind which sought to know the nature of the human soul and the way of a complete and wholly satisfying life in conformity with human nature. Amidst the chaos of thought and existence, he sought to know himself — both through experience, and through study of the noble minds of antiquity — and through the human nature within himself, to know the human nature of all mankind. The historians and moral philosophers of antiquity were his greatest teachers: Plutarch and Seneca, especially, among others. The result was a serene way of life founded essentially on classical rather than Christian thought, in which the guidance of reason as master of the passions became habitually natural. Although conservative and loyal in his actual adherence to existing institutions of church and state, he would even suggest that self-knowledge, reason, conscience can become a sufficient guide in one's own private life to live independent of either. The only truth he could arrive at was that obtained through the reason and senses of his human experience; the divine truth of supernatural revelation was impossible of human attainment and beyond human apprehension. "It is an absolute and, as it were, divine perfection to be able to enjoy obediently one's existence. We seek other conditions because we do not understand the use of our own, and go outside of ourselves because we know not what is taking place . . . The finest lives are, to my thinking, those which are conformed to the common human model, with regularity, with nothing wonderful or extravagant." As an anonymous writer in the London *Times Literary Supplement* (March 16, 1933, p. 174) wrote, "it was as though, in Montaigne and Shakespeare, Nature had come to her own in man once more, and inspired him, as she must in her perfection, with a new reverence for man."

SELECTED BIBLIOGRAPHY

EDITIONS

Edition Municipale des Essais (Bordeaux Edition), ed. F. Strowski, F. Gebelin, and P. Villey, Bordeaux, Pech, 1906–33, 5 vols. For general use, the following editions: ed. Pierre Villey, Paris, Alcan, 1930–31, 3 vols.; ed. A. Armaingaud, Paris, Conrad, 1924–27, 6 vols.; ed. J. Plattard, Paris, Roches, 1931–33, 6 vols.; ed. F. Strowski, Paris, 1927–30, 7 vols.

TRANSLATIONS

Essays, trans. John Florio (1603), pub. in Tudor Translations, Temple Classics, Everyman's Lib.; trans. Charles Cotton (1685) later ed. W. Carew Hazlitt, London, 1865; trans. George B. Ives, Harvard Univ. Press, 1925, 4 vols.; trans. Jacob Zeitlin, New York, Knopf, 1934–36, 3 vols.; trans. E. J. Trechmann, London, Oxford Univ. Press, 1935, 2 vols., also in Modern Lib. Giant edit.; *Selected Essays,* trans. Donald M. Frame, New York, Classics Club, Black, 1943. *Journal of Travels in Italy,* trans. W. G. Waters, London, Murray, 1903, 3 vols.; trans. E. J. Trechmann, New York, Harcourt Brace, 1929.

BIOGRAPHY AND CRITICISM

Pierre Villey, *Les Sources et Evolution des Essais de M.*, Paris, Hachette, 2nd edit. 1933, 2 vols.; Gustave Lanson, *Les Essais de M. Etude et Analyse,* Paris, Doumic, 1930; Fortunat Strowski, *Montaigne,* Paris, Alcan, 2nd edit., 1931; P. Villey, *Montaigne,* Paris, Rieder, 1933; Jean Plattard, *Montaigne et Son Temps,* Paris, Boivin, 1933; Maturin Dréano, *La Pensée Religieuse de M.,* Paris, Beauchesne, 1936; F. Strowski, *Montaigne, Sa Vie Publique et Privée,* Paris, Nouv. Rev. Critique, 1938; Paul Bonnefon, *Montaigne, l'Homme et l'Oeuvre,* Paris, Picard, 1943; Charles Dédéyan, *Montaigne chez Ses Amis Anglo-Saxons,* Paris, Boivin, 1946, 2 vols.

R. W. Emerson, "Montaigne; or, the Skeptic" in *Representative Men,* Boston, 1850; Walter Pater, "Suspended Judgment" in *Gaston de Latour,* London, 1896; M. E. Lowndes, *Michel de Montaigne. A Biographical Study,* Cambridge Univ. Press, 1898; Edward Dowden, *Michel de Montaigne* (French Men of Letters), Philadelphia, Lippincott, 1906; Edith Sichel, *Michel de Montaigne,* New York, Dutton, 1911; Irene C. Willis, *Montaigne,* New York, Knopf, 1927; F. L. Lucas, "The Master-Essayist" in *Studies French and German,* London, Cassell, 1934; Marvin Lowenthal, *The Autobiography of M. de Montaigne,* Boston, Houghton Mifflin, 1935; André Gide ed., *Montaigne* (Living Thoughts Lib.), New York, Longmans, 1939; Donald M. Frame, *Montaigne in France, 1812–1852,* Columbia Univ. Press, 1940.

SPECIAL STUDIES

B. R. Headstrom, "The Philosophy of Montaigne's Skepticism," *Personalist,* XII (1931), 259–66; H. L. Stewart, "The Montaigne Quater-Centenary," *Univ. Toronto Quar.,* III (1934), 208–27; A. D. Menut, "Montaigne and the Nicomachean Ethics," *Mod. Philol.,* XXXI (1934), 225–42; J. Murray, "The Significance of Montaigne's Journal de Voyage in Relation to his Essays," *Mod. Lang. Rev.,* XXIX (1934), 291–96; W. H. Alexander, "The Sieur de Montaigne and Cicero," *Univ. Toronto Quar.,* IX (1940), 222–30, and "Montaigne's Classical Book-shelf," *ibid.,* XI (1942), 78–86; E. Marchand, "Montaigne and the Cult of Ignorance," *Romanic Rev.,* XXXVI (1945), 275–82; D. M. Frame, "Did Montaigne Betray Sebond?" *Rom. Rev.,* XXXVIII (1947), 297–329; also "A Detail in Montaigne's Thought: The Source of Our Ignorance Is the Source of Our Happiness," *Word,* V (1949), 159–65; H. Kurz, "Montaigne and La Boétie in the Chapter on Friendship," *Pub. Mod. Lang. Assoc.,* LXV (1950), 483–530; E. H. Henderson, "Montaigne and Modern Philosophy," *Personalist,* XXXIV (1953), 278–89.

ESSAYS

Translated by JACOB ZEITLIN

[Taken from *The Essays of Michel de Montaigne,* translated by Jacob Zeitlin, 3 vols., Alfred A. Knopf, New York, 1934.]

TO THE READER

This, READER, is an honest book. It apprises you at the very outset that I proposed no other aim to myself than a domestic and private one. I have had no view therein either to thy service or my glory. My powers are not capable of any such design. I have intended it for the particular benefit of my kinsfolk and friends, so that when they have lost me (which they soon must do) they may therein recover some features of my character and humour, and by that means keep alive more entirely and more vividly the knowledge they have had of me. Had it been my purpose to seek the favour of the world, I should have taken more pains in my adornment and have appeared before it in a studied posture. I desire that men should see me in my simple, natural, and ordinary fashion, without straining or artifice: for it is myself that I portray. My defects will there be read to the life, and my native form, so far as respect for the public has permitted me to display it. Had I belonged to one of those nations which are still said to live in the sweet liberty of nature's first laws, I assure you that I should very gladly have painted myself at full length and in all my nakedness. Thus, reader, I am myself the substance of my book: there is no reason why you should take up your time with so frivolous and so vain a subject.

Farewell, then, from Montaigne, this first day of March, fifteen hundred and eighty.

BOOK ONE

CHAPTER 26

OF THE EDUCATION OF CHILDREN

To Madame Diane de Foix, Comtesse de Gurson

* * * * * *

Madame, learning is a great ornament and an instrument of marvelous utility, especially in persons raised to that degree of fortune in which you are. In truth, in hands of mean and low condition it does not have its true employment. It takes much more pride in lending its powers in the conduct of war, in the government of peoples, in securing the friendship of a prince or a foreign nation, than in constructing a dialectical argument or in prescribing a package of pills. Wherefore, Madame, believing you will not omit this feature in the education of your children, you who have tasted its sweetness and who come of a lettered race (for we still have the writings of the ancient Counts of Foix, from whom Monsieur the Count your husband and yourself are both descended; and François, Monsieur de Candale, your uncle, every day brings forth others which will extend the knowledge of this quality in your family to many ages), I will impart to you on this theme a single fancy of my own which is contrary to general usage: it is all I am able to contribute to your service in this affair.

The office of the tutor you shall provide for your son, upon the choice of whom depends the whole success of his education, has several important duties which I shall not mention, as being unable to add anything of moment concerning them; and in this particular wherein I take upon me to give him advice, he may believe me so far only as his reason shall approve.

For a child of noble family, who is earnestly interested in letters, not for the sake of gain (for so abject a purpose is unworthy of the grace and favour of the Muses, and moreover is directed toward and dependent upon other persons), nor so much for external advantages as for those that concern him individually, and to enrich and adorn himself within, the desire being to make of him an accomplished man rather than a man of learning, I would wish that care should be taken to choose for him a tutor who has rather a well-made head than a well-filled one, and that both things should be required of him, but character and understanding more than learning, and that he should conduct himself in his responsibility after a new method.

Our schoolmasters are eternally shouting into our ears as though they were pouring into a funnel, while our business is only to repeat what the others have said. I would have the tutor correct this practice, and that at the very outset he should, according to the capacity of the mind he has to deal with, begin to put it to the test, making it taste things, select them, and distinguish among them by itself, sometimes opening a path for it, sometimes leaving it to open it for itself. I would not have him do all the thinking and speaking; I would have him hear his pupil speak in turn. Socrates, and after him Arcesilaus, first made their scholars speak, and then they spoke to them. "The authority of the teacher is generally an obstacle for those who wish to learn" (Cicero). It is good to make him trot before him that he may judge of his paces and how much he should abate of his own speed to accommodate himself to his strength. For want of this proportion we spoil all; to learn to hit upon it and to conduct oneself therein with due measure is one of the most arduous tasks that I know, and it is the action of a high and strong nature to know how to condescend to its childish steps and direct them. I walk with surer and firmer step up hill than down.

If teachers, according to our common way, undertake with one and the same lesson and a similar standard of guidance to govern a number of minds so diverse in their measure and shape, it is no wonder if in a whole multitude of children they scarcely find two or three who bear away any good fruit from their instruction.

Let the master demand an account not only of the words of his lesson, but of the sense and substance of it, and let him judge of the profit he has made, not by the testimony of his memory but by that of his life. Let him make him put what he has learned into a hundred forms and apply it to as many different subjects, to see if he has yet rightly comprehended it and made it his own, informing himself of his progress according to the pedagogic method of Plato. It is a sign of crudity and indigestion to disgorge what we eat just as it was swallowed. The stomach has not performed its office unless it has altered the form and condition of what was given to it to concoct.

Our minds work only upon trust, being bound and constrained to the appetites of another's fancy, enslaved and held fast under the authority of another's instruction. We have been so subjected to leading-strings that we no longer have any freedom of movement. Our vigour and liberty is extinguished. "They have never become masters of their own thoughts" (Seneca).

I had some private conversation at Pisa with an excellent man, but so great an Aristotelian that his most pervasive doctrine was: "That the touchstone and rule of all solid speculation and of all truth is its conformity to the teaching of Aristotle, that all besides is nothing but inanity and chimera, that he has seen all and said all." This position, for having been a little too broadly and unfairly interpreted, brought him once and long kept him in great danger of the Inquisition at Rome.

Let the tutor make his pupil sift everything, and lodge nothing in his head upon simple authority and trust. Let not the principles of Aristotle be principles to him, any more than those of the Stoics and the Epicureans. Let this diversity of opinions be laid before him; he will choose, if he be able; if not, he will remain in doubt. Only fools are sure and immovable.

> Doubting pleases me no less than knowing. (Dante)

For if he embrace the opinions of Xenophon and Plato by his own reason, they will no longer be theirs, they will become his own. Who follows another, follows nothing. He finds nothing, nay, he seeks nothing. "We are not subjects of a king: let each one claim his own freedom" (Seneca). Let him at least know that he knows. He must imbibe their essence, not learn their precepts. Let him boldly forget, if he will, where he has learned them, but let him know how to apply them to his use. Truth and reason are common to every one, and no more belong to him who spoke them first than to him who speaks them after. It is no more according to Plato than according to me, since he and I understand it and view it alike. Bees pilfer from this flower and that, but afterwards make honey thereof which is all their own; it is no longer thyme and marjoram; so the pieces he borrows from others, he will transform and fuse to make of them a work that shall be absolutely his own, that is to say, his judgment. His education, his labour and study, tend to nothing else but to form that.

Let him conceal where he has gained his assistance and show only what he has made of it. Pillagers and borrowers make a display of their purchases and buildings, not of that which they have taken from others. You do not see the "gratuities" of a magistrate, but you see the alliances he has made and the honours he has obtained for his children. No one publishes the nature of his revenue; but every one publishes his acquisitions. The gain from our study is to become better and wiser thereby.

It is the understanding, said Epicharmus, that sees and hears, it is the understanding that improves everything, that orders everything, that acts, rules, and reigns: all other things are blind, and deaf, and without soul. Truly we render it abject and cowardly in not allowing it the liberty to do anything of itself. Who ever asked his pupil what he thought of rhetoric or grammar, and of such and such a thought of Cicero? Our masters stick them, full feathered, in our memories, like oracles in which the letters and syllables are of the substance of the thing. To know by rote is no knowledge; it is only to retain what has been given into the keeping of our memory. That which a man rightly understands he disposes of without looking at the pattern, without turning his eyes toward his book. What a sorry proficiency is a proficiency that is merely bookish! I look to have it serve for ornament, not for a foundation, according to the opinion of Plato, who says that constancy, faith, and sincerity are the true philosophy, and that sciences that are directed to other ends are nothing but face-paint. I could wish that Paluel or Pompey, those splendid dancers of my time, might teach us their capers only by seeing them done without stirring from our places, as these men pretend to inform the understanding without ever setting it to work; or that we should be taught to manage a horse, or a pike, or a lute, or the voice, without the trouble of practice, as these attempt to teach us to judge and speak well without exercising us in judging or speaking. Now for the instruction that I propose, whatsoever presents itself before us is book sufficient; a roguish trick of a page, a stupid mistake of a servant, a remark at the table, are so many new subjects.

For this reason, intercourse with men is extremely suitable, as well as travel in foreign countries, not only to bring back, in the manner of our French nobility, an account of how many paces Santa Rotonda is in circuit, or of the richness of Signora Livia's petticoats, or, like some others, how much Nero's face in a statue of some old ruin is longer or broader than on some medal of equal antiquity, but chiefly to bring back an impression of the peculiarities of these nations and their customs, and that we may rub and sharpen our wits against those of others. I would have a boy sent abroad very young, and first, so as to kill two birds with one stone, to those neighbouring nations whose language is most removed from our own, and to which, if it be not formed betimes, the tongue cannot be made supple.

It is also an opinion generally accepted that it is not right for a child to be brought up in the lap of his parents; their natural affection makes them too tender and lax, even the wisest of them. They are capable neither of chastising his faults nor of seeing him brought up hardily, as he should be, and hazardously. They will not endure to see him return, all dust and sweat, from his exercise, drink when he is hot or when he is cold, nor see him mount a rearing horse, nor take a foil in hand against a sturdy fencer, nor with his first musket in his hand. For there is no remedy; if one would make a proper man of him, it is certain that one must not spare him when young, and must very often transgress the rules of physic:

> To live beneath the open sky,
> Alert at danger's call. (Horace)

It is not enough to toughen his spirit, his muscles also must be toughened. For the spirit is too greatly strained if it is not supported, and would have too hard a task to discharge two offices alone. I know how mine pants in the company of a body so delicate, so sensitive, and that leans so heavily upon it. And often in my reading I perceive that our masters, in their writings, make examples pass for magnanimity and strength of courage which really are rather toughness of skin and hardness of bone. I have seen men, women, and children naturally so constituted that a cudgeling is less to them than a flirt with a finger to me; who do not utter a sound nor wink an eyelash at the blows they receive. When athletes imitate philosophers in patience, it is strength of nerves rather than of heart. Now, to be accustomed to undergo labour is to be accustomed to endure pain: "toil induces a certain callousness to pain" (Cicero). A boy is to be broken to the pain and harshness of exercise, so as to be trained up to the pain and harshness of dislocations, cholics, cauteries, and also of imprisonment and the rack. For he may fall a prey even to the last of these, which, in times like ours, light upon the good as well as the bad. We have living proof of it. Whoever draws his sword against the laws threatens the honestest men with the whip and the halter.

And moreover, the authority of the tutor, which ought to be sovereign over the boy, is checked and hindered by the presence of parents; to which may be added that the respect the whole household pay to him, and the consciousness he has of the power and greatness of his house are, in my opinion, no small disadvantages at that age.

In this school of intercourse with men I have often observed this vice, that instead of taking cognizance of others, we make it our whole business to give cognizance of ourselves, and are more concerned to make sale of our own wares than to acquire a stock of the new. Silence and modesty are very advantageous qualities in this intercourse. The boy will be trained to be sparing and economical of his accomplishment when he has acquired it, and not to take exception to idle sayings or ridiculous stories that will be told in his presence, for it is an unmannerly annoyance to bristle up at everything that is not to our own taste. Let him be satisfied with correcting himself and not seem to condemn everything in another that he would not do himself, nor set himself in opposition to common customs. "A man may be wise without parade and without arousing enmity" (Seneca). Let him avoid these overbearing and uncivil airs, and this childish ambition of wishing to appear cleverer by being different and to gain a reputation by censoriousness and originality. For as it becomes none but great poets to make use of the licences of their art, so it is intolerable for any but great and illustrious minds to assume a privilege above the authority of custom. "Because Socrates and Aristippus have done something contrary to the manners and established customs of the city, let him not think he has a right to do the same: they have gained this privilege for themselves by great and divine talents" (Cicero). He will be instructed not to engage in argument or dispute but with a champion worthy of him, and even then not to make use of all the arts that may serve his purpose, but only of those that may serve him best. Let him be taught to be fastidious in the choice and sorting of his arguments, loving pertinence and, consequently, brevity. But above all let him be instructed to surrender and lay down his arms to the truth so soon as ever he shall discover it, whether it comes to light in his opponent's argument or upon better consideration of his own. For he will not be placed in a professor's chair to read a set lecture. He is bound to no cause save in so far as he approves it. Nor will he follow a calling in which the liberty to repent and acknowledge one's error is sold for ready money. "Nor is he constrained by any necessity to defend everything that has been prescribed and enjoined" (Cicero).

If his tutor be of my humour, he will form his will to be a very loyal subject to his prince, very affectionate and very courageous; but he will cool in him the desire of attaching himself to his service otherwise than by public duty. Besides several other disadvantages which through these private obligations strike at our liberty, the judgment of a man who is bought and receives wages either operates with less integrity and freedom, or it is tainted both with indiscretion and ingratitude. A courtier can have neither the right nor the wish to speak or think otherwise than favourably of a master who, among so many thousands of other subjects, has chosen him to foster and advance with his own hand. This favour and benefit corrupt his freedom, not without some reason, and dazzle him. Therefore the language of these people is generally observed to be different from all other language spoken in a nation and is very little to be trusted in matters of this sort.

Let his conscience and virtue shine forth in his speaking, and have only reason for their guide. Make him understand that to acknowledge the error he shall discover in his own argument, though it is observed only by himself, is an act of judgment and sincerity, which are the principal things he is to seek after; that obstinacy and contentiousness are common qualities, most often seen in the meanest minds, that to change his mind and correct himself, to forsake a bad position at the height of his ardour, are tokens of rare, strong, and philosophical qualities.

Let him be warned, when he is in company, to have his eyes everywhere, for I find that the chief seats are commonly seized upon by the least capable man, and that greatness of fortune is seldom joined with ability. I have been present when, while those at the upper end of the table were amusing themselves with talk of the beauty of the arras or the flavour of the malmsey, many fine remarks were lost at the other end. Let him sound every man's capacity; a cowherd, a mason, a passer-by—he must put them all to work and borrow from each according to his wares, for everything is of use in a household; the very folly and weakness of others will serve him for instruction. By observing the graces and manners of each one, he will beget in himself a desire of good manners and a contempt of the bad.

Let an honest curiosity be instilled in his mind for inquiring after all things; whatever singular thing there is in his neighbourhood, let him go and see it—a building, a fountain, a man, the site of an ancient battle, the place where Cæsar or Charlemagne have passed,

> What lands are frozen, what are parched, explore,
> And what wind bears us to the Italian shore. (Propertius)

Let him inquire into the characters, resources and alliances of princes. These are things very pleasant to learn and very useful to know.

In this intercourse with men I mean to include, and as the chief part, those who live only in the memory of books. By means of histories he will hold converse with the great minds of the best ages. It is a vain study if one makes it so, but also, if one makes it so, it is a study of inestimable fruit and value, and the only study, as Plato reports, that the Lacedæmonians reserved to themselves.

What profit shall he not reap in this quarter by reading the lives of our Plutarch? But let my governor remember to what end his instructions are directed, and let him not so much imprint in his pupil's memory the date of the ruin of Carthage as the characters of Hannibal and Scipio; nor so much where Marcellus died, as why it was unworthy of his duty to die there. Let him not teach him so much the facts of history as how to judge them. It is, in my opinion, the subject matter of all others to which our minds apply themselves in the most differing manners. I have read a hundred things in Livy that another has not. Plutarch has read a hundred more there than ever I could find or than, peradventure, the author ever put there. To some it is merely a grammatical study, to others the anatomy of philosophy, in which the most abstruse parts of our human nature penetrate. There are in Plutarch many extended discourses very worthy to be observed, for he is, in my opinion, the master workman in this craft; but there are a thousand others which he has no more than touched upon; he only points with his finger to direct us which way we may go, if we like, and contents himself sometimes with a single thrust at the quick of a question. It is for us to extricate them and place them where they will do business. As, for example, his saying that the inhabitants of Asia came to be subjects to one man, for not having been able to pronounce one single syllable, which is No, gave perhaps matter and occasion to La Boétie to write his *Voluntary Servitude.* Only to see him pick out a slight action in a man's life, or a word that does not seem to amount to anything, is in itself a whole discourse. It is a pity that men of understanding should be so fond of brevity; no doubt their reputation is the better by it, but we are worse off. Plutarch had rather we should applaud his judgment than his knowledge; he had rather leave us with an appetite for him than with satiety. He knew that a man may say too much even upon the best subjects, and that Alexandridas justly reproached the man who was making a very good speech to the Ephors, but too long: "O stranger, you say what you should, but differently than you should." Such as have lean bodies stuff them out with padding; such as have slender substance inflate it with words.

The human judgment is marvellously enlightened by going about in the world. We are all confined and pent up within ourselves, and our view is shortened to the length of our own noses. Someone asked Socrates of what country he was. He did not answer, "Of Athens," but "Of the world." He, whose imagination was fuller and wider, embraced the whole world as his city, and extended his acquaintance, his society, and affections to all mankind; not as we do, who look no further than our feet. When the vines of my village are nipped with the frost, my parish priest presently concludes that the wrath of God is gone out against all the human race and that the cannibals have already got the pip. Who is there that, seeing these civil wars of ours, does not cry out that the machine of the world is being destroyed, and that the day of judgment has us by the throat; without reflecting that many worse things have occurred and that, meanwhile, people are having a very good time in a thousand other parts of the earth? For myself, considering the licence and impunity that attends such commotions, I wonder they are so mild and moderate. To him who feels the hailstones about his ears the whole hemisphere appears to be in storm and tempest. The Savoyard said that if that fool of a French king had known how to manage his fortune, he might have become steward of his master the Duke. His imagination could not conceive a more exalted grandeur than that of his master. We are all of us insensibly in this error, an error of serious consequence and harm. But whoever shall represent to his fancy, as in a picture, that great image of our mother Nature, in her full majesty; whoever in her countenance shall read so universal and so constant a variety; whoever shall observe himself therein, and not only himself, but a whole kingdom, as a point made with an extremely delicate touch, that man alone estimates things according to their true proportion.

This great world, which some yet multiply as a species under one genus, is the mirror wherein we are to behold ourselves in order to know ourselves from the true angle. In short, I would have this to be my scholar's book. So many humours, sects, judgments, opinions, laws and customs, teach us to judge healthily of our own and teach our understanding to recognize its imperfection and its natural infirmity, which is not a trivial lesson. So many revolutions of states and changes of public fortune teach us to make no great miracle of our own. So many names, so many victories and conquests buried in oblivion, render ridiculous our hopes of eternizing our names by the taking of half-a-score of troopers or a henroost, which is known only by the fact of its fall. The pride and arrogance of so many foreign pomps, the puffed-up majesty of so many courts and grandeurs, give strength and steadiness to our sight, so that it can view the splendour of our own without blinking. So many millions of men buried before us encourage us not to fear to seek such good company in the other world. And so of all the rest.

Our life, said Pythagoras, resembles the great and populous assembly of the Olympic games. Some exercise the body to gain glory in the games; others bring merchandise to sell for profit. There are some, and they not the worst, who pursue no other advantage than to observe how and why everything is done, and to be spectators of the lives of other men, in order to judge and regulate their own.

To examples may appropriately be joined all the profitable arguments of philosophy, to which human actions ought to be referred as to their standard. The boy will be told,

> What we should wish for, how we may discern
> The bounds of wealth, and its true uses learn;
> How fix the portion which we ought to give
> To friends, relations, country — how to live
> As fits our station; and how best pursue
> What God has placed us in this world to do,
> Learn what we are, and for what purpose born; (Persius)

what it is to know and what to be ignorant; what ought to be the aim of study; what valour, temperance, and justice are; the difference between ambition and avarice, servitude and submission, licence and liberty; by what token a man may know true and solid contentment; to what extent death, suffering, and shame are to be feared,

> In what way
> He may shun or suffer each particular toil; (Virgil)

by what secret springs we move, and the reason for so great a variety of impulses within us. For, methinks, the first lessons with which one should slake his understanding ought to be those which regulate his morals and his sense, which will teach him to know himself and how both to die well and to live well.

Among the liberal arts let us begin with that which makes us free. They all serve in some measure to the formation and use of life, as all other things in some fashion do; but let us make choice of that which directly and professedly serves to that end. If we were able to restrict the functions of our life to their just and natural limits, we should find that most of the sciences in use are of no use to us, and that even in those that are, there are useless stretches and abysses which we should do better to let alone, and following the teaching of Socrates, limit the extent of our studies in those subjects which are lacking in utility.

> So, then, have courage to be wise! Begin!
> He that would mend his life, yet still delays
> To set to work, is like the clown who stays
> Till the broad stream that bars his way is gone,
> But on still flows the stream, and ever will flow on. (Horace)

It is a great folly to teach our children

> What influence Pisces and fierce Leo have
> Or Capricorn, bathed in Hesperian wave, (Propertius)

the knowledge of the stars and the motion of the eighth sphere, before their own movements:

> What are the Pleaides to me,
> And what to me Boötes' stars? (Anacreon)

Anaximenes writing to Pythagoras: "With what sense can I amuse myself in searching out the secrets of the stars, having death or slavery continually present to my eyes?" (for the kings of Persia were at that time preparing to invade his country). Everyone ought to say thus: "Being assaulted by ambition, avarice, temerity, superstition, and having within me so many other enemies of life, shall I go speculating about the revolutions of the earth?"

After having taught him what will make him wiser and better, you may then take up with him the meaning of logic, physics, geometry, rhetoric; and the science which he shall choose when his judgment is already formed he will quickly make his own. The instruction ought to be carried on sometimes by conversation and sometimes by books; sometimes his tutor shall put into his hands the author himself, whom he thinks appropriate for his instruction, and sometimes he will give him the marrow and substance well digested. And if he is not himself familiar enough with books to find all the fine passages that are in them for his purpose, some man of letters may be associated with him, who as each need arises shall supply him with the provision he requires, to deal it out and dispense it to his pupil. And who can doubt but that this way of teaching is more easy and natural than that of Gaza. In the latter the precepts are so thorny and disagreeable and the words so empty and fleshless that there is no hold to be taken of them, nothing that rouses the mind. In the other the mind has something to bite into and feed upon. The fruit of it is greater beyond comparison, and yet it will be much sooner ripe.

It is a singular thing that matters should be at such a pass in this age of ours that philosophy, even with men of understanding, should be a vain and fantastic name, a thing of no use, no value, both in common opinion and in fact. I think those ergotisms, by seizing the approaches to it, are the cause. It is entirely wrong to represent it to children as a thing of so difficult access, and with such a frowning, grim, and formidable countenance. Who is it that has marked it with this false, pale, and hideous face? There is nothing more gay, more sprightly, more frolic, and I might almost say more wanton. She preaches nothing but merrymaking and jollity. A mournful and dejected look shows that she does not inhabit there. Demetrius the grammarian, finding in the temple of Delphi a knot of philosophers seated together, said to them, "Either I am deceived or, judging by your serene and cheerful countenances, you are engaged in no very deep discourse." To which one of them, Heracleon the Megarean, replied: "It is for those who are inquiring whether the future tense of the verb βάλλω be spelt with a double λ, or who hunt after the derivation of the comparatives χεῖρον and βέλτιον and the superlatives χεῖριστον and βέλτιστον, to knit their brows while discoursing of their science. But as to philosophical discussions, they are wont to enliven and delight those that are engaged in them and never deject them or make them sad."

Still we find
The face the unerring index of the mind,
And as this feels or fancies joys or woes,
That pales with sorrow, or with rapture glows. (Juvenal)

The soul that lodges philosophy ought by its healthiness to make the body healthy too. It ought to make its tranquillity and gladness shine forth. It should fashion the outward behaviour to its own mould, and consequently arm it with a graceful pride, an active and spirited carriage, and a contented and gracious countenance. The most manifest sign of wisdom is a constant cheerfulness; her state is like that of things in the regions above the moon, always serene. It is "Baroco" and "Baralipton" that render their disciples so dirty and smoky, and not she; they know her but by hearsay. What! She makes it her business to calm the tempests of the soul and to teach famine and fevers to laugh, not by certain imaginary epicycles but by natural and palpable arguments. She has virtue for her end; which is not, as the schoolmen say, situated upon the summit of an abrupt mountain, rugged and inaccessible. Such as have approached her find her, quite on the contrary, seated in a fair plain, fertile and flowering, whence she easily observes all things beneath her; but any one may arrive there, if he but know the way, through shady, green, and sweetly blooming avenues, pleasantly, by an easy and smooth slope, like that of the celestial vaults. For not having associated with this supreme, beautiful, triumphant, loving, alike delicious and courageous virtue, this professed and implacable enemy to sourness, trouble, fear, and constraint, having Nature for her guide, Fortune and Pleasure for her companions, they have gone, according to their own weakness, and created this ridiculous, this stupid image, mournful, querulous, sulky, threatening, scowling, and placed it upon a rock apart, amid brambles, a hobgoblin to terrify people.

My tutor, who knows that he ought to fill the soul of his pupil as much or more with affection than with awe toward virtue, will be able to tell him that the poets express the common feeling, and will make him see plainly that the gods have placed perspiring toil in the approaches to the chambers of Venus and not of Minerva. And when he shall arrive at a consciousness of himself and have offered to him a Bradamante or an Angelica for a mistress to be enjoyed — a natural, active, spirited, not mannish but manly beauty, alongside of a soft, affected, effeminate, artificial beauty — the one in the habit of a youth, wearing a glittering helmet, the other dressed like a girl, adorned with a head-dress of pearls — he will then judge even his love to be masculine, if he shall choose quite differently from that effeminate shepherd of Phrygia.

He will put before him this new lesson, that the worth and height of true virtue consists in the facility, usefulness, and pleasure of its exercise, so far removed from difficulty that children as well as men are capable of it, the simple as well as the subtle. Moderation is the means to acquire it, not effort. Socrates, her first favourite, deliberately renounces all effort, to slide into the natural and smooth course of her progression. She is the nursing mother of human pleasures. By making them upright, she makes them pure and permanent. By moderating them, she keeps them in breath and appetite. By eliminating those which she refuses, she whets our desire for those which she leave us; and she leaves us abundantly all that nature requires, even to satiety, like an indulgent mother, if not to lassitude; unless, perchance, we mean to say that the regimen which stops the toper before the point of drunkenness, the glutton before indigestion, and the lecher before he has lost his hair, is an enemy to our pleasures. If the common sort of fortune plays her false, she rises above it or does without it, and forms for herself another, wholly her own, not so fickle and unsteady. She can be rich, potent, and learned, and lie upon perfumed beds. She loves life, she loves beauty, and glory, and health. But her proper and peculiar function is to know how to enjoy the use of these good things with self-control, and how to bear their loss with firmness: a function much more noble than troublesome, without which the whole course of life is unnatural, turbulent, and deformed, and one may fairly associate with it those rocks, those thickets, and those monsters.

If this pupil should happen to be of so unpromising a disposition that he had rather listen to a tale of a tub than the narrative of some noble expedition or some wise conversation, when he happens to hear it; if, at the sound of the drum that excites the youthful ardour of his companions, he turns aside to another that invites him to the jugglers; if he does not by preference find it more pleasant and sweet to return dusty and victorious from a combat, with the prize of that exercise, than from tennis or from a ball, I see no other remedy than that, ere it be too late, his tutor should strangle him, if there are no witnesses, or that he be apprenticed to a pastry-maker in some good town, though he were the son of a duke, pursuant to Plato's precept that children are to be placed not according to the quality of their father, but according to the qualities of their own minds.

Since philosophy is that which instructs us to live, and since childhood has its lessons in it as well as other ages, why is it not communicated to children?

> But yet thou art a moist and yielding clay:
> Call for some plastic hand without delay,
> Nor cease the labour, till the wheel produce
> A vessel nicely formed, and fit for use. (Persius)

They begin to teach us to live when life has gone by. A hundred students have got the pox before they have come to read Aristotle on temperance. Cicero said that though he should live two men's lives, he should never find leisure to study the lyric poets; and I find these sophists still more deplorably unprofitable. The boy we would breed has much less time to spare; he owes but the first fifteen or sixteen years of his life to pedagogy; the remainder belongs to action. Let us, therefore, employ that short time in the necessary instruction. They are abuses: away with all these thorny subtleties of dialectics by which our lives can never be amended. Take the simple teachings of philosophy, learn how to select them and give them point; they are easier to understand than a tale of Boccaccio. A child newly weaned is more capable of them than of learning to read or write. Philosophy has teachings for the birth of man as for his decrepitude.

I am of Plutarch's mind, that Aristotle did not so much trouble his illustrious pupil with the trick of constructing syllogisms or with the elements of geometry, as with infusing in him good precepts concerning valour, prowess, magnanimity, temperance, and the assurance that knows no fear; and, with this provision, he sent him, while yet a boy, to subjugate the empire of the whole earth, with no more than thirty thousand foot, four thousand horse, and but forty-two thousand crowns. For the other arts and sciences, he says, Alexander honoured them and commended their excellence and charm, but for all the pleasure that he took in them, he was not easily seduced by a desire to practise them.

> Seek then, both old and young, from truths like these,
> That certain aim which life's last cares may ease. (Persius)

It is what Epicurus says in the beginning of his letter to Meniceus: "The youngest should not refuse to study philosophy nor the oldest grow weary of it." Whoever does otherwise seems to say that either the time of living happily is not yet come or that it is already past.

For all these reasons, I would not have this pupil of ours imprisoned. I would not have him given up to the morose humour of a violent schoolmaster. I would not have his spirit debased by confining him to torture and toil, as they do the others, fourteen or fifteen hours a day, like a porter. Neither should I think it good, if by virtue of a solitary and pensive disposition he is discovered to be addicted with an indiscreet application to the study of books, to foster that propensity in him; that renders them unfit for social intercourse and diverts them from better employments. And how many have I not seen in my time brutified by an immoderate thirst after knowledge! Carneades was so besotted with it that he had no time to attend to his hair and nails. Neither would I have his noble manners spoiled by contact with the incivility and barbarism of others. The French wisdom was once upon a time proverbial for a wisdom which was early in gaining a hold, but slight in duration. In truth, we still see that there is nothing so charming as little children in France, but ordinarily they deceive the hope that has been conceived of them, and as grown men they are without distinction. I have heard men of understanding say that these schools to which we send them, of which we have an abundance, make them such animals as they are.

But to our pupil a closet, a garden, the table, the bed, solitude, company, morning and evening, all hours shall be the same, and all places serve him for a study; for philosophy, which, as the moulder of judgment and character, will be his principal lesson, has this priviledge of intruding everywhere. The orator Isocrates, being at a feast entreated to speak of his art, all the company felt that he was right in answering, "It is not now the time for what I can do; and that for which it is now time I cannot do." For to deliver harangues and rhetorical disputations in a company met together to laugh and make good cheer would result in a discordant medley. And as much might be said of all the other sciences. But as to what concerns philosophy, in that part which treats of man and of his duties and functions, it has been the common opinion of all wise men that, in view of the sweetness of her conversation, she is never to be excluded either from feastings or games. And Plato having invited her to his banquet, we see how she entertains the company in a delicate manner, suited both to time and place, though it be one of his most elevated and salutary discourses:

truths that rich and poor concern,
Which young and old are lost unless they learn. (Horace)

Thus, doubtless, he will spend less time in idling than the others. But as the steps we take in walking to and fro in a gallery, though three times as many, do not tire us as much as those we employ in a fixed journey, so our lesson, occurring as it were accidentally, without being bound to time or place, and mingling with all our actions, will glide by without being felt. Our very games and exercises will be a good part of our study: running, wrestling, music, dancing, hunting, the management of horses and of weapons. I would have his outward manners, and his social behaviour, and the carriage of his person formed at the same time with his mind. It is not a mind, it is not a body that we are training; it is a man, and he ought not to be divided into two parts. And, as Plato says, we must not train one without the other, but drive them abreast like two horses harnessed to the same pole. And, to listen to him, does he not seem to bestow more time and more care on the exercise of the body and to hold that the mind thereby gets its exercise at the same time, and not the reverse?

As to the rest, this education ought to be carried on with a severe sweetness, not as it is now done. Instead of alluring children to letters, they do in truth present them with nothing but horror and cruelty. Away with violence and compulsion! There is nothing which in my opinion so powerfully corrupts and stupefies a well-born nature. If you would have him stand in fear of shame and chastisement, do not harden him to them. Harden him to toil and cold, to wind and sun, and to dangers that he ought to despise; wean him from all effeminacy and delicacy in clothes and sleep, eating and drinking; accustom him to everything. Let him not be a pretty and lady-like boy, but a lusty and vigorous youth. In childhood, in manhood, in old age, I have ever believed and thought in the same way. But among other things, the discipline of most of our schools has always displeased me. They might perhaps have erred less perniciously by leaning toward indulgence. It is a veritable jail of imprisoned youth. They become undisciplined by being punished before they are so. Enter the room when they are about their lesson: you shall hear nothing but the cries of boys undergoing chastisement and of masters beside themselves with rage. What a way to arouse an eagerness for their lessons in these delicate and timid minds, to lead them to it with a terrifying visage and an armful of rods! A wicked and pernicious proceeding! Besides what Quintilian has very well observed, that this imperious authority is attended by very dangerous consequences, and particularly with our way of chastising. How much more becoming would it be to have their classes strewn with flowers and with leaves than with the bloody stumps of birches! I should paint the school with the pictures of Joy and Gladness, of Flora and the Graces, as the philosopher Speusippus did in his school. Where their profit is, let their pleasure be also. One should sweeten the food that is wholesome for the child and dip in gall what is harmful to him. It is marvellous to see how solicitous Plato is in his Laws concerning the gayety and diversion of the youth of his city, and how he dwells upon their races, games, songs, jumping and dancing, of which he says that antiquity has given the ordering and patronage to the gods themselves, to Apollo, the Muses and Minerva. He spreads himself in a thousand precepts for his gymnasium; as to the literary studies, he wastes very little time over them and seems to recommend poetry particularly only for the sake of the music.

All strangeness and peculiarity in our habits and modes of conduct is to be avoided as inimical to social intercourse and savouring of the monstrous. Who would not be astonished at the constitution of Demophon, steward to Alexander the Great, who sweated in the shade and shivered in the sun? I have seen men run from the smell of an apple more swiftly than from a musket-shot, others take fright at a mouse, others vomit at the sight of cream, others at the making of a feather bed; and Germanicus could endure neither the sight nor the crowing of a cock. There may, perhaps, be some occult cause in these cases; but in my opinion a man might stifle it if he applied himself to it in time. Education has prevailed thus far with me (it is true that it was not without some trouble) that, beer excepted, my appetite accommodates itself indifferently to all sorts of diet. While the body is yet supple, one should on that account adjust it to all fashions and customs. And provided he can hold the appetite and the will under control, let us boldly make a young man fit for all nations and all companies, even to irregularity and excess, if need be. Let his practice follow the custom. Let him be able to do everything, but love to do nothing but what is good. The philosophers themselves do not find it praiseworthy in Callisthenes that he forfeited the favour of his master Alexander the Great by refusing to keep pace with him in drinking. Let him laugh, make merry, and live riotously with his prince. I would that even in his dissipation he should excel his companions in vigour and endurance, and that he should not give over doing evil either for want of power or knowledge, but for want of will. "There is a great difference between not wishing and not knowing enough to do evil" (Seneca). I thought I was doing honour to a gentleman, who was as far removed from those excesses as any man in France, by asking him in the presence of good company how many times in his life he had got drunk in the interest of the king's business in Germany. He took it as it was intended, and answered, "Three times," recounting the occasions. I know some who for want of this faculty have found a great inconvenience in negotiating with that nation. I have often with great admiration reflected upon the wonderful constitution of Alcibiades, that could so easily adjust itself to fashions so various without any prejudice to his health, one while outdoing the Persians in pomp and luxury, and another the Lacedæmonians in austerity and frugality; as pure in Sparta as he was voluptuous in Ionia,

> Old Aristippus every dress became,
> In every state and circumstance the same. (Horace)

I would have my pupil be such,

> But lift the man into a higher sphere,
> Who in a blanket wrapped his lore austere,
> And I'll admire him greatly, if he bear
> His change of life with a becoming air. (Horace)

These are my lessons. He who puts them in practice has reaped more advantage by them than he who merely knows them. If you see him, you hear him; if you hear him, you see him.

God forbid, says someone in Plato, that to philosophize were only to learn a number of things and to discuss the arts! "This the most fruitful of all arts, which teaches the way of right living, they promoted more by their lives than by their writings" (Cicero). Leon, prince of the Phliasians, asking Heraclides Ponticus of what art or science he made profession, received the answer: "I know neither art nor science, but I am a philosopher." Someone reproached Diogenes that, being ignorant, he should meddle with philosophy. "I meddle with it," said Diogenes, "all the more appropriately." Hegesias entreated that he would read him some book. "You jest," said he; "you choose real and natural figs, not painted ones; why do you not also choose real and natural activities instead of the written sort?"

He will not so much speak his lesson as do it. He will repeat it in his actions. We shall discover if there be prudence in his undertakings, if there be goodness and justice in his deportment, if there be judgment and grace in his speaking, if there be constancy in his sickness, if there be moderation in his pastimes, temperance in his pleasures, indifference in his palate, whether it be flesh or fish, wine or water, order in his domestic economy: "Who think that the tenets of their school are not a display of knowledge but a law of life, who submit to their own control and obey their own injunctions" (Cicero). The true mirror of our doctrines is the conduct of our lives.

* * * * *

CHAPTER 28

OF FRIENDSHIP

As I was considering the way in which a painter whom I employ goes about his work, I was taken with a desire to imitate him. He chooses the fairest place, the middle of each wall, and puts there a picture, elaborated with all his skill; and the space all about it he fills with grotesques, which are fantastic pictures having no other charm than their variety and strangeness. And in truth, what are these things of mine but grotesque and monstrous bodies, pieced together of sundry members, without definite shape, having neither order, coherence, or proportion, except by accident?

So that a woman, lovely to a wish,
Goes tailing off into a loathsome fish. (Horace)

In this second point indeed I go hand in hand with my painter, but fall short in the first and better part; for my skill does not reach so far that I dare to undertake a picture that is rich, finished, and shaped according to art. It therefore occurred to me to borrow one from Etienne de la Boétie, which shall do honour to all the rest of this work. It is a discourse to which he gave the name of *Voluntary Servitude;* but those who did not know it have since fitly enough rebaptized it *Le Contre Un.* He wrote it in his early youth by way of essay, in honour of liberty against tyrants. It has long been circulating among men of understanding, not without singular and merited commendation, for it is a fine thing and as full as can be. And yet it lacks much of being the best that he could do; and if in that more mature age wherein I knew him he had conceived a design like this of mine, to commit his thoughts to writing, we should see a great many rare things, such as would bring us very near to the honour of antiquity; for in natural gifts especially I know no man comparable to him. But he has left nothing behind him save this treatise (and that only by chance, and I believe he never saw it after it left his hands), and some observations upon that Edict of January, made famous by our civil wars, which will perhaps yet find a place elsewhere. These were all I could recover of what he left (I, to whom, with such loving trust, in the very throes of death, he by his last will bequeathed his library and papers), except for the little volume of his works which I have had published. And the particular obligation I have to this treatise is that it served as the occasion of our first acquaintance. For it was shown to me long before I had met him, and gave me the first knowledge of his name, thus preparing the way for that friendship which we cherished, so long as it was God's will, with such entirety and such perfection that certainly the like is hardly to be found in books, and among the men of this age there is no trace in practice of any such thing. It needs so many concurring factors to build it up that it is much if fortune attain to it once in three centuries.

There is nothing to which Nature seems so much to have inclined us as to society. And Aristotle says that the good legislators have been more concerned about friendship than justice. Now the highest point in the perfection of society is this of friendship. For, generally, all those bonds that pleasure or profit, public or private interest, create and nourish are so much the less beautiful and noble, and so much the less friendships, as they mix another cause and design and fruit with friendship, than friendship itself. Neither do the four kinds recognized in antiquity — natural, social, hospitable, venerian — either separately or jointly sort with friendship.

The feeling of children for their fathers is rather respect. Friendship is nourished by communication, which cannot exist between these because of too great inequality, and would perhaps do injury to the duties of nature. For neither are all the secret thoughts of fathers capable of being communicated to children, lest it beget an unbecoming intimacy between them, nor can the admonitions and reproofs, which are among the principal offices of friendship, be administered by children to fathers. There have been nations where it was the custom for children to kill their fathers, and others where the fathers killed their children, to avoid the embarrassment they might sometimes cause one another; and by the operation of nature the prosperity of the one depends upon the ruin of the other. There have been philosophers who have disdained this natural tie, witness Aristippus, who, being closely pressed about the affection he owed to his children, as being come out of him, began to spit, saying that this also came out of him, and that we also breed worms and lice. And another, whom Plutarch wished to induce to be reconciled with his brother, said: "I make no greater account of him for having come out of the same hole."

This name of brother is indeed a beautiful name, and full of winsomeness, and on that account did he and I form our alliance. But the complication of property, the divisions of estates, and the fact that the wealth of the one is the poverty of the other wondrously weakens and loosens the fraternal cement. Brothers having to pursue the advancement of their fortune by the same path and at the same pace, they must of necessity often jostle and clash with one another. Besides, why should the harmony and kinship which begets true and perfect friendship exist in these relations? The father and the son may be of quite differing natures, and so may brothers. This is my son, this is my kinsman, but he is a surly fellow, a rascal, or a fool. And moreover, to the extent that these are friendships that the law and natural obligation impose upon us, there is less in them of our own choice and free will. And our free will has no product that is more properly its own than this of affection and friendship. Not but that I have in my own person experienced all that one possibly can on that score, having had the best father that ever was, and the most indulgent, even in his extreme old age, and being of a family for many generations famous and exemplary in this matter of brotherly concord,

And I myself am known
For loving-kindness fatherlike
To all my brothers shown. (Horace)

To compare with it the affection we bear to women, though it spring from our own choice, is not possible, nor to place it in this class. Its fire, I confess,

Nor is that Goddess unaware of me,
Who blends with pain our bitter-sweet delight, (Catullus)

is more active, more scorching and more violent. But it is a reckless and fickle flame, wavering and inconstant; a fever flame, subject to paroxysms and intermissions, and that holds us but by one corner. In friendship it is a general and universal warmth, but temperate and even, a constant and settled warmth, all gentleness and smoothness, with nothing in it of roughness or poignancy. What is more, in love there is nothing but frantic desire for that which flies from us:

Like hunters that the flying hare pursue
O'er hill and dale, through heat and morning dew,
Which being ta'en, the quarry they despise,
Being only pleased in following that which flies. (Ariosto)

As soon as it enters into the terms of friendship — that is to say, into an agreement of wills — it grows faint and languishing. Enjoyment destroys it, as having only a fleshly end, and subject to satiety. Friendship, on the contrary, is enjoyed proportionably as it is desired; and is bred, nourished, and increased only by enjoyment, as being of essence spiritual, and the soul growing refined by practice. Beneath the level of this perfect friendship those fleeting affections once found a place in me, to say nothing of him, who confesses it but too much in his verses. So these two passions have entered into me, each aware of the other, but never in competition, the first keeping its course with a lofty and proudly conscious flight and looking down disdainfully upon the other, flying at a far humbler pitch below.

As concerning marriage, besides that it is a bargain to which only the entrance is free (the continuance in it is forced and compulsory, depending upon other things than our own will), and a bargain commonly made for other ends, there almost always happen in it a thousand extraneous tangles to unravel, enough to break the thread and to trouble the course of a lively affection, whereas friendship has no manner of business or traffic with aught but itself. Moreover, to say truth, the ordinary talent of women is not such as answers the requirements of that converse and intercourse which is the nurse of this sacred tie; nor does their soul seem to be so firm as to endure the strain of so hard and durable a knot. And assuredly, but for this, if there could be such a free and voluntary familiarity contracted, where not only the souls might have this complete enjoyment, but the bodies also might share in the alliance, in which the entire man was engaged, it is certain that the friendship would be more full and perfect thereby. But this sex has in no instance ever yet attained to it, and, by the common agreement of the ancient schools, it is excluded from it.

And that other Grecian licence is justly abhorrent to our morals. There being, moreover, according to their practice, so necessary a disparity of age and difference of services between the lovers, it answered no better to the perfect union and harmony that we here require: "For what is this so-called love of friendship? Why is it no one is in love with either an ugly youngster or a handsome old man?" (Cicero). For even the picture that the Academy presents of it will, as I think, not refute me when I say that this first frenzy inspired by the son of Venus in the heart of the lover for an object in the flower of tender youth, to which they allow all the insolent and passionate actions that an immoderate ardour can produce, was simply founded upon external beauty, the deceptive image of corporeal generation. For it could not be grounded in the soul, whose quality as yet lay concealed, since it was only in its birth and before the age of budding. If this frenzy seized upon a base heart, the means by which it preferred its suit were wealth, presents, influence in advancement to dignities, and other such base merchandise, which they disapprove. If it fell on a more generous heart, the means of ingratiation were also generous: philosophical instruction, precepts to revere religion, to obey the laws, to die for the good of one's country, examples of valour, wisdom, and justice; the lover studying to render himself acceptable by the grace and beauty of his soul, that of his body being long since faded, and hoping by this mental society to establish a more firm and lasting contract. When this courtship had its effect in due season (for that which they do not require in the lover — namely, leisure and discretion in his pursuit — they strictly require in the person loved, inasmuch as he had to judge of an internal beauty, difficult of knowledge and deeply hidden from discovery), there sprang in the person loved the desire of a spiritual conception by the mediation of a spiritual beauty. This was here the principal matter; the corporeal was accidental and secondary: quite the reverse of the lover's case. For this reason they prefer the person beloved, maintaining that the gods also prefer him, and severely rebuke the poet Æschylus for having, in the love of Achilles and Patroclus, given the lover's part to Achilles, who was in the first and beardless bloom of his youth, and the handsomest of all the Greeks. After the formation of this general companionship, the sovereign and most worthy part of it exercising its functions and predominating, they say that useful fruits resulted therefrom both of a private and public nature; that it constituted the strength of the countries where it prevailed and the chief security of liberty and justice: witness the salutary loves of Harmodius and Aristogeiton. Therefore they call it sacred and divine and conceive that nothing but the violence of tyrants and the baseness of the common people are inimical to it. In short, all that can be said in favour of the Academy is that it was a love which ended in friendship, which does not ill agree with the Stoical definition of love: "Love is an endeavour to form a friendship inspired by the beauty of the object" (Cicero).

I return to my description of a more just and equal kind of friendship. "As a rule only those are to be deemed friendships that have been formed after strength and stability have been reached in mind and years" (Cicero). For the rest, what we commonly call friends and friendships are nothing but acquaintance and familiarities, contracted either by some chance or for convenience, by which our minds hold intercourse. In the friendship I speak of, they mingle and unite one with the other in a blend so perfect that the seam which has joined them together is effaced and can never be found again. If I should be pressed to say why I loved him, I feel that it cannot be expressed, except by answering: "Because it was he, because it was I."

There is, beyond all my reasoning and all that I am able specifically to say, I know not what inexplicable and fated power that brought on this union. We sought one another before we met, and by the reports we heard of one another, which wrought upon our affections a greater impression than, in reason, mere reports should do; I believe it was by some decree of heaven. We embraced one another by our names. And at our first meeting, which happened by chance at a great festival assembly in the city, we found ourselves so mutually taken, so well acquainted, and so bound to one another, that thenceforward nothing was so near to us as each to the other. He wrote an excellent Latin satire, which is published, wherein he excuses and explains the precipitation of our mutual intelligence, so quickly grown to its perfection. Having so short a time to endure, and having begun so late (for we were both full-grown men, and he some years the elder), it had no time to lose, nor to arrange itself by the example of those mild and regular friendships that require so many precautions of long preliminary intercourse. This has no other ideal than in itself, and can only be referred to itself. It is not one special consideration nor two, nor three, nor four, nor a thousand. It is I know not what quintessence of all this mixture which, having seized my whole will, brought it to plunge and lose itself in his; which, having seized his whole will, brought it with equal hunger and emulation to plunge and lose itself in mine. I may truly say lose, since we reserved to ourselves nothing that was our own, nor that was either his or mine.

When Lælius, in the presence of the Roman consuls, who, after they had condemned Tiberius Gracchus, prosecuted all those who had been in his confidence, came to ask Caius Blossius (who was his chief friend) how much he would have been willing to do for him, he answered: "Everything." "How! Everything?" said Lælius. "And what if he had commanded you to fire our temples?" "He would never have commanded me that," replied Blossius. "But what if he had?" said Lælius. "I would have obeyed him," said the other. If he was so perfect a friend to Gracchus as the histories say, he had no occasion to offend the consuls by this bold and extreme confession, and he ought not to have forsaken the assurance he had of the purposes of Gracchus. However, those who accuse this answer as seditious do not well understand this mystery and do not presuppose, what was true, that he held the will of Gracchus in his sleeve, both through his power over him and knowledge of him. They were friends more than citizens, friends to one another more than either friends or enemies to their country, or than friends to ambition and disturbance. Having absolutely given themselves up to one another, each held absolutely the reins of the other's inclination; and supposing this team to be guided by virtue and the conduct of reason (and without these it is quite impossible to harness it), the answer of Blossius is such as it should have been. If their actions were off the handle, they were neither, according to my measure, friends to one another nor friends to themselves. As to the rest, this answer carries no better sound than mine would do to one that should question me in this fashion: "If your will should command you to kill your daughter, would you do it?" and I should answer that I would. For this carries no proof of consent to such an act, because I have no doubt of my own will, and just as little of the will of such a friend. It is not in the power of all the arguments in the world to dislodge me from the certainty I have of the intentions and judgments of my friend. No action of his, what face soever it might bear, could be presented to me of which I could not instantly find out the moving cause. Our souls have pulled so unitedly together, they have considered each other with so ardent an affection, and with the like affection laid open the very bottom of our hearts to one another's view, that I not only knew his as well as my own, but should certainly have trusted myself more willingly with him than with myself.

Let no one, therefore, rank other common friendships with such a one as this. I have as much knowledge of them as another, and of the most perfect of their kind, but I do not advise anyone to confuse their rules, for they would find themselves deceived. In these other friendships you must walk with the bridle in hand, with prudence and circumspection, for in them the knot is never so secure that a man is quite without ground for distrust. "Love him," said Chilo, "as if you were one day to hate him; and hate him as if you were one day to love him." This precept, which is abominable in the sovereign and perfect friendship, is sound in the practice of the common and customary ones, in regard to which one may employ the saying that Aristotle had frequently in his mouth: "O my friends, there is no friend."

In this noble relationship, good offices and benefits, by which other friendships are fostered, do not deserve even to be taken into account; and the cause of it is the complete fusion of our wills. For as the love I bear to myself receives no increase for any assistance I give myself in time of need, whatever the Stoics may say, and as I do not feel grateful to myself for any service I do myself, so the union of such friends, being truly perfect, causes them to lose the feeling of such duties and makes them loathe and banish from their thoughts these words of division and distinction — benefit, obligation, gratitude, entreaty, thanks, and the like. All things being in effect common between them — wills, thoughts, opinions, goods, wives, children, honour, and life, and their alliance being that of one soul in two bodies, according to that very apt definition of Aristotle, they can neither lend nor give anything to one another. This is the reason why the law-makers, to honour marriage with some imaginary resemblance to this divine union, interdict all gifts between man and wife, desiring to imply thereby that all should belong to each of them, and that they have nothing to divide or to give to each other.

If, in the friendship of which I speak, one could give to the other, the receiver of the benefit would be the man that obliged his friend. For each of them above all things studying how to confer a benefit on the other, he that provides the matter and occasion is the liberal man, in giving his friend the satisfaction of doing that toward him which he most desires. When the philosopher Diogenes wanted money, he used to say that he asked it back of his friends, not that he asked it. And to show how this works in practice, I will recount an ancient example of it, of a singular kind.

Eudamidas of Corinth had two friends, Charixenus, a Sycionian, and Aretheus, a Corinthian. When he came to die, being poor, and his two friends rich, he made his will after this manner: "I bequeath to Aretheus my mother, to support and maintain her in her old age; to Charixenus I bequeath the care of marrying my daughter, and to give her as good a dower as he is able; and in case one of these should die, I substitute the survivor in his place." They who first saw this will made merry over it, but when the heirs were notified, they accepted it with a singular satisfaction. And one of them, Charixenus, dying five days later, and the substitution thus falling open in favour of Aretheus, he supported the mother with very great care, and of five talents he had in his estate, he gave two and a half in marriage with an only daughter of his own, and two and a half in marriage with the daughter of Eudamidas, and the same day solemnized both their nuptials.

This example is quite complete but for one objection: namely, the number of friends. For this perfect friendship of which I speak is indivisible; each one gives himself so entirely to his friend that he has nothing left to distribute to others; on the contrary, he is sorry that he is not double, triple, or quadruple, and that he has not several souls and several wills, to confer them all upon this one object. Common friendships will admit of sharing: one may love the beauty of this person, the good humour of that, the liberality of a third, the paternal affection of a fourth, the fraternal love of a fifth, and so of the rest; but this friendship that possesses the soul and rules it with an absolute sovereignty cannot possibly be double. If two at the same time should call to you for succour, to which of them would you run? Should they require of you contradictory services, how would you reconcile them? Should one commit a thing to your silence that it were useful for the other to know, how would you disengage yourself? A unique and dominant friendship dissolves all other obligations. The secret I have sworn not to reveal to any other I may without perjury communicate to him who is not another: he is myself. It is a great enough miracle for a man to double himself, and those that talk of tripling themselves do not know the height of the thing. Nothing is superlative that has its like. And he who shall suppose that of two men I love one as much as the other, that they love one another and me as much as I love them, multiplies into a confraternity the most single and unified of things, whereof, moreover, one single case is the rarest thing in the world to find.

The rest of this story agrees very well with what I was saying, for Eudamidas bestows upon his friends the kindness and favour of employing them for his needs. He leaves them heirs to this liberality of his, which consists in putting into their hands the means of conferring a benefit upon him. And doubtless the force of friendship appears much more richly in this act of his than in that of Aretheus. In short, these are effects beyond the imagination of such as have not tasted them, and they make me wondrously honour the answer of that young soldier to Cyrus, when the King asked him how much he would take for a horse with which he had just won the prize of a race, and whether he would exchange him for a kingdom? "No, truly, Sire, but I would give him with all my heart to get thereby a friend, could I find a man worthy of such alliance." He did not say ill in saying: "could I find"; for one easily meets with men qualified for a superficial acquaintance. But in this, where a man deals from the very bottom of his heart, without any manner of reservation, it is surely needful that all the springs be perfectly clean and true.

In associations that hold but by one end, we have only to provide against the imperfections that particularly concern that end. It can be of no importance to me of what religion my physician or my lawyer is. This consideration has nothing to do with the friendly offices which they owe me. And in the domestic relations that my servants contract with me I have the same attitude. I inquire little into the chastity of a footman; I try to learn if he be diligent. And I am not so much afraid of a gaming muleteer as of an idiotic one, nor of a swearing cook as an incompetent one. I do not take upon me to say what people should do in the world (there are others enough to do that), but only what I do there myself.

> For me 'tis needful so — do you as you see best. (Terence)

With the familiarity of the table I associate the agreeable rather than the wise; in bed, beauty before goodness; in the exchange of ideas, ability even when it is without complete candour; and so in other things.

As he that was found astride upon a stick, playing with his children, entreated the man who surprised him in that posture to say nothing of it till himself came to be a father, supposing that the feeling that would then be born in his soul would make him a fair judge of such an action; so I, also, could wish to speak to such as have had experience of what I say. But knowing how remote a thing such a friendship is from the common practice and how rarely it is to be found, I do not look to meet with any competent judge. For even the discourses left us by antiquity upon this subject seem to me flat in comparison with the feeling I have of it. And, in this particular, the facts surpass even the precepts of philosophy:

> Nothing, no, nothing on this earth,
> Whilst I have reason, shall I e'er
> With a true-hearted friend compare. (Horace)

The ancient Menander declared that man happy who had been able to meet with but the shadow of a friend. He was assuredly right in saying it, particularly if he spoke from experience. For, in truth, if I compare all the rest of my life, though with the grace of God it has passed sweetly and easily and, except for the loss of such a friend, free from any grievous affliction and in great tranquillity of mind, seeing I was content with my natural and original advantages without seeking others, if I should compare it all, I say, with the four years that were granted to me to enjoy the sweet companionship and society of that man, it is nothing but smoke, nothing but a dark and irksome night. From the day that I lost him,

which I
Shall ever hold, for so ye gods have willed,
Sacred to grief and honour without end, (Virgil)

I have only led a languishing life; and the very pleasures that present themselves to me, instead of bringing me comfort, redouble my grief for his loss. We were co-partners in everything; it seems to me that I defraud him of his part,

And that for me all joy in life were impious
Till safely he returns to share it all with me. (Terence)

I was already so moulded and habituated to be double in all places that methinks I am now no more than a half.

Ah, since untimely Fate hath snatched from hence
My soul's more precious part,
Why should I linger on, with deadened sense,
And ever-aching heart,
A worthless fragment of a fallen shrine?
No, no, one day hath seen thy death and mine. (Horace)

There is no action or thought of mine wherein I do not miss him, as I know he would have missed me. For as he surpassed me infinitely in every other accomplishment and virtue, so did he also in the duty of friendship.

Why should we stop the flowing tear?
Why blush to weep for one so dear? (Horace)

But, brother, what with mirth was once so rife
Is turned to sadness by thy timeless doom;
Dead with thy death is all that cheered my life,
And all our house is buried in thy tomb!
Gone are the joys that, whilst thou yet wert here,
Were by thy sweet affection fanned and fed;
All studies, all delights, that once were dear,
I've banished from my soul, since thou art dead.
Oh, is thy voice forever hushed and still?
Oh, brother, dearer far than life, shall I
Behold thee never? But in sooth I will
Forever love thee, as in days gone by. (Catullus)

* * * * *

CHAPTER 31

OF CANNIBALS

When King Pyrrhus passed over into Italy, having surveyed the ordering of the army the Romans sent out against him, he said, "I do not know what kind of barbarians these may be (for so the Greeks called all foreign nations), but the disposition of this army that I see has nothing of the barbarous in it." As much did the Greeks say of the army which Flaminius brought into their country, and also Philip, when he beheld from an eminence the order and distribution of the Roman camp formed in his kingdom under Publius Sulpicius Galba. Thus it appears how cautious men ought to be about clinging to vulgar opinions, and that we should judge by the method of reason and not by common report.

I had dwelling with me for a long time a man who had lived ten or twelve years in that other world which has been discovered in our time, in that place where Villegaignon landed, which he called Antarctic France. This discovery of so vast a country seems to be worthy of consideration. I cannot be sure that hereafter there may not be another, so many greater men than we having been deceived in this. I am afraid our eyes are bigger than our bellies, and that we have more curiosity than capacity. We grasp at all, but catch nothing but wind.

Plato brings in Solon telling a story that he had heard from the priests of Saïs in Egypt, that in olden days before the Deluge there was a great island called Atlantis, situate directly at the mouth of the Strait of Gibraltar, which contained more countries than Africa and Asia put together, and that the kings of that country, who not only possessed that isle, but extended their dominion so far into the continent that they held the breadth of Africa as far as Egypt and the length of Europe as far as Tuscany, attempted to encroach upon Asia and to subjugate all the nations that border upon the Mediterranean, as far as the Black Sea; and to that end overran all Spain, Gaul, and Italy as far as Greece, where the Athenians checked them; but that some time after, both the Athenians and they and their island were swallowed by the Deluge.

It is very likely that this extreme inundation of water made wonderful changes in the habitations of the earth, as it is supposed the sea has cut off Sicily from Italy,

> For this region once, 'tis said,
> By violence and huge convulsion torn,
> Leapt into twain, that were one land before,
> Continuous; (Virgil)

Cyprus from Syria, the isle of Eubœa from the mainland of Bœotia; and elsewhere united lands that had been divided, by filling up the channel between them with sand and mud,

> the marsh, once waste and watery, now
> Feeds neighbour towns, and grows beneath the plough. (Horace)

But there is no great probability that this island was the New World that we have lately discovered, for it almost touched Spain, and it were an incredible effect of an inundation to have forced it back where it is, more than twelve hundred leagues; besides that our modern navigators have already almost discovered it to be no island, but terra firma, holding together with the East Indies on one side and with the lands under the two poles in another direction; or, if it be separated from them, it is by so narrow a strait and interval that it deserves not the name of an island for that.

It would seem that in these great bodies, as in our own, there are two sorts of motions, the one natural, and the other febrific. When I consider the encroachment that my river, the Dordogne, is making in my time, on the right bank in its descent, and that in twenty years it has gained so much and undermined the foundations of so many houses, I clearly see that it is an extraordinary disturbance, for if it had always gone on at this rate, or were hereafter to do it, the aspect of the world would be totally changed. But rivers are subject to changes; sometimes they overflow on one side and sometimes on the other; sometimes they keep the channel. I do not speak of sudden inundations, the causes of which we understand. In Médoc, by the seashore, the Sieur d'Arsac, my brother, sees an estate of his being buried under the sands which the sea vomits before it; the tops of some houses are yet to be seen; his rents and domains have been converted into thin pasturage. The inhabitants say that for some time the sea has been pushing so vigorously toward them that they have lost four leagues of land. These sands are her harbingers; and we now see great mounds of moving sand that march half a league before her and occupy the land.

The other testimony from antiquity, which some would connect with this discovery, is in Aristotle, at least if that little book, *Of Unheard-of Wonders,* be his. He there relates that certain Carthaginians, having launched across the Atlantic Ocean beyond the Strait of Gibraltar and sailed a very long time, discovered at last a great and fruitful island, covered all over with forests and watered by broad and deep rivers, far removed from any mainland; and that they, and others after them, allured by the goodness and fertility of the soil, went thither with their wives and children and began to make a settlement there. The lords of Carthage, perceiving their land little by little becoming depopulated, issued an express prohibition, that none, upon pain of death, should any longer journey thither, and they drove out the new inhabitants, fearing, 'tis said, lest in the course of time they should so multiply as to supplant themselves and ruin their state. This narration of Aristotle agrees no better with our new-found lands than the other.

This man that I had was a plain ignorant fellow, which is a character likely to bear true witness; for your clever men are much more curious observers, and notice more things, but they gloss them; and to give the greater weight to their interpretation and make it persuasive, they cannot forbear a little to alter the story; they never represent things to you simply as they are, but bend and mask them according to the appearance which they had for them; and to gain faith for their judgment, and to induce you to accept it, are willing to add something of their own to the matter, to expand it and amplify it. We need either a very truthful man or one so simple that he has not wherewithal to build and to give a colour of truth to false stories, and who has espoused no theories. Such was my man; and besides, he has at divers times brought to me several seamen and merchants whom he knew on that voyage. I therefore content myself with his information, without inquiring what the cosmographers say about it.

We need topographers to give us an exact description of the places where they have been. But for having the advantage over us of having seen the Holy Land, they wish to enjoy the privilege of telling us new tales about all the rest of the world. I would have everyone write what he knows, and as much as he knows, not in this only, but on all other subjects; for a person may have some particular knowledge and experience of the nature of some river or fountain who, as to other things, knows no more than what everybody knows. Yet, to give currency to this shred of information, he will undertake to write the whole body of physics. From this vice spring many great disadvantages.

Now, to return to my subject, I find that there is nothing barbarous and savage in this nation, as far as I have been informed, except that everyone calls barbarism that which is not his own usage; as, indeed, we seem to have no other level of truth and reason than the example and pattern of the opinions and practices of the country wherein we live. There one finds always the perfect religion, the perfect government, the most perfected and accomplished usage in all things. They are savages in the same sense that we say fruits are wild, which nature produces by herself and in her usual course; whereas in truth, we ought rather to call wild those whose natures we have changed by our artifice and diverted from the common order. In the former, the genuine and the most useful and natural virtues and properties are alive and vigorous, which in the latter we have bastardized, and we have only adapted them to the pleasure of our corrupted palate. And yet, for all this, our taste confesses a flavour and delicacy, excellent even in comparison with ours, in several uncultivated fruits of those countries. It is not reasonable that art should gain the point of honour over our great and powerful mother Nature. We have so loaded the beauty and richness of her works with our inventions that we have altogether smothered her. Yet wherever she shines forth in her purity, she marvellously puts to shame our vain and frivolous undertakings,

> Best thrives the ivy when no culture spoils,
> The strawberry fairest grows in shaded soils;
> The song of birds is sweeter without art. (Propertius)

Our utmost efforts cannot attain to so much as to reproduce the nest of the smallest of birds, its contexture, its beauty, and its convenience: not so much as the web of a poor spider. All things, says Plato, are produced by nature, by fortune, or by art; the greatest and most beautiful by one or other of the first two, the least and most imperfect by the last.

These nations, then, seem to me to be so far barbarous as they have received very little fashioning from human wit, and are still very near to their original simplicity. The laws of Nature govern them still, very little debased with any mixture of ours; but they are in such a state of purity that I am sometimes vexed that the knowledge of them did not come earlier, at a time when there were men better able to judge of them than we are. I am sorry that Lycurgus and Plato did not know them; for it seems to me that what we now actually see in those nations, does not only surpass all the pictures with which the poets have adorned the golden age and all their inventions in feigning a happy state of man, but even the conceptions and the very desire of philosophy. They could not imagine so pure and simple an innocence as we by experience see to be in them; nor could they have believed that human society could be maintained with so little artifice and human cementing. This is a nation, I should say to Plato, wherein there is no manner of traffic, no knowledge of letters, no science of numbers, no name of magistrate or political superiority, no use of service, no riches or poverty, no contracts, no successions, no partitions of property, no employments but those of leisure, no respect of kinship save the common ties, no clothing, no agriculture, no metal, no use of corn or wine. The very words that signify lying, treachery, dissimulation, avarice, envy, detraction, pardon, never heard of. How far distant from this perfection would he find the republic of his imagination: "mortals fresh from the gods" (Seneca).

These are the modes that nature first ordained. (Virgil)

For the rest, they live in a country very pleasant and temperate, so that, as my witnesses inform me, one rarely hears of a sick person; and they have assured me that they never saw any man either palsied, blear-eyed, toothless, or bent with age. They are settled along the sea, and shut in on the land side by great and high mountains, there being a stretch about a hundred leagues in breadth between the mountains and the sea. They have great store of fish and flesh, that have no resemblance to ours, and they eat them without any other art than that of plain cookery. The first man who rode a horse thither, though in several other voyages he had contracted an acquaintance with them, put them into so terrible a fright in that posture that they killed him with their arrows before they could recognize him.

Their buildings are very long and capable of holding two or three hundred people, covered with the bark of tall trees, fastened in the ground at one end and leaning against and supporting one another at the ridgepole, as in some of our barns, the covering of which hangs down to the ground and serves for the side-walls. They have a wood so hard that they cut with it, and they make their swords of it and grills to broil their meat. Their beds are of cotton weave, suspended from the roof, like those in our ships, every man having his own; for the women lie apart from their husbands.

They rise with the sun, and as soon as they are up, eat for the whole day, for they have no other meal. They do not drink at that time like some other people of the East, of whom Suidas tells, that never drank at their meals; but they drink several times a day, and copiously. Their drink is made of a certain root and is of the colour of our claret. They drink it only lukewarm. This beverage will not keep above two or three days; it has a somewhat sharp taste, is not at all heady, is wholesome for the stomach, and laxative to those who are not used to it; it is a very pleasant drink for such as are accustomed to it. In place of bread they use a certain white substance like coriander comfits. I have tasted it; the flavour is sweet and a little flat.

The whole day is spent in dancing. Their young men go a-hunting after wild beasts with bows and arrows. Some of their women are employed meanwhile in warming their drink, which is their chief duty. One of their old men, in the morning before they begin to eat, preaches to the whole barnful, walking from one end to the other and repeating the same sentence several times, till he has finished the round (for the buildings are at least a hundred yards long). He enjoins only two things upon them: valour against their enemies, and love for their wives. And they never fail, by way of refrain, to point out this obligation, that it is their wives who keep their drink warm and well seasoned.

There may be seen in a number of places, including my own house, the fashion of their beds, of their ropes, of their wooden swords, and the bracelets of wood with which they cover their wrists when they go to fight, and of the big canes, open at one end, by the sound of which they keep the cadence of their dances. They are close shaven all over and perform the process much more neatly than we, with nothing but a razor of wood or stone. They believe in the immortality of the soul, and that those who have merited well of the gods are lodged in that part of heaven where the sun rises, and those who are accursed in the west.

They have some kind of priests and prophets, who very rarely present themselves to the people, having their abode in the mountains. On their arrival, there is a great feast and solemn assembly of many villages (each barn, as I have described it, makes a village, and they are about a French league distant from one another). This prophet speaks to them in public, exhorting them to virtue and their duty; but their whole ethical science is comprised in these two articles: resolution in war, and affection to their wives. He also prophesies to them events to come and the issues they are to expect from their enterprises, and prompts them to war or dissuades them from it; but it is on condition that when he fails to prophesy correctly and anything falls out otherwise than he has foretold, he is cut into a thousand pieces if he is caught, and condemned for a false prophet. For that reason, he who has once miscalculated is never seen again.

Divination is a gift of God; that is why its abuse ought to be a punishable imposture. Among the Scythians, when their diviners failed in their prediction, they were laid, bound hand and foot, upon carts loaded with brushwood and drawn by oxen, on which they were burned. Those who manage things subject to the conduct of human capacity are excusable if they do the best they can. But these others, who come to delude us with assurances of an extraordinary faculty beyond our understanding, ought they not to be punished when they do not make good their promise, and for the temerity of their imposture?

They have their wars with the nations that live farther inland on the other side of the mountains, to which they go quite naked, and without other arms than their bows, and wooden swords pointed at one end, like the tongues of our spears. It is marvellous what obstinacy they display in their battles, which never end without great slaughter and effusion of blood; for as to flight and terror, they know not what it is. Everyone for a trophy brings home the head of an enemy he has killed, and fixes it over the entrance of his dwelling. After treating their prisoners well for a long time and with all the indulgences they can think of, he to whom the prisoner belongs assembles a great company of his acquaintances. He ties a rope to one of the arms of the prisoner, by the end of which he holds him, but at a safe distance, for fear of being struck, and gives to his best friend the other arm to hold in the same manner; and they two, in the presence of the whole assembly, dispatch him with their swords. After that they roast and eat him in common and send some pieces to their absent friends. They do not do this, as some think, for nourishment, as the Scythians anciently did, but to express an extreme revenge. That this is the case will appear by the following circumstances: having observed that the Portuguese, who were in league with their enemies, inflicted a different sort of death upon those whom they took prisoners, which was to bury them up to the waist, to shoot the rest of the body full of arrows, and then hang them, they thought that these people from the other world (as men who had sown the knowledge of a great many vices among their neighbours, and who were much greater masters in all sorts of mischief than they) did not exercise this sort of revenge without a reason, and that it must needs be more painful than their own; so they began to leave their old way and to follow this. I am not sorry that we should take notice of the barbarous horror of such acts, but I am sorry that, seeing so clearly into their faults, we should be so blind to our own. I conceive there is more barbarity in eating a man alive than in eating him dead, in tearing by rack and torture a body that is still full of feeling, in roasting it bit by bit, in causing it to be mutilated by dogs and swine (as we have not only read but seen within fresh memory, not among inveterate enemies, but among neighbours and fellow citizens, and, what is worse, under colour of piety and religion), than in roasting and eating him after he is dead.

Chrysippus and Zeno, heads of the Stoic sect, were indeed of opinion that there was no harm in making use of our dead carcasses in any way for our necessity, and in feeding upon them too, as did our own ancestors when, being besieged by Cæsar in the city of Alésia, they resolved to support the famine during the siege with the bodies of their old men, women, and other persons who were useless for fighting.

> The Gascons once (the story yet is rife)
> With such dire sustenance prolonged their life. (Juvenal)

And physicians are not afraid of employing it in all sorts of ways for our health, applying it either inwardly or outwardly. But there never was any opinion so extravagant as to excuse treachery, disloyalty, tyranny, and cruelty, which are our common vices.

We may then call these people barbarians in respect to the rules of reason, but not in respect to ourselves, who surpass them in all sorts of barbarity. Their warfare is consistently noble and generous and has as much excuse and beauty as is compatible with that human malady; it has with them no other foundation than the sole jealousy of valour. Their disputes are not for the conquest of new lands, for they still enjoy that natural fruitfulness which provides them, without labour or trouble, with all things necessary, in such abundance that they have no need to enlarge their borders. They are still in that happy state of not desiring any more than their natural necessities demand; all beyond that is superfluous to them.

Men of the same age generally call one another brothers; those who are younger they call children; and the old men are fathers to all the rest. These leave to their heirs in common the full possession of goods, without any manner of division, or any other title than that pure one which Nature bestows upon her creatures in bringing them into the world. If their neighbours cross the mountain to attack them and obtain a victory, all the victors gain by it is glory only, and the advantage of having proved themselves superior in valour and virtue; for otherwise they have no use for the goods of the conquered, and so return to their own country, where they have no want of anything necessary, nor want even that great possession, to know how to enjoy their condition happily and be content with it. These in their turn do the same. They demand of their prisoners no other ransom than the confession and acknowledgement of being vanquished; but there is not one found, in a whole century, who will not rather choose death than either by word or look to abate a single point from the grandeur of an invincible courage. There is not a man among them who would not rather be killed and eaten than so much as request that he may not. They treat them with all liberality in order that their lives may be so much the dearer to them; and they commonly entertain them with menaces of their approaching death, of the torments they are to suffer, of the preparations being made for the purpose, of the cutting up of their limbs, and of the feast that is to be made at their expense. All this is done with no other aim but to extort some weak or submissive word from them or to fill them with a desire to run away, that they may obtain the advantage of having terrified them and shaken their constancy. For indeed, if rightly taken, it is in this point only that a true victory consists;

> No victory is complete,
> But when the vanquished own their just defeat. (Claudian)

The Hungarians, very bellicose fighters, in former days did not pursue their advantage further than to reduce the enemy to their mercy. For, having wrested this confession from them, they let them go without damage and without ransom, except, at the most, to extract from them a pledge never to bear arms against them again.

We gain a number of advantages over our enemies that are borrowed advantages, not really our own. It is the attribute of a porter and not of valour to have sturdier arms and legs; adroitness is a dead and corporeal quality; it is a stroke of fortune that makes our enemy stumble or dazzles his eyes with the light of the sun; to be a skilful fencer is a trick of science and art, and one that may be acquired by craven and worthless fellows. The estimation and value of a man consists in the heart and in the will; there his true honour lies. Valour is strength, not of legs and arms, but of the heart and the soul; it does not lie in the goodness of our horse or of our arms, but in our own. He that falls obstinate in his courage, "if he falls, he will fight on his knees" (Seneca). He who, for any danger of imminent death, abates nothing of his assurance; who, in yielding up his soul, still gazes at his enemy with a firm and disdainful look, he is beaten, not by us, but by fortune; he is killed, not vanquished. The most valiant are sometimes the most unfortunate.

There are also defeats which vie with victories in triumph. Never could those four sister victories, the fairest the sun ever beheld with its eyes, of Salamis, Platæa, Mycale, and Sicily, dare to oppose all their united glories to the single glory of the discomfiture of King Leonidas and his men at the pass of Thermopylæ.

Who ever ran with a more glorious and ambitious desire to the winning of a battle than Captain Ischolas to defeat? Who has more ingeniously and painstakingly assured himself of his safety than he did of his destruction? He was charged with the defence of a certain pass in the Peloponnesus against the Arcadians. Finding himself quite incapable of accomplishing this because of the nature of the place and the inequality of the forces, and being convinced that all who presented themselves to the enemy must inevitably be left upon the spot; on the other hand, deeming it unworthy both of his own virtue and magnanimity and of the Lacedæmonian name to fail in his charge, he chose a middle course between these two extremes, in this manner: the youngest and fittest men he preserved for the service and defence of their country and sent them back; and with the rest, whose loss would not be felt so much, he resolved to hold the pass, and with their death make the enemy buy their entry as dearly as possible. And thus it fell out; for being presently surrounded on all sides by the Arcadians, after having made a great slaughter of the enemy, he and his men were all cut to pieces. Is there any trophy dedicated to victors which was not much more due to these vanquished? The role of true victory is in contesting, not in coming off with safety; and the honour of valour consists in fighting, not in overcoming.

To return to our story. These prisoners are so far from submitting, in spite of all the tortures inflicted upon them, that, on the contrary, during the two or three months they are kept, they carry a cheerful countenance; they urge their masters to make haste to bring them to the test; they defy them, insult them, reproach them with cowardice and the number of battles they have lost against their own country. I have a song composed by a prisoner in which he bids them all to come boldly and assemble to dine upon him, for they will eat their own fathers and grandfathers, whose flesh has served to feed and nourish his body. "These muscles," he says, "this flesh and these veins, are your own, poor fools that you are; you little think that the substance of the limbs of your ancestors is here yet; relish them well, and you will find in them the taste of your own flesh." This is an idea that has no suggestion of the barbarian. Those that paint these people dying and depict the execution represent the prisoner spitting in the faces of his slayers and making wry mouths at them. In truth, to the very last gasp they never cease to brave and defy them both by word and by gesture. To be quite straightforward, here are men who are savages indeed in comparison with us; for either they must be so in good earnest, or else we are savages; there is an amazing distance between their character and ours.

The men there have several wives, and the higher their reputation for valour, the greater is the number of their wives. It is a remarkably beautiful feature in their marriages that the same jealousy our wives have to hinder us from the love and kindnesses of other women, theirs employ to procure these things for them. Being more concerned for the honour of their husbands than for any other thing, they exert themselves to seek out and possess as many companions as they can, inasmuch as it is a proof of the husband's virtue.

Our ladies will cry, "Miracle!" It is not so. It is properly a matrimonial virtue, but of the highest order. And in the Bible, Leah, Rachel, Sarah, and the wives of Jacob gave their beautiful handmaids to their husbands; and Livia seconded the passions of Augustus to her own disadvantage; and Stratonice, the wife of King Deiotarus, not only allowed her husband the use of a very beautiful young chambermaid who was in her service, but carefully brought up the children he had by her, and assisted them in obtaining the succession to their father's estates.

And that it may not be supposed that all this is done through a simple and servile bondage to common usage, or through the pressure of the authority of their ancient custom, without reasoning or judgment, and because their minds are so stupid that they cannot take any other course, I must give some evidence of their talents. In addition to what I have just quoted from one of their songs of war, I have another, a love-song, that begins thus: "Adder, stay; stay, adder, that by the pattern of thy markings my sister may draw the fashion and work of a rich girdle which I may present to my beloved; so shall thy beauty and the disposition of thy scales forever be preferred before all other serpents." This first couplet makes the refrain of the song. Now, I am familiar enough with poetry to judge thus much: that not only is there nothing of the barbarous in this fancy, but that it is altogether Anacreontic. Their language, moreover, is a soft language, agreeable in sound, resembling the Greek in its terminations.

Three men of this nation, unaware of how costly their knowledge of the corruptions of this part of the world will one day be to their happiness and repose, and that from this intercourse will be born their ruin, which I suppose is already well under way (miserable men to suffer themselves to be deluded with desire of novelty and to leave the serenity of their own sky to come and gaze at ours!), were at Rouen at the time that the late King Charles the Ninth was there. The King talked to them a good while; they were shown our fashions, our pomp, and the form of a fair city. Then someone asked their opinion and wanted to know what they found most to be wondered at. They spoke of three things, of which I have forgotten the third, and am very sorry for it; but two I still remember. They said that in the first place they thought it very strange that so many big men, bearded, strong, and well armed, who were about the King (it is likely they meant the Swiss of his guard) should submit to obey a child, and that they did not rather choose one of their own to command them. Secondly (they have a way in their language of speaking of men as halves of one another), that they had observed that there were among us men full and crammed with all sorts of good things, while their halves were begging at their doors, emaciated with hunger and poverty; and they thought it strange that these necessitous halves were able to suffer such an injustice, and that they did not take the others by the throat or set fire to their houses.

I talked a long time with one of them, but I had an interpreter who followed my meaning so badly and who was so hindered by his stupidity in grasping my ideas that I could hardly get any satisfaction from him. When I asked him what advantage he reaped from his superior position among his people (for he was a captain and our sailors called him king), he told me that it was to march foremost in war. By how many men was he followed? He indicated a piece of ground to signify as many as could be contained in such a space, which might be four or five thousand men. Did all his authority expire with the war? He said that this remained, that when he visited the villages depending on him, they prepared paths for him through their thickets by which he might pass at his ease.

All this does not sound very ill. But stay! They wear no breeches!

BOOK TWO

CHAPTER 12

APOLOGY FOR RAIMOND SEBOND

* * * * *

But to return to my subject. We have for our share inconstancy, irresolution, uncertainty, sorrow, superstition, solicitude about things to come even after we shall be no more, ambition, avarice, jealousy, envy, disordered, insane, and untamable appetites, war, falsehood, disloyalty, detraction, and curiosity. In truth, we have paid a strangely high price for that splendid reason on which we plume ourselves and that capacity of judging and knowing, if we have bought it at the cost of that infinite number of passions to which we are eternally a prey. Unless it shall please us to make a point, as Socrates indeed does, of this notable prerogative over other animals: that whereas Nature has prescribed to them certain seasons and limits for the delights of Venus, she has left us a free rein in them for all hours and all occasions.

"Just as it is better, because though occasionally beneficial it is more often injurious, not to administer wine to the sick at all than in the hope of a doubtful cure to incur a manifest peril, so I scarcely know whether it had not been better for the human race if that swift movement of thought, that wit and subtlety which we call reason, had not been given to it at all than so generously and liberally given, seeing that it is mischievous to the many and salutary only to the few" (Cicero).

Of what benefit can we suppose the understanding of so many things was to Varro and Aristotle? Did it exempt them from human troubles? Were they freed from the accidents that lie heavy upon a porter? Did they derive from their Logic some consolation for the gout? Because they knew how this humour is lodged in the joints, did they feel it the less? Did they make their peace with Death from knowing that some nations rejoice at it, and with cuckoldry from knowing that in some regions women are enjoyed in common? On the contrary, though they held the highest rank in knowledge, the one among the Romans, the other among the Greeks, and in a time when learning was in its most flourishing state, we have not heard, for all that, that they displayed any special excellence in the conduct of their lives; nay, the Greek has enough to do to clear himself from some notable blemishes in his.

Has it ever been found that pleasure and health have a finer relish for one who understands Astrology and Grammar?

> Is not the unlettered churl as fit
> For Venus' service as the wit? (Horace)

and that shame and poverty are less vexatious?

> Disease thy couch shall flee,
> And sorrow and care, and thou indeed shalt see
> Long years of happiness, till now unknown. (Juvenal)

I have seen in my time a hundred artisans, a hundred labourers, wiser and happier than university rectors, and whom I would rather resemble. Learning, in my opinion, has a place among the things necessary to life, like glory, nobility, dignity, or, at most, like beauty, riches, and other such qualities, which are indeed useful to it, but remotely so, and a little more in imagination than by nature.

We scarcely need more functions, rules, and laws of living in our society than cranes and ants do in theirs; and yet we see that they conduct themselves in a very orderly manner without erudition. If man were wise, he would estimate the true value of each thing according to its utility and appropriateness for his life.

Whoever will reckon us with reference to our actions and behaviour will find a greater number of excellent men among the ignorant than among the learned; I mean in every sort of virtue. The older Rome seems to me to have produced men of greater worth, both for peace and for war, than that learned Rome that ruined herself. Though they might be equal in all other respects, integrity and innocence at least would remain on the side of the earlier age, for these qualities dwell in singular harmony with simplicity.

But I leave this disquisition, which would lead me further than I should be inclined to follow. I shall only say this much more, that humility and submission alone have the power to make a good man. We must not leave to the judgment of each man the understanding of his duty; we must prescribe it to him, and not leave it to his reason to make the choice. Otherwise, in view of the imbecility and infinite variety of our reasons and opinions, we should in the end create duties for ourselves that would, as Epicurus says, set us to eating one another.

The first law that ever God gave to man was a law of pure obedience. It was a naked and simple commandment, in which there was nothing that man needed to know or to argue about, inasmuch as obedience is the principal function of a reasonable soul acknowledging a heavenly superior and benefactor. From obedience and yielding spring all other virtues, as all sin from presumption. And, on the contrary, the first temptation that came to human nature through the devil, its first poison, insinuated itself into us through the promises he made of learning and of knowledge: "Ye shall be as gods, knowing good and evil" (Genesis). And the sirens, in Homer, to beguile Ulysses and draw him into their dangerous and ruinous snares, offer him the gift of knowledge. The plague of man is the presumption of knowledge. That is why ignorance is so recommended to us by our religion, as a quality suited to faith and obedience. "Beware lest any man spoil you through philosophy and vain deceits, after the rudiments of the world." (Saint Paul) . . .

But though knowledge did, in effect, do what they say, though it blunted the edge and abated the severity of the misfortunes that attend us, what does it do other than what ignorance does much more simply and more evidently? The philosopher Pyrrho, being in the peril of a great storm at sea, had nothing to offer for the imitation of those who were with him but the unconcern of a pig that was travelling with them and looking at the tempest without dismay. Philosophy, when she comes to the end of her precepts, refers us to the examples of an athlete and a muleteer, in whom we commonly observe much less sensibility to death, pain, and other discomforts, and greater fortitude than learning ever furnished to anyone who was not born and prepared to suffer them of himself by a natural disposition. What is the reason that one cuts and makes incisions on the tender limbs of a child more easily than on our own, if it is not ignorance? And on those of a horse? How many have been made ill by the mere power of imagination? It is usual to see men bled, purged, and physicked to be cured of diseases they feel only in their minds. When real infirmities fail us, learning lends us her own. This colour and this complexion portend some catarrhal inflammation; this hot season threatens you with an attack of fever; this break in the life-line of your left hand warns you of the approach of some serious indisposition. And in the end it makes open assault on health itself. This youthful sprightliness and vigour cannot endure without change; some blood must be withdrawn, your strength reduced, lest it turn to your prejudice. Compare the life of a man enslaved to such imaginations with that of a labourer who suffers himself to be led by his natural appetites, measuring things only by the immediate sensation, without learning and without prognostics, who is ill only when he is ill; whereas the other often has the stone in his mind before he has it in the bladder. As if it were not time enough to suffer the evil when it shall come, he anticipates it in imagination and runs to meet it. . . .

What we are told of the people of Brazil, that they never die but of old age, which is attributed to the serenity and tranquillity of their climate, I rather attribute to the serenity and tranquillity of their souls, free from all passion, thought, and intense or disagreeable occupations — people that pass their lives in an admirable simplicity and ignorance, without letters, without law, without king, without any manner of religion.

And whence comes this, which we know by experience, that the grossest and stupidest fellows are more vigorous and more desirable in amorous performances, and that the love of a muleteer often makes itself more acceptable than that of a gentleman, if it be not that in the latter the agitation of the soul distracts his bodily strength, dissolves and wearies it? As it also commonly wearies and distracts itself. What deranges it, what more usually drives it to madness, but its vivacity, its acuteness, its agility, and, in short, its own strength? Whence does the most subtle madness proceed but from the most subtle wisdom? As great enmities spring from great friendships, and mortal maladies from vigorous health, so the most exorbitant and lively agitations of our souls: it is but half a turn of the peg from one to the other.

In the actions of the insane we see how exactly madness consorts with the most vigorous operations of our soul. Who does not know how imperceptible is the boundary that separates madness from the joyous exaltation of a free spirit and from the actions of a supreme and extraordinary virtue? Plato says that melancholic persons are the most teachable and the most excellent; nor indeed are there any in whom there is so great a tendency to madness. Innumerable minds are ruined by their own strength and mobility. What a lapse, owing to his excitability and high-spiritedness, has just been suffered by one who is more judicious, ingenious, and more in tune with the spirit of that antique and pure poesy than any other Italian poet has been for a long time? Has he not cause to be grateful to this vivacity that has murdered him, to this light that has blinded him, to this exact and intense apprehension of reason that has left him without reason, to this careful and laborious search after learning that has reduced him to stupidity, to that rare aptitude for the exercises of the mind which has left him without exercise and without mind? I felt even more irritation than compassion to see him at Ferrara in so pitiful a state, surviving himself, oblivious of both himself and his works, which, without his knowledge, and yet before his very eyes, were given to the world without connection and without final shaping.

Would you have a man healthy, would have him normal, and in a state of stability and security? Muffle him up in darkness, in sloth, and in stupidity. We must be made level with the beasts that we may be wise, and blinded that we may be led. . . .

O Presumption, how much dost thou hinder us! When Socrates was informed that the God of Wisdom had conferred upon him the title of the Sage, he was astonished, and searching and examining himself thoroughly, he could find no foundation for this divine judgment. He knew men as just, temperate, valiant, and learned as himself, and more eloquent, more handsome, and more useful to their country. At last he concluded that he was distinguished from others and was wise only because he did not think himself so, and that his God considered a belief in one's own knowledge and wisdom a singular folly in man, and that his best knowledge was knowledge of his ignorance, and his best wisdom simplicity.

The holy word pronounces miserable those of us who have a good opinion of ourselves. "Dust and ashes," it says to them, "what hast thou to glory in?" And in another place: "God has made man like unto a shadow, of which who shall judge when by the departure of the light it shall have vanished?" We are indeed a thing of naught. Our powers are so far from being able to conceive the divine height that of the works of our Creator those best bear his mark and are most peculiarly His which we least understand. It is for Christians an occasion to believe when they meet with something unbelievable. It is all the more according to reason, because it is contrary to human reason. If it were according to reason, it would no longer be a miracle; and if it were according to some precedent, it would no longer be a singular thing. "God is best known in not being known," says Saint Augustine; and Tacitus: "It is more pious and more reverent to believe in the works of the gods than to comprehend them." And Plato thinks there is some sin of impiety in inquiring too curiously into God and the world and the first causes of things. "To discover the parent of this universe is difficult; and to reveal him to the multitude, when you have discovered him, is sinful," says Cicero.

We say, indeed, Power, Truth, Justice: these are words which signify some great thing; but that thing we do not see at all, nor do we conceive it. We say that God fears, that God is angry, that God loves,

> Branding immortal things with mortal names; (Lucretius)

these are all perturbations and emotions which cannot dwell in God, according to our form, nor can we imagine Him according to His. It belongs to God alone to know Himself and to interpret His works.

And He does it in our language, inexactly, in order to stoop and descend to us, who are on the earth, grovelling. Wisdom, which is the choice between good and evil, how can it be attributed to Him, seeing that no evil can touch Him? What has He to do with reason and understanding, which we make use of to arrive at things apparent by things that are obscure, seeing that nothing is obscure to God? Justice, which distributes to each man what belongs to him, a thing created for the society and community of men—how can it be in God? How Temperance, which is the moderation of bodily pleasures, which have no place in divinity? Fortitude to support pain, toil, and danger just as little appertains to Him, these three things having no access to Him. Therefore Aristotle holds Him equally exempt from virtue and from vice. "He can be affected neither by kindness nor by anger, because all such things are the effects of weakness" (Cicero).

The share we have in the knowledge of truth, such as it is, is not acquired by our own strength. God has made that sufficiently clear to us through the witnesses He has chosen from the common people, simple and ignorant men, to instruct us in His wondrous secrets. Our faith is not of our acquiring; it is a pure gift from the bounty of another. It is not by virtue of our reason and our understanding that we have received our religion; it is by authority and by command from without. The weakness of our judgment is of more assistance to it than our strength, and our blindness more than our clear-sightedness. It is by the mediation of our ignorance more than of our learning that we know anything of this divine wisdom. It is no wonder if our natural and earthly means cannot conceive that supernatural and celestial knowledge; let us bring to it from our own stock only obedience and submission, for, as it is written, "I will destroy the wisdom of the wise, and bring to nothing the understanding of the prudent. Where is the wise? Where is the scribe? Where is the disputer of this world? Hath not God made foolish the wisdom of this world? For after that in the wisdom of God the world by wisdom knew not God, it pleased God by the foolishness of preaching to save them that believe" (Saint Paul to the Corinthians).

I must also examine, finally, whether it be in the power of man to find what he seeks, and whether the search in which he has been engaged for so many ages has enriched him with any new power or any solid truth. I believe he will confess, if he speaks from his conscience, that all he has gained by so long a pursuit is that he has learned to know his weakness. The ignorance that was naturally in us we have by long study confirmed and verified. It has happened with the truly wise as with the ears of corn: they shoot up and raise their heads erect and proud as long as they are empty, but when they are full and swollen with grain in maturity, they begin to humble themselves and lower their horns. Similarly men, having tried all things and sounded all things, and having found in that mass of knowledge and in all that various provision nothing solid and firm, nothing but vanity, they have renounced their presumption and acknowledged their natural condition. It is the reproach levelled by Velleius against Cotta and Cicero that they had learned from Philo that they had learned nothing.

Pherecydes, one of the Seven Sages, writing to Thales from his death-bed, said: "I have given orders to my people, after they have buried me, to bring my writings to you. If they satisfy you and the other sages, publish them; if not, suppress them. They contain no certainty with which I myself am satisfied. Neither do I profess to know the truth nor to attain to it. I rather uncover things than discover them." The wisest man that ever lived, when he was asked what he knew, answered that he knew this much, that he knew nothing. He verified the saying that the greatest part of what we know is the least part of what we do not know; that is to say, that even what we think we know is but a fraction, and a very small one, of our ignorance. We know things in a dream, says Plato, and are ignorant of them in reality. "Nearly all the ancients have said that nothing could be known, nothing perceived, nothing learned; that our senses were restricted, our minds feeble, the course of life too short" (Cicero).

Of Cicero himself, who was indebted to learning for all of his merit, Valerius says that in his old age he began to despise letters. And during the time that he was actively occupied with them it was without binding himself to any faction, following what he thought probable now in one sect, now in another, always preserving the doubting attitude of the Academy. "I must speak, but in such a way as to affirm nothing, question everything, generally learning to doubt, and distrusting myself" (Cicero).

I should have too easy a task if I were to consider man in his ordinary condition and in the gross, and yet I might fairly do it by his own rule, since he judges Truth not by the weight of the votes, but by their number. Let us leave the multitude out of it,

> Which snores while it's awake,
> Whose life's a living death while yet it lives, (Lucretius)

which is not conscious of itself, which does not judge itself, which lets most of its natural faculties lie idle. I will take man in his highest state.

Let us consider him in that small number of excellent and chosen men who, having been endowed by nature with a fine and exceptional talent, have further strengthened and sharpened it by care, by study, and by art and raised it to the highest pitch of wisdom to which it is capable of attaining. They have so shaped their mind that it is adjusted to every direction and every angle; they have supported it and propped it up with every external help that was suited to it, and enriched and adorned it with all that they could borrow for its advantage from within the world and from without. It is in them that the supreme elevation of human nature appears. They have brought order into the world by means of governments and laws, they have instructed it in arts and sciences, and instructed it also by the example of their admirable conduct. I shall take into account only these men, their testimony, and their experience. Let us see how far they have gone and to what they have held. The maladies and defects that we shall find in that company of men the rest of the world may boldly avow as their own.

Whoever goes in search of anything must come to this point: he says either that he has found it, or that it cannot be found, or that he is still upon the quest. All philosophy is divided into these three kinds. Its design is to seek for Truth, Knowledge, and Certainty. The Peripatetics, Epicureans, Stoics, and others thought they had found it. These have established the sciences that we have, and have treated them as matters of certain knowledge. Clitomachus, Carneades, and the Academics have despaired in their quest and decided that Truth could not be conceived by our capacity. For these men the conclusion was the weakness and ignorance of man. This sect has had the greatest following and the noblest partisans. Pyrrho and other Skeptics, or Ephectics — whose doctrines were by many ancients held to be derived from Homer, the Seven Sages, Archilochus, Euripides, and they join with them Zeno, Democritus, Xenophanes — say that they are still in search of the truth. These conclude that the others, who think they have found it, are vastly deceived, and that there is even too daring a vanity in the second sort, who affirm that human power is not capable of attaining it. For to establish the measure of our power, to know and judge of the difficulty of things, that is the great and utmost point of knowledge, of which they doubt whether man is capable.

Then if a man believes that naught is known,
He surely cannot tell if it be so
Or not, since he knows nothing. (Lucretius)

The ignorance that knows itself, that judges and condemns itself, is not an absolute ignorance: to be this, it must be ignorant of itself. So that the profession of the Pyrrhonians is to waver, doubt, and inquire, to be sure of nothing, to be answerable for nothing. Of the three actions of the soul, the imaginative, the appetitive, and the consenting, they accept the first two; the last they hold in suspense and declare to be ambiguous, without inclination or approbation one way or the other, however slight. . . .

Is there not some advantage in being disengaged from the necessity that curbs others? Is it not better to remain in suspense than to get entangled in the innumerable errors that the human fancy has brought forth? Is it not better to suspend one's belief than to get mixed up with these wrangling and seditious factions? What shall I choose? "Whatever you please, provided you choose." A foolish answer, that! And yet it seems to be the one in which all dogmatism terminates, which does not permit us to be ignorant of that of which we are ignorant.

Take the most famous side; it will never be so sure but that, to defend it, you will have to attack and combat hundreds of contrary positions. Is it not better to keep out of this fracas? You are permitted to espouse, as though your honour and your life depended on it, the opinion of Aristotle on the eternity of the soul and to contradict and give the lie to what Plato says on that subject; and shall they be forbidden to be doubtful about it? If it is permissible for Panætius to suspend his judgment about auguries, dreams, oracles, vaticinations, concerning which the Stoics entertain no doubts at all, why shall not a wise man dare in all things what this man dares in those which he has learned of his masters and which were regarded as settled by the common consent of the school whose doctrines he followed and professed? If it is a child that judges, he knows not what it is; if it is a scholar, he is prejudiced. The Pyrrhonians have reserved for themselves a marvellous advantage in the combat, having freed themselves of any concern for their own defence. It does not matter to them if they are struck, provided they strike; and they make everything serve their purpose. If they win, your argument is lame; if you, theirs. If they make a mistake, they confirm the case for ignorance; if you make a mistake, you confirm it. If they prove that nothing is known, it is well; if they cannot prove it, it is well just the same. "So that, when on the same subject the arguments appear equally balanced for and against, the judgment may more easily be suspended on either side" (Cicero). And it is their point that one can much more easily find out why a thing is false than that it is true; and that which is not, than that which is; and what they do not believe, than what they believe.

Their way of speaking is: "I settle nothing; it is no more thus than thus, or no more one than the other; I understand it not; the probabilities are equal in all cases; it is equally possible to speak for and against. Nothing seems true that may not seem false." Their sacramental word is ἐπέχω; that is to say: "I am in suspense, I do not budge." This is the burden of their song, and others of like stuff. The result of it is a pure, complete, and very perfect surcease and suspension of judgment. They make use of their reason to inquire and to debate, but not to decide and choose. Whoever can imagine a perpetual confession of ignorance, a judgment without bias or inclination, upon any occasion whatever, can have a conception of Pyrrhonism. I express this notion as well as I can, because many find it hard to conceive; and the authors of it themselves present it somewhat obscurely and variously.

As to what concerns the actions of life, they belong in this respect to the common sort. They yield and adapt themselves to the natural inclinations, to the impulse and constraint of the passions, to the constitutions of laws and customs, and to the tradition of arts. "For God did not wish us to know those things, but only to use them" (Cicero). They suffer their ordinary actions to be guided by those things without forming any opinion or judgment. For which reason I cannot well reconcile with this mental attitude the things that are said of Pyrrho. They describe him as dull and inert, leading an eccentric and unsociable kind of life, waiting to be knocked down by carts, exposing himself on the edge of precipices, refusing to conform to the laws. That is to exaggerate the import of his teaching. He did not mean to make himself a stock or a stone; he meant to show himself a living, thinking, reasoning man, enjoying all the natural pleasures and comforts, putting into play and utilizing all of his bodily and mental faculties in regular and correct fashion. The fantastic, imaginary, and false privileges that man has usurped of teaching, of regulating, of establishing the truth, he has sincerely quitted and renounced.

Besides, there is no sect which is not constrained to permit its sage to do many things neither comprehended, nor perceived, nor assented to, if he desires to live. And when he goes to sea, he follows that course without knowing whether it will turn out to his advantage; he relies on the goodness of the ship, the experience of the pilot, the fitness of the season, circumstances merely probable, but according to which he is bound to go, and let himself be governed by appearances, provided there is nothing expressly unfavourable in them. He has a body, he has a soul; the senses push him, the mind spurs him on. Although he does not find in himself that singular property that marks him out for passing judgment, and although he perceives that he ought not to pledge his assent, considering there may be some false thing resembling the true, he nevertheless carries on the functions of his life fully and satisfactorily. How many arts are there that profess to consist in conjecture more than in knowledge, that do not decide between the true and the false and follow only that which seems? There is, they say, a true and a false, and there is within us the means to seek it, but no touchstone to settle it. We are better off to let ourselves be swayed by the order of the world, without any inquiry. A soul secured against prejudice makes a marvellous advance toward tranquillity. Men who judge and who correct their judges never duly submit to them. How much more docile and easily led, in the laws both of religion and of civil government, are simple and incurious minds than those minds that act as monitors and schoolmasters over divine and human causes!

There is no human conception that carries so great a show of likelihood and usefulness. It presents man naked and empty, acknowledging his natural weakness, fit to receive from on high some strength not his own, unprovided with human knowledge and therefore more apt to admit divine knowledge, annihilating his judgment to make more room for faith, neither disbelieving, nor maintaining any dogma contrary to the common observances; humble, obedient, teachable, zealous, a sworn enemy of heresy and consequently free from the vain and irreligious opinions introduced by the false sects. It is a blank sheet, prepared to receive from the finger of God such characters as it shall please Him to engrave upon it. The more we resign and commit ourselves to God and the more we repudiate ourselves, the better off we are. "Receive things in good part," says Ecclesiastes, "according to the aspect and flavour with which they appear to you from day to day; the rest is out of thy knowledge." "The Lord knoweth the thoughts of man, that they are vain" (Psalms). . . .

Democritus, having eaten at his table some figs that tasted of honey, immediately began to seek in his mind for the reason of this unusual sweetness, and in order to clear the matter up he was about to rise from the table to see the situation of the place where the figs had been gathered. His maid, realizing the cause of this movement, laughingly told him that he need give himself no more trouble on that score, for the reason was that she had put them into a dish which had contained honey. He was vexed that she had deprived him of an occasion for investigation and robbed his curiosity of matter to work upon. "Go thy way," said he; "you have made me angry; but for all that I shall not give up searching for the cause as if it were natural." And he would not have failed to discover some true cause for a false and imaginary effect.

This story of a great and famous philosopher illustrates very clearly the passion for study that beguiles us into the pursuit of things which we have no hope of acquiring. Plutarch recounts a like case of one who did not wish to be enlightened concerning a thing on which he stood in doubt, that he might not lose the pleasure of inquiring into it; like another, who would not have his physician allay the thirst of his fever that he might not lose the pleasure of quenching it by drink. "It is better to learn useless things than nothing" (Seneca). Just as in all feeding there is often only the pleasure of eating, and not every agreeable thing that we eat is nutritive or wholesome, similarly what our mind derives from learning does not cease to be pleasurable, even though it is neither nourishing nor healthful.

This is what they say: "The consideration of Nature is a diet proper for our minds; it lifts us up and expands us, making us disdain low and earthy things in comparison with the high and heavenly; the mere act of inquiry into great and occult things is very pleasant, even if one acquires nothing by it but a sense of reverence and awe in judging of them." These are the words they profess. The vain image of that sickly curiosity shows itself even more definitely in this other example that they hold in honour and have so often in their mouths. Eudoxus desired and prayed the gods that he might but once see the sun near at hand, comprehend its form, its size, and its beauty, though on penalty of being instantly burned up by it. He wishes, at the price of his life, to purchase a knowledge of which the use and possession should in the same instant be taken from him, and for this momentary and fleeting knowledge he would lose all other knowledge that he has or may in the future acquire.

I am not easily persuaded that Epicurus, Plato, and Pythagoras have given us their Atoms, their Ideas, and their Numbers for current coin. They were too wise to establish their articles of faith upon such uncertain and debatable things. But in the darkness and ignorance of the world each of these great men strove to introduce some idea of the light, whatever it might be, and they exercised their minds in speculations that might at least have a pleasant and ingenious appearance, provided that, false though it might be, it could hold its ground against opposing ideas: "these things are imagined by each one according to his wit, not by virtue of his knowledge" (Seneca).

One of the ancients who was reproached for making a profession of philosophy, by which, however, in his own judgment he set no great store, answered that this was truly to philosophize. It has been their aim to consider everything, to weigh everything, and they have found that occupation suited to the natural curiosity that is in us. Some things they have written for the needs of society, such as their religious beliefs; and in considering these things it was but reasonable that they should not scrutinize common opinions too closely, for fear of troubling the obedience to the laws and customs of their country.

Plato's device in the treatment of this mystery is quite transparent. For when he writes as for himself, he prescribes nothing with certainty. When he plays the legislator, he borrows a magisterial and positive style, and yet boldly inserts his most fantastic ideas, which are as useful for persuading the multitude as they are ridiculous for persuading himself, knowing how fit we are to receive all sorts of impressions, and, above all, the wildest and most extravagant. And therefore, in his laws, he takes great care that only those poems should be sung in public whose fabulous stories tend to some useful purpose; and it being so easy to imprint all sorts of phantasms on the human mind, he thought it unfair not to feed it rather on profitable truths than on untruths that are either unprofitable or harmful. He says quite unequivocally, in his *Republic,* that for the profit of men it is often necessary to deceive them.

It is easy to discern that some of the schools have been more interested in the pursuit of truth, others in the pursuit of utility, whereby the latter have gained the credit. It is the misery of our condition that often what appears to our imagination as the most true does not also appear as the most useful to life. The boldest sects, the Epicurean, the Pyrrhonian, the New Academic, are yet, after all is said and done, constrained to submit to the civil law.

Other subjects there are that they have passed through their sieves and tossed to the right or the left, everyone labouring to give them some kind of colour, right or wrong. For, having found nothing so abstruse that they would not discuss it, they are often forced to forge weak and foolish conjectures; not that they themselves take them as a foundation for anything or for the establishing of any truth, but merely for exercise in their study: "Not so much because they believed what they said, as from a wish to exercise their minds with the difficulty of the matter" (Quintilian).

And if we did not take it thus, how should we defend so great an inconsistency, variety, and vanity of opinions as we see to have been produced by those excellent and admirable minds? For, by way of example, what can be more vain than to desire to guess at God by our analogies and conjectures, to make Him and the world conform to our capacities and our laws, and to utilize, at the expense of the Deity, that little shred of power which it has pleased Him to assign to our natural condition? And because we cannot stretch our view to the height of His glorious throne, to bring Him down to a level with our corruptions and our miseries?

Of all human and ancient opinions concerning religion, that seems to me to have had most probability and most justification which recognized in God an incomprehensible power, the source and preserver of all things, all goodness, all perfection, receiving and accepting graciously the honour and reverence that human beings rendered Him, under whatever aspect, under whatever name, and in whatever way:

> Almighty Jove, of things, and kings, and gods
> Begetter and conceiver. (Valerius Soranus)

This zeal has in all places been looked upon by Heaven with a gracious eye. All societies have reaped fruit from their devotion: impious men and impious actions have everywhere met with an appropriate fate. Pagan histories recognize authority, order, justice, prodigies, and oracles employed for their profit and instruction in their fabulous religions; God, in His mercy, perhaps vouchsafing by these temporal benefits to foster the tender roots of a kind of brutish knowledge that natural reason has given us of Him amid the false images of our dreams. Not only false, but also impious and harmful are those that man has forged by his own invention.

And of all the religions that Saint Paul found in repute at Athens, that which they had dedicated to a hidden and unknown Deity seemed to him the most defensible.

Pythagoras shadowed forth the truth a little more nearly, deeming that the knowledge of this First Cause and Being of Beings ought to be indefinite, without circumscription, without explanation; that it was nothing else than the supreme effort of our imagination toward perfection, everyone amplifying the idea of it according to his capacity. But if Numa attempted to make the worship of his people conform to this design, to attach it to a religion purely intellectual without any fixed object and without material admixture, he attempted something that was of no utility. The human mind could not maintain itself afloat in such an infinity of formless thoughts; it must needs arrange them in a certain shape according to its own model. The divine majesty has thus to some extent suffered itself to be circumscribed in corporeal limits for our benefit. His supernatural and heavenly sacraments bear signs of our earthly conditions; His worship is expressed by means of rites and words that speak to the senses; for it is man who believes and prays. I omit the other arguments that are employed on this subject. But it would be hard to make me believe that the sight of our crucifixes, the picture of that piteous agony, the ornaments and the ceremonious movements in our churches, the voices attuned to the devoutness of our thoughts, and all that excitement of the senses did not warm the souls of the people with a religious emotion of very advantageous effect. . . .

Thales, who was the first to inquire into such things, thought God was a spirit that made all things of water; Anaximander, that the gods were dying and being born at different seasons and that they were worlds infinite in number; Anaximenes, that the air was God, that it was brought forth and immense, always in motion. Anaxagoras was the first who held that the form and fashion of all things was controlled by the power and reason of an infinite mind. Alcmæon ascribed divinity to the sun, the moon, the stars, and the soul. Pythagoras made God a spirit diffused through the nature of all things, from which our souls detached themselves; Parmenides, a circle encompassing the heavens and supporting the world by the intensity of its light. Empedocles declared the four elements, of which all things are composed, to be gods; Protagoras declared that he could not say whether they are or are not, or what they are. Democritus was one moment of the opinion that the images of objects and their circular movements were gods; at another moment, the nature that darts out those images; and, again, that our knowledge and understanding were gods. Plato disperses his beliefs in a variety of shapes. He says, in the *Timæus,* that the father of the world cannot be named; in the *Laws,* that men must not inquire into his nature; and elsewhere in the same books he makes the world, the heaven, the stars, the earth, and our souls gods; and he accepts, besides, those which have been accepted by ancient institutions in every state. Xenophon reports a similar confusion in the teachings of Socrates: one while we are not to inquire into the form of God, and then he makes him maintain that the sun is God, and the soul God; first he says that there is only one God, and then that there are many. Speusippus, the nephew of Plato, makes God a certain power procuring all things and says that it is animal. Aristotle now says it is the mind and now the world; now he gives another master to this world, and again he makes God the heat of heaven. Xenocrates makes eight of Him: five named among the planets, the sixth composed of all the fixed stars as its members, the seventh and eighth, the sun and moon. Heraclides Ponticus does nothing but wander in a maze of opinions, and finally deprives God of feeling and makes Him shift from one form to another, and then says that He is heaven and earth. Theophrastus strolls with similar indecision among all his fancies, attributing the superintendence of the world now to the understanding, now to heaven, and then again to the stars. Strato says it is Nature, having the power of generation, augmentation, and diminution, without form and feeling. Zeno says it is the Law of Nature, commanding good and forbidding evil, which law is an animated being; and he abolishes the customary gods, Jupiter, Juno, and Vesta. Diogenes of Apollonia says that it is Age. Xenophanes makes God round, seeing, hearing, not breathing, having nothing in common with human nature. Aristo thinks the form of God to be incomprehensible, deprives Him of senses, and knows not whether He is an animated being or something else. Cleanthes now declares him to be Reason, and, again, the world; now the Soul of Nature, and, again, the supreme heat, encircling and enveloping all things. Perseus, Zeno's disciple, held that men have given the title of gods to such as have contributed any notable benefit to human life, and even to the benefits themselves. Chrysippus made a confused heap of all the preceding ideas, and among the thousand forms of gods that he fashions he reckoned also those men that were immortalized. Diagoras and Theodorus flatly denied that there were any gods at all. Epicurus made the gods shining beings, through whom light and air might pass, lodged between two worlds as between two forts, secure from shocks, invested with a human shape and limbs like ours, which limbs are of no use to them.

> I've said, and always shall, that there are gods in heaven,
> But what men do on earth concerns them not, I ween. (Ennius)

Trust now to your philosophy, boast that you have found the bean in the cake when you hear all this rattling of philosophical brains! The confusion in the ways of the world has gained this advantage for me: that manners and notions different from my own do not displease me as much as they instruct me, nor do they puff me up with pride as much as they humble me, when I compare them; and every other choice than that which comes expressly from the hand of God seems to me a choice of little advantage. I leave out of account the monstrous and unnatural modes of life. The governments of the world are no less contradictory in this regard than the schools; whereby we may learn that Fortune herself is not more variable and inconstant than our reason, nor more blind and heedless. . . .

Now, nothing of ours can be likened or compared in any way whatever with the divine nature without blemishing and tarnishing it with so much imperfection. How can that infinite beauty, power, and goodness admit of any correspondence or similitude with so abject a thing as we are, without loss and derogation of its divine grandeur? "The weakness of God is stronger than men, and the foolishness of God is wiser than men" (Saint Paul). When Stilpo the philosopher was asked whether the gods took pleasure in the honours and sacrifices we offered them, he replied: "You are indiscreet; let us draw aside if you wish to talk of that."

Nevertheless, we prescribe bounds to God, we subject His power to the siege of our reasons (I call reason our random thoughts and dreams, with the permission of Philosophy, which says that even the foolish and the wicked are mad by reason, but it is a particular kind of reason), we would make Him subservient to the vain and feeble conjectures of our understanding, Him who has made both us and our knowledge.

Because nothing is made of nothing, God could not have formed the world without matter! What! has God put into our hands the keys and most secret springs of His power? Has He bound Himself not to trespass beyond the limits of our knowledge? Put the case, O man, that thou hast been able to observe here some traces of His operations; dost thou think that He has employed therein all His powers, and has crowded all His forms and all His ideas into this work? Thou seest nothing but the order and the government of this little cave in which thou art lodged, if indeed thou seest that much; His divinity has an infinite jurisdiction beyond; this fragment is nothing in comparison with the whole:

> All things in heaven, on earth, and in the sea
> Are all as nothing in the sum entire
> Of the all-Sum: (Lucretius)

it is a local law that thou allegest; thou knowest not what is the universal law. Tie thyself to that to which thou art subject, but do not tie Him; He is not of thy brotherhood, nor thy fellow-citizen or companion. If He has in some sort communicated Himself unto thee, it is not to abase Himself to thy littleness nor to give thee supervision over His power. The human body cannot soar up into the clouds — that is a law that affects thee; the sun runs its usual course without repose; the boundaries of the seas and the earth cannot be confounded; water is unstable and without solidity; a wall in which there is no breach is impenetrable to a solid body; a man cannot preserve life in the flames; he cannot be with his body both in heaven and upon earth, and in a thousand places at the same time. It is for thee that He has made these rules; it is thee that they bind. He has given proof to the Christians that He has transcended them all, when it has pleased Him. In truth, why, all-powerful as He is, should He have confined His powers within certain bounds? In favour of whom should He have renounced His privilege? Of no other thing does thy reason persuade thee with greater likelihood and better foundation than of the plurality of worlds:

> Heaven and earth, sun, moon, and sea, and all
> That is, are never single in their kind,
> But rather are in number numberless. (Lucretius)

The most famous minds of the past believed it, and some even of our own age, compelled by the probabilities of human reasoning. Inasmuch as in this fabric that we behold there is nothing single and one,

> In the sun there is
> No one thing single of its kind in birth,
> And single and sole in growth, (Lucretius)

and all the kinds are multiplied in some number, therefore it seems not to be likely that God should have created this work alone without a companion and that the matter of this form should have been totally exhausted in this sole individual object:

> Again and again we must confess there are
> Such congregations of matter otherwhere,
> Like this one world which the vast Ether holds
> Within its huge embrace: (Lucretius)

especially if it is an animated being, which its motions render so credible that Plato asserts it, and many of our people either confirm it or do not venture to deny it; no more than the ancient opinion that the heaven, the stars, and other portions of the universe are creatures composed of body and soul, mortal in respect of their composition, but immortal by the determination of the creator.

Now, if there be many worlds, as Democritus, Epicurus, and almost all philosophy has believed, how do we know that the principles and rules that govern this world of ours equally affect the others? Perhaps they have another aspect and another polity. Epicurus imagines them either like or unlike. We see in this world an infinite difference and variety arising solely from the distance between places. Neither corn nor wine nor any of our animals is to be seen in the new lands discovered by our fathers; everything there is different. And, in times past, do but consider in how many parts of the world they had no knowledge of either Bacchus or Ceres. If we are to believe Pliny and Herodotus, there are, in certain places, species of men who bear a very slight resemblance to ours. And there are mongrel and ambiguous forms between human beings and brutes. There are countries where men are born without heads, having their eyes and mouth in their breast; where they are all androgynous; where they walk on all fours; where they have but one eye in the forehead, and a head more like a dog's than like ours; where they are half fish below, and live in the water; where the women bear at the age of five, and live only eight years; where the head and the skin of the forehead are so hard that a sword cannot bite into them, but is blunted by the contact; where the men are beardless; nations without the use and knowledge of fire; others that eject sperm of a black colour.

What shall we say of those that naturally change into wolves, mares, and then into men again? And if it be true, as Plutarch says, that in a certain place in the Indies there are men without mouths, who feed on the smell of certain odours, how many of our descriptions are false! He is no longer the animal that laughs, nor perhaps capable of reason and society. The arrangement and cause of our internal structure would, for the most part, be to no purpose.

Moreover, how many things are there within our knowledge that are opposed to those fine rules we have cut out for and prescribed to Nature! And yet we will undertake to bind God Himself to them! How many things do we not call miraculous and contrary to Nature! That is done by every man and by every nation according to the measure of their ignorance. How many occult properties and quintessences do we not discover! For, with us, to go according to nature is nothing else than to go according to our understanding, as far as that is able to follow and as far as we are able to see; whatever is beyond is unnatural and irregular. Now, by this reckoning, all things will be unnatural to the most sensible and the most competent, for they are the ones who have been persuaded by human reason that it has no kind of footing or foundation, not so much as to assure them whether snow is white (and Anaxagoras said it was black), whether there is anything or whether there is nothing; whether there is knowledge or ignorance (Metrodorus of Chios denied that man was able to determine it); or whether we live, since Euripides doubts whether the life we live is life, or whether what we call death be not life:

> *Τὶς δ' οἴδεν ει ζῆν τουθ ὁ κίκληται θανεῖν*
> *Τὸ ζῆν δὲ θνέσκειν ἔστι.* (Stobaeus)

And not without plausibility: for why do we take our title to existence from this instant, which is but a flash in the infinite course of an eternal night, and so brief an interruption of our perpetual and natural condition, death possessing all that went before and all that comes after this moment, and even a good part of the moment itself? Others swear that there is no motion, that nothing stirs, like the followers of Melissus (for if there be only One, He cannot be served by spherical motion, nor by movement from one place to another, as Plato proves), that there is neither generation nor corruption in Nature.

Protagoras says that there is nothing in Nature but doubt, that we may equally dispute concerning all things, and even concerning this very point, whether we may equally dispute concerning all things; Nausiphanes declares that of things which seem to be, nothing is, any more than it is not; that there is nothing certain but uncertainty; Parmenides, that of that which seems to be, there is nothing in general, that there is only One; Zeno, that even One is not, and that there is nothing. If One were, it would be either in another or in itself; if it is in another, there are two; if it is in itself, there are still two — the containing and the contained. According to these doctrines, the nature of things is only a shadow, either false or void of meaning.

It has always seemed to me that in a Christian it is highly indiscreet and irreverent to speak after this fashion: "God cannot die, God cannot unsay what He has said, God cannot do this or that." I do not approve of having the divine power confined within the laws of our speech. And the surmise which offers itself to us in these propositions ought to be presented more reverently and more religiously.

Our language has its weaknesses and defects like everything else. Most of the occasions of disturbance in the world spring from grammar. Our lawsuits arise only from disputes over the interpretation of laws; and most wars proceed from the inability to express in clear language the conventions and articles of agreement among princes. How many quarrels, and what momentous ones, has doubt about the meaning of the syllable HOC created in the world!

Let us take the clearest statement that Logic itself can offer us. If you say: "It is fine weather" and are telling the truth, then it is fine weather. Is not this a very certain way of speaking? And yet it will deceive us. To prove this, let me follow up the example. If you say: "I lie," and are telling the truth, then you do lie. The art, the reason, the force of the conclusion of this statement are the same as in the other; yet there we are, stuck in the mire!

The Pyrrhonian philosophers, I see, cannot express their general conception in any kind of speech; for they would require a new language. Ours is made up altogether of affirmative propositions, which to them are entirely hostile; so that when they say: "I doubt," they are immediately seized by the throat and made to confess that they at least know and are sure of this, that they doubt. So they have been constrained to take refuge in that medical comparison without which their peculiar attitude would be inexplicable: when they declare: "I do not know" or: "I doubt," they say that this proposition carries itself off with the rest, neither more nor less than rhubarb that drives out the evil humours and carries itself off with them.

This notion is more surely conceived by an interrogation: "What do I know?" as represented on my shield, with the emblem of a pair of scales. . . .

We must observe that to every creature nothing is more dear and of higher estimation than its own being (the lion, the eagle, the dolphin prize nothing above their own species); and that each one relates the qualities of all other things to its own peculiar qualities, which we may indeed expand and contract, but that is all. For outside of this relationship and this principle our imagination cannot move, can divine nothing that is different; it is impossible that it should find an outlet from that and pass beyond it. Whence arise those ancient conclusions. "Of all forms the most beautiful is that of man; God therefore is of that form. No one can be happy without virtue, nor can virtue exist without reason, and no reason can dwell anywhere else than in the human shape; God, therefore, is clothed in human shape." "Our minds are so informed by preconceptions that when a man would think of God, the human shape is what instantly occurs to him" (Cicero).

Therefore it was that Xenophanes wittily said that if the animals fashion any gods for themselves, as it is probable they do, they certainly fashion them in their own likeness, and glorify themselves therein as we do. For why shall not a goose say thus: "All the parts of the universe have me in view; the earth serves me to walk upon, the sun to light me, the stars to shed their influence upon me; I enjoy this benefit from the winds, that from the waters; there is nothing that yon heavenly vault looks upon so favourably as on me; I am the darling of Nature; is it not man who maintains me, who gives me shelter, who serves me? It is for me that he sows and grinds: if he eats me, he also eats man, his companion, and so do I the worms that kill him and eat him." As much might be said by a crane, and even more magnificently, on account of the freedom of its flight and its possession of that high and beautiful region: "Such a smooth procuress and such a seducer of herself is Nature!" (Cicero)

Now then, by this same course of reasoning, for us are the Destinies, for us the world; it shines, it thunders for us; both the creator and the creatures, everything is for us. It is the goal and aim to which the universality of things is directed. Look into the records that Philosophy has kept, for two thousand years and more, of the affairs of heaven: the gods have acted, have spoken, only for man; she ascribes to them no other deliberation and no other function. . . .

Let us see if we have a little more light in the knowledge of human and natural things. Is it not a ridiculous undertaking to go about devising another body and imparting a false form of our own invention to those to which, by our own confession, our knowledge is not able to attain, as is manifest in the movement of the planets, to which, seeing our mind cannot arrive at nor conceive their natural course, we lend material, gross, and corporeal springs from our own stock:

Gold was the axle, and the beam was gold;
The wheels with silver spokes on golden circles rolled. (Ovid)

You would say that we had had coach-makers, carpenters, and painters who went up on high to set up contrivances with various movements, and to arrange the wheels and interlacings of the heavenly bodies in variegated colours around the spindle of Necessity, according to Plato:

The world's a mansion, too vast to be told,
Which thundering zones, in number five, enfold,
Through which a girdle, painted with twelve signs,
And that with sparkling constellations shines,
Obliquely traversing the lofty air,
Admits the moon with chariot and pair. (Varro)

These are all dreams and fanatical follies. Why does not Nature take it into her head some day to lay open her bosom to us and reveal to us the true means and conduct of her movements, and prepare our eyes to see them? Good God, what blunders, what miscalculations should we discover in our poor science! I am mistaken if it apprehends any one thing as it really is; and I shall depart hence more ignorant of all other things than of my own ignorance.

Have I not read in Plato this divine saying: that Nature is nothing but enigmatic poetry; as we should say, perhaps, a veiled and shadowy picture, gleaming here and there with an infinite variety of false lights to exercise our conjectures? "All those things lie hidden and enveloped in the thickest shades, and there is no human wit so sharp as to penetrate to heaven or into the depths of the earth" (Cicero). And certainly philosophy is nothing else than a sophisticated poetry. Whence do the ancient writers derive all their authority but from the poets? And the first of them were poets themselves and treated philosophy in the style of that art. Plato himself is but a disconnected poet. Timon insultingly calls him a great fabricator of miracles.

Just as women make use of ivory teeth when their natural teeth are wanting, and in place of their true complexion make one of some foreign substance; just as they make up their thighs with cloth or felt, and their hips with cotton, and in the view and knowledge of everyone beautify themselves with a false and borrowed beauty, so does science (and even our jurisprudence, they say, has its legal fictions on which it bases the truth of its justice); she gives us as current pay and presupposition things which she herself informs us were invented; for those epicycles, eccentrics, concentrics, which Astrology calls to its aid in order to guide the motions of its stars, she gives us as the best thing she has been able to devise on that subject; as also, for that matter, Philosophy offers us not that which is, or what she believes, but what she makes up with the greatest show of probability and attractiveness. Plato, in discussing the state of our bodies and that of beasts, says: "Of the truth of what we have said we should be sure if we had thereon the confirmation of an oracle; we are only sure that it is the most likely to be true of anything we could say." . . .

Those persons who find Sebond's arguments too weak, who are ignorant of nothing, who guide the course of the world, who know it all:

> What causes the wild oceans sway,
> The seasons what from June to May;
> If free the constellations roll,
> Or move by some supreme control;
> What makes the moon obscure her light,
> What pours her splendour on the night;
> Whence concord rises from the jar
> Of atoms that discordant are; (Horace)

have they not sometimes amid their books sounded the difficulties that present themselves in knowing their own being? We see indeed that the finger moves and that the foot moves; that some parts move of themselves, without our leave, and that we stir others by our volition; that a certain kind of impression occasions blushes, a certain other kind produces pallor; one kind of imagination works only on the spleen, another kind on the brain; one causes laughter, another tears; still another stupefies and paralyses all our senses and arrests the movements of our limbs. At one object the stomach will rise, at another a member that lies below it. But how a spiritual impression should make such a breach in a massive and solid substance, and the nature of the connection and linking of these wonderful mechanisms, are what no man has ever known. "All these things are inscrutable to reason and concealed in the majesty of Nature," says Pliny; and Saint Augustine: "The manner in which spirits are united with bodies is altogether marvellous and cannot be comprehended by man; yet this it is which is man."

And yet no one ever raises a doubt about it; for the opinions of men are adopted in conformity with ancient beliefs, upon authority and trust, as if they were religion and law. What is commonly believed about it is accepted as if by rote. This truth, with its whole structure and equipment of arguments and proofs, is received as though it were a firm and solid body which is not to be shaken, not to be subjected to judgment. On the contrary, everyone, as best he may, cements and fortifies this belief with the utmost power of his reason, which is a supple and pliable instrument, and adaptable to every shape. And thus the world comes to be filled and stuffed with inanities and falsehoods.

The reason why men raise so few doubts is that they never put common impressions to the test. They do not dig to the root, where lie the fault and the weakness; they only argue about the branches. They do not ask whether such and such a thing is true, but whether it has been understood so or so. They do not ask whether Galen has said anything worth while, but whether he has pronounced himself thus or otherwise. In truth there was good reason why this curb and constraint on the liberty of our judgments, and this tyranny over our beliefs, should be extended to the schools and arts. The god of scholastic learning is Aristotle; it is an impiety to dispute his decrees, as it was to dispute those of Lycurgus at Sparta. His doctrine, which is perhaps as false as any other, is by us treated as magisterial law. I do not know why I should not as readily accept either the Ideas of Plato, or the Atoms of Epicurus, or the Plenum and Vacuum of Leucippus and Democritus, or the Water of Thales, or the Infinity of Nature of Anaximander, or the Air of Diogenes, or the Numbers and Symmetry of Pythagoras, or the Infinite of Parmenides, or the One of Musæus, or the Water and Fire of Apollodorus, or the Similar Parts of Anaxagoras, or the Discord and Friendship of Empedocles, or the Fire of Heraclitus, or any other opinion of that infinite confusion of views and judgments which this fine human reason of ours begets with its certitude and clear-sightedness on every subject with which it meddles, as I should accept the opinion of Aristotle on this matter of the principles of natural things; which principle he builds up of three parts—Matter, Form, and Privation. And what can be more pointless than to make emptiness itself the cause of the production of things? Privation is a negative; by what peculiar process of thought could he have made it the cause and origin of things that are? And yet all this no man must dare to disturb except for an exercise in logic. Nothing therein is discussed with a view to raising doubts, but only to defend the founder of the school against objections from without. His authority is the mark beyond which it is not permitted to inquire.

It is very easy, upon granted foundations, to build whatever we please; for in accord with the law and rules of this beginning the remaining parts of the edifice are easily carried out without violation of harmony. In this way we find our reasoning well grounded and argue with entire confidence. For our masters occupy and win in advance as much room in our belief as they need for drawing afterwards the conclusions that they please, in the manner of geometricians with their axioms: the consent and approval we grant them giving them the means to pull us to the right or left and to whirl us about at their pleasure. Whoever is believed in his presuppositions is our master and our god; he will lay the plan of his foundations so amply and so easily that by their means he will, if he so please, lift us up to the clouds.

* * * * *

BOOK THREE

CHAPTER 2

OF REPENTANCE

Others form man; I describe him, and portray a particular one, ill fashioned enough, and whom, if I had to mould him anew, I should certainly make very different from what he is. But that's past recalling. Now, the features of my portrait are not random, though they change and vary. The world is but a perennial whirligig. All things therein are incessantly in motion, the earth, the rocks of the Caucasus, the pyramids of Egypt, both with the general movement and their own. Constancy itself is nothing but a more languid motion. I cannot fix my object; it keeps tottering and reeling by a natural intoxication. I take it as it is at the instant that I am occupied with it. I do not paint its being. I paint its passage: not a passage from one age to another, or, as the people say, from seven years to seven years, but from day to day, from minute to minute. I must accommodate my history to the hour. I may presently change, not only by fortune, but also by intention. It is a record of various and changeable occurrences, and of unsettled and, as sometimes befalls, contradictory ideas, whether it be that I am then another self or that I take hold of subjects by other circumstances and considerations. So it is that I may perhaps contradict myself, but the truth, as Demades said, I do not contradict. Could my soul once take footing, I would not essay, I would resolve; but it is always in a state of apprenticeship and making trial.

I set forth a life that is humble and without distinction: it all comes to the same thing. All of moral philosophy can be applied as well to a common and private life as to one of richer stuff. Every man carries in himself the entire form of the human state.

Authors communicate themselves to people by some special and extrinsic mark; I, the first of any, by my universal being, as Michel de Montaigne, not as a grammarian, a poet, or a lawyer. If the world find fault that I speak too much of myself, I find fault that they do not so much as think of themselves.

But is it reasonable that, being so private in my way of living, I should aspire to present myself to public knowledge? And is it reasonable, too, that I should offer to the world, where style and art have so much credit and authority, the crude and simple products of Nature, and of a rather weak nature to boot? Is it not like building a wall without stone or some such material, to construct books without learning and without art? The fancies of music are guided by art, mine by chance.

This at least I have in keeping with the rules, that never any man treated of a subject which he understood and knew better than I do the one that I have undertaken, and that in this I am the most learned man alive; secondly, that never any man penetrated further into his matter, nor more thoroughly analyzed its elements and connections, nor more exactly and fully arrived at the end he had proposed for his labours. To accomplish it, I need bring nothing but fidelity to the work; and that is there, the most pure and sincere that is anywhere to be found. I speak truth, not as completely as I should like, but as much as I dare; and I dare a little more as I grow older, for it seems that custom allows to age more liberty of prating and more indiscretion in talking of oneself. It cannot happen here, as I often see elsewhere, that the artificer and his product contradict one another: "Can a man who is so sensible in conversation have written so foolish a book?" or: "Do such learned writings proceed from a man so feeble in conversation?"

If the talk of a man is ordinary and his writing distinguished, it means that his ability lies in the place from which he borrowed it, and not in himself. A learned man is not learned in all things; but a man of talent is always a man of talent, even in ignorance.

Here my book and I go hand in hand together, and keep the same pace. Elsewhere men may commend or censure the work apart from the workman; here they cannot. Who touches the one, touches the other. He who shall judge the one without knowing the other, will wrong himself more than me; he who has come to know the work, gives me all the satisfaction I desire. Happy beyond my desert if I enjoy only this much of public approbation, to make men of understanding feel that I was capable of profiting by learning, had I had it, and that I deserved to be better assisted by my memory.

Let me excuse myself here for what I often repeat, that I rarely repent, and that my conscience is satisfied with itself, not as the conscience of an angel or of a horse, but as the conscience of a man; always adding this refrain, not by way of formality, but in sincere and real submission, that I speak as one who questions and does not know, purely and simply referring myself for the decision to the common and legitimate beliefs. I do not teach, I relate.

There is no vice truly a vice which is not hurtful, and which a sound judgment does not condemn; for there is in it so manifest an ugliness and disadvantage that they are perhaps in the right who say that it is chiefly begotten by stupidity and ignorance. So hard it is to imagine that a man may know it without hating it. Malice sucks up the greater part of its own venom and poisons itself with it. Vice leaves repentance in the soul like an ulcer in the flesh, which is always scratching itself and drawing blood. For reason effaces all other griefs and sorrows, but it begets that of repentance, which is so much the more grievous as it springs from within; as the cold and heat of fevers are more sharply felt than that which comes from without. I hold for vices (but each according to its measure) not only those which reason and nature condemn, but also those which the opinion of men has created, even though it be a false and erroneous opinion, provided it has the authority of law and custom.

There is likewise no good action which does not rejoice a well-born nature. There is assuredly a kind of gratification in well-doing that causes inward rejoicing, and there is a generous pride that accompanies a good conscience. A soul daringly wicked may perhaps arm itself with security, but with this complacency and satisfaction it cannot supply itself. It is no little pleasure to feel oneself preserved from the contagion of so depraved an age, and to say to oneself: "If anyone should look into my very soul, he would yet not find me guilty either of the affliction or ruin of anyone, or of revenge or envy, or of offending the public laws, or of innovation and disturbance, or of failing in my word; and though the licence of the time permits and teaches everyone to do so, yet have I not laid my hand on any Frenchman's goods or thrust my fingers into his purse, and have lived only on what is my own, in war as well as in peace; neither have I set any man to work without paying him his hire." These testimonies of a good conscience are pleasant, and this natural rejoicing is very beneficial to us, and the only reward that we can never fail of.

To ground the recompense of virtuous actions upon the approbation of others is to adopt too uncertain and shaky a foundation. Especially in so corrupt and ignorant an age as this, the good opinion of the people is injurious. On whom can you rely to see what is commendable? God defend me from being an honest man according to the descriptions of honour I daily see every man give of himself. "Those things which once were vices are now moral" (Seneca).

Some of my friends have at times taken it upon them to school and lecture me with great plainness, either of their own accord or at my request, as acquitting themselves of an office which to a well-composed soul surpasses, not only in utility but in kindness, all other offices of friendship. I have always received it with the most open arms of courtesy and of gratitude. But to speak of it now in all sincerity, I have found so much false measure both in their blame and praise that if I had sinned instead of doing well, I should hardly have committed a sin according to their notions. Those of us in particular who live private lives, not exposed to any other view than our own, ought to have fixed a pattern within ourselves by which to test our actions, and, according to that pattern, sometimes hug and sometimes flog ourselves. I have my own laws and my court-room to judge me, and I refer to these more than to any other authority. I do indeed restrain my actions according to others, but I extend them only according to myself. None but yourself knows if you are cowardly and cruel, or loyal and devout. Others do not see you, they guess at you by uncertain conjectures. They do not so much see your nature as your art. Therefore do not hold by their opinions; hold by your own. "You must use your own judgment. In the matter of virtues and vices, a man's own conscience carries great weight: take that away, and everything lies in ruins" (Cicero).

But the saying that repentance follows close upon the sin does not seem to have in view sin in its high estate, which is lodged in us as in its proper domicile. We may disown and retract the vices which take us by surprise and into which we are hurried by passion; but those which by long habit are rooted and anchored in a strong and vigorous will are not capable of being gainsaid. Repentance is no other than a recanting of the will and an opposition to our fancies, which leads us about in all directions. It makes this person disown his former virtue and continency:

Why to my youth was not the wisdom given
Which now I share?
Or with my old desires why come not back
Youth's cheeks as fair? (Horace)

It is a rare life that preserves its orderly procedure even in private. Everyone can play his part in the farce and represent an honest character on the platform; but within, and in his own bosom, where all is permitted, where all is concealed, to be disciplined there—that is the point! The state nearest to it is to be so in our own house, in our ordinary actions, for which we are accountable to no man; where there is no study, no artifice. And therefore Bias, describing an ideal domestic establishment, says it is one of which the master is the same within, of his own free will, as he is without, from fear of the law and of what people might say. And it was a worthy saying of Julius Drusus to the workmen who offered, for three thousand crowns, to put his house into such a condition that his neighbours would no longer be able to look into it as they had done. "I will give you," he said, "six thousand, if you will make it possible for everybody to see into it from all sides." It is observed to the honour of Agesilaus that in his travels he was accustomed to take up his lodgings in churches, so that the people and the gods themselves might see into his private actions. Some men have seemed miraculous to the world, in whom their wives and valets have never observed anything that was even noteworthy. Few men have been admired by their own household.

No one has been a prophet, not only in his own house, but in his own country, says the experience of history. It is the same in things of no consequence. And in this following humble example a reflection of greater ones may be seen. In my region of Gascony they think it a droll thing to see me in print; the farther off from my own lair the knowledge of me spreads, the more highly am I valued. I buy the printers in Guienne; elsewhere they buy me. On this circumstance do those people base their expectations, who keep concealed while living and present, to gain a reputation when they are dead and absent. I prefer to have less of it, and only throw myself upon the world for that portion of it that I actually draw on. Beyond that, I hold it quit.

See this fellow whom the people, after a public function, escort to his door with loud acclaim. Along with his gown he puts off the part he has been playing; his drop is as deep as his climb was high. Within, in himself, all is in confusion and base. And even though order should exist there, it requires a lively and well-sifted judgment to perceive it in those humble and private actions. Besides, order is a dull and sombre virtue. To enter a breach, conduct an embassy, govern a people, are brilliant actions. To scold, laugh, sell, pay, love, hate, to hold pleasant and reasonable converse with oneself and one's family, not to let go of oneself nor to be false to oneself, that is a rarer and more difficult matter, and not so much remarked. Retired lives, whatever people may say, are thereby subject to duties as severe and strenuous as those of other lives, if not more so. And private persons, says Aristotle, render a higher and more difficult service to virtue than do those who are in authority. We prepare ourselves for eminent occasions more out of glory than conscience. The shortest way to arrive at glory would be to do for the sake of conscience what we do for the sake of glory. And the virtue of Alexander in his great theatre seems to me to display much less vigour than that of Socrates in his humble and obscure activity. I can easily imagine Socrates in the place of Alexander, but Alexander in that of Socrates, I cannot. If you will ask the former what he can do, he will answer: "Subdue the world"; if you put the same question to the latter, he will say: "Carry on human life conformably with its natural condition": a skill of much more general importance, more difficult, and more legitimate.

The worth of the soul does not consist in mounting aloft, but in walking at an orderly pace. Its greatness is not exercised in greatness, but in a middle state. As those who judge and test our inner being make no great account of the lustre of our public actions, and see that these are only drops and thin tricklings of water oozing from a thick and slimy bottom; so likewise they who judge us by this brave outward appearance, infer a similar quality in our internal constitution, and are unable to couple common faculties, just like their own, with these other faculties that astonish them and are so far beyond their scope. So we endow demons with monstrous shapes. And who does not picture Tamerlane with raised eyebrows, open nostrils, a dreadful visage, and a prodigious stature, which is the figure that the imagination has constructed from the report of his name? Once upon a time, if I had been brought into the presence of Erasmus, it would have been hard for me not to take for adages and apothegms anything he might have said to his servingman and his hostess. We find it more in keeping to imagine an artisan on his close-stool or on his wife than a great president, venerable by his bearing and his talent. From their high thrones, it seems to us, they will hardly abase themselves so low as to live.

As vicious souls are often incited by some extraneous impulse to do good, so are virtuous souls to do evil. We must therefore judge them by their settled state, when they are at home, if they ever are; or at least when they are closest to repose and to their natural state. Natural inclinations are assisted and reinforced by education, but they are scarcely altered and overcome. A thousand natures in my time have escaped toward virtue or toward vice athwart a training that led in the opposite direction:

> As when wild beasts, long time in cages shut,
> Grow tame and lay aside their threatening looks,
> Learning to suffer the control of man;
> But if a little warm blood touch their mouths,
> Their savage fury and their rage return,

At the forgotten taste their jaws distend,
They burn with thirst, and hardly can be kept
From springing at their trembling master's throat. (Lucan)

These original qualities are not to be rooted out; they may be covered, they may be concealed. The Latin tongue is, as it were, natural to me; I understand it better than French, but it is forty years since I have made any use of it for speaking or writing. Yet in extreme and sudden states of excitement, such as I have fallen into two or three times in my life (once, when I saw my father, though in perfect health, fall upon me in a swoon), the first words that rushed from the depths of my breast were always in Latin, Nature surging up and forcibly expressing herself in spite of long disuse. The same experience is related of many others.

They who in my time have attempted to revise the morals of the world by new ideas, reform external vices; the essential vices they leave as they were, if they do not increase them. And the increase is what is to be feared. We are apt to rest from all other well-doing on the strength of these external, arbitrary reformations, which are less costly and bring greater recognition, and by this means we atone at a cheap rate for the other natural, consubstantial, and internal vices. Consider a little how our own experience in the matter stands. There is no man who, if he listens to himself, does not discover within himself an individual principle, a ruling principle, which struggles against education and against the tempest of passions that are hostile to it. For my part, I am not much agitated by sudden gusts; I am nearly always in my place, like heavy and cumbrous bodies. If I am not at home, I am always very close to it. My excesses do not carry me very far away. There is in them nothing strange or extreme; and yet I have healthy and vigorous changes of feeling.

The true condemnation, the one which affects the common run of men, is that even their retirement is full of corruption and filth; their idea of reformation is blurred, their penitence is sick and faulty, almost as much so as their sin. Some, either because they are by nature cemented to vice, or because of long habituation, are no longer aware of its ugliness. Others (of the regiment to which I belong) feel the weight of vice, but they counterbalance it with pleasure, or some other circumstance; they suffer it and submit to it, for a certain price, but viciously and basely, nevertheless. Yet it might be possible to imagine a disproportion so great between the pleasure and the sin that the pleasure might with justice excuse the sin, as we say that utility excuses it; not only if it were incidental, something apart from the sin itself, as in theft, but in the very exercise of the sin, as in the enjoyment of women, where the provocation is violent and, it is said, some times irresistible.

The other day at Armagnac, on the estate of a kinsman of mine, I saw a country fellow whom everybody called by his nickname, Thief. He gave the story of his life as follows: Born a beggar and realizing that by toiling with his hands for a living he would never succeed in securing himself against want, he decided to turn thief, and by the aid of his physical strength he had practised his trade throughout his youth in safety. For he gathered his harvest and his vintage from other men's lands, but at such a great distance and in such great heaps that it is hard to imagine how one man could have carried off so much in a single night on his own shoulders. And besides, he was careful to equalize and distribute the damage that he did, so that the loss to each individual was of less consequence. Now, in his old age, he is rich for a man in his position, thanks to this traffic, which he openly confesses. And to make his peace with God for his ill-gotten gains, he says he is daily engaged in compensating by favours the successors of those whom he robbed; and if he does not finish his task (for to do it all at once is out of his power), he will charge his heirs with it, in proportion to the wrong which he alone knows he has done to each. By this description, be it true or false, it appears that this man regards theft as a dishonest action and hates it, but not so much as he hates poverty; he repents of it quite simply, but in so far as his wrong action was counterbalanced and compensated by certain benefits, he does not repent of it. This is not what I mean by that habit which incorporates us with vice and brings even our understanding into conformity with it, nor by that impetuous whirlwind which in gusts confuses and blinds our soul and hurls us for the time, judgment and all, into the power of vice.

Customarily, whatever I do, I do it as a whole, and I move in one piece. I have hardly a motion that hides and steals away from my reason, and that is not guided by the consent of nearly all parts of me, without division, without internal sedition. My judgment has all the blame or all the praise of it. And the blame it once has, it always has, for almost since its birth it has been one: the same inclination, the same road, the same strength. And in the matter of general opinions, I established myself in youth in the position where I had to stay.

There are sins that are impetuous, instantaneous, and sudden: let us set them aside. But with respect to those other sins, so many times repeated, meditated, and considered, or constitutional sins, even sins flowing from our profession and vocation, I cannot conceive that they should have remained lodged for so long a time in one and the same heart unless the reason and the conscience of the man who harbours them constantly wills and means that it should be so. And the repentance which, according to his boast, overcomes him at a certain prescribed moment is for me a little hard to imagine and conceive.

I do not follow the opinion of the Pythagorean sect, that men take up a new soul when they repair to the images of the gods to receive their oracles. Unless he meant to say that it must needs be extrinsic, new, and borrowed for the time being: their own showing so little sign of the purification and cleanness that is becoming to such an office.

They act quite contrary to the Stoical precepts, which do indeed command us to correct the imperfections and vices which we acknowledge to be in us, but forbid us to be troubled and chagrined on account of them. Those men make us believe that they feel great regret and remorse within; but of amendment and correction, or cessation, there is no symptom. Yet there can be no cure if the disease is not thrown off. If repentance were heavy in the scale of the balance, it would weigh down the sin. I know of no quality so easy to counterfeit as devoutness, if the conduct of life is not brought into conformity with it. Its essence is abstruse and occult; its forms are easy and ceremonial.

For my own part, I may desire in general to be other than I am; I may dislike and condemn my whole nature and implore God for my entire reformation and for pardon of my natural infirmity. But this I ought not to call repentance, methinks, any more than my dissatisfaction at not being an angel or Cato. My actions are ordered in conformity with what I am and with my condition. I can do no better. And repentance does not properly affect things that are not in our power; regret, indeed, does. I can imagine innumerable natures loftier and more orderly than mine; I do not for all that improve my faculties, just as neither my arm nor my mind grows more vigorous by conceiving those of another to be so. If to imagine and desire a nobler way of acting than ours produced repentance of our own, we should have to repent of our most innocent actions, inasmuch as we may well suppose that in a more excellent nature they would have been performed with greater dignity and perfection; and we should wish to do likewise.

When I reflect on the behaviour of my youth in comparison with that of my old age, I find that in general I have conducted myself with order in both, according to my notion; this is all that my resistance can do. I am not flattering myself: in similar circumstances I should always be the same man. It is not a spot, but rather a tincture with which I am stained all over. I know of no superficial, half-way, and merely formal repentance. It must affect me in every part before I can call it so; it must pierce my bowels and afflict them as deeply and as entirely as God sees into them.

As to business, many good opportunities have escaped me for want of successful management. And yet my plans were well enough laid, in relation to the circumstances they were faced with; it is their way always to choose the easiest and safest course. I find that in my former deliberations I have, according to my rule, proceeded wisely, considering the state of the business that was put before me, and I should do the same a thousand years from now in similar situations. I do not consider what it is at this moment, but what it was when I deliberated on it.

The strength of every decision is bound up with the time; circumstances and things ceaselessly revolve and shift about. I have in my life committed some serious and grievous errors, not for lack of good counsel, but for lack of good fortune. In the objects which we handle there are secret elements, not to be guessed at, particularly in the natures of men; mute conditions, that make no show, unknown sometimes by the possessor himself, that are brought out and awakened by occasions as they arise. If my prudence was unable to penetrate into and foresee them, I am not in the least aggrieved at it. Its function is confined within its own limits. It is the event that gets the better of me, and if it favours the side that I have rejected, there is no remedy. I do not blame myself; I accuse my fortune, not my work. This cannot be called repentance.

Phocion had given the Athenians some advice which was not followed. When the affair nevertheless, contrary to his opinion, passed off prosperously, someone said to him: "Well, Phocion, are you glad that things go so well?" "I am indeed glad," he replied, "that it has fallen out thus, but I do not repent of having counselled otherwise." When my friends apply to me for advice, I give it freely and clearly, without hesitating, as nearly everybody does, at the thought that, the matter being subject to hazard, it may fall out contrary to my idea and they may reproach me for my advice: about that I am quite indifferent. For it will be wrong of them to blame me, and I had no right to refuse them that office.

I have hardly anyone but myself to blame for my errors or mishaps. For, in fact, I rarely make use of the advice of others, unless by way of respectful formality, except when I have need of scientific information or knowledge of fact. But in things wherein I stand in need of nothing but judgment, other men's reasons may serve to support me, but have little effect in deterring me. I lend a favourable and courteous ear to all of them, but, as far as I can remember, I have hitherto trusted to none but my own. In my view they are but flies and atoms that lead my will hither and yon. I set small value on my opinions, but I set as little on those of other men. Fortune pays me properly. If I do not accept advice, I give still less. I am consulted very little, but I am heeded even less; and I know of no public or private undertaking that has been reformed and set right by my advice. Even those whom Fortune had in some manner tied to my direction, have been more disposed to let themselves be guided by any other brains. And as a man who is as jealous of the rights of my repose as of the rights of my authority, I would rather have it so. By letting me alone, people humour me in what I profess, which is to be settled and contained wholly within myself. It is a pleasure to me not to be interested in the affairs of others and not to be involved in any responsibility for them.

With respect to any business, when once it is over, I have little regret, however it may have turned out. For this idea relieves me of worry, that the thing had to happen just so. It is seen to be a part of the great stream of the universe and of the chain of Stoical causes. Your imagination cannot by wish or thought disturb one tittle without overturning the whole order of things, both past and future.

As to the rest, I hate that repentance which the accident of old age brings with it. He who said of old that he was obliged to the years for having rid him of sensual pleasure, was of a different opinion from mine. I can never be beholden to impotence for any good it may do me. "Nor will providence ever appear so unfriendly to her own work that debility should be ranked among the best things" (Quintilian). Our desires are few in old age; a profound satiety overcomes us after the act. In this I see no manifestation of conscience. Melancholy and weakness imprint in us a sluggish and rheumatic virtue. We must not let ourselves be so wholly carried away by natural changes that our judgment is corrupted by them. Youth and pleasure did not formerly disable me from recognizing the face of vice in sensual pleasure; nor does the distaste which the years bring me disable me from recognizing that of sensual pleasure in vice. Now that I am no longer in it, I judge of it as though I were. I, who agitate it briskly and attentively, find that my reason is the very same that it was in my licentious years, unless, perhaps, in so far as it is weakened and impaired by growing old. And I find that though it refuses to embroil me with this pleasure out of consideration for the good of my bodily health, it would not refuse it, any more than formerly, for the sake of my spiritual health. I do not regard it as more valiant for being out of the battle. My temptations are so broken and mortified that they are not worth its resistance. By merely stretching out my hands, I exorcize them. Should it be confronted with the old concupiscence, I fear it would have less strength to resist it than it formerly had. I do not see that of itself it judges things otherwise than it did then, nor that it is endowed with any new light. Wherefore, if there is any improvement in it, it is a maimed sort of improvement. Miserable kind of remedy, to owe one's health to the disease!

It does not belong to our misfortune to perform this office; it belongs to the good fortune of our judgment to do so. I cannot be made to do anything by evils and afflictions, except to curse them. That is for people who can only be aroused by the strokes of a lash. My reason runs a freer course in prosperity. It is much more distraught and taken up with digesting pains than pleasures. I see much more clearly in fair weather. The admonitions of health, as they are more cheerful, so also are they more useful than those of sickness. I advanced as far as was in my power toward a reformed and well-regulated life when I had health to enjoy. I should be ashamed and resentful that the wretchedness and misfortune of my decrepitude should be given the preference over my good, healthful, sprightly, vigorous years, and that I should be estimated not by what I have been, but by what I have ceased to be. In my opinion it is the happy living, not (as Antisthenes said) the happy dying that constitutes human felicity. I have not strained myself to tack on in monstrous fashion the tail of a philosopher to the head and body of a libertine, nor to have this wretched remainder of existence disown and belie the fairest, richest, and longest part of my life. I wish to present myself and to be seen uniformly throughout. If I had to live my life over again, I should live it just as I have lived it. I neither complain of the past nor fear the future. And if I do not deceive myself, my inner movements have been approximately like my outward ones. It is one of the principal obligations that I have to my fortune, that the course of my bodily states has been run according to the season suited to each one. I have seen the grass, the flower, and the fruit; and now I see the drying up. Happily, since it is naturally. I endure much more mildly the infirmities that I have, because they come in their own time, and also because they make me remember more kindly the long felicity of my past life. So also it may well be that my wisdom is of the same proportions in this age as in the other, but it used to be much more enterprising and of better grace when it was fresh, gay, and natural, than now that it is bowed down, peevish, and painful. I repudiate, therefore, those casual and sorrowful reformations.

God must touch our hearts. Our conscience must amend of itself by the reinforcement of our reason, not by the weakening of our appetites. In itself sensual pleasure is neither pale nor discoloured, though it appear so to dim and bleary eyes. Temperance should be loved for its own sake and out of reverence to God, who has commanded it, and also chastity; what a catarrh imposes on us and what I owe to the favour of my colic, is neither chastity nor temperance. A man cannot boast that he despises and resists sensual pleasure if he does not see it, if he is not acquainted with it, with its charms, its powers, and most alluring beauty. I know them both, I am in a position to speak. But it seems to me that in old age our souls are subject to more troublesome ailments and imperfections than in youth. This I used to say when I was young; then they threw my beardless chin up to me. I still say it, now that my grey hairs give me the authority to do it. We give the name of wisdom to the harshness of our humours and the distaste of present things. But in truth, we do not so much give up our vices as we change them, and, in my opinion, for the worse. Aside from a silly and tottering pride, a tedious garrulity, bristling and unsociable humours, superstition, and an absurd eagerness for riches after the use of them has been lost, I find there more of envy, of injustice, and of malice. Old age imprints more wrinkles in our minds than in our faces; and never, or very rarely, do we find a soul that in growing old does not acquire a sour and musty smell. Man moves all together both toward his growth and toward his decay.

As I observe the wisdom of Socrates and many circumstances of his condemnation, I should dare to believe that he in some sort purposely lent himself to it by prevarication, seeing that, at the age of seventy years, he would soon have to suffer the stupefaction of the rich activity of his mind and the dimming of its accustomed brightness.

What metamorphoses do I see old age daily bring about in numbers of my acquaintances! It is a powerful malady, and it steals upon us naturally and imperceptibly. It needs a great provision of study and great precaution to avoid the imperfections with which it loads us, or at least to slow up their progress. I feel that, notwithstanding all my entrenchments, it gains foot by foot upon me. I resist as long as I can. But I myself do not know whither it will bring me in the end. But come what may, I am content the world should know from what height I shall have fallen.

CHAPTER 12

OF PHYSIOGNOMY

Almost all the opinions we have are taken on authority and trust. There is no harm in this: we could not choose worse than by ourselves in so feeble an age. That idea of the speeches of Socrates which his friends have handed down to us we approve only out of respect to the general approval they have gained; it is not from our own knowledge. They are not in our manner. If anything of the kind should at this moment make its appearance, there are few men who would value it.

We perceive no beauties that are not sharpened, puffed out, and inflated by artifice. Such as glide along in their naturalness and simplicity easily escape so gross a sight as ours. Theirs is a delicate and hidden beauty; it needs a clear and well-purged sight to discover that secret light. Is not simplicity, as we regard it, near akin to folly and a matter of reproach? Socrates makes his soul move with a natural and ordinary motion. A peasant says this, a woman says that. He never has anybody in his mouth but carters, joiners, cobblers, and masons. His are inductions and similitudes drawn from the commonest and most familiar actions of men; everyone understands him. Under so mean a form we should never have recognized the nobility and splendour of his admirable ideas, we who think all things low and flat that are not set off by learning, who discern no riches but in pomp and show. This world of ours is only formed for ostentation. Men only puff themselves up with wind, and bound hither and yon like balls. Socrates proposed to himself no idle fancies; his aim was to furnish us with things and precepts that have a real and close application to the service of life,

> To keep the mean, his end still to observe,
> And follow Nature. (Lucan)

He was, moreover, always one and the same, and raised himself to the highest pitch of vigour, not spasmodically, but by his natural disposition. Or, to put it better, he raised nothing, but rather lowered and reduced vigour and all asperities and difficulties to his own original and natural level and brought them under its subjection. For in Cato it is very evident that we have a pace strained beyond that of ordinary men; in the brave exploits of his life and in his death one feels that he is always mounted on his high horse. The other moves easily over the ground, and at a gentle and ordinary pace treats of the most useful matters; and both at his death and in the thorniest passages that may be encountered, his conduct remains on the plane of human life.

It has fallen out fortunately that the man most worthy to be known and to be offered to the world as an example should be the one of whom we have the most certain knowledge. He has had light thrown upon him by the most clear-sighted men that ever lived; the testimonies we have of him are admirable both in fidelity and competence.

It is a great thing that he was able to impart such order to an imagination pure as that of a child that without altering or straining it he drew forth from it the most beautiful productions of our soul. He does not show it as either elevated or rich; he only shows it as healthy, but assuredly with a brisk and pure health. By means of those common and natural devices, by means of those ordinary and familiar notions, without excitement and without fuss, he established not only the best-regulated but the most exalted and vigorous beliefs, actions, and morals that ever were. It is he who brought human wisdom down again from heaven, where she was losing her time, and restored her to man, with whom her normal and her most toilsome and useful business lies. See him plead before his judges; observe with what reasons he rouses his courage in the hazards of war, with what arguments he fortifies his patience against calumny, tyranny, death, and against the bad temper of his wife. There is nothing borrowed from art and science; the simplest may there recognize their own means and strength; it is not possible to move more retiringly and more humbly. He has done human nature a great kindness in showing how much it can do of itself.

We are, each one of us, richer than we think, but we are trained to borrow and to hunt, and are taught to make use of what is another's more than of our own. In nothing is man able to stop at what is needful; of pleasure, riches, power he grasps more than he can hold; his greed is incapable of moderation. I find it is the same with the curiosity for knowledge. He cuts out for himself more work than he can manage and much more than he has any business with, assuming that the usefulness of knowledge is coextensive with its matter. "In learning, as in all other things, we suffer from intemperance" (Seneca). And Tacitus is right to commend the mother of Agricola for having curbed in her son a too burning appetite for learning. It is, looking at it with a firm gaze, a good which, like the other goods belonging to man, has in it a great deal of vanity and weakness proper and natural to itself, and it costs dear.

Its employment is far more hazardous than that of any other food or drink. For with other things, what we have bought we carry off to our dwelling in some vessel, and there we have leisure to examine its value and to decide how far we shall partake of it, and when. But the sciences we cannot at the outset stow into any other vessel than our mind; we swallow them in the act of buying, and as we leave the market-place we are already either infected or improved. There are some that only obstruct and overload our stomachs instead of nourishing us, and still others which, under the colour of curing, poison us.

It gave me pleasure to see men in a certain place vow themselves out of piety to ignorance, as well as to chastity, poverty, and penitence. It is also a gelding of our unruly appetites to blunt that cupidity which pricks us on to the study of books and to deprive the soul of that voluptuous complacency which tickles us with the notion of being learned. It is richly to fulfil the vow of poverty to add to it that of the mind. We need hardly any learning to live comfortably. And Socrates teaches us that it is in us, and the way to discover it and utilize it. All these abilities of ours that are in excess of the natural are well-nigh vain and superfluous. It is much if they do not burden and cumber us more than they do us good. "A sound mind has need of only a little learning" (Seneca). These are feverish excesses of our mind, a turbulent and unquiet instrument. Collect yourself; you will find in yourself the true arguments of Nature against death and the best-suited to serve you in your need; they are those which make a peasant and whole nations die with as much steadfastness as a philosopher. Should I have died less cheerfully before I had read the *Tusculans*? I think not. And when I meditate on it rightly I feel that my tongue has been enriched by them, my courage not at all; this is just as Nature framed it for me, and it arms itself for the conflict with the defences used by ordinary people. Books have served me not so much for instruction as for exercise. What if knowledge, while trying to arm us with new defences against natural evils, has impressed their magnitude and their weight on our imagination more strongly than it has impressed the arguments and subtle reasonings with which to protect us against them? They are, indeed, subtleties, with which she often alarms us to very little purpose. Look even at the most compact and wisest writers and see how about one good argument there is planted a quantity of others that are trivial and, if you observe them closely, without body. They are but clever arrangements of words, and deceptive. But as long as they deceive advantageously, I do not wish to probe them any further. There are enough arguments of the kind to be found in different parts of this book, either borrowed or imitated. Yet we ought to take some care and not call force that which is only nice phrasing, or solid that which is only acute, or good that which is only beautiful: "which give more pleasure in a sip than in a large draught" (Cicero). Not everything that tastes good is nourishing. "When it is a question not of the wit but of the soul" (Seneca).

To see the trouble Seneca takes to prepare himself for the shock of death, to see him sweating and panting in the effort to stiffen and reassure himself, and bustling so long on that perch, would have shaken his reputation with me if he had not in dying very valiantly maintained it. His agitation, so intense, so frequent, shows that he was himself hot and impetuous. "A great spirit speaks more negligently and more confidently" (Seneca). "A man's mind does not differ in colour from his soul" (Seneca). He must be convicted at his own expense. And it shows in some sort that he was hard pressed by his enemy. The style of Plutarch, in so far as it is more disdainful and less tense, is in my view the more virile and persuasive; I could easily believe that the movements of his soul were more assured and better regulated. The one, being more sharp, pricks us and makes us leap, touches the spirit more. The other, more sedate, constantly forms, settles, and strengthens us, touches the understanding more. The former ravishes our judgment, the latter wins it.

I have likewise seen other writings, even more revered, which, in painting the struggle they undergo against the goads of the flesh, represent them as being so piercing, so powerful and invincible that we ourselves, who are of the common herd, must wonder as much at the strangeness and unheard-of force of their temptation as at their resistance.

To what end do we go arming ourselves with this laborious learning? Let us look at the earth and see the poor people who are scattered over it, their heads bowed over their toil, who know neither Aristotle nor Cato, neither example nor precept. From them Nature every day extracts actions of constancy and of endurance purer and stronger than those we study so painstakingly in school. How many do I see in my usual rounds who are unconcerned over their poverty, how many who desire death or who face it without alarm and without distress! This man who is digging my garden has this morning buried his father or his son. The very names by which they call their diseases soften and mitigate their harshness; phthisis is for them a cough; dysentery is a looseness of the bowels; a pleurisy is a cold; and as they give them gentle names, so also they endure them gently. Their ailments must be grave indeed when they interrupt their ordinary labour; they take to their beds only to die. "That frank and simple virtue has been converted into hidden and crafty knowledge" (Seneca).

I was writing this about the time when a great load of our troubles had for some months been pressing down with all its weight directly upon me. On the one hand I had the enemy at my door, on the other the freebooters, worse enemies: "they fight not with arms but with crimes" (Livy); I experienced simultaneously every kind of mischief the soldiery can inflict.

> To right and left the dreaded foe appears,
> With imminent terror threatening all sides. (Ovid)

A monstrous war! Other wars work outwardly, this also against itself, biting into its own vitals and destroying itself with its own poison. It is of so malignant and ruinous a nature that it ruins itself along with all the rest, and rends and dismembers itself with rage. We see it more often dissolving of itself than from the want of any necessary thing or by the power of the enemy. All discipline flies from it. It comes to cure sedition, and is full of it; it would chastise disobedience, and gives an example of it; and, being employed in defence of the laws, plays the part of a rebel against its own laws. What a state are we in! Our medicine carries infection,

Our disease is multiplied
By the remedies applied.

It mounts still higher, more inflamed with healing. (Virgil)

The mad confusion of all right and wrong
Has turned from us the just will of the gods. (Catullus)

In these diseases of the people one can distinguish in the beginning the sound from the sick; but when they last, as ours are doing, the whole body is infected from head to heels; no part is free from the taint. For there is no air that is so greedily drawn in, that so spreads and penetrates, as the air of licence. Our armies are no longer tied and held together except with an alien cement; of Frenchmen a steadfast and orderly army-corps is no longer to be formed. What shame! There is no discipline except what is displayed by borrowed soldiers. As for ourselves, we carry on at our own discretion and not the chief's, every man as he pleases: the chief has more to do within than without. It is the commander who has to follow, to pay court, and to bend the knee; he alone has to obey, all the rest is free and dissolute. It gives me pleasure to see how much weakness and pusillanimity there is in ambition, how much abjectness and servility is needed for the attainment of its goal. But it gives me no pleasure to see fine natures, capable of uprightness, every day corrupted in exercising command over this confusion. Prolonged compliance begets habit, habit begets consent and imitation. We had ignoble souls enough without spoiling the good and generous ones. So that, if we keep this up, there will hardly remain a person to whom to entrust the health of this state, in case Fortune should restore it.

Keep not this youth, at least,
From bringing succour to a world o'erturned. (Virgil)

What has become of that ancient precept that soldiers ought to fear their chief more than the enemy? And that wonderful example of the apple-tree that happened to be enclosed within the precincts of a Roman army-camp, and of the army decamping the next day and leaving to the owner the full count of his ripe and delicious apples? I could wish that our youth, instead of the time they spend in less useful travels and less honourable apprenticeships, would bestow half of it in observing naval warfare under some good captain-commander of Rhodes, and the other half in observing the discipline of the Turkish armies; for it differs in many ways from ours and is in many ways superior. For example, our soldiers become more licentious on a campaign, theirs more restrained and timid; for offences or thefts committed upon humble folk, which in times of peace are punished with flogging, are capital in war; for an egg taken without payment there is a predetermined penalty of fifty blows with a stick; for any other thing, not suitable for food, however small it may be, they are impaled or beheaded without ado. I was amazed in reading the history of Selim, the most cruel conqueror that ever was, to observe that in the course of his subjugation of Egypt the wonderful gardens around the city Damascus, abounding in delicate fruits, remained undefiled by the hands of his soldiers, all free and unenclosed as they were.

But is there any malady in a government so bad that it is worth while to combat it with so deadly a drug? Not even, said Favonius, the usurpation of tyrannical power over a state. Plato, likewise, will not consent to have the repose of his country violated for the sake of curing it and will not accept a reformation that costs the blood and ruin of the citizens, defining it to be the duty of a good man in that case to leave things alone, only praying to God to lend His extraordinary aid. And he seems to be displeased with his great friend Dion for having gone about it somewhat differently. I was a Platonist on this point before I knew there had been a Plato in the world. And if such a man is to be absolutely excluded from our communion, one who by the purity of his conscience earned the divine favour of penetrating so deeply into the light of Christianity amidst the general darkness of the world in his time, I do not think it very well becomes us to let ourselves be taught by a pagan how great an impiety it is not to look to God for an assistance that is simply His own and without any co-operation from us. I often doubt whether among so many men that meddle in such business a single one has been found of such feeble understanding as to be really persuaded that he was on the way to reformation by the worst of deformations, that he was moving toward his salvation by the most manifest principles that we know of a very certain damnation, that by overthrowing the government, the official authorities, and the laws under whose guardianship God has placed him, dismembering his mother and giving the pieces to her ancient enemies to devour, filling the hearts of brothers with parricidal hatreds, calling the devils and furies to his aid, he could bring assistance to the most holy sweetness and justice of the divine word. Ambition, avarice, cruelty, revenge have not sufficient natural impetuosity of their own; let us apply the spark and set them ablaze with the glorious title of justice and piety. It is not possible to imagine a worse state of things than when wickedness becomes legitimate and with the leave of the magistrate puts on the cloak of virtue. "Nothing carries a more deceptive face than false religion, when a pretext is made of piety to cover our crimes" (Livy). The extreme form of injustice is attained, according to Plato, when the unjust is regarded as the just.

The common people suffered greatly at that time, not present losses only,

> Such great disturbance reigns throughout the land, (Virgil)

but future losses also. The living had to suffer; so did those who were not yet born. They were pillaged, and consequently I, even of hope, having torn from them all the means of providing for their livelihood for long years to come.

> What they can't carry off or lead away
> The wicked rabble wantonly destroy,
> And burn the innocent hovels of the poor. (Ovid)

> There is no trust in walls, and all the fields
> Lie waste and desolate. (Claudian)

Besides this shock I suffered others. I incurred the disadvantages which moderation entails in diseases of that kind. I was belaboured from all quarters; to the Ghibelline I was a Guelph, to the Guelph a Ghibelline. One of my poets uses this expression, but I do not know where it is. The situation of my house and the neighbours with whom I was intimate showed me in one light, my life and my actions in another. There were no formal accusations made against me, for there was nothing they could sink their teeth into. I never overstep the laws; and if anyone had called me to account, he might have found himself in a worse plight than I. There were only mute suspicions that had a secret currency, to which there is never lacking plausibility in such a mixed confusion of affairs, any more than there is a lack of envious or silly heads. I usually assist the unfair presumptions that Fortune scatters abroad against me by a way I have always had of refraining from justifying, excusing, and explaining myself, believing that to plead for my conscience is to compromise it. "A clear case is clouded by argument" (Cicero). And, as if everyone saw as clearly into me as I do myself, instead of recoiling from an accusation I advance to meet it and rather enhance it by an ironical and scornful confession, if I do not keep absolutely silent, as if it were something that did not deserve an answer. But those who look upon it as a too haughty self-confidence are scarcely less displeased with me than those who regard it as the weakness of an indefensible cause, particularly the great, with whom want of submission is the great fault, harsh toward every manifestation of righteousness that is conscious of itself, that does not feel itself lowly, humble, and suppliant. I have often knocked my head against that pillar. So it is that over what befell me then an ambitious man would have hanged himself; and an avaricious man would have done the same.

I have not the least interest in acquiring wealth.

> Let me possess
> The goods that now I have, or even less;
> Live for myself the days I have to live,
> If the gods please a few days more to give. (Horace)

But the losses that befall me through a wrong done to me by another, whether by theft or violence, afflict me about as much as they do a man who is sick and tormented with avarice. The sense of injury is immeasurably bitterer than the loss.

A thousand different kinds of trouble descended upon me, one after another; I should have suffered them more cheerfully if they had all come at once. I was already meditating to whom among my friends I could entrust a needy and unhappy old age; after allowing my eyes to wander in every direction, I found myself stripped to my shirt. To let oneself fall plumb down, and from such a height, it must be into the arms of an affection, solid, vigorous, and favoured by fortune; such an affection is rare, if it exists at all. In the end I recognized that the surest course was to entrust myself and my need to myself, and if it should fall out that Fortune was cold in her favours to me, that I should recommend myself the more strongly to my own favour, attach myself and look more closely to myself. On all occasions men cast themselves for support on the props of others in order to spare their own, which are the only sure ones, the only powerful ones, if a man knows how to equip himself with them. Every man runs elsewhere and into the future, because no man has arrived at a knowledge of himself. And I came to the conclusion that my troubles had their uses, inasmuch as, firstly, bad scholars must be admonished with the rod, when reason does not serve, as a piece of warped wood is restored to straightness by fire and the force of wedges. It is such a long time that I have been preaching to myself the wisdom of sticking to my own concerns and of keeping aloof from the affairs of others; nevertheless I always keep casting sidelong glances. A nod, a friendly word from a great man, a gracious look, tempt me. God knows if there is any dearth of them in these times, and whether they signify anything! I still listen without wrinkling my brows to the seductions that are held out to me to lure me into the general traffic, and I defend myself so feebly against them that it looks as though I should quite willingly let myself be overcome by them. Now, a spirit so indocile needs the lash; and it needs some good sound strokes of the mallet to force down and tighten the hoops of this cask which is getting loose and weak in the seams and going completely to pieces. Secondly, that misfortune served me as an exercise to prepare me for a worse, in case I, who hoped, through the kindness of Fortune and through the character of my conduct, to be among the last, should turn out to be among the first to be overtaken by the storm: teaching me betimes to restrict my mode of life and to fit it for a new situation. True freedom is to have power over oneself in all things. "He is most powerful who has power over himself" (Seneca).

In a time of ordinary tranquillity a man prepares for the common and moderate mischances, but in the confusion in which we have been living for the last thirty years every Frenchman, whether as a private individual or as a member of the community, sees himself at any moment on the point of the total ruin of his fortune. Therefore we must have our courage all the better supplied with strong and vigorous defences. Let us be grateful to the destiny that has placed our lives in an age that is neither soft nor languid nor indolent. Many a man who could never have been so by other means will become famous by his misfortune.

As I seldom read in histories of those upheavals in other states without a feeling of regret that I was not able to study them more closely by living in their midst, so from my curiosity I get a kind of satisfaction in seeing with my own eyes this notable spectacle of our public death, its symptoms and its form. And since I am unable to retard it, I am content that I was destined to be present at it and to get a lesson from it. Thus do we eagerly desire to see the representation of the tragic plays of human fortunes, though it be but in a shadow and in the fictions of the theatre.

It is not without compassion at what we hear, but there is a pleasure in having an emotion of pain aroused within us because of the rareness of those pitiful events. Nothing tickles that does not pain. And the good historians avoid the narration of peaceful events like stagnant waters or a dead sea in order to come to the seditions, the wars, to which they know that we summon them. I doubt whether I am honest enough to confess with how very small cost to the repose and tranquillity of my life I have passed more than half of it amidst the ruin of my country. I buy my patience at somewhat too cheap a price in the misfortunes that do not grip me personally, and, to lodge a complaint against myself, I consider not so much what is taken from me as what remains safe, both within and without. There is a comfort in dodging now one, now another of the evils that successively fly in our direction and find their marks all around us. Moreover, in the case of public calamities, the more universally my sympathy is dispersed, the weaker it is. To which may be added that it is almost certain that "we feel public calamities only so far as they affect our private interests" (Livy), and that the state of health from which we declined was such as to bear its own solace for the regret that we should have had for it. It was health but, only by comparison with the sickness that followed it. We have hardly fallen from a great height. The corruption and the brigandage which have official standing and form part of the established order seem to me the least tolerable. We are less outraged at being robbed in a wood than in a place of safety. It was a universal cohesion of members each one more diseased than the others, and for the most part with inveterate ulcers that no longer admitted of cure or asked for it.

This collapse, then, really raised my spirits more than it depressed me, being assisted by my conscience, which bore itself not only peaceably but proudly, and I found no reason to complain of myself. Also, as evil is never sent to us by God quite unmixed, any more than good, my health during all that time remained unusually good; and, as I can do nothing without health, there are few things that I cannot do with it. It afforded me the means of mustering my resources and of deflecting the stroke which might easily have made a deeper wound. And by what I endured I found that I had something with which I could make a stand against Fortune, and that it would take a severe shock to hurl me out of my saddle. I do not say this to provoke her to make a more vigorous onset against me. I am her servant, I hold out my hands to her, let her be content, in God's name! Do I feel her assaults? Indeed I do. As those whom grief overwhelms and possesses will yet at intervals let themselves be caressed by some pleasurable sensation and allow a smile to escape them, so I too have sufficient power over myself to make my ordinary condition peaceable and free from troublesome imaginings; but I allow myself nevertheless to be surprised at moments by the stings of those unpleasing thoughts which assail me even as I am arming myself to drive them away or to wrestle with them.

Behold now a further aggravation of the evil which came upon me in the wake of the others. Both outside and within my house I was greeted by a plague of the utmost severity. For as healthy bodies are subject to graver maladies because they can be overcome by these alone, so my very salubrious air, where in the memory of man no contagion, though it had been in the vicinity, had ever been able to get a footing, becoming poisoned, produced very unusual results.

Young and old drop hour by hour;
No single head is spared by ruthless Proserpine. (Horace)

I had to put up with the queer situation of feeling that the sight of my house was frightful to me. Everything in it was unguarded and at the mercy of anyone who might wish to take it. I myself, who am so hospitable, was engaged in the painful hunt of a retreat for my family: a family all astray, frightening to their friends and to themselves, filling with horror every place where they tried to settle, and having to shift their abode as soon as one among them began to feel a pain in his finger. Every ailment is taken for the plague; people do not give themselves the time to examine it. And the humour of it is that, according to the rules of the profession, whenever the danger appears, you have to spend forty days in anxiety over that sickness, the imagination meanwhile working its will upon you and turning even your health into a fever.

All this would have affected me much less if I had not had to feel for the sufferings of others and to serve for six months in misery as a guide to this caravan. For my own preservatives, which are resolution and patience, I carry within myself. Apprehension, which is particularly feared in this disease, does not cause me much distress. And if I had been alone and wished to take flight, it would have been a much more cheerful flight and to a greater distance. It is not a kind of death which I regard as among the worst: it is generally quick, dazed, painless, taking comfort in being shared by many, without ceremony, without mourning, without the attendance of a crowd. But as for the people about us, not a hundredth part could save themselves:

> Deserted you may see the shepherd's realms,
> And far and wide their glades untenanted. (Virgil)

In this place the best part of my revenue is from manual labour; the land that a hundred men tilled for me lay idle for a long time.

But what an example of fortitude did we not then see in the simplicity of all these people! As a general thing each one renounced all concern for life. The grapes remained hanging on the vines, the principal wealth of the country, all men indifferently preparing themselves and expecting death that evening or on the morrow, with a countenance and voice in which there was so little fear that it seemed as if they had come to terms with that necessity and that it was a universal and inevitable doom. Death is always such. But on how slight a thread hangs our fortitude in dying! The difference of a few hours in our distance from it, the mere consideration of having company, makes a difference in our feeling toward it. Observe these people: because they die in the same month, children, young men and old, they are no longer shocked, they no longer bewail one another. I saw some who were afraid of being left behind, as in a dreadful solitude, and I observed generally that they had no other concern than for their burial. It distressed them to see the bodies scattered in the fields, at the mercy of the wild beasts that promptly infested them. (How divergent are the fancies of men! The Neorites, a nation subjugated by Alexander, throw the bodies of their dead into the deepest parts of their forests to be eaten up, the only sepulture reputed happy among them.) Some, still sound in health, were already digging their graves; others lay down in them while yet alive. And a labourer of mine pulled the earth over himself with his hands and feet as he was dying. Was not this like drawing the covers over himself that he might go to sleep more peacefully? An action in a way as lofty as that of the Roman soldiers who were found after the battle of Cannæ with their heads thrust into holes which they had made and filled up with their own hands while they were suffocating. In short, by practice alone a whole nation was quickly placed in a state which for undauntedness yields nothing to the most studied and premeditated fortitude.

Most of the instructions by which learning seeks to strengthen our courage have in them more of show than of power and more of ornament than of effect. We have abandoned Nature and would teach her our lessons, her who was guiding us so happily and so surely. And meanwhile from the traces of her instruction and from the little which remains of her image, by the favour of ignorance, imprinted in the lives of this rustic rout of unpolished men, learning is constrained every day to borrow patterns of constancy, innocence, and tranquillity for her disciples. It is fine to see how these persons, filled with all their beautiful knowledge, have to imitate that foolish simplicity, and to imitate it in the primary actions of virtue, and how our sapience draws from the beasts themselves the most useful instructions for the greatest and most necessary concerns of our life: how we ought to live and die, husband our wealth, love and bring up our children, maintain justice—a singular testimony of human infirmity; and how the reason, which we control at will, always discovering something different and something novel, leaves in us no apparent trace of Nature. Men have done with Nature as perfumers with oil, they have sophisticated her with so many arguments and far-fetched reasonings that she has become variable and special to each person and has lost her own uniform and universal countenance, and we must seek in beasts for any testimony of her that is not subject to favour, corruption, or diversity of opinions. For it is indeed true that even beasts do not always go exactly in the path of Nature, but they swerve so little from it that you can always perceive the track. Just as horses that are led by hand do much prancing and leaping, but no further than the length of their halters, and for all that they follow the steps of the man who leads them; and just as the hawk takes its flight, but under the restraint of its leash. "Meditate upon exile, torture, war, disease, shipwreck, so that you be not unschooled to any misfortune" (Seneca).

What is the good of that solicitude of ours in anticipating all the evils of human nature and in preparing ourselves with so much trouble to face even those which perhaps will never touch us? "The possibility that they may suffer makes them as gloomy as those that really suffer" (Seneca). Not only the blow, but the wind and the noise strike us. Or why, like one in a great frenzy, for truly it is a frenzy, go and have yourself flogged at once because it may happen that Fortune will one day make you undergo the lash, and why put on your furred gown in midsummer because you will stand in need of it at Christmas? "Rush in and make trial of the evils that may befall you, especially of the greatest evils. Test yourself in them," they say, "and make sure of yourself." On the contrary, the easiest and most natural way would be to banish even the thought of them. One would suppose that they will not come soon enough, that their true duration is not long enough; our mind must extend and prolong them, must absorb them within itself beforehand and nourish itself on them, as if they did not reasonably weigh upon our senses. "They will weigh heavily enough when they come," says one of the masters, not of some tender sect, but of the sternest. "In the meantime, please yourself. Believe what you like best. What good will it do you to run ahead to extend a greeting to your evil fortune and lose the present through fear of the future, to make yourself miserable now because you are fated to be so in time?" These are his words. Learning doubtless does us a good office when it instructs us in the exact dimensions of our evils,

> Whetting with cares the minds of mortal men. (Virgil)

What a pity it would be if any part of their burden should escape our feeling and our knowledge!

It is certain that to most men the preparation for death has occasioned more torment than death itself. It was once truly said and by a very judicious writer: "The suffering itself afflicts the senses less than the meditation of it" (Quintilian).

The feeling that death is at hand sometimes of itself animates us with a quick resolve no longer to avoid that which is utterly inevitable. Many gladiators in times past, after having fought timorously, have been known to swallow death courageously, offering their throats to the sword of the enemy and inviting it. To contemplate death in the future calls for a firmness that is slow of pace and therefore difficult to provide. If you do not know how to die, never mind. Nature will instruct you on the spot, fully and adequately. She will do that job neatly for you; do not bother your head about it.

> Mortals, in vain you seek to learn of death
> The uncertain hour, or by what road it comes. (Propertius)

> 'Tis smaller pain to meet a sudden blow
> Than what one fears a long time to foreknow. (Maximianus)

We trouble life with our cares about death, and death with our cares about life. The one torments us, the other frightens us. It is not against death that we make our preparations; that is too momentary an affair. A quarter of an hour's suffering, without consequence, without troublesomeness, does not deserve a special course of lessons. To speak truly, we prepare ourselves against the preparations for death. Philosophy orders us to keep death ever before our eyes, to foresee it and meditate it before the time comes, and then gives us rules and precautions to prevent that foresight and that thought from hurting us. That is what the physicians do who bring sickness upon us that they may have an occasion for employing their drugs and their art. If we have not known how to live, there is no justice in teaching us how to die, and in giving to the end a different form from the whole. If we have known how to live steadfastly and tranquilly, we shall known how to die in the same way. They may boast as much as they please. "The whole life of a philosopher is a meditation on death" (Cicero). But it seems to me that it is indeed the end but not the aim of life; it is its termination, its extreme point, not its object, however. Life ought to be an aim to itself, its own purpose; its true study is to regulate itself, guide itself, suffer itself. In the number of the many other duties comprised in the general and principal chapter of "Knowing how to live" is this article of "Knowing how to die"; and it is one of the lightest, save when our fear gives it weight.

To judge them by their utility and by the naked truth, the lessons of simplicity yield little to those which learning preaches to us in the contrary sense. Men differ in feeling and in strength; they must be guided to their welfare according to their dispositions and by different routes. "Wherever the tempest drives me, there I land" (Horace). I never saw a peasant in my neighbourhood cogitating with what countenance and assurance he should go through that final hour. Nature teaches him not to think of death except when he is dying. And then he carries himself with a better grace than Aristotle, upon whom death presses doubly, because of its own proper weight and because it has been so long in his thoughts. That is why Cæsar was of the opinion that the least premeditated death was the happiest and the easiest. "He suffers more than is needful who suffers before it is needful" (Seneca). The bitterness of this imagination springs from our curiosity. We are always impeding ourselves in this way by trying to forestall and put to school the prescriptions of Nature. It is only for learned doctors to have their dinner spoiled by it while in the best of health and to knit their brows at the idea of death. The plain people have no need of remedy or consolation till the blow strikes, and they meditate on it precisely as long as they feel it. Is it not as we say, that the stolidity and lack of imagination of the common people give them that patience under present evils and that profound unconcern for the sinister events of the future; that their souls, because they are thick and obtuse, are less penetrable and less shakable? If this be so, let us in God's name henceforth keep a school of stupidity. It is the utmost benefit that learning promises us, to which stupidity so gently leads her disciples.

We shall not lack good tutors, interpreters of natural simplicity. Socrates shall be one. For, as well as I can remember, he speaks in some such sense as this to the judges who are deliberating on his doom: "I am afraid, gentlemen, if I entreat you not to put me to death, I shall involve myself in the charge of my accusers, which is that I pretend to be wiser than others, as having some more secret knowledge of things that are above and below us. I know that I have had no intercourse or acquaintance with death, nor have I known anyone who has had any experience of its nature and was able to inform me concerning it. Those who fear it assume that they know it. As for me, I neither know what it is nor what takes place in the other world. Perhaps death is a thing indifferent, perhaps it is desirable. (We may believe, however, if it is a migration from one place to another, that there is a gain in going to live with so many of the illustrious dead and in being freed from having any more to do with unjust and corrupt judges. If it is an annihilation of our being, it is still a gain to enter on a long and peaceful night. We know of no sweeter sensation in life than a tranquil repose and a profound sleep, without dreams.) The things that I know to be evil, such as to injure one's neighbour and disobey one's superior, whether God or man, I sedulously avoid. Such as I do not know whether they be good or evil, I cannot fear. If I go to my death and leave you alive, the gods alone can see with whom it will go better, with you or with me. Therefore, as far as I am concerned, you may decree as you please. But in keeping with my method of counselling just and profitable things, I say to you that for the sake of your conscience you will do better to set me free, unless you see further than I do into my case, and judging by my past actions, both public and private, by my intentions, and by the profit which so many citizens, both young and old, daily derive from my conversation, and the fruit that you all reap from me, you cannot duly discharge your obligation to my merits except by ordering that, in view of my poverty, I should be maintained in the Prytaneum at the public expense, a thing I have often known you, with less reason, grant to others. Do not impute it to obstinacy or disdain if I do not, according to custom, become a suppliant and try to move you to commiseration. I have friends and kindred (not being, as Homer says, begotten of a block or of a stone, any more than others) who might appear before you in tears and in mourning, and I have three desolate children with whom to appeal to your pity. But I should bring shame upon our city if, at my age and with such a reputation for wisdom as I here stand charged with, I should degrade myself to such abject devices. What would men say of other Athenians? I have always admonished those who have listened to me not to redeem their lives by a dishonourable action. And in the wars of my country, at Amphipolis, at Potidæa, at Delium, and others in which I took part, I showed in act how far I was from securing my safety by my shame. Besides, I should make you violate your duty and induce you to do unbecoming things; for it is not my entreaties that ought to persuade you, but the pure and solid arguments of justice. You have sworn to the gods to conduct yourselves in this manner: it would seem as if I meant to suspect you and to retort against you the charge of believing that there are no gods. And thus I should be testifying against myself, that I do not believe in them as I ought, distrusting their conduct of affairs and refusing to commit my own entirely to their hands. I wholly rely upon them, and hold it for certain that they will do in this what shall be most fitting both for you and for me. No good man, whether in life or after death, has any reason to fear the gods."

Is not this a pointedly sound pleading, but at the same time natural and plain, of an inconceivable loftiness, truthful, frank, and honest beyond all example? And in what a critical need employed! Truly, he had reason to prefer it to what the great orator Lysias had put into writing for him, admirably couched in the forensic style, but unworthy of so noble a criminal. Should a supplicating tone have issued from the mouth of Socrates? Should that superb virtue have slackened sail at the moment when it had the chance to display its utmost strength? And should his rich and powerful nature have committed her defence to art and, in her greatest trial, have renounced the truth and sincerity which were the ornaments of his speech to deck herself out in the tawdry figures and artifices of an oration learned by rote? He did very wisely, and like himself, not to corrupt the tenor of an incorrupt life and so sacred a model of humanity, to prolong his decrepitude by another year and to cheat us of the undying memory of that glorious end. He owed his life not to himself but to the world, as an example. Would it not have been a public loss if he had terminated it in an idle and obscure fashion? Assuredly, such a light and indifferent way of regarding his death deserved that posterity should regard it the more seriously in his behalf: which it did. And there is nothing in justice so just as that which Fortune ordained for his glory. For the Athenians held those who had been the cause of his death in such abomination that they shunned them like excommunicated persons; they looked upon everything as polluted that had been touched by them; no one would wash with them in the baths; no one would salute or accost them, so that at last, unable any longer to support this public hatred, they hanged themselves.

If anyone should think that among so many examples of the sayings of Socrates that were available to me for the purpose of my argument I have been ill-advised in choosing this particular one, and if he judges that this speech is elevated far above common ideas, I must say that I have chosen it deliberately. For my own judgment of it is different, and I hold that it is a speech ranking in naturalness much behind and below common ideas. In a boldness artless as a fledgling's and in a childlike assurance it reproduces the pure and primary impression and ignorance of Nature. For it may be believed that we have a natural fear of pain, but not of death on its own account: it is a part of our being, no less essential to it than is life. To what end should Nature have begotten in us a hatred and horror of it, seeing that it performs a function of very great use to her in fostering the succession and vicissitude of her works, and that in this universal republic it conduces more to birth and increase than to loss or ruin?

Thus does the universe renew itself. (Lucretius)

The failure of one life is a passage to a thousand other lives. Nature has imprinted in animals the care for their own preservation. They go so far as to be afraid of impairing their lot, of being struck or wounded, of being chained and beaten by us, accidents that come within their senses and experience. But that we should kill them they cannot fear, nor have they the faculty for imagining or inferring such a thing as death. So it is said also that they have been observed not only to suffer death cheerfully (most horses neigh as they die, and swans greet it with a song), but even to court it at need, as many examples of elephants tend to show.

Besides, is not the method of arguing which Socrates here employs equally admirable for its simplicity and vigour? Truly, it is much easier to speak like Aristotle and live like Cæsar than to speak and live like Socrates. There lies the extreme degree of perfection and difficulty; art cannot reach to it. Our faculties are not trained in this way. We do not test them and we do not know them. We invest ourselves with those of others and let our own lie idle.

Precisely so might it be said of me that I have here only brought together a mass of flowers from other people's gardens, supplying nothing of my own but the thread that ties them. Truly, I have yielded to public opinion in letting these borrowed ornaments accompany me. But I do not intend that they should cover me and hide me; that is the very reverse of my design, who wish to make a show of nothing but what is mine, and of what is mine by nature. And if I had trusted myself I should at all hazards have spoken out absolutely in my own person. I load myself with these borrowings every day more heavily contrary to my intention and my real nature, following the fancy of the age and the exhortation of others. If it is unsuited to me, as I think it is, no matter; it may be useful to someone else. Some persons quote Plato and Homer who have never looked at them. And I myself have taken passages far enough from their source. Without trouble and without learning, having a thousand volumes about me in the place where I am writing, I could immediately, if I liked, borrow from a dozen such botchers, fellows whose books I seldom handle, the wherewithal to enamel this treatise of Physiognomy. I need only the preliminary epistle of some German to stuff me with quotations; and that is how we go in pursuit of an enticing glory, to cheat the silly world.

These concoctions of commonplaces by which so many men spare themselves the trouble of studying are of little use but for commonplace subjects, and serve us only for display and not for guidance in life — a ridiculous issue of learning which Socrates so humorously threshes out in his argument with Euthydemus. I have known books to be made up out of things that were never studied nor understood, the author assigning to sundry of his learned friends the investigation of this or that material to build it up with, contenting himself, for his share, with having projected the plan and industriously piled up the stack of meaningless matter; the ink and paper, at least, are his. This, in all conscience, is to buy or borrow a book, not to make it. It is to prove to men not that you can make a book but, what they might otherwise be in doubt about, that you cannot make one. A President boasted in my hearing that he had heaped up two hundred and odd citations from other writers in one of his presidential judgments. In proclaiming this to everybody it seemed to me that he was effacing the glory that was awarded to him for it. A small-minded and absurd boast, in my opinion, for such a matter and in such a personage! Amidst so many borrowings I am glad to be able to steal one on occasion, disguising and changing its shape for some new service. At the risk of having it said that it was through failure to understand its proper application, I give it a particular turn with my own hand, so as to make it less purely the property of another. These others parade their thefts and give an account of them, and so they enjoy a better standing with the laws than I. We believers in Nature think that the honour of invention is greatly and incomparably to be preferred to the honour of quotation.

If I had wished to speak in the way of learning, I would have spoken sooner. I would have written in a time nearer to my studies, when I had more wit and memory; and I should have trusted more to the vigour of that earlier age than to the present one if I had wished to adopt the profession of writing. Moreover, such gracious favour as Fortune might have offered me by the mediation of this work would then have come in a more propitious season. Two of my acquaintances, great men in that calling, have, in my opinion, lost half of the benefit in refusing to publish at the age of forty in order to wait till they were sixty. Maturity has its drawbacks, as well as greenness, and worse. And old age is as unsuited for this kind of work as for any other. He who sends his decrepitude to press commits a folly if he hopes to squeeze out of it any humours that do not have a suggestion of the disagreeable, of dreaminess, and of drowsiness. Our mind becomes constipated and sluggish as it grows old. I deliver my ignorance lavishly and with an air, my learning meagrely and piteously; the latter as accessory and incidental, the former as my express and principal design. And I do not specifically treat of anything except of nothing, nor of any knowledge except that of no-knowledge. I have chosen a time when my life, which I have to portray, lies wholly before me: what remains of it is more closely connected with death. And even of my death, if I should find it talkative, as others do, I should willingly give an account at the moment of my departure.

It vexes me that Socrates, who was the pattern of perfection in all great qualities, should have been endowed with so ugly a body and a face as they say he had, and so out of keeping with the beauty of his soul, he who was so in love and so infatuated with beauty! Nature did him wrong. There is nothing more probable than the conformity and the relation of the body to the spirit. "It makes a great difference what sort of body it is in which the souls are actually placed; for many conditions of body tend to sharpen the mind and many to blunt it" (Cicero). Cicero is speaking of an unnatural ugliness and deformity of limbs. But we call ugliness also an unsightliness at first glance which resides chiefly in the face and often disgusts us for a very slight cause: the complexion, a spot, a roughness in the countenance, or some inexplicable cause, when the members are symmetrical and perfect. The ugliness which clothed a very beautiful soul in La Boétie was of this order. This superficial ugliness, which nevertheless makes a strong impression, is the least injurious to the state of the soul and is not very certain in its influence on the opinions of men. The other, which is more properly called deformity, is more substantial and is more apt to penetrate inwardly. It is not the shoe that is made of smooth leather but the well-modelled shoe that shows the shape of the foot within. So Socrates said of his ugliness, that it betrayed what would have been just as great an ugliness in his soul if he had not corrected it by education. But in saying this I believe he was jesting, as his custom was. A soul so excellent was never of its own making.

I cannot often enough repeat how high a value I place upon beauty, as a quality that gives power and advantage. Socrates called it "a brief tyranny," and Plato "the privilege of Nature." We have none that surpasses it in prestige. It holds the first place in the intercourse of men; it shows itself in the foreground, seduces and prepossesses our judgments with great authority and wonderful impressiveness. Phryne would have lost her case, although it was in the hands of an excellent advocate, if she had not opened her robe and corrupted the judges by her dazzling beauty. And I find that Cyrus, Alexander, Cæsar, those three masters of the world, did not leave beauty out of the reckoning in the conduct of their great affairs. No more did the first Scipio. One and the same word in Greek embraces the beautiful and the good. And the Holy Ghost often calls good those whom it would designate as beautiful. I should be inclined to approve the order in which the good things of life are ranked in the song, taken from some ancient poet, which Plato says was current in his day: health, beauty, riches. Aristotle says that to the beautiful belongs the right of commanding, and if there are any whose beauty approaches our idea of the beauty of the gods, that veneration is equally their due. To one who asked him why the society of the beautiful was longer and more frequently sought after, he replied: "That question ought only to be raised by a blind man." Most philosophers, and the greatest of them, paid for their schooling and acquired their wisdom by the favour and mediation of their beauty.

Not only in the men who serve me, but in animals too, I regard it as within two fingers' breadth of goodness. Yet it seems to me that the features and mould of the face and those lineaments from which one infers certain inward dispositions and our destiny in the future, are not things that fall very directly and simply under the chapter of beauty and ugliness. No more than every good odour and clear atmosphere carried a promise of health, nor every thick atmosphere and putrid odour a threat of infection in times of pestilence. Those who accuse the ladies of contradicting their beauty by their conduct do not always hit the mark; for in a face that is not too well shaped there may dwell an air of honesty that inspires trust, as, on the contrary, I have sometimes read in a pair of beautiful eyes menaces of a malign and dangerous nature. There are propitious physiognomies; and in a throng of victorious enemies you will promptly pick out, among men you do not know, one rather than another to whom to surrender and entrust your life, and not exactly from considerations of beauty.

A man's countenance is a feeble security; nevertheless it has some importance. And if it were my business to lash the wicked, I should scourge more severely those who belie and betray the promises which Nature had planted in their foreheads. I should inflict a sharper punishment on the evil that wore an air of gentle goodness. It seems as if some faces were lucky, others unlucky. And I believe that there is some art in distinguishing the affable from the merely simple faces, the severe from the rough, the malicious from the surly, the scornful from the melancholy, and such other closely related qualities. There are beauties that are not only haughty but sour; there are others that are gentle, and still beyond that, insipid. As to prognosticating future events from them, these are matters that I leave undecided.

I have, as I said elsewhere, quite simply and crudely adopted for my own behoof this ancient rule: that we cannot make a mistake in following Nature, that the sovereign precept is to conform ourselves to her. I have not, like Socrates, corrected my natural disposition by the power of reason and I have in no way disturbed my native inclination by art. I let myself go as I have come; I combat nothing; the two principal parts of my being live of their own accord in peace and good understanding; but my nurse's milk was, thank God, tolerably wholesome and temperate.

Shall I say this much in passing, that I see a greater value than it is worth attached to a certain notion of scholastic probity, the only one almost that is current among us, a slave to precepts and under the constraint of hope and fear? The kind that I like is one which would not be the work of laws and religions but only be perfected and authorized by them, which would have the means of sustaining itself without other aid, springing up in us with its own roots from a seed of reason implanted in every man not perverted by nature. This Reason, which straightens Socrates from his vicious bend, makes him obedient to the men and the gods who rule in his city, courageous in death, not because his soul is immortal, but because he is mortal. It is a teaching ruinous to every society, and much more injurious than ingenious and subtle, which persuades people that religious belief is enough, by itself and without moral living, to satisfy the divine justice. Use enables us to see the enormous difference there is between devoutness and conscience.

I have a prepossessing bearing both in outward appearance and in the idea of me that it conveys.

> Have, did I say? No, Chremes, I once had! (Terence)
>
> Alas, 'tis but the bones that you behold of a worn body, (Maximianus)

and one which makes a showing opposite to that of Socrates. It has often befallen me that on the bare assurance of my presence and my countenance persons who had no knowledge of me have placed great confidence in me, whether it concerned their own affairs or mine; and in foreign countries I have derived rare and special benefits from this fact. But the two following experiences, perhaps, are particularly worth recounting.

A certain person planned to take by surprise my house and myself. His scheme was to arrive at my gate by himself and rather importunately to demand admission. I knew him by name and had reason to trust him as a neighbour and a sort of connection. I had the gates opened to him as I do to everybody. There he was, in a terrible fright, his horse out of breath, very jaded. He entertained me with this cock-and-bull story: That he had been set upon half a league away by an enemy of his, whom I also knew and of whose quarrel with him I had heard; that this enemy was hot at his heels in pursuit, and that, having been caught in disorder and with inferior numbers, he had cast himself at my gates for refuge; that he was in great trouble for his followers, who, he professed to believe, were either dead or captured. I tried in all innocence to comfort, reassure, and reanimate him. Soon after, behold four or five of his soldiers with the same terrified aspect coming up and wishing to enter; and then others, and still others after these, well mounted and well armed, to the number of twenty-five or thirty, all pretending that the enemy were at their heels. This mystery began to awaken my suspicion. I was not unaware in what age I was living, how much my house might be an object of envy, and I knew of several examples of others of my acquaintance who had had similar misadventures. However, feeling there was nothing to be gained by the courtesy with which I had begun if I did not go through with it, and not being able to get out of my embarrassment without ruining everything, I followed the most natural and the simplest course, as I always do, giving orders to have them all admitted.

The truth is that I am by nature little given to distrust and suspicion. I generally lean toward excuse and the mildest interpretation. I take men according to the general run, and do not believe in those perverted and unnatural inclinations unless I am forced to it by the weight of the evidence, any more than I believe in monsters and miracles. And besides, I am a man who readily commit myself to Fortune and throw myself recklessly into her arms. Whereby I have hitherto had more reason to applaud than to blame myself; and I have found her both more prudent and more friendly with respect to my affairs than I am myself. There have been actions in my life of which the performance might fairly have been called difficult or, if you like, prudent; but even of these actions, assuming that a third part of the credit belonged to me, two thirds were undoubtedly and richly hers. We err, I think, in not trusting ourselves sufficiently to Heaven, and we look for more from our own conduct than we have any right to. That is why our designs so often miscarry. Heaven is jealous of the scope that we assign to the claims of human wisdom at the expense of its own, and abridges them in proportion as we magnify them.

These men remained on horseback in my courtyard while their leader was with me in my hall, having declined to have his horse stabled and saying that he would have to retire promptly as soon as he got news of his men. He saw himself master of his enterprise, and nothing now remained but its execution. He has often said since, for he was not ashamed to tell this story, that my countenance and my frankness had wrested the treachery out of his hands. He remounted his horse, his men having their eyes steadily fixed upon him to see what signal he would give them and being very much astonished to see him depart and give up his advantage.

Another time, relying on some truce that had just been proclaimed between our armies, I started on a journey through a remarkably ticklish part of the country. They had no sooner got wind of me than three or four parties of horsemen sallied forth from different points to seize me; one of them came up with me on the third day, when I was set upon by fifteen or twenty masked gentlemen followed by a troop of mounted archers. There I was, seized and made a prisoner, withdrawn into the thick of a neighbouring forest, dismounted, robbed, my coffers rifled, my money-box taken, my horses and equipage divided among new masters. We spent a long time in that thicket disputing over the matter of my ransom, which they set so high that it was quite clear that I was not very well known to them. They carried on a dispute over my life. Indeed, there were many circumstances which carried a manifest threat of danger to me in that situation.

> Then of thy courage was there need, Æneas,
> Then need of a stout heart. (Virgil)

I kept insisting on my rights under the truce, being willing to give up to them only the gain they had made in despoiling me, which was not to be despised, without promise of any other ransom. After we had been there two or three hours, and they had set me on a jade that was not likely to run away from them, and put me under a special guard of fifteen or twenty musketeers, and scattered my servants among the others with orders that we should be led as prisoners by different routes, and when I had already been conducted a distance of two or three musket-shots from the spot,

> Praying for help to Castor and to Pollux, (Catullus)

behold a sudden and altogether unexpected change that came over them. I saw the leader returning to me with gentler language, going to the trouble of searching for my scattered articles among the troopers, and having them restored to me as quickly as he could recover them, even to my money-box. The best present which they made me was, after all, my freedom. The rest did not much affect me at that particular moment.

As for the true cause of so unheard-of a change and reversal of feeling, without any apparent motivation, and of so miraculous a repentance in such a time in an enterprise that had been deliberately planned and which had come to be sanctioned by custom (for I openly confessed to them at the outset to what party I belonged and what road I was taking), really, I do not even now know what it is. The most conspicuous among them, who took off his mask and told me his name, repeated to me several times that I owed this deliverance to my face, to the freedom and firmness of my speech, which showed that I did not deserve such a mishap, and he begged me to assure him of similar treatment. It is possible that the divine goodness wished to make use of this insignificant instrument for my preservation. It defended me the next day from other and worse ambushes, of which these very men had given me warning. The gentleman who figures in this incident is still on earth to tell the story; the other was killed not long since.

If my face did not answer for me, if men did not read the innocence of my intention in my eyes and in my voice, I should not have lived so long a time without quarrels and without offence, in view of my indiscreet freedom in speaking out, right or wrong, whatever comes into my head and in judging things so heedlessly. This manner may with reason be thought uncivil and not in harmony with our usage, but I never knew any person who thought it outrageous and malicious or who took offence at my freedom, if he heard it from my own lips. Words when they are repeated carry a different sense as they carry a different sound. Moreover, I hate no one; and I am so loth to injure anyone that I cannot do it on behalf of Reason itself. And when circumstances required me to condemn criminals, I preferred to fall short in point of justice. "I had rather there should be no more crimes committed than have the heart to punish them when they are committed" (Livy).

Aristotle, it is said, was reproached for having been too merciful to a wicked man. "I was," he said, "indeed merciful to the man, but not to the wickedness." Common judgments are exasperated to vengeance by the horror of the misdeed. It is this very thing that cools my judgment: the horror of the first murder makes me afraid of a second, and hatred of the first cruelty makes me hate every imitation of it. To me, who am but the knave of clubs, may be applied what was said of Charillus, King of Sparta: "He cannot be good, since he is not bad to the wicked." Or rather thus, for Plutarch gives it to us in these two ways, as he does a thousand other things, with a different and contradictory turn: "He must needs be good, since he is so even to the wicked." As I dislike to take a hand in actions, even though legitimate, when they affect persons who would be offended by them, so, to tell the truth, I am not sufficiently scrupulous to refrain from taking a hand in them, even though illegitimate, when they affect persons who consent to them.

CHAPTER 13

OF EXPERIENCE

* * * * *

I, who am a very earthy being, hate that unhuman kind of wisdom that would make us disdainful and hostile to the cultivation of the body. I look upon it as an equal injustice to loathe natural pleasures and to be too much in love with them. Xerxes was a blockhead who, enveloped in all human delights, offered a reward to the man who would invent others for him; but he is hardly less a blockhead who cuts off those which Nature has invented for him. They should neither be pursued nor shunned; they should be accepted. I accept them a little more liberally and kindly and allow myself more easily to follow my natural inclination. We have no need to exaggerate their emptiness; it reveals itself sufficiently and makes itself adequately felt. Thanks to our sickly, kill-joy mind, which disgusts us with them as with itself, it treats both itself and all that it receives, now better, now worse, according to its insatiable, erring, and versatile nature.

In a foul vessel everything turns sour. (Horace)

I, who boast that I embrace the comforts of life so diligently and so particularly, find in them, when I contemplate them thus minutely, little more than wind. What then? We are all wind throughout. And the wind itself, more wisely than we, likes to bluster and veer about, and is content with its own functions, not desiring stability and solidity, qualities that do not belong to it.

The pleasures and the troubles which are wholly the product of the imagination, some say are the greatest, as Critolaus expressed it with his balances. It is no wonder: she composes them to her own liking and cuts them out of whole cloth. Of this I see every day notable examples, and perhaps desirable. But I, who am of a mixed and coarse substance, cannot so entirely bite at this single and simple object of the imagination without allowing myself quite grossly to run after the immediate pleasures springing from the universal human law, intellectually sensible and sensibly intellectual. The Cyrenaic philosophers hold that the bodily pleasures, like the bodily pains, are more powerful, as being both twofold and more real. There are some who from a savage stupidity, as Aristotle says, are disgusted with them; some I know who are so from ambition. Why do they not also forswear breathing? Why do they not live on their own air? Why do they not refuse light because it shines gratis and costs them neither invention nor effort? Let Mars or Pallas or Mercury provide them with sustenance instead of Venus, Ceres, and Bacchus, and see what will happen. Will they not try to square the circle while perched over their wives? I hate to be required to have my mind in the clouds while my body is at table. I would not have the mind nailed there nor wallowing, but paying proper heed; let it sit there, not go to sleep. Aristippus vindicated the body alone, as if we had no soul; Zeno espoused only the soul, as if we had no body. Both were mischievous. Pythagoras, they say, followed a philosophy that was all contemplation; Socrates, one that was all conduct and action; Plato found the just balance between the two. But they express it so for the sake of talking, and the true balance is found in Socrates, and Plato is much more Socratic than Pythagorean, and it becomes him better.

When I dance, I dance; when I sleep, I sleep. Yes, and when I am taking a solitary stroll in a beautiful orchard, if my thoughts are engaged for part of the time by extraneous incidents, for another part I recall them to the walk, to the orchard, to the sweetness of the solitude, and to myself. Nature has with a motherly tenderness observed this principle: that the actions she has enjoined for our need should also be pleasurable to us; and she invites us to them not only through reason but also through appetite. It is wrong to infringe her laws.

When I see both Cæsar and Alexander in the very thick of their most serious business so fully enjoying natural, and therefore necessary and reasonable pleasures, I do not say that it is a relaxing of their minds, I say that they are bracing them, subjecting their violent employments and laborious thoughts by the force of spirit to the ordinary usage of life. Wise had they been if they had believed that the latter was their ordinary, the former their extraordinary vocation!

We are great fools. "He has passed his life in idleness," we say; "I have done nothing today." What! Have you not lived? That is not only the fundamental but the most eminent of your occupations. "Had I been given charge of great affairs, I should have shown what I could do!" Have you known how to think out and manage your own life? You have then performed the greatest work of all. In order to reveal and develop her powers, Nature has no need of Fortune; she reveals herself equally in all grades, and behind a curtain as well as without one. Our duty is to compose our character, not to compose books, and to win, not battles and provinces, but order and tranquillity in our conduct. Our great and glorious masterpiece is to live appropriately. All other things, to rule kingdoms, to lay up treasure, to build, are at most but slight appendices and supports thereto.

I take pleasure in seeing a general of an army, at the foot of a breach he is about to assault, giving himself up wholly and freely to his dinner and to conversation with his friends; and in the spectacle of Brutus, with heaven and earth conspiring against him and the freedom of Rome, stealing an hour from his nightly rounds to read and annotate Polybius in all security. It is the character of a little soul, buried under the weight of business, not to be able to disengage itself clearly, not to know how to lay it aside and take it up again:

> Oh, ye brave souls,
> Who oft with me have suffered sterner fates,
> Banish your cares with wine. Tomorrow we
> Over the mighty main shall take our course. (Horace)

Whether it be in jest or earnest that the theological and Sorbonical wine has passed into a proverb, and their banquets too, I think it reasonable that they should dine more comfortably and pleasantly for having employed the morning profitably and seriously in their scholastic labours. The consciousness of having spent the other hours well is a proper and savoury sauce for the dinner-table. Thus have the sages lived. And that inimitable striving after virtue which amazes us in the two Catos, that disposition of theirs, austere to the point of extravagance, has thus gently submitted itself and taken pleasure in the laws of human existence, both in Venus and Bacchus, according to the precepts of their school, which require the perfect sage to be as expertly versed in the use of natural pleasures as in all the other duties of life. "A wise palate should consort with a wise heart" (Cicero).

The ability to unbend and be at ease does wondrous credit, methinks, and is most becoming to a strong and generous soul. Epaminondas did not think that to mingle in the dance with the young men of his city, to sing, to play an instrument, and to enter into these things with his whole heart, in any way derogated from the honour of his glorious victories and the perfect purity of manners that belonged to him. And among so many admirable actions of Scipio, the grandfather, a person worthy to be reputed of heavenly extraction, there is none that makes him appear more charming than to see him carelessly engaged in the childish pastime of picking up and selecting shells, and running potato-races along the beach with Lælius, and in bad weather amusing himself merrily by writing comedies to represent the vulgarest and meanest actions of men, and, with his head full of that wonderful campaign against Hannibal and Africa, visiting the schools of Sicily and attending lectures on philosophy to the extent of supplying weapons to the blind envy of his enemies in Rome. Nor is there anything more remarkable in Socrates than that in his old age he found time to take lessons in dancing and the playing of instruments, and thought it time well spent.

This same man was once seen in a trance, standing through the entire day and night in the presence of the whole Greek army, his mind caught and transported by some profound thought. He was seen, the first among so many valiant men of the army, running to the relief of Alcibiades, who was being overwhelmed by the enemy, shielding him with his own body and extricating him from the press by sheer force of arms; and the first among all the people of Athens, outraged like him at so shameful a spectacle, to come to the rescue of Theramenes, who was being led to his death by the satellites of the Thirty Tyrants, and, though he was followed but by two other persons, he desisted from this bold attempt only at the remonstrance of Theramenes himself. Though courted by a beauty with whom he was in love, he was known at need to maintain a severe abstinence. He was seen at the battle of Delium to raise up and save Xenophon, who had fallen from his horse. He was seen constantly walking to war or trotting over the ice in bare feet, wearing the same gown in winter and in summer, surpassing all his companions in the endurance of toil, eating no differently at a banquet than at an ordinary meal. He was seen for twenty-seven years to endure with the same countenance hunger, poverty, the intractableness of his children, the clawings of his wife; and in the end, calumny, tyranny, imprisonment, fetters, and poison. But when this man was invited to a drinking-bout by the obligation of civility, he was the one in the army with whom the advantage remained. And he never refused to play at nuts with children, nor to ride the hobby-horse with them, and he did it gracefully; for all actions, says

Philosophy, are equally becoming and equally creditable to a wise man. There is material enough, and we ought never to weary of presenting the image of this great man as a pattern of all kinds of perfection. There are very few examples of a pure and complete life, and it is committing a wrong against our education to put before us every day feeble and defective models, scarcely good for a single aptitude, which rather pull us backward, corrupters rather than correctors.

People deceive themselves: it is much easier to go along the sides, where the outer edge serves as a boundary and guiding line, than to go in the middle of the road, which is broad and open; and it is easier to go according to art than according to Nature, but it is much less noble and commendable. Greatness of soul consists not so much in mounting high and pressing forward as in knowing how to regulate and circumscribe oneself. It regards as great anything that is enough, and shows its elevation by preferring a moderate level to eminence. There is nothing so beautiful and so just as to play the man well and fittingly, nor is there any science so arduous as to know how to live this life well and naturally; and of all our ills the most inhumane is to despise our being.

Whoever has a mind to send his soul abroad, let him do it boldly, if he can, when the body is unwell, so as to free it from the contagion; otherwise, however, let the mind give aid and comfort to the body and let it not refuse to participate in its natural pleasures and find conjugal satisfaction in it, bringing moderation thereto, if it is wiser, lest through indiscretion the pleasures be confounded with pain. Intemperance is the plague of pleasure, and temperance is not its scourge, but its seasoning. Eudoxus, who erected it as the sovereign good, and his fellows, who set so high a value upon it, savoured it in its greatest charm and sweetness through the means of that temperance which was in them so remarkable and exemplary a quality.

I enjoin my soul to look upon pain and pleasure with a gaze equally regular ("for it is from one and the same defect that the soul expands in joy and is contracted in sorrow" [Cicero]) and equally firm, but gaily at the one, severely at the other, and, as far as it is able, to be as painstaking to extinguish the one as to prolong the other. A sane view of the good has for its consequence a sane view of evil. Pain has something of the unavoidable in its tender beginnings, as pleasure has something to be avoided in its excessive end. Plato couples them together and maintains that it is the duty of fortitude to fight equally against pain and against the immoderate and alluring blandishments of pleasure. They are two springs, at which whoever draws where, when, and how much is needful, be it city, man, or beast, is very fortunate. The first is to be taken medicinally and from necessity, very sparingly; the other from thirst, but not to intoxication. Pain, pleasure, love, hatred, are the first things a child feels; if, when Reason arrives, they attach themselves to her, that is virtue.

I have a special vocabulary of my own. I "pass the time" when it is bad and unpleasant weather; when the weather is fair, I do not wish to pass it, I savour it, I cling to it. We must speed over the bad and settle upon the good. This common phrase of "pastime" and "passing the time" represents the usage of those wise folk who think they can make no better reckoning of their life than to let it slide, and to escape from it, to pass it away, to deflect it, and, as much as in them lies, to ignore it and to shun it as a tedious and contemptible thing. But I know it to be otherwise, and find it agreeable and worthy to be prized, even in its decline, in which I now enjoy it; and Nature has put it into our hands equipped with such favouring conditions that we have only ourselves to blame if it afflicts us or escapes from us unprofitably. "The fool's life is without satisfaction, full of fears, given over wholly to the future" (Seneca). Nevertheless I prepare myself to lose it without regret, but as a thing which by its nature has to be lost, not as something troublesome and vexatious. Moreover, not to dislike the idea of dying is properly becoming only to those who like to live. It calls for good management to enjoy it. I enjoy it twice as much as others; for the measure of the enjoyment depends on the greater or lesser degree of application that we devote to it. Especially now, when I perceive my time to be so brief, I mean to increase it in weight. I wish to check the rapidity of its flight by the rapidity of my grasp, and by my eagerness in employing it make up for the hurry of its flow. In the proportion that my possession of life is shorter, I must make it deeper and fuller.

Others feel the sweetness of contentment and prosperity; I feel it as well as they, but not in watching it pass by and slip away. Rather should one study it, savour it, and ruminate upon it, in order to give due thanks to Him who grants it to us. They enjoy other pleasures as they do that of sleep, without being conscious of it. To the end that not even sleep should escape from me thus insensibly, I used to contrive to have it interrupted, and so to gain a glimpse of it. I meditate upon any cause of contentment, I do not skim over it; I take its soundings and bend my reason, now grown peevish and tasteless, to give it welcome. Do I find myself in some state of tranquil composure? Is there some sensual pleasure that tickles me? I do not allow it to be filched by the senses; I make my soul join in it, not so that she gets involved, but that she takes satisfaction in it; not so that she loses, but that she finds herself in it. And I employ her on her own part to view herself in this prosperous state, to weigh and appreciate the happiness of it and to amplify it. She makes due reckoning of how much she stands indebted to God that she is at peace with her conscience and free from other intestine passions, that her body is in its natural state, duly and adequately enjoying the tender and soothing functions by which He of His grace is pleased to compensate the sufferings wherewith His justice in its turn chastises us; of how great her advantage is in being so situated that wherever she casts her eye the heavens are calm about her, that no desire, no fear or doubt disturbs her atmosphere, that there is no difficulty, past, present, or future, over which her imagination does not pass without hurt. This consideration acquires great lustre in a comparison with conditions differing from my own. Thus I place before myself in a thousand aspects those who are carried away and storm-tossed by fortune or their own error, and also those who, resembling me more closely, accept their good fortune so feebly and indifferently. These are men who really "pass their time"; they pass over the present and that which they possess to make themselves the slaves of hope and for the shadows and vain images which fancy dangles before them,

> Like phantoms that, folk say, flit after death,
> Or visions that befool the slumbering sense, (Virgil)

which hasten and prolong their flight the more they are pursued. The fruit and object of their pursuit is to pursue, as Alexander said that the end of his labour was to labour,

> Believing nothing done while aught remained to do. (Lucan)

For my part, then, I love life and cultivate it, such as it has pleased God to bestow it upon us. I do not go about desiring that it may be free from the necessity of eating and drinking, and it would seem to me an error equally inexcusable to desire that the necessity might be double ("The wise man is the keenest seeker for natural riches" [Seneca]), or that we may sustain ourselves by merely putting into our mouth a little of that drug by which Epimenides took away his appetite and kept himself alive, or that we may beget children insensibly with our fingers or heels, but, with reverence be it spoken, that we may rather beget them voluptuously with our fingers and heels, or that the body should be without desire and without titillation. These are ungrateful and unfair complaints. I accept cheerfully and gratefully what Nature has done for me, and am well pleased with myself and proud of myself to do so. A man does wrong to the great omnipotent giver in refusing, nullifying, or disfiguring His gift. All goodness Himself, He has made all things good. "All things that are according to Nature are worthy of esteem" (Cicero).

Of philosophical opinions I preferably embrace those that are most solid; that is to say, most human, and most our own. My reflections, in conformity with my character, are low and humble. Philosophy plays the child, to my thinking, when, investing herself in her ergotisms, she preaches to us that it is a barbarous alliance to marry the divine with the earthly, the reasonable with the unreasonable, the severe with the indulgent, the honest with the dishonest, that the pleasure of the senses is a brutish thing unworthy to be tasted by the wise man: the only pleasure he derives from the enjoyment of a fair young wife is pleasure in the consciousness of performing an orderly action, like putting on one's boots for some useful errand. If only her followers had no more right or nerve or juice in deflowering their wives than there is in her lessons!

That is not what Socrates, her teacher and ours, says. He values as he ought the pleasure of the body, but he prefers that of the mind, as having greater strength and stability and flexibility and variety and dignity. The latter, in his opinion, goes by no means alone (he is not so fantastic), it merely comes first. Temperance with him is the moderator, not the adversary of pleasures.

Nature is a gentle guide, but not more gentle than wise and just. "We must penetrate into the nature of things and get an intimate view of what it requires" (Cicero). I seek her footprints everywhere. We have obscured them with artificial tracks, and on this account the sovereign good of the Academics and Peripatetics, which is "to live according to her," becomes difficult to limit and explain, as does that of the Stoics, closely allied to it, which is "to acquiesce in Nature." Is it not an error to esteem any actions less worthy because they are necessary? So they will not beat it out of my head that the marriage of pleasure with necessity (with which, one of the ancients says, the gods always conspire) is not a very fitting one. To what end do we dismember by divorce a structure built of so close and brotherly correspondence of parts? On the contrary, let us tie it together by mutual offices. Let the mind rouse and quicken the heaviness of the body, and the body check and stabilize the levity of the mind. "He who extols the nature of the soul as the chief good, and condemns the nature of the flesh as evil, assuredly is fleshly both in his love of the soul and hatred of the flesh; for these his feelings arise from human vanity, not from divine truth" (Saint Augustine). There is no part unworthy of our care in this present that God has made us; we stand accountable for it even to the last hair. And the charge enjoined upon man to conduct human life according to its condition is not enjoined for form's sake; it is express, plain, and of chief importance, and has been imposed upon us by the Creator seriously and severely. Authority alone prevails over common understandings, and it carries greater weight in a foreign language. Let us again enforce the charge. "For who would not say that it was a mark of folly to do in a slothful and rebellious spirit what has to be done, or to urge the body in one direction and the mind in another, and thus to be torn between the most conflicting emotions?" (Seneca)

Come now, to make proof of this, ask anyone to tell you some day what are the notions and fancies with which he occupies his head, and for the sake of which he diverts his thoughts from a good meal and complains of the time which he spends in feeding. You will find there is nothing so insipid in all the dishes at your table as this fine entertainment of his mind (for the most part we would be better off to go quite to sleep than to stay awake to such a purpose as occupies our waking thoughts), and you will find that his speeches and his ideas are not worth your commonest stew. Though they were the raptures of Archimedes himself, what then? I am not here referring to or confounding with the rabble of us ordinary men, or with the vanity of the thoughts and desires that distract us, those venerable souls exalted by the ardour of devotion and religion to a constant and conscientious meditation on divine things, who, anticipating by force of a lively and vehement hope the enjoyment of eternal nourishment, the final aim and last step of Christian desires, the only constant and incorruptible pleasure, disdain to apply themselves to our beggarly, fleeting, and ambiguous comforts, and readily resign to the body the care and enjoyment of sensual and temporal provender. That is a privileged study. Between ourselves, I have ever observed that there is a singular accord between supercelestial thoughts and subterrestrial conduct.

Æsop, that great man, saw his master make water as he walked. "What!" said he, "must we drop excrement as we run?" Let us manage our time as well as we can, there will yet remain a great deal that is idle and ill employed. It is likely that our mind has not other hours enough wherein to do its business, without dissociating itself from the body for that little space that it must have for its necessity. They wish to get out of their own skins and escape from the man. It is folly: instead of transforming themselves into angels they transform themselves into beasts; instead of raising, they lower themselves. These transcendental humours frighten me, like lofty and inaccessible places; and nothing in the life of Socrates is so hard for me to digest as his ecstasies and his dæmonisms, and nothing is so human in Plato as that for which they say he was called divine. And of our sciences those seem to me the most terrestrial and low that have made the highest flight. And I find nothing so humble and so mortal in the life of Alexander as his fancies about his immortalization. Philotas taunted him wittily in his answer: he congratulated him by letter on having been placed among the gods by the oracle of Jupiter Ammon, saying: "As far as you are concerned, I am glad of it, but those men are to be pitied who will have to live with and obey a man who exceeds and is not contented with the measure of a man." "Because you submit to the gods, you exercise sway over men" (Horace).

The pretty inscription wherewith the Athenians honoured the entry of Pompey into their city is in agreement with my view:

> So much thou hast of Deity
> As thou dost own of man in thee. (Plutarch)

It is an absolute perfection and, as it were, divine for a man to know how to enjoy his existence as he ought. We seek other conditions because we do not understand the use of our own, and we go out of ourselves because we do not know what there is within us. So it is no use to mount upon stilts, for even on stilts we must walk with our own legs. And even on the most exalted throne in the world we are only sitting on our own bottom.

The fairest lives, in my opinion, are those which conform to the common and human model, with order, but without miracle and without extravagance. Now old age stands in need of being treated a little more tenderly. Let us commend it to that god who is the protector of health and wisdom, but a gay and sociable wisdom:

Grant me, Latona's son, but health,
  Grant me a mind entire,
Contentment and a dignified old age,
  Not lacking in the sweetness of the lyre. (Horace)

TORQUATO TASSO

(1544–1595)

Although Torquato Tasso lived in the age of the Counter Reformation, in the Italy dominated by the Spanish and the Papacy, he was at heart a spirit of the past and the last great poet of the Italian Renaissance.

He was born in Sorrento, on the southern side of the Bay of Naples, on the 11th of March 1544. His father, Bernardo Tasso, of a noble family originally of Bergamo, was the noted author of the *Amadigi,* then secretary to Ferrante Sanseverino, Prince of Salerno; his mother was Porzia de' Rossi, a Neapolitan of a noble family formerly of Pistoia. He had an older sister, Cornelia.

From his boyhood, misfortune and tragedy haunted Torquato's family. His father, involved in the political downfall of the prince, left his family in Naples when Torquato was seven and eventually followed his master as an exile from the Kingdom of Naples. His mother, young and beautiful, but unfit to hold her own alone, was persecuted by her brothers and her mother on account of her dowry which they controlled. When Torquato was ten, it was decided that he should join his father in Rome, after a fruitless attempt had been made to secure his mother's departure from Naples. Torquato never saw his mother again. Two years later, word came of her death; it was believed that she had been poisoned.

In Naples the boy had been placed in a Jesuit school where his sensitiveness had been prematurely pressed to a precocious religiosity. In Rome his father directed his education. In 1557, Bernardo entered the service of Guidobaldo II della Rovere at Urbino, and here Torquato became the companion of Prince Francesco Maria and shared the instruction of the young prince's masters. Here, also, was open to him the association of literati and courtiers and the glamorous and exciting world of the unstable court life of the age. Deprived of a normal home life, and being the son of his father, Torquato accepted its surface values and idealized it. In 1559, Bernardo went to Venice, accepting an offer for the printing of his *Amadigi,* and here Torquato experienced the life of the fascinating city of the lagoons with both its refined taste and voluptuous magnificence, at a time when Titian, Paolo Veronese, and Tintoretto were painting.

In 1560, at the age of sixteen, his father sent him to the University of Padua to study law; a year later, he transferred to courses in philosophy and eloquence. Here he wrote his youthful romance, the *Rinaldo,* printed in 1562, which brought him fame. He continued his studies at Bologna, but returned to Padua in 1564 to become a member of the Accademia degli Eterei (The Ethereals), which his intimate friend Scipione Gonzaga had recently organized. In this group he read his youthful love poems and discussed poetic theory, continuing his philosophical studies at the university at the same time.

In 1565, following inevitably the career of his father, he took service with the Cardinal Luigi d'Este in Ferrara. The Ferrarese court of this late age still maintained its surface brilliance. Duke Alfonso II, the Cardinal's brother, now ruled, and the court was adorned by his two sisters, the Princess Lucrezia, later to become Duchess of Urbino, and the Princess Leonora, of delicate health and semi-secluded life. Into this court the youthful Tasso, handsome, to the manor born, already a famed poet, was accepted with acclaim. It offered him the life to which he was attuned and in which his poetic creativeness was nourished. In 1570 he followed the Cardinal to Paris, where he came to know the poetry of Ronsard. He remained there with the Cardinal only a few months, however, and was back in Ferrara the next year, where he entered the service of the Duke Alfonso. Probably the happiest years of Tasso's life then followed, 1572–74. He was the favorite of the Duke and the princesses and was smiled upon by the whole court. His poetry flourished: for a court festival in 1573, he composed his pastoral drama, the *Aminta;* his epic, the *Jerusalem Delivered,* was completed in 1575. These proved to be his two greatest works.

With the completion of his epic poem, however, the turn came in Tasso's life. He began to find himself dissatisfied at Ferrara. Proud, supersensitive, and lacking in tact, his highly-strung nervous system gradually reacted to the labors of poetic creation and the long strain of the court life to which he gravitated. The success of his epic enlarged his expectations, nor was his temperament such as to avoid the envy and antagonism which his superiority caused among other courtiers. He thought of leaving the Estensi and negotiated with their rivals, the Medici, at Florence. The melancholy depression which he had known from his boyhood increased. Lacking in confidence and irresolute, he submitted his poem to four critics to be judged for its adherence to the rules of the epic. Fearing he had offended the Church in his poem, and indeed solicitous over the spiritual health of his own soul, he submitted himself to examination by the Inquisition. He was taken with suspicions, obsessions, hallucinations; he feared a plot to poison him, or to deliver him over to the Inquisition as a heretic.

Alfonso at first seems to have shown considerable patience. On the evening of the 17th of June 1577, however, in the apartments of the Duchess Lucrezia, thinking that a servant — who was probably placed to watch — was spying upon him, he impulsively drew his knife. The Duke then saw fit to place him in confinement, at first in rooms in court, later in his villa that he might have the care of physicians, and finally in the convent of the Franciscans. During the night of the 26th–27th of July, he escaped from the convent, donned the garb of a peasant, and made on foot the long wandering journey to join his sister in Sorrento. The rest of Tasso's life is filled with pathos. Incapable of living outside the atmosphere of courts, he was back in Ferrara by April 1578. Leaving again, he wandered from city to city, to Mantua, to Padua, to Venice, to Pesaro, to Turin, returning again to Ferrara in February 1579. Finally, in March 1579, Alfonso found it wise to place him in Sant' Anna, the Ferrarese hospital for the insane.

The cause of Tasso's madness has given rise to much speculation. A romantic legend arose, used by Goethe and Byron, that it was caused by Tasso's love for the Princess Leonora which was returned, that the jealous Duke Alfonso compelled him to feign madness in order to protect the honor of his house, that the Duke imprisoned and tortured him, that he escaped at last to die of a broken heart. This legend was proved to be without foundation by Angelo Solerti in 1895 in his distinguished biography. It is doubtful if Tasso was capable of such a romantic passion. Close analysis of his many letters reveals that his life became increasingly self-centered. Deprived from earliest years of the wholesome influence of home life, and geared to the life of illusion of the court, his final condition was the inevitable result of his temperament, of his nervous constitution, and of the life he inherited and led. As De Sanctis wrote, "Instead of doctors and medicines, the thing he needed was a calm life in some place of quiet seclusion, with his books, and with a mother beside him, or a sister, or friends made intelligent by affection."

Tasso remained in Sant' Anna for seven years. After the first year, his treatment was improved: he was given decent rooms, received frequent and distinguished visitors, and was allowed at times to go out under accompaniment. He continued his writing, but wrote many letters of appeal for assistance. Finally, on the 12th of July 1586, the Duke permitted Vincenzo Gonzaga, Prince of Mantua, to take him to his own city. For a short time he seemed happy, but his old restlessness and melancholy returned and a little over a year later he fled from Mantua.

Much of the time during his last years was spent in Rome, first at the house of his old friend Scipione Gonzaga, and then either at the Quirinal or the Vatican as a guest of Cinzio Passeri and Pietro Aldobrandini, nephews of Clement VIII. In melancholy depression, he asked gifts and favors from friends and sought patronage from the wealthy and powerful. Late in 1594, Pope Clement VIII conferred a pension upon him. Finally, the lawsuit over his mother's property which he had taken up was settled. Clement planned to have bestowed upon him the poet's crown of laurel. But in April 1595 he had himself taken to the monastery of San Onofrio on Janiculum Hill. He died there on April 25th; he lies buried in the Church of San Onofrio.

Tasso's greatest poem, the *Gerusalemme Liberata,* was published in its correct form in 1581. Immediately it was compared with Ariosto's *Orlando* and a literary debate arose over epic theory and the comparative merits of the two poems. In his youth Tasso had set forth his own epic theory in his *Discorsi . . . del Poema Eroica,* which he later rewrote in 1594. In it he argued that the poem should reconcile the unity of the classical epic with the rich variety of the romance. Distracted, however, over both religious and artistic criticism, he first sought to justify the *Gerusalemme* by writing an allegorical interpretation the year after it was completed, and later completely rewrote the original poem in the greatly inferior *Gerusalemme Conquistata,* completed in 1592.

A little less than 2000 of Tasso's lyrics remain: sonnets, *canzoni,* madrigals, and octaves, in the Petrarchan style. He wrote 31 dialogues, many of them in Sant' Anna, on various subjects, philosophical, ethical, and literary. A little less than 1700 letters have been collected, written in artistic style, and revealing intimately his inner life. Among other writings of lesser merit is a tragedy, *Il Torrismondo,* completed at Mantua in 1586, and a religious poem on the creation of the universe, the *Mondo Creato,* completed in 1594.

Deeply rooted in Tasso's personal tragedy, one discerns a basic conflict in his essentially noble although egoistic spirit. At heart, he longed for the chivalric idealism of the past, the beauty and glamour of romance, the pagan gladness and rich sensuous experience of the High Renaissance. But he lived in the era of the Council of Trent, the Spanish Inquisition, and the predominance of pedantic critical theory over free creation. Essentially lyric and subjective in temperament, he sought to write an epic poem. His finest poetry is the expression of the inner world of his dreams, idyllic and elegiac; in it is found the sensitive melancholy of a dreamer of the unattainable.

SELECTED BIBLIOGRAPHY

EDITIONS

Opere, ed. G. Rosini, 33 vols., Pisa, Campurro, 1821–32; also edit. in "Scrittori d'Italia" series, Bari, Laterza, now in process of publication; *Opere Minori in Versi,* ed. A. Solerti, 3 vols., Bologna, Zanichelli, 1891–95; *La Gerusalemme Liberata,* ed. E. Allodoli, Milan, Vallardi, 1933, good annotated edit. for general use.

TRANSLATIONS

Jerusalem Delivered, trans. Edward Fairfax, 1600; trans. John Hoole, London, 1763; trans. J. H. Wiffen, Bohn Library, London, Bell, 1824; trans. Sir John Kingston James, 2 vols., London, Kegan Paul, 1884. *Rinaldo,* trans. John Hoole, London, 1792. *Aminta,* trans. Ernest Grillo, New York, Dutton, 1924; trans. Louis E. Lord, Oxford Univ. Press, 1931. *Discourses on the Heroic Poem,* trans. A. H. Gilbert, in *Literary Criticism: Plato to Dryden, 466–503,* New York, Am. Book Co., 1940.

BIOGRAPHY AND CRITICISM

Angelo Solerti, *Vita di T. Tasso,* 3 vols., Turin, Loescher, 1895; Eugenio Donadoni, *T. Tasso: Saggio Critico,* 2 vols., Florence, 2nd edit., 1936; U. Bosco, "T. Tasso," in *Enciclopedia Italiana,* XXXIII, 308–17, 1937.

Elizabeth J. Hasell, *Tasso,* Philadelphia, Lippincott, 1882; William Boulting, *Tasso and His Times,* New York, Putnam, 1907; George E. Woodberry, "Tasso," in *Inspiration of Poetry,* 142–71, New York, Macmillan, 1910; C. M. Bowra, "Tasso and the Romance of Christian Chivalry," in *From Virgil to Milton,* 139–93, London, Macmillan, 1945; Giacomo Grillo, *Poets of the Court of Ferrara,* Boston, Excelsior Press, 1943.

SPECIAL STUDIES

E. Koeppel, "Die Englischen Tassoübersetzungen des XVI Jahrhunderts," *Anglia,* XI (1889), 341–62; W. P. Mustard, "Tasso's Debt to Vergil," *Class. Weekly,* XIII (1920), 115–20; H. H. Blanchard, "Imitations from Tasso in the Faerie Queene," *Stud. in Philol.,* XXII (1925), 198–221; H. M. Briggs, "Tasso's Theory of Epic Poetry," *Mod. Lang. Rev.,* XXV (1930), 457–73; J. G. Fucilla, "Contributions to a Tasso Bibliography," *Philol. Quar.,* XII (1933), 170 ff.; A. H. Krappe, "The Subterranean Voyage," *Philol. Quar.,* XX (1941), 119–30; E. K. Waterhouse, "Tasso and the Visual Arts," *Ital. Studies,* III (1946), 146–62; C. C. Bell, "A History of Fairfax Criticism," *Pub. Mod. Lang. Assoc.,* LXII (1947), 644–56; E. Roditi, "T. Tasso: The Transition from Baroque to Neo-Classicism," *Jour. of Aesthetics and Art. Crit.,* VI (1948), 235–45; H. Hatzfeld, "A Clarification of the Baroque in the Romance Literatures," *Compar. Lit.,* I (1949), 113–39; C. C. Bell, "Fairfax's Tasso," *Compar. Lit.,* VI (1954), 26–52; R. M. Durling, "The Bower of Bliss and Armida's Palace," *Compar. Lit.,* VI (1954), 335–47.

JERUSALEM DELIVERED

Translated by J. H. Wiffen

[Taken from *The Jerusalem Delivered of Torquato Tasso*, translated by J. H. Wiffen, Bohn Library, G. Bell & Sons, London, 1824.]

[The *Jerusalem Delivered* combines in structure the unity of the classical epic with the elaboration by episode of medieval romance.

The epic subject of the poem is the First Crusade, in which appear the historic characters, Godfrey of Bouillon, Count Raymond of Toulouse, and Tancred of Sicily. Upon this historic framework are created also the romantic episodes involving the fictitious characters of Rinaldo of Este, Armida, Erminia, and the martial Clorinda, with whom the historic Tancred is also associated.

The poem opens near the end of the Crusade, in 1099, the year in which Jerusalem was taken. Knowledge is assumed of the Council of Clermont in 1095, of the preaching of Peter the Hermit, of the marching of armies in 1096 from Provence, Lorraine, southern Italy to meet at Constantinople, of the taking of Edessa, of Antioch, and of Tripoli. As the poem opens, Godfrey of Bouillon is by divine command elected head of all the crusading armies, and the Christian host approaches Jerusalem. Meanwhile, within the city, the aged King Aladine prepares the defence.]

CANTO III

ARGUMENT

Clorinda bravely meets the Franks in fight,
When at Jerusalem the host arrives;
Erminia's love awakens at the sight
Of Tancred in the field; his own revives,
When a strange knight, with whom in war he strives,
Appears unmasked; Argantes at a blow
The brave Adventurers of their Chief deprives;
Dudon interred, for timbers to lay low
The town, to antique groves the Latin soldiers go.

1.

The odorous air, morn's messenger, now spread
Its wings to herald, in serenest skies,
Aurora issuing forth, her radiant head
Adorned with roses plucked in Paradise;
When in full panoply the hosts arise,
And loud and spreading murmurs upward fly,

Ere yet the trumpet sings; its melodies
They miss not long, the trumpet's tuneful cry
Gives the command to march, shrill sounding to the sky.

2.

The skilful Captain, with a gentle rein
Guides their desires, and animates their force;
And though 't would seem more easy to restrain
Charybdis in its mad volubil course,
Or bridle Boreas in, when gruffly hoarse
He tempests Apenninus and the grey
Ship shaking Ocean to its deepest source,—
He ranks them, urges, rules them on the way;
Swiftly they march, yet still with swiftness under sway.

3.

Wing'd is each heart, and winged every heel;
They fly, yet notice not how fast they fly;
But by the time the dewless meads reveal
The fervent sun's ascension in the sky,
Lo, towered Jerusalem salutes the eye!
A thousand pointing fingers tell the tale;
"Jerusalem!" a thousand voices cry,
"All hail, Jerusalem!" hill, down, and dale
Catch the glad sounds, and shout, "Jerusalem, all hail!"

4.

Thus, when a crew of fearless voyagers,
Seeking new lands, spread their audacious sails
In the hoar Arctic, under unknown stars,
Sport of the faithless waves and treacherous gales;
If, as their little bark the billow scales,
One views the long-wished headland from the mast,
With merry shouts the far-off coast he hails,
Each points it out to each, until at last
They lose in present joy the troubles of the past.

5.

To the pure pleasure which that first far view
In their reviving spirits sweetly shed,
Succeeds a deep contrition, feelings new,—
Grief touched with awe, affection mixed with dread;
Scarce dare they now upraise the abject head,
Or turn to Zion their desiring eyes,
The chosen city! where Messias bled,
Defrauded Death of his long tyrannies,
New clothed his limbs with life, and reassumed the skies!

6.

Low accents, plaintive whispers, groans profound,
Sighs of a people that in gladness grieves,
And melancholy murmurs float around,
Till the sad air a thrilling sound receives,
Like that which sobs amidst the dying leaves,
When with autumnal winds the forest waves;
Or dash of an insurgent sea that heaves
On lonely rocks, or locked in winding caves,
Hoarse through their hollow aisles in wild low cadence raves.

7.

Each, at his Chief's example, lays aside
His scarf and feathered casque, with every gay
And glittering ornament of knightly pride,
And barefoot treads the consecrated way.
Their thoughts, too, suited to their changed array,
Warm tears devout their eyes in showers diffuse,—
Tears, that the haughtiest temper might allay;
And yet, as though to weep they did refuse,
Thus to themselves their hearts of hardness they accuse.

8.

"Here, Lord, where currents from thy wounded side
Stained the besprinkled ground with sanguine red,
Should not these two quick springs at least, their tide
In bitter memory of thy passion shed!
And melt'st thou not, my icy heart, where bled
Thy dear Redeemer? still must pity sleep?
My flinty bosom, why so cold and dead?
Break, and with tears the hallowed region steep!
If that thou weep'st not now, for ever shouldst thou weep!"

9.

Meanwhile the Guard that from a lofty tower
In the far city cast abroad his view,
Marked the dust rise, and like a thunder-shower
Printed in air, turn dark the' ethereal blue;
The gloomy cloud seemed pregnant as it flew
With fire,—anon, bright metals flashed between
Its shaken wreaths, and as it nearer drew,
Dim through the storm were apparitions seen—
Spearmen, and issuing steeds, and chiefs of godlike mien.

10.

He saw, and raised his terrible alarm;
"Oh rise, all citizens below, arise;
Mount to the walls; haste! arm! this instant arm!
Lo, what a dust upon the whirlwind flies,

And lo, the lightning of their arms!" he cries, —
"The foeman is at hand!" then, yet more loud,
He calls, "Shall the swift foe the town surprise?
Quick, seize your weapons; mark the dusty cloud
That hither rolls! it wraps all heaven within its shroud!"

11.

The simple infant and the aged sire,
Matrons and trembling maids, to whom belong
Nor strength, nor skill to make defence, retire,
A pale, disconsolate, and suppliant throng,
In sad procession to the mosques: the strong
In spirit as in limbs obey the call;
Seizing their arms in haste, they speed along,
Part flock to guard the gates, part man the wall;
The king to all parts flies, sees, cares, provides for all.

12.

His orders given, for every need prepared,
He from the thickening tumult has withdrawn,
And scales a tower that 'twixt two portals reared,
O'erlooks the plain, and holds the hills in scorn.
His steps Erminia, lovely as the morn,
At call attends; with all respect received,
His royal Court her winning charms adorn,
Since Antioch by the Christians was achieved,
And o'er her kingly sire the orphan-princess grieved.

13.

Meantime Clorinda hastes against the Franks,
First of her band, with many a gallant knight,
Whilst in a secret porch Argantes ranks
His troops, prepared for rescue or for fight.
Her words, intrepid as her mien, excite
Fire in all hearts, as thus the heroine spoke:
"Well it becomes us, armed in Asia's right,
To found the loosening of her hated yoke
On the auspicious base of some determined stroke!"

14.

Lo, Fortune, as she speaks, the' occasion yields!
A band of Franks sent onward to forecast
The army's wants, from foraging the fields,
Near them, with flocks and herds returning, passed;
She towards them, and to her rushed as fast
Their Chief, when he beheld her silver crest; —
Guardo his name, a man of puissance vast,
But weak with her the laurel to contest; —
Onward abrupt they drove, their lances laid in rest.

15.

Breathless to earth the hapless Frank was strook
By the fierce shock, in either army's sight;
From his mischance the shouting Pagans took
Their joyous augury of the future fight:
Onward she flew upon the rest, the might
Of numbers flashing in her single blade;
Fast in their serried ranks she poured the light;
Her warriors followed through the gap she made,
Where her assault had been, where yet her falchion played.

16.

Soon from the spoiler they the spoil obtain;
The Franks give way, yet to their standard keep,
Till slow the summit of a hill they gain,
And stand assisted by the rising steep:
When as a tempest, which the whirlwinds sweep
Abroad, breaks loose, and in aërial dance
Warm from its skirts the vivid lightnings leap,
Tancred at Godfrey's beck made swift advance
With his Italian troop, and couched his quivering lance.

17.

The king beheld him from his tower, and deemed
Him of all men the choicest cavalier,
So young, so resolute, so brave he seemed,
And bore with such a grace his beamy spear;
Whence he bespake the fair Erminia near,
Whose palpitating heart in secret thrilled
As at the sight of something deeply dear;
"Well shouldst thou know, in many a fighting field
Marked out, each Christian knight, howe'er in arms concealed.

18.

"Who then is this, that in fierce grace outstrips
All other knights?" In room of a reply,
The quick breath fluttered round her lovely lips,
The big tear trembled in her full blue eye:
These she reclaimed, yet not so carelessly
As to escape regard,—a conscious red
Tinged her averted cheek, the sudden sigh,
Choked to a groan, spoke plain of feeling fled,
And o'er her tearful eyes a radiant circlet spread.

19.

In these delusive words her answer ran,
Veiling her love beneath a mask of hate;
"Too well I know the' inexorable man,
And should, amidst a thousand! but of late,

His savage soul I saw him satiate
With slaughter, — saw him flesh his angry steel
Upon the best of our Assyrian state:
Cruel are all his strokes! the wounds they deal,
No magic charm can stanch, no breathing balsam heal!

20.

"He is Prince Tancred; oh that he, some day,
Might be my slave! I would not wish him dead;
Glad that he lives, so might I thus repay
In sweet revenge my wrongs upon his head!
That would indeed be some small joy," she said,
And the king failed not, as she wished, to wrest
The meaning of her words, ascribed, instead
Of love, to hate: she ceased, but from her breast
Stole forth a mournful sigh that would not be repressed.

21.

Meanwhile Clorinda rushes to assail
The Prince, and level lays her spear renowned;
Both lances strike, and on the barred ventayle
In shivers fly, and she remains discrowned;
For, burst its silver rivets, to the ground
Her helmet leaped, (incomparable blow!)
And by the rudeness of the shock unbound,
Her sex to all the field emblazoning so,
Loose to the charmed winds her golden tresses flow.

22.

Then blazed her eyes, then flashed her angry glance,
Sweet e'en in wrath; in laughter then what grace
Would not be theirs! — but why that thoughtful trance?
And, Tancred, why that scrutinizing gaze?
Know'st not thine idol? lo, the same dear face,
Whence sprang the flame that on thy heart has preyed!
The sculptured image in its shrine retrace,
And in thy foe behold the noble maid,
Who to the sylvan spring for cool refreshment strayed.[1]

23.

He, who her painted shield and silver crest
Marked not at first, stood spell-bound at the sight;
She, guarding as she could her head, still pressed
The' assault, and struck, but he forebore the fight,
And to the rest transferring his despite,

1. See I, 45–49, not given in these selections. At Antioch, Tancred, retiring from the battle at noon to a woodland spring, met there the pagan warrior-maid, Clorinda, from Persia, who had also come there for refreshment, with helmet removed. Although they were separated immediately by the coming of troops, Tancred was taken with love for her at once.

Plied fast his whirling sword; yet not the less
Ceased she to follow and upbraid his flight,
With taunt and menace heightening his distress;
And, "Turn, false knight!" she cried, loud shouting through the press.

24.

Struck, he not once returns the stroke, nor seeks
So much to ward the meditated blow,
As in those eyes and on those charming cheeks
To gaze, whence Passion's fond emotions flow:
"Void," to himself he says, "too cruel foe,
Void fall the strokes which that beloved arm
Distributes in its wrath! no fatal throe
Is that thy scimitar creates; the harm
Is in thy angry looks, that wound me while they charm!"

25.

Resolved at length not unconfessed to fall,
Though hopeless quite her pity to obtain,
That she might know she struck her willing thrall,
Defenceless, suppliant, crouching to her chain;
"O thou," said he, "that followest o'er the plain
Me as thine only foe, of all this wide
Presented people! yet thy wrath restrain;
The press let us forsake, so may aside
Thy force with mine be proved, my skill with thine be tried.

26.

"Then shalt thou measure in the face of day
Thy strength with mine, nor own my valour less."
Pleased she assents, and boldly leads the way,
Unhelmed, — he follows in his mute distress.
Already stood the' impatient Warrioress
Prepared, already had she struck, when he
Exclaimed; "Hold! hold! ere we ourselves address
To the stern fight, 't is fit we should agree
Upon the terms of strife; fix first what these shall be!"

27.

Her arm she stayed; strong love and wild despair
A reckless courage to his mind impart;
"These be the terms," said he, "since you foreswear
All peace with me, pluck out my panting heart,
Mine own no more! I willingly shall part
With life, if farther life thy pride offend;
Long have I pined with love's tormenting smart;
'T is fit the fond and feverish strife should end;
Take then the worthless life which I will ne'er defend.

28.

"Behold! my arms are offered, — I present
My breast without defence, — spare not to smite;
Or shall I speed the task? I am content
To strip my cuirass off, and thus invite
Thy cruel steel!" — In harsher self-despite,
The mournful youth would have proclaimed his woes,
But suddenly, in craft or panic fright,
The Pagans yield to their pursuing foes,
And his brave troops rush by, and numbers interpose.

29.

Like driven deer before the' Italian band
They yield, they fly in swiftness unconfined;
One base pursuer saw Clorinda stand,
Her rich locks spread like sunbeams on the wind,
And raised his arm in passing, from behind,
To stab secure the undefended maid;
But Tancred, conscious of the blow designed,
Shrieked out, "Beware!" to warn the' unconscious maid,
And with his own good sword bore off the hostile blade.

30.

Still the stroke fell, and near the graceful head
Her snowy neck received the point, which drew
Some rosy drops, that crimsoned, as they shed,
Her yellow curls with their bespangling dew;
E'en thus gold beams with the blush-rose's hue,
When round it rubies sparkle from the hand
Of some rare artist; trembling at the view,
His wrath the Prince no longer may command,
But on the caitiff falls, and shakes his threatening brand.

31.

The villain flies, and full of rage the knight
Pursues, — as arrows swift, they scour the plains;
Perplexed she stands, and keeps them both in sight
To a great distance, nor to follow deigns,
But quickly her retreating band regains; —
Sometimes she fronts in hostile attitude
The' arrested Franks, now flies, and now disdains
To fly, — fights, flies again, as suits her mood,
Nor can she well be termed pursuer or pursued.

32.

So in the Circus the fierce bull turns back
To gore the baying mastiffs that pursue;
They pause — but still as he resumes his track,
Their ruffian clamours savagely renew.

She, as she fled, above her shoulders threw
Her guardian buckler, like an orbed sun;
So at their sports gymnastic may we view
The fugitive Morescos shielded run,
Dexterous the darted balls on nimble feet to shun.

33.

Whilst these give chase, and those assaulted fly,
To the town-walls they now approaching drew,
When on the sudden, with a frightful cry,
Back on the Christians came the Pagan crew;
First wheeling far aloof, and then anew
Returning nigh, with circumventing skill
They on the wings and rear tempestuous flew;
Whilst undisguised Argantes down the hill
Moved to assail the front, and shouted wild and shrill.

34.

Before his troop the fierce Avenger passed,
All eager first to pounce upon the prey;
Over and over, at one charge he cast
The horse and rider that first crossed his way;
And ere to shivers flew his lance, there lay
Whole heaps of such in his encumbered track;
Then from its scabbard leaps his sword, and aye
Whom it but fully reaches to attack,
It either kills, or wounds, or beats affrighted back.

35.

In rivalry of him Clorinda slew
Ardelio brave, of years now most mature,
But though by age untamed, and fenced by two
Bold sons, he was not from her sword secure:
For a sharp wound which he could ill endure,
First from the sire removed his eldest pride,
Unblest Alcander; and his trust, the sure
Young Polypherne, assistant at his side,
For his own menaced life but barely could provide.

36.

But Tancred, finding that he vainly chased
The ruffian, who a swifter steed displayed,
Looked back and saw how far intemperate haste
Hurried the valour of his bold brigade;
Hemmed in he saw it, to the sword betrayed,
And spurring back, to the corrected rein,
His gallant steed, came quickly to their aid;
Nor he alone, but that adventurous train,
Who every risk of war unshrinkingly sustain.

37.

Dudon's choice phalanx to the rescue throng,
The flower of heroes, dragons of the fight;
And noblest, bravest, foremost rushed along,
The gay and versatile Rinaldo, light
As the wild wind; Erminia knew the knight
By his bold port and azure-tincted shield,
Where the bird argent spreads its plumes for flight,[2]
And to the king, who watched him through the field,
Exclaimed, "Lo there the youth to whom all knights must yield!

38.

"But few or none in tournament can vie
With him, though yet but into boyhood grown;
Could Europe six such paragons supply,
Salem were not, and Syria were o'erthrown;
The South her strong supremacy would own,
Kingdoms that lie beneath the morning star
Stoop to her rule, and in the burning zone,
Vainly perhaps would Nilus seek afar,
Amid his secret springs, a refuge from the war!

39.

"Rinaldo is his name; his angry sword
More threats your walls than the most huge machine:
But turn to where I point; yon noble lord,
Glittering in armature of gold and green,
Is gallant Dudon, to whose call convene
The band to which I see your eyes advert,
Adventurers chivalrous, — a warrior keen,
Who high-born, active, and in arms expert,
Greatly transcends in years, nor yields in true desert.

40.

"That towering figure, sheathed in brown, has birth
From Norway's king, Gernando is his name:
No prouder creature breathes, throughout the earth;
A single foible sullying all his fame.
But lo, urged on for ever by one aim,
Where Edward and his dear Gildippe move!
Their mantles, arms, and ornaments the same,
Argent! in bridal harmony they rove,
Famed both for deeds of arms, and loyalty of love."

41.

Whilst thus Erminia communes with the king,
Below, yet deeper carnage dyes the fields;

2. The coat-of-arms of the House of Este at Ferrara, and thus of Tasso's patron, Duke Alfonso.

There Tancred and Rinaldo break the ring,
Dense with conflicting men and serried shields;
Then pour the' Adventurers in, and bravely wields
Each knight the weapon of his sharp disdain;
Argantes' self, the proud Argantes yields;
Beat by Rinaldo backward on the plain
In sudden shock, he scarce his footing can regain:—

42.

Nor e'er had he renewed the stern debate,
But the same instant fell Rinaldo's steed,
And from the pressure of its cumbrous weight
The noble youth not easily was freed.
Meanwhile, diffused in flight, with headlong speed,
On to the barbican the Pagans hied;
Argantes and Clorinda sole impede—
Mounds to its wrath—the' irruptions of the tide
That on them bursts behind with such insulting pride.

43.

Last they retire, and the pursuing force
Of battle hold in check, and so restrain,
That those who flee before, screened in their course,
With less of ruin gored the city gain.
Still Dudon, flushed with conquest, gave the rein
To his curvetting horse, that with a bound
Bore down the fierce Tigranes; not in vain
The sharp sword struck; he headless fell to ground,
And, savage e'en in death, superb defiance frowned.

44.

Nought his fine hauberk Algazel avails,
Nought his strong helmet Corbano defends;
Them through the nape and back he so assails,
That through the face and breast the steel protends:
With fell Almanzor next two valiant friends,
Mahmoud and Amurath, his trenchant brand
From pleasant life to Lethe quickly sends;
The valour flashing from his armed hand,
Not e'en Circassia's Duke could unannoyed withstand.

45.

He frets within himself, with rage he burns,
Oft stops, wheels round, yet still the field forsakes;
At last so sudden on his foe he turns,
And with a spring like the uncoiling snake's,
At Dudon's side so fierce a thrust he makes,
That deep within, it bathes the griding blade,
And from the Chief all power of motion takes;

He falls; and his shut eyes, with pain o'erweighed,
An adamantine sleep and quietude invade.

46.

Thrice he unclosed them, and the sun's sweet light
Sought to enjoy; thrice on his arm arose,
And thrice fell back; then dark the veil of night
Involved his eyes, which, tired, for ever close.
His limbs relax; from all his members flows
A dead cold sweat; the pulses cease their play,
And sensibly an icy stiffness grows:
Upon the knight now dead, no idle stay
The fierce Argantes makes, but instant hies his way.

47.

Yet turning, as he speeds, his cruel eye
On his antagonists, he cries aloud:
"This falchion, streaming with so bright a dye,
Is that which yesterday your Prince bestowed!
Quick! be its quittance to his ear avowed;
Tell him what havoc it has done today;
Glad will he be to find a gift so proud,
Brought to its trial, stand the sharp assay;
How I must prize it, think,—how I have used it, say!

48.

"Tell him, that soon he may expect to see
In his own bowels proof of it more sure;
That if he hastes not to the battle, we
Will drag him from his tented coverture;"
The irritated Franks but ill endure
The brutal message and insulting call;
All pressed to charge him; but he passed secure
Beneath the favour of the guarded wall,
And reached the rest that fled, unhurt, unharmed of all.

49.

Then from the battlements of either tower,
A storm of stones obscured the sleety air,
And arrows, an immitigable shower,
Innumerable archers fulmine there
From the tough bow; the Christians pause,—they dare
No further press, but shrinking from the storm,
Perforce the relics of the Pagans spare;
'Twas then Rinaldo showed his martial form,
Freed from his fallen horse, as Jove's red lightnings warm.

50.

He came, on the barbaric homicide
Slain Dudon's debt with usury to repay,
And to his pausing troops sublimely cried,
"What wait you for? what means this base delay?
Slain is the gallant lord, your Chieftain, — say,
What is it stays you? what is it appals?
Forward this instant, and the town essay!
What! when so great a cause for vengeance calls,
Shall we be held in check by these weak mouldering walls?

51.

"No! though with adamant each charmed tower
Were flanked, or triply fenced with stubborn steel,
Safe in its pale the' assassin should not cower,
But the full measure of your vengeance feel;
On! on!" and seconding the high appeal
By instant action, to the walls, before
All else he rushes; in his ardent zeal
Scorning with guarded head the shower and roar
Of stones, and shafts, and darts, that from the engines pour.

52.

He shakes his sable plumes, he lifts his face,
So full of fierce resolve, that it enchains
The energies of all who guard the place, —
An icy fear runs thrilling through their veins
While thus the seized advantage he maintains,
And those to menace seeks, and these to cheer,
In rushes one who his desire restrains;
Godfrey has sent to them the good Sigièr,
Of his discreet commands the' executor severe:

53.

Who in his reverenced name commands them back,
And chides a step so rash and so absurd:
"This is no time," he cries, "for the attack;
Godfrey recalls you from the risk incurred.
Back! back!" Rinaldo, who the rest had spurred
To the near danger, thus compelled to yield,
Slowly receded, uttering not a word,
But inly chafed, and outwardly revealed
More than one pregnant sign of anger, ill concealed.

54.

Unharassed of the foe, by due degrees,
The Franks bore off, and full of sorrow paid
The last sad rites and solemn offices
Due to the person of the noble dead;

Borne in their pious arms, his friends conveyed
The sacred weight along, — whilst on the height
Of fair Mount Olivet, the Duke surveyed
The city's strength, appliances, and site;
Rampire, and battled crag, and fastness shaped for fight.

55.

On two bold hills Jerusalem is seen,
Of size unequal, face to face opposed;
A wide and pleasant valley lies between,
Dividing hill from hill; three sides the coast
Lies craggy, difficult, and high, disposed
In steep acclivities; the fourth is cast
In gentlest undulations, and enclosed
By walls of height insuperable and vast,
That seem to brave the sky, and face the Arctic blast.

56.

Cisterns for rain, canals, and living fountains
Make glad the thirsting city; but around,
Barren, and bare, and naked are the mountains,
And scarce one solitary flower is found
To blossom near: no sylvans, sun-embrowned,
Shut out the fervid noon; no valley shines
With lapse of lakes, nor falling waters sound;
One forest yet the blue horizon lines,
Black with the baleful shades of cypresses and pines.

57.

Here, toward the regions of the orient day,
The stately Jordan leads its happy wave;
There, where the solemn sunset fades away,
A sandy shore Levantine billows lave;
North, with Samaria Bethel stands, which gave
Fires to the Golden Calf, of hell beguiled;
And last, where Auster from his southern cave
Let loose the showery winds and tempests wild,
Bethlehem, whose matron lap received the Heaven-born Child.

58.

Now as the Chief the city's walls espied —
Its strength, its site — and in his wisdom weighed
Where best he could encamp, and on which side
The hostile towers might safest be essayed,
To Aladine divine Erminia said,
Her eager finger pointing to the place;
"That Godfrey is, in purple robes arrayed!
Observe, with what a military grace
He moves! august his port, and dignified his pace!

59.

"He of a truth was born for empire: yes!
So well he knows to govern and command;
Great as a general, as a knight no less,
Sceptre and sword were fashioned to his hand!
I know not one of all that countless band,
More warlike, or more wise; Raymond the sage,
Perhaps in counsel by his side might stand,
Rinaldo, Tancred equal warfare wage,
These from their sprightlier youth, and Raymond from his age."

60.

"Him," the king answered, "I remember well:
I saw him at the splendid Court of France,
When envoy there from Egypt, and could tell
How gallantly in joust he bore his lance;
And though his years, which then did scarce advance
Beyond gay boyhood, had begun to grave
No manly lines in his smooth cheek, his glance,
Bold deeds, reflective mind, and semblance brave,
Of loftiest hopes e'en then a certain presage gave.

61.

"Too sure, alas!" and here his troubled eyes
He cast to earth, till gathering voice, he said:
"But who is he that as an equal vies
With him, in mantle of resplendent red?
How like in form and visage! e'en his tread
Betrays a strange similitude, though less
I deem his stature:" "That," rejoined the maid,
"Is Baldwin, like in aspect and address,
But brother most in soul and princely nobleness.

62.

"Now mark the man near Godfrey, in the guise
Of an adviser; he deserves all praise!
That is Earl Raymond, prudent, close, and wise,
Of reverend tresses white with length of days;
Such politic manœuvres none displays—
Latin or Frank—in battle to o'erwhelm,
Or to deceive; but he that blinds our gaze,
The sunshine playing on his gilded helm,
Is William, the young hope of Britain's distant realm.

63.

"With him is Guelph, in rich estates, high blood,
And thirst for honour equal with the best;
I know him well by his firm attitude,
By his broad shoulders and dilated chest:

But my chief foe, for whom in eager quest
I have so long looked round, I nowhere see,
Fell Bohemond, the' assassin! he oppressed
My subjects, slew my sire, and left to me
No joy but that of tears, no friends but Heaven and thee!"

64.

Thus commune they; whilst, having well surveyed
The City, Bouillon joined his hosted train,
And as he judged that battery and scalade
On all sides else would be assayed in vain,—
Against the Northern Gate, on the near plain
Fixing his standard, he encamps; and thence
His quartered troops extending, till they gain
The Corner Tower, the whole vast field presents
One long continuous scene of equipage and tents.

* * * *

CANTO IV

ARGUMENT

The Prince of Darkness in the realms below
His powers assembles, and in grief and rage
From Orcus lets them loose, a war of woe
With all their art against the Franks to wage.
By them incited, Idraote the Sage
Burns with ambition, and in flattering style
Studies Armida's influence to engage;
Urged, she proceeds to smooth by her sweet smile
His way,—her only arms, wit, beauty, youth, and guile.

1.

Whilst thus in fervent toil the artisan
His warlike engines framed, of largest size,
To storm the city, the grand foe of man
Against the Christians turned his livid eyes;
And seeing them in glad societies,
On the new works successfully engaged,
Bit both his lips for fury, and in sighs
And bellowings, like a wounded bull enraged,
Roared forth his inward grief, and envy unassuaged.

2.

Then, having run through every mode of thought
To work them sharpest ills, he gave command
That all his angels should make swift resort
To his imperial court, a horrid band!
As though it were a trivial thing to stand
(O fool!) the' antagonist of God, and spite
His will divine! unmindful of the hand

That, thundering thro' all space, from heaven's blessed height
Hurled him of yore down — down to Tartarus and Night.

3.

Its hoarse alarm the Stygian trumpet sounded
Through the dark dwellings of the damned; the vast
Tartarean caverns tremblingly rebounded,
Blind air rebellowing to the dreary blast:
Hell quaked with all its millions: never cast
The' ethereal skies a discord so profound,
When the red lightning's vivid flash was past;
Nor ever with such tremors rocked the ground,
When in its pregnant womb conflicting fires were bound.

4.

The Gods of the Abyss in various swarms
From all sides to the yawning portals throng,
Obedient to the signal — frightful forms,
Strange to the sight, unspeakable in song!
Death glares in all their eyes; some prance along
On horny hoofs, — some, formidably fair,
Whose human faces have the viper's tongue,
And hissing snakes for ornamental hair,
Ride forth on dragon folds that lash the lurid air.

5.

There might you hear the Harpy's clangorous brood,
The Python's hiss, the Hydra's wailing yell,
Mad Scylla barking in her greedy mood,
And roaring Polypheme, the pride of hell;
Pale Gorgons, savage Sphinxes, Centaurs fell,
Geryons, Chimeras breathing flakes of fire,
Figures conceptionless, innumerable,
Multiform shapes conjoined in monsters dire,
To the vast halls of Dis in hideous troops aspire.

6.

They took their stations right and left around
The grisly king; he, cruel of command,
Sate in the midst of them, and sourly frowned,
The huge, rough sceptre waving in his hand.
No Alpine crag, terrifically grand,
No rock at sea in size with him could vie;
Calpe, and Atlas soaring from the sand,
Seemed to his stature little hills, so high
Reared he his horned front in that Tartarean sky.

7.

A horrid majesty in his fierce face
Struck deeper terror, and increased his pride;

His bloodshot eyeballs were instinct with rays
That like a baleful comet, far and wide,
Their fatal splendor shed on every side;
In rough barbaric grandeur his hoar beard
Flowed to his breast, and like the gaping tide
Of a deep whirlpool his grim mouth appeared,
When he unclosed his jaws, with foaming gore besmeared.

8.

His breath was like those sulphurous vapours born
In thunder, stench, and the live meteor's light,
When red Vesuvius showers, by earthquakes torn,
O'er sleeping Naples in the dead of night
Funereal ashes! whilst he spoke, affright
Hushed howling Cerebus, the Hydra's shriek;
Cocytus paused in its lamenting flight;
The' abysses trembled; horror chilled each cheek;
And these the words they heard the fallen Archangel speak.

9.

"Princes of Hell! but worthier far to fill
In Heaven, whence each one sprang, his diamond throne;
Ye, who with me were hurled from the blest hill,
Where brighter than the morning-star we shone,
To range these frightful dungeons! ye have known
The ancient jealousies and fierce disdains
That goaded us to battle; overthrown,
We are judged rebels, and besieged with pains,
Whilst o'er his radiant hosts the happy victor reigns.

10.

"And for the' ethereal air, serene and pure,
The golden sun, and starry spheres, his hate
Has locked us in this bottomless obscure,
Forbidding bold ambition to translate
Our spirits to their first divine estate:
Then, ah the bitter thought! 'tis this which aye
Stings me to madness, — then did he create
The vile worm man, that thing of reptile clay,
To fill our vacant seats in those blue fields of day.

11.

"Nor this sufficed: to spite us more, he gave
His only Son, his darling to the dead;
He came, he burst hell's gates, and from the grave,
Compassed our kingdoms with audacious tread;
The souls in torment doomed to us, he led
Back to the skies — his richly-ransomed throng;
And, in our teeth, hell's conquered ensigns spread,

Abroad on heaven's bright battlements uphung,
The whilst ten thousand saints their halleluiahs sung.

12.

"But why renew afflictions so severe,
By numbering up our wrongs, already known!
When, or on what occasion did ye hear
He paused in wrath, and left his works undone?
No more o'er past indignities I run,
But present injuries and future shame—
Shall we pass these? Alas! we cannot shun
The consciousness, that now his envious aim
Is the wide nations round from darkness to reclaim.

13.

"What! shall we pass in sloth the days and hours,
Cherish no wrath-born lightnings in our veins,
But leave his principalities and powers
To reap fresh laurels on the Asian plains?
To lead Judea in their servile chains,
And spread his worshipped name from clime to clime?
Sound it in other tongues, in other strains,
And on fresh columns sculpture it sublime,
To teach the future age, and mock almighty Time?

14.

"Must then our glorious idols be o'erthrown?
Our altars change to his? our temples nod?
Gold, incense, vows, be paid to him alone,
And Baäl bow before the shrine of God?
In the high Groves where erst we made abode
Must priest, nor charm, nor oracle remain?
And shall the myriad spirits who bestowed
Tribute on us, that tribute now disdain,
And o'er dispeopled realms abandoned Pluto reign?

15.

"No! for our essences are yet the same,
The same our pride, our prowess, and our power,
As when with sharp steel and engirding flame,
In godlike battle we withstood the flower
Of heaven's archangels: we in evil hour
Were foiled, I grant; but partial chance, not skill,
Gave them the victory;—still we scorned to cower;
Victory was theirs, but an unconquered will
Nobly remained to us—it fires our spirits still!

16.

"Why longer then delay! arise, take wing,
My hope, my strength, my trusty cohorts, fly;

Plagues and swift ruin on these Christians bring,
Ere reinforced by any fresh ally;
Haste! quench the spreading flame of chivalry,
Ere in its blaze Judea all unites;
Your arts exert, your strong temptations ply;
Enter at will among their armed knights,
Now practise open force, and now use secret sleights.

17.

"Let what I will, be fate; give some to rove
In exile, some in battle to be slain;
Let some, abandoned to a lawless love,
Make woman's smiles and frowns their joy and pain,
And brilliant eyes their idols; let some stain
Their swords in civil strife; let some engage
In crimes against their Chief; let murder reign
With treason, rage with murder, hate with rage;
So perish all — priest, king, prince, noble, serf, and sage!"

18.

Ere yet the Anarch closed his fierce harangue,
His rebel angels on swift wings were flown,
Glad to revisit the pure light; — a clang
Of pinions passed, and he was left alone.
As in their deep Eolian grottoes moan
The Spirits of the storm — as forth they sweep,
Or ere the signal of the winds is blown,
With howling sound, high carnival to keep,
And in wild uproar all embroil both land and deep; —

19.

So the loosed Fiends o'er valley, wave, and hill,
Spreading their nimble wings, themselves dispersed;
Solicitous to frame, with demon-skill,
New-fancied snares, and urge their arts accursed:
But say, sweet Muse! of various ills, what first
Their malice wrought, and by what agents, say;
Thou know'st it; Fame the tidings has rehearsed,
But in the gloom remote of times grown grey,
Long ere it reach our ear, her weak voice melts away.

20.

A mighty wizard in Damascus reigned,
Prince Idraotes; who from childhood pored
O'er dark divining volumes, till he gained
The potent knowledge which his soul adored;
But what availed his whole collected hoard
Of signs and charms, if he could not foretel
The war's uncertain issues? his search soared

To heaven — no star, no planet owned the spell,
Nor would one parleying ghost divulge the truth from hell.

21.

And yet he thought (blind human wit, how vain
And crooked are thy thoughts!) that Heaven had blessed
The Paynim arms, and surely would ordain
Death to the' unconquered armies of the West;
He judged that Egypt from their grasp would wrest
The palm of war, and from the dazzling game
Depart a winning victor, and impressed
With this delusive hope, resolved to claim
Part in the grand award of conquest, wealth, and fame.

22.

But as their prowess drew his high esteem,
The war's vague chances he forbore to dare,
And long revolved how by some deep-laid scheme
The Christian princes he might best ensnare,
And by diminishing their strength, prepare
The path for Egypt; when, with ruin rife,
Her hosts the conquering sword abroad should bear;
His evil angel marked the mental strife,
Made quick the embryo thought, and pushed it into life.

23.

He framed the fraud, the counsel he inspired,
And made his purpose easy to pursue;
He had a niece, whose beauty was admired
Of the whole Orient, paralleled by few,
And to the echo vaunted; one who knew
Each fine discretion, each beguiling art
Of virgin and enchantress; her he drew
To his saloon, and thus to her apart,
In nectarous words made known the wishes of his heart.

24.

"Dear niece! that underneath these locks of gold,
And that fair face, so young yet so divine,
Dost hide a heart, wise, masculine, and bold,
And magic skill transcendent over mine,—
I nurse a mighty project: the design
But needs thy gentle guidance to commend
My hopes to sure success; the thread I twine,
Weave thou the web, the lively colours blend;
What cautious Age begins let dauntless Beauty end.

25.

"Go to the hostile camp; weep, tremble, sigh,
Each female charm that lures to love employ;

Let the lips aid the witchcraft of the eye,
Smiles flash through tears, and grief despond in joy:
Now shrink from notice, now with prayers annoy;
In weeping beauty o'er the wise prevail;
Go! storm the' obdurate bosom, win the coy,
In seeming truth clothe fiction's specious tale,
And with deep maiden shame thy bold advances veil.

26.

"First, if thou canst, take Godfrey in the thrall
Of thy sweet looks and amiable address,
Till his soul sickens at the trumpet's call,
And the world's war dissolves in a caress;
But if this feat surpass thy skill, possess
His bravest nobles, and in friendship's guise
Transport them to some boundless wilderness,
Ne'er to return:" — he opens his device,
And adds — "All means our faith — our country sanctifies!"

27.

Armida, in her youth and beauty's pride,
Assumed the' adventure, and at close of day,
Eve's vesper star her solitary guide,
Alone, untended, took her secret way.
In clustering locks and feminine array,
Armed but with loveliness and frolic youth,
She trusts to conquer mighty kings, and slay
Embattled hosts; meanwhile false rumors soothe
The light censorious crowd, sagacious of the truth.

28.

Few days elapsed, ere to her wishful view
The white pavilions of the Latins rise;
The camp she reached, — her wondrous beauty drew
The gaze and admiration of all eyes;
Not less than if some strange star in the skies,
Or blazing comet's more resplendent tire
Appeared; a murmur far before her flies,
And crowds press round, to listen or inquire
Who the fair pilgrim is, and soothe their eyes' desire.

29.

Never did Greece or Italy behold
A form to fancy and to taste so dear!
At times, the white veil dims her locks of gold,
At times, in bright relief they reappear:
So, when the stormy skies begin to clear,
Now through transparent clouds the sunshine gleams;

Now, issuing from its shrine, the gorgeous Sphere
Lights up the leaves, flowers, mountains, vales and streams,
With a diviner day — the spirit of bright beams.

30.

New ringlets form the flowing winds amid
The native curls of her resplendent hair;
Her eye is fixed in self-reserve, and hid
Are all Love's treasures with a miser's care;
The Rival Roses upon cheeks more fair
Than morning light, their mingling tints dispose;
But on her lips, from which the amorous air
Of paradise exhales, the crimson rose
Its sole and simple bloom in modest beauty throws.

31.

Crude as the grape unmellowed yet to wine,
Her bosom swells to sight; its virgin breasts,
Smooth, soft, and sweet, like alabaster shine,
Part bare, part hid by her invidious vests;
Their jealous fringe the greedy eye arrests,
But leaves its fond imagination free,
To sport, like doves, in those delicious nests,
And their most shadowed secrecies to see;
Peopling with blissful dreams the lively phantasy.

32.

As through pure water or translucent glass
The sunbeam darts, yet leaves the crystal sound,
So through her folded robes unruffling pass
The thoughts, to wander on forbidden ground:
There daring Fancy takes her fairy round,
Such wondrous beauties singly to admire;
Which, in a pleasing fit of transport bound,
She after paints and whispers to Desire,
And with her charming tale foments the' excited fire.

33.

Praised and admired Armida passed amid
The wishful multitudes, nor seemed to spy,
Though well she saw, the interest raised, but hid
In her deep heart the smile that to her eye
Darted in prescience of the conquests nigh:
Whilst in the mute suspense of troubled pride
She sought with look solicitous, yet shy,
For her uncertain feet an ushering guide
To the famed Captain's tent, young Eustace pressed her side.

34.

As the winged insect to the lamp, so he
Flew to the splendour of her angel face,
Too much indulgent of his wish to see
Those eyes which shame and modesty abase;
And, drawn within the fascinating blaze,
Gathering, like kindled flax, pernicious fire
From its resplendence, stupid for a space
He stood — till the bold blood of blithe desire
Did to his faltering tongue these few wild words inspire.

35.

"O Lady! if thy rank the name allow,
If shapes celestial answer to the call —
For never thus did partial Heaven endow
With its own light a daughter of the Fall, —
Say on what errand, from what happy hall,
Seek'st thou our camp? and if indeed we greet
In thee one of the tribes angelical,
Cause us to know — that we, as were most meet,
May bend to thee unblamed, and kiss thy saintly feet."

36.

"Nay," she replied, "thy praises shame a worth
Too poor to warrant such a bold belief;
Thou see'st before thee one of mortal birth,
Dead to all joy, and but alive to grief;
My harsh misfortunes urge me to your Chief, —
A foreign virgin in a timeless flight;
To him I speed for safety and relief,
Trusting that he will reassert my right:
So far resounds his fame, for mercy and for might.

37.

"But, if indulgent courtesy be thine,
To pious Godfrey give me strait access!"
"Yes, lovely pilgrim," he replied, "be mine
The task to guide thee in thy young distress:
Nor is my interest with our Chieftain less
Than what a brother may presume to vaunt;
Thy suit shall not be wanting in success;
Whate'er his sceptre or my sword can grant,
Shall in thy power be placed, to punish or supplant."

38.

He ceased, and brought her where, from the rude crowd
Apart, with captains and heroic peers,
Duke Godfrey sate; she reverently bowed,
A sweet shame mantling o'er her cheek, and tears

Stifling her speech: he reassured her fears,
Chid back the blush so beautifully bright,
Till, sweeter than the music of the spheres,
Their captive senses chaining in delight,
Her siren voice broke forth, and all were mute as Night.

39.

"Unconquered Prince!" she said, "whose name supreme
Flies through the world on such a radiant plume,
That kings and nations conquered by thee, deem
Their deed of vassalage a glorious doom,—
Well known thy valour shines, thy virtues bloom;
And whilst thy foes revere them and admire,
They, on their part, invite us to assume
The confidence we need, and to desire
Aid at thy hands, and aid requested to acquire.

40.

"Thus I, though nurtured in the faith you hate,
And strive to cancel from the world's wide page,
Hope to regain by thee my lost estate,
My sceptre, and ancestral heritage:
Others, oppressed by foreign force, engage
The succours of their kindred; I, alas!
Defrauded of their pity at an age
Which claims it most, against my kindred, pass,
And hostile arms invoke—the ghost of what I was!

41.

"To thee I call, on thee depend, for thou
Alone canst conquer back mine ancient crown;
Nor shouldst thou be less prompt to raise the low
Than on the proud to call destruction down;
Lovelier is Mercy's smile than Valour's frown,
A suppliant cherished than a foe undone:
And 'twere less glorious to thy just renown,
Whatever hazards in the task were run,
To lay whole realms in dust than thus relumine one.

42.

"But if our varying faiths—my Gentile creed—
Move thee to disregard my humble prayer,
Let my sure faith in thine indulgence plead
My cause, nor prove an illusory snare;
Lo! before universal Jove I swear—
God over all, from whom all empire flows,—
A juster quarrel never claimed thy care;
But listen! frauds, conspiracies, and foes,
Of these my story treats, a tale of many woes!

43.

"The daughter I of Arbilan, who reigned
In fair Damascus — less by birth made great
Than merit; Queen Cariclea he obtained
In marriage, and with her possessed the state:
Her death, alas! did almost antedate
My worthless life! I issued from the womb
As she expired; the self-same hour of fate,
(Oh birth too dearly bought! oh ill-starred doom!)
Me to the cradle gave, my mother to the tomb.

44.

"Five summer-suns had scarcely spent their fire,
Since Death's pale Angel called her to the skies,
Than, yielding to the lot of all, my sire
Rejoined her sainted shade in Paradise.
He left his brother, by his last devise,
Sole regent of the kingdom and of me;
Thinking that if the natural pieties
In mortal breast had mansion, they must be
Locked in his kindred heart with virtue's strictest key.

45.

"Thus then he played the tutor to my youth,
And with such show of kindness, that each wind
Voiced far and near his uncorrupted truth,
Paternal love, and bounty unconfined:
Whether the guilty movements of his mind
Beneath a flattering face he thought to hide,
Or that he then sincerely was inclined
To make me happy, as the destined bride
Of his ungracious son — 'twere idle to decide.

46.

"I grew in years, and with me grew his son;
But to no brave accomplishments, no store
Of sciences or arts could he be won,
He hated knightly deeds and princely lore:
Beneath a hideous countenance he bore
A baser soul, whilst pride and avarice
His heart pervaded to its inmost core;
Savage in manners, slave to drink and dice,
None but himself could be his paragon in vice.

47.

"And now it was that my kind guardian strove
To wed me with this ill-assorted thing,
A goodly gallant for a lady's love,
To charm as bridegroom, and to reign as king!

Rhetoric he used — he used address to bring
The ardent hopes with which his fancy swelled
To their vowed end, but never could he wring
From me the fatal promise, — I rebelled,
And all his golden lures disdainfully repelled.

48.

"At last he left me with a gloomy face,
His elvish heart transpicuous in his look;
Too well my future story could I trace
In the dire leaves of that prophetic book!
Thenceforth each night alarming visions shook
My slumbers, — in my ears strange outcries shrilled,
And phantoms frowned on me; my spirit took
The ghastly impress of their forms, and thrilled
With dread forebodings, since — how fatally fulfilled!

49.

"And oft my mother's piteous ghost appeared;
Ah! how unlike her smiling face portayed
In picture, loving, lovely, and endeared,
Now all illusion, and a pallid shade!
'Fly! oh my child, fly! fly!' the figure said,
'Instant death threatens thee, and swift as Light
Will the stroke fall; — the traitor's toils are laid; —
The poison in its gay glass sparkles bright:'
This said, it glided by, and melted into night.

50.

"But what, alas! availed it that my heart
Received this presage of the perils near,
When, unresolved to act the counselled part,
My sex and tender age gave way to fear!
To rove through deserts, woods, and mountains drear
In willing exile, — undefenced to go
From my paternal realm, seemed more severe
Than to yield up the struggle to my foe,
And there to close mine eyes where first they woke in woe.

51.

"I dreaded death; yet, (will it be believed?)
With death at hand, I durst not flee away;
I feared e'en lest my fear should be perceived,
And thus accelerate the fatal day:
Thus restless, thus disturbed, without one ray
Of comfort, I dragged on my wretched life,
In a perpetual fever of dismay;
Like the doomed victim, who, in thought's last strife,
Feels, ere the' assassin stabs, the' anticipated knife.

52.

"But, whether my good Genius ruled, or Fate
Preserved me yet for days of deeper gloom,
One of the noblest ministers of state,
Whose youth my sire had fostered, sought my room;
In brief disclosing that the hour of doom,
Fixed by the fiend, was now upon the wing;
That he himself had promised to assume
The murderous office, and the poison wring,
That night, in the sherbert my page was wont to bring.

53.

"Flight, he assured me, was my sole resource
In this my crisis of despair, and prayed
That since bereft of every other force,
I would accept his own effective aid:
His counsels, full of comfort, soon persuade
My undetermined spirit; to the wind
I gave my fears, and only now delayed
Till eve's grey veil the tell-tale light should blind,
To leave all that I loved and hated, far behind.

54.

"Night fell; an ebon darkness, more obscure
Than usual, its kind shadows round us spread,
When with two favourite maids I passed secure
The guarded palace, joined my guide, and fled:
But through the trembling tears I ceaseless shed,
Long looked I back on the receding towers,
Insatiate with the sight; all objects fed
My sorrow; each one spoke of happier hours,
The hills, the lamp-lit mosques, and hallowed cypress-bowers.

55.

"To them my looks, my thoughts, my sighs were given,
As on I speeded, malcontent though free;
I fared like an unanchored pinnace driven
From its loved port by whirlwinds far to sea:
All the long night and following day we flee,
By paths no human foot had ever pressed;
Till on the confines of my realm we see
Its last baronial seat, — there, tired, we rest,
Just as the sun's slow orb forsook the fulgent west.

56.

"It was the castle of the generous knight,
Arontes, who had made my life his care;
But when the baffled traitor by our flight
Perceived I had escaped the mortal snare,

His rage flamed forth against us both; and ere
I could arraign him, intricate in ill,
Gathering a fresh presumption from despair,
He charged on us his own all-evil will,—
The selfsame crime which he was studious to fulfil.

57.

"He said I had the false Arontes bribed
To mix destroying poisons in his bowl,
Impatient of the maxims he prescribed
To curb my lust, that free from all control
I might pursue the bias of my soul,
And with voluptuous blandishments commend
My beauty to a thousand youths: — Skies! roll
Your thunders, let avenging fires descend,
Ere I thy sacred laws, blest Chastity, offend!

58.

"That avarice and ambition, pride and pique
Urge him to shed my guiltless blood, must claim
Grief and alarm; but that the wretch should seek
To fix dishonour on my spotless name,
Goes to my heart: he, fearing now the flame
Of popular rage, with smooth-tongued eloquence,
Forges a thousand falsehoods to my shame;
So that the city fluctuates in suspense
Betwixt the guilt of both, nor arms in my defence.

59.

"Yea, though he sits on mine authentic throne,
Though my tiara sparkles on his brow,
Dominion spurs him but more keenly on
To work me farther injury, shame, and woe:
With fire and sword he threatens to o'erthrow
Arontes in his fortress, if in chains
He yield not, and on me denounces now
Not merely war, but stripes and fearful pains,
Whilst flows one drop of blood in my rebellious veins.

60.

"This — under colour of a lively zeal
To purge away the stains of my disgrace,
And to its ancient purity anneal
The golden sceptre which my crimes debase!
But the true motive is a wish to place
His claims beyond dispute: whilst I remain
Heir to the crown, he fears no plea can grace
His kingly usurpation, so is fain
To build upon my death the basis of his reign.

61.

"And e'en such end awaits his fell desire;
He must enjoy what he is fixt to gain,
And in my heart's blood quench the boundless ire
Which all my tears were powerless to restrain,
If thou, alas, my suppliant prayer disdain!
To thee — a wretched girl, weak, innocent,
Orphaned — I fly; must my sad tears in vain
Fall on thy holy robes? relent! relent!
Oh, by the knees I grasp, forbid his fierce intent!

62.

"By these thy feet, that on the proud and strong
Triumphantly have trod; by thy right hand;
By thy past victories, a choral throng!
And by the temples of this sacred land,
Freed by the sword, or to be freed, — withstand,
Thou only canst, his merciless decree;
My crown, my life preserve, secure, command,
Merciful Sire! but vain is mercy's plea,
If first religious right and justice move not thee.

63.

"Beloved of Heaven! thou destined to desire
That which is just, and thy desires achieve,
Save me! my kingdom thou wilt thus acquire,
Which I in fief shall thankfully receive;
Let ten of these heroic champions leave
The camp beneath my conduct; their renown,
Spread through the city, will my cause retrieve,
Will win my faithful people to strike down
With ease the man of crime, and repossess my crown.

64.

"Yea, more: a Noble to whose keeping falls
A secret gate, has promised me access,
At dead of night, to my paternal halls;
But some small aid he counselled me to press:
The least, the least thou grantest to redress
The grievances I suffer, will inflame
His hopes with surer prospects of success,
Than if from other kings whole squadrons came,
So high he ranks thy flag, so high thy simple name!"

65.

She ceased; but still her mute imploring eye
Spoke eloquence beyond the reach of prayer;
Doubtful alike to grant as to deny,
A thousand various thoughts, absorbed in care,

Godfrey revolved; he feared some Gentile snare
Couched in her tears, some ambuscade of art;
He knew who kept not faith with God, would dare
Break league with man; still pity pleads her part,
Pity — which never sleeps within a noble heart.

66.

His native ruth inspires the wish that she
Deserved the grace; and policy on ruth
Succeeding, whispers it were wise to free,
And fix in rich Damascus one whose truth,
Enforced by the dependency of youth,
May much avail him, with her feudal arms,
The course of his sublime designs to smooth, —
To minister supplies against the' alarms
Of Egypt's mustered tribes and tributary swarms.

67.

Whilst thus from wavering thought to thought he flies,
Revolves, and re-revolves, the eager maid
Fixed on his downcast face her pleading eyes,
And its least workings breathlessly surveyed;
And when his answer longer was delayed
Than she had hoped, she trembled, drooped, and sighed;
Her quivering lips the heart's alarm betrayed;
Pale grew her face: at length the Prince replied,
And in these courteous words mildly her suit denied.

68.

"If God's own quarrel had not claimed these swords,
Now oath-bound to his cause, thy hopes might rest
Thereon in perfect trust, — not pitying words,
But valid actions had thy wrongs redressed;
But whilst his heritage is thus oppressed
Beneath the harsh rod of a tyrant king,
How can we grant, fair Lady, thy request?
Divided hosts declining fortunes bring,
And check the flowing tide of victory in its spring.

69.

"But this I promise, — firmly may'st thou trust
The word I pledge, and live secure from fear, —
If e'er we conquer from a yoke unjust
These towers, to Heaven and piety so dear,
To pity's voice I will incline mine ear,
Thee on thy lost throne to exalt; but now,
No pitying sympathies must interfere
To cancel what to the Most High we owe,
And for a mortal's sake dissolve our solemn vow."

70.

At this the mournful Princess drooped her head,
And stirless stood, as Niobe of yore;
Then raised her eyes, impearled, to heaven, and said,
Whilst all the woman at their founts ran o'er —
"Lost! lost! O skies! O stars! what evils more
Do ye prescribe? did ever one fulfil
A doom so harsh, so merciless before!
Woe's me! all natures change; the world grows chill;
I only vary not, immutable in ill!

71.

"Now farewell hope! now welcome misery!
All prayer in human breasts has lost its force;
Am I to hope the tears that touch not thee
Will move the barbarous tyrant with remorse? —
Yet, though denied this pitiful resource,
With no reproach thy rigour shall be paid;
It is my Genius I accuse — the source
Of all my ills, — my Genius, who has made
Godfrey's a ruthless heart, — 't is him that I upbraid.

72.

"Not to thee, gracious Chieftain! not to thee
Lay I this crime, but to imperious Fate;
Oh, that her active tyranny would free
My weary spirit from a world I hate!
Was 't not enough, stern Power, to dedicate
Mother and sire e'en in their morn of life
To the dark grave, that from my high estate
Thou hast now tossed me on this sea of strife,
And given thy victim bound and blinded to the knife!

73.

"Now holy sanctitude and maiden shame
Urge me to go, but whither shall I fly?
There is no refuge for a blighted name;
Earth holds no spot beneath the boundless sky
So secret, but the tyrant's active eye
Will find it, and transpierce me; but — I go;
The Angel of Death approaching I descry;
Nought now is left but to forestal his blow;
None but Armida's arm shall lay Armida low!"

74.

She ceased: a generous and majestice scorn
Fired all her features to a rose-like red,
And then she made as she would have withdrawn,
With grief and anger in her farewell tread:

Her eyes, 'twixt sorrow and resentment, shed
Tears thick as summer's heat-drops — tears, that shine,
With the sun's golden rays athwart them spread,
Like falling pearls, like crystals argentine,
Or sparkling opal-drops from some far Indian mine.

75.

Her fresh cheeks, sprinkled with those living showers,
Which to her vesture's hem, down gliding, cling,
Appear like snowy and vermilion flowers
Humid with May-dews, when romantic Spring,
In shadow of the green leaves whispering,
Spreads their closed bosoms to the amorous air;
Flowers, to which sweet Aurora oft takes wing,
Which with gay hand she culls with such fond care
In morn's melodious prime, to bind her vagrant hair.

76.

But the clear drops that, thick as stars of night,
On those fair cheeks and on that heaving breast
So shine, have all the' effect of fire, and light
A secret flame in each beholder's breast:
O Love! the marvellous rod by thee possessed,
For ever powerful over Nature, draws
Lightning from tears, and gives to grief a zest
Beyond the bliss of smiles; but nature's laws
Its magic far transcends, in this thy darling's cause.

77.

Her feigned laments from roughest warriors call
Sincerest tears; — their hearts to her incline;
Each is afflicted at her grief, and all
At Godfrey's speech thus whisperingly repine:
"Surely he made the vext sea-roaring brine
His nursing cradle, and wild wolves that rave
On the chill crags of some rude Apennine,
Gave his youth suck: oh, cruel as the grave,
Who could view charms like hers, and not consent to save!"

78.

But Eustace, in whose young and generous blood
Pity and love flowed strongest, whilst the rest
But murmured and were silent, forward stood,
And dauntlessly his brother thus addressed:
"My Lord! far too inflexibly thy breast
Keeps to the firmness of its first design,
If to the common voice which would obtest
Thy clemency, thou dost not now incline;
Reverent of mercy's claims and quality divine.

79.

"Think not I urge the princedoms and the powers
Who rank dependent tribes beneath their care,
To turn their arms from these assieged towers,
And the first duties of the camp forswear;
But, warriors of adventure, we, who bear
Nor feudal flag nor delegated trust,
Who act without restriction, well may spare
At thy wise choice, and in a cause most just,
Ten guardian knights to one so helpless, so august.

80.

"Know, he assists the cause of God, who toils
The rights of outraged virgins to maintain;
And precious in his sight must be the spoils
Which freemen hang in Freedom's holy fane,
The glorious trophies of a tyrant slain:
Though then no interest counselled to the deed,
Duty would urge, and Knighthood would constrain
Me to assist the damsel in her need,
And without scruple go, where'er her voice may lead.

81.

"Oh, by yon bright sun, tell it not in France!
Publish it not where courtesy is dear!
That of our nobles none would break a lance
In Beauty's quarrel, let not Europe hear!
Henceforth, my lord, sword, corslet, helm, and spear,
I toss aside, and bid farewell to fame;
No generous steed shall bear me in career
With swordless chiefs, where Chivalry weds Shame,—
I will no longer bear the knight's degraded name!"

82.

Thus spoke the youth, and all his Order there
Applausive murmured in loud unison;
Praised his good counsel, and with urgent prayer
Closed round their Captain on his ducal throne.
"I yield," at length he said, "but yield alone
To the desire of numbers, since the plea
Is one my private judgment would disown;
Grant we her boon, if such your pleasure be;
But know the' advice is yours, it not proceeds from me:

83.

"And, far as Godfrey's counsel can persuade,
Temper your sympathies, be closely wise:"
He said no more, it was enough,—they paid
The kind concession with delighted cries.

What cannot Beauty, when her pleading eyes
From their deep fountains shower down tears of pain,
And to her amorous tongue sweet speeches rise?
From her divine lips glides a golden chain,
That wins to her dear will who most those tears disdain.

84.

Eustace recalled her, took her passive hand,
And said, "Now cease, dear Lady, to repine;
The utmost succours that thy fears demand,
(Weep not) shall all, and speedily be thine:"
Then the dark aspect of her face grew fine,—
With her white veil she wiped the tears away,
And gave a smile so brilliant and benign,
You would have thought the' enamoured God of Day
In sunshine kissed the lips whose lustre shamed his ray.

85.

And in her sweet voice and pathetic tone,
She gave them thanks for their exceeding grace;
Saying it should to the wide world be known,
And ever and forever have a place
Within her grateful heart: her working face,
And gestures with impassioned meanings fraught,
Told what the tongue was powerless to express;
Thus masking in false smiles the end she sought,
Her varied web of guile she unsuspected wrought.

86.

Who but Armida now exults to see
How fortune and kind fate the fraud befriend?
Who o'er each dark suggestion broods, but she,
To bring the plot to a successful end?
With beauty and sweet flatteries to transcend
Whate'er Medea's witchcraft e'er designed,
Or Circe's incantations wrought,—to blend
Mischief with mirth, and the most watchful mind
As in Elysian sleep with siren songs to bind?

87.

All arts the' enchantress practised to beguile
Some new admirer in her well-spread snare;
Nor used with all, nor always the same wile,
But shaped to every taste her grace and air;
Here cloistered is her eye's dark pupil, there
In full voluptuous languishment is rolled;
Now these her kindness, those her anger bear,
Spurred on or checked by bearing frank or cold,
As she perceived her slave was scrupulous or bold.

88.

If she marked some too bashful to advance,
Sick if unnoticed, diffident if seen,
Forth flew her radiant smile, her thrilling glance,
Sunny as summer and as eve serene:
Thus reassured, their dying hopes grow keen;
The faint belief, the languishing desire
Reviving brighten in their eager mien;
Those looks a thousand amorous thoughts inspire,
And Fear's pale frost-work melts in Fancy's lively fire.

89.

If some make bold to press her virgin palm,
Too rashly building on her former cheer,
She grows a miser of her eye's mild charm,
Spares her fond smile, and frowns them into fear;
But through the wrath that fires her front austere,
And ruffles her sweet cheek, they may discern
Rays of forgiving pity reappear;
Thus do they droop, but not despair, and yearn
Towards her in deepest love when she appears most stern.

90.

Sometimes in lonely places she dissembled
Deep grief — the voice, the action, and the tread;
And oft when in her eye the loose tear trembled,
Crushed, or reclaimed it to the fountain-head.
Soon as those tragic gestures were ared,
A thousand striplings, vanquished by her art,
Would come and weep around her: Envy fed
Their frenzy; and Love, tempering his keen dart
In Pity's scalding tears, shot torture through the heart.

91.

Anon she starts from her abstraction, wakes
With hope's fresh whispers to her spirit; seeks
Her many lovers, talks to them, and shakes
The bright locks on her brow for joy, that speaks
Life to her lips, and to her glowing cheeks
New smiles; her eyes then sparkle as in scorn
Of their late griefs, — as when Apollo streaks
With fire the opening eyelids of the morn,
And every darkening cloud to distance has withdrawn.

92.

But whilst she sweetly speaks and sweetly smiles,
And with this twofold sweetness lulls the sense,
She from its blissful cage well-nigh exiles
The soul, unused to rapture so intense;

Ah cruel Love! whether thy hand dispense,
Wreathed with the cypress or the lotos-leaf,
Thy gall or nectar-cup, its quintessence
Maddens with ecstasy, or blights with grief;
Fatal thy sickness is, and fatal thy relief!

93.

Through all these shifting tempers, whilst each knight
Fluctuates disturbed, uncertain of her choice,
Through fire and frost, smiles, tears, fear, hope, delight,
The beauteous witch his agony enjoys:
If any e'er presumes with trembling voice
To tell his secret pain, her guilefulness
The glorious vision of his soul destroys;
She nor perceives his meaning, nor can guess,—
The very fool of Love and frank unconsciousness.

94.

Or, casting down to ground her bashful eyes,
The blush of honour o'er her face she throws,
So that the alabaster white, which lies
In sweet confusion underneath the rose
That her celestial cheek irradiates, glows
Like the rich crimson on Aurora's face,
When from the Orient first her form she shows;
And the red flush of anger keeping pace
With shame, combines to shed round shame a sweeter grace.

95.

But if she one perceives resolved to' avow
His warm desire, she stops her charmed ears;
Now shuns his converse, grants an audience now,
Then flies, returns, smiles, frowns, and disappears:
Thus in a war of wishes, sighs, and tears,
In vain pursuit he wastes his life away;
And with deluding hopes, afflicting fears,
Fares like the hunter who at dying day
Has lost in pathless woods all traces of his prey.

96.

These were the arts by which Armida took
A thousand spirits captive to her sleight,
Or rather, these the arms, with which she strook,
And made them bondslaves in their own despite.
What marvel elder Love subdued the might
Of Theseus fierce, and Hercules the strong;
When those who drew the sword in Jesu's right,
Soothed by a siren's smile,—a siren's song,
Wore his enfeebling chains, and gloried in the wrong!

CANTO VI

ARGUMENT

Argantes dares the Franks to single fight;
His prowess first the' undaunted Otho shows,
Too rashly; tumbled from his steed, by right
Of martial law he into thraldom goes.
Tancred, whom Godfrey for his champion chose,
Renews the conflict, and his falchion plies
Till twilight's gathering glooms a truce impose;
To cure her wounded lord, Erminia hies
From the well-guarded town, at dew-fall, in disguise.

1.

But better hopes inspirit and make blithe
The hearts of the besieged: beside the grain
Stored from the reaping sickle and the scythe,
Beneath night's favouring darkness they obtain
Fresh stores; and flank, and fortify amain
With engines and grim frieze the Northern wall;
Which, grown to giant height, seems to disdain
The shock of brazen rams, as idle all,
Nor dreads what man can do to work its purposed fall.

2.

Yet still at morn, at eve, at radiant noon,
The Monarch higher gives his towers to soar;
Nor quits his labour when the stars and moon
Silver the dusk of night; and evermore,
New arms for battle forging to the roar
Of sweltering fires, armourer and artisan
Toil with strong limbs, till vigour be no more.
As thus the' intolerable moments ran,
To him Argantes came, and boastful thus began:

3.

"How long in these vile walls must we be bound,
Rebellious prisoners, tamed by slow blockade?
I hear the clang of anvils; the shrill sound
From hauberk, helm, and shield, my ears invade;
But to what purpose is the proud parade?
These robbers at their license don the crest;
Scour all our fields; our palaces invade;
Yet none of us their progress dare molest,
Or one clear trumpet sound, to scare their golden rest.

4.

"Them the gay lute and bounding dance employ,
Unbroken banquets and secure delights;
Their day is one long carnival of joy,
And ease and quiet crown their blissful nights:
But thou at length, when fiercely famine bites,
Conquered must fall, and with submission buy
The victor's insults and the foe's despites;
Or die without a blow, as cowards die,
If Cairo send not soon our lingering, late ally.

5.

"Ne'er o'er the dial of my life shall run
The oblivious darkness of a death it hates;
Not e'en the lustre of another sun
Shall see me shut within these cursed gates!
With this, my life's poor fragment, let the Fates
Do what is fixed for it in heaven or hell;
None e'er shall say in these inglorious straits,
That with his sword in sheath Argantes fell;
He will revenge disgrace, and earn his tomb too well.

6.

"But if one spark of thy first chivalry
Still in thy bosom shed its fervent charm,
I should not hope in noble strife to die,
But live, enriched with honour's proudest palm;
With one accord let us resolve to arm,
Confront the Christians, and the field contest;
How oft in deepest peril and alarm,
The most audacious strokes have proved the best;
And ills which Care increased, Distraction has redressed!

7.

"But if thou dread'st to play so bold a game;
If to stake all thy forces to decide
The war at once, be judged a frantic aim,—
At least in duel let the strife be tried:
And that with livelier willingness and pride
The Captain of the Franks may entertain
Our challenge, and the' arbitrement abide,
Let him choose arms, take vantage of the plain,
And fix the terms of fight as he himself may deign.

8.

"Then, if no hundred-handed Briareus
Arm on his side, how fierce soe'er he be,
Dread not that evil chance thy cause will lose,
Upheld by justice, and secured by me;

In place of fate and fortune's blind decree,
My strong right hand shall from the stars pluck down
Consummate conquest for thy realms and thee:
Grasp it in pledge; now, by my old renown,
Trust me, they shall not shake one jewel from thy crown!"

9.

He ceased, and Aladine replied: "In truth,
Though Age my pristine vigour has defaced,
Think not this scrupulous hand, too fervent youth,
A traitor to the sword it once embraced;
Think not my spirit slothful or debased;
Sooner with honour by the sword or spear
Would I expire, than die a death disgraced;
If I could entertain misdoubt or fear
That the distressful ills, announced, were really near.

10.

"Allah such shame avert! What deep my art
From others hides, to thee shall now be shown:
The mighty Solyman, who burns in part
To' avenge the loss of his Nicean throne,
Has roused Arabia from her utmost zone
Of sand to Alcaïro, and relies
On all her tribes, when once his trumpet's blown,
In the black night the foeman to surprise,
And pour into the town fresh succour and supplies.

11.

"Soon will he join us; if meanwhile they reign
In our spoiled castles, blinded by conceit
And careless ease, fret not, whilst I retain
My purple mantle and imperial seat;
But that rash courage and intemperate heat
Which hurries thee to such excess, abate;
And for a dignified occasion, meet
For thy renown and my deep vengeance, wait;—
Soon the black storm will burst, and lightnings seal their fate."

12.

The haughty Pagan frowned at this: high pride
And bitter spite boiled in his breast, to hear
How on this Nicene prince the king relied,
His ancient rival and most fierce compeer:
"Sir," he replied, in icy tone austere,
"'T is thy undoubted right to wage or end
War at thy pleasure; I have done; wait here
The shivered sword of Solyman thy friend;
Let him who lost his own thy kingdoms safe defend.

13.

"Proud as a patron God let him advance
To free thy people from their yoke abhorred;
Myself am my palladium 'gainst mischance,
Nor freedom ask but from this single sword.
But whilst the rest repose, the grace accord,
That I at least may my own wrongs requite;
That from the town descending to the sward,
Not as thy champion but a private knight,
I may at least engage the Franks in single fight."

14.

The king replied, "Although thou shouldst reserve
Thy sword and anger for a nobler use,
That thou defy some knight, if that will serve
Thy purpose, Aladine will not refuse."
His herald then without a moment's truce
Argantes spake, and with the daring boast
Dilating said: "Give all thy swiftness loose;
And let this not mean challenge be proposed
To the Frank Duke below, in hearing of his host.

15.

"Say, that a knight who longer scorns to crouch
Within the marble ramparts of the town,
Burns in the eye of angels to avouch,
By fact of arms, his prowess and renown;
That he to duel hastens to come down
Upon the plain midway 'twixt tent and tower;
To prove his valour on the golden crown
Of whatsoever Frank, of Franks the flower,
Dares to accept the gage, and try his martial power.

16.

"And that not only is he girt to wage
Victorious battle with a single foe,
But with the third, fourth, fifth he will engage,
Villain or lord, with highborn or with low;
The vanquished shall the victor serve, for so
The rules of war ordain:" his message done,
The silver-sceptred herald turned to go,
And lightly threw his purple surcoat on,
Emblazed with golden arms that glittered in the sun.

17.

When reached the tent of Godfrey the divine,
In presence of his Barons, "Prince," he said,
"May perfect liberty of speech be mine
To tell a daring message without dread?"

He in assent inclined a haughty head,
And answered, "Ay! without the thought of fear,
Before us be the mighty venture spread:"
Then thus the herald, "Now will it appear
If the great news sound sweet or frightful to your ear."

18.

The knight's defiance he at large exposed,
In glorying terms, magnificent and high;—
Loud murmured the fierce Lords, and round him closed,
Scorn on each lip, and pride in every eye:
Quickly their Lion-leader gave reply:
"A modest task methinks the knight has mused:
What think ye, Peers? dare we the battle try?
Much I misdoubt when he his sword has used
On the fourth knight, the fifth will wish to stand excused!

19.

"But let him put it to the proof; I grant
Safe field and liberal; we have some shall dare
Advance, to lessen his presumptuous vaunt,—
They shall no vantage use, nor fact unfair,
I lift my sceptre to the stars, and swear:"
This heard, the sovereign of the silver mace
Turned back by the same path he trod whilere;
Nor till he saw Argantes face to face
Slacked, for a moment slacked, the swiftness of his pace.

20.

"Arm!" he exclaimed, "why hesitate to arm?
The challenge they accept with glad surprise;
Like sovereign heroes there the meanest swarm
To front you,— vizors close, and lances rise;
I saw rage lighten in a thousand eyes;
I saw a thousand hands caress the sword
In passion for the fight; hark, how the skies
Sound to their shout, as though a river roared!—
Safe guard and ample field their Captain will afford."

21.

He heard, he called his Squire, and hurriedly
Braced on his mail, impatient for the plain;
Whilst to the fair Clorinda standing by,
The king exclaimed: "Brave Lady! to abstain
From arms, and in the city to remain,
Whilst free Argantes issues out to fight,
Suit not thy rank; take then an armed train
For surer safety, and attend the knight;
At distance range their spears, but keep the lists in sight."

22.

He ceased, and soon under the open sky
The troop rode forth in beautiful array,
And marked far on before how gallantly
The knight, in wonted arms and trappings gay,
Cheered to the frequent spur his ardent bay: —
A plain there was, seemed formed by art, between
The camp and town; of wide extent it lay,
As though the Campus Martius it had been
Before another Rome, unswelling, smooth, and green.

23.

There singly he descended; there, in sight
Of the collected Camp his station took;
By his brave heart, great bulk, and brawny might
Magnificent, and menacing in look
As huge Goliath by the vale's clear brook,
Or grim Enceladus, before whose stride
The' aërial pines, and fields of Phlegra shook;
But many without fear the giant eyed,
For none his utmost strength in battle yet had tried.

24.

Though Godfrey yet no champion had selected,
Whose bravery best the Camp might represent,
It was no secret whom they most affected —
All eyes, hopes, wishes were on Tancred bent;
To him the favour of all faces lent,
Spoke him the' ascendant genius of the crowd;
And first a whisper round the circle went,
Which, faint awhile, grew momently more loud;
Nor less the General's looks his own desire avowed.

25.

To him the rest give place, nor silent then
Remained the Duke; "The tilt be thine," he cried;
"Tancred, meet thou the ruffian Saracen,
Repress his fury, and abase his pride."
In Tancred's face I would you had descried
What exultation shone, what boldness glowed;
Proud to be named the' antagonist defied,
He called for helm and steed; his steed bestrode;
And straight with numerous friends from forth the' entrenchments rode.

26.

Within a bowshot of the ample field
Wherein Argantes for his champion stayed,
On the near hill, upgazing, he beheld

The warlike figure of his Persian maid:
White were the vests that o'er her armour strayed,
As snows on Alpine glaciers, and her face,
(For she her vizor had thrown up), displayed
Grandeur sublime so sweetening into grace,—
The region seemed to him some heavenly-haunted place.

27.

He noted not where the Circassian reared
His frightful face to the affronted skies,
But to the hill-top where his Love appeared,
Turned, slackening his quick pace, his amorous eyes,
Till he stood steadfast as a rock, all ice
Without, all glowing heat within;—the sight
To him was as the gates of Paradise;
And from his mind the memory of the fight
Passed like a summer cloud, or dream at morning light.

28.

The' impatient Pagan, seeing none appear
In act preparative for battle, cried:
"Desire of gallant conflict brought me here;
Come forward one, and let the tilt be tried."
Still Tancred stood as he were stupified;
The hero's shout broke not his thoughtful trance;
But Otho, striking in his courser's side
His shining rowels, bravely made advance
First in the vacant lists, and couched his eager lance.

29.

He was of those whose ardent hope and aim
It was, with fierce Argantes to have fought;
To Tancred he indeed resigned his claim,
And with the rest that Prince to battle brought;
But noticing him now, absorbed in thought,
Fail the desired advantage to employ,—
Seeing the tourney he before had sought
Free to his lance, the bold impatient boy
Seized on the offered chance with rash and greedy joy.

30.

Swift as the tiger or voracious pard
Springs through the crashing forest, Otho pressed
To the stout Mussulman, who, on good guard,
Laid his tremendous spear in sudden rest:
Then Tancred first awoke; then from the zest
Of amorous thoughts as from a sweet dream started;
And cried, "The fight is mine! his course arrest!"

But the young champion now too far had darted
Within the lists, to be from his opponent parted.

31.

Therewith he stayed, whilst wrath and crimson shame
Glowed on his cheek, and in his bosom boiled,
Deeming it worse than falsehood to his fame,
Thus of the field's first risks to be beguiled:
Meantime in mid career the hardy Childe
Struck the Circassian's burganet, and tore
The feathers from its crown; but he, half wild,
With naked spear implacable for gore,
Quite clove his Redcross shield, and through the breast-plate bore!

32.

Pushed from his seat by rudeness of the blow,
The Christian fell, half senseless from the shock;
But his more vigorous and athletic foe
Bore it unbowed, impassive as a rock;
And thus began the prostrate knight to mock,—
Fierce was his gesture, insolent his tone,—
"Yield thee my slave! where proudest nobles flock,
'T will be enough for thy renown, to own
That thou hast fought with me, and thus been overthrown!"

33.

"No!" said the youth, "not quite so soon we use
To yield our arms and ardour on command;
Let others as they list my fall excuse,
I will revenge it, or die sword in hand!"
Fierce as Alecto, pitilessly grand,
With all the Gorgon raging in his face,
And breath like that of Atè's flaming brand,
Argantes said, "And scorn'st thou my good grace?
Learn then my power!" he spoke, and speaking spurned the place.

34.

His rampant steed he drove at him, nor heeded
What to his chivalry was due; the Frank
From the rude onset, quick as thought, receded,
And dealt, in passing, at his dexter flank
A stroke so strong, that through his armour sank
The sword, incarnadine with blood; — the ground
Some rosy drops of the libation drank;
But what availed it to inflict a wound
That raised the conqueror's rage, and left his vigour sound?

35.

He curbed his courser, whirled him round, bore back,
And almost in the twinkling of an eye,
Ere his charged foe could guard against the' attack,
Trampled him down in grim ferocity:
Short drew his breath; quivered in agony
His legs, and with a faint, lamenting shriek
He swooned away; now low behold him lie,—
On the hard earth thrown panting, bruised, and weak;
Half closed the languid eye, and pale the suffering cheek.

36.

Argantes, drunk with rage, enforced his way
With high curvettings o'er his victim's chest;
And cried, "Let all proud knights obedience pay,
Like him whom thus my horse's hoofs have pressed:"
Undaunted Tancred in his manly breast
At this barbaric action could restrain
His wrath no longer; shaking his black crest,
He forward spurred, ambitious to regain
His wonted fame eclipsed, and clear its recent stain.

37.

"And oh," he cried, advancing, "spirit base!
E'en in thy conquests, infamous! what meed,
What title to esteem, what claim to praise
Hop'st thou, accurst, from such a villain's deed!
With Arab robbers or the like fierce breed
Of ruffians, surely thou wert bred;—away!
Back to thy loathed den of darkness speed;
Midst hills and woods go raven for thy prey
With other wolves by night, more savage far than they!"

38.

The Pagan Lord, to such affronts unused,
Bit both his lips, wrath's strangled orators;
He would have spoke, but only sounds confused
Broke forth, such sounds as when a lion roars;
Or, as when lightning cleaves the stormy doors
Of heaven, to rouse from its reluctant rest
The thunder growling as the tempest pours;
For every word which he with pain expressed,
Escaped in tones as gruff, from his infuriate breast.

39.

When by ferocious threats they each had fired
His rival's pride, and fortified his own,
Some paces back they rapidly retired,
And met, like two black clouds together blown.

Queen of the Lyre! down from thy Delphic throne
Descend with all thy talismans and charms;
Breathe in my ringing shell thy hoarsest tone,
That to their rage attempered, its alarms
May with the shock, repeat the clangour of their arms!

40.

Both placed in rest, and levelled at the face
Their knotty lances; — ne'er did tiger's spring,
Nor ardent charger in the rushing race,
Match their swift course, nor bird of swiftest wing;
Here Tancred, there Argantes came! — to sing
The force with which they met, would ask the cry
Of angels, — sudden the shocked helmets ring;
Their spears are broke; and up to the blue sky
A thousand lucid sparks, a thousand shivers fly.

41.

That shrill blow shook Earth's firm volubil ball;
The mountains, sounding as the metals clashed,
Passed the dire music to the towers, till all
The City trembled; but the shock, which dashed
Both steeds to earth, as each for anguish gnashed
Its teeth, and shrieked its noble life away,
Scarce bowed their haughty heads; they, unabashed,
Sprang lightly up, war's perfect masters they,
Drew their gold-hilted swords, and stood at desperate bay.

42.

Warily deals each warrior's arm its thrust,
His foot its motion, its live glance his eye;
To various guards and attitudes they trust;
They foin, they dally, now aloof, now nigh,
Recede, advance, wheel, traverse, and pass by,
Threat where they strike not, where they threat not, dart
The desperate pass; or, with perception sly,
Free to the foe leave some unguarded part,
Then his foiled stroke revenge, with art deriding art.

43.

Prince Tancred's thigh the Pagan knight perceives
But ill defended, or by shield or sword;
He hastes to strike, and inconsiderate leaves
His side unshielded as he strides abroad;
Tancred failed not instinctively to ward
The stroke, beat back the weapon, and, inspired
With eager hope, the guardless body gored;
Which done, of either gazing host admired,
He nimbly back recoiled, and to his ward retired.

44.

The fierce Argantes, when he now beheld
Himself in his own gushing blood baptized,
In unaccustomed horror sighed and yelled,
With shame discountenanced, and with pain surprised;
And, both by rage and suffering agonised,
Raised with his voice his sword aloft, to quit
The sharp rebuke; but Tancred, well advised
Of his intent, afresh the' assailant smit,
Where to the nervous arm the shoulder-blade was knit.

45.

As in its Alpine forest the grim bear,
Stung by the hunter's arrow, from its haunts
Flies in the face of all his shafts to dare
Death for the wild revenge, no peril daunts;
Just so the mad Circassian fares, so pants
For blood, as thus the foe his soul besets,
When shame on shame, and wound on wound he plants;
And his revenge his wrath so keenly whets,
That he all danger scorns, and all defence forgets.

46.

Joining with courage keen a valour rash,
And untired strength with unexampled might,
He showers his strokes so fast, that the skies flash,
And earth e'en trembles in her wild affright:
No time has the alarmed Italian knight
To deal a single blow; from such a shower
Scarce can he shield himself, scarce breathe; no sleight
Of arms is there to' assure his life an hour
From the man's headstrong haste and brute gigantic power.

47.

Collected in himself, he waits in vain
Till the first fury of the storm be past;
Now lifts his moony targe; now round the plain
Fetches his skilful circles, far and fast;
But when he sees the Pagan's fierceness last
Through all delay, his own proud blood takes fire;
And, staking all his fortunes on the cast,
He whirls his sword in many a giddy gyre,
Requiting strength with strength, and answering ire with ire.

48.

Judgment and skill are lost in rage; rage gives
Resentment life; fresh force resentment lends;
Where falls the steel, it either bores or cleaves
Chainplate or mail; plumes shiver, metal bends,

Helms crack, and not a stroke in vain descends;
The ground is strewed with armour hewn asunder,
Armour with blood, with ruby blood sweat blends;
Each smiting sword appears a whirling wonder,
Its flash the lightning's fire, its sullen clang far thunder.

49.

Both gazing nations anxious hung suspended
Upon a spectacle so wild and new;
With fear, with hope, the issue they attended,
Some good or ill perpetually in view;
Not the least beck or slightest whisper flew
Mid the two hosts so lately in commotion;
All nerve alone, all eye, all ear, they grew
Fixt, mute, and soundless as an eve-lulled ocean,
Save what the beating heart struck in its awful motion.

50.

Now tired were both; and both, their spirits spent,
Had surely perished on the field of fight,
Had not dim eve her lengthening shadows sent,
And e'en of nearest things obscured the sight;
And now on either side in apposite
Array, a reverend herald rose, and sought
From the keen strife to separate each his knight;
This Aridos, Pindoro that, who brought
Of late the' insulter's boast, and terms on which they fought.

51.

Safe in the sacred laws of nations kept
Religiously from hallowing age to age,
The swords of both they dare to intercept
With their pacific sceptres, and the sage
Pindoro spoke, "Suspend, my sons, your rage:
Equal your glory, equal is your might;
No longer then the' inveterate warfare wage,
Nor with rude sounds unamiable affright
Rashly the holy ear of quiet-keeping Night!

52.

"Lulled in soft rest by night each creature lies;
Man should but toil while shines the daily sun,
And noble bosoms will but lightly prize
E'en noble deeds in silent darkness done."
Argantes then: "To quit the strife begun
Pleases me ill, though darkness ride the air;
Yet worthier far will be my conquest won
Beneath the eye of day; then let him swear,
Here for fresh proof of arms again to make repair."

53.

To whom the high Italian: "Thou too plight
Thy promise to return, and bring with thee
Thy captive to the lists, or ne'er, proud knight,
Look thou for other time than this from me."
Thus swear they both by what may holiest be;
And the choice heralds meditate what time
May best subserve the combat; they decree,
(Considerate of their wounds) the hour of prime,
When the sixth morning's breeze sheds coolness through the clime.

54.

This dreadful battle left in every heart
Deep horror, mighty wonder, and chill fear,
Which cannot be forgot, nor soon depart,
And open gloom and counterfeited cheer.
The force and valour shown by either peer
Alone the talk of all employed—how well,
And stubbornly they fought; but which with clear
Pre-eminence of power did most excel,
Perplexed the vulgar thought; in sooth no tongue could tell.

55.

All wait in sharp anxiety to see
What fate will crown the strife; if rage shall quail
To the calm virtue of pure chivalry,
Or giant strength o'er hardihood prevail:
But deepest cares and doubts distract the pale
And sensitive Erminia; her fond heart
A thousand agonies and fears assail;
Since, on the cast of war's uncertain dart,
Hangs the sweet life she loves, her soul's far dearer part.

56.

She, daughter to Cassano, who the crown
Wore of imperial Antioch, in the hour
When the flushed Christians won the stubborn town,
With other booty fell in Tancred's power:
But he received her as some sacred flower,
Nor harmed her shrinking leaves; midst outrage keen
Pure and inviolate was her virgin-bower;
And her he caused to be attended, e'en
Amidst her ruined realms, as an unquestioned queen.

57.

The generous knight in every act and word
Honoured her, served her, soothed her deep distress,
Gave her her freedom, to her charge restored
Her gems, her gold, and bade her still possess

Her ornaments of price: the sweet Princess,
Seeing what kingliness of spirit shined
In his engaging form and frank address,
Was touched with love; and never did Love bind
With his most charming chain a more devoted mind.

58.

Thus, though in person free, her spirit ever
Remained his willing thrall; and many a tear,
Many a last look, many a vain endeavour,
It cost her to depart from one so dear,
And quit her blissful cage; but shame austere,
And princely chastity, whose least command
The high-souled lady ever must revere,
Forced her to take her aged mother's hand,
And an asylum seek in some far friendly land.

59.

To towered Jerusalem she came, and there
Was richly entertained; but 't was her doom,
Too soon the sable vests of woe to wear,
And plant the cypress round her mother's tomb;
But not the grief, the sickness, and the gloom,
Not all that bitter exile could inspire,
From her delicious cheek might brush the bloom,
The rosy bloom of amorous desire,
Or quench in her soft heart pure Passion's lingering fire.

60.

She loved, she glowed, poor girl! and yet was far
From happy, for her love hoped no return;
Indeed she turned far oftener to the star
Of Memory, than of Hope; as in an urn
Hiding within her breast the thoughts that burn
Fiercest in secret; to foment the flame,
Vain as it was, was long her sole concern;
Till with the war to Salem, Tancred came,
And Hope again flashed forth like lightning through her frame.

61.

Others beheld with gloom and pale dismay
Such tameless numbers to the plain advance:
But her dark looks at once grew bright, and gay
She marked the banners float, the white plumes dance;
And rolled throughout the host an eager glance,
The generous hero of her heart to see;
Oft the vain search her sadness would enhance;
Yet oft she recognised him, in fond glee
Shook her rich locks, and said: "That, that indeed is he!"

62.

Near to the walls, within the palace, soared
A lofty tower antique, from whose steep height
The eye at its own pleasant will explored
The camp, the mountains, and the field of fight;
There would she sit from the first hour that light
Bathed the grey battlements, till seas and skies
Grew dark with the impurpling hues of night; —
There would she sit, fond dreamer! with her eyes
Turned to the Christian camp, and spend her soul in sighs.

63.

'T was thence she viewed that battle, whose least blow
Made her heart tremble in its dainty cell,
And send its strong pulsations to and fro,
As if in solemn tone it tolled the knell
Of hope, and sounded to her soul — "Farewell
To Tancred!" troubled thus, with fear profound
She watched each fortune that her knight befel;
And ever as the Pagan's sword flew round,
Felt in her own fond heart and brain the' inflicted wound.

64.

But when the fatal tidings reached her ear
That the fierce conflict must afresh be tried,
Her sick blood curdled in its flow; blank fear
Appalled her, and her heart within her died;
Now she poured forth wild tears; now sorely sighed;
And now to unseen glooms stole, seeking there
The strong convulsions of her soul to hide;
Grief in her gaze, distraction in her air,
She seemed the passive slave and picture of Despair.

65.

And frightful shapes and images possessed
The organs of her fancy; types and themes
More drear than death, if e'er she sank to rest,
Thronged to her sleep, and shook her midnight dreams:
Now to her sight her loved Crusader seems
Mangled and bleeding, or assaulted rears
To her his fond beseeching arms, and screams
For her vain help; till leaping with her fears,
She wakes, and finds her eyes and bosom bathed with tears.

66.

But dread of future ills was not the worst
Of her solicitudes; rude visitings
Of fancy thoughtful of his wounds unnursed,
Ruffled her soul, and loosed its silver springs;

Nor less each fresh report that Rumour brings
In her fallacious circuit, magnifies
Her picturings of unknown and distant things,
Till she at length admits the wild surmise,
That at the point of death her languid warrior lies.

67.

And as her mother taught her in her youth
The virtues of all herbs by saint or sage
For medicine culled, with all the charms that soothe
The thrilling wound, and calm the fever's rage,—
An art which from the Patriarchal Age
The East's prescriptive usages accord
To virgins e'en of princely parentage—
With her own hand would she, of risk unawed,
Tend, and to health restore the bruises of her lord.

68.

To heal her love was her desire, to cure
His foe her bitter task: she thought to seek
Sometimes for poisonous herbs that might ensure
His death; but such malignant arts her meek
And pious hands recoiled from—she could speak,
Not execute the scheme: but she might nurse
At least the wish, her piety to pique,
That some kind power the blessings would reverse
Of all her balms and spells, and change them to a curse.

69.

She had no fear to go midst adverse nations,
Who was so much a pilgrim; she had seen
The anarchy of battle, desolations,
Adversities, and slaughters; and had been
So tossed by Fate through each tumultuous scene,
That now her gentle mind a strength displayed
That was not in its nature—fixed, serene;
No more to shake with every wind that played
Amongst the midnight woods, nor shriek at every shade.

70.

But more than all, Love, headstrong Love, removed
From her all sense of fear: she would have faced,
Devoid of terror, for the man she loved,
The snakes and lions of the Lybian waste,
And deemed her passage sure; but though in haste
To please her will existence she disdained,
She trembled lest her name should be disgraced:
Two potent rivals, Love and Honour, reigned
Within her maiden breast, and dubious strife maintained.

71.

"Beloved young Virgin," Honour whispered, "well
Hast thou preserved my statutes to this hour!
Think how I kept, by mine immortal spell,
Chaste thy fair limbs when in the spoiler's power;
And wilt thou, now that thou art free, the flower
Of holy Chastity unwooed resign,
So closely treasured then? beshrew thy bower?
How canst thou once indulge the dread design!
What thoughts, alas, what hopes, dear maid, are these of thine!

72.

"Hold'st thou thy glory at a price so slight,
The priceless glory of a maiden's fame,
That thou must go, Love's paranymph, by night
Mid adverse hosts to court unquestioned shame?
'No,' the proud victor coolly will exclaim,
'Thou with thy throne thy dignity of mind
Hast lost — a prize so worthless I disclaim;' —
Say, canst thou brook to be by one so kind
To some more vulgar feere contemptuously resigned?"

73.

Next Love, the flattering sophist, with a tongue
Sweet as the nightingale's, her soul beguiled;
"Thou wert not, gentle maid, from rude rocks sprung,
Or nursed by wild wolves in the fruitless wild,
That thou shouldst scorn soft Cytherea's child,
His admirable bow and dulcet dart,
Forswearing bliss; then blush not to be styled
His votaress, young and charming as thou art —
Heaven ne'er has cursed that form with an unyielding heart.

74.

"Go then where mild Desire thy steps invites!
Canst thou conceive thy victor harsh or vain,
Who know'st how much thy grief his grief incites,
How thy complaints e'en move him to complain?
'T is not his harshness then, but thy disdain
That thou shouldst deprecate, who with so slow
An inclination mov'st to ease his pain:
Thy virtuous Tancred dies, stern girl, and lo —
Thou must be sitting here to aid his worthless foe!

75.

"Yes, cure Argantes, that his sword may smite
Thy benefactor to the dead! what then,
Wouldst thou thus cancel, wouldst thou thus requite
The' unmeasured kindness of the best of men?

Canst thou once doubt, that the vile Saracen
Will fail on Tancred and on thee to bring
Yet sharper pangs, restored to arms again?
Let the mere dread and horror of the thing
Suffice to speed thee hence as on the turtle's wing.

76.

"It would be some humanity to stand
His dutiful physician! what delight
Would it not be to lay thy healing hand
Upon the brave man's breast! how exquisite
To watch, as at thy call, the roseate light
Of health descend with freshness to displace
The pallid hues which now his beauty blight;
And on the colouring roses of his face,
As on thine own rich gifts, admiringly to gaze!

77.

"So shouldst thou share in all the after-fame
Of his romantic exploits; so should sweet
And unreproved caresses crown thy flame;
And prosperous nuptials make thy joy complete:
Then into beauteous Italy, the seat
Of high-born worth, thou go'st, a glorious bride;
Whilst Latin girls and mothers at thy feet
Scatter young flowers, and point at thee with pride,
Seated in Tancred's car, like Love by Valour's side."

78.

With these light hopes, sweet simple girl, upbuoyed,
She fondly deemed all Paradise her own;
Yet still a thousand doubts her mind annoyed—
How could she pass out through the gates, unknown;
For trumpets at the least alarm were blown,
And stationed guards paraded, without pause,
The court, the streets, and ramparts of the town;
Nor might the gates, by Aladine's wise laws,
Be night or day unbarred, but on some urgent cause.

79.

It was Erminia's wont, long hours, to hold
Converse with brave Clorinda: them the sun
Together viewed, as down the skies he rolled—
Them, when his orient progress was begun;
And when his circuit through the heavens was run,
On the same couch together they reposed;
And all her thoughts and feelings, save the one
Her glowing spirit loved and mused on most,
Were to the Persian maid familiarly disclosed.

80.

This only secret to herself alone
She kept; and if she did but once complain,
Or unawares let fall a sigh or groan,
Straight she disguised it on pretence of pain
For her remembered home: so strict the chain
Of their connexion now was grown, that ne'er
Did mute or maiden offer to restrain
Erminia's access to her, whatsoe'er
Might be the' immediate theme that claimed their Lady's care.

81.

She came one eve — Clorinda was away, —
Yet pensive she sat down, and inly weighed
Each mode of art by which she might essay
The so-much-wished departure, unbetrayed;
There whilst a thousand thoughts her mind, unstayed
In its designs, revolved, nor could decide
Which to adopt, by the mild light that played
On the white walls, suspended she descried
Clorinda's arms and vest: she saw them, and she sighed:

82.

And sighing, thus exclaimed: "Heroic dame,
How envy I thy fortune! not that thou
Art lovely in thy might, — not for the fame
And vaunt of thy wild beauty, Dearest, no!
But thee no envious cell restrains; no flow
Of cumbrous garments curbs thy steps, — thy weeds
Are of the beaten silver: thou canst go
By night or day where'er thy humour leads;
No fear thy course controls, no bashfulness thy deeds.

83.

"Ah, wherefore did not Heaven to me accord
A strength like hers; then might I change the veil
For the plumed helm, the quiver for the sword,
And pall of purple for the shirt of mail:
Then neither thunder, heat, nor hoary hail
Should mew my love within these towers of stone:
But or in open day, or by the pale
Pure planet of the night, would I begone,
Armed, to the Christian camp, attended or alone.

84.

"Then thou, accurst Argantes, hadst not fought
First with my lord: I would have sought the plain,
And struck, perhaps a noble conquest wrought,
And hither brought my vassal to sustain,

Forged by revengeful Love, a red-rose chain
Gay as the light, and playful as the air;
Charmed with that fond beguilement of my pain,
I should have felt the bonds he makes me wear,
Sweet for my servant's sake, and passing light to bear.

85.

"Or else his hand the passage had explored
To my poor heart, and piercing through my breast,
His kindly-cruel and unhindered sword
Had cured the wound his image there impressed:
Then would my weary spirit be at rest;
Perchance the victor, piteous of my doom,
With one kind tear my obsequies had graced;
Raised the lone urn, and o'er my early tomb
Bade the green cypress wave, the' unwithering laurel bloom.

86.

"Alas, I dream wild things! what have I said?
My thoughts are in a maze of follies lost;
Shall I then stay, lamenting, yet afraid
To act, like a weak slave or shivering ghost?
I will not! no! mount, spirits, to your post!
My bold heart, fortify my timorous cheek!
Can I not use these arms for once? at most,
It is but a brief hardship that I seek;
Can I not bear their weight, though tender, faint, and weak?

87.

"I can; I will; true Love will make me strong,—
Love gives the weakest strength: e'en the tame deer,
Pricked by his kindly heat, to battle throng
In antlered vigour, without care or fear:
I have no wish indeed with helm or spear
To war, like them; but only, by their rape,
Like my beloved Clorinda to appear;
If I of her but take the armed shape,
Beneath the pleasant fraud I make my sure escape.

88.

"The warders will not dare but ope for her
The portal-gates, and a free pass allow;
I think again . . . no other means occur;
This method only can avail my vow.
O, gentle Love! in this sharp need, do thou
Favour my flight, as thou inspir'st my wit;
And Fortune, stand benignant! even now
Prove I your power,—this is the time most fit,
Whilst yet Clorinda's cares the masked attempt permit."

89.

Thus, fixed was her resolve; delay was none;
By the rash fervour of her passion swayed,
From her friend's near apartment to her own,
Clorinda's arms she secretly conveyed,—
For at her entrance each attendant maid
Retired, and she remained alone; whilst Night,
Blind patroness of thefts and frolics played
By gentle lovers, favourer of her flight,
Rose o'er the silent world, and hid the spoils from sight.

90.

She, when she saw the bloom of sunset fade,
And Love's pale star put forth its sparkling fire,
No moment of her precious time delayed,
But sent a secret summons for her squire,
And for her favourite maid, in whose entire
Devotion to her person she reposed
Implicit trust: to them her strong desire
To quit the' invested city she disclosed;
But feigned that other cause the timeless step imposed.

91.

Quick was the squire, and active to provide
What for the journey he conceived was meet;
Whilst young Erminia laid her vests aside,
That hung for pomp below her graceful feet;
And to her flowered cymar disrobed complete,
Never did virgin bride a shape display
So elegantly slender; charms so sweet
Surpass the power of fancy to portray:
Prompt stands the favourite maid her Lady to array.

92.

The hard cold steel oppresses and offends
Her delicate smooth neck and golden hair;
Her arm, unequal to the burden, bends
Beneath the huge shield she aspires to bear:
Armed, the bright Virgin cast a dazzling glare,
And fashioned her nice step and aspect mild
To a proud stride and military air;
Love near her clapped his little wings, and smiled,
As when in female weeds Alcides he beguiled.

93.

Oh, how fatiguing every moment grew
The' unequal weight! how slow her faltering pace!
Faint to her handmaid for support she drew,
And by her help moved onward a short space;

But Love renews her spirits, bright hopes brace
Her sinews strengthening as her fear abates;
So that at length they reach the chosen place,
Where the mute squire for their arrival waits,
Vault on their steeds, and seek at once the guarded gates.

94.

Disguised they went, the least-frequented ways
Selecting well; yet passed they many a band
Of soldiers under arms, and saw the blaze
Of bickering armour flash on every hand;
But none of those they met with, durst withstand
Their uncommissioned progress, nor presume
E'en to require the signal of command;
Awed they passed on, for through the evening gloom
All knew the silver arms and dreaded tigress plume.

95.

Erminia, though this homage had dispersed
The strongest of her doubts, was ill at ease;
Still for her bold design she feared the worst;
And heard discovery sound in every breeze.
But now the portals of the town she sees;
Checks her alarm, and in commanding state
Boldly confronts the keeper of the keys:
"For Aladine!" she cries, "unbar the gate!
Heave the portcullis up! the hour is waxing late."

96.

Her female tone and form give added power
To the masked fraud; (for who would think to see
Armed and in saddle, at so dusk an hour,
A gentle lady of her high degree?)
So that the guard obeys at once, and she,
With the two pressed attendants that partake
Her flight, proceeds; for full security
Resolved to thread the vales, by bush and brake
Gliding in noiseless stealth, long winding tracks they take.

97.

But when Erminia saw herself at last
Deep in the lonely vales, she curbed her steed;
For her first peril she accounted past,—
And well aware that she had now no need
For apprehension, gave attentive heed
To the still voice of prudence, which, she grieved,
Had been in her desire's impetuous speed
Passed by unheard: her access she perceived
Would prove more hard to win, than she at first believed.

98.

She now perceived the folly of a flight
In borrowed arms amid her angry foes;
Nor, on the other hand, till to the knight
She came, would she her rank or name disclose;
But, secret and reserved as the moss-rose
In its enfolding leaves, would first acquire
Pledge of deserved reception; whence she goes
More gently o'er the grass, and her desire,
Lowered to cool caution's key, thus trusts to her sure squire.

99.

"My faithful servant! thee have I designed
For my precursor; but be swift and wise:
Haste to the camp, and some auxiliar find
To introduce thee where Prince Tancred lies;
Him of my coming tranquilly apprise:
Say, 'That a pitying lady comes to pour
Oil in his wounds, and on his grace relies
For peace, whom warring Love has wounded sore;
So may our mutual gifts our mutual ease restore!

100.

" 'One, who on him does such full trust repose,
That in his hands she fears nor wrong nor scorn:'
This only — to his private ear disclose,
And if he wishes aught beside to learn,
Tell nothing, nothing know, but straight return;
I (for the spot a sense of safety brings)
Will meanwhile in the valley make sojourn:"
This said, her faithful herald forward springs;
And scours the vale as though endued with actual wings.

101.

With such a dexterous skill his aim he wrought,
He won the jealous sentries, passed them clear,
And to the warrior on his couch was brought,
Who heard the message with delighted ear.
Left to himself, the' astonished cavalier
Lay full of thought, and in his fancy weighed
A thousand doubtful things, by hope and fear
At once possessed: the answer which he made
Was, that she safe might come, and secret as the shade.

102.

But she meanwhile impatient, in whose eyes
Each moment seemed an age, to care a prey,
Counts to herself each separate step, and cries,
"Now he arrives, now speaks, now hastes away;"

Next she upbraids his indolent delay;
Chides his unusual want of diligence;
And, weary grown of his eternal stay,
Spurs till she gains the nearest eminence,
Whence her dilating eye discerns the distant tents.

103.

On high were the clear stars; the gentle Hours
Walked cloudless through the galaxy of space,
And the calm moon rose, lighting up the flowers
With frost of living pearl: like her in grace,
The' enamoured maid from her illumined face
Reflected light where'er she chanced to rove;
And made the silent Spirit of the place,
The hills, the melancholy moon above,
And the dumb valleys round, familiars of her love.

104.

Seeing the Camp, she whispered: "O ye fair
Italian tents! how amiable ye show!
The breathing winds that such refreshment bear,
Ravish my soul, for 'tis from you they blow!
So may relenting Heaven on me bestow,—
On me, by froward Fate so long distressed,—
A chaste repose from weariness and woe,
As in your compass only lies my quest;
As 'tis your arms alone can give my spirit rest.

105.

"Receive me then, and in you let me find
Love's gentle voice, which spoke of pity, true;
And that delightful music of the mind,
Which in my blest captivity I drew
From my lord's mercy; patronised by you,
I have no wish to re-obtain and wear
My regal crown,—adieu, vain pomps, adieu!
Enough for me if Tancred grants my prayer;
More blest in you to serve, than reign a queen elsewhere."

106.

Ah, little does she think, while thus she dreams,
What is prepared for her by Fortune's spite!
She is so placed, that the moon's placid beams
In line direct upon her armour light;
So far remote into the shades of night
The silver splendour is conveyed, and she
Surrounded is with brilliancy so bright,
That whosoe'er might chance her crest to see,
Would of a truth conclude it must Clorinda be.

107.

And, as Fate willed, close couched in the high fern,
In stations due of distance interposed,
Two brave Italian brothers, Polypherne,
And, paramount, Alcander, had disposed
Full fifty youths, the flower of Tancred's host,
To intercept the Saracens' supply
Of flocks and herds from the Arabian coast;
Erminia's servant but escaped their eye
By his long winding track, and speed in gliding by.

108.

Watchful young Polypherne, whose aged sire
Before his eyes Clorinda lately slew,
Saw the white arms, the feminine attire,
And the charged helmet for Clorinda's knew;
Rash and unguarded in his wrath, he drew
His urged attendants from the covert near;
And, as on fire for vengeance forth he flew,
Shouted aloud, " 'Tis well; death waits thee here!"
And lanced, but lanced in vain, his formidable spear.

109.

As when a hind, inflamed with fervid thirst,
Seeking the cool refreshing fountains, sees
A clear spring gushing from a crag, or burst
Of some cascade o'er bowered with leafy trees,—
If, while she thinks to taste the shade at ease,
And quaff the waves up that so sweetly roar,
The hunter's horn sounds shrilly in the breeze,
Back, back she rushes, nor remembers more
The faintness, thirst, and heat, that fired her limbs before:

110.

So she, who thought in Tancred's pure embrace
To quench the love which she began to find
Inflame her heart, and, anchored on his grace,
To woo repose to her so weary mind,
Hearing the clang of weapons on the wind,
And the loud menace of the hunters armed
To thwart her pleasures, tremblingly resigned
Thought of the joy that wooed, the wish that warmed,
And spurred her courser back, distracted and alarmed.

111.

Away the Princess flies, her snorting steed
Trampling with swift intelligential feet
The echoing soil; with imitative speed
Flies too her handmaid, while with steps less fleet

The troop pursue; and now the squire discreet
With his untimely tidings comes in sight
Of the pale maid, perceives her in retreat,
And, pressed, participates her dubious flight;
Wide o'er the plains they speed, diversely driven by fright.

112.

But the more wise Alcander, though he too
Had the same counterfeit Clorinda seen,
Would not the' already challenged maid pursue,
But kept still close within his leafy screen;
And sent to say, that through the valleys green
Nor fleecy sheep had passed, nor lowing steer;
And that no foe had intercepted been,
But strong Clorinda, who in panic fear
Fled from his brother's call and close-pursuing spear;

113.

And that he could not reasonably conceive
That she, the Lady Chieftain of the land,
Not a mere warrioress, would choose to leave
The town at such an hour, but on some grand
And hardy enterprise, for mischief planned
Against the camp; yet, ere he shifted thence,
He looked for Godfrey's counsel or command;
The scout that brought the news of these events,
Passing, divulged it first amid the' Italian tents.

114.

Tancred, who yet had scarce the doubts allayed
Raised by the message which the Syrian bore,
Thinks, what if for my sake the courteous maid
Risks her dear life! ah! what if all be o'er!
He leaps from off his couch, assumes no more
Than half his arms, in still and secret haste
Climbs to his steed, the strange event to' explore,
And, following the clear footmarks freshly traced,
Glides like a shooting star across the moonbright waste.

CANTO VII

ARGUMENT

A hospitable shepherd entertains
Forlorn Erminia; her undaunted knight
Seeking the frighted damsel, in the trains
Of false Armida, is entrapped by sleight.
Raymond with proud Argantes dares the fight,
And gains an Angel for his guard; betrayed
By rage to deepest risk, in helpless plight

The Pagan stands, till Belzebub, in aid,
Blends the two gazing hosts in uproar, storm, and shade.

1.

Through the brown shade of forests ivied o'er
With age, meanwhile, divine Erminia fled;
Her trembling hand the bridle ruled no more;
And she appeared betwixt alive and dead.
The steed that bore her with the' instinctive dread
Of danger, at its own wild mercy, through
Such winding paths and bosky mazes sped,
That it at length quite rapt her from the view;
Baffling the eager hopes of those that would pursue.

2.

As when, after some long and toilsome chase,
The hounds return, a sad and panting train,
Leaving the prey it mocks their skill to trace,
Lodged in some thicket from the open plain;
So, full of shame, resentment, and disdain,
Their far pursuit the weary knights resigned;
Yet still the timid Virgin fled amain
Through the drear woods, disconsolate of mind,
Nor once looked back to mark if yet they pressed behind.

3.

All night she fled; and all the day succeeding,
Still without guidance or reflection, flies
O'er dale and hill, nought listening to, or heeding,
But her own tears, but her own mournful cries;
Till now, what time the sun, descending, dyes
The clouds with crimson, leaving earth in shade,
Fair Jordan's lucid current she descries;
There first her steed's bewildered step she stayed;
Her bed the chill green bank, her bower the wild woods made.

4.

Repast she yet had none; her only diet
The food that sorrow from remembrance brings;
But Sleep at length, pain's balm, and care's sweet quiet,
O'er her closed eyes displays his brooding wings;
Seals with his opiate rod the many springs
Of thought, and in serene oblivion steeps
Her sense of grief; but forms of visioned things
Disturb her fluttering spirit whilst she sleeps,—
Still Fancy's pictured porch unsilenced Passion keeps.

5.

She slept, till in her dreaming ear the bowers
Whispered, the gay birds warbled of the dawn;
The river roared; the winds to the young flowers
Made love; the blithe bee wound its dulcet horn:
Roused by the mirth and melodies of morn,
Her languid eyes she opens, and perceives
The huts of shepherds on the lonely lawn;
Whilst seeming voices, 'twixt the waves and leaves,
Call back her scattered thoughts, — again she sighs and grieves.

6.

Her plaints were silenced by soft music, sent
As from a rural pipe, such sounds as cheer
The Syrian shepherd in his summer tent,
And mixed with pastoral accents, rude but clear.
She rose; and gently, guided by her ear,
Came where an old man on a rising ground
In the fresh shade, his white flocks feeding near,
Twig-baskets wove, and listened to the sound
Trilled by three blooming boys, who sate disporting round.

7.

They at the shining of her silver arms
Were seized at once with wonder and despair;
But sweet Erminia soothed their vain alarms,
Discovering her dove's eyes, and golden hair.
"Follow," she said, "dear innocents, the care
Of favouring Heaven, your fanciful employ!
For the so formidable arms I bear,
No cruel warfare bring, nor harsh annoy,
To your engaging tasks, to your sweet songs of joy!

8.

"But, Father, say, whilst the destructive fire
Of war lays waste the country wide and far,
How live you free from military ire,
Beneath the charm of what benignant star?"
"My son," said he, "from the rude wrongs of war
My family and flocks in this lone nook
Were ever safe; no fears my quiet mar;
These groves to the hoarse trumpet never shook;
Calm rolls yon stately stream, calm flows each woodland brook.

9.

"Whether it be that Heaven protects in love
The chaste humility of shepherd swains,
Or, as its lightnings strike the crag's tall grove,
But leave untouched the roses of the plains,—

That so the wrath of foreign swords disdains
To harm the meek heads of the lowly poor,
Aiming alone at lofty kings,—our gains
Tempt not the greedy soldier to our door;
Safe stands our simple shed, despised our little store.

10.

"Despised by others, but so dear to me,
That gems and crowns I hold in less esteem;
From pride, from avarice is my spirit free,
And mad ambition's visionary dream.
My thirst I quench in the pellucid stream,
Nor fear lest poison the pure wave pollutes;
With flocks my fields, my fields with herbage teem;
My garden-plot supplies nutritious roots;
And my brown orchard bends with Autumn's wealthiest fruits.

11.

"Few are our wishes, few our wants; Man needs
But little to preserve the vital spark:
These are my sons; they keep the flock that feeds,
And rise in the grey morning with the lark.
Thus in my hermitage I live; now mark
The goats disport amid the budding brooms;
Now the slim stags bound through the forest dark;
The fish glide by; the bees hum round the blooms;
And the birds spread to heaven the splendour of their plumes.

12.

"Time was (these grey hairs then were golden locks),
When other wishes wantoned in my veins;
I scorned the simple charge of tending flocks,
And fled disgusted from my native plains.
Awhile in Memphis I abode, where reigns
The mighty Caliph; he admired my port,
And made me keeper of his flower-domains;
And though to town I rarely made resort,
Much have I seen and known of the intrigues of court.

13.

"Long by presumptuous hopes was I beguiled,
And many, many a disappointment bore;
But when with youth false hope no longer smiled,
And the scene palled that charmed so much before,—
I sighed for my lost peace, and brooded o'er
The' abandoned quiet of this humble shed;
Then, farewell State's proud palaces! once more
To these delightful solitudes I fled;
And in their peaceful shades harmonious days have led."

14.

This his discourse so sweetly did subdue
The secret sorrows of the listening maid,
Each word, descending to her heart, like dew,
The feverish passion of her soul allayed:
That, when the measure she had inly weighed—
Her present peace, and her so late dismay,—
She stood resolved within the silent shade
Of these sweet solitudes, at least to stay,
Till for her safe return kind Heaven might smooth the way.

15.

And thus replied: "Oh fortunate and wise!
Who hast thyself experienced, nor forgot
The ills of cruel fortune! if the skies
Be nothing jealous of thy blissful lot,
Pity my woes, and to this pleasant spot
Deign to receive me, stung with sorrow's smart;
In the safe shelter of thy welcome cot
And these still shades, I may perhaps in part
Lose the oppressive weight that hangs around my heart!

16.

"And, if what crowds fall down to and adore
As idols, gold and jewels, thou shouldst prize,
Rich e'en in ruin, I have here a store
That well thine utmost wishes may suffice."
Then, showering from her bright benignant eyes
Tears like those dropt from heaven's resplendent bow,
Part of her history she told: with sighs
And tears, in concord with her own that flow,
The pitying shepherd heard the narrative of woe:

17.

And straight, with all a father's love and zeal,
He took her to his heart, soothed her distress,
And to his wife, whose heart alike could feel
For others' sorrows, led the fair Princess.
Her arms she changes for a pastoral dress,
And with rude ribbon binds her dainty hair;
Yet still, her graceful manner of address,
Movement of eyes and steps the truth declare,—
Was never woodland girl so delicately fair!

18.

Those rustic weeds hid not the princely fire
And grandeur so instinctively her own;
In every action through her quaint attire,
The latent spirit of the Lady shone;

Whether she drove her flocks to range alone
The thymy down, or penned them in the fold;
Or to wild ditties sung in mournful tone,
The dulcet cream in churns revolving rolled,
Till firm the fluid fixed, and took the tinge of gold.

19.

Oft when her flocks, from summer's noontide rays,
Lay in cool shades o'erarched by gadding vines,
She carved on beeches and immortal bays
Her Tancred's name, and left the mossy pines
With sad inscriptions flourished, silent signs
Of the unhappy flame her fancy fed;
And when again she saw her own fond lines,
As she the melancholy fragments read,
Fresh tears of grief unchecked her lovely eyes would shed:

20.

And weeping she would say: "Forever be,
O ye dear trees, historians of my woe!
That when two faithful lovers rest, like me,
In the cool shade your verdant boughs bestow,
Their hearts with generous sympathy may glow;
And, as this volume of my griefs they view,
Say to themselves, 'Ah, never may we know
Her pangs, poor maid! 'tis hard a love so true
Should be so ill repaid by Love and Fortune too!'

21.

"Perhaps, if Heaven benignly hears the vow
And prayer affectionate of girls unblest,
He who cares nothing for Erminia now,
May wander to these woods, where buried rest
Her virgin relics, early dispossessed
Of life's pure fire, — may, glancing on my grave,
White with spring's violets, beat his manly breast,
And to my griefs — the first he ever gave —
Yield a few gracious tears, too late, alas, to save!

22.

"Thus, though in life most miserable, in death
Bliss to my spirit shall at least arise;
And my cold ashes, quickened by his breath,
Enjoy what now my evil star denies."
Whilst thus, the tears fast streaming from her eyes,
To the deaf trees she talked in fondest phrase,
The' unconscious object of her plaintive cries,
As chance or froward fortune guides him, strays
In search of her, far-off, through dark and dreary ways.

23.

Following the impress of her horse's hoof,
He reached the neighbouring wood; there brier and fern
So choked the way, and from its leafy roof
The chequered shade grew momently so stern,
That he no more could 'mid the trees discern
The recent prints, but through the gloom profound
Wandered perplexed; at almost every turn
Listening if, chance, from the deep glens around,
Of arms or trampling steeds his ear might catch the sound.

24.

And if but the night breeze in beech or oak
Shook the still leaves, if but a timid bird
Sped through the rustling boughs, from slumber woke,
Or fiercer creature in the thicket stirred,
To the vague murmur instantly he spurred;
At length he issued from the wood's blind maze,
And to a noise mysterious, which he heard
Remote — beneath the yellow moon's bright rays,
Rode, till he held the cause subjected to his gaze.

25.

A steep he reached, where from the living stone
Fell in full streams a beautiful cascade;
Which, curbed into a flood, went roaring on,
And the whole valley like a garden made.
Here he his fruitless steps dejected stayed;
He called — but Echo of his eager cries
Made mockery, vocal from the greenwood shade —
None else; meanwhile he saw — with tranquil eyes,
Blooming with white and red the new Aurora rise.

26.

He sighed, he stormed, he angrily repined,
And of his disappointment Heaven accused;
But deepest vengeance vowed, if he should find
That the dear maid had been at all abused.
Back to the Camp at length, when he had mused
What step to take, his course he fixed to steer,
Although the way was dubious and confused;
For well he knew the stated time drew near,
When he again should fight the' Egyptian cavalier.

27.

Through many a winding path as he advanced,
He heard the sound of hoofs; nor was it long,
Ere up the narrow vale in prospect, pranced
One, courier-like, who shook a waving thong;

Gay at his side by chains of silver hung
An ivory horn, in our Italian mode
Across his shoulders negligently slung;
Tancred of him inquired the nearest road
To Godfrey's camp, which strait the ready stranger showed:

28.

Adding in Tuscan: "Thither am I bent,
By Bohemond's command;" the knight, this heard,
Deemed him his uncle's post, and with him went,
In full reliance on his guileful word.
They came at length to where, alike unstirred
By breeze or storm, a stagnant lake embayed
A castle; huge the pile its waters gird:
On the dark towers the sun one moment played,
Then sudden sank to sea, and left the world in shade.

29.

Arrived, the courier blew his signal horn,
Instant a drawbridge fell athwart the fosse;
"Sir Knight," he said, "thou here canst rest till morn,
If Frank thou art, or follower of the Cross;
These towers Cosenza's Earl, with little loss,
Three days since wrested from the Turk:" the knight
Gazed on the antique structure—grey with moss,
Gloomy, yet grand it showed, of giant height,
Nobly defenced by art, impregnable in site.

30.

A pile so strong, concealed, he was afraid,
Some secret treason or malignant charm;
But, to all risks accustomed, he betrayed
Neither by sound nor sign the least alarm:
For well he trusted in his own right arm,
Where'er by choice or Fortune led, to make
Terms of complete security from harm;
But, pledged already, and his fame at stake,
No fresh adventure now he cared to undertake.

31.

Before the Castle, where in the green lea
The drawbridge ceased to span the sullen tide,
He therefore paused; nor would persuaded be
To follow o'er the flood his wily guide.
But now an armed warrior he descried
On the pontoon, of fierce and scornful mien;
Sublime his stature, haughty was his stride;
In his right hand a naked sword was seen,
And thus he spake in terms decisive, stern, and keen.

32.

"Oh thou whom choice conducts, or fortune charms
To tread, beguiled, Armida's fatal lands!
Think not of flight; strip off those idle arms,
And to her chains submit thine abject hands.
Free to thy feet her guarded palace stands,
The bliss to taste, the fealty to swear,
Which she to others offers, and commands:
Look not to see heaven's sunshine more, whate'er
May be thy youth of years, or hoariness of hair; —

33.

"Unless thou swear her edicts to enforce,
And with her other slaves to death pursue
All Christ's detested sons:" at this discourse
The knight regarded him, on closer view,
The arms and accents recognised, and knew
Rambaldo for his foe — the Gascon base,
Who with Armida from the camp withdrew,
Pagan became, and here, to his disgrace,
Maintained the evil rules and customs of the place.

34.

The pious warrior blushed with holy scorn,
And answered: "Curst apostate! know that I
That Tancred am, who aye for Christ have borne
The warrior's weapon on my martial thigh.
Strong in His strength, his rebels I defy,
And tame; as thou, if thou but enterprise
Thy sword with mine, shalt surely testify;
For the just anger of the' insulted skies
Has chosen this strong right hand thy treason to chastise."

35.

Aghast at mention of his glorious name
Stood the false knight, but cloaked his fear, and said:
"Ill-starred the hour when to these shores you came,
In Eblis' halls to join the silent dead!
Here shall thy crest be shorn, thy spirits shed;
To the last drop thy heart's blood will I spill,
And to your Captain send that haughty head,
In gift of grace, if but my prowess still
Be, what it ever was, consistent with my will."

36.

Whilst thus the Pagan spoke, the shades of night
Shut up their view; when swift, around, on high,
Cressets, and lamps, and urns of golden light
Filled the dusk element with brilliancy:

Gay shone the Castle to the' enchanted eye,
As in a theatre the shifted scene,
When gorgeous Tragedy sweeps sceptred by;
And in her lofty latticed bower, the Queen
Unmarked spectatress sate, and smiled behind her screen.

37.

Meanwhile the Christian Chief begins to fit
His arms and courage to the coming fight,
Nor on his feeble courser will he sit,
His foe on foot, but generously alight.
The foe comes covered with his buckler; bright
The helmet glitters on his head, and bare
Shines his raised scimetar in act to smite;
'Gainst him the Prince too flies, his worst to dare,
Like thunder sounds his voice, his eyes like lightnings glare.

38.

That, in wide circles wheels averse, in strict
Defence of art, feigns, motions, falsifies;
This though late wounds and faintness sore afflict,
With bold impatience the near conflict plies;
And when his foe draws back, in quick surprise
Springs with the utmost speed he can command,
To intercept, or smite him as he flies;
Whilst ever and anon his active hand
To the unguarded face directs its flashing brand.

39.

With yet more eagerness the Prince assails
The vital parts, and every stroke he deals
Quits with high threats; the Gascon's courage fails,
His ears ring inward, and his blood congeals:
Now here, now there in panic fear he wheels,
Lithe and alert as an assaulted snake;
With live eye circumspect his blows he steals;
And now with sword, now shield, essays to make
The knight's impetuous steel a slant direction take.

40.

But he to ward off harm is not so swift
As that fierce foe is active to assail;
Battered his helm, his shield's already cleft,
And bored and bloody is his plated mail.
Of Tancred's meditated blows, none fail
Of their effect, not one descends in vain;—
Each keenly wounds; the renegade turns pale,
And his heart writhes at once beneath the pain
Of anger, pride, remorse, love, conscience, and disdain.

41.

On one last effort of despairing pride
Resolved at length his dying hopes to set,
He casts the fragment of his shield aside,
Grasps with both hands his sword, uncrimsoned yet,
And, closing nimbly with his foe, to get
The full command and vantage of the ground,
Quits with so sharp a stroke his heavy debt,
That through both plate and mail the flesh it found,
And in the warrior's side impressed a grisly wound.

42.

Next on his spacious brows he struck, — the steel
Like an alarm-bell rang; a stroke so dire
And unexpected made the warrior reel
Some paces back, yet left the helm entire,
Red grew the Prince's cheeks for very ire;
In agony of shame his teeth he gnashed;
His eyes were like two coals of living fire,
And every glance that through his visor flashed,
Blasted the Gascon's pride, both blasted and abashed.

43.

He heard the hissing of the' Avenger's steel,
Brandished aloft; its shining he descried;
Already in his breast he seemed to feel
The' accelerated sword his heart divide,
And tremblingly recoiled; the blow fell wide
On an antique pilaster that embossed
The marble bridge, — sparks flashed on every side;
Fragments sprang forth and in the skies were lost;
Whilst to the traitor's heart fear shot its arrowy frost.

44.

Back to the bridge he rushed, in speed reposing
His hopes of life, — behind, the' Avenger hung
On his fleet steps, now near, now nearer closing,
One hand already to his shoulder clung;
When lo! from trembling air the lights are wrung;
The cressets disappear; the tapers die; —
Gone was each star that in blue ether hung;
The yellow moon drew in her horns on high;
And all grew hideous shade beneath the vacant sky.

45.

Through the thick glooms of witchcraft and of night
Nought could the Prince distinguish to pursue;
Still he pressed on, though ignorant if aright,
His steps confused and dubious as his view:

Bewildered thus, he to the portals drew,
By evil chance the threshold he passed o'er,
And of his fatal entrance nothing knew,
Till hoarse behind, with repercussive roar,
The sullen hinge flew back, and locked the closing door.

46.

As from our seas to the Comachian bay,
Urged by the fury of the driving tide,
The vext fish joys to cleave its wanton way
Where calm and smooth the silent waters glide,
And locks itself unconsciously inside
The marshy gaol; nor finds, till it would dart
Back to the ocean, all escape denied;
For the strange estuary, with curious art,
To all free access yields, but lets not one depart:

47.

So Tancred there (such artful springs involved
The wizard work of that mysterious den),
Entered with ease, but found, on flight resolved,
No human foot might pass its walls again.
He shook the massy gate with might and main;
The lock essayed; the brazen hinges tried;
But found the effort void, the project vain:
"In vain," a loud voice in the distance cried,
"Seek'st thou to flee from hence, lorn thrall of queen Armide!

48.

"Here thou, thus livingly entombed, shalt waste
(Fear not for death) thy days and years alone:"
The hardy knight replied not, but compressed
Within his heart affliction's rising groan.
Love inly he accused, — love, fate, his own
Small wit, and his false guide's deceptions fell;
" 'Tis not," he murmured in desponding tone,
" 'Tis not to bid the cheerful sun farewell
Can make my heart with grief or proud resentment swell.

49.

"That were small suffering; but I lose, alas,
Of a diviner sun the lovelier grace!
Ignorant if e'er these gates I shall repass,
Or e'er again the blissful sight embrace
Of my love's stately form and radiant face:"
Therewith the image of Argantes came,
And deepened his distress: "O dire disgrace!"
He cried: "with too just cause will he defame
My truth; alas the' affront! the fixt eternal shame!"

[Armida finally obtained from Godfrey ten of his leading knights, many others then deserted and followed her; all of these she imprisoned in her magic castle on the Dead Sea. All her powers, however, had met with no success in Rinaldo and Tancred. At the close of the last selection, Tancred is unwittingly lured into her castle. In the meantime, back at the Christian camp, the aged Count Raymond goes forth the next morning to meet Argantes in Tancred's stead.

Early in the fighting, Dudon — captain of Godfrey's daring band of Adventurers — had been killed. Rinaldo and Gernando of Norway then competed for his position. When Gernando insulted Rinaldo beyond endurance, a duel was fought between them and Gernando was killed. Rather than undergo trial for this offense, Rinaldo fled from the camp.

Armida saw fit to send her band of captive knights under guard to Egypt for permanent capture. Rinaldo, in his wanderings, came across this band — including Tancred — and set them free. Armida, in revenge, discovering a cast-off suit of Rinaldo's armor, cleverly clad a headless corpse with it, so that when it was found by knights from Godfrey's army, they reported that Rinaldo was dead. This report created rebellion against Godfrey, who was accused of having him murdered. The Christian knights set free by Rinaldo immediately returned to the army before Jerusalem at a crucial point in the battle, however, and reported that Rinaldo was very much alive.

In the first assault upon the city, the Crusaders used a rolling wooden tower as high as the city-walls, from the top of which by a movable bridge they planned to pass over onto the walls themselves. At the close of the first day of the assault, the tower is withdrawn for repairs. On this night, Clorinda conceives of the daring plan to set fire to the tower.]

CANTO XII

ARGUMENT

First from her faithful slave Clorinda learns
The secret story of her birth; then goes,
Masked, on a high adventure, and returns
Safe to the gates, successful o'er her foes;
But, chased by Tancred to the vales, they close
In mortal battle, and she falls; yet ere
She dies, the rite of baptism he bestows;
Sorely the Prince bewails his slaughtered fair; —
Argantes vows revenge, and soothes the crowd's despair.

1.

'T was night; nor yet had either wearied host
Found soft refreshment in the arms of sleep;
But here the Christians, wakeful at their post,
Guard o'er the workmen round the engine keep;
And there the Pagans their defenses steep,
Trembling and nodding to their fall, repair;
And, to build up the breaches wide and deep
Of the dismantled walls, no labour spare;
And each their wounded tend, with like considerate care.

2.

At length the wounds are bandaged, and complete
Is every one of their nocturnal tasks;
The rest they leave; and, wooed to slumber sweet
By gentler quiet, and the gloom that masks
The world at noon of night, their cumbrous casques
They cast aside: not so the Warrior maid;
Hungering for fame, she still for action asks,—
Action, from which fatigues all else dissuade;
With her Argantes walked, and inly thus she said:

3.

"Deeds rare and wonderful indeed this day
Have the bold Soldan and divine Argaunt
Accomplished, by themselves to take their way,
Huge towers beat down, and hostile millions daunt;
Whilst I, (the utmost merit I can vaunt,)
Cooped in on high, with distant shafts but checked
Their eager escalade; my shafts, I grant,
Flew fair enough, some fatal, I suspect;
But is this then the whole we women can effect?

4.

"Better it were in woods and wilds again
To stags and wolves my arrows to confine,
Than trifle thus, a damsel, in the train
Of knights whose actions so superior shine;
Why not the cuirass and the sword resign?
Resume my woman's weeds, and live dissolved
In careless ease?" thus mused she; but in fine
A daring project in her breast revolved,—
Turned to the knight, and thus broke forth with soul resolved:

5.

"I know not what blest ardour sets ablaze
My restless mind,—or do the Gods inspire
The daring thought that on my spirit preys,
Or make we Gods of each sublime desire?
Far lie the Franks encamped: look forth! admire
The twinkling lights that burn towards the west;
There will I go with torch and sword, and fire
Their rolling fort; this passion of my breast
Let me but see fulfilled, and Heaven arrange the rest!

6.

"But, if I chance to be by Fate debarred
From measuring back my steps, to thee, my friend,
The man that loves me with a sire's regard,
And my devoted damsels I commend:

Each kind protection to their griefs extend,
And back to Egypt, with the dear old sage,
The' inconsolable girls in safety send;
Promise me this! their sex and his great age
May well thy care demand, thy sympathies engage."

7.

Argantes stood amazed; touched in his breast
Were all the springs of glory, and he cried:
"Wilt thou do this? and leave thy friend, disgraced,
Here with the' inglorious vulgar to abide?
Safe from the risk shall I with joy or pride
See the fire kindle? no, Clorinda, no!
If I have ever been in arms allied
With thee, with thee this night too will I go,
And all thy fortunes share, betide me weal or woe!

8.

"I have a heart too can scorn death, and feel
The bauble life well flung for fame away:"
"To this," she answered, "an eternal seal
Didst thou in thy brave sally set to-day;
But I am a mere woman in the way;
Feeble indeed are my poor powers, and small
The aid I lend; my death would none dismay;
But (Heaven avert the omen!) shouldst thou fall,
Who will remain behind to guard the sacred wall?"

9.

"Why these excuses vain?" the knight replied;
"Fixed is my will, and settled mine intent;
Allowed, I follow; but, if once denied,
I go before thee, and thy zeal prevent:"
Thus overpowered, Clorinda gave consent,—
They seek the King, with emir, prince, and peer
Engaged in high and serious argument;
Then thus the Virgin spoke: "Oh Sire, give ear,
And what we wish to say with kind acceptance hear!

10.

"Argantes swears (nor vain will be the boast)
To fire yon rolling fort—the same swear I;
We wait alone till on the guardian host
Deep sleep falls heavy; those who wake shall die!"
The hoary King held up his hands on high;
A tear of joy streamed down his withered cheek;
"And praised," he said, "be Thou, who yet dost eye
With gracious care thy worshippers, and seek
Still to preserve my crown, and guard these kingdoms weak!

11.

"Fall they shall not, whilst in their sure defence
Two such undaunted demigods are found:
To your deserts what equal recompense
Can I decree? Oh, evermore renowned!
Let Fame her golden trumpet take, and sound
Your glory, tuned to music's loftiest pitch,
And fill the' enchanted Universe around!
The deed itself be your reward; to which
No trifling part I add of realms esteemed as rich!"

12.

He said, and fondly to his bosom strained
Now him, now her; to equal transport charmed,
The Soldan stood, nor in his heart contained
The generous envy that his spirit warmed:
But cried: "And not for nothing am I armed
With this good sword, nor shall I be less slow
To toss the fires!" the Amazon, alarmed
For her endangered fame, replied, "Not so:
Are all to make the' attempt? who stays, if thou shouldst go?"

13.

Argantes too, with features full of pride,
Stood ready to reject his scorned request;
But this the King forestalled, and first replied
With placid aspect to his regal guest;
"Forward thou ever art to manifest
Thyself emphatically great, a knight
Prompt to dispute the laurel with the best,
Consistent with thyself, untired in fight,
Whom no new shape of death or danger can affright!

14.

"I know that, sallying forth, thou deeds wouldst do
Worthy the Soldan; but for all to quit
Your wonted stations in the town, of you,
My bravest heroes, were a thing unfit,
Fraught with alarm; I would not e'en permit
These to depart, with such a jealous care
Guard I their lives, if I could well commit
To other hands the enterprise they dare—
Or if the deed itself of less importance were.

15.

"But since around the' immeasurable tower
The guards so thick are stationed, that a few
Would not suffice, and numbers at this hour
Could not conveniently be spared on new

Fatiguing services, e'en let the two
That, to such risks accustomed, first proposed
The noble task, with prospering stars pursue
Their schemes alone, and realise a boast
Made in no idle mood: they are themselves a host.

16.

"Do thou, as best becomes a king, remain
As regent of the gates; and when the pair,
Of whose success sure hopes I entertain,
Have fired the pile and back their footsteps bear,
Prest by the Christians, with thy Turks repair,
Beat off the fierce pursuers, and prevent
The harms which else revenging rage may dare:"
Thus spoke the King; the Soldan, ill content,
Said not another word, but smiled a sour assent.

17.

"Yet go not," said Ismeno, "till I mix,
Of various grain impregn'd with fiery spume,
Tartareous balls, that where they strike shall fix,
Fixing ignite, and blazing, soon consume
The tower to dust: the witching hour of gloom
Draws nigh; by then the soldiers may remit
Their watch, o'erpowered by languor, and the fume
Of sleep;" all praise the sorcerer's pregnant wit,
And parting wait the hour by him determined fit.

18.

Her sculptured helm, her greaves of silver plate,
And burnished mail aside Clorinda laid;
And in a suit prophetic of her fate,
Sable, and rough with rust, her limbs arrayed,
Where no bright jewel flashed, nor plumage played:
For thus she thought unseen to leave beguiled
The watch, swift stealing through the friendly shade;
'T was then her eunuch came, Arsetes mild,
Who had her cradle rocked, and nursed her from a child.

19.

All careless of fatigue, the good old man
Tended her still; and, chancing now to see
The surreptitious arms, he soon began
To comprehend her risk; and on his knee,
Sore weeping, by the pious memory
Of his past offices, by locks grown grey
In her dear service, and by every plea
Of love and pity, did he long time pray
Her to resign the' attempt, and still she answered nay.

20.

At length he said: "Since in its wrong thy mind
Is obstinate, since to my feeble years,
Since to my silver tresses thou art blind,
Blind to my love, and proof to all my tears,
My piteous prayers, and too prophetic fears,—
Lo, from thy hitherto unknown descent
I rend the veil! that known, do what appears
Good in the sight:"—amazed, Clorinda bent
On him her large dark eyes, and thus the story went.

21.

"In former days o'er Ethiopia reigned,
Happy perchance reigns still, Senapo brave;
Who with his dusky people still maintained
The laws which Jesus to the nations gave:
'T was in his court, a Pagan and a slave,
I lived, o'er thousand maids advanced to guard,
And wait with authorised assumption grave,
On her whose beauteous brows the crown instarred;
True, she was brown, but nought the brown her beauty marred.

22.

"The King adored her, but his jealousies
Equalled the fervours of his love; the smart
At length of sharp suspicion by degrees
Gained such ascendance in his troubled heart,
That from all men in closest bower apart
He mewed her, where e'en Heaven's chaste eyes, the bright
Stars, were but half allowed their looks to dart;
Whilst she, meek, wise, and pure as virgin light,
Made her unkind lord's will her rule and chief delight.

23.

"Hung was her room with storied imageries
Or martyrs and of saints; a Virgin here,
On whose fair cheeks the rose's sweetest dyes
Glowed, was depicted in distress; and near,
A monstrous dragon, which with poignant spear
An errant knight transfixing, prostrate laid:
The gentle Lady oft with many a tear
Before this painting meek confession made
Of secret faults, and mourned, and Heaven's forgiveness prayed.

24.

"Pregnant meanwhile, she bore (and thou wert she)
A daughter white as snow; the' unusual hue,
With wonder, fear, and strange perplexity
Disturbed her, as though something monstrous too:

But, as by sad experience well she knew
His jealous temper and suspicious haste,
She cast to hide thee from thy father's view;
For in his mind (perversion most misplaced!)
Thy snowy chasteness else had argued her unchaste.

25.

"And in thy cradle to his sight exposed
A negro's new-born infant for her own;
And, as the tower wherein she lived enclosed
Was kept by me and by her maids alone, —
To me whose firm fidelity was known,
Who loved and served her with a soul sincere,
She gave thee, beauteous as a rose unblown,
Yet unbaptised; for there, it would appear,
Baptised thou couldst not be in that thy natal year.

26.

"Weeping she placed thee in my arms, to bear
To some far spot; what tongue can tell the rest!
The plaints she used; and with what wild despair
She clasped thee to her fond maternal breast:
How many times 'twixt sighs, 'twixt tears caressed;
How oft, how very oft her vain adieu
Sealed on thy cheek; with what sweet passion pressed
Thy little lips! at length a glance she threw
To Heaven, and cried: 'Great God, that look'st all spirits through! —

27.

" 'If both my heart and members are unstained,
And nought did e'er my nuptial bed defile, —
(I pray not for myself; I stand arraigned
Of thousand sins, and in thy sight am vile;)
Preserve this guiltless infant, to whose smile
The tenderest mother must refuse her breast,
And from her eyes their sweetest bliss exile!
May she with chastity like mine be blessed;
But stars of happier rule have influence o'er the rest!

28.

" 'And thou, blest knight, that from the cruel teeth
Of the grim dragon freed'st that holy maid,
Lit by my hands if ever odorous wreath
Rose from thy altars; if I e'er have laid
Thereon gold, cinnamon, or myrrh, and prayed
For help, through every chance of life display,
In guardianship of her, thy powerful aid!'
Convulsions choked her words, — she swooned away —
And the pale hues of death on her chill temples lay.

29.

"With tears I took thee, in a little ark
So hid by flowers and leaves that none could guess
The secret, brought thee forth 'twixt light and dark,
And, unsuspected, in a Moorish dress,
Passed the town walls: as through a wilderness
Of forests horrid with brown glooms, I took
My pensive way, I saw, to my distress,
A tigress issuing from a bosky nook,
Rage in her scowling brows, and lightning in her look.

30.

"Wild with affright, I on the flowery ground
Cast thee, and instant climbed a tree close by;
The savage brute came up, and glancing round
In haughty menace, saw where thou didst lie;
And, softening to a mild humanity
Her stern regard, with placid gestures meek,
As by thy beauty smit, came courteous nigh;
In amorous pastime fawning licked thy cheek;
And thou on her didst smile, and stroke her mantle sleek.

31.

"With her fierce muzzle and her cruel front
Thy little hands did innocently play;
She offered thee her teats, as is the wont
With nurses, and adapted them, as they,
To thy young lips; nor didst thou turn away,—
She suckled thee! a prodigy so new
Filled me with fresh confusion and dismay;
She, when she saw thee satisfied, withdrew
Into the shady wood, and vanished from my view.

32.

"Again I took thee, and pursued my way
Through woods, and vales, and wildernesses dun;
Till in a little village making stay,
I gave thee secretly in charge to one,
Who fondly nursed thee till the circling sun,
With sixteen months of equatorial heat,
Had tinged thy face; till thou too hadst begun
To prattle of thy joys in murmurs sweet,
And print her cottage floor with indecisive feet.

33.

"But, having passed the autumn of my years,
As sprightly vigour failed and life declined,
Rich in the gold that with her farewell tears
Thy bounteous mother to my hands consigned,

I for my native country inly pined;
After my many toils and wanderings wide,
I longed amidst old faces left behind,
In my dear birthplace tranquil to reside,
And spend life's wintry eve at my own warm fireside.

34.

"To Egypt then, where first my eyes unclosed,
I took, conducting thee, a secret road,
And reached a flood, to equal risks exposed,—
Here robbers chased me, there the torrent flowed:
What should I do? resign my cherished load?
No! yet how shun the meditated theft?
A moment's thought hereon when I bestowed,
I braved the stream; with one bold arm I cleft
Venturous the roaring waves, and bore thee in my left.

35.

"Swift as an arrow flowed the flood; midway,
The jangling tides for ever boil and spin;
There, as a curling snake devours its prey,
The volumed whirlpool gaped, and sucked me in;
Giddy, tossed round, distracted with the din,
Thee then I missed; but the wild waves upbore,—
Propitious breezes caught thy garments thin,
And laid thee safe on the smooth sandy shore;
Which I at length too reached, when hope almost was o'er.

36.

"With joy I took thee up; eve's dusky light
The landscape veiled, when, slumbering on the sand,
Methought the figure of a frowning knight
Came near, and pointing at my breast his brand,
Imperiously exclaimed: 'No more withstand
The solemn charge with which thou long hast striven,
A mother's precept! christen, I command,
This babe, the choice inheritant of heaven;—
To my peculiar care the orphan child is given.

37.

"''T was I gave mercy to the' infuriate brute,
Life to the wind, and mildness to the stream;
And woe to thee, if thou my words dispute,
Or as a vacant phantom disesteem
The heavenly form I am!' with morn's first beam
I woke, and, shaking off the dews of night,
Went forward; but, as false I judged the dream,
And true my faith, I scrupled not to slight
The angel's threat, and still withheld the sacred rite;—

38.

"But as a Pagan bred thee, nor revealed
The secret of thy birth; whilst thou hast grown
Valiant in arms, the phœnix of the field,
And o'er thy sex and Nature's self hast shown
Thyself victorious; hosts hast thou o'erthrown;
Won riches, realms, and palms for ever green;—
What since has happened, thou thyself hast known;
And how in peace, in battle, I have been
Thy sire at once and slave, through each succeeding scene.

39.

"Last morn a sleep, the simile of death,
Ere yet the stars had faded from the sky,
Sank on my soul, and by our holy faith
Again thy Genius in my sleep passed by;
But haughtier was his look, more fierce his cry,—
'Traitor!' he said, 'the hour to disunite
Clorinda from the bonds of earth draws nigh;
Mine shall she yet become in thy despite;
Be thine the woe!' he frowned, and heavenward took his flight.

40.

"Thus, then, be warned! for sadly I suspect
O'er thee, my love, strange accidents impend;
Perhaps the heavens are wroth when we reject
The faith our wise forefathers did commend;
Perhaps that faith is true; oh, condescend,
Deign, I entreat thee, to put off this vest
Of sable, deign thy purpose to suspend!"
He ceased, and wept; fear thrilled her pensive breast,
For on her heart a like remembered vision pressed.

41.

But soon her aspect she serened, and said:
"This faith, which surely strikes my mind as true,
Which thou wouldst have me doubt in thy vain dread,
The faith that with my nurse's milk I drew,
Still will I keep; nor yet resign (beshrew
The soul that would!) my old heroic spear,
And plighted purpose; no, not if I knew
That Death, with that fierce visage which strikes fear
Into the hearts of men, would dog me as a deer!"

42.

She soothes him, smiles on him, and straight retires,
For now the hurrying hours to action call;
And with the dauntless hero who desires
To share her hazard, seeks the palace hall:

Ismeno joins them, and with words of gall
Spurs on the daring hearts that little need
Renewed excitements; gives to each a ball
Of pitch and sulphur; in a hollow reed
Shuts up the fatal flame, and bids them do the deed.

43.

Charged, they depart; and over dale and hill
Circling the valleys, through the darkness scud
With speed incessant, side by side, until
They near the spot where the vast engine stood;
There high their spirit rises, hot the blood
Boils in their veins; desire and scorn combine
To cheer them on, and in their madding mood,
Drawn are their swords; the watch behold the shine
Of coming arms, and loud demand the passing sign.

44.

Mute they move on; "To arms!" exclaim the guard;
Their sudden shouts the valiant couple stun,
But nought their generous enterprise retard,—
They bound abroad, and all concealment shun:
As from the' electric cloud or levelled gun,
At the same instant comes the flash, the thunder,
And bolt of ruin; so for them to run,
Arrive, strike, penetrate, and cleave asunder
The phalanx, is but one, one moment's work of wonder.

45.

Through thousand arms, amidst a thousand blows
They pass, and execute their glorious aim;
Their glimmering lights secreted they disclose,
And tip the black combustible with flame;
Tossed, to the tower it fixes; words are tame
To picture how it creeps, expands, aspires;
How soon it runs o'er all the timbered frame;
How thick the smoke, and in what billowy gyres,
Climbs to the lofty stars, and cloaks their shining fires.

46.

Vast globes of fire amid the ceaseless whirl
Of smoke voluminous, now dim, now bright,
As the cloud fluctuates, high to heaven upcurl,—
The blustering winds add fury to their flight:
Then joined the scattered flames; a sudden light
Strikes the awed host,—they arm in mute amaze;
'T is done! the pile, so terrible in fight,
Sinks in a lofty, broad, columnar blaze;
And one brief hour destroys the workmanship of days.

47.

Two bands meantime to where the pile is burning
Haste from the Camp; which when Argantes sees,
He shouts, "Your blood shall quench the fire!" and turning
His sword against them, with wild menaces
Keeps them at bay; but, yielding by degrees
With fair Clorinda, to the brown hill's bent
Retires, while fast behind the crowds increase,
Like headlong floods which August rains augment;
Hotly they press the chase, and climb with them the' ascent.

48.

The Golden Gate turns on its hinge; and there,
With his armed people stands the Turkish King,
Ready to welcome back the dauntless pair,
If favouring fortune should them homeward bring;
High o'er the ruins of the fosse they spring
Before a grove of spears — the Soldan stout
Gives the known word, the portals wide they fling,
Drive back the Franks, and, wheeling swift about,
Close the strong gates — alas! these shut Clorinda out.

49.

For at the moment when the Turks let fall
The pendulous portcullis, forth she flew
To wreak her ire on Arimon the tall,
Whose daring sword had cut her hauberk through;
This she revenged, nor yet Argantes knew
That she was separate from his side; the glare
Of steel, the anarchy of fight, the crew
That pressed behind, and denseness of the air,
Wholly his sight confused, distracting every care.

50.

But when her sultry anger she had quenched
In the proud blood of dying Arimon,
Saw the gates closed, and how she stood intrenched,
She deemed Clorinda utterly undone,
And looked alone for death; but soon, as none
Pierced her disguise, fresh hopes of safety rose.
With other turns of wit, she feigns her one
Of the same troop, a bold demeanour shews,
And with cool unconcern slips in amidst her foes.

51.

Then, as the still wolf glides to the green wood,
Conscious of crime, and in close ambush lies;
So, by the tumult favoured, and unviewed,
Through the dun shade of the nocturnal skies,

Dissevered from the press, Clorinda flies:
Tancred alone, it seems, the secret knew
Both of her fatal chance and sly device;
Arriving there as Arimon she slew,
He saw her, marked her out, and kept in constant view.

52.

Her would he fight with, deeming her a man
Glorious in arms as lively in address;
Around the winding ramparts swift she ran,
In at some other gate to gain access;
As swift behind her did the' avenger press;
Nor was it long, ere on the gusty breath
Of the night-wind she heard, with some distress,
The sound of arms; whence, turning, "Halt!" she saith;
"What fleet foot news bring'st thou?" He answered, "War and death!"

53.

"War shalt thou have," saith she, "and death, if these
Are thy request;" and here her step she stayed;
Tancred his steed abandons, when he sees
His foe on foot, by lonely hills embayed:
Then she her sabre, he his poignant blade
Draws from the sheath; they stand as mortal foes;
Wrath nerves the hero, haughtiness the maid;
Like two young bulls each smarting with the throes
Of envy, rage, and love, in desperate strife they close.

54

Worthy of royal lists, and the clear shine
Of suns would be the battle, if descried;
Dark Abbess! thou that in thy Gothic shrine
The mouldering relics of their tale dost hide!
Grant me to lift thy cowl, to waft aside
The curtain, and in radiant numbers braid
Their deeds, for endless ages to abide;
So with their glory, glorious shall be made,
In page of high Romance, the memory of thy shade.

55.

They shrink not, trifle not, strive not to smite
By artificial rules, with wary will;
Stand not on postures or on points, the night
And their blind rage forbid the tricks of skill;
But swords crash horribly with swords, and shrill
The mountain echo shrieks along the plain;
Not a foot stirs, — where stood, there stand they still;
But aye their hands in motion they maintain;
And not a lounge, or foin, or slash descends in vain.

56.

Shame stings disdain to vengeance, vengeance breeds
New shame, — thus passion runs a ceaseless round;
To spite despite, to rage fresh rage succeeds,
The agony to strike, the lust to wound:
And now the battle blends in narrower ground;
No room have they to foin, no room to lash;
Their blades flung back, like butting rams they bound,
Fight with the hilts, wild, savage, raging, rash,
And shield at sounding shield, and helm at helmet dash.

57.

Thrice in his boisterous arms the maid he pressed,
And thrice was forced to loose his sinewy clasp;
She had no fancy to be so caressed;
Empassioned Love is not an angry asp.
Again with eagerness their swords they grasp,
And tinge them ruddy as Vesuvian fire,
In blood of many wounds; till, tired, they gasp
For every breath, — some paces back retire;
And from their long fatigues all pantingly respire.

58.

Faint on their swords, with like exhausted frame,
Alike they rest, and echo gaze for gaze:
Fades the last star; Aurora, robed in flame,
Unbars Elysium, and the morning plays;
Tancred perceives, beneath its grateful rays,
From her the trickling blood profusely rain,
And glories in the languor she displays;
Oh man, vain man! poor fool of pride and pain!
Puffed up with every breath from Fortune's wavering vane!

59.

Why that proud smile? sad, oh how sad, shall be
Thy acted triumphs when the' illusion clears!
Thine eyes shall weep, if still the light they see,
For every drop of blood a sea of tears:
Thus resting, gazing, full of hopes and fears,
The bleeding warriors, silent as the dead,
Stood for a space; at length some feelings fierce
Tancred deposed, — kind thoughts rose in their stead,
He wished her name to know, and, breaking silence, said:

60.

"Hard is our chance, our prowess thus to spend
On deeds which silence and these shades conceal;
To which thwart Fortune yields no praise, no friend
On our viewed acts to set his speaking seal!

Yet, if amid the sullen shock of steel
Prayers may have access, courtesies find place,
Thy name, thy country, and thy rank reveal;
That I, whatever issue crown the case,
May know at least who gives my death or victory grace."

61.

Sternly she said: "Thy prayer no access wins;
Custom forbids; but, whatsoe'er my name,
Thou seest before thee one of those brave twins,
Who gave your towering structure to the flame."
Fired at her answer, Tancred made exclaim:
"In evil hour hast thou thy guilt avowed;
Thy speech and silence are to me the same,
Discourteous wretch, contemptible as proud!
Both chide my sloth, and both for vengeance plead aloud."

62.

Rage to their hearts returns, and spurs them on,
Though weak, to war; dire war! from which the sleights
Of art are banished, whence all strength is gone,
And in the room of both, brute fury fights:
Oh, sharp his falchion, sharp her sabre smites!
What bloody gaps they make through plate and chain,
In their soft flesh! revenge, revenge requites;
If life parts not, 'tis only that disdain
Knits it in pure despite to the rebellious brain.

63.

As the deep Euxine, though the wind no more
Blows, that late tossed its billows to the stars,
Stills not at once its rolling and its roar,
But with its coasts long time conflicting jars;
Thus, though their quickly-ebbing blood debars
Force from their blades as vigour from their arms,
Still lasts the frenzy of the flame which Mars
Blew in their breasts; sustained by whose strong charms,
Yet heap they strokes on strokes, yet harms inflict on harms.

64.

But now, alas! the fatal hour arrives
That must shut up Clorinda's life in shade;
In her fair bosom deep his sword he drives;
'Tis done — life's purple fountain bathes the blade!
The golden flowered cymar of light brocade,
That swathed so tenderly her breasts of snow,
Is steeped in the warm stream: the hapless maid
Feels her end nigh; her knees their strength forego;
And her enfeebled frame droops languishing and low.

65.

He, following up the thrust with taunting cries,
Lays the pierced Virgin at his careless feet;
She, as she falls, in mournful tones outsighs,
Her last faint words, pathetically sweet;
Which a new spirit prompts, a spirit replete
With charity, and faith, and hope serene,
Sent dove-like down from God's pure mercy-seat;
Who, though through life his rebel she had been,
Would have her die a fond repentant Magdalene.

66.

"Friend, thou hast won; I pardon thee, and oh
Forgive thou me! I fear not for this clay,
But my dark soul — pray for it, and bestow
The sacred rite that laves all stains away:"
Like dying hymns heard far at close of day,
Sounding I know not what in the soothed ear
Of sweetest sadness, the faint words make way
To his fierce heart, and, touched with grief sincere,
Streams from his pitying eye the' involuntary tear.

67.

Not distant, gushing from the rocks, a rill
Clashed on his ear; to this with eager pace
He speeds — his hollow casque the waters fill —
And back he hurries to the deed of grace;
His hands as aspens tremble, whilst they raise
The locked aventayle of the unknown knight; —
God, for thy mercy! 'tis her angel face!
Aghast and thunderstruck, he loathes the light;
Ah, knowledge best unknown! ah, too distracting sight!

68.

Yet still he lived; and mustering all his powers
To the sad task, restrained each wild lament,
Fain to redeem by those baptismal showers
The life his sword bereft; whilst thus intent
The hallowing words he spoke, with ravishment
Her face transfigured shone, and half apart
Her bland lips shed a lively smile that sent
This silent speech in sunshine to his heart:
"Heaven gleams; in blissful peace behold thy friend depart!"

69.

A paleness beauteous as the lily's mixt
With the sweet violet's, like a gust of wind
Flits o'er her face; her eyes on Heaven are fixt,
And Heaven on her returns its looks as kind:

Speak she can not; but her cold hand, declined,
In pledge of peace on Tancred she bestows;
And to her fate thus tenderly resigned,
In her meek beauty she expires, and shows
But as a smiling saint indulging soft repose.

70.

But when he saw her starlike spirit set,
The self-possession which had manned his soul,
Bent to the storm of anguishing regret
That o'er his bosom burst beyond control:
Pangs of despair convulsed his heart; life stole
As to its last recess; death's icy dew
Bathed his pale brow, his blood forebore to roll;
Till like the breathless dead the living grew,
In chillness, silence, air, and attitude, and hue.

71.

And sure his life, impatient of the light,
Struggling had burst in its rebellious scorn
From its weak chain, and followed in its flight
The beauteous spirit, that, but just re-born,
Had spread its wings in sunshine of the morn,—
Had not a party of the Franks, dispread
In search of water o'er the gleaming lawn,
By providential guidance thither led,
Seen where he lay supine, the dying by the dead.

72.

Their Chief, though distant, by his armour knew
The Latin Prince, and hastened to the place;
The lifeless beauty he remembered too
For Tancred's love, and mourned her fatal case;
He would not leave a form so full of grace,
Albeit a Pagan, as he deemed, a prey
To wolves, but lifting, in a little space,
To others' arms both bodies whence they lay,
Took straight to Tancred's tent his melancholy way.

73.

Not yet the knight, so equably and slow
They marched, from his dark trance awakened was;
But feeble groans at intervals might shew
Some sands still glided in his vital glass;
The Lady lay a mute and stirless mass,
Nor breath, nor pulse gave hope that life was there
Incorporate with its beauty: thus they pass;
Thus, side by side, the two, lamenting, bear;
And in adjoining rooms dispose with silent care.

74.

His pitying squires drew nigh; with busy pain
Chafed his chill temples, and his mail unbound;
His languid eyes at length he oped again,
Felt the physician's hand, the smarting wound,
And heard, yet dubious of his sense, the sound
Of whispering lips, — where was he, and with whom?
Long with bewildered gaze he looked around;
At length his squires, at length he knew the room,
And in low feeble words lamented thus his doom:

75.

"Yet do I breathe? yet live to view the beams
Of this curst day, more odious than the shade?
Clear witness of my blind misdeed, it streams
To' accuse my rashness, and my guilt upbraid:
Ah, coward hand! why now art thou afraid,
Thou, so well versed in all the turns of strife,
The impious minister of death repaid
In infamy, to grasp the vengeful knife,
And cut the pall-black thread of this opprobrious life!

76.

"Take the fell steel, and hide it to the hilt
Within me, — my sad heart in sunder cleave!
But thou, perhaps, inured to deeper guilt,
May'st deem it mercy such quick ease to give:
Then as a dire example let me live,
Monster of luckless Love! a mark for men
To point at and abhor; this base reprieve
To shameful life will be the' alone fit pain
For such enormous guilt, and of so dark a grain.

77.

"Vext by just Furies, anguish, grief, and care,
A wandering maniac must I live — to run,
Shrieking, from phantoms with which sleep shall scare
My soul, when Night her orgies has begun;
To hold in horror and in hate the Sun,
That did my fatal error shew; to eye
Myself with fear, and strive myself to shun; —
Evermore flying, evermore to fly,
Whilst hell's pursuing fiends are ever howling nigh!

78.

"But where, alas, where lie the relics chaste
Of my slain angel? what my cruel scorn
Left whole, perchance some savage of the waste —
The lion mangles, or the wolf has torn;

Ah spoils for them too rich! dear beauty, born
To different end! too sweet, too precious fruit!
Poor injured maiden! whom the shades forlorn
And lone hills have betrayed, first in dispute
To me, and next in prey to some ferocious brute.

79.

"Yet will I go, and the loved spoils collect;
Dear limbs! where late the hues of beauty bloomed;
But if the wolf, in hungry disrespect,
Those virgin relics has indeed consumed,
In the same cavern let me be entombed,
Let the same jaws ingulf me! hailed by me
Will the stroke come; but, preyed on or inhumed,
A glorious sepulchre, my love, 'twill be,
Where'er thy bones are cast, to be inurned with thee."

80.

But being told that her lamented form
Lay in his tent, a beam of joy appeared,
Like lightning flashing through a sable storm,
To light his aspect, and the darkness cleared;
Straight from the couch of his repose he reared
The heavy burden of his limbs, and slow—
Weak as an infant, full of pain, but cheered
By her dear image, thither strove to go,
On frail unsteady steps, loose staggering to and fro.

81.

But when he came, and in her beauteous breast
Saw the red gash his murderous hand had made,
And her late radiant aspect calmed to rest,
Like a nocturnal sky, in livid shade—
His heightening colour was perceived to fade;
A trembling ague rocked his frame; and there
Would he have sunk, but for immediate aid;
"Sweet face," he sighed, "thou canst make death look fair,
But hast not power to soothe or sweeten my despair!

82.

"Fair hand! dear pledge of pardoning amity!
Late forceful pleader, uttering love's farewell!
What do I find thee now? ah, what am I!
And you, light limbs, that did in flight excel
The graceful motions of the fleet gazelle,
What but upbraiding vestiges are ye
Of my irreparable rage? too well
My stony eyes and cruel hand agree,
When, what the one destroyed, the other brooks to see;—

83.

"And see without a tear! then weep, my blood,
Since my remorseless eyes to weep forbear!"
Frantic he spoke; and in his madding mood,
Strong with desire of death, began to tear
His bands away, and to his nails laid bare
Each irritated wound, — the blood like rain
Gushed forth, and in this fit of wild despair
He must have died, had not excess of pain
Caused him to swoon away, and life perforce retain.

84.

Borne to his bed again, his fluttering sprite
Back to its hated mansion they reclaim;
The dire mischance and anguish of the knight
This while was widely spread by babbling fame;
And thither came the Chief; and thither came,
With his loved friends, the Solitary Sage;
But neither grave admonishment could tame,
Nor pity soothe, nor gentlest prayers assuage
Of his distracted grief the stubbornness and rage.

85.

As in a tender limb the serpent's sting,
With oils fomented, doth the keener smart;
So their kind solaces of love but bring
Acuter pangs to his afflicted heart!
But reverend Peter, who the faithful part
Of a good shepherd ever undertook
With his sick flock, blest counsels to impart,
His long romantic passion would rebuke,
And from its frenzied trance, his wilful spirit shook:

86.

"O Tancred! Tancred! how unlike that mind,
Whose first unfoldings did so bright appear!
What cloud, what darkness does thy vision blind,
What sorcery shuts thy intellectual ear?
This thy sore trouble is instruction clear
Sent from the Lord; dost thou not see the ray
That would direct thy feet? dost thou not hear
The voice that calls thee to the safer way,
Wherein thou first didst walk, whence now thy footsteps stray?

87.

"To actions worthy thy first love, his voice
Recals thee, vowed to this divine crusade;
Which thou hast left (unwise, unworthy choice!)
For the blind worship of a Pagan maid.

Happy misfortune! Heaven on thee has laid
In tenderest clemency its chastening rod;
Thy fault, thyself has it the agent made
Of thine own good; and is it in this mode
That thou the gift receiv'st, and own'st the grace bestowed?

88.

"Scorn'st thou then, ingrate, the salubrious gift
Of God, with God incensed? unhappy! think
Whither this angry whirlwind bears thee — swift
O'er dark Eternity's tremendous brink;
Down the deep precipice about to sink,
Thou hang'st at mercy of the slenderest breath;
Call, I entreat, call back thy senses, shrink
From the momentous danger, look beneath,
And curb this impious woe, that leads to endless death!"

89.

That second death the sufferer's soul alarmed,
And, all relinquishing his wish to die,
Their soothing words he entertained, and calmed
The hurricane within; yet still a sigh —
A groan at times escaped; by fits his eye
Would weep, and his sad tongue lament aloud,
Now holding with himself wild colloquy,
Now with his love, who from some rosy cloud
To his fond plaints perchance an ear of pity bowed.

90.

On her at smile of morn, for her at frown
Of eve he calls, he murmurs, and complains;
Like a lorn nightingale when some rude clown
Has stol'n her plumeless brood; in piercing strains
She fills the dying winds, and woods, and plains
With her sweet quarrel; all night long she weeps,
And to the listening stars repeats her pains,
Till morn with rosy tears the forest steeps; —
Then on his streaming eyes awhile calm slumber creeps.

91.

And, clad in starry robes, the maid for whom
He mourned, appears amid his morning dreams;
Fairer than erst, but by the deathless bloom
And heavenly radiance that around her beams,
Graced, not disguised; in sweetest act she seems
To stoop, and wipe away the tears that flow
From his dim eyes: "Behold what glory streams
Round me," she cries; "how beauteous now I show,
And for my sake, dear friend, this waste of grief forego!

92.

"Thee for my bliss I thank; Earth's sordid clod
Thou by a happy error forced to quit,
And for the glorious Paradise of God
By sacred baptism mad'st my spirit fit:
There now midst angels and blest saints I sit
In rapturous love and fellowship divine;
There may our souls together yet be knit,
And there in fields where suns eternal shine,
Shalt thou at once enjoy their loveliness and mine;—

93.

"If by thy passions unseduced, if thou
Grudge not thyself the bliss; live then, Sir Knight,
Know that I love thee, far as Love can bow
For aught of earthly mould a Child of Light!"
As thus she spoke, her glowing eyes shone bright
With an immortal's fervour—rosy red,
She in the mild irradiance shut from sight
Her face, like a sweet flower, her fans outspread,
And in his drooping soul celestial comfort shed.

94.

Soothed he awoke, and to the hands discreet
Of skilled practitioners his wounds resigned;
The whilst his friends interred, with spices sweet,
The limbs late vital with so great a mind:
And if the tomb to which they were consigned
Was not of pure Pentelican, nor graced
With sculptures planned by architects refined,
The stone was choice, and wrought with all the taste
The urgent time allowed, in form antiquely chaste.

95.

There by bright lamps that in long order shine,
With many a dirge, her bones in earth they lay;
And on the smooth trunk of a leafless pine
Her arms, hung round with cypress and with bay,
In trophy to her fame aloft display;
And thither did the Prince his footsteps turn
All languid as he was, at break of day,
With awe and melancholy calm concern,
Unseen her grave to view, and clasp her reverenced urn.

96.

When reached the tomb, his spirit's dolorous gaol,
Prescribed by Heaven's inscrutable decree,
Long on the pile, mute, motionless, and pale,
His hollow eyes in absent reverie

He fixed: at length to his relief a sea
Of tears gushed forth; and, gathering voice, he said,
His accents prefaced with a sigh: "Oh ye
So loved, so honoured tablets of the dead,
In which my soul abides, o'er which my tears are shed!—

97.

"Not of unliving dust are ye the shrine,
But Love's quick ashes, canonised by woe;
From you I catch his wonted fires divine,
Less sweet, less grateful, but as warm they glow;
Take the sad sighs and kisses I bestow,
Bathed in the fondest tears that ever blessed
The grave of luckless beauty; take, and oh
Convey each sigh breathed forth, each kiss impressed,
To the beloved remains that in your bosom rest!

98.

"For if to her fair spoils that fairest Saint
E'er gives a glance, thy pity and my love
Will not offend; since, neither can the taint
Of scorn or hatred reach the blest above;
She who forgave my crime, can ne'er reprove
My zeal—this hope alone my tears can dry;
It was, she knows, my hand alone that drove
The murdering sword; nor can it irk that I,
Who lived adoring her, adoringly should die.

99.

"And die adoring her I shall; blest day,
Whenever it arrives! but far more blest,
If as now round thy polished sides I stray,
I then be taken to thy sacred breast!
Ah! let our blending souls together rest
In heaven, our ashes in the self-same tomb!
If I by death be of the bliss possessed
Which life denied me,—might I but presume
This, this to hope indeed, delightful were my doom!"

100.

Meanwhile in Salem, of Clorinda's fall
At first confused and floating whispers rise;
Till, ascertained and soon divulged, through all
The' astonished City the loud rumour flies,
Mingled with tears, and shrieks, and women's cries;
As though the town itself, the sacred town,
Were now by storm become the victor's prize;
And in the rage of flying flames went down
Their temples, spires, abodes, and towers of old renown.

101.

But every eye was on Arsetes turned,
Who stood, a piteous spectacle of care;
He not as others his dear mistress mourned;
His eyeballs, stony with supreme despair,
Shed not a tear; but fiercely did he tear
His face, his bosom, and with ashes strowed
The hoary honours of his silver hair:
As thus he drew the' attention of the crowd,
Midst them Argantes came, and thus harangued aloud:

102.

"Much did I wish, when conscious that the gate
Was closed against the' incomparable maid,
To follow straight,—I ran to share her fate,
Protect her life, or be beside her laid;
What did I not? what said I not? I prayed,
Adjured the King, by all that was most dear,
To' unbar the gates: he, of the Franks afraid,
Denied my suit, though tendered with a tear;
And, men of Syria! he has sole dominion here.

103.

"Ah! had I then gone forth, or safe from strife
I the brave heroine had brought off, or closed
Where she has made earth purple, my sad life
In memorable decease, a glorious ghost!
But what could I do more? the starry host,
And counsels both of Gods and men were set
In adverse influence, to my wish opposed;
Cold in her grave the Virgin lies; but yet,
There are some mournful dues which I will ne'er forget.

104.

"Hear, all Jerusalem, my vow! Heaven, hear!
And, if I fail my promise to fulfil,
Blast me with fire! deep, deep revenge I swear,
On the base Frank that did Clorinda kill!
Never from battle shall my sword lie still,
However fully fleshed upon the foe;
Ne'er be dissevered from my side, until
I stab curst Tancred to the heart, and throw
His ruffian carcase out, to feed the hound and crow!"

105.

The warrior ceased; and to his fierce harangue
From the soothed crowds applauding shouts succeed;
Hushed their sore weeping, lost is every pang,
In the mere fancy of the' expected deed.

Oh blind, presumptuous vow! far different seed
Than flowering hope imagines, to his scythe
Time will devote; thyself, thyself shalt bleed,
In equal battle bleed, and dying writhe
Beneath his sword o'er whom thou now exultest blithe!

CANTO XIV

ARGUMENT

Godfrey, in vision rapt to Paradise,
Is warned of God to call back to the host
The good Rinaldo, wherefore he replies,
When his recal the Princes have proposed,
With favour; Peter, whom the Holy Ghost
Had previously instructed, now prepares
To send two knights where on the nigh sea-coast
A courteous wizard lives, who first declares
To them Armide's deceits, then how to scape her snares.

1.

Now from the fresh soft lap and twilight bower
Of her still mother flew the gentle Queen
Of Shade, with light airs compassed, and a shower
Of starlight dews, pure, precious and serene:
And, shaking o'er the universal scene
The humid border of her veil, impearled
With honey-balm the flowers and forests green;
Whilst the sweet zephyrs their still wings unfurled,
And fanned to dulcet sleep and peace the' o'erwearied world.

2.

Each busy thought of rude disturbing day
In sweet oblivious quietude was drowned;
But He, whose wisdom heaven and earth doth sway,
Yet kept his ruling watch, insphered and crowned
With ceaseless light; and from heaven's starry round
Casting on Godfrey the ecstatic beam
Of his mild eye, to him in sleep profound,
By silent precept of a missioned dream,
Of his Almighty Mind revealed the will supreme.

3.

In the rich Orient, near the valves of gold
Whence the sun sallies, turns a crystalline
Clear gate, whose doors in harmony unfold,
Ere pale the planets and the day-beams shine:
'Tis thence the glorious dreams which the Divine
In grace to pure and holy spirits sends,

Issuing fly forth; from that pictorial shrine
This dream to pious Godfrey now descends,
And o'er his placid face its radiant wings extends.

4.

Nor dream nor gifted vision e'er portrayed
Such beautiful or lively forms, as here
To Godfrey's fancy this, which now displayed
Of heaven and of its stars the secrets clear;
As in the mirror of a glassy sphere,
All was at once presented to his sight
That in them is; he seemed, in swift career,
Caught up to an expanse of perfect white,
Adorned with thousand flames that gave a golden light.

5.

Here, as the moving spheres, the vast blue sky,
The lights, and the rich music he admires,
Lo, to his side a winged knight draws nigh,
With sunbeams crowned, and circumfused with fires!
And in a voice to which the clearest choirs
And perfect marriage of sweet sounds below,
Breathed out from beauteous lips or golden wires,
Would be but discord, said: "Canst thou bestow
No smile, or dost thou not thy once loved Hugo know?" [1]

6.

To which the Duke replied: "That aspect new,
Which like the glowing sun so brightly shines,
Has dazzled so mine intellectual view
That it can ill recal its ancient lines:"
And saying this, to greet him he inclines;
Thrice with a fond affectionate embrace
Around his neck his loving arms he twines;
And thrice the' encircled form and radiant face
Fly like a summer cloud, or shade the sunbeams chase.

7.

Prince Hugo smiled: "And think not, as of old,"
He said, "that earthly robes my limbs invest;
My naked spirit here dost thou behold,
A simple shape; I dwell, a glorious guest,
In this the' illumined City of the Blest:
This is the temple of our God, the' abode
Of his true knights; and here thou too shall rest:"
"Ah, when?" he cried; "if aught in me this mode
Of bliss obstruct, loose now, O loose the' encumbering load!"

1. Brother to the King of France, a military leader who was prevented by death from taking part in the Crusade. See I, 37, not included in these selections.

8.

"Soon!" replied Hugo; "soon in glory thou
Shalt gathered be to our triumphant band;
But many a laurel first must grace thy brow,
Much blood be shed by thy victorious hand;
The Pagan armies yet thou must withstand,
And from their grasp by many a toilsome deed
Wresting the sceptre of the Holy Land,
Fix the Frank empire; then it is decreed,
That to thy gentle rule thy brother shall succeed.

9.

"But now look round more fixedly; behold—
To quicken for the skies thy pure desires,
These lucid halls and starry orbs of gold,
Which, whirling round, the' Eternal Mind inspires!
Observe the beauty of those siren choirs
Of seraphs; hear the' angelical sweet strains,
In concord sung to their celestial lyres;
Next view," he said, and pointed to the plains
Of earth, below, "what yon terrestrial globe contains.

10.

"Think of your earthly titles and designs;
With what a vile reward is virtue crowned!
Mark what a little ring your pride confines,
What naked deserts your vain glories bound!
Earth like an island the blue sea flows round,
Now, called the Mighty Deep from coast to coast,
Now, the vast Ocean; to that pompous sound
Nought corresponds, to authorise such a boast—
'Tis but a shallow pool, a narrow marsh at most."

11.

The Spirit said: and he his sight let fall
On earth, and smiled with a serene disdain;
Shrunk to a point, seas, streams, and mountains tall
He sees, remote, but here distinguished plain;
And much he wondered that weak man should strain
At shades and mists, that swim before his eyes,
And chase those radiant bubbles of the brain—
Capricious Fame, and Power, that, followed, flies,
Nor heed the' inviting voice that calls him to the skies.

12.

Wherefore he answered: "Since not yet thy God
Is pleased to call me from this cage of clay,
Which path of life is safest to be trod
Mid Earth's erroneous windings, deign to say."

Hugo replied: "The least fallacious way
To happiness, indeed the' alone sure track,
Is that thou walkest; turn not then astray;
Alone I would advise thee, be not slack
From his far exile now to call Rinaldo back.

13.

"For, as by Providence divine to thee
The golden sceptre, the supreme command
Of that adventure is consigned, so he
As sovereign agent of thy schemes, must stand
Assistant to the task: the first and grand
Office is thine; the second the Most High
Concedes to him; he is the army's hand,
And thou the head, — none other can supply
His place, not e'en thyself, thy state does this deny.

14.

"He, he alone has license to cut down
The forest guarded by such magic art;
From him thy troops, despairing of the town
From the deserters they have seen depart,
On flight themselves debating, shall take heart,
And, nerved with livelier strength by the mere sight
Of one so valiant, fresh for conquest start;
The bulwarks he shall shatter, scale their height,
And the vast Memphian hosts o'erpower in mortal fight."

15.

He ceased, and Godfrey answered: "His return
Would be most grateful to my feelings; thou,
Who every secret purpose dost discern,
Know'st if I love him, as I here avow:
But say, what offers must I make him? how
Soothe his vext spirit? where my heralds send?
Wilt thou that I for his recal allow
Courtship, or use command? declare, blest friend,
How I to make this suit may fitly condescend."

16.

"God" — in reply the' angelic spirit said,
"Who with such high regards thy rank has graced,
Wills, that to thee all reverence yet be paid
By those who under thy command are placed;
Shew thou not then facility nor haste;
Make no request; for, haply, this would lead
To scorn, and thus thy dignity, debased,
Might fall into contempt; but asked, concede
And yield, when first thy knights shall for forgiveness plead.

17.

"Guelph shall petition thee (by God inspired)
To' absolve the headstrong youth of that offence
To which intemperate wrath his spirit fired,
That he to honour may return; dispense
Thy grace; and though in loosest indolence
And love intoxicate, he now reclines
On a far foreign shore, doubt not but thence
He will return, ere many a morning shines,
Apt for thy pressing needs and difficult designs.

18.

"Your Hermit Peter, to whose piercing sight
Heaven of its secrets gives perception clear,
Shall thy sent messengers direct aright,
Where certain tidings they of him shall hear;
The sage to whose abode their ship must steer,
Will shew the arts and methods they must use
To free, and home conduct the wandering peer;
Thus Heaven at length shall, partial to thy views,
Beneath the sacred Cross each errant chief reduce.

19.

"Farewell! yet ere I end, hear one brief thing,
Which will, I know, delight thy noble mind;
Your blood shall mix, and from that union spring
A glorious issue, dear to all mankind!"
He said; and like a cloud before the wind,
Or azure mist upon the mountain's crest
By the hot shining of the sun refined,
Vanished away; sleep fled, and left his breast
With wonder and deep joy confusedly possessed.

20.

His eyes he opes, and sees the Orient blaze
With the high-risen Aurora; from repose
He starts, in iron robes his limbs arrays,
And o'er his back the purple mantle throws;
Then takes his seat; for, soon as morning glows,
To his pavilion throng the knights of state,
In customary council to expose
Their sentiments, and of the war debate;
Thither they all were met, and round in silence sate.

21.

Then Guelph arose, full of the new design
Which had his mind inspired, and drawing near,
To Godfrey thus made suit: "O, Prince benign,
What I propose receive with favouring ear!

I come to ask, with all thy nobles here,
Grace for a crime, and, if it must be said,
A crime yet recent; whence it may appear,
Perchance, that my request is hasty made,
In an untimely hour, ere yet maturely weighed.

22.

"But when I think that to a Prince so mild
My suit is proffered, and for whose brave sake,
That, too, the intercessor is not vilde
Nor mean of rank, I cannot choose but take
The prayer for granted, which will surely make
All happy, and obtain deserved applause;
Recal Rinaldo! I my honour stake
That he his blood will, in the common cause,
Shed to redeem his fault, and satisfy the laws.

23.

"What daring hand but his those haunted bowers,
So feared, shall e'er successfully assail?
Who, of a firmer heart, more vigorous powers,
May hope the risks of death to countervail?
Thou shalt behold him o'er yon towers prevail,
Shatter the wall, beat down the brazen door,
And singly, before all, the rampart scale:
Restore him to the camp, kind Sire, restore!
Its hope, its heart, its hand! by Jesu I implore!

24.

"To me a nephew, to thyself restore
An agent, prompt for each sublime attack;
Leave him not sunk in slumber, I implore,—
To glory, to himself, invite him back;
Let him but follow the triumphal track
Of thy blest flag, the world shall witness be
Of his improvement: he shall not be slack
To do illustrious deeds, beholding thee,
Ranked beneath thy command, fulfilling thy decree!"

25.

Thus sued the high-born Guelpho, and the rest
With partial murmurs the request improved;
Godfrey, as though revolving in his breast
A thing before unthought of, as behoved,
Paused, and made answer: "Can I but be moved
To grace and mercy, when you all are bent
To press me? your petition stands approved;
Let rigour yield — what you with one consent
Desire, shall be my law: I yield, and am content.

26.

"Let the brave youth return, but let him rein
Henceforth his rage more wisely; and take heed,
That the high hopes our armies entertain
Of his maturing years, be matched indeed
By equal actions; now, my lord, proceed —
'Tis fit the wanderer be recalled by thee;
Return he will, I trust, with willing speed;
Choose then the messengers, and o'er the sea
Or sands direct them where you judge the knight to be."

27.

He ceased, and thus the warrior Dane: "I pray
To be the man commissioned; I shall slight
All danger, doubt, or distance of the way,
So I may give this sword to whom of right
It henceforth must belong:" the Danish knight
Was resolute of heart, and brave of hand;
The offer thus gave Guelpho much delight:
"Thy wish," said he, "is mine; and with thee bland
Ubaldo, sage and sure, the mission will demand."

28.

Ubald in early lifetime had surveyed
Much of the world, in various realms had been;
From frozen zones to where palmettos shade
The sultry Ethiop, had most nations seen;
Their rites observed, and with perception keen
Learned, at whatever port his bark might touch,
To imitate the language, mode, and mien
Of the rude native; thus, his parts were such,
That, in his court retained, Lord Guelpho loved him much.

29.

These were the knights appointed to recal
The noble fugitive; and Guelph ordained
That they should shape their journey to the hall
Where Bohemond in kingly splendour reigned;
For that the warrior there was entertained,
By public fame had through the host been spread,
And as a certain fact was still maintained:
The Hermit, knowing they were much misled,
Amidst them entered now, and interposing said: —

30.

"In following, Signior, the fallacious breath
Of public rumour, you pursue a guide
Headstrong and treacherous, which, if not to death,
From the right path will lead your steps aside:

No! give your pinnace o'er the sea to glide;
To Ascalon's near shores your sails commend;
Where a swift stream rebuts the salt sea-tide,
A hermit you will meet, my trusty friend,
Of your intent forewarned — to all his words attend.

31.

"Much from the foresight of his own clear mind,
Much of your voyage has he learned from me;
Wise as he is, the Senior you will find
As much distinguished for his courtesy,
His affable discourse, and manners free."
Instructed thus, no more did Charles inquire,
Nor Ubald more; but, as a fixt decree,
Obeyed those accents, which celestial fire
Was, as they surely knew, accustomed to inspire.

32.

They bid adieu; impatience spurs them on —
Without delay they launch, and drive before
The willing wind direct for Ascalon,
Where the blue ocean breaks against the shore:
Scarce had they caught the hoarse and hollow roar
Of breakers on the coast than they beheld
The' anticipated stream its waters pour
Into the sea, by recent torrents swelled,
And o'er its rocky banks with headlong force impelled.

33.

High o'er its banks the unrestricted flood,
Swift as a flying shaft, its waters rolled:
Whilst in confusion and suspense they stood,
A Sire appeared, right venerably old,
Crowned with beech-leaves; long robes his limbs enfold
Of whitest grain — he shook a charming-rod —
The surge grew calm; and, curious to behold,
With unwet feet, in only sandals shod,
He on the waters walked, and toward the vessel trod.

34.

As o'er the Rhine when winter its broad tide
Has in smooth chains of solid silver bound,
The village girls in crowds securely glide,
With long swift strokes, in many a playful round;
So on these orient waves, though neither sound
Nor crystallised to ice, this ancient man
Walked to the deck on which in awe profound
The knights stood fixt, stood stupified to scan
This singular, strange sight; he came, and thus began:

35.

"Oh friends, a perilous and painful quest
You urge, and much in need of guidance stand!
The knight you seek, far in the golden West
Lies on a wild, unknown, and Gentile strand:
Much, oh how much for you remains on hand
To dare and do! what coasts must you not clear,
What spacious seas, and what long tracts of land!
Beyond the limits of our eastern sphere,
You must your search extend, your winged pinnace steer!

36.

"Yet scorn not first to view the hidden cell
Which I my secret hermitage have made:
Momentous things you there shall hear me tell,
Most requisite for you to know;"—he said,
And made the waves yield passage; they obeyed—
Murmuring sweet music, they receded swift;
And, here and there dividing, high o'erhead
Hung curling, like some proud and beetling clift,
That o'er the mining deep is seen its brows to lift.

37.

He took them by the hand and led them down
The river's depth beneath the roaring main,
By such pale light, as through some forest brown
Streams from the yellow moon, when in her wane;
They see the spacious caverns that contain
The weight of waters which above-ground break
So freely forth; that in one lucid vein
Burst in clear springs, or, more expansive, make
The broad smooth-sliding stream, slight pool, or sheeted lake.

38.

The cisterns there whence Ganges takes his course,
Po, and renowned Hydaspes, strike their eye;
Don, Eúphrates, and Tanais; nor its source
Mysterious does the Nile to them deny;
More deep, a river flowing brightly by
O'er beds of living sulphur they behold,
Brimmed with quicksilver; these the sun on high
Ripens, refines, and in their secret mould
Binds in resplendent veins of silver, zinc, or gold.

39.

And the rich flood did all its banks instar
With precious stones, enchanting to the sight;
Which, like bright lamps, illumined wide and far
The den's black gloom with luxury of light:

There, in blue lustre, shone the sapphire bright,
Heaven's native tint; the jacinth glistered mild;
Flamed the fine ruby, flashed the diamond white,
In virgin state, on sparkling opals piled,
And, gay with cheerful green, the lovely emerald smiled.

40.

In dumb amazement the two warriors passed,
And all their thoughts to these strange scenes applied
Said not a word! Ubaldo spake at last,
And thus in faltering speech addressed his guide:
"O Father, say where now we are! this tide—
Where does it flow? thine own estate explain;
Do I behold aright? or is this pride
And prodigality of wealth a vain
Illusion? scarce I know, such wonder wraps my brain."

41.

"You," he replied, "are in the spacious womb
Of earth, the general mother! not e'en ye
Could ever thus have pierced into the gloom
Of her rich bowels, unless brought by me:
I lead you to my home, which you will see
Illumed with curious light, a splendid place—
I was by birth a Pagan; but, set free
From Pagan sin, regenerate grown by grace,
I was baptised, and now Christ's holy rule embrace.

42.

"Think not my magic wonders wrought by aid
Of Stygian angels summoned up from hell;
Scorned and accurst be those who have essayed
Her gloomy Dives and Afrits to compel,
By fumes or voices, talisman or spell!—
But by perception of the secret powers
Of mineral springs, in nature's inmost cell,
Of herbs, in curtain of her greenwood bowers,
And of the moving stars, on mountain-tops and towers.

43.

"For in these caves mid glooms and shadows brown,
Far from the sun, not always I abide;
But oft on sacred Carmel's flowery crown,
And oft on odorous Lebanon reside;
There without veil I see the planets glide;
Notice each aspect; chronicle each phase
Of Mars and Venus; every star beside,
That, swift or slow, of kind or froward rays,
Revolves and shines in heaven, is naked to my gaze.

44.

"Beneath my feet I view, or rare or dense,
The clouds, now dark, now beautiful in show;
Of rains and dews the generation; whence,
Thwart or direct, the winds and tempests blow;
How lightnings kindle, why they dart below
In orb'd or writhen rays; so near I scan
The fireball, comet, and the showery bow
Wove in Heaven's loom, that I at length began,
Puffed up with pride, myself to fancy more than man.

45.

"So overweening of myself, that now
I thought my powers could compass or command
Knowledge of all above, around, below,
That sprang to birth from God's creative hand!
But when your Hermit, visiting this strand,
From sin my soul, from error purged my mind,
He taught my thoughts to soar, my views to' expand,
And I perceived how little and confined
They of themselves had been, how vain, how weak, how blind!

46.

"I saw how, like night-owls at rise of sun,
Our minds with Truth's first rays are stupified;
Smiled at the futile webs my folly spun;
Scorned my vain-glory, and renounced my pride;
But still my genius, as he wished, applied
To the deep arts and philosophic quest
In which I joyed before, but, purified
And changed from what I was, with nobler zest;
Ruled by the Seer on whom implicitly I rest; —

47.

"My guide and lord! what his sagacious wit
Points out, I execute; he not disdains
Now to my poor direction to commit
Works that might grace himself — from servile chains
To free the' unconquered knight whom sloth detains
By strong enchantment in a witch's hold,
Where amorous Revel high misrule maintains;
Long for your coming have I looked, of old
By the prophetic Seer in signs to me foretold."

48.

Whilst with this tale the knights he entertained,
They reached his dwelling: large it was and fair;
Shaped like a grot, and in itself contained
Galleries, and rooms, and spacious halls; whate'er

Of wild or precious, beautiful or rare,
Earth breeds in her rich veins, shone forth to view;
Nor one romantic ornament was there,
That from arranging art its glory drew,
But, formed in Nature's freaks, in native wildness grew.

49.

Nor failed there pages, numberless, untold,
To serve the guests with ready active haste;
Nor failed there urns of crystal, pearl, and gold,
On stands magnificent of silver placed,
Heaped high with whatsoe'er might please the taste:
And when with meats and wines their appetite
Was satisfied, rich fruits the table graced;
And the sage spoke: " 'Tis time that I invite
To what will be, methinks, of more refined delight.

50.

"Armida's deeds, her purposes, her guile,
And secret snares in part to you are known;
How to your camp she came, and by what wile
She charmed and led your warriors to her lone
Enchanted fortress; how they then were thrown
By their false hostess into chains, and lay
Long time, their amorous follies to atone;
Till, sent with thousand guards to Gaza, they
Were by Rinaldo freed; — mark well what now I say.

51.

"Things yet unknown to you do I declare,
Strange, but most true: when the fair witch perceived
That the rich prey it took such toil to snare,
Was rescued from her grasp, she stormed, she grieved,
Stamped, and in anger scarce to be conceived,
That her designs should be so clearly crost,
Burst forth: 'Let not the wretch be so deceived,
As to suppose the prisoners I have lost,
Are to be repossessed without revenge or cost!

52.

" 'If he has set them free, he in their place
Shall suffer lingering misery, hopeless thrall:
Nor shall this serve; the dues of my disgrace
Shall on the whole curst Camp in vengeance fall!'
And, raving thus, she in her heart of gall
Framed what I now disclose to you, a sleight
The most malignant and refined of all;
She came where young Rinaldo had in fight
Her warriors late subdued, or massacred outright.

53.

"Rinaldo there had thrown his arms aside,
And in a Turkish suit himself disguised;
Thinking perchance that he should safer ride,
In an array less known and signalised:
The' Enchantress came; his arms she recognised;
A headless figure in them cased, and threw
Upon a brook's green banks, where, she surmised,
It would be sure to meet the Christians' view,
When to the shaded stream for waters fresh they drew.

54.

"Nor was their coming hard to be foreseen;
For she a thousand spies on all sides sent,
Who every day brought tidings to their queen
Of the far Camp, who came, returned, or went;
Oft too her dexterous spirits would present,
After long talk with them in hall or grot,
Familiar picturings of each fresh event;
And thus the corse she cast in such a spot,
As best subserved her aim, and deep insidious plot.

55.

"Near, the most shrewd of her deceitful train
She slily placed, in shepherd's weeds arrayed;
And, what he was to do, to say, to feign,
Taught in all points, and was in all obeyed;
He, seized whilst hurrying from the forest shade,
Spoke with your soldiers, and amongst them sowed
Seeds of suspicion; which, maturing, swayed
The Camp to discord, till rebellion showed
Fearless her face abroad, and fires intestine glowed.

56.

"For, as she planned, all thought Rinaldo dead,
By Godfrey slain, his error to atone;
Albeit indeed their vague suspicions fled,
When the first beams of truth prevailing shone:
Thus with a craft peculiarly her own,
Armida wove her wiles; the second well
Chimed with the first, as will be seen anon;
The sequel of her scheme I now shall tell,
How she Rinaldo chased, and what from thence befel.

57.

"O'er hill and dale Armida watched the youth,
Till now his steps the swift Orontes stayed,
Where the clear stream its waters parting smooth,
Soon to rejoin, a flowery island made:

Here on the banks, under the greenwood shade,
A sculptured column might the Prince behold,
Near which a little shallop floating played;
The marble white, its workmanship and mould,
As he admired, he read in words engraved of gold: —

58.

" 'Oh thou, whoe'er thou art, whom sweet self-will,
Or chance, or idlesse to this region guides!
No greater wonder in design or skill
Can the world shew, than that this islet hides;
Pass o'er and see!' Enticed, he soon divides
The boat's gilt chain, and, so divinely smile
Those summer waters, o'er them tilting rides;
But as the skiff was slight, he leaves the while
His knights ashore, and seeks alone the' inviting isle.

59.

"Landing, he looks around; yet nothing sees
To claim his curious sight but waters sheen,
Rocks, mossy grots, dells, fountains, flowers, and trees,
So that he deems his fancy to have been
Mocked by the marble; yet the place, the scene,
Were such as might enchant the rudest minds;
So down he sits on banks of pleasant green,
Disarms his face, and sweet refreshment finds
In the cool fanning breath of odoriferous winds.

60.

"Meanwhile the river gurgles with a sound
New to his ear, and thither calls his sight;
One placid billow in the midst whirled round,
And sudden sank, then rose to greater height;
From which peeped forth, with golden tresses bright,
A virgin's beauteous face — her neck — her breast —
Then her two lily paps of purest white,
Their budded nipples rosily expressed; —
Whilst whispering billows flung their silver round the rest.

61.

"So on the midnight stage some water-maid,
Or fairy-queen slow rises from the floor;
And though no Siren, but a painted shade,
Yet all the fascinating grace she bore
Of those same treacherous Sisters, that of yore
Haunted the smooth sunshiny waters nigh
The Tuscan coast; as bright a bloom she wore;
As musical her voice, her smile as shy;
And thus aloud she sang, enchanting air and sky.

62.

" 'Oh happy youths, whom Spring with roses sweet
Robes and adorns! let not false glory's ray,
Nor virtue's smooth insidious beauty cheat
Your tender minds, and lead your steps astray;
Who crops the lily ere it fades away,
Who follows pleasure, he alone is sage!
Press then the purple grape of life — be gay —
This Nature bids; and will you warfare wage
With her divine decrees, nor fear the frowns of age?

63.

" 'Fools! to fling from you, without taste or care,
The brief enjoyments of your passing prime;
Names without object, idols all of air,
Are the vain toys to which you warriors climb:
The fame which charms with such a golden chime
Proud heroes' hearts, the glories that persuade,
Are but an echo in the ear of Time, —
A dream, a shade, the shadow of a shade;
With the bright rainbow born, they swift as rainbows fade.

64.

" 'But let your tranquil souls with all sweet things
Your happy senses cheer, whilst fresh and fair;
Past woes forget: nor with the anxious wings
Of expectation speed the steps of care:
Heed not if thunders roll, or lightnings glare;
Let the storm threaten as it will, rejoice!
With languor rest, with rest enjoyment share;
This is Elysium, this true Wisdom's choice,
This Nature's self requires, — slight not her charming voice!'

65.

"So sings the Phantom, and her soft sweet tune
To settling sleep allures his heavy eyes;
Sense after sense dissolves in gentle swoon;
From limb to limb lethargic sweetness flies;
Till he of death the passive picture lies,
Nor e'en the bellowing thunder now could break
The magic trance: when this Armida spies,
She, issuing swift and silent as the snake,
From her close ambush runs, her sworn revenge to take.

66.

"But on his face when she had gazed awhile,
And saw how placidly he breathed, how sweet
A light seemed e'en in his closed eyes to smile,
(Ah, were they open, what were her conceit!)

She paused in doubt, and near him took her seat;
The more she gazed, the more fond pity sprung
To her stern heart; till, of all angry heat
Charmed, o'er the boy, those greens and flowers among,
With loving, lovely eyes, Narcissus-like she hung.

67.

"The living heat-dews that impearled his face,
She with her veil wiped tenderly away;
And, to cool more the fervours of the place,
Her turban took, and fanned him as he lay;
And called the mild winds of the west to play
Round the rich cheeks that so divinely glow;
Mark but the change! Love's intellectual ray
Has from her savage bosom thawed the snow,
And to the kindest friend transformed the sternest foe.

68.

"With bluebells, lilies, woodbines, and wild roses,
That flowered in thousands through those pleasant plains,
She next with admirable skill composes
Garlands, festoons, and odoriferous chains,
Which round his neck, and arms, and feet she strains
Tightly yet tenderly; and o'er his eyes
Whilst sleep her shadowy government maintains,
Bears upon tiptoe the imprisoned prize
To her enchanted car, and, mounting, cuts the skies.

69.

"Not now to rich Damascus does she fly,
Nor where her castle crests the' Asphaltine tide;
But, jealous of a pledge so dear, and shy
Of her new passion, betwixt shame and pride,
In the Atlantic sea resolves to hide,
Where rarely mortal oar was known to comb,
Or ne'er, green Neptune's curling waves; there, wide
Of all mankind, she singles for her home
A little isle, round which the billows loneliest foam.

70.

"One of a cluster to which Fortune lends
Her name, the' Elysian fields of old renown;
There she a mountain's lofty peak ascends,
Unpeopled, shady, shagged with forests brown;
Whose sides, by power of magic, half way down
She heaps with slippery ice, and frost, and snow,
But sunshiny and verdant leaves the crown
With orange woods and myrtles — speaks — and lo!
Rich from the bordering lake a palace rises slow.

71.

"Here in perpetual May her virgin sweets
She yields him, lapt in amorous wild delight;
From that far palace, from those secret seats,
Your task must be to disenthral the knight;
To brave, encounter with, and put to flight
The guards her timorous jealousy has set
To keep the marble hall and shaded height;
Nor shall you need or guide or gondolet,
Nor added arms divine, the' adventure to abet.

72.

"A damsel, old in years, though young in show,
When from the stream we issue, you will find,
With long rich tresses curling round her brow,
And garments beauteous as the bird of Ind;
She, through the ocean, swifter than the wind
Or wing of eagles, shall direct your track,
And leave the lightning in her flight behind;
Nor will you find her as a guide less slack,
Or less secure of trust, to speed you safely back.

73.

"At the hill's foot whereon the Sorceress reigns,
Bulls bellow, hydras roar, and serpents hiss,
Revengeful lions rear their frightful manes,
And bears and panthers ope the grim abyss
Of their devouring jaws; shake then but this
My fascinating wand, and at the sound
They will recede, or crouch your feet to kiss:
But on the summit of that guarded ground
More fearful perils lurk — and subtler charms abound.

74.

"For there a fountain plays, whose dancing, pure,
And smiling rills the gazer's thirst excite,
Yet the cool crystals but to harm allure, —
Strange poison lurks within its waves of light;
One little draught the soul inebriates quite,
Mounts to the brain, and to the wit supplies
A host of gay ideas; till delight
Starts into voice, shrill peals of laughter rise,
Mirth overpowers the man, he laughs, and laughing dies.

75.

"Turn then, oh turn your lips away with dread;
Scorn the false wave that to such ills persuades;
Be not allured by wines or viands spread
By fountain sides, or under green arcades;

Let no fond gestures of lascivious maids—
The smile that flatters, or the tune that calls
To amorous blandishments in myrtle shades,
Move the fine pulse; each glance, each word that falls,
Leave for the ivory gates, and tread the' interior halls.

76.

"Within, a maze of circling corridors
Verge and diverge a thousand winding ways;
But of its various galleries, walks and doors,
A lucid plan this little chart displays
To guide your steps: in centre of the maze,
A spacious garden flings its fragrance round,
Where not a light leaf shakes, or zephyr strays,
But breathes out love; here, on the fresh green ground,
In his fair lady's lap the warrior will be found.

77.

"But when the' Enchantress quits her darling's side,
And elsewhere turns her footsteps from the place,
Then, with the diamond shield which I provide,
Step forth, and so present it for a space,
That he may start at his reflected face,
His wanton weeds and ornaments survey;
The sight whereof, and sense of his disgrace,
Shall make him blush, and without vain delay
From his unworthy love indignant break away.

78.

"Enough! it were superfluous to say more,
Than that tomorrow you may hence proceed;
And when your pleasant voyage ends, explore
The secret paths that to the lovers lead,
With safe success and all convenient speed;
For neither shall the powers of sorcery
Your voyage hinder or your plans impede;
Nor (so superior will your guidance be,)
Shall the fair witch have skill your coming to forsee.

79.

"Nor less securely from her fairy halls
Shall you depart and wend your homeward way;
But now the midnight hour to slumber calls,
And we must be abroad by break of day."
This said, he rose; and, ushering them the way,
His wondering guests to their apartments brought;
And leaving them to slumber's peaceful sway,
In reveries of glad and solemn thought,
His own nocturnal couch the good old Hermit sought.

CANTO XV

ARGUMENT

The Seer's instructions the two knights pursue;
They reach the ready ship that rides in port,
Embark, set sail, and in the distance view
The fleet and army of the' Egyptian court.
Propitious winds within the canvass sport,
Fast bounds the vessel to the pilot's hand
O'er the blue ocean, making long seem short;
On a lone isle remote at last they land,
And every tempting sound and spectacle withstand.

1.

Scarce had Aurora ris'n with grateful ray,
Or Syrian shepherd led his flocks from fold,
Than the Sage, coming where the warriors lay,
Produced the chart, the shield, and wand of gold;
And "Rise!" he said, "ere yet the sun has told
His rosary on the hills — soft breezes swell
To waft you on your voyage; here behold
The promised gifts that will have power to quell
Armida's witchcrafts all, and thaw each murmured spell."

2.

But they the' expected summons had forerun,
Were up, and robed in arms from head to feet,
And straight, by paths ne'er gazed on by the sun,
Following their host, returning they repeat
The steps they took to his romantic seat
The previous day; but to the river side
When they were come, the Senior stayed to greet
His parting guests: "Farewell, my friends!" he cried,
"Here must I leave you; go, good-fortune be your guide!"

3.

Embarked, the river with harmonious flow
The stranded vessel buoyantly upbore,
As, tossed into the stream, a leafy bough
Is wont to rise, and, without sail or oar,
Floated them gently to the verdant shore;
There, as the spacious ocean they surveyed, —
A little vessel with vermilion prore
Steered nigh, wherein was seen the destined maid,
And well the bounding bark her guiding hand obeyed.

4.

Her locks hung curled around her brow; her eyes
Were like the dove's, kind, tender, calm and true;

Her face an angel's, bright, and Paradise
Was in each radiant smile and look she threw;
Her robe from white to red, from red to blue,
Lilach, green, purple, fleetingly and fast,
Long as you looked, diversified its hue;
You gaze again, the precious purple's past,
And a fresh tint appears, diviner than the last.

5.

The feathers thus which on the neck genteel
Of the impassioned dove their circles spread,
Not for one moment the same tint reveal,
But in the sun ten thousand colours shed;
Now they a necklace seem of rubies red,
Of emeralds now they imitate the light,
Then — let the gentle bird but turn its head —
They shift from green to black, from black to bright,
Then take the tints of all, still more to charm the sight.

6.

"Enter," she said, "O happy youths! the bark,
Wherein from sea to sea I safely ply;
In which the heaviest weights grow light, the dark
Rough billows smooth, and calm the stormiest sky;
Me in his love and favour the Most High
Sends as your guide:" the Lady spake, and now
Guiding her painted gondola more nigh,
O'er the glad waves that round in homage bow,
The green saluted shore strikes lightly with her prow.

7.

Her charge received, the cable she upcurls,
Frees the fixed keel, and launches from the land;
Loose to the wind the silken sail unfurls,
And rules the rudder with a dexterous hand;
Swell the full sails, as glorying to be fanned;
Heaves the swoln stream, so deep with recent rain,
It might have borne a fleet well gunned and manned;
But her light frigate it would well sustain,
Though to its usual state the waters were to wane.

8.

Shrill airs unusual sing within the sails,
And swiftly speed them from the verdant shore;
The waters whiten to the active gales,
And round the vessel murmur, foam, and roar.
But now they reach to where its loud waves hoar
The river quiets in a broader bed;

There, by the greedy sea embraced, its store
Melts into nought, or nought apparent, wed
With the vast world of waves before them greenly spread.

9.

The sounding margin of the rough rude main
Is scarcely touched by the enchanted pine,
Than the black clouds that lowered, presaging rain,
Clear off at once, and leave the morning fine;
The mountain-waves, smoothed by a charm divine,
Fall flat, or if a zephyr intervene,
It does but curl the clear blue hyaline;
And ne'er in heaven's benignant face was seen
A smile so sweet as now, a purple so serene.

10.

She sails past Ascalon, and cheerly drives
Her beauteous bark betwixt the south and west;
And near to stately Gaza soon arrives,
Once but a haven held in slight request,
But year by year increasing as the rest
Went to decay, a city now it stands,
Of power, and strength, and merchandise possessed;
And at this instant, countless as its sands,
Myriads of armed men o'erspread the bordering lands.

11.

To land the warriors look, and see the plains
With countless rich pavilions whitened o'er,
And knights, and squires, and steeds with glistening reins
Pass to and fro betwixt the town and shore;
Camels and burdened elephants, whose roar
Comes mellowed o'er the main, pace side by side,
And stamp the sands to dust; with many an oar
Flash the vext waves, and in the harbour wide,
Galleys, and light caiques, and ships at anchor ride.

12.

Some with strong rowers brushed the buxom wave;
Some spread their wings out to the winds, and flew;
Their sharp swift beaks the liquid seas engrave;
Foam the raised billows as the keels glide through.
"Though," said the Lady then, "the ocean blue
And yellow plains are filled, as you behold,
With hosts and navies of the trustless crew,
Fresh bands on bands, beneath his moon of gold,
By the strong tyrant yet remain to be enrolled.

13.

"Sole from his own or neighbouring realms are drawn
These troops; more distant aid he yet awaits;
For to the regions of the noon and morn
Extends his influence with barbaric states;
So that I hope we shall, with prosperous fates,
Have made return, ere from this subject-coast
He to Jerusalem his camp translates;
He, or whatever Captain in his post
May o'er his other chiefs be raised to rule the host."

14.

Then as an eagle passes one by one
All lesser birds, and soars to such a height,
That she appears confounded with the sun,
Her form unfixed by the acutest sight;—
So, betwixt ship and ship, her rapid flight
The gay and graceful gondola holds on,
Without a fear or care, however slight,
Who may arrest or chase her, and anon
Is from the sailors flit, and out of prospect gone.

15.

Past Raffia town she in a moment flew,
The first in Syria seen by those who steer
From fruitful Egypt, and had soon in view
The barren isle of lonely Rhinocere;
Not distant, trees o'er waving trees appear
To clothe a hill embrowning all the deep
That bathes its base; not unremembered here,
Urned in its heart, the bones of Pompey sleep;
Round sigh the winds and woods; beneath, the waters weep.

16.

They next behold, by Damietta driven,
How to the sea proud Nile the tribute pays
Of his celestial treasures, by his seven
Famed mouths, and by a hundred minor ways:
Then past the City built in ancient days
By the brave youth of Macedon, who bore
Palms from all lands, she sails, and soon surveys
The Pharian isle, an isle at least of yore,
But by an isthmus now connected with the shore.

17.

She leaves to starboard Rhodes and Crete unseen,
And to the' adjacent shore of Libya stands;
Along the sea productive, tilled, and green,
But inly thronged with snakes and barren sands:

Barca she passes — passes by the lands
Where stood Cyrene, who no more presides
Queen of the silent waste! and soon commands
With Ptolomet the cypress wood, whence guides
Lethe the fabled flow of his oblivious tides.

18.

Syrtes, the seamen's curse, before the wind
She flies aloof, and far to seaward steers;
And, doubling Cape Judeca, leaves behind
Swift Magra's stream, till Tripoli appears
Crowning the coast; due north, low Malta rears
Her cliffs, but Malta they not now behold;
To shun the lesser Syrtes, which she fears,
She tacks; but, past Alzerbo, coasts more bold
The land where dwelt the mild Lotophagi of old.

19.

Next on the crooked shore they Tunis see,
Whose bay a hill on either side embrowns —
Tunis, rich, stately, honourable, and free,
Beyond all other Mauritanian towns;
Right opposite to which Sicilia crowns
The sea, and, roughly rising o'er the flood,
In sombre shade Cape Lilybæum frowns;
Here now the Damsel points where Carthage stood,
Rival so long of Rome, and drunk with Roman blood.

20.

Low lie her towers; sole relics of her sway,
Her desert shores a few sad fragments keep;
Shrines, temples, cities, kingdoms, states decay;
O'er urns and arcs triumphal deserts sweep
Their sands, or lions roar, or ivies creep;
Yet man, proud worm, resents that coming Night
Should shroud his eyes, in no perpetual sleep!
Biserta now they reach in silent flight,
Sardinia's distant isle receding on the right.

21.

Then scudding by the vast Numidian plains,
Where wandering shepherds wont their flocks to feed,
Bugia and Algiers, the accursed dens
Of corsairs, rise, approach, and retrocede;
By Oran's towers they pass with equal speed,
And, coasting the steep cliffs of Tingitan,
Now named Morocco, famous for its breed
Of elephants and lions, they began
Granada's adverse shores through azure mists to scan.

22.

And now Al Tarik's Straits they intersect,
Alcides' work, as gray traditions feign;
Haply an isthmus did the shores connect,
Till some concussion rent its rocks in twain;
And, by irruption of the horned main,
Abyla here and Calpe there was placed;
And Libya, sundered from romantic Spain,
No more as friends, but foes each other faced —
Such power Time hath to change, and lay strong bulwarks waste!

23.

Four times the morn has tinted Ocean's cheek,
Since the gay bark its voyage first begun;
Nor has it entered once or port or creek,
For rest or stores, — well furnished, need was none;
It now the entrance of the strait has won,
Shoots the slight pass, and, far as sight can flee,
Into the pathless infinite is run:
If, land-locked, here so spacious seems the sea,
There, where it rolls round earth, what must the' appearance be!

24.

No longer now each city that succeeds
Rich Cadiz o'er the billows they descry;
Fast wealthy Cadiz, fast all land recedes,
Sky girds the Ocean, Ocean bounds the sky:
Said Ubald then: "Fair pilot! make reply,
If on the boundless sea through which we glide
So swift, bark e'er before was known to ply —
And if beyond this world of waves reside
Men of like modes with ours?" The Gondolier replied:

25.

"When Hercules the monsters had subdued
That haunted Libya and the realms of Spain,
Through all your coasts his conquests he pursued,
Yet durst not tempt the' unfathomable main;
Here then he raised his Pillars, to restrain
In too close bounds the daring of mankind;
But these his marks Ulysses did disdain,
And, fond of knowledge still, his curious mind
E'en by Alcides' laws refused to be confined.

26.

"The straits he passed, and on the' Atlantic sailed,
Bold as the Sea-God in his fish-drawn shell;
But nought, alas, his naval skill availed,
The roaring billows rang his funeral knell!

The secrets of his fate no records tell,
Where bleached his bones, or whither drove his sail;
If any since were driven out by the swell
Of wave or wind, they perished in the gale,
Or came not back, at least, to tell the' adventurous tale.

27.

"Thus still this sea rests unexplored; it boasts
A thousand isles, a thousand states unknown;
Nor void of men, nor barren are the coasts,
But fertile, rich, and peopled as your own;
Nor can the sun which cheers your milder zone,
Be in its quickening virtue lifeless there,
But earth is heaped with fruits and blossoms blown:"
Said Ubald then: "Of this new world so fair,
Be pleased the worship, laws, and customs to declare."

28.

"As various as the tribes," she made reply,
"Their rites, and languages, and customs are;
Some Earth, the general mother, glorify,
Some worship beasts, the sun, and morning star;
Whilst some in woods and wildernesses far
Spare not to deify the Prince of Hell,
And heap their boards with captives slain in war;
In short, most impious are their rites, and fell
The faith of all the tribes that west of Calpe dwell."

29.

"Will then," the knight rejoined, "that God who came
From heaven to' illuminate the human heart,
Shut every ray of Truth's celestial flame
From that, which forms of earth so large a part?"
"No," she replied, "each humanising art
Shall yet be theirs; e'en kings shall coincide
The holy Faith and Gospels to impart;
Nor think indeed that this extent of tide
Shall from your world these tribes for ever thus divide.

30.

"The time shall come, when ship-boys e'en shall scorn
To have Alcides' fable on their lips,
Seas yet unnamed, and realms unknown adorn
Your charts, and with their fame your pride eclipse;
Then the bold Argo of all future ships
Shall circumnavigate and circle sheer
Whate'er blue Tethys in her girdle clips,
Victorious rival of the Sun's career—
And measure e'en of Earth the whole stupendous sphere.

31.

"A Genoese knight shall first the' idea seize,
And, full of faith, the trackless deep explore;
No raving winds, inhospitable seas,
Thwart planets, dubious calms, or billows' roar,
Nor whatsoe'er of risk or toil may more
Terrific show, or furiously assail,
Shall make that mighty mind of his give o'er
The wonderful adventure, or avail
In close Abyla's bounds his spirit to impale.

32.

" 'T is thou, Columbus, in new zones and skies,
That to the wind thy happy sails must raise,
Till Fame shall scarce pursue thee with her eyes,
Though she a thousand eyes and wings displays!
Let her of Bacchus and Alcides praise
The savage feats, and do thy glory wrong,
With a few whispers tossed to after days;
These shall suffice to make thy memory long
In history's page endure, or some divinest song."

33.

She said, and sliced through foam towards the west
Her course awhile, then to the south inclined,
And saw — now Titan rolling down to rest,
And now the youthful Morning rise behind;
And when with rosy light and dews refined
Aurora cheers the world, more sail she crowds;
Till, in blue distance breaking, as the wind
Curls off the mist that all the' horizon shrouds,
They see a mountain rise, whose summits reach the clouds.

34.

As they advance the vapours melt, nor more
Their wished inspection of the isle prevent;
Like the vast pyramids 'twas seen to soar,
Sharp in its peak, and widening in extent
Down to its base; it seemed to represent
The burning hill 'neath which the Giant lies
That warred on Jove, for with like sulphurous scent
It smokes by day, and still, as daylight dies,
With ruddy fires lights up the circumambient skies.

35.

Then other islands, other mountains mild,
Less steep and lofty, their regards engage;
The Happy Isles, the Fortunate! so styled
By the fond lyrists of the antique age;

Which warrior, sophist, priest, and gifted sage
Believed so favoured by the heavens benign,
As to produce, untilled, in every stage
Of growth, its fruits; unpruned the fancied vine
At once flowered, fruited, filled, and gushed with generous wine.

36.

Here the fat olive ever buds and blooms,
And golden honeys from old oaks distil,
And rivers slide from mountain-greens and glooms,
In silver streams, with murmurs sweet or shrill:
And here cool winds and dews all summer chill
The heats, and the calm halycon builds her nest,
With every beauteous bird of tuneful bill;
And here are placed the' Elysian Fields, where rest,
In fair unfading youth, the spirits of the blest.

37.

To these the Lady made: "And now," said she,
"The destined haven of your hopes is near;
The promised isles of Fortune now you see,
Whose fame has reached, if not fatigued your ear
With its uncertain echoes; Fiction here
Has not been idle; rich they are, and gay,
And pleasant, but not quite what they appear
In poesy:" she said, and in her way,
Passed the first isle of ten that clear in prospect lay.

38.

Then Charles: "If, Lady, with our enterprise
The' excursion suits, now let us leap ashore,
And mark what yet no European eyes
Have viewed — the people see, the place explore,
The rites they use, the Genius they adore,
And whatsoe'er may prompt the' inquiry keen
Of envying sages; that, recounting o'er
The perils braved, the strange new objects seen,
I may with honest pride exclaim, 'Yes! there I've been!'"

39.

"Worthy," the Gondolier replied, "of thee
The' entreaty surely is; but what can I,
If Heaven's severe, inviolable decree
The least compliance with thy wish deny.
The perfect period fixed by God on high
To give this great discovery to the day,
Is not yet come; and thus for you to eye
The Secrets of the Deep, and back convey
The' authentic news, would be his will to disobey.

40.

"To you 'tis granted, by peculiar grace
And superhuman skill, the fame to' acquire
Of rescuing to your world from thraldom base,
A youth whom nations ardently desire;
Let this suffice, for farther to aspire,
Would be to war with fate:" whilst she replies,
The first green isle seems lessening to retire
From notice, and the next sublime to rise,
So blithely o'er the wave the charmed pinnace flies.

41.

They now behold how in the same degree
All in long order shun the realms of morn,
And by what equal distances of sea
The happy isles are each from each withdrawn:
Huts, curling smoke, white flocks, and ripening corn
Spoke seven of them inhabited; the rest
Were waste, o'errun with heath and shagged with thorn;
Where, fixed in long hereditary rest,
Secure the lion prowls, the vulture builds her nest.

42.

In one they find a lone sequestered place,
Where, to a crescent curved, the shore extends
Two moony horns, that in their sweep embrace
A spacious bay — a rock the port defends;
Inward it fronts, and broad to ocean bends
Its back, whereon each dashing billow dies,
When the wind rises and the storm descends;
Whilst here and there two lofty crags arise,
Whose towers, far out at sea, salute the sailor's eyes.

43.

Safe sleep the silent seas beneath; above,
Black arching woods o'ershade the circled scene;
Within, a grotto opens in the grove,
Pleasant with flowers, with moss, with ivies green,
And waters warbling in the depth unseen;
Needed nor twisted rope nor anchor there
For weary ships: into that so serene
And sheltered hermitage, the maiden fair
Entered, her slender sails unfurling from the air.

44.

"Behold," she said, "the cupolas and towers
That on yon mountain's lofty summit shine!
There Christ's lethargic champion wastes his hours
In dalliance, idlesse, folly, feast and wine:

That slippery, steep ascent of palm and pine
Mount with the rising sun; nor let delay
Seem to you grievous; influences malign
The' important scheme to ruin will betray,
If any hour but that be fixed for the essay.

45.

"You yet with easy speed may reach the foot
Of the seen mountain, ere the day's expired:"
Their lovely guide in parting they salute,
And lightly pace at length the shore desired.
They found the way so much to be admired,
So full of goodly prospects, cool with shade,
And smooth withal to tread, that nothing tired;
And when they issued from the last green glade,
High o'er the landscape yet the evening sunbeams played.

46.

They see that to the mountain's stately head
O'er nodding crags and ruins they must climb;
Below, with snows and frosts each path was spread,
For bloomy heath exchanged and odorous thyme;
Cedar, and pine, and cypress more sublime
Round its white shoulders tossed their verdant locks;
Sweet lilies peeped from forth the hoary rime,
Whilst (force of magic!) pinks, geraniums, stocks,
And roses, fully flowered, hung clustering round the rocks.

47.

Within a savage cave beneath the mount,
Closed in with shades, the warriors passed the night;
But when the Sun from heaven's eternal fount
Through the brown forest shed his golden light,
"Up, up!" at once they cried; and either knight
With rival zeal along the track of frost
Began the' ascent; when, on their startled sight,
Whence they knew not, in various colours glossed,
Their onward path a fierce and frightful serpent crossed.

48.

Her head and scaly crest of pallid gold
She raised erect, and swelled her neck with ire;
Lightened her eyes; and, hiding as she rolled
A length of way, she poison breathed and fire;
Now she recoiled into herself, now nigher
Her tangled rings distending many a yard,
She slid along with mischievous desire,
Presenting all her stings the pass to guard,—
Much she the knights amazed, but did not much retard.

49.

Already Charles, the monster to assail,
Had drawn his sword, when out Ubaldo spake:
"Soft! what is it you do? by arms so frail
How can you hope to quell the' enchanted snake?"
His golden wand of an immortal make
He shook, so that the demon, smit with fear,
No longer hissing, sought the tangled brake;
Needed no second sound to warn its ear;
Instant it slipt away, and left the passage clear.

50.

A little further on, with sour disdain
A roaring lion the strict pass denied;
Tossing aloft the terrors of his mane,
And his voracious jaws expanding wide,
He with redoubling fury lashed his side,
And to the knights advanced with hasty tread;
But when the wand immortal he espied,
A secret instinct chilled his heart with dread,
And quelled his native fire; he howled, and howling fled.

51.

Their track the venturous couple follow fast,
But numerous legions yet before them rise
Of savage beasts, terrific as the past,
Differing in voice, in movement, and in guise;
All monstrous forms, all wild enormities,
All the grim creatures in their sternest moods
That betwixt Nile and Atlas Titan eyes,
Seemed gathered there, with all the raging broods
That haunt the' Ercynian caves or old Hyrcanian woods.

52.

But e'en this phalanx, massy, fierce, and bold
As it appeared, could not the pair affright,
Much less repel; for of the wand of gold
A single motion put them all to flight.
And now they climb victorious to the height
Of the rude precipice, without delay;
Save that the Alpine cliffs and glaciers, white
With drifted snows that round austerely lay,
Of their sublime ascent more tedious make the way.

53.

But when at length the steep acclivity
Is scaled, and passed the snows and breezes keen,
Beneath the sunshine of a summer sky
They find an even, smooth, and spacious green.

Here in a clime delightfully serene
His wings the everlasting Zephyr shakes,
And breathes a ceaseless sweetness o'er the scene;
For here the sun one golden measure makes,
Nor ever charms asleep, nor e'er the wind awakes.

54.

Not as elsewhere with fervours frosts severe,
Or clouds with calms divide the happy hours;
But heaven, than whitest crystal e'en more clear,
A flood of sunshine in all seasons showers;
Nursing to fields their herbs, to herbs their flowers,
To flowers their smell, to leaves the' immortal trees;
Here by its lake, the splendid palace towers
On marble columns rich with golden frieze,
For leagues and leagues around o'ergazing hills and seas.

55.

The warriors weary found themselves and faint,
From their long travel up the steep rough hill:
And loitering through the pleasant gardens went,
Walking or resting at their own sweet will;
When lo, a fountain whose light music shrill
Allures the thirsty pilgrim, gleamed in view!
In one tall column it descended chill,
And in a thousand crystal fragments flew,
Sprinkling with orient pearl the plants that round it blew.

56.

But through the grass these delicate cascades
The same deep channel in conclusion found,
And under curtain of perpetual shades
Ran warbling by, cool, tranquil, and embrowned;
Yet still so clear, that in its depths profound
Each glistening wave amid the sands was seen,
With all its curls of beauty; whilst around,
The mossy banks formed couches soft and green,
Inlaid with odorous herbs, and violets strewn between.

57.

"See here the fount of laughter! see the stream
To which such fatal qualities belong!
Now," they exclaimed, "let us avoid the dream
Of warm desire, and in resolve be strong;
Now shut our ears to the fair Siren's song,
And to each smile of feminine deceit
Close the fond eye!" thus warned, they pass along,
Until they reach to where the waters sweet
Break out a broader bed, and form a spacious sheet.

58.

Here, served on ivory, stood all sumptuous food
That Taste could wish, or Luxury purvey,
And chattering, laughing, in the crystal flood
Two naked virgins, full of wanton play;
Now kissing, wrestling, breaking now away,
Now striving which the other should outswim;
Now diving, floating, as the waters sway,
Sometimes above, sometimes below the brim,
Marking their course concealed by some voluptuous limb.

59.

These swimming damsels, beautiful and bare,
These warriors' bosoms somewhat did subdue;
So that they stayed to watch them, whilst the pair
Seemed all intent their pastimes to pursue:
One meanwhile, starting upward, full to view
Of the clear heavens her swelling breasts displayed,
And all that might with rapture more endue
The eye, to the white waist; the waves that played
Round her, each limb beneath pellucidly arrayed.

60.

As from the waves the glittering Star of morn
Comes, dropping nectar; or, as rising slow
From Ocean's fruitful foam when newly born,
The Queen of Love and Beauty seemed in show,
So she appeared, so charmed; her tresses so
From all their golden rings bright humour rained,
Rich with the colours of the showery bow;
Whilst looking round, the knights but then she feigned
To see, and back recoiled, offended, shocked, and pained.

61.

Her tresses knotted in a single braid,
She in an instant loosened and shook down;
Which, thickly flowing to her feet, arrayed
Her polished limbs as with a golden gown:
But oh! when fell the curtain from her crown,
What an enchanting spectacle was fled!
Yet 'twas enchantment, so to find it flown:
Thus gloriously with locks and waves o'er spread,
She from them turned askance, rejoicing, rosy red.

62.

She smiled, she crimsoned deep, and all the while
Her smile the sweeter shewed the more she blushed,
And the sweet crimson sweeter for the smile
That o'er her tender face in sunshine rushed;

Then with a voice so mild it might have hushed
The nightingale, and taken an angel prey,
Rich from her warbling lips these accents gushed:
"O happy pilgrims! favoured to survey
Regions so full of peace, a Paradise so gay!

63.

"This is the haven of the world; here Rest
Dwells with Composure, and that perfect bliss,
Which in the Golden Age fond men possessed,
In liberty and love unknown to this;
You now may lay aside the' incumbrances
Of arms, and safely hang them on the trees,
Sacred to Peace; all else but folly is;
Seek then soft quiet, seek indulgent ease,
Love's the sole captain here, young Love's the lord to please.

64.

"The fields of battle here are mosses green
And beds of roses, where — you dream the rest;
We will conduct you to our fairy queen,
The queen whose bounty makes her servants blest.
You of that happy band shall be impressed,
Whom she has destined for her joys; but first,
Your weary limbs of those rude arms divest,
In these cool waters be your dust dispersed,
And at yon board indulge your hunger, taste, and thirst."

65.

Thus sang the one; her sister played the mime,
In act and glance outpleading her appeal,
As swift or slow to the melodious chime
Of lutes and viols the blithe dancers wheel.
But to these wiles the knights in triple steel
Of stern resolve had shut their souls; and hence,
The tunes they sing, the beauties they reveal,
Their angel looks and heavenly eloquence,
But circle round and round, nor reach the seat of sense.

66.

Or if of such sweet airs and glowing charms
Aught stirs the soil where buds unchaste Desire,
The heart soon Reason fills with her alarms,
And with strong hand roots up each rising brier:
Vanquished the nymphs remain; the knights retire,
And, without bidding them adieu, pass on;
These reach the palace, those with fruitless ire
Crimsoning afresh at the repulse, anon
Dive in the waves, and deep beyond all sight are gone.

CANTO XVI

ARGUMENT

The spacious palace of the' enchanting Dame
The warriors tread, where lost Rinaldo lies;
And speed so well, that, full of wrath and shame,
He bursts his bonds, and with them quickly flies:
She, to retain her loved deserter, tries
All powers of language and of tears — in vain —
He parts; to' avenge her wrongs, on Dis she cries,
Destroys her palace, and, in high disdain,
Flies through the stormy skies in her aerial wain.

1.

Round is the spacious pile; and in its heart,
Set like a gem, a garden is insphered,
More decked by nature and enriched by art,
Than the most beautiful that e'er appeared
To flower in old romance; and round it, reared
The Stygian sprites unnumbered galleries,
Harmonious, seen at distance, but, when neared,
A trackless maze discordant to the eyes, —
Through all these tortuous coils their secret passage lies.

2.

Through the chief gate they tread the marble floors,
For full a hundred grace the spacious hold;
Of fine and figured silver, here the doors
On their smooth hinges sing, of shining gold:
A while they pause the figures to behold
Cast on the squares; for, with extreme surprise,
They see the metal rivalled by the mould;
Speech fails alone, but, to the trusting eyes,
The sprightly shapes e'en speak, and limbed with life arise.

3.

Here midst Mæonian girls the Grecian Mars
Sits, telling fond romantic tales; and he
Who stormed black Orcus, and upheld the stars,
Now twirls the spindle with a maiden's glee;
Young Love looks on and laughs; whilst Iole
In her unwarlike hands is seen to bear
His murderous arms with proud mock-majesty,
And on her back the lion's hide to wear,
Too rough a vest for limbs so finely turned and fair!

4.

Near heaved a sea whose azure surface changed,
As close you looked, and into silver splashed;

Two adverse navies in the midst were ranged
For war — blue lightnings from the armour flashed;
In gold the bright and burning billows dashed,
And all Leucate did on fire appear,
Ere the beaks grappled, and the falchions clashed;
Augustus there all Rome, Antonius here,
Brought up his Eastern kings, and couched his Memphian spear.

5.

You would declare the rifted Cyclades
Concurred, and mountains did with mountains jar,
When with their tower-like vessels those and these
Rushed o'er the brine, and shocked in mortal war:
Here, like the sparkles of a glancing star,
Darts fly, and fire-balls blaze; there, bloody dyes
The virgin whiteness of the waters mar:
Whilst neither wins, lo where, with heavy eyes,
O'er the vexed waves, alarmed, the' Egyptian beauty flies!

6.

And flies her Chief? can he relinquish here
The glorious world to which his hopes aspire?
He flies not, no, nor fears; he does not fear,
But follows her, drawn on by fond desire:
You see him (like a man whom now the fire
Of love torments, and now, as shame prevails,
Disdain,) alternately regard, as ire
And tenderness were cast in equal scales,
Now the still dubious fight, and now her lessening sails.

7.

Then in the secret creeks of fruitful Nile
He in her lap appears for death to wait,
And with the pleasure of her lovely smile
Sweetens the bitter stroke of hasting fate. —
With such like arguments of various date
And issue in Love's story, were embossed
The glittering metals of that princely gate;
The figured tales long time the knights engrossed;
At length the charm they broke, and o'er the threshold crossed.

8.

As 'twixt its crooked banks Meander plays,
Curls and uncurls in its uncertain course,
Now to its spring, now to the Ocean strays,
Now meets itself returning to its source:
Such, only intertangled with a force
Yet more mysterious, of this mazy spot

The paths appear; but now they have recourse
To the clear chart, which, pointing out both what
To shun, and what pursue, resolves the' enchanted knot.

9.

These windings passed, the garden gates unfold,
And the fair Eden meets their glad survey,—
Still waters, moving crystals, sands of gold,
Herbs, thousand flowers, rare shrubs, and mosses grey;
Sunshiny hillocks, shady vales; woods gay,
And grottos gloomy, in one view combined,
Presented were; and what increased their play
Of pleasure at the prospect, was, to find
Nowhere the happy Art that had the whole designed.

10.

So natural seemed each ornament and site,
So well was neatness mingled with neglect,
As though boon Nature for her own delight
Her mocker mocked, till fancy's self was checked;
The air, if nothing else there, is the' effect
Of magic, to the sound of whose soft flute
The blooms are born with which the trees are decked:
By flowers eternal lives the' eternal fruit,
This running richly ripe, whilst those but greenly shoot.

11.

Midst the same leaves and on the self-same twig
The rosy apple with the' unripe is seen;
Hung on one bough the old and youthful fig,
The golden orange glows beside the green;
And aye, where sunniest stations intervene,
Creeps the curled vine luxuriant high o'erhead;
Here the sour grape just springs the flowers between,
Here yellowing, purpling, blushing ruby red,
Here black the clusters burst, and heavenly nectar shed.

12.

The joyful birds sing sweet in the green bowers;
Murmur the winds; and, in their fall and rise,
Strike from the fruits, leaves, fountains, brooks, and flowers,
A thousand strange celestial harmonies;
When cease the birds, the zephyr loud replies;
When sing the birds, it faints amidst the trees
To whispers soft as lovers' farewell sighs;
Thus, whether loud or low, the bird the breeze,
The breeze obeys the birds, and each with each agrees.

13.

One bird there flew, renowned above the rest,
With party-coloured plumes and purple bill,
That in a language like our own expressed
Her joys, but with such sweetness, sense, and skill,
As did the hearer with amazement fill;
So far her fellows she outsang, that they
Worshipped the wonder; every one grew still
At her rich voice, and listened to the lay:
Dumb were the woods — the winds and whispers died away.

14.

"Ah see," thus she sang, "the rose spread to the morning
Her red virgin leaves, the coy pride of all plants!
Yet half open, half shut midst the moss she was born in,
The less shews her beauty, the more she enchants;
Lo, soon after, her sweet naked bosom more cheaply
She shews! lo, soon after she sickens and fades,
Nor seems the same flower late desired so deeply
By thousands of lovers, and thousands of maids!

15.

"So fleets with the day's passing footsteps of fleetness
The flower and the verdure of life's smiling scene:
Nor, though April returns with its sunshine and sweetness,
Again will it ever look blooming or green;
Then gather the rose in its fresh morning beauty,
The rose of a day too soon dimmed from above;
Whilst, beloved, we may love, let — to love, be our duty,
Now, now, whilst 'tis youth, pluck the roses of love!"

16.

She ceased; and, as approving all they heard,
That tender tune the choirs of birds renew;
The turtles billed, and every brute and bird
In happy pairs to unseen glooms withdrew.
It seemed that the hard oak, the grieving yew,
The chaste sad laurel, and the whole green grove —
It seemed each fruit that blushed, each bud that blew,
The earth, air, sea, and rosy heavens above,
All felt divine desire, and sighed out sweetest love.

17.

Midst melody so tender, midst delights
So passing sweet, and midst such tempting snares,
Cautious, serene, and serious go the knights,
And steel their souls to the loose Lydian airs.
Lo, betwixt leaves and leaves, at unawares

Advancing slow, they see, or seem to see —
They see most surely, crown of all their cares!
The lover and his darling lady; he
In the fair lady's lap, on herbs and violets she.

18.

Her veil, flung open, shews her breast; in curls
Her wild hair wooes the summer wind; she dies
Of the sweet passion, and the heat that pearls,
Yet more her ardent aspect beautifies:
A fiery smile within her humid eyes,
Trembling and tender, sparkles like a streak
Of sunshine in blue fountains; as she sighs,
She o'er him hangs; he on her white breast sleek
Pillowing his head reclines, cheek blushing turned to cheek.

19.

His hungry eye-balls, fixt upon her face,
For her dear beauty pine themselves away;
She bows her head, and in a fond embrace,
Sweet kisses snatches, betwixt war and play,
Now of his just touched eyes, in wilder prey
Now of his coral lips; therewith he heaves
Sighs deep as though his spirit winged its way
To transmigrate in her: amidst the leaves,
This amorous dalliance all each watchful knight perceives.

20.

A polished glass, whose sheen the stars excelled,
Strange arms! hung pendant at Rinaldo's thigh;
He rose, and to the fair the crystal held,
Her chosen page in each love-mystery:
Both — she with smiling, he with glowing eye,
Mark but one scene of all the scenes they view;
Her angel form and aspect they descry,
She in the glass, he, fond enthusiast! through
A sweeter medium far — her eyes of heavenly blue.

21.

She in herself, he glories but in her;
He proud of bondage, of her empire she;
"And why," he murmurs, "so to this recur?
Turn, my beloved, turn thine eyes on me —
Those smiling eyes, that no less blessed be,
Than blessed make; ah, know'st thou not, that best
They in mine eye-balls must thy beauty see?
And know'st thou not thy graces are expressed
Less clear in this gay glass than in my faithful breast!

22.

"Though me thou scorn, thou might'st at least consent
To mark thine own most interesting face;
Those looks, else unrepaid, must rest content
With joy, if on themselves themselves they place;
So rare an image can no crystal trace,
No glass a perfect Eden can comprise
In its small round; to see aright thy grace
Thou must consult the mirror of the skies;
Heaven is thy glass, the stars reflect thy sparkling eyes."

23.

Armida smiled at this, yet not the less
Kept to her toilet, gathering up behind
Her hair, restricting each resplendent tress
That in loose tangles wantoned in the wind;
The less she curled in rings, and with them twined
Flowers that, like lazuli in gold, impressed
A deeper charm on the beholder's mind;
Then to the native lilies of her breast
She joined the foreign rose, and smoothed her veil and vest.

24.

Not Juno's bird such beauty spreads to show
In her eyed plumes so ravishingly bright,
Nor Iris such, when her celestial bow
Spans the dark cloud with gold and purple light;
But rich beyond all richness shines to sight
The glorious cest which 'tis her wont to wear
At all times, e'en though naked, and at night;
A local shape she gave to things of air,
And in it blended all of lovely, sweet, and rare: —

25.

Tender disdains, repulses mild, feigned fears,
Kind looks, sweet reconcilements, blissful stings,
Smiles, little love-words, sighs, delicious tears,
Hopes, turtle kisses, music, marriage rings;
Embraces dear, and all ambrosial things
She fused, commingled slowly in the chaste
Bright fire, attempered in cool Lydian springs,
And fashioned thus this talisman of Taste,
Which, in itself a charm, clasps round her charming waist.

26.

At length, their courtship o'er, she farewell took,
Gave him a kiss, sighed, smiled, and went her way;
For o'er the pages of her magic book,
Murmuring her charms, she spent some hours each day.

He, by a kind of charm compelled to stay,
Remained; for not one moment from these groves
Her jealous fear allowed his steps to stray:
Alone mid bees, birds, fountains, flowers, alcoves,
And grots, save when with her, the hermit lover roves.

27.

But when the soft and silent shade recals
The ready lovers to their stolen delights,
Under one roof within the palace walls
They meet, and happy pass harmonious nights.
Now when Armida for severer rites
Had left her hermit love, her pleasant play,
And variegated garden, the two knights,
From the green bushes, where concealed they lay,
Rushed forth in radiant arms whose light enriched the day.

28.

As the fierce steed, from busy war withdrawn
A while to riot in voluptuous ease,
Midst his loved mares loose wantons o'er the lawn,
If chance he hears once more upon the breeze
The spirit-stirring trumpet sound, or sees
The flash of armour, thither, far or near,
He bounds, he neighs, he prances o'er the leas,
Burning to whirl to war the charioteer,
Clash with the rattling car, and knap the sparkling spear,

29.

So fared Rinaldo, when the sudden rays
Of their bright armour on his eye-balls beat;
At once those lightnings set his soul ablaze,
His ardour mounts to all its ancient heat;
Their vivid beam his sparkling eyes repeat,
Drowned though he was, and drunken with the wine
Of siren wantonness: on footsteps fleet,
Ubald meanwhile to where he lay supine
Came, and the diamond shield turned to him, pure and fine.

30.

Upon the lucid glass his eyes he rolled,
And all his delicacy saw: his dress,
Breathing rich odours, how it gleamed with gold!
How trimly curled was each lascivious tress!
And with what lady-like luxuriousness
His ornamented sword addressed his side!
So wrapt with flowers it swung, that none could guess
If 'twas a wounding weapon, or applied
As a fantastic toy, voluptuous eyes to pride.

31.

As one by heavy sleep in bondage held,
Comes to himself when the long dream takes flight,
So woke the youth when he himself beheld,
Nor could endure the satire of the sight:
Down fell his looks; and instantly, in spite
Of recollected pride, the colour came
Across his face; — in this embarrassed plight,
A thousand times he wished himself in flame,
Ocean, in earth, the' abyss, to shun the glowing shame.

32.

Then spake Ubaldo: "Hearken and give ear!
Asia and Europe to the battle crowd;
Whoever counts or faith or glory dear,
Stands to the strife for Christ against Mahmoud.
Thee, son of Berthold, thee alone, the vowed
To honour and renown, loose idlesse charms
To a small angle of the world, more proud
To play the lover in a lady's arms,
Than champion deathless deeds, — thee only nought alarms!

33.

"What sleep, what lethargy, what base delights
Have melted down thy manhood, quenched thy zeal?
Up! up! thee Godfrey, thee the camp invites;
For thee bright Victory stays her chariot wheel.
Come, fated warrior, set the final seal
To our emprise! thy coming all expect;
Let the false Saracens confounded feel
That sword from which no armour can protect;
Haste, and in total death destroy the impious sect!"

34.

He ceased; the noble Infant for a space
Stood stupified, attempting no defence;
But soon as bashfulness to scorn gave place,
Scorn, the fine champion of indignant sense,
Then, with a yet diviner eloquence,
Another redness than of shame rushed o'er
His cheeks, almost atoning his offence;
The rich embroidered ornaments he wore,
Away with hasty hand indignantly he tore.

35.

Begone he would, and through the intricate
Labyrinth of galleries from the garden fled;
Meanwhile Armida, by the regal gate
Starts to behold her savage keeper dead.

At first a vague suspicion, a blind dread,
Then a quick feeling of the fatal truth
Instinctive flashed across her mind; her head
She turned, and saw (too cruel sight!) the youth
Haste from her blest abode, without concern or ruth.

36.

"Oh cruel! leav'st thou then Armida spurned?"
She would have said, but choking sorrow drowned
The issuing cry, and the faint words returned
With bitter echo in her heart to sound:
Poor wretch! her happiness its term has found;
A power and wisdom above hers constrain
The youth to hurry from the' enchanted ground
With so much speed; she sees it, and in vain
Tries all her wonted arts, the recreant to retain.

37.

All dreadful strains that e'er Thessalian lips
Spoke to lost spirits, every potent spell
That could arrest the planets, or eclipse,
And call up demons disenchained from hell,
She knew, she tried, yet could not now compel
One gibbering ghost to answer to her cry;
Thus she gave o'er her incantations fell,
And would essay if stronger sorcery
Dwelt in pale Beauty's tear and supplicating eye.

38.

Careless of honour, off she ran, she flew;
Where are her vaunts, ah, where her triumphs now!
She who the total sway of Love o'er threw,
And judgment gave but by her bending brow;
And like her pride was her disdain! oh how,
Loving their love, did she her slaves despise!
Herself alone could she at all allow
To pleasure her, nor aught in man could prize,
Beyond the' effect produced by her two radiant eyes.

39.

Left and neglected now, she follows swift
Him who forsakes her in his careless scorn;
And summons all her tears up, the poor gift
Of her rejected beauty to adorn:
Headlong she runs, unchecked by brier or thorn;
O'er rugged Alpine rocks and glaciers hoar
Her tender feet adventure to be torn;
Loud cries, as messengers, she sends before,
Which reach not him, till he has reached the winding shore.

40.

Madly she cries: "Oh cruel fugitive!
That bear'st with thee my dearer half away,
Either take this, or that restore, or give
Death to them both together: stay, O stay!
Let my last words to thee at least find way,
I say not kisses: these sweet gifts from thee
Some worthier favourite may receive, delay
Thy flight, unkind! what dost thou fear from me?
Thou canst as well refuse, when thou hast ceased to flee."

41.

"Signior," said then Ubaldo, "to refuse
Her wish, would be unkindness too severe:
Most sweetly bathed in sorrow's briny dews,
Armed with fond prayers and beauty she draws near;
Thy tempted virtue will shine forth more clear,
If, listening to the siren, thou remain
Proof to her winning voice and starting tear;
So Reason shall resume her peaceful reign
O'er sense, and thus refined, her native light regain."

42.

At this he stayed until she reached the shore;
Pale she came up, faint, breathless, all in tears,
And mournful past expression; but the more
She mourns, her beauty more divine appears:
Eager she eyes him; but mistrustful fears,
Disdain, amazement, or excess of woe
Keeps her quite mute; Rinaldo volunteers
No look, no glance at her, at least in show,
But stands with bashful eyes at stealth unclosing slow.

43.

As skilful singers, ere they strain on high
Their voice in the loud song's symphonious flow,
Prepare the mind for the full harmony,
By sweetest preludes, warbled soft and low:
Thus she, who had not, e'en in deepest woe,
Wholly lost memory of her fraudful art,
First breathed a symphony of sighs forth, so
By just degrees to predispose the heart,
To which her words the print of pity would impart.

44.

Then thus: "Expect not I shall fondly bow,
Cruel! to thee, as loves to lovers should;
Such once we were — if such no longer now,
If e'en the thought of thine impassioned mood

Move thy displeasure, as I judge, be wooed,
At least, my mournful plea to entertain,
As foemen the proud prayers of foes subdued;
My suit is such, as thou with little pain
Mayst grant, and yet keep all thy harshness and disdain.

45.

"If me thou hate, and in it tak'st delight,
Hate on, I come not to disturb thy joy;
Just it may seem, just be it, for with spite
Thy sect, thyself I laboured to destroy!
What fierce expedients did I not employ,
A Pagan born, to sap your power! nay, more,
Thee did I hate, thee chase, and thee decoy
To the strange borders of an unknown shore,
Far from the din of arms, where only sea-waves roar.

46.

"And, which seems most to move thy grief and shame,
Add with how much of tender, kind, and sweet,
Thy frozen heart I fondled into flame,
An impious fondness, sure, a vile deceit!
To let my virgin fruit be plucked and eat;
My blooms be spoiled; my tamelessness subdued,
And cast my beauties at a tyrant's feet!
Those youthful charms for which a thousand sued,
To a mere stranger given, unhoped, unwished, unwooed!

47.

"Yes! number them amongst my sins, and let
These many crimes against thee hasten more
Thy prompt departure; heed not, but forget
This thy fair mansion, so beloved before!
Go, pass the seas; fight, glut thyself with gore;
Quick to the task! I bid thee o'er the brine;
Destroy our faith — 'twill be but what you swore;
What say I? ours? ah no! not mine! not mine!
I, cruel idol! seek alone thy reverenced shrine!

48.

"Let me but follow thee! 'tis all I crave;
This mightst thou grant, though I had proved unkind;
Seldom the conqueror parts without his slave,
The robber rarely leaves his prey behind:
Me with thy other hapless prisoners bind
For exhibition; to each other aim
At praiseful acts, let this, I pray, be joined —
That all may point the finger, and exclaim,
'There the proud scorner goes, now scorned with equal shame!'

49.

"A bondslave spurned, why longer do I keep
My locks unshorn, by thee now rendered vile?
Cut them clean off! the ground they shall not sweep,
To mock the misery of my servile style.
Thee will I follow from this hated isle;
Thee, when most fervent glows the fight, pursue
Through hostile crowds; I shall not want the while
Spirit or strength a thousand things to do,—
Bear darts, guide steeds, and strain myself the bending yew.

50.

"Either thy shield or shield-bearer, which best
May please thee, I in thy defence will be;
Nor spare my person—through this throat and breast
The sword shall pass, before it injures thee;
The foe will scarce have so much cruelty
As to strike then, but will perhaps direct
Their darts elsewhere, not to endanger me;
And smother their fierce vengeance, in respect
Of these poor charms, to which thou dost such strange neglect.

51.

"Wretch! do I still presume, still place my worth
In these scorned charms, which nothing can obtain!"
More would she say, but bitter tears gush forth,
Like springs from Alpine rocks, or falling rain;
She sought to grasp his hand; she sought to strain,
In suppliant attitude, his robes; but no—
Himself he curbed, his tenderness restrained,
And started back; love found no entrance, though
The swelling tears rolled high, and stood prepared to flow.

52.

Love entered not, to fan within his breast
The ancient flame which reason had congealed;
But Pity entered in its place at least,
Love's chaste companion, ever prone to yield;
And touched him so, that scarcely he concealed,
Scarce, with much pain, the yearning tears repressed;
Yet, though she loudly to his heart appealed,
The fond emotion he within compressed,
And when he could, the fair thus tranquilly addressed.

53.

"I feel for thee, Armida! if my powers
Were such, how gladly would I cure the pain
Of the ill-starred warm passion that devours
Thy soul—I have no hatred, no disdain;

No wish for vengeance moves me; peace I fain
Would give thee! wrongs I know not of, much less
Thee as a slave or foe would I retain;
True, thou hast erred; and now all tenderness,
Now all dislike, hast loved and hated to excess:

54.

"But these are frailties shared by all, and them
Thy native laws, thy sex, and youth excuse;
I too have sinned, nor thee can I condemn,
If thou to pardon me dost not refuse.
Midst the dear images I ne'er can lose,
Thine shall be dearest still; on thee, sweet maid,
In joy and woe 'twill be my bliss to muse;
Thy champion still — thou still shalt be obeyed,
Far as with honour suits, and our divine crusade.

55.

"Let now our mutual faults and follies cease,
And with our faults our shame too have an end;
And in this lonely island sleep in peace
Their sad sweet memories, let them here descend
As to the silent grave; where'er I wend,
This only act of mine let no one trace,
None whisper to the wind; nor thou, dear friend,
Do, I implore thee, aught that would debase
Thy name, thy worth, thy charms, or shame thy princely race!

56.

"Farewell! I go; thy wishes must be vain,
Fate grants them not; Armida, thou art wise!
Or go some happier way, or here remain,
And calm the thoughts that to such wildness rise."
She, whilst the pensive warrior thus replies,
Restless, disturbed, could scarce her passion stay;
Long time she rolled on him her angry eyes,
Nor knew in what fierce terms her scorn to say;
At length the storm broke loose, and these mad words found way: —

57.

"Thee no Sophia bore, no Azzo gave
Blood for thy being! thy fierce parents were
The icy Caucasus, the mad sea-wave,
Some Indian tiger or Hyrcanian bear!
Why should I longer fawn? did the man e'er
Show but one sign of warm humanity?
Changed he his colour at my sharp despair?
Did he but dash one tear drop from his eye?
Or breathe for all my pangs a single suffering sigh?

58.

"What things shall I pass over, what repeat?
He swears he's mine, yet with the whirlwind flies;
Good, merciful, kind victor! to forget,
And pardon your fond foe's indignities.
Hear how he counsels! hark but to his wise
And modest words! this coy Xenocrates,
Hear how he talks of love! O Gods! O skies!
And can you suffer holy men like these,
To burn your towers and towns, and act what sins they please?

59.

"Begone, false wretch, with all that peace of mind
Thy treason leaves to me! begone, I say!
Soon shall my ghost, a haunting shade behind,
From which thou canst not tear thyself away,
Dog all thy thoughts by night, thy steps by day;
With snakes and torches, a new Fury, I,
Much as I loved thee, so much will dismay;
And if it be thy fate the strife to try,
Scaped from the roaring waves and tempests of the sky —

60.

"There, midst the dead and dying, thou shalt fall,
And pay for all my wrongs, false chevalier!
Oft on Armida's name distracted call,
In thy last groans, which soon I hope to hear!"
But there the mourner's spirit failed, nor clear
Were the last accents; her sweet colour flies,
She faints, she falls, her speaking lips adhere,
An icy sweat on her cold forehead lies,
Droops her dejected head, and close her radiant eyes.

61.

Thine eyes are closed, Armida; the stern powers
Of fate deny all solace to thy woe;
Look up, poor girl, and see what bitter showers
Stream from the eyes of thine imagined foe!
Couldst thou but hear his sighs, couldst thou but know
The pain he feels, it must thy love renew,
And in thy bitter cup fresh sweetness throw;
All that he can, he gives to thee, still true,
And takes (thou think'st it not), a last — a fond adieu.

62.

What should he do? leave on the naked sands
The Lady thus, betwixt alive and dead?
Pity forbids, and courtesy withstands,
But hard necessity compels — 'tis sped;

One farewell kiss — he parts; the grot they tread,
And launch from land; mild blow the western gales
Midst the rich tresses of the pilot's head;
Fast o'er green ocean glide the golden sails:
To land he looks, till land his grieving vision fails.

63.

Waked from her trance, Armida, with a start,
Looked round her — all was silence; all was shade;
"And *is* he gone?" she said, "and *had* he heart
To leave me thus, nor for a moment stayed,
In doubt of life or death, a little aid
To lend? nor for one moment lingered o'er,
To watch the pale, mute ruin he had made?
And do I love him still, and on this shore
With folded arms still sit, still unrevenged deplore?

64.

"Why weep I longer? other arms and arts
Command I not? I will the wretch pursue;
Nor shall the deep o'er which his bark departs,
Nor heaven's high vault secure him from his due;
I will o'ertake him; cleave his heart in two,
And hang his severed head upon a spot
Where all like traitors may the monster view;
Versed as he is in guile, I will outplot
His brain — alas, I rave! I talk I know not what!

65.

"Then, wretched girl! thou shouldst have wreaked thy hate,
When he lay safely curling in thy chain;
That had been something worth! now all too late
Come thy hot wrath and thy incensed disdain!
But, if my beauty and ingenious brain
Can nothing here, not fruitless shall this strong
And passionate desire of mine remain;
Oh my scorned charms! yours, yours was all the wrong;
To you shall the dear task of vengeance now belong.

66.

"These charms of mine shall be the fixed reward
Of him who slays the man! your swords prepare,
Oh my famed lovers! though the task seem hard,
Yet great and glorious is the deed you dare:
I, who in independent state shall wear
The crown of rich Damascus, will be nigh,
In guerdon of the victim; if this rare
Reward appear too poor, revenge to buy,
Nature! I thank thee not for charms ill praised so high.

67.

"False, fatal gifts! I spurn you back; I scorn
The hated kingdom which I have to give;
I hate my life, the hour when I was born,
Alone in hope of sweet revenge I live!"
In broken words, enraged, thus does she grieve,
Thus rave; then turns with a distracted pace
From the lone shore, the moments to retrieve;
Showing what fury in her heart found place,
By her dishevelled hair, fierce eyes, and crimsoning face.

68.

Reached her abode, with foaming lips she called
Three hundred ghosts from Tartarus the dun;
Black clouds the tranquil face of heaven appalled,
Pale in a moment grew the' eternal sun;
The whirlwinds blustered on the hills, air spun,
Hell bellowed at her feet; then might you hear
Through the enchanted halls the damned run,
Unchained and raging, now far-off, now near —
Shrieks, hissings, yells, drear groans, and whisperings yet more drear.

69.

A raven shade, more dark than darkest night,
Cloaked all the hill, enlivened by no ray,
Save now and then dull flashes of blue light,
That made the following gloom yet more dismay:
Slowly at length the blackness cleared away;
The round pale sun shone out, but nothing clear;
Gloomy the earth, the air was aught but gay,
Nor of the palace did one trace appear,
Nor would you venture now, e'en to exclaim, 'twas here.

70.

As when the clouds at summer eve have drawn
In air huge towers and temples, they remain
Till wind or sunshine comes, and straight they're gone,
Like a dream figured in the sick man's brain:
So melt the' enchanted towers, with all their train
Of rich delights, and leave but for the eye
The hoary face of nature — the still main,
Brown hills, and frowning woods. Her chariot nigh
She as is usual mounts, and fast away doth fly.

71.

The clouds she cleaves, and round her doth enrol
Thunders and tempests, lightnings, wave, and wind;
The regions subject to the southern pole,
And all their unknown natives left behind,

Calpe she crossed; nor, in her fretful mind,
Stooped to the Spaniard, or the Moor, but o'er
The Midland Sea her winged car inclined;
Nor to the right, nor to the left hand bore,
Till in mid air she reached the known Assyrian shore.

72.

Not now to fair Damascus does she post,
But shuns the aspect of her once dear land,
And guides her chariot to the Dead Sea coast,
Where the strongholds of the Enchantress stand.
Alighting here, she from her duteous band
Of damsels and of pages hides her face,
And, wandering lonely on the sea-beat strand,
Fluctuates from scheme to scheme in doubtful case,
But soon all shame to rage and wished revenge gives place.

73.

"Yes, hence I will," she cried, "before his swarms
The' Egyptian king shall move in Sion's aid;
Each art react, remuster all my charms,
To every uncouth thing my sex degrade,
That may assist my purpose; — undismayed,
Handle the brand and bow, become the flame
Of the most potent, and direct his blade;
Let me but have the just revenge I claim,
Farewell, vain self-respect! farewell, fond maiden shame!

74.

"And for the faults I shall hereby commit,
Let my sage guardian blame himself, not me;
He first to thoughts and offices unfit
Set my frail sex and daring spirit free;
He made me first a gadding damsel, he
Spurred on my ardour, loosed me from the rein
Of timorous awe and shame-faced modesty;
His be the guilt of all then that may stain —
All I have done through love, or may do through disdain."

75.

Thus fixed, she gathered in, on Arab steeds,
Damsels, and knights, and servitors in haste;
And in their sumptuous arms and woman's weeds,
Displayed at once her fortune and fine taste.
Forward she set; and, journeying the wild waste,
Took nor repose by night, nor rest by day,
Till her keen eye along the' horizon traced
The' Egyptian hosts, that in their mailed array
Wide o'er the sunbright sands of antique Gaza lay.

[Armida goes to the Egyptian host encamped at Gaza — about to advance to the relief of Jerusalem, presents herself to the King of Egypt, and offers her hand to that one of his captains who shall slay Rinaldo. Godfrey sends Tancred's squire, Vafrino, to the Egyptian army as a spy to bring back information. After Rinaldo's return, the Christians scale the walls and capture the city; Tancred slays Argantes in single combat. In the following selection, Vafrino travels to the Egyptian camp. The last canto tells of the victory over the Egyptian host which completes the Christian conquest, and of the end of the story of Armida.]

CANTO XIX

ARGUMENT

Tancred in single combat slays his foe,
The terrible Argantes; Aladine
Flees to the citadel, and saveth so
His host; Erminia challenges Vafrine;
Of the leagued hosts reveals the masked design,
Accompanies him back, and on the sands
Finds her loved lord half dead beneath a pine;
First mourns, then cures him; Godfrey understands
Ormondo's plot, and acts as circumstance demands.

* * * * *

57.

The lark was warbling sweet her evening song,
When through the shadows of declining day
Vafrino left the' encampment; all night long
He travelled on his dark and lonely way;
High Ascalon he passed, ere morning grey
O'er the dim landscape shed its grateful light,
And when the sun with culminating ray
Had reached its hot meridian, to the right
The vast, the boundless camp burst proudly on his sight.

58.

Millions of tents, o'erwaved with flags unfurled,
Green, purple, gold, and crimson, he espies;
And hears such strange wild tongues, and such a world
Of savage sounds from barbarous metals rise,
Trumpet, and horn, and gong, with camels' cries,
Roarings of elephants, and neighings clear
Of shrill-voiced coursers, climbing to the skies,
That to himself he says, with soul sincere,
"All Asia, Libya, all are sure transported here!"

59.

He first the' encampment and its strength surveys,
The circling rampart, its extent, and height,

Then seeks no more obscure and winding ways,
But boldly issues to the public sight;
And with an air most unconcerned and light
Enters the regal gates direct, and now
Asks, and now answers questions, with a sleight
But to be equalled by the frank bold brow
Which makes his answers good, and greets it cares not how.

60.

Through the long crowded streets, the tents and squares,
Now here, now there, solicitous he turns;
The horses, armours, chiefs, the name each bears,
Their arts and customs he observes and learns;
Nor satisfied with this, his spirit burns,
And partly manages to know the bent
Of their most secret projects and concerns;
So well he speeds beneath his fair ostent,
As e'en to win access to the imperial tent.

61.

Here, looking round, he marked a rent, through which
The voice within found egress, and whereby
The Viceroy's private cabinet, a rich
Recess, was obvious to the curious eye;
So that whoever chose thereto to' apply
His ear without, might gather whatsoe'er
Transpired within; at this the matchless spy
Planted himself, as with assiduous care
The tent's defective seam adroitly to repair.

62.

The Chief bareheaded stood, in arms, and wore
A vest of Tyrian purple; in the rear
Two pages his bright shield and helmet bore;—
Thoughtful he stood, and, leaning on his spear,
Gave heed to one who with a look severe,
Tall in his stature, sinewy in his frame,
High points discussed; Vafrino was all ear;
And, surely fancying that he heard the name
Of Bouillon's lord, yet more inquisitive became.

63.

He heard the Chieftain question: "Art thou then
So sure of Godfrey's death?" "So sure," said he,
"I take my oath by Allah, ne'er again
But as a matador thy face to see;
I will outstrip all those who are with me
Sworn to the deed; nor ask I other bliss,

Than to hang up in trophy, by decree
Of our great prince, in his metropolis,
The man's rich arms, subscribed with some such verse as this: —

64.

" 'These arms in war from the Frank Chief, the curse
And scourge of Asia, brave Ormondo tore,
When him he slew; the fame whereof, this verse
And trophied marble laud for evermore!' "
"Of this," the armed Leader said, "no more;
Think not the king will leave unglorified
A deed which both the Egypts must adore;
Thy wish, be sure, he will fulfil with pride,
And grace thy conquering brows with priceless gems beside.

65.

"Now then the counterfeited arms prepare,
For the great day of fight approaches fast:"
"They are all ready," he replied, and there
Both ended parle, and from the chamber passed.
Suspense and doubt Vafrino's mind o'ercast;
Long as he weighed the seeming aim and end
Of their discourse, the project to the last
Remained obscure, — he could not comprehend,
What by this feint of arms the traitors could intend.

66.

Thence he departed, nor the livelong night
His eyes to slumber or repose resigned;
But when that mighty camp at morning light
Unfurled its thousand banners to the wind,
He in their march the hostile squadrons joined,
Like the trained hound sequacious of its scent;
With them he halted when the day declined,
And, as before, stalked slow from tent to tent,
Eager to gather more of this disguised intent.

67.

On a rich throne, mid knights and damsels gay,
Searching around, Armida he descries;
Forlorn she sits, and inly seems to weigh
Some deep sad thought, for as she sits she sighs.
On her white hand in melancholy guise
She leans her rosy cheek, and so would fain
Hide the love-darting radiance of her eyes;
Weeps she or no he knows not, but 'tis plain
The stars in heaven are dim, and lower, presaging rain,

68.

In front of her Adrastus sits, nor heeds
Aught but her charms, — he moves not, scarce respires,
So stedfastly he hangs on her, and feeds
His pining hopes and unappeased desires.
But Tisaphernes now the dame admires,
Now eyes the savage, whom in soul he spurns
From her dear sight; the whilst with changeful fires
His visage dark and radiant shews by turns,
As Love's mild watchlight shines, or Wrath's hot beacon burns.

69.

Then Altamore he views, where more apart
He stands, enclosed amidst her virgins bright;
He lets not loose his glances, but with art
Rules his fond fancy and his wishful sight:
His left eye marks her hand, her face, his right
Glides down voluptuous on a sweeter quest,
And secretly slips in, to its delight,
Where the too careless and indulgent vest
Reveals, at every swell, the beauty of her breast.

70.

At length Armida raised her eyes, and straight
Her brow cleared up; and through the clouds of grief
With which her pensive features gloomed of late,
Flashed a sweet smile in beautiful relief.
"Prince," she said, turning to the Indian Chief,
"Thy vaunts have power my sorrows to assuage;
For they confirm me in the fond belief
That I shall have quick vengeance: sweet is rage,
When willing Hope takes up Revenge's daring gage."

71.

"For Allah's sake, serene," the Indian said,
"Thy mournful aspect, and thy griefs control;
For soon indeed Rinaldo's hated head
I in glad vengeance at thy feet will roll;
Or, if it more thy sorrow should console,
In chains conduct him to whatever jail
May please thee most; I swear it on my soul."
His rival, hearing thus the ruffian rail,
Deigned not a word himself, but gnawed his bitter nail.

72.

She, turning then on Tisapherne a smile,
Said: "What say'st thou, and how dost thou decide?"
"I, who am backward in this vaunting style,"
The noble Prince in irony replied,

"Will follow this grim champion with a stride
Less stately, and at distance:" his sharp sneer
Stung the fierce savage to the quick, who cried:
"And fit it is that he whose arm must fear
To match the king of Inde's, *should* linger far arear."

73.

The Persian, nettled at the word, tossed high
The haughty plumes upon his head, and said:
"Oh, were I master of my will, had I
But free permission to unsheath my blade,
Which was the lingerer should be soon displayed!
Nor thee, nor thy big vaunts, ferocious brute!
But Heaven and unconsenting Love I dread:"
He ceased; Adrastus rushed to the dispute;
But then Armida rose, and twixt them placed her foot.

74.

"Why will you thus retract the oaths," said she,
"Which you so oft have given? respect my woes;
Both are my champions; let that title be
The bond your fatal discords to compose:
He that is wroth, is wroth with me; who throws
Scorn on his comrade, spares not to provoke
My just displeasure; to your cost be foes!"
Thus she exclaimed; and thus, beneath a yoke
Stronger than steel, their hot, rebellious spirits broke.

75.

Vafrine was there; and, treasuring in his mind
All he heard mentioned, from the tent retired;
Some deep dark plot he clearly saw designed,
Some plot, that was not thus to have transpired;
But this was all; he busily inquired
The naked fact, but fruitlessly; defeat
And difficulty but the more inspired
The anxious wish his mission to complete;
Fixed or to learn the truth, or there his death to meet.

76.

A thousand tricks and subtleties of brain,
A thousand unimagined means he tried,
To worm the secret out, but still in vain,—
The plan was still unknown, the arms unspied;
Fortune at length, when wit alone could guide
His steps no farther, lent her gracious aid,
And the dark knot of all his doubts untied;
So that all points of the dire project laid
Against good Bouillon's life, before him were displayed.

77.

Thither he turned again, where still among
Her armed lovers sat the Syrian queen,
Judging the truth would soonest find a tongue,
Where such a crowd of visitors convene.
Here now he greets a damsel with the mien
Of one in all polite enchantments versed,
As though the lady he before had seen,
And but renewed some friendship that had erst
'Twixt them subsisted long; and frankly he conversed.

78.

"Fain would I too," he sportively began,
"Become the champion of some charming maid,
And, in fulfilment of the purposed plan,
The blood of Bouillon or Rinaldo shed;
Ask then some boon, my Beauty, that may wed
My soul to your sweet service; what you please,
Or stout earl's heart or barbarous baron's head:"
Thus he commenced, intending by degrees
To slip from gay to grave, and learn the chief's decrees.

79.

But as he spake, he smiled; and in a way
So natural and unfeigned, that to his side
Another damsel, who had marked the play
Of his expressive face, drew near, and cried:
"Nay! for thy falchion choose no other bride
Than my commands, for on its aid my heart
Is set; nor think such love misplaced,—beside
By old consent my knight indeed thou art,
And e'en as such, we two must have some talk apart."

80.

Withdrawn, she spoke: "I know thee well, Vafrine!
Me too thou needs must know;" the subtle Spy
Felt his heart fail him, but with lively mien
Her glance returned, and smiling made reply:
"Nay, gracious lady! ne'er before have I,
That I remember, seen your face, although
Its beauty asks the gaze of every eye
Fitly to praise it; this alone I know,
My name is much unlike the one which you bestow.

81.

"My mother bore me on Biserta's plains,
Her name Lesbina, mine is Almanzore:"
Quick she replied: "All that to thee pertains
I long have known, dissemble it no more;

Hold not thyself so secret, I implore;
I am thy friend, and for thy good would dare
No little risk, — Erminia I, of yore
A Queen's blest daughter and a King's rich heir,
Then good Prince Tancred's thrall, and subject to thy care.

82.

"Two blessed months thy captive I remained,
A reverenced nun in a delightful cell,
And in all courteous modes was entertained, —
The same, the same I am; behold me well!"
The squire failed not, when on her beauty fell
His closer gaze, to recognise the fair:
"All fears," she added, "from thy mind expel;
Fear not for me, thy life shall be my care;
By the bright sun in heaven, by heaven itself I swear!

83.

"Nay, when thou partest, take me back, my friend,
To my dear prison — (pardon me the phrase);
For here in bitter liberty I spend
Whole restless nights and melancholy days;
And if perchance thou'rt lingering here to gaze
Upon our camp, and with ingenious brain
Pry through our plans, great cause hast thou to praise
Thy happy stars; for I will things explain,
Which else thy utmost skill had failed to ascertain."

84.

Thus she: but, thoughtful of Armida's snares,
He silent stood, considering in his mind,
"Woman's a false and chattering thing, — she swears,
And will and will not, just as sits the wind;
Simple's the man, and credulous, and blind,
Who trusts a word she says;" at length he cried,
After long thought, "If thou'rt indeed inclined
To go, so be it; I will be thy guide;
Leave we the rest to wait a more convenient tide."

85.

And now the gongs and trumpets sound to horse,
And through the host an apt confusion reigns;
Vafrino leaves her tent, whilst she perforce
Rejoins her friends, a while with them remains,
And in gay talk their idlesse entertains
With jocund praises of her new-made knight;
Then steals off slyly; mounts her palfrey; gains
The place prescribed, and with Vafrino light
O'er the wide champaign takes her unregarded flight.

86.

When they had reached the desert, and in air
Beheld the distant towers of Gaza fade,
Vafrino begged the virgin to declare
What secret plot was against Godfrey laid:
She then the whole conspiracy displayed,
The treacherous web unwinding, fold by fold;
"Eight warriors are there of the court," she said,
"In this insidious bond of guilt enrolled,
Of whom the most renowned is Ormond, base as bold.

87.

"These, whether moved by hatred or disdain,
Have thus conspired, and 'tis their shrewd design,
When in pitched battle, or to lose or gain
These Asian realms, the two great armies join,
To bear upon their coats the Red-cross sign,
And armed like Franks commingle in the fight;
And as 'tis known the guards of Godfrey shine
In *or* and *argent,* they themselves will dight
In the like foreign vests, emblazoning gold and white.

88.

"But all will wear some token on the crest,
Whereby their friends may know them for allies;
And when both armies lay their spears in rest,
And the war thickens and the tumults rise,
They will your Chief track out, and in the guise
Of guards with amicable zeal crowd round,
To pierce his bosom; if they strike, he dies;
For know, their swords with poison have been ground,
That death may be dealt out in every separate wound.

89.

"And as their Chieftain learned from public fame
That none with surer skill could signify
Your arms and dress, he fixed on me to frame
Their feigned array, and forced me to comply.
This is the cause I leave the camp; I fly
The' imperious biddings which that Asp of Nile
Might further give; his trains of treachery
My heart abhors, nor ever shall such guile
Or masked deceit again my virgin heart defile.

90.

"This is the cause, nor this alone,"—and here
She ceased, and, colouring to a rosy red,
Cast down her eyes, nor could Vafrino hear
Well the last words, which much she wished unsaid.

Solicitous to know what thoughts could shed
Such deep confusion o'er her cheek, he pressed
The virgin home, — "Of little faith!" he said,
"Why the true causes hide from one whose breast
Is, as thou know'st, of trust? blush not, but speak the rest."

91.

Her bosom heaved with a tumultuous swell,
And from her lips the trembling accents came
Abrupt and prefaced by a sigh: "Farewell,
Ill-timed reserve and unavailing shame!
It is in vain — I am no more the same —
In vain concealed and close you strive to hide
Love's glowing fires beneath your specious flame!
Due were such scruples ere I stept aside;
But now a wandering maid, farewell the' imperfect pride!

92.

"My loss," she added, "on that night of grief,
When my poor country yielded to her foes,
Surpassed the' appearance; not that then my chief
Misfortune happened, but from thence it rose.
My sceptre lost, my realms subdued, were woes
Easy to bear, resigned with little cost;
But with my high estate, my heart's repose
Was also gone; ah me! what folly crost
My brain? then sense was wrecked, and peace for ever lost!

93.

"Thou know'st, Vafrine, with what a trembling awe,
Seeing such slaughter and foul spoil, I sped
To thy kind lord and mine, when first I saw
Armed in my halls the warrior fix his tread;
Thou know'st with what an agony of dread
His knees I grasped, and of his conquering glaive
Prayed strong protection: 'Mercy, Prince,' I said,
'I pray not for my life, but save, oh save
My virgin flower unstained; 'tis all I come to crave!'

94.

"He waited not to hear my finished plea,
But took my hand in his, and said, 'Arise!
Fear not, fair maiden! I myself will be
Thy sure defence; cloud not those charming eyes!'
Ah, then I felt, with a divine surprise,
I know not what strange sweetness seize my frame!
Which by degrees, in gratitude's disguise,
Securely creeping through my soul, became
Ere well I wist, a wound, a sickness, and a flame.

95.

"He visited me oft, he saw me grieve,
And with mild accents would my woes allay;
'Thy perfect liberty,' he said, 'receive;
Take back thy treasures, and be cheered, I pray.'
Ah, this was cruelty, not kindness! gay
I could not be, when, whilst he drew the dart,
He rudely snatched me from myself away;
These he restored to me, the cheaper part,
But in restoring played the tyrant o'er my heart.

96.

"Love's hard to hide; with thee I oft apart
Asked of my lord in garden, hall, and grove;
Thou the strong workings of my mind and heart
Perceiving, saidst, 'Erminia, thou'rt in love!'
This I denied — can maids do less? and strove
To dissipate the' idea; but my sighs
Too well sufficed the assertion to disprove;
And whilst my tongue was mute, perchance my eyes
Shone with the' impassioned warmth I studied to disguise.

97.

"Unhappy silence! had I then but sought
The fitting medicine for my wounds, I ne'er
Had loosed my wishes on a fancy fraught
With no relief, nor fled I know not where.
I left him, hiding in my breast with care
The flame I nursed; — what tongue my pangs can paint?
For death alone I looked; till with despair
Love in my succour strove, and in the' attaint,
Loosed me from every tie of feminine restraint.

98.

"So that to seek my lord I went, that he
Might cure the lingering sickness he had made;
But on my moonbright way, I chanced to be,
By villains ambushed in the greenwood shade,
Chased and assaulted; scarce could I evade
Their savage grasp, so hotly they pursued;
To a lone cell at length my palfrey strayed,
And there I dwelt in genial solitude,
A simple shepherd-girl, a tenant of the wood.

99.

"But when that fond desire which sore dismay
Had for a while suppressed, revived again,
Daring the same adventure, on my way
The same misfortune met with me as then;

Nor could I now escape; for in the glen
The lurking freebooters were close at hand;
Thus was I chased and quickly seized, — the men
Were, I soon gathered, an Egyptian band,
Who straight for Gaza made, swift journeying o'er the sand.

100.

"They took me to their Chief, whose ear my prayer
And mournful story so completely gained,
That he mine honour did respect, and there
With kind Armida have I since remained.
Thus oft have I been harshly entertained;
Thus oft have I escaped; ah, see, Vafrine,
What scenes I have passed through, what ills sustained!
Yet free, yet captured oft as I have been,
Still my first chains I wear, preserved through every scene.

101.

"Ah, let not him who round my soul entwined
The chains from which no power can set me free,
Let him not say, 'Go, vagrant maid, and find
Some other home, thou shalt not stay with me,' —
But kind and dear may my reception be!
'Take back,' Vafrino! to thy master say,
'This trembling dove, and treat her tenderly!' "
Thus spake the Princess; and thus, night and day,
They side by side rode on, and talked the time away.

102.

The beaten road Vafrino left erewhile,
Seeking a shorter or securer way;
They reached at length, what time with farewell smile
The sun hung hovering o'er the landscape grey,
Near to the town, a vale of pine and bay;
Sprinkled with crimson was the green, and nigh,
Grovelling in blood, a lifeless warrior lay
Across the path; though dead, his Gorgon eye
Yet seemed to menace death, upstaring on the sky.

103.

The fashion of his arms and foreign mien
Spoke him a Pagan; on Vafrino sped,
And somewhat farther on the encircled green,
As to the right he chanced to turn his head,
Perceived a second: "This," he inly said,
"Must surely be a Christian, by the grain
Of his dark vest;" he sees the Cross of Red,
Leaps from his steed, the face discovers plain,
And, "O my God!" he cried, "here lies Prince Tancred slain."

104.

The pitying Princess had paused to gaze
On the grim form of the Circassian peer,
When that sad voice of anguish and amaze
Came like an arrow on her heart and ear;
At Tancred's name, she spurred like one whom fear
Or wine had rendered mad, her palfrey fleet;
And when she saw indeed the form so dear,
Pale, and wrapt round as with the winding-sheet
Of death, she stept not, — no, she darted from her seat!

105.

And, with a bursting groan, a stormy shower
Of tears, low bending o'er the' unconscious knight,
"Fortune!" she cried, "in what ill-omened hour
Bring'st thou me here? O dire, O fatal sight!
Long wished, long sought for, is it in this plight
I find and view thee, oh my love! laced o'er
With wounds, and all unable to requite
With one kind look the bitter plaints I pour?
No sooner found again, than lost for evermore!

106.

"Ah! never did I dream that to these eyes
Thou could'st be aught, love, but a pleasing care!
Would they were dark, no more this blank disguise
Of thy dear face to mark, which ill they dare.
Where is its once expressive smile? ah where
The mildness beaming from the eye? the cheek's
Divine carnations, and the brow that bare
Itself so bravely? — not a feature speaks, —
Gone! beyond reach, alas, of groans, or tears, or shrieks!

107.

"But, though thus pale and dim, thou charm'st me still;
Fair soul! if yet thou light'st this seeming clay,
Yet hear'st my plaints, forgive my daring will
And too rash ardour the fond theft which they
Tempt me to take, — forgive me if I lay
To thine my virgin lips, and one cold kiss
Steal from the dull caresses of decay!
Warmer I looked for, but 'twill be some bliss
To seize in death's despite, and die remembering this.

108.

"Receive my soul, which flutters to be free,
And thither guide it where thine own is fled!"
Groaning she spoke, and weeping seemed to be
Apace dissolving with the tears she shed.

Bathed by this quickening balm, as from the dead,
The knight revived, and opened for a space
His languid lips, — dark slumber still o'erspread
His heavy eyes, but as she kissed his face,
One blending sigh from him repaid her blest embrace.

109.

A gleam of hope, at his reviving breath,
Cheered the sad maid: "Look up, dear love," she cried,
"On the last melancholy rites of death
Which I with pious tears and sighs provide!
Look on me, Tancred, a funereal bride,
Fain in companionship with thee to take
The long dark path and perish at thy side!
Fly not, fly not so soon, for pity's sake!
'Tis the last boon I ask, the last request I make."

110.

Tancred his eyes unclosed, and closed again,
Heavy and dim; and she renewed her plaint;
"This," said Vafrine, "soothes not the hero's pain,
First cure the wounded, then bewail the' attaint."
He strips him of his arms; Erminia, faint
And trembling, aids him as she can, applies
Her skilful hand, like a ministrant saint,
To search his wounds, and with experienced eyes,
Symptoms of hopeful show rejoicingly descries.

111.

By loss of blood and faintness she perceives
The trance is caused, and by the chill night wind;
But in this lonely wilderness of leaves
Nought save her veil occurs, his wounds to bind:
But Love romantic bandages can find,
And dictate arts of pity strange and sweet, —
For with her radiant tresses, disentwined,
She stanched the flowing blood, (divine conceit!)
And swathed the grisly wounds that so acutely beat; —

112.

Severing the tresses with his sword; for ill
Her thin short veil the' occasion could suffice;
Nor sage nor crocus, dittany nor dill
Found she at hand; but charms of equal price
She knew, she used, and from his weary eyes
That deadly sleep already shakes away;
Lightly he lifts them, and with glad surprise
Beholds his servant, and, in strange array,
The maid who o'er him hangs with such benign dismay.

113.

"How com'st thou here, Vafrino?" soft he said,
"And thou, my kind physician! who art thou?"
She wept, she blushed, rejoicing, rosy-red,
She sighed, she smiled, she felt she wist not how.
"Thou shalt know all, prince," she replied, "but now
(Thus thy physician bids) be still and rest;
Health shall return to thy bewildered brow,
Prepare the guerdon that shall make me blest;"
And then his head she placed upon her beauteous breast.

114.

Vafrino mused how he might best, ere night,
Remove the warrior from the bosky glen,
When lo! a band of soldiers came in sight,
Whom soon he noted for Lord Tancred's men;
They on the tower were fighting round him, when
He met the fierce Circassian, blade to blade,
And in appeal of battle dared him; then
Bade not to follow, they the prince obeyed,
But anxious sought him now, so long the hero stayed.

115.

Numbers beside pursued the search, but these
Alone had the good chance their wish to gain;
Their arms they join, whereon with perfect ease
To all, the wounded hero they sustain:
"Shall then Argantes," said the knight, "remain,
Brave as he was, the prey of wild birds? no!
Leave not the hero; bear him from the plain;
His gallant relics shall not feed the crow,
Nor want such praise or tomb as Tancred can bestow!

116.

"I war not with the pale dumb corse, — he died
Bold as a lion on the hunter's spear;
Funereal rites 'tis fit that we provide,
The last poor honours that can serve him here."
He said; his troops construct a simple bier,
And thus in solemn march behind him bear
His slaughtered foe; Vafrino in the rear
His station takes beside the' enamoured fair,
And tends her o'er the downs with all a page's care.

117.

"Not home," said Tancred, "to my wonted tent,
But bear, O bear me to the sacred Town!
That if cut short by human accident,
I there may lay my feverish being down:

Haply a spot of such revered renown
Where died the Lamb of God, may make my way
To heaven more easy; and 'twill be the crown
Of all my toils, with life's declining ray,
Low at his worshipped shrine my pilgrim vows to pay!"

118.

He said, and thither was he borne, and laid
On a soft bed, and in a calm repose
Was soon entranced; Vafrino for the maid
A near apartment close and secret chose;
And, leaving her to cheer her amorous woes
With kindling hope's serene perspective, went
Where Godfrey sojourned, unforbid by those
Who there kept guard, though then in crowded tent
On the next stroke of war his dubious thoughts were bent.

119.

Beside the bed, whence Raymond scarce uprears
His yet enfeebled frame, the Duke was found;
By a brave garland of his noble peers
And of his wisest counsellors compassed round:
The Squire his tale begins, and a profound
Regard is marked on each beholder's mien;
None interrupts him: "Sire," he says, "renowned
Through the wide world! at thy desire I've been
Amidst the' Egyptian tents, and all their forces seen.

120.

"But fancy not that of the mighty host
The countless swarms can be by me ared;
I saw the hills, and plains, and valleys lost,
E'en as I looked, beneath their darkening tread;
I saw, where'er they came, where'er they spread,
Rich earth despoiled of all her grass and grain,
And the flood shrink in its exhausted bed;
Not Jordan's stream, nor Syria's wide champaign
Can e'er, methinks, suffice, such myriads to sustain.

121.

"But of their horse and of their foot by far
The greater part are merely useless shows;
Troops that no signals use nor arts of war,
But at a distance fight with slings and bows;
Yet are there some choice warriors who compose
The Persian host, well mailed, with sword in hand,
And helmets on their heads; but chiefly those
Illustrious myrmidons my praise demand,
Who guard the' imperial flag, the king's Immortal Band.

122.

"Immortal called, for when a soldier's lost,
Its number not diminishes; the knight
Next in renown fills up the vacant post,
As though succeeding to his comrade's right;
The Captain, Emireno named, for might
In deeds of arms and wisdom in divan,
Has but few peers; his orders are, despite
Thy utmost phlegm, by all the arts he can,
Into a general fight to force thee or trepan.

123.

"Nor can the army its approach retard
Beyond the second day, for 'tis on fire
To act — look well, Rinaldo, then to guard
Thy head, 'gainst which so many knights conspire:
The most renowned have whet their swords in ire,
And pledged their honour on the dreadful deed;
Whilst, yet the more to raise incensed desire,
Herself Armida promises in meed
Of him who or by guile or prowess shall succeed.

124.

"Chief of the warriors who have sworn thy death
Is Altamore, the king of Samarcand;
Adrastus too, whose realms are by the breath
Of young Aurora at her rising fanned;
As big and bold a giant as e'er spanned
A sword in battle; so unlike his kind,
His reins a monstrous elephant command;
And Tisapherne, to whom, of milder mind,
The sovereign palm of worth and prowess is assigned."

125.

This heard, Rinaldo's soul was all ablaze,
His eyes with generous indignation fill,
He burns to rush amidst his foes, he lays
Hand on his sword, nor stands a moment still.
"This," said Vafrine, "is one impending ill,
But their chief plot, the crowning stroke of all,
Remains to be disclosed; their utmost skill
In arms, their guile, their hatred, and their gall,
Will be employed to work thine own determined fall."

126.

He then proceeded, part by part to' unveil
The latent risk, the meditated fraud,
The poisoned arms, devices, shirts of mail,
The vaunt, the promise, and designed reward;

Much was inquired, much answered; all applaud
The spy's quick genius and accomplished vow:
Silence ensued; until the chief, unawed
By the near danger, raised his tranquil brow,
And to Count Raymond said, "What counsel offerest thou?"

127.

"Not as was fixed," he said, "at rise of sun
To press our foes, but, more to their chagrin,
The tower so strictly to besiege, that none
May at his pleasure or pass out or in;
Meanwhile refresh our forces, which begin
To need the respite; strengthened thus with rest,
The last great battle we may hope to win;
But judge thyself at leisure if 'twere best,
Boldly, or here at bay the battle to contest."

128.

"But, above all things, of thyself be sure
Take every care, as 'tis through thee, they own,
Our armies conquer; who can else secure
The field, and Europe o'er the East enthrone?
And that the traitors may be clearly known,
Change the devices of thy guardian band;
So shall the villains for their crime atone,
Caught in the very scheme themselves have planned,
And thou be still preserved our armies to command."

129.

"As is thy wont," the pious Chief replied,
"Thy kind regard and wisdom dost thou show;
But what thou leav'st unfixed, I now decide—
We will march forth against the haughty foe.
Shall armies, recent from the overthrow
Of the proud East, from tower or rampart fight,
When too by such foul guile insulted? No!
Our well-proved swords the traitors shall requite
Both in the open field and all-beholding light!

130.

"Neither the rumour of our conquered spoils
Shall they sustain; nor, when in frowns revealed,
The victor's aspect, or his arms; our toils
Are crowned; and in their fall our empire's sealed:
The tower, their last lorn confidence, shall yield,
Or, unrelieved of any, be possessed,
When the first engine to its walls is wheeled!"
Here ceased the high-souled Chief, for down the west
The glittering stars declined, and called them to their rest.

CANTO XX

ARGUMENT

The host arrives, and with the Christian power
Joins in fell battle; Solyman disdains
To be cooped up in the blockaded tower,
And sallies out, to war upon the plains;
With him the king in blood his sabre stains;
Both fall by noble hands; the godlike boy
Soothes his forlorn Armida; daylight wanes,
But the flushed Croises all their foes destroy,
And to the long-sought shrine proceed with duteous joy.

* * * * *

53.

The Moors, the Ethiops, and the Arabs then,
To the dull discord of the atabal,
Spread out their dusky skirts of moving men,
And on the dexter wing revolving fall;
Already with their bows and slings they gall
The army from afar, when, like the din
Of earthquake and of thunder, at the call
Of young Rinaldo, his bold knights begin
With shouts their rushing march, and hem the' assailants in.

54.

The first he met was Asimire, who led
The Moors of Meröe, an illustrious name;
Rinaldo smote him where the swarthy head
Towers on the neck, and shore it from the frame;
And when this taste of victory and of fame
Had whet his angry appetite, the youth
So nobly bore him in the bloody game,
That to relate his deeds would be in sooth
To give mute wonder wing, and wed romance to truth.

55.

More deaths than blows he deals, yet momently
His falchion smites: and as the angry snake
Seems in its single tongue to vibrate three,
With such a fearful swiftness does it shake,
So in dismay these charged barbarians take
The single sword which furiously the knight
Whirls round, for three; its rapid motions make
The first illusion to the trusting sight,
And awe the portent seals in superstitious fright.

56.

Down, down to Tophet, fast the Negro kings
And Ethiopic tyrants bleeding go;
Each gallant comrade in his footsteps springs,
Upon the rest — with rival zeal they glow:
The Pagan multitudes to earth they mow
With terrible contempt; and these prepare
No vain defence, but die without a blow:
A massacre it is, no conflict, where
They yield up here their swords, present their bosoms there.

57.

Yet long they stand not to receive their wounds
In noble parts, but scour away — away;
Fear spurs them on, despair their ranks confounds,
Lost is all art, relaxed their fair array;
But the flushed hero still pursues his prey,
Strikes down their standards, breaks their strong crossbows,
Till spent in utter rout their powers decay;
He then returns, for on defenceless foes
His fiery soul relents, his zeal less fiercely glows.

58.

As the strong wind tenfold its rage augments
When hills or sturdy woods its blasts oppose,
But o'er the ample plain at once relents,
And in soft murmurs more serenely blows, —
As on the rock the dashing ocean throws
Its rough, its roaring billows, and boils high,
But in the open main more gently flows,
Rinaldo so, thus unopposed, lays by
Much of his noble rage, and calms his angry eye.

59.

Then, on the backs of this defenceless force
Scorning to spend his generous wrath in vain,
He to the infantry directs his course,
Late flanked by Asimire and Artabane,
Arab and dusky African; now plain
It stood and naked, for the tribes that well
Might have defenced it, were dispersed or slain;
Crosswise he came, and on their flank, in selle,
With all his men-at-arms in sworded fury fell.

60.

He snapt their bristling spears, the ranks they form
He clove in twain, and in their pierced array
Plunged, beating down their troops; the windy storm
Whirls the reaped harvests with less ease away.

On every side around him does he lay
A bloody pavement, pebbled thick with lance,
Shield, and lopt limb; along whose broad highway,
The following horse, for Palestine and France,
Uncurbed, with battering hoofs in gorgeous frenzy prance.

61.

The Hero came where his forlorn Armide
In warlike pomp stood in her golden car,
Girt by a noble band, who for the meed
Of her sweet smile escort her through the war;
He by his armour known whilst yet afar,
Was viewed by her with eyes which from desire
And passion trembled like a sparkling star;
He changed but slightly; she, 'twixt love and ire,
From red to deadly pale, from frost to flushing fire.

62.

The Knight declined the chariot of the dame,
And like a man that would elsewhere bestow
His thoughts, passed on; but her sworn knights for shame
Let not their rival scape without a blow;
One drew his crooked sabre, one couched low
His lance, his arbalist another bent;
Herself an arrow planted in her bow,
Scorn strung her hand, and nerved her fierce intent,
But love the mood appeased, nor yet the shaft was sent.

63.

Love against anger rose, and their dispute
Proved that her flame still glowed, though hid from view;
Three times her arms she stretched abroad to shoot,
Three times took aim, and thrice her aim withdrew;
Disdain at length prevailed: again the yew
She with an eager and unshrinking arm
Bent, and the bowstring twanged; the shaft outflew,—
Out flew the shaft, but with the shaft this charm
She the next moment breathed: "God grant it do no harm!"

64.

She would have bade the weapon turn again,
And smite the heart whose sternness she resents;
O, well indeed she must have loved him, when
In hate's last pass her soul so soon relents!
But straight again her fondness she repents,
Straight to her stormy heart fresh furies rise;
Thus she the shaft now joys in, now laments,
She will, she will not it should smite, and eyes
With a tumultuous heart the arrow as it flies.

65.

Not quite in vain was it discharged; the reed
Smote the young knight's hard coat of mail, too hard
In fact, for female weapons to succeed, —
The steel, instead of piercing it, was jarred
Itself to shivers, nor the silver marred;
He turned away, — she thought in scorn, and ground
Her teeth with anger at his disregard;
Ofttimes she shot, but still no entrance found
Her shafts, and while she shot, love dealt her wound on wound.

66.

"What! is he then impassive, that he mocks
All hostile force!" she murmurs; "must he mail
His limbs in adamant like that which locks
His haughty spirit in its stubborn scale?
Against his heart nor glancing eyes prevail,
Nor weaponed knight, armed proof from top to toe;
Whilst I, alas! at all points foiled, bewail,
Armed or unarmed, alike or friend or foe,
My thousand arts despised, and droop my pennons low!

67.

"Now what new art, what charm shall I essay;
In what new form can I myself present?
Wretch that I am, there is no hope! my day
Of rule is o'er, and all my forces spent!
My knights, where are they? 'tis too evident
All power, all arms are weak to his; in vain
The spear is levelled, and the crossbow bent:"
Thus she repined; for now throughout the plain
She saw her champions pierced, beat down, dispersed, or slain.

68.

Alone, she felt defenceless, stood in fear
To be enthralled or slain; nor can the aid
Of Dian or Minerva's arms — the spear
Or formidable bow, her heart persuade;
But as the delicate white swan, dismayed,
O'er which the eagle with fierce pounce impends,
Crouches to earth, and her broad wings displayed
Folds in mute terror, — to the storm she bends;
Just such her motions seem, just such wild looks she sends.

69.

But brave Prince Altamore, whose might till now
Had held in check Gildippe, had upheld
The Persian flag when it began to bow,

And by his single arm the Franks repelled,
When in distress his Goddess he beheld,
Rushed, or flew rather from the near attack
To her; though honour at the step rebelled,
Him neither honour nor his host kept back;
So she but rescued be, the world may go to wrack!

* * * * *

112.

Wonders that day good Tisaphernes wrought —
The Normans in his wrath he overthrew;
Scourged the stout Flemings, and, as still he fought,
Young Gernier, Gerard, and De Rosel slew;
And when by deeds of so divine a hue
He to the measure of eternal fame
His brief existence had prolonged, he flew
At the sublimest risk of all the game,
Like one to whose concern life laid no further claim.

113.

He spied Rinaldo, and though now his shield
Had changed its tincture to a tricolór,
Though the pearl eagle in its sapphire field
With ruby beak and wings was seen to soar,
Known was the proud emblazonry it bore;
"And lo!" he cried, "the dragon of the fight!
Heaven nerve my arm to do the deed I swore;
Let but my blade Armida's wrongs requite;
Thine, good Mahmoud, shall be the trophies of the knight!"

114.

Thus prayed the Persian, but his prayers were vain,
Mahmoud heard not upon his couch of fire;
But as a lion, bristling up his mane,
With lashing tail provokes his native ire,
So on the whetstone of his wild desire
His scorn he sharpens, whets his eager zeal,
And, mustering all his strength up for the dire
Assault, coil'd safe behind his shield, his steel
He lifts — and bounds the barb beneath his angry heel.

115.

Rinaldo saw him with his sabre raised,
And rushed to meet him in as swift career;
Far fell the near assailants back, and gazed
On the stern scene, with mingled awe and fear.
Such was the might and fame of either peer,

Such strokes resounded when their weapons crossed,
That each his own strong cause for grief or cheer,
And the whole host of passions that engrossed
His soul — at once forgot, in breathless wonder lost.

116.

That struck alone; this struck, and wounded, blest
With greater strength and arms more sure and sound;
With cloven shield, pierced helm, and shattered crest,
The Persian's noble blood distains the ground:
The fair Enchantress sees her champion's wound,
Sees his pierced armour, his half-helmless head,
And, worse, his failing prowess; gazing round,
She finds the rest disheartened, slain, or fled,
And her own safety hang on fortune's slenderest thread.

117.

Late girt by thousand warriors in the strife,
She now stands lonely in her rubied wain;
Desperate of victory as revenge, her life
She holds in hate, she dreads the victor's chain,
And straight, 'twixt terror, fury, and disdain,
Her chariot quitting, on a palfrey near
Springs, and takes instant flight, — her only train
Scorn and unconquered love, that in her rear
Hang like two eager hounds behind a hunted deer.

118.

So in sharp battle fled alone of yore
Scared Cleopatra, leaving to the blade
Of fortunate Augustus, midst the roar
Of waves and weapons, her fond knight betrayed;
And e'en as he, by tenderness o'er swayed,
False to himself and to the world he wooed,
Followed her solitary sails displayed,
So the fond Persian would have fain pursued
His pearl of beauty too, but this the foe withstood.

119.

To the sad Pagan, when his love was lost,
Day seemed to darken and the sunshine fled,
And to the knight who thus his wishes crossed,
He turned enraged, and smote his helmed head;
More lightly falls to fabricate the red
And writhen thunderbolts, at Jove's behest,
Bronte's vast hammer; well the weapon sped, —
Its ponderous stroke alighting on his crest,
Made the knight's head bow down benignly to his breast.

120.

But soon recovering, in his seat erect
Rinaldo rose, and with his whirling sword
Clove the fine hauberk, 'twixt the ribs direct
Plunged the sharp steel, which in its wrath explored
So deep a passage to the heart it gored,
That far beyond life's citadel it went;
Entering the breast, the Pagan's back it bored,—
The steel drawn forth, supplied a double vent,
Through which the noble soul took straight its wing'd ascent.

121.

The conqueror paused to contemplate where next
He should his falchion ply, where render aid,—
His foes in all their movements were perplexed,
Their colours struck, and scarce a spear displayed:
Here then his terrible career he stayed,
Curbed in his courser, to the sheath resigned
His sword, his martial ecstasy allayed,
And, calming every passion, called to mind
Armida's helpless plight and destinies unkind.

122.

Her flight he well observed; mild pity now
Called for his courtesy and gracious cheer,
And the remembrance of his parting vow
To stand her firm and faithful chevalier,
Came o'er his mind, with feelings sweet and dear;
So that he followed where the dinted ground
Betrayed her goaded palfrey's swift career:
She the meanwhile a dreary glen had found,
Fit place for secret deaths, with cypress compassed round.

123.

Well pleased she was at heart, that chance should guide
Her wandering steps to so retired a place;
Here she alighted then, and cast aside
Her bow, her arrows, and their golden case:
"There lie," she murmured, "in your deep disgrace,
Unhappy arms! that from the war return
With scarce a spot your mistress to aggrace;
There buried lie, there rust amidst the fern,
Since to avenge my wrongs you've shewn such small concern!

124.

"Ah! midst so many weapons could not one
At least return with hostile crimson blest?
If other hearts to you seem marble, shun,
Spare not your points to pierce a woman's breast;

In this mine own, stript naked for the test,
Achieve your triumphs, and your fame restore;
Tender it is, Heaven knows, to wounds impressed
By Love's sharp arrows, Love — who evermore
Strikes wheresoe'er he aims, and hurts the sufferer sore.

125.

"Shew yourselves sharp on me and strong; (your past
Degeneracy I pardon;) O poor heart!
Into what straits of fortune art thou cast,
When these alone can peace to thee impart;
But since no other solace to my smart
Remains, none other passport to repose,
Go to! the wounds of this consenting dart
Shall cure the wounds of love, — a few brief throes,
And death shall bring the balm that soothes all earthly woes!

126.

"Blest, if in dying I bear not with me
This my long plague to pester Hell's foul host;
Hence, Love! come only, dear Disdain, and be
The' eternal partner of my injured ghost!
Or, rising with it from the Stygian coast,
To the false wretch that did me such despite,
In such a whirlwind of resentment post,
With such grim shapes, that all his dreams by night
May be one ceaseless round of agonised affright!"

127.

She ceased; and, fixt in her intention, drew
The best and sharpest arrow from her case;
Rinaldo reached the wood, and caught a view
Of her mad gesture and disordered pace;
Saw her last act, and with how wild a grace
She to the fatal stroke her soul addressed;
Already death's pale hue o'erspread her face,
When, just in time her purpose to arrest,
The knight stept in behind, and saved her beauteous breast.

128.

Armida turned; and saw, to her surprise,
The knight, for unperceived was his advance;
Shrieking, she snatched away her angry eyes
From his loved face, and sunk in Passion's trance;
She swooned, she sank, like a sweet flower by chance
Snapt half in two, that, with its bells abased,
Droops on its stem; he with distracted glance
Upheld her, falling, round her charming waist
Threw his sustaining arm, her clasping zone unbraced;

129.

And o'er her snowy breast and face deprived
Of life's warm hues, fond tears of pity shed; —
As by the summer morning's dew revived,
The fading rose resumes its native red,
So she, recovering, raised her drooping head
And cheek, revived by this celestial rain;
Thrice her unclosing eyes sought his, thrice fled
The bitter-sweet enchantment, nor again
Would she look up, but blushed 'twixt wrath and warm disdain;

130.

And with her languid hand would have repelled
The nervous arm by which she was sustained;
Oft she essayed, but he the faster held,
The more she strove, the more she was enchained:
Yielding herself at length, like one constrained,
To that dear bond, for still perchance 'twas dear,
Despite the scorn she shewed, the hate she feigned,
She sighing thus broke forth, whilst tear on tear
Gushed from the downcast eyes she did not, would not rear.

131.

"O! ever, parting and returning, ever
Cruel alike! what dark devices guide
Thy movements now? 'tis strange thou shouldst endeavour
To save the life whose strings thou dost divide;
Thou seek to save me; to what scorn beside
Am I reserved? what modes of misery
Am I to suffer next? no! no! thy pride
And traitorous purpose well we know; but I
Am weak indeed, if e'er I want the power to die.

132.

"Thy honours truly must be incomplete,
If unsaluted; there must be displayed,
Chained to thy car, or suppliant at thy feet,
A dame, now seized by force, as first betrayed!
This be thy noblest boast: time was, I prayed
To thee for peace and life, now sweet would fate
Prove to my grief, — but ne'er, false renegade,
Kneel I to thee for it! there's not a state
Which, if it were thy gift, I should not hold in hate!

133.

"Of myself, traitor! hope I to unloose,
Some way or other, this most wretched frame
From thy fierce tyranny; and if the noose,
Dagger, and drug, and precipice, and flame

Fail thy chained slave, by means as sure my aim,
Thank Heaven, I yet can compass, and defeat
No less thy malice than thy guile; for shame!
Cease thy base flatteries; cease thy false deceit;
How yet he strives with hope my sorrowing soul to cheat!"

134.

Thus she laments; and with the floods of tears
Which love and scorn distil from her fair eyes,
A sympathising part his sorrow bears,
Where some chaste sparks of love and pity rise:
And with a voice sweet as the west wind's sighs,
He to her troubled heart speaks peace: "I crave
Thy grace, Armida! calm thyself," he cries;
"Not to be scorned, but crowned, thy life I save;
No foe, but still, yes still, thy champion, yea, thy slave!

135.

"Mark in my eyes, if you my words alone
Distrust, the fervour of my soul: I swear
Again to seat thee on thy father's throne,
And make thy comfort my peculiar care;
And O, would Heaven, auspicious to my prayer,
Chase from thy mind with its celestial flame
Those mists of Pagan darkness which impair
Its inward grace and beauty, not a dame
In the whole East should match thy glory, power, and fame!"

136.

Thus does he soothe, thus sue to her; and so
Tempers his suit with tears, his tears with sighs,
That, like a virgin wreath of mountain snow
When zephyr breathes or sunshine warms the skies,
Her haughty scorn, that wore so stern a guise,
And all her cherished anger melt away,
And milder wishes in their room arise:
"Behold," she says, "thy handmaid; I obey:
Thy lips my future life, thy will my fortune sway!"

137.

This while, the' Egyptian Captain in the strife
Sees his imperial standard fall to ground,
Sees too stout Rimedon deprived of life,
Despatched by Godfrey in a single wound;
And all his men, discomfited around,
Dead, or in flight across the boundless plain;
He in his last sharp act will not be found
Recreant like them, but seeks (nor seeks in vain)
Some noble hand by which he may be nobly slain.

138.

Spurring his steed, he against Godfrey rode,
No worthier foe he knew could be descried;
And wheresoe'er he passed or came to, shewed
The last brave tokens of despairing pride:
But ere he reached his foe, aloud he cried:
"Lo, Chief! I come to spend my final hour
And hopes with thee; but yet it shall be tried
If, overpowered, I too cannot o'erpower,
And on my conqueror fall, as falls a thundered tower!"

139.

This said, they each at each indignant dashed;
With lifted swords at once they meet, they smite;
Broken the shield, the vantbrace cleft, and gashed
Is the left shoulder of the Christian knight:
He, on his part, discharged with matchless might
On the left cheek a blow that prostrate laid
The Pagan chief; and in bewildered plight
As to regain the saddle he essayed,
Through the abdomen thrust, his life-blood bathed the blade.

140.

Prince Emirene thus dead, but few remain
Of all that countless host; as he pursued
The vanquished, Godfrey saw, and checked his rein,
How Altamore on foot, in blood embrued,
With half a sword, and half a helm on, stood,
Breasting a hundred bristling spears, that poured
Round the doomed Prince, whose prowess still they rued;
"Cease, cease," he cried, "Sir Knights! and thou, brave lord,
Yield, ('tis Duke Godfrey speaks,) yield up thy useless sword!"

141.

He, who had never till that hour abased
To any act like this his lofty soul,
When now he heard the name which heaven had graced
With such renown from Nubia to the pole,
Yielding his arms, replied: "To thy control
(For thou deserv'st the homage), I my knee
Submit; then midst thy other spoils enrol
The name of Altamoro, who will be
Neither in fame nor wealth a prize unworthy thee.

142.

"The gold and gems of kingdom shall my kind
And faithful lady grant for my release:"
"Heaven has endowed me with a nobler mind,"
Godfrey replied, "than to desire increase

Of earthly treasure; still retain in peace
All that from Ind or Persia swells thy store,
Bocharian mantle, and Tartarian fleece,
I set no price on life; on Asia's shore
I war in Europe's right, not trade in Asian ore!"

143.

This said, he gives him to his guards to tend,
And after those that fled, pursues amain;
These to the rampired camp their lives commend,
Yet thence small respite to their fate obtain;
Soon is it won; the trench is choked with slain,
From gay pavilion to pavilion glide
Streams of warm blood, with whose vermilion stain
Each sumptuous trophy of barbaric pride —
Plumes, corslets, turbans, helms, and shields are deeply dyed.

144.

Thus conquered Godfrey; and as yet there glowed
A flush of glory in the fulgent West,
To the freed City, the once loved abode
Of Christ, the pious Chief and armies pressed:
Arm'd as he was, and in his sanguine vest,
With all his knights in solemn cavalcade,
He reached the Temple; there, supremely blest,
Hung up his arms, his bannered spoils displayed,
And at the sacred TOMB his vowed devotions paid.

MIGUEL DE CERVANTES SAAVEDRA

(1547–1616)

The desire to know about the author of *Don Quixote* began even during his lifetime. A Spanish official has recorded the following conversation held with certain foreign diplomats: "They inquired very particularly as to his age, his pursuits, his condition and fortune. I was obliged to say that he was an old man, a soldier, a gentleman, and poor; to which one replied in these precise words: 'But does not Spain keep such a man rich, supported out of the public exchequer?' Another of these gentlemen broke in with this sentiment, saying with much acuteness: 'If it is necessity obliges him to write, may God send he may never have abundance, so that, poor himself, he may enrich the whole world with his works.'" (Watts translation.)

Evidence for the major facts of Cervantes' career is adequately furnished by the documents we possess. Since his writings are largely based upon his own experience, the documents may be greatly illuminated by what he wrote. But documents and writings alike have only served to confirm the picture given by the Spanish official as authentic through four centuries. Cervantes' life was one of misfortune, poverty, and frustration, but from it was wrought a work which has taken its place in the world's literature.

He was born some twenty miles northeast of Madrid in the little town of Alcalá de Henares, then the seat of a famous university. He was baptized there on the 9th of October 1547; although the date of his birth is unknown, it may have been that of the feast of his patron saint, St. Michael, the 29th of September. His father, Rodrigo de Cervantes — although the son of a lawyer of considerable prestige, and of gentle blood — seems himself to have been a poor physician, moving from place to place, with little professional training or success. Little is known of his mother, Leonor de Cortinas. Her heroic efforts to ransom her two sons from Algerian captivity probably depleted permanently whatever resources the family possessed. Of the seven children, Miguel was the second son and fourth child. Two sisters lived in his household in later years.

Save for his early love of poetry and the drama, nothing is actually known about the formative period of his life, his first twenty-one years. It was only in 1569 that a humanist schoolmaster in Madrid, Juan López de Hoyos, named him as his beloved pupil; this constitutes the only documentary evidence of his education. From accounts in his narratives, it has been imagined that he had previous schooling at Seville, that he was a poor student at the University of Salamanca, or that he had seen military service in Flanders, but it is not probable that his formal education was either prolonged or thorough.

By December 1569, he was living in Rome. It was probably at this time that he was valet to Giulio Acquaviva, later cardinal. What sent him to Italy is not known, possibly to escape arrest in Madrid after a duel. Soon after, he enlisted as a private in the Spanish army. He was on board the *Marquesa* in the fleet of Don John of Austria at the battle of Lepanto, the 7th of October 1571. Even though suffering from a fever on the day of the battle, he refused to remain below, declaring that he would rather die for his God and his king. He was given command of a boat of twelve men and received three wounds, from one of which his left hand remained paralyzed for life. In the years that followed, he was engaged in several military operations and was stationed at garrisons at Naples and Palermo. Finally, in September 1575, together with his younger brother Rodrigo who had joined him, he left Naples on leave to Spain to press his claim for a captaincy. Off the coast near Marseilles his boat was captured by Turkish galleys and the brothers were carried as captives to Algiers.

The brothers became slaves of the Greek renegade, Dalí-Mamí, who had captured them. Since Miguel carried letters of commendation from Don John of Austria and the viceroy of Italy, they were held for ransom. Although handcuffed, put in chains, and placed in a dungeon, their treatment was later considerably relaxed. Cervantes' slavery lasted for five years, during which he demonstrated the stoic patience in adversity that characterized his life career. At least four times he organized plots for escape which, for courage and daring, drew admiration from his fellows and seem even to have inspired consideration from his masters. Hassan Pasha, Dey of Algiers, who bought him from his captor, is reported to have declared: "So long as I have the maimed Spaniard in my keeping, my Christians, ships — aye, and the whole city — are safe." Meanwhile, his mother, Doña Leonor, made heroic efforts to raise money for his ransom. Rodrigo was ransomed after two years. It was not until September 1580, when he was already placed in chains and irons aboard ship to sail for Constantinople, that — through the efforts of two Trinitarian monks, and the generosity of Spanish traders in Algiers — Miguel was finally released to embark for Spain. Aubrey F. G. Bell has well remarked: "If an enterprising publisher had persuaded him to write his autobiography, we might have possessed a book as fascinating as *Don Quixote* itself." (*Cervantes,* p. 52.)

Cervantes was back in Madrid in December 1580; Madrid can perhaps be considered his center for the next seven years. But to make a living proved difficult. At first he seems to have been employed as official messenger to Portugal, and to Algeria. Then he began writing, in association with men of letters at Madrid. Some "twenty or thirty plays" are mentioned of which only two survive; they were not apparently successful. His pastoral romance, *La Galatea,* was published in 1585. During these years he entered upon his intrigue with Ana Franca de Rojas, perhaps a Madrid actress; their natural daughter, Isabel de Saavedra, was his only child and was to cause him much concern in later years. In December 1584, he was married to Catalina de Salazar y Palacios, of a well-to-do peasant family at Esquivias — north of Toledo. He was thirty-seven and she nineteen. Although there is scant evidence concerning their married life, it seems dubious from the tone of his writings that it brought him much happiness.

Reluctantly but inevitably Cervantes was compelled to abandon writing to make ends meet. In 1587 he was appointed a commissary in Andalusia to requisition oil, wheat, and other supplies for the Invincible Armada. Seville became his center for over ten years, for he retained this position after the Armada was defeated. His position was fraught with difficulties. Collection of supplies from those who did not wish to yield them involved many troubles. Official red tape and accounts became exceedingly complex. Official investigations were relentless and constantly occurring. A Seville banker to whom he had paid large sums for transmission to Madrid went bankrupt. Moreover, his own pay was frequently in arrears. Three times we find him imprisoned. In 1590, he applied for one of four posts in the New World, but without success. In 1594, he was commissioned to collect royal taxes in the province of Granada. From the evidence of surety which he sought in order to buy common necessities, he would seem to have been still beset by poverty. At the same time, however, he must have had abundant experience of the Andalusian countryside: its roads, its inns, and its characters.

By the summer of 1604, he was living at Valladolid, temporarily the capital of Spain. Here the official license for the first part of *Don Quixote* was issued, and the book appeared early in 1605. It was a commercial success at once. In this year Cervantes with his household — including his wife and daughter, two sisters, and a niece — were living in the Calle del Rastro, in a poor quarter of the city. One night a well-known rake with distinguished connections was murdered at the door of their house. Cervantes and three members of his immediate household were arrested. The accusations brought against them proved utterly false, but they suffered the chance hazards of the district in which they were forced to live.

When the capital was moved again to Madrid, Cervantes followed. He was lodging there with his wife, sisters, and niece by 1609 and probably before, and Madrid was his home for the rest of his life. In 1608, his natural daughter was married in Madrid. Unappreciative, shrewd, and grasping, she finally involved her father in the deceitful scheming of her marriage and married life, and seems to have lived alienated from his family. Although the *Don Quixote* brought Cervantes fame at home and abroad, many friends and admirers, and no less than two patrons, he lived poor to the end, as the quotation in the first paragraph above indicates. His spirit and energy, however, remained unimpaired. His continued writing shows that his genius was at its height, and he died with further projects in mind. In 1613, the *Exemplary Novels* were published, twelve narratives which for artistry rank with his best work. In 1614, the *Jour-*

ney to Parnassus was issued, a critique of the poets of his old age, written in *terza rima.*

In the Prologue to the *Exemplary Novels,* Cervantes had indicated that he was writing a continuation to *Don Quixote.* The Second Part appeared in 1615, when he was sixty-eight years of age. He had apparently reached its fifty-ninth chapter before he learned that a spurious Part Two had appeared under the name of a certain Alonzo Fernandez de Avellaneda. This, together with the insolent preface it contained, he deeply resented, as he shows in the last fifteen chapters of his work. In the same year of 1615, the dramatic writing of his last period was also issued, the *Eight Comedies and Eight Interludes.* After his death, in 1617, his last novel, the *Persiles and Sigismunda,* was printed.

To know of his personal appearance, perhaps one can do no better than to take his own self-portrait, written in his last years. In the Prologue to the *Exemplary Novels,* he described himself as "with aquiline visage, with chestnut hair, smooth and unruffled brow, with sparkling eyes, and a nose arched, although well proportioned, a silver beard, although not twenty years ago it was golden, large moustache, small mouth, teeth not important, for he has but six of them and those in ill condition and worse placed because they do not correspond the one with the other, the body between two extremes, neither large nor small, the complexion bright, rather white than brown, somewhat heavy-shouldered, and not very nimble on his feet." (Maccoll translation.)

He had, a few years before, taken the habit of the Franciscan Tertiaries at Alcalá de Henares. He died in Madrid on the 23rd of April 1616 and was buried in the convent of the Barefooted Trinitarian nuns in the Calle de Cantarranas, although the exact identification of his grave there has been lost. His widow, Doña Catalina, lived until 1626. Isabel, his natural daughter, lived until 1652. With her death his family became extinct.

A knowledge of Cervantes' life is necessary to reach the deeper levels of meaning in his writing. The *Don Quixote* and *Exemplary Novels* are creations of one who had lived in slavery, poverty, and frustration; who obtained by hard experience his intimate knowledge of the roads and inns, the men and women of Spain in her Golden Age. The wise and humorous spirit that informs them is that of a man who found within himself resources of character to meet a fortune he could not control, as well as a glad escape and freedom in the creative world of his imagination.

SELECTED BIBLIOGRAPHY

EDITIONS

Obras Completas, ed. Adolf Bonilla and Rudolph Schevill, Madrid, Gráficas Reunidas, 1914–41, 19 vols.

TRANSLATIONS

Don Quixote, trans. Thomas Shelton (1612, 1620), introd. J. Fitzmaurice-Kelly, Tudor Translations, London, Nutt, 1896, 4 vols.; trans. P. Motteux (1700), in Everyman's Lib., and Modern Lib.; trans. Charles Jarvis (1742), in World's Classics; trans. A. J. Duffield, London, Kegan Paul, 1881; trans. John Ormsby, New York, Macmillan, 1885; trans. H. E. Watts, London, Quaritch, 1888; trans. Robinson Smith, Hisp. Soc. of Am., 1932; trans. Samuel Putnam, 2 vols., New York, Viking, 1949, also in *The Portable Cervantes,* Viking, 1953; trans. J. M. Cohen, Penguin Classics, 1950. *La Galatea,* trans. H. Oelsner and A. B. Welford, Glasgow, Gowans & Gray, 1901. *Exemplary Novels,* trans. James Mabbe (1640), Philadelphia, Lippincott, 1900; trans. Norman Maccoll, Glasgow, Gowans & Gray, 1902. *Three Exemplary Novels,* trans. Samuel Putnam, New York, Viking, 1950. *Journey to Parnassus,* trans. James Y. Gibson, London, Kegan Paul, 1883. *The Wanderings of Persiles and Sigismunda,* trans. Louise D. Stanley, London, Cundall, 1854. *The Interludes of Cervantes,* trans. S. Griswold Morley, Princeton Univ. Press, 1948.

BIOGRAPHY AND CRITICISM

J. R. Lowell, "Don Quixote" in *Democracy and Other Addresses,* 159–86, Boston, 1887; A. F. Jaccaci, *On the Trail of Don Quixote, a Record of Rambles in . . . La Mancha,* New York, Scribner, 1896; S. M. Crothers, "Quixotism" in *The Gentle Reader,* 271–302, Boston, 1903; G. E. Woodberry, "Cervantes" in *Great Writers,* New York, McClure, 1907; James Fitzmaurice-Kelly, *M. de Cervantes Saavedra. A Memoir,* Oxford, Clarendon Press, 1913; J. Fitzmaurice-Kelly, *Cervantes and Shakespeare,* London, Milford, 1916; Rudolph Schevill, *Cervantes* (Master Spirits of Lit.), New York, Duffield, 1919; Américo Castro y Quesada, *El Pensamiento de Cervantes,* Madrid, Hernando, 1925; J. W. Krutch, "Cervantes" in *Five Masters,* 61–105, New York, Cape & Smith, 1930; Sadie E. Trachman, *Cervantes' Women of Literary Tradition,* New York, Inst. de la Españas, 1932; Roger Boutet de Monvel, *Cervantes and the Magicians,* London, Hurst & Brackett, 1934; Mariano Tomás, *The Life and Misadventures of M. de Cervantes,* London, Allen & Unwin, 1934; Bruno Frank, *A Man Called Cervantes,* New York, Viking Press, 1935; Salvador de Madariaga, *Don Quixote: An Introductory Essay in Psychology,* Oxford, Clarendon Press, 1935; William J. Entwistle, *Cervantes,* Oxford, Clarendon Press, 1940; A. F. G. Bell, *Cervantes,* Univ. of Oklahoma Press, 1947; Angel Flores and M. J. Benardete, editors, *Cervantes across the Centuries,* New York, Dryden Press, 1947.

SPECIAL STUDIES

G. T. Northup, "Cervantes' Attitude toward Honor," *Mod. Philol.,* XXI (1924), 397–421; A. F. G. Bell, "The Character of Cervantes," *Rev. Hispanique,* LXXX (1930), 653–717, and "Cervantes and the Renaissance," *Hispanic Rev.,* II (1934), 89–101; J. D. M. Ford and Ruth Lansing, *Cervantes: A Tentative Bibliography,* Harvard Univ. Press, 1931; F. C. Tarr, "Recent Trends in Cervantes Studies," *Romanic Rev.,* XXXI (1940), 16–28; A. Castro, "The Prefaces of Don Quixote," *Philol. Quar.,* XXI (1942), 65–96; M. F. Heiser, "Cervantes in the United States," *Hispanic Rev.,* XV (1947), 409–35; H. A. Hatsfield, "Thirty Years of Cervantes Criticism," *Hispania,* XXX (1947), 321–8; Eleanor O'Kane, "The Proverb: Rabelais and Cervantes," *Compar. Lit.*, II (1950), 360–9; L. G. Crocker, "*Don Quijote,* Epic of Frustration," *Rom. Rev.*, XLII (1951), 178–88; E. Goggio, "The Dual Role of Dulcinea in Cervantes' *Don Quijote,*" *Mod. Lang. Quar.*, XIII (1952), 285–91.

THE INGENIOUS GENTLEMAN DON QUIXOTE OF LA MANCHA

Translated by John Ormsby

[First published in 1885 by Smith, Elder & Co., London, and The Macmillan Co., New York; a recent edition of Ormsby's translation was published by Alfred A. Knopf, New York, 2 vols., 1926, with introduction by George E. Woodberry.]

PART ONE

CHAPTER I

Which treats of the character and pursuits of the famous gentleman Don Quixote of La Mancha

In a village of La Mancha, the name of which I have no desire to call to mind, there lived not long since one of those gentlemen that keep a lance in the lance-rack, an old buckler, a lean hack, and a greyhound for coursing. An olla of rather more beef than mutton, a salad on most nights, scraps on Saturdays, lentils on Fridays, and a pigeon or so extra on Sundays, made away with three-quarters of his income. The rest of it went in a doublet of fine cloth and velvet breeches and shoes to match for holidays, while on week-days he made a brave figure in his best homespun. He had in his house a housekeeper past forty, a niece under twenty, and a lad for the field and market-place, who used to saddle the hack as well as handle the bill-hook. The age of this gentleman of ours was bordering on fifty; he was of a hardy habit, spare, gaunt-featured, a very early riser and a great sportsman. They will have it his surname was Quixada or Quesada (for here there is some difference of opinion among the authors who write on the subject), although from reasonable conjectures it seems plain that he was called Quixana. This, however, is of but little importance to our tale; it will be enough not to stray a hair's breadth from the truth in the telling of it.

You must know, then, that the above-named gentleman whenever he was at leisure (which was mostly all the year round) gave himself up to reading books of chivalry with such ardour and avidity that he almost entirely neglected the pursuit of his field-sports, and even the management of his property; and to such a pitch did his eagerness and infatuation go that he sold many an acre of tillage-land to buy books of chivalry to read, and brought home as many of them as he could get. But of all there were none he liked so well as those of the famous Feliciano de Silva's composition, for their lucidity of style and complicated conceits were as pearls in his sight, particularly when in his reading he came upon courtships and cartels, where he often found passages like *"the reason of the unreason with which my reason is afflicted so weakens my reason that with reason I murmur at your beauty;"* or again, *"the high heavens, that of your divinity divinely fortify you with the stars, render you deserving of the desert your greatness deserves."* Over conceits of this sort the poor gentleman lost his wits, and used to lie awake striving to understand them and worm the meaning out of them; what Aristotle himself could not have made out or extracted had he come to life again for that special purpose. He was not at all easy about the wounds which Don Belianis gave and took, because it seemed to him that, great as were the surgeons who had cured him, he must have had his face and body covered all over with seams and scars. He commended, however, the author's way of ending his book with the promise of that interminable adventure, and many a time was he tempted to take up his pen and finish it properly as is there proposed, which no doubt he would have done, and made a successful piece of work of it too, had not greater and more absorbing thoughts prevented him.

Many an argument did he have with the curate of his village (a learned man, and a graduate of Siguenza) as to which had been the better knight, Palmerin of England or Amadis of Gaul. Master Nicholas, the village barber, however, used to say that neither of them came up to the Knight of Phœbus, and that if there was any that could compare with *him* it was Don Galaor, the brother of Amadis of Gaul, because he had a spirit that was equal to every occasion, and was no finikin knight, nor lachrymose like his brother, while in the matter of valour he was not a whit behind him. In short, he became so absorbed in his books that he spent his nights from sunset to sunrise, and his days from dawn to dark, poring over them; and what with little sleep and much reading his brains got so dry that he lost his wits. His fancy grew full of what he used to read about in his books, enchantments, quarrels, battles, challenges, wounds, wooing, loves, agonies, and all sorts of impossible nonsense; and it so possessed his mind that the whole fabric of invention and fancy he read of was true, that to him no history in the world had more reality in it. He used to say the Cid Ruy Diaz was a very good knight, but that he was not to be compared with the Knight of the Burning Sword who with one back-stroke cut in half two fierce and monstrous giants. He thought more of Bernardo del Carpio because at Roncesvalles he slew Roland in spite of enchantments, availing himself of the artifice of Hercules when he strangled Antæus the son of Terra in his arms. He approved highly of the giant Morgante, because, although of the giant breed which is always arrogant and ill-conditioned, he alone was affable and well-bred. But above all he admired Reinaldos of Montalban, especially when he saw him sallying forth from his castle and robbing everyone he met, and when beyond the seas he stole that image of Mahomet which, as his history says, was entirely of gold. And to have a bout of kicking at that traitor of a Ganelon he would have given his housekeeper, and his niece into the bargain.

In short, his wits being quite gone, he hit upon the strangest notion that ever madman in this world hit upon, and that was that he fancied it was right and requisite, as well for the support of his own honour as for the service of his country, that he should make a knight-errant of himself, roaming the world over in full armour and on horseback in quest of adventures, and putting in practice himself all that he had read of as being the usual practices of knights-errant; righting every kind of wrong, and exposing himself to peril and danger from which, in the issue, he was to reap eternal renown and fame. Already the poor man saw himself crowned by the might of his arm Emperor of Trebizond at least; and so, led away by the intense enjoyment he found in these pleasant fancies, he set himself forthwith to put his scheme into execution.

The first thing he did was to clean up some armour that had belonged to his great-grandfather, and had been for ages lying forgotten in a corner eaten with rust and covered with mildew. He scoured and polished it as best he could, but he perceived one great defect in it, that it had no closed helmet, nothing but a simple morion. This deficiency, however, his ingenuity supplied, for he contrived a kind of half-helmet of pasteboard which, fitted on to the morion, looked like a whole one. It is true that, in order to see if it was strong and fit to stand a cut, he drew his sword and gave it a couple of slashes, the first of which undid in an instant what had taken him a week to do. The ease with which he had knocked it to pieces disconcerted him somewhat, and to guard against that danger he set to work again, fixing bars of iron on the inside until he was satisfied with its strength; and then, not caring to try any more experiments with it, he passed it and adopted it as a helmet of the most perfect construction.

He next proceeded to inspect his hack, which, with more quartos than a real and more blemishes than the steed of Gonela, that *"tantum pellis et ossa fuit,"* surpassed in his eyes the Bucephalus of Alexander or the Babieca of the Cid. Four days were spent in thinking what name to give him, because (as he said to himself) it was not right that a horse belonging to a knight so famous, and one with such merits of his own, should be without some distinctive name, and he strove to adapt it so as to indicate what he had been before belonging to a knight-errant, and what he then was; for it was only reasonable that, his master taking a new character, he should take a new name, and that it should be a distinguished and full-sounding one, befitting the new order and calling he was about to follow. And so, after having composed, struck out, rejected, added to, unmade, and remade a multitude of names out of his memory and fancy, he decided upon calling him Rocinante, a name, to his thinking, lofty, sonorous, and significant of his condition as a hack before he became what he now was, the first and foremost of all the hacks in the world.

Having got a name for his horse so much to his taste, he was anxious to get one for himself, and he was eight days more pondering over this point, till at last he made up his mind to call himself Don Quixote, whence, as has been already said, the authors of this veracious history have inferred that his name must have been beyond a doubt Quixada, and not Quesada as others would have it. Recollecting, however, that the valiant Amadis was not content to call himself curtly Amadis and nothing more, but added the name of his kingdom and country to make it famous, and called himself Amadis of Gaul, he, like a good knight, resolved to add on the name of his, and to style himself Don Quixote of La Mancha, whereby, he considered, he described accurately his origin and country, and did honour to it in taking his surname from it.

So then, his armour being furbished, his morion turned into a helmet, his hack christened, and he himself confirmed, he came to the conclusion that nothing more was needed now but to look out for a lady to be in love with; for a knight-errant without love was like a tree without leaves or fruit, or a body without a soul. As he said to himself, "If, for my sins, or by my good fortune, I come across some giant hereabouts, a common occurrence with knights-errant, and overthrow him in one onslaught, or cleave him asunder to the waist, or, in short, vanquish and subdue him, will it not be well to have some one I may send him to as a present, that he may come in and fall on his knees before my sweet lady, and in a humble, submissive voice say, 'I am the giant Caraculiambro, lord of the island of Malindrania, vanquished in single combat by the never sufficiently extolled knight Don Quixote of La Mancha, who has commanded me to present myself before your Grace, that your Highness dispose of me at your pleasure?'" Oh, how our good gentleman enjoyed the delivery of this speech, especially when he had thought of some one to call his Lady! There was, so the story goes, in a village near his own a very good-looking farm-girl with whom he had been at one time in love, though, so far as is known, she never knew it nor gave a thought to the matter. Her name was Aldonza Lorenzo, and upon her he thought fit to confer the title of Lady of his Thoughts; and after some search for a name which should not be out of harmony with her own, and should suggest and indicate that of a princess and great lady, he decided upon calling her Dulcinea del Toboso — she being of El Toboso — a name, to his mind, musical, uncommon, and significant, like all those he had already bestowed upon himself and the things belonging to him.

CHAPTER II

Which treats of the first sally the ingenious Don Quixote made from home

These preliminaries settled, he did not care to put off any longer the execution of his design, urged on to it by the thought of all the world was losing by his delay, seeing what wrongs he intended to right, grievances to redress, injustices to repair, abuses to remove, and duties to discharge. So, without giving notice of his intention to anyone, and without anybody seeing him, one morning before the dawning of the day (which was one of the hottest of the month of July) he donned his suit of armour, mounted Rocinante with his patched-up helmet on, braced his buckler, took his lance, and by the back door of the yard sallied forth upon the plain in the highest contentment and satisfaction at seeing with what ease he had made a beginning with his grand purpose. But scarcely did he find himself upon the open plain, when a terrible thought struck him, one all but enough to make him abandon the enterprise at the very outset. It occurred to him that he had not been dubbed a knight, and that according to the law of chivalry he neither could nor ought to bear arms against any knight; and that even if he had been, still he ought, as a novice knight, to wear white armour, without a device upon the shield until by his prowess he had earned one. These reflections made him waver in his purpose, but his craze being stronger than any reasoning he made up his mind to have himself dubbed a knight by the first one he came across, following the example of others in the same case, as he had read in the books that brought him to this pass. As for white armour, he resolved, on the first opportunity, to scour his until it was whiter than an ermine; and so comforting himself he pursued his way, taking that which his horse chose, for in this he believed lay the essence of adventures.

Thus setting out, our new-fledged adventurer paced along, talking to himself and saying, "Who knows but that in time to come, when the veracious history of my famous deeds is made known, the sage who writes it, when he has to set forth my first sally in the early morning, will do it after this fashion? 'Scarce had the rubicund Apollo spread o'er the face of the broad spacious earth the golden threads of his bright hair, scarce had the little birds of painted plumage attuned their notes to hail with dulcet and mellifluous harmony the coming of the rosy Dawn, that, deserting the soft couch of her jealous spouse, was appearing to mortals at the gates and balconies of the Manchegan horizon, when the renowned knight Don Quixote of La Mancha, quitting the lazy down, mounted his celebrated steed Rocinante and began to traverse the ancient and famous Campo de Montiel;' " which in fact he was actually traversing. "Happy the age, happy the time," he continued, "in which shall be made known my deeds of fame, worthy to be moulded in brass, carved in marble, limned in pictures, for a memorial for ever. And thou, O sage magician, whoever thou art, to whom it shall fall to be the chronicler of this wondrous history, forget not, I entreat thee, my good Rocinante, the constant companion of my ways and wanderings." Presently he broke out again, as if he were love-stricken in earnest, "O Princess Dulcinea, lady of this captive heart, a grievous wrong hast thou done me to drive me forth with scorn, and with inexorable obduracy banish me from the presence of thy beauty. O lady, deign to hold in remembrance this heart, thy vassal, that thus in anguish pines for love of thee."

So he went on stringing together these and other absurdities, all in the style of those his books had taught him, imitating their language as well as he could; and all the while he rode so slowly and the sun mounted so rapidly and with such fervour that it was enough to melt his brains if he had any. Nearly all day he travelled without anything remarkable happening to him, at which he was in despair, for he was anxious to encounter some one at once upon whom to try the might of his strong arm.

Writers there are who say the first adventure he met with was that of Puerto Lapice; others say it was that of the windmills; but what I have ascertained on this point, and what I have found written in the annals of La Mancha, is that he was on the road all day, and towards nightfall his hack and he found themselves dead tired and hungry, when, looking all around to see if he could discover any castle or shepherd's shanty where he might refresh himself and relieve his sore wants, he perceived not far out of his road an inn, which was as welcome as a star guiding him to the portals, if not the palaces, of his redemption; and quickening his pace he reached it just as night was setting in. At the door were standing two young women, girls of the district as they call them, on their way to Seville with some carriers who had chanced to halt that night at the inn; and as, happen what might to our adventurer, everything he saw or imagined seemed to him to be and to happen after the fashion of what he had read of, the moment he saw the inn he pictured it to himself as a castle with its four turrets and pinnacles of shining silver, not forgetting the drawbridge and moat and all the belongings usually ascribed to castles of the sort. To this inn, which to him seemed a castle, he advanced, and at a short distance from it he checked Rocinante, hoping that some dwarf would show himself upon the battlements, and by sound of trumpet give notice that a knight was approaching the castle. But seeing that they were slow about it, and that Rocinante was in a hurry to reach the stable, he made for the inn door, and perceived the two gay damsels who were standing there, and who seemed to him to be two fair maidens or lovely ladies taking their ease at the castle gate.

At this moment it so happened that a swineherd who was going through the stubbles collecting a drove of pigs (for, without any apology, that is what they are called) gave a blast of his horn to bring them together, and forthwith it seemed to Don Quixote to be what he was expecting, the signal of some dwarf announcing his arrival; and so with prodigious satisfaction he rode up to the inn and to the ladies, who, seeing a man of this sort approaching in full armour and with lance and buckler, were turning in dismay into the inn, when Don Quixote, guessing their fear by their flight, raising his pasteboard visor, disclosed his dry, dusty visage, and with courteous bearing and gentle voice addressed them, "Your ladyships need not fly or fear any rudeness, for that it belongs not to the order of knighthood which I profess to offer to anyone, much less to high-born maidens as your appearance proclaims you to be." The girls were looking at him and straining their eyes to make out the features which the clumsy visor obscured, but when they heard themselves called maidens, a thing so much out of their line, they could not restrain their laughter, which made Don Quixote wax indignant, and say, "Modesty becomes the fair, and moreover laughter that has little cause is great silliness; this, however, I say not to pain or anger you, for my desire is none other than to serve you."

The incomprehensible language and the unpromising looks of our cavalier only increased the ladies' laughter, and that increased his irritation, and matters might have gone farther if at that moment the landlord had not come out, who, being a very fat man, was a very peaceful one. He, seeing this grotesque figure clad in armour that did not match any more than his saddle, bridle, lance, buckler, or corselet, was not at all indisposed to join the damsels in their manifestations of amusement; but, in truth, standing in awe of such a complicated armament, he thought it best to speak him fairly, so he said, "Señor Caballero, if your worship wants lodging, bating the bed (for there is not one in the inn) there is plenty of everything else here." Don Quixote, observing the respectful bearing of the Alcaide of the fortress (for so innkeeper and inn seemed in his eyes), made answer, "Sir Castellan, for me anything will suffice, for

"My armour is my only wear,
My only rest the fray."

The host fancied he called him Castellan because he took him for a "worthy of Castile," though he was in fact an Andalusian, and one from the Strand of San Lucar, as crafty a thief as Cacus and as full of tricks as a student or a page. "In that case," said he,

"Your bed is on the flinty rock,
Your sleep to watch alway;

and if so, you may dismount and safely reckon upon any quantity of sleeplessness under this roof for a twelvemonth, not to say for a single night." So saying, he advanced to hold the stirrup for Don Quixote, who got down with great difficulty and exertion (for he had not broken his fast all day), and then charged the host to take great care of his horse, as he was the best bit of flesh that ever ate bread in this world. The landlord eyed him over, but did not find him as good as Don Quixote said, nor even half as good; and putting him up in the stable, he returned to see what might be wanted by his guest, whom the damsels, who had by this time made their peace with him, were now relieving of his armour. They had taken off his breastplate and backpiece, but they neither knew nor saw how to open his gorget or remove his make-shift helmet, for he had fastened it with green ribbons, which, as there was no untying the knots, required to be cut. This, however, he would not by any means consent to, so he remained all the evening with his helmet on, the drollest and oddest figure that can be imagined; and while they were removing his armour, taking the baggages who were about it for ladies of high degree belonging to the castle, he said to them with great sprightliness:

"O, never, surely, was there knight
So served by hand of dame,
As served was he, Don Quixote hight,
When from his town he came;
With maidens waiting on himself,
Princesses on his hack —

— or Rocinante, for that, ladies mine, is my horse's name, and Don Quixote of La Mancha is my own; for though I had no intention of declaring myself until my achievements in your service and honour had made me known, the necessity of adapting that old ballad of Lancelot to the present occasion has given you the knowledge of my name altogether prematurely. A time, however, will come for your ladyships to command and me to obey, and then the might of my arm will show my desire to serve you."

The girls, who were not used to hearing rhetoric of this sort, had nothing to say in reply: they only asked him if he wanted anything to eat. "I would gladly eat a bit of something," said Don Quixote, "for I feel it would come very seasonably." The day happened to be a Friday, and in the whole inn there was nothing but some pieces of the fish they call in Castile "abadejo," in Andalusia "bacallao," and in some places "curadillo," and in others "troutlet;" so they asked him if he thought he could eat troutlet, for there was no other fish to give him. "If there be troutlets enough," said Don Quixote, "they will be the same thing as a trout; for it is all one to me whether I am given eight reals in small change or a piece of eight; moreover, it may be that these troutlets are like veal, which is better than beef, or kid, which is better than goat. But whatever it be let it come quickly, for the burden and pressure of arms cannot be borne without support to the inside." They laid a table for him at the door of the inn for the sake of the air, and the host brought him a portion of ill-soaked and worse cooked stockfish, and a piece of bread as black and mouldy as his own armour; but a laughable sight it was to see him eating, for having his helmet on and the beaver up, he could not with his own hands put anything into his mouth unless some one else placed it there, and this service one of the ladies rendered him. But to give him anything to drink was impossible, or would have been so had not the landlord bored a reed, and putting one end in his mouth poured the wine into him through the other; all which he bore with patience rather than sever the ribbons of his helmet.

While this was going on there came up to the inn a sow-gelder, who, as he approached, sounded his reed pipe four or five times, and thereby completely convinced Don Quixote that he was in some famous castle, and that they were regaling him with music, and that the stockfish was trout, the bread the whitest, the wenches ladies, and the landlord the castellan of the castle; and consequently he held that his enterprise and sally had been to some purpose. But still it distressed him to think he had not been dubbed a knight, for it was plain to him he could not lawfully engage in any adventure without receiving the order of knighthood.

CHAPTER III

Wherein is related the droll way in which Don Quixote had himself dubbed a knight

Harassed by this reflection, he made haste with his scanty pothouse supper, and having finished it called the landlord, and shutting himself into the stable with him, fell on his knees before him, saying, "From this spot I rise not, valiant knight, until your courtesy grants me the boon I seek, one that will redound to your praise and the benefit of the human race." The landlord, seeing his guest at his feet and hearing a speech of this kind, stood staring at him in bewilderment, not knowing what to do or say, and entreating him to rise, but all to no purpose until he had agreed to grant the boon demanded of him. "I looked for no less, my lord, from your High Magnificence," replied Don Quixote, "and I have to tell you that the boon I have asked and your liberality has granted is that you shall dub me knight to-morrow morning, and that to-night I shall watch my arms in the chapel of this your castle; thus to-morrow, as I have said, will be accomplished what I so much desire, enabling me lawfully to roam through all the four quarters of the world seeking adventures on behalf of those in distress, as is the duty of chivalry and of knights-errant like myself, whose ambition is directed to such deeds."

The landlord, who, as has been mentioned, was something of a wag, and had already some suspicion of his guest's want of wits, was quite convinced of it on hearing talk of this kind from him, and to make sport for the night he determined to fall in with his humour. So he told him he was quite right in pursuing the object he had in view, and that such a motive was natural and becoming in cavaliers as distinguished as he seemed and his gallant bearing showed him to be; and that he himself in his younger days had followed the same honourable calling, roaming in quest of adventures in various parts of the world, among others the Curing-grounds of Malaga, the Isles of Riaran, the Precinct of Seville, the Little Market of Segovia, the Olivera of Valencia, the Rondilla of Granada, the Strand of San Lucar, the Colt of Cordova, the Taverns of Toledo, and divers other quarters, where he had proved the nimbleness of his feet and the lightness of his fingers, doing many wrongs, cheating many widows, ruining maids and swindling minors, and, in short, bringing himself under the notice of almost every tribunal and court of justice in Spain; until at last he had retired to this castle of his, where he was living upon his property and upon that of others; and where he received all knights-errant, of whatever rank or condition they might be, all for the great love he bore them and that they might share their substance with him in return for his benevolence. He told him, moreover, that in this castle of his there was no chapel in which he could watch his armour, as it had been pulled down in order to be rebuilt, but that in a case of necessity it might, he knew, be watched anywhere, and he might watch it that night in a courtyard of the castle, and in the morning, God willing, the requisite ceremonies might be performed so as to have him dubbed a knight, and so thoroughly dubbed that nobody could be more so. He asked if he had any money with him, to which Don Quixote replied that he had not a farthing, as in the histories of knights-errant he had never read of any of them carrying any. On this point the landlord told him he was mistaken; for, though not recorded in the histories, because in the author's opinion there was no need to mention anything so obvious and necessary as money and clean shirts, it was not to be supposed therefore that they did not carry them, and he might regard it as certain and established that all knights-errant (about whom there were so many full and unimpeachable books) carried well-furnished purses in case of emergency, and likewise carried shirts and a little box of ointment to cure the wounds they received. For in those plains and deserts where they engaged in combat and came out wounded, it was not always that there was some one to cure them, unless indeed they had for a friend some sage magician to succour them at once by fetching through the air upon a cloud some damsel or dwarf with a vial of water of such virtue that by tasting one drop of it they were cured of their hurts and wounds in an instant and left as sound as if they had not received any damage whatever. But in case this should not occur, the knights of old took care to see that their squires were provided with money and other requisites, such as lint and ointments for healing purposes; and when it happened that knights had no squires (which was rarely and seldom the case) they themselves carried everything in cunning saddle-bags that were hardly seen on the horse's croup, as if it were something else of more importance, because, unless for some such reason, carrying saddle-bags was not very favourably regarded among knights-errant. He therefore advised him (and, as his godson so soon to be, he might even command him) never from that time forth to travel without money and the usual requirements, and he would find the advantage of them when he least expected it.

Don Quixote promised to follow his advice scrupulously, and it was arranged forthwith that he should watch his armour in a large yard at one side of the inn; so, collecting it all together, Don Quixote placed it on a trough that stood by the side of a well, and bracing his buckler on his arm he grasped his lance and began with a stately air to march up and down in front of the trough, and as he began his march night began to fall.

The landlord told all the people who were in the inn about the craze of his guest, the watching of the armour, and the dubbing ceremony he contemplated. Full of wonder at so strange a form of madness, they flocked to see it from a distance, and observed with what composure he sometimes paced up and down, or sometimes, leaning on his lance, gazed on his armour without taking his eyes off it for ever so long; and as the night closed in with a light from the moon so brilliant that it might vie with his that lent it, everything the novice knight did was plainly seen by all.

Meanwhile one of the carriers who were in the inn thought fit to water his team, and it was necessary to remove Don Quixote's armour as it lay on the trough; but he seeing the other approach hailed him in a loud voice, "O thou, whoever thou art, rash knight that comest to lay hands on the armour of the most valorous errant that ever girt on sword, have a care what thou dost; touch it not unless thou wouldst lay down thy life as the penalty of thy rashness." The carrier gave no heed to these words (and he would have done better to heed them if he had been heedful of his health), but seizing it by the straps flung the armour some distance from him. Seeing this, Don Quixote raised his eyes to heaven, and fixing his thoughts, apparently, upon his lady Dulcinea, exclaimed, "Aid me, lady mine, in this the first encounter that presents itself to this breast which thou holdest in subjection; let not thy favour and protection fail me in this first jeopardy;" and, with these words and others to the same purpose, dropping his buckler he lifted his lance with both hands and with it smote such a blow on the carrier's head that he stretched him on the ground so stunned that had he followed it up with a second there would have been no need of a surgeon to cure him. This done, he picked up his armour and returned to his beat with the same serenity as before.

Shortly after this, another, not knowing what had happened (for the carrier still lay senseless), came with the same object of giving water to his mules, and was proceeding to remove the armour in order to clear the trough, when Don Quixote, without uttering a word or imploring aid from anyone, once more dropped his buckler and once more lifted his lance, and without actually breaking the second carrier's head into pieces, made more than three of it, for he laid it open in four. At the noise all the people of the inn ran to the spot, and among them the landlord. Seeing this, Don Quixote braced his buckler on his arm, and with his hand on his sword exclaimed, "O Lady of Beauty, strength and support of my faint heart, it is time for thee to turn the eyes of thy greatness on this thy captive knight on the brink of so mighty an adventure." By this he felt himself so inspirited that he would not have flinched if all the carriers in the world had assailed him. The comrades of the wounded perceiving the plight they were in began from a distance to shower stones on Don Quixote, who screened himself as best he could with his buckler, not daring to quit the trough and leave his armour unprotected. The landlord shouted to them to leave him alone, for he had already told them that he was mad, and as a madman he would not be accountable even if he killed them all. Still louder shouted Don Quixote, calling them knaves and traitors, and the lord of the castle, who allowed knights-errant to be treated in this fashion, a villain and a low-born knight whom, had he received the order of knighthood, he would call to account for his treachery. "But of you," he cried, "base and vile rabble, I make no account; fling, strike, come on, do all ye can against me, ye shall see what the reward of your folly and insolence will be." This he uttered with so much spirit and boldness that he filled his assailants with a terrible fear, and as much for this reason as at the persuasion of the landlord they left off stoning him, and he allowed them to carry off the wounded, and with the same calmness and composure as before resumed the watch over his armour.

But these freaks of his guest were not much to the liking of the landlord, so he determined to cut matters short and confer upon him at once the unlucky order of knighthood before any further misadventure could occur; so, going up to him, he apologized for the rudeness which, without his knowledge, had been offered to him by these low people, who, however, had been well punished for their audacity. As he had already told him, he said, there was no chapel in the castle, nor was it needed for what remained to be done, for, as he understood the ceremonial of the order, the whole point of being dubbed a knight lay in the accolade and in the slap on the shoulder, and that could be administered in the middle of a field; and that he had now done all that was needful as to watching the armour, for all requirements were satisfied by a watch of two hours only, while he had been more than four about it. Don Quixote believed it all, and told him he stood there ready to obey him, and to make an end of it with as much despatch as possible; for, if he were again attacked, and felt himself to be a dubbed knight, he would not, he thought, leave a soul alive in the castle, except such as out of respect he might spare at his bidding.

Thus warned and menaced, the castellan forthwith brought out a book in which he used to enter the straw and barley he served out to the carriers, and, with a lad carrying a candle-end, and the two damsels already mentioned, he returned to where Don Quixote stood, and bade him kneel down. Then, reading from his account-book as if he were repeating some devout prayer, in the middle of his delivery he raised his hand and gave him a sturdy blow on the neck, and then, with his own sword, a smart slap on the shoulder, all the while muttering between his teeth as if he was saying his prayers. Having done this, he directed one of the ladies to gird on his sword, which she did with great self-possession and gravity, and not a little was required to prevent a burst of laughter at each stage of the ceremony; but what they had already seen of the novice knight's prowess kept their laughter within bounds. On girding him with the sword the worthy lady said to him, "May God make your worship a very fortunate knight, and grant you success in battle." Don Quixote asked her name in order that he might from that time forward know to whom he was beholden for the favour he had received, as he meant to confer upon her some portion of the honour he acquired by the might of his arm. She answered with great humility that she was called La Tolosa, and that she was the daughter of a cobbler of Toledo who lived in the stalls of Sanchobienaya, and that wherever she might be she would serve and esteem him as her lord. Don Quixote said in reply that she would do him a favour if thenceforward she assumed the "Don" and called herself Doña Tolosa. She promised she would, and then the other buckled on his spur, and with her followed almost the same conversation as with the lady of the sword. He asked her name, and she said it was La Molinera, and that she was the daughter of a respectable miller of Antequera; and of her likewise Don Quixote requested that she would adopt the "Don" and call herself Doña Molinera, making offers to her of further services and favours.

Having thus, with hot haste and speed, brought to a conclusion these never-till-now-seen ceremonies, Don Quixote was on thorns until he saw himself on horseback sallying forth in quest of adventures; and saddling Rocinante at once he mounted, and embracing his host, as he returned thanks for his kindness in knighting him, he addressed him in language so extraordinary that it is impossible to convey an idea of it or report it. The landlord, to get him out of the inn, replied with no less rhetoric though with shorter words, and without calling upon him to pay the reckoning let him go with a Godspeed.

CHAPTER IV

Of what happened to our knight when he left the inn

Day was dawning when Don Quixote quitted the inn, so happy, so gay, so exhilarated at finding himself dubbed a knight, that his joy was like to burst his horse-girths. However, recalling the advice of his host as to the requisites he ought to carry with him, expecially that referring to money and shirts, he determined to go home and provide himself with all, and also with a squire, for he reckoned upon securing a farm-labourer, a neighbour of his, a poor man with a family, but very well qualified for the office of squire to a knight. With this object he turned his horse's head towards his village, and Rocinante, thus reminded of his old quarters, stepped out so briskly that he hardly seemed to tread the earth.

He had not gone far, when out of a thicket on his right there seemed to come feeble cries as of some one in distress, and the instant he heard them he exclaimed, "Thanks be to heaven for the favour it accords me, that it so soon offers me an opportunity of fulfilling the obligation I have undertaken, and gathering the fruit of my ambition. These cries, no doubt, come from some man or woman in want of help, and needing my aid and protection;" and wheeling, he turned Rocinante in the direction whence the cries seemed to proceed. He had gone but a few paces into the wood, when he saw a mare tied to an oak, and tied to another, and stripped from the waist upwards, a youth of about fifteen years of age, from whom the cries came. Nor were they without cause, for a lusty farmer was flogging him with a belt and following up every blow with scoldings and commands, repeating, "Your mouth shut and your eyes open!" while the youth made answer, "I won't do it again, master mine; by God's passion I won't do it again, and I'll take more care of the flock another time."

Seeing what was going on, Don Quixote said in an angry voice, "Discourteous knight, it ill becomes you to assail one who cannot defend himself; mount your steed and take your lance" (for there was a lance leaning against the oak to which the mare was tied), "and I will make you know that you are behaving as a coward." The farmer, seeing before him this figure in full armour brandishing a lance over his head, gave himself up for dead, and made answer meekly, "Sir Knight, this youth that I am chastising is my servant, employed by me to watch a flock of sheep that I have hard by, and he is so careless that I lose one every day, and when I punish him for his carelessness and knavery he says I do it out of niggardliness, to escape paying him the wages I owe him, and before God, and on my soul, he lies."

"Lies before me, base clown!" said Don Quixote. "By the sun that shines on us I have a mind to run you through with this lance. Pay him at once without another word; if not, by the God that rules us I will make an end of you, and annihilate you on the spot; release him instantly."

The farmer hung his head, and without a word untied his servant, of whom Don Quixote asked how much his master owed him.

He replied, nine months at seven reals a month. Don Quixote added it up, found that it came to sixty-three reals, and told the farmer to pay it down immediately, if he did not want to die for it.

The trembling clown replied that as he lived and by the oath he had sworn (though he had not sworn any) it was not so much; for there were to be taken into account and deducted three pairs of shoes he had given him, and a real for two blood-lettings when he was sick.

"All that is very well," said Don Quixote; "but let the shoes and the blood-lettings stand as a set-off against the blows you have given him without any cause; for if he spoiled the leather of the shoes you paid for, you have damaged that of his body, and if the barber took blood from him when he was sick, you have drawn it when he was sound; so on that score he owes you nothing."

"The difficulty is, Sir Knight, that I have no money here; let Andres come home with me, and I will pay him all, real by real."

"I go with him!" said the youth. "Nay, God forbid! no, señor, not for the world; for once alone with me, he would flay me like a Saint Bartholomew."

"He will do nothing of the kind," said Don Quixote; "I have only to command, and he will obey me; and as he has sworn to me by the order of knighthood which he has received, I leave him free, and I guarantee the payment."

"Consider what you are saying, señor," said the youth; "this master of mine is not a knight, nor has he received any order of knighthood; for he is Juan Haldudo the Rich, of Quintanar."

"That matters little," replied Don Quixote; "there may be Haldudos knights; moreover, everyone is the son of his works."

"That is true," said Andres; "but this master of mine — of what works is he the son, when he refuses me the wages of my sweat and labour?"

"I do not refuse, brother Andres," said the farmer; "be good enough to come along with me, and I swear by all the orders of knighthood there are in the world to pay you as I have agreed, real by real, and perfumed."

"For the perfumery I excuse you," said Don Quixote; "give it to him in reals, and I shall be satisfied; and see that you do as you have sworn; if not, by the same oath I swear to come back and hunt you out and punish you; and I shall find you though you should lie closer than a lizard. And if you desire to know who it is lays this command upon you, that you may be more firmly bound to obey it, know that I am the valorous Don Quixote of La Mancha, the undoer of wrongs and injustices; and so, God be with you, and keep in mind what you have promised and sworn under those penalties that have been already declared to you."

So saying, he gave Rocinante the spur and was soon out of reach. The farmer followed with him his eyes, and when he saw that he had cleared the wood and was no longer in sight, he turned to his boy Andres, and said, "Come here, my son, I want to pay you what I owe you, as that undoer of wrongs has commanded me."

"My oath on it," said Andres, "your worship will be well advised to obey the command of that good knight — may he live a thousand years — for, as he is a valiant and just judge, by Roque, if you do not pay me, he will come back and do as he said."

"My oath on it, too," said the farmer; "but as I have a strong affection for you, I want to add to the debt in order to add to the payment;" and seizing him by the arm, he tied him up to the oak again, where he gave him such a flogging that he left him for dead.

"Now, Master Andres," said the farmer, "call on the undoer of wrongs; you will find he won't undo that, though I am not sure that I have quite done with you, for I have a good mind to flay you alive as you feared." But at last he untied him, and gave him leave to go look for his judge in order to put the sentence pronounced into execution.

Andres went off rather down in the mouth, swearing he would go to look for the valiant Don Quixote of La Mancha and tell him exactly what had happened, and that all would have to be repaid him sevenfold; but for all that, he went off weeping, while his master stood laughing.

Thus did the valiant Don Quixote right that wrong, and, thoroughly satisfied with what had taken place, as he considered he had made a very happy and noble beginning with his knighthood, he took the road towards his village in perfect self-content, saying in a low voice, "Well mayest thou this day call thyself fortunate above all on earth, O Dulcinea del Toboso, fairest of the fair! since it has fallen to thy lot to hold subject and submissive to thy full will and pleasure a knight so renowned as is and will be Don Quixote of La Mancha, who, as all the world knows, yesterday received the order of knighthood, and hath to-day righted the greatest wrong and grievance that ever injustice conceived and cruelty perpetrated: who hath to-day plucked the rod from the hand of yonder ruthless oppressor so wantonly lashing that tender child."

He now came to a road branching in four directions, and immediately he was reminded of those cross-roads where knights-errant used to stop to consider which road they should take. In imitation of them he halted for a while, and after having deeply considered it, he gave Rocinante his head, submitting his own will to that of his hack, who followed out his first intention, which was to make straight for his own stable. After he had gone about two miles Don Quixote perceived a large party of people, who, as afterwards appeared, were some Toledo traders, on their way to buy silk at Murcia. There were six of them coming along under their sunshades, with four servants mounted, and three muleteers on foot. Scarcely had Don Quixote descried them when the fancy possessed him that this must be some new adventure; and to help him to imitate as far as he could those passages he had read of in his books, here seemed to come one made on purpose, which he resolved to attempt. So with a lofty bearing and determination he fixed himself firmly in his stirrups, got his lance ready, brought his buckler before his breast, and planting himself in the middle of the road, stood waiting the approach of these knights-errant, for such he now considered and held them to be; and when they had come near enough to see and hear, he exclaimed with a haughty gesture, "All the world stand, unless all the world confess that in all the world there is no maiden fairer than the Empress of La Mancha, the peerless Dulcinea del Toboso."

The traders halted at the sound of this language and the sight of the strange figure that uttered it, and from both figure and language at once guessed the craze of their owner; they wished, however, to learn quietly what was the object of this confession that was demanded of them, and one of them, who was rather fond of a joke and was very sharp-witted, said to him, "Sir Knight, we do not know who this good lady is that you speak of; show her to us, for, if she be of such beauty as you suggest, with all our hearts and without any pressure we will confess the truth that is on your part required of us."

"If I were to show her to you," replied Don Quixote, "what merit would you have in confessing a truth so manifest? The essential point is that without seeing her you must believe, confess, affirm, swear, and defend it; else ye have to do with me in battle, ill-conditioned, arrogant rabble that ye are; and come ye on, one by one as the order of knighthood requires, or all together as is the custom and vile usage of your breed, here do I bide and await you, relying on the justice of the cause I maintain."

"Sir Knight," replied the trader, "I entreat your worship in the name of this present company of princes, that, to save us from charging our consciences with the confession of a thing we have never seen or heard of, and one moreover so much to the prejudice of the Empresses and Queens of the Alcarria and Estremadura, your worship will be pleased to show us some portrait of this lady, though it be no bigger than a grain of wheat; for by the thread one gets at the ball, and in this way we shall be satisfied and easy, and you will be content and pleased; nay, I believe we are already so far agreed with you that even though her portrait should show her blind of one eye, and distilling vermilion and sulphur from the other, we would nevertheless, to gratify your worship, say all in her favour that you desire."

"She distils nothing of the kind, vile rabble," said Don Quixote, burning with rage, "nothing of the kind, I say, only ambergris and civet in cotton; nor is she one-eyed or humpbacked, but straighter than a Guadarrama spindle: but ye must pay for the blasphemy ye have uttered against beauty like that of my lady."

And so saying, he charged with levelled lance against the one who had spoken, with such fury and fierceness that, if luck had not contrived that Rocinante should stumble midway and come down, it would have gone hard with the rash trader. Down went Rocinante, and over went his master, rolling along the ground for some distance; and when he tried to rise he was unable, so encumbered was he with lance, buckler, spurs, helmet, and the weight of his old armour; and all the while he was struggling to get up, he kept saying, "Fly not, cowards and caitiffs! stay, for not by my fault, but my horse's, am I stretched here."

One of the muleteers in attendance, who could not have had much good nature in him, hearing the poor prostrate man blustering in this style, was unable to refrain from giving him an answer on his ribs; and coming up to him he seized his lance, and having broken it in pieces, with one of them he began so to belabour our Don Quixote that, notwithstanding and in spite of his armour, he milled him like a measure of wheat. His masters called out not to lay on so hard and to leave him alone, but the muleteer's blood was up, and he did not care to drop the game until he had vented the rest of his wrath, and gathering up the remaining fragments of the lance he finished with a discharge upon the unhappy victim, who all through the storm of sticks that rained on him never ceased threatening heaven, and earth, and the brigands, for such they seemed to him. At last the muleteer was tired, and the traders continued their journey, taking with them matter for talk about the poor fellow who had been cudgelled. He when he found himself alone made another effort to rise; but if he was unable when whole and sound, how was he to rise after having been thrashed and well-nigh knocked to pieces? And yet he esteemed himself fortunate, as it seemed to him that this was a regular knight-errant's mishap, and entirely, he considered, the fault of his horse. However, battered in body as he was, to rise was beyond his power.

CHAPTER V

In which the narrative of our knight's mishap is continued

Finding, then, that in fact he could not move, he bethought himself of having recourse to his usual remedy, which was to think of some passage in his books, and his craze brought to his mind that about Baldwin and the Marquis of Mantua, when Carloto left him wounded on the mountain side, a story known by heart by the children, not forgotten by the young men, and lauded and even believed by the old folk; and for all that not a whit truer than the miracles of Mahomet. This seemed to him to fit exactly the case in which he found himself, so, making a show of severe suffering, he began to roll on the ground and with feeble breath repeat the very words which the wounded knight of the wood is said to have uttered:

Where art thou, lady mine, that thou
My sorrow dost not rue?
Thou canst not know it, lady mine,
Or else thou art untrue.

And so he went on with the ballad as far as the lines:

O noble Marquis of Mantua,
My Uncle and liege lord!

As chance would have it, when he had got to this line there happened to come by a peasant from his own village, a neighbour of his, who had been with a load of wheat to the mill, and he, seeing the man stretched there, came up to him and asked him who he was and what was the matter with him that he complained so dolefully.

Don Quixote was firmly persuaded that this was the Marquis of Mantua, his uncle, so the only answer he made was to go on with his ballad, in which he told the tale of his misfortune, and of the loves of the Emperor's son and his wife, all exactly as the ballad sings it.

The peasant stood amazed at hearing such nonsense, and relieving him of the visor, already battered to pieces by blows, he wiped his face, which was covered with dust, and as soon as he had done so he recognized him and said, "Señor Don Quixada" (for so he appears to have been called when he was in his senses and had not yet changed from a quiet country gentleman into a knight-errant), "who has brought your worship to this pass?" But to all questions the other only went on with his ballad.

Seeing this, the good man removed as well as he could his breastplate and backpiece to see if he had any wound, but he could perceive no blood nor any mark whatever. He then contrived to raise him from the ground, and with no little difficulty hoisted him upon his ass, which seemed to him to be the easiest mount for him; and collecting the arms, even to the splinters of the lance, he tied them on Rocinante, and leading him by the bridle and the ass by the halter he took the road for the village, very sad to hear what absurd stuff Don Quixote was talking. Nor was Don Quixote less so, for what with blows and bruises he could not sit upright on the ass, and from time to time he sent up sighs to heaven, so that once more he drove the peasant to ask what ailed him. And it could have been only the devil himself that put into his head tales to match his own adventures, for now, forgetting Baldwin, he bethought himself of the Moor Abindarraez, when the Alcaide of Antequera, Rodrigo de Narvaez, took him prisoner and carried him away to his castle; so that when the peasant again asked him how he was and what ailed him, he gave him for reply the same words and phrases that the captive Abencerrage gave to Rodrigo de Narvaez, just as he had read the story in the "Diana" of Jorge de Montemayor where it is written, applying it to his own case so aptly that the peasant went along cursing his fate that he had to listen to such a lot of nonsense; from which, however, he came to the conclusion that his neighbour was mad, and so made all haste to reach the village to escape the wearisomeness of this harangue of Don Quixote's; who, at the end of it, said, "Señor Don Rodrigo de Narvaez, your worship must know that this fair Xarifa I have mentioned is now the lovely Dulcinea del Toboso, for whom I have done, am doing, and will do the most famous deeds of chivalry that in this world have been seen, are to be seen, or ever shall be seen."

To this the peasant answered, "Señor — sinner that I am! — cannot your worship see that I am not Don Rodrigo de Narvaez nor the Marquis of Mantua, but Pedro Alonso your neighbour, and that your worship is neither Baldwin nor Abindarraez, but the worthy gentleman Señor Quixada?"

"I know who I am," replied Don Quixote, "and I know that I may be not only those I have named, but all the Twelve Peers of France and even all the Nine Worthies, since my achievements surpass all that they have done all together and each of them on his own account."

With this talk and more of the same kind they reached the village just as night was beginning to fall, but the peasant waited until it was a little later that the belaboured gentleman might not be seen riding in such a miserable trim. When it was what seemed to him the proper time he entered the village and went to Don Quixote's house, which he found all in confusion, and there were the curate and the village barber, who were great friends of Don Quixote, and his housekeeper was saying to them in a loud voice, "What does your worship think can have befallen my master, señor licentiate Pero Perez?" for so the curate was called; "it is six days now since anything has been seen of him, or the hack, or the buckler, lance, or armour. Miserable me! I am certain of it, and it is as true as that I was born to die, that these accursed books of chivalry he has, and has got into the way of reading so constantly, have upset his reason; for now I remember having often heard him saying to himself that he would turn knight-errant and go all over the world in quest of adventures. To the devil and Barabbas with such books, that have brought to ruin in this way the finest understanding there was in all La Mancha!"

The niece said the same, and, indeed, more: "You must know, Master Nicholas" — for that was the name of the barber — "it was often my uncle's way to stay two days and nights together poring over these unholy books of misventures, after which he would fling the book away and snatch up his sword and fall to slashing the walls; and when he was tired out he would say he had killed four giants like four towers; and the sweat that flowed from him when he was weary he said was the blood of the wounds he had received in battle; and then he would drink a great jug of cold water and become calm and quiet, saying that this water was a most precious potion which the sage Esquife, a great magician and friend of his, had brought him. But I take all the blame upon myself for never having told your worships of my uncle's vagaries, that you might put a stop to them before things had come to this pass, and burn all these accursed books — for he has a great number — that richly deserve to be burned like heretics."

"So say I too," said the curate, "and by my faith to-morrow shall not pass without public judgment upon them, and may they be condemned to the flames lest they lead those that read them to behave as my good friend seems to have behaved."

All this the peasant heard, and from it he understood at last what was the matter with his neighbour, so he began calling aloud, "Open, your worships, to Señor Baldwin and to Señor the Marquis of Mantua, who comes badly wounded, and to Señor Abindarraez, the Moor, whom the valiant Rodrigo de Narvaez, the Alcaide of Antequera, brings captive."

At these words they all hurried out, and when they recognised their friend, master, and uncle, who had not yet dismounted from the ass because he could not, they ran to embrace him.

"Hold!" said he, "for I am badly wounded through my horse's fault; carry me to bed, and if possible send for the wise Urganda to cure and see to my wounds."

"See there! plague on it!" cried the housekeeper at this: "did not my heart tell the truth as to which foot my master went lame of? To bed with your worship at once, and we will contrive to cure you here without fetching that Hurgada. A curse I say once more, and a hundred times more, on those books of chivalry that have brought your worship to such a pass."

They carried him to bed at once, and after searching for his wounds could find none, but he said they were all bruises from having had a severe fall with this horse Rocinante when in combat with ten giants, the biggest and the boldest to be found on earth.

"So, so!" said the curate, "are there giants in the dance? By the sign of the Cross I will burn them to-morrow before the day is over."

They put a host of questions to Don Quixote, but his only answer to all was — give him something to eat, and leave him to sleep, for that was what he needed most. They did so, and the curate questioned the peasant at great length as to how he had found Don Quixote. He told him all, and the nonsense he had talked when found and on the way home, all which made the licentiate the more eager to do what he did the next day, which was to summon his friend the barber, Master Nicholas, and go with him to Don Quixote's house.

[On the next day, while Don Quixote is still sleeping, the curate and the barber gain admission to his library, go through his more than hundred books, select those that have caused the mischief, and throw them out of the window to be burned in the yard. Chapter VII begins the account of Don Quixote's second sally.]

CHAPTER VII

Of the second sally of our worthy knight Don Quixote of La Mancha

At this instant Don Quixote began shouting out, "Here, here, valiant knights! here is need for you to put forth the might of your strong arms, for they of the Court are gaining the mastery in the tourney!" Called away by this noise and outcry, they proceeded no farther with the scrutiny of the remaining books, and so it is thought that "The Carolea," "The Lion of Spain," and "The Deeds of the Emperor," written by Don Luis de Avila, went to the fire unseen and unheard; for no doubt they were among those that remained, and perhaps if the curate had seen them they would not have undergone so severe a sentence.

When they reached Don Quixote he was already out of bed, and was still shouting and raving, and slashing and cutting all round, as wide awake as if he had never slept.

They closed with him and by force got him back to bed, and when he had become a little calm, addressing the curate, he said to him, "Of a truth, Señor Archbishop Turpin, it is a great disgrace for us who call ourselves the Twelve Peers, so carelessly to allow the knights of the Court to gain the victory in this tourney, we the adventurers having carried off the honour on the three former days."

"Hush, gossip," said the curate; "please God, the luck may turn, and what is lost to-day may be won to-morrow; for the present let your worship have a care of your health, for it seems to me that you are over-fatigued, if not badly wounded."

"Wounded no," said Don Quixote, "but bruised and battered no doubt, for that bastard Don Roland has cudgelled me with the trunk of an oak tree, and all for envy, because he sees that I alone rival him in his achievements. But I should not call myself Reinaldos of Montalvan did he not pay me for it in spite of all his enchantments as soon as I rise from this bed. For the present let them bring me something to eat, for that, I feel, is what will be more to my purpose, and leave it to me to avenge myself."

They did as he wished; they gave him something to eat, and

once more he fell asleep, leaving them marvelling at his madness.

That night the housekeeper burned to ashes all the books that were in the yard and in the whole house; and some must have been consumed that deserved preservation in everlasting archives, but their fate and the laziness of the examiner did not permit it, and so in them was verified the proverb that sometimes the innocent suffer for the guilty.

One of the remedies which the curate and the barber immediately applied to their friend's disorder was to wall up and plaster the room where the books were, so that when he got up he should not find them (possibly the cause being removed, the effect might cease), and they might say that a magician had carried them off, room and all; and this was done with all despatch. Two days later Don Quixote got up, and the first thing he did was to go and look at his books, and not finding the room where he had left it, he wandered from side to side looking for it. He came to the place where the door used to be, and tried it with his hands, and turned and twisted his eyes in every direction without saying a word; but after a good while he asked his housekeeper whereabouts was the room that held his books.

The housekeeper, who had been already well instructed in what she was to answer, said, "What room or what nothing is it that your worship is looking for? There are neither room nor books in this house now, for the devil himself has carried all away."

"It was not the devil," said the niece, "but a magician who came on a cloud one night after the day your worship left this, and dismounting from a serpent that he rode he entered the room, and what he did there I know not, but after a little while he made off, flying through the roof, and left the house full of smoke; and when we went to see what he had done we saw neither book nor room: but we remember very well, the housekeeper and I, that on leaving, the old villain said in a loud voice that, for a private grudge he owed the owner of the books and the room, he had done mischief in that house that would be discovered by-and-by: he said too that his name was the Sage Muñaton."

"He must have said Friston," said Don Quixote.

"I don't know whether he called himself Friston or Friton," said the housekeeper, "I only know that his name ended with 'ton.'"

"So it does," said Don Quixote, "and he is a sage magician, a great enemy of mine, who has a spite against me because he knows by his arts and lore that in process of time I am to engage in single combat with a knight whom he befriends and that I am to conquer, and he will be unable to prevent it: and for this reason he endeavours to do me all the ill turns that he can; but I promise him it will be hard for him to oppose or avoid what is decreed by Heaven."

"Who doubts that?" said the niece; "but, uncle, who mixes you up in these quarrels? Would it not be better to remain at peace in your own house instead of roaming the world looking for better bread than ever came of wheat, never reflecting that many go for wool and come back shorn?"

"Oh, niece of mine," replied Don Quixote, "how much astray art thou in thy reckoning: ere they shear me I shall have plucked away and stripped off the beards of all who would dare to touch only the tip of a hair of mine."

The two were unwilling to make any further answer, as they saw that his anger was kindling.

In short, then, he remained at home fifteen days very quietly without showing any signs of a desire to take up with his former delusions, and during this time he held lively discussions with his two gossips, the curate and the barber, on the point he maintained, that knights-errant were what the world stood most in need of, and that in him was to be accomplished the revival of knight-errantry. The curate sometimes contradicted him, sometimes agreed with him, for if he had not observed this precaution he would have been unable to bring him to reason.

Meanwhile Don Quixote worked upon a farm labourer, a neighbour of his, an honest man (if indeed that title can be given to him who is poor), but with very little wit in his pate. In a word, he so talked him over, and with such persuasions and promises, that the poor clown made up his mind to sally forth with him and serve him as esquire. Don Quixote, among other things, told him he ought to be ready to go with him gladly, because any moment an adventure might occur that might win an island in the twinkling of an eye and leave him governor of it. On these and the like promises Sancho Panza (for so the labourer was called) left wife and children, and engaged himself as esquire to his neighbour. Don Quixote next set about getting some money; and selling one thing and pawning another, and making a bad bargain in every case, he got together a fair sum. He provided himself with a buckler, which he begged as a loan from a friend, and, restoring his battered helmet as best he could, he warned his squire Sancho of the day and hour he meant to set out, that he might provide himself with what he thought most needful. Above all, he charged him to take alforjas with him. The other said he would, and that he meant to take also a very good ass he had, as he was not much given to going on foot. About the ass, Don Quixote hesitated a little, trying whether he could call to mind any knight-errant taking with him an esquire mounted on ass-back, but no instance occurred to his memory. For all that, however, he determined to take him, intending to furnish him with a more honourable mount when a chance of it presented itself, by appropriating the horse of the first discourteous knight he encountered. Himself he provided with shirts and such other things as he could, according to the advice the host had given him; all which being settled and done, without taking leave, Sancho Panza of his wife and children, or Don Quixote of his housekeeper and niece, they sallied forth unseen by anybody from the village one night, and made such good way in the course of it that by daylight they held themselves safe from discovery, even should search be made for them.

Sancho rode on his ass like a patriarch with his alforjas and bota, and longing to see himself soon governor of the island his master had promised him. Don Quixote decided upon taking the same route and road he had taken on his first journey, that over the Campo de Montiel, which he travelled with less discomfort than on the last occasion, for, as it was early morning and the rays of the sun fell on them obliquely, the heat did not distress them.

And now said Sancho Panza to his master, "Your worship will take care, Señor Knight-errant, not to forget about the island you have promised me, for be it ever so big I'll be equal to governing it."

To which Don Quixote replied, "Thou must know, friend Sancho Panza, that it was a practice very much in vogue with the knights-errant of old to make their squires governors of the islands or kingdoms they won, and I am determined that there shall be no failure on my part in so liberal a custom; on the contrary, I mean to improve upon it, for they sometimes, and perhaps most frequently, waited until their squires were old, and then when they had had enough of service and hard days and worse nights, they gave them some title or other, of count, or at the most marquis, of some valley or province more or less; but if thou livest and I live, it may well be that before six days are over, I may have won some kingdom that has others dependent upon it, which will be just the thing to enable thee to be crowned king of one of them. Nor needst thou count this wonderful, for things and chances fall to the lot of such knights in ways so unexampled and unexpected that I might easily give thee even more than I promise thee."

"In that case," said Sancho Panza, "if I should become a king by one of those miracles your worship speaks of, even Juana Gutierrez, my old woman, would come to be queen and my children infantes."

"Well, who doubts it?" said Don Quixote.

"I doubt it," replied Sancho Panza, "because for my part I am persuaded that though God should shower down kingdoms upon earth, not one of them would fit the head of Mari Gutierrez. Let me tell you, señor, she is not worth two maravedis for a queen; countess will fit her better, and that only with God's help."

"Leave it to God, Sancho," returned Don Quixote, "for he will give her what suits her best; but do not undervalue thyself so much as to come to be content with anything less than being governor of a province."

"I will not, señor," answered Sancho, "especially as I have a man of such quality for a master in your worship, who will be able to give me all that will be suitable for me and that I can bear."

CHAPTER VIII

Of the good fortune which the valiant Don Quixote had in the terrible and undreamt-of adventure of the windmills, with other occurrences worthy to be fitly recorded

At this point they came in sight of thirty or forty windmills that there are on that plain, and as soon as Don Quixote saw them he said to his squire, "Fortune is arranging matters for us better than we could have shaped our desires ourselves, for look there, friend Sancho Panza, where thirty or more monstrous giants present themselves, all of whom I mean to engage in battle and slay, and with whose spoils we shall begin to make our fortunes; for this is righteous warfare, and it is God's good service to sweep so evil a breed from off the face of the earth."

"What giants?" said Sancho Panza.

"Those thou seest there," answered his master, "with the long arms, and some have them nearly two leagues long."

"Look, your worship," said Sancho; "what we see there are not giants but windmills, and what seem to be their arms are the sails that turned by the wind make the millstone go."

"It is easy to see," replied Don Quixote, "that thou art not used to this business of adventures; those are giants; and if thou art afraid, away with thee out of this and betake thyself to prayer while I engage them in fierce and unequal combat."

So saying, he gave the spur to his steed Rocinante, heedless of the cries his squire Sancho sent after him, warning him that most certainly they were windmills and not giants he was going to attack. He, however, was so positive they were giants that he neither heard the cries of Sancho, nor perceived, near as he was, what they were, but made at them shouting, "Fly not, cowards and vile beings, for it is a single knight that attacks you."

A slight breeze at this moment sprang up, and the great sails began to move, seeing which Don Quixote exclaimed, "Though ye flourish more arms than the giant Briareus, ye have to reckon with me."

So saying, and commending himself with all his heart to his lady Dulcinea, imploring her to support him in such a peril, with lance in rest and covered by his buckler, he charged at Rocinante's fullest gallop and fell upon the first mill that stood in front of him; but as he drove his lance-point into the sail the wind whirled it round with such force that it shivered the lance to pieces, sweeping with it horse and rider, who went rolling over on the plain, in a sorry condition. Sancho hastened to his assistance as fast as his ass could go, and when he came up found him unable to move, with such a shock had Rocinante fallen with him.

"God bless me!" said Sancho, "did I not tell your worship to mind what you were about, for they were only windmills? and no one could have made any mistake about it but one who had something of the same kind in his head."

"Hush, friend Sancho," replied Don Quixote, "the fortunes of war more than any other are liable to frequent fluctuations; and moreover I think, and it is the truth, that that same sage Friston who carried off my study and books, has turned these giants into mills in order to rob me of the glory of vanquishing them, such is the enmity he bears me; but in the end his wicked arts will avail but little against my good sword."

"God order it as he may," said Sancho Panza, and helping him to rise got him up again on Rocinante, whose shoulder was half out; and then, discussing the late adventure, they followed the road to Puerto Lapice, for there, said Don Quixote, they could not fail to find adventures in abundance and variety, as it was a great thoroughfare. For all that, he was much grieved at the loss of his lance, and saying so to his squire, he added, "I remember having read how a Spanish knight, Diego Perez de Vargas by name, having broken his sword in battle, tore from an oak a ponderous bough or branch, and with it did such things that day, and pounded so many Moors, that he got the surname of Machuca, and he and his descendants from that day forth were called Vargas y Machuca. I mention this because from the first oak I see I mean to rend such another branch, large and stout like that, with which I am determined and resolved to do such deeds that thou mayest deem thyself very fortunate in being found worthy to come and see them, and be an eye-witness of things that will with difficulty be believed."

"Be that as God will," said Sancho, "I believe it all as your worship says it; but straighten yourself a little, for you seem all on one side, may be from the shaking of the fall."

"That is the truth," said Don Quixote, "and if I make no complaint of the pain it is because knights-errant are not permitted to complain of any wound, even though their bowels be coming out through it."

"If so," said Sancho, "I have nothing to say; but God knows I would rather your worship complained when anything ailed you. For my part, I confess I must complain however small the ache may be; unless indeed this rule about not complaining extends to the squires of knights-errant also."

Don Quixote could not help laughing at his squire's simplicity, and he assured him he might complain whenever and however he chose, just as he liked, for, so far, he had never read of anything to the contrary in the order of knighthood.

Sancho bade him remember it was dinner-time, to which his master answered that he wanted nothing himself just then, but that *he* might eat when he had a mind. With this permission Sancho settled himself as comfortably as he could on his beast, and taking out of the alforjas what he had stowed away in them, he jogged along behind his master munching deliberately, and from time to time taking a pull at the bota with a relish that the thirstiest tapster in Malaga might have envied; and while he went on in this way, gulping down draught after draught, he never gave a thought to any of the promises his master had made him, nor did he rate it as hardship but rather as recreation going in quest of adventures, however dangerous they might be. Finally they passed the night among some trees, from one of which Don Quixote plucked a dry branch to serve him after a fashion as a lance, and fixed on it the head he had removed from the broken one. All that night Don Quixote lay awake thinking of his lady Dulcinea, in order to conform to what he had read in his books, how many a night in the forests and deserts knights used to lie sleepless supported by the memory of their mistresses. Not so did Sancho Panza spend it, for having his stomach full of something stronger than chicory water he made but one sleep of it, and, if his master had not called him, neither the rays of the sun beating on his face nor all the cheery notes of the birds welcoming the approach of day would have had power to waken him. On getting up he tried the bota and found it somewhat less full than the night before, which grieved his heart because they did not seem to be on the way to remedy the deficiency readily. Don Quixote did not care to break his fast, for, as has been already said, he confined himself to savoury recollections for nourishment.

They returned to the road they had set out with, leading to Puerto Lapice, and at three in the afternoon they came in sight of it. "Here, brother Sancho Panza," said Don Quixote when he saw it, "we may plunge our hands up to the elbows in what they call adventures; but observe, even shouldst thou see me in the greatest danger in the world, thou must not put a hand to thy sword in my defence, unless indeed thou perceivest that those who assail me are rabble or base folk; for in that case thou mayest very properly aid me; but if they be knights it is on no account permitted or allowed thee by the laws of knighthood to help me until thou hast been dubbed a knight."

"Most certainly, señor," replied Sancho, "your worship shall be fully obeyed in this matter; all the more as of myself I am peaceful and no friend to mixing in strife and quarrels: it is true that as regards the defence of my own person I shall not give much heed to those laws, for laws human and divine allow each one to defend himself against any assailant whatever."

"That I grant," said Don Quixote, "but in this matter of aiding me against knights thou must put a restraint upon thy natural impetuosity."

"I will do so, I promise you," answered Sancho, "and I will keep this precept as carefully as Sunday."

[Don Quixote and Sancho, having encountered a company of more than twenty Yanguesan carriers and been badly beaten with stakes by them, find their way to an inn, which Don Quixote insists is a castle.]

CHAPTER XVI

Of what happened to the ingenious gentleman in the inn which he took to be a castle

The inkeeper, seeing Don Quixote slung across the ass, asked Sancho what was amiss with him. Sancho answered that it was nothing, only that he had fallen down from a rock and had his ribs a little bruised. The innkeeper had a wife whose disposition was not such as those of her calling commonly have, for she was by nature kind-hearted and felt for the sufferings of her neighbours, so she at once set about tending Don Quixote, and made her young daughter, a very comely girl, help her in taking care of her guest.

There was besides in the inn, as servant, an Asturian lass with a broad face, flat poll, and snub nose, blind of one eye and not very sound in the other. The elegance of her shape, to be sure, made up for all her defects; she did not measure seven palms from head to foot, and her shoulders, which over-weighted her somewhat, made her contemplate the ground more than she liked. This graceful lass, then, helped the young girl, and the two made up a very bad bed for Don Quixote in a garret that showed evident signs of having formerly served for many years as a straw-loft, in which there was also quartered a carrier whose bed was placed a little beyond our Don Quixote's, and, though only made of the pack-saddles and cloths of his mules, had much the advantage of it, as Don Quixote's consisted simply of four rough boards on two not very even trestles, a mattress, that for thinness might have passed for a quilt, full of pellets which, were they not seen through the rents to be wool, would to the touch have seemed pebbles in hardness, two sheets made of buckler leather, and a coverlet the threads of which any one that chose might have counted without missing one in the reckoning.

On this accursed bed Don Quixote stretched himself, and the hostess and her daughter soon covered him with plasters from top to toe, while Maritornes — for that was the name of the Asturian — held the light for them, and while plastering him, the hostess, observing how full of wheals Don Quixote was in some places, remarked that this had more the look of blows than of a fall.

It was not blows, Sancho said, but that the rock had many points and projections, and that each of them had left its mark. "Pray, señora," he added, "manage to save some tow, as there will be no want of some one to use it, for my loins too are rather sore."

"Then you must have fallen too," said the hostess.

"I did not fall," said Sancho Panza, "but from the shock I got at seeing my master fall, my body aches so that I feel as if I had had a thousand thwacks."

"That may well be," said the young girl, "for it has many a time happened to me to dream that I was falling down from a tower and never coming to the ground, and when I awoke from the dream to find myself as weak and shaken as if I had really fallen."

"There is the point, señora," replied Sancho Panza, "that I without dreaming at all, but being more awake than I am now, find myself with scarcely less wheals than my master, Don Quixote."

"How is the gentleman called?" asked Maritornes the Asturian.

"Don Quixote of La Mancha," answered Sancho Panza, "and he is a knight-adventurer, and one of the best and stoutest that have been seen in the world this long time past."

"What is a knight-adventurer?" said the lass.

"Are you so new in the world as not to know?" answered Sancho Panza. "Well, then, you must know, sister, that a knight-adventurer is a thing that in two words is seen drubbed and emperor, that is to-day the most miserable and needy being in the world, and to-morrow will have two or three crowns of kingdoms to give his squire."

"Then how is it," said the hostess, "that, belonging to so good a master as this, you have not, to judge by appearances, even so much as a county?"

"It is too soon yet," answered Sancho, "for we have only been a month going in quest of adventures, and so far we have met with nothing that can be called one, for it will happen that when one thing is looked for another thing is found; however, if my master Don Quixote gets well of this wound, or fall, and I am left none the worse of it, I would not change my hopes for the best title in Spain."

To all this conversation Don Quixote was listening very attentively, and sitting up in bed as well as he could, and taking the hostess by the hand he said to her, "Believe me, fair lady, you may call yourself fortunate in having in this castle of yours sheltered my person, which is such that if I do not myself praise it, it is because of what is commonly said, that self-praise debaseth; but my squire will inform you who I am. I only tell you that I shall preserve for ever inscribed on my memory the service you have rendered me in order to tender you my gratitude while life shall last me; and would to Heaven love held me not so enthralled and subject to its laws and to the eyes of that fair ingrate whom I name between my teeth, but that those of this lovely damsel might be the masters of my liberty."

The hostess, her daughter, and the worthy Maritornes listened in bewilderment to the words of the knight-errant, for they understood about as much of them as if he had been talking Greek, though they could perceive they were all meant for expressions of good-will and blandishments; and not being accustomed to this kind of language, they stared at him and wondered to themselves, for he seemed to them a man of a different sort from those they were used to, and thanking him in pot-house phrase for his civility they left him, while the Asturian gave her attention to Sancho, who needed it no less than his master.

The carrier had made an arrangement with her for recreation that night, and she had given him her word that when the guests were quiet and the family asleep she would come in search of him and meet his wishes unreservedly. And it is said of this good lass that she never made promises of the kind without fulfilling them, even though she made them in a forest and without any witness present, for she plumed herself greatly on being a lady and held it no disgrace to be in such an employment as servant in an inn, because, she said, misfortunes and ill-luck had brought her to that position. The hard, narrow, wretched, rickety bed of Don Quixote stood first in the middle of this star-lit stable, and close beside it Sancho made his, which merely consisted of a rush mat and a blanket that looked as if it was of threadbare canvas rather than of wool. Next to these two beds was that of the carrier, made up, as has been said, of the pack-saddles and all the trappings of the two best mules he had, though there were twelve of them, sleek, plump, and in prime condition, for he was one of the rich carriers of Arévalo, according to the author of this history, who particularly mentions this carrier because he knew him very well, and they even say was in some degree a relation of his; besides which Cid Hamet Benengeli was a historian of great research and accuracy in all things, as is very evident since he would not pass over in silence those that have been already mentioned, however trifling and insignificant they might be, an example that might be followed by those grave historians who relate transactions so curtly and briefly that we hardly get a taste of them, all the substance of the work being left in the ink-bottle from carelessness, perverseness, or ignorance. A thousand blessings on the author of "Tablante de Ricamonte" and that of the other book in which the deeds of the Conde Tomillas are recounted; with what minuteness they describe everything!

To proceed, then: after having paid a visit to his team and given them their second feed, the carrier stretched himself on his pack-saddles and lay waiting for his conscientious Maritornes. Sancho was by this time plastered and had lain down, and though he strove to sleep the pain of his ribs would not let him, while Don Quixote with the pain of his had his eyes as wide open as a hare's. The inn was all in silence, and in the whole of it there was no light except that given by a lantern that hung burning in the middle of the gateway. This strange stillness, and the thoughts, always present to our knight's mind, of the incidents described at every turn in the books that were the cause of his misfortune, conjured up to his imagination as extraordinary a delusion as can well be conceived, which was that he fancied himself to have reached a famous castle (for, as has been said, all the inns he lodged in were castles to his eyes), and that the daughter of the innkeeper was daughter of the lord of the castle, and that she, won by his high-bred bearing, had fallen in love with him, and had promised to come to his bed for a while that night without the knowledge of her parents; and holding all this fantasy that he had constructed as solid fact, he began to feel uneasy and to consider the perilous risk which his virtue was about to encounter, and he resolved in his heart to commit no treason to his lady Dulcinea del Toboso, even though the queen Guinevere herself and the dame Quintañona should present themselves before him.

While he was taken up with these vagaries, then, the time and the hour — an unlucky one for him — arrived for the Asturian to come, who in her smock, with bare feet and her hair gathered into a fustian coif, with noiseless and cautious steps entered the chamber where the three were quartered, in quest of the carrier; but scarcely had she gained the door when Don Quixote perceived her, and sitting up in his bed in spite of his plasters and the pain of his ribs, he stretched out his arms to receive his beauteous damsel. The Asturian, who went all doubled up and in silence with her hands before her feeling for her lover, encountered the arms of Don Quixote, who grasped her tightly by the wrist, and drawing her towards him, while she dared not utter a word, made her sit down on the bed. He then felt her smock, and although it was of sackcloth it appeared to him to be of the finest and softest silk: on her wrists she wore some glass beads, but to him they had the sheen of precious Orient pearls: her hair, which in some measure resembled a horse's mane, he rated as threads of the brightest gold of Araby, whose refulgence dimmed the sun himself: her breath, which no doubt smelt of yesterday's stale salad, seemed to him to diffuse a sweet aromatic fragrance from her mouth; and, in short, he drew her portrait in his imagination with the same features and in the same style as that which he had seen in his books of the other princess who, smitten by love, came with all the adornments that are here set down, to see the sorely wounded knight; and so great was the poor gentleman's blindness that neither touch, nor smell, nor anything else about the good lass that would have made any but a carrier vomit, were enough to undeceive him; on the contrary, he was persuaded he had the goddess of beauty in his arms, and holding her firmly in his grasp he went on to say in a low, tender voice, "Would that I found myself, lovely and exalted lady, in a position to repay such a favour as that which you, by the sight of your great beauty, have granted me; but fortune, which is never weary of persecuting the good, has chosen to place me upon this bed, where I lie so bruised and broken that though my inclination would gladly comply with yours it is impossible; besides, to this impossibility another yet greater is to be added, which is the faith that I have pledged to the peerless Dulcinea del Toboso, sole lady of my most secret thoughts; and were it not that this stood in the way I should not be so insensible a knight as to miss the happy opportunity which your great goodness has offered me."

Maritornes was fretting and sweating at finding herself held so fast by Don Quixote, and not understanding or heeding the words he addressed to her, she strove without speaking to free herself. The worthy carrier, whose unholy thoughts kept him awake, was aware of his doxy the moment she entered the door, and was listening attentively to all Don Quixote said; and jealous that the Asturian should have broken her word with him for another, drew nearer to Don Quixote's bed and stood still to see what would come of this talk which he could not understand; but when he perceived the wench struggling to get free and Don Quixote striving to hold her, not relishing the joke he raised his arm and delivered such a terrible cuff on the lank jaws of the amorous knight that he bathed all his mouth in blood, and not content with this he mounted on his ribs and with his feet tramped all over them at a pace rather smarter than a trot. The bed, which was somewhat crazy and not very firm on its feet, unable to bear the additional weight of the carrier, came to the ground, and at the mighty crash of this the innkeeper awoke and at once concluded that it must be some brawl of Maritornes', because after calling loudly to her he got no answer. With this suspicion he got up, and lighting a lamp hastened to the quarter where he had heard the disturbance. The wench, seeing that her master was coming and knowing that his temper was terrible, frightened and panic-stricken made for the bed of Sancho Panza, who still slept, and crouching upon it made a ball of herself.

The innkeeper came in exclaiming, "Where art thou, strumpet? Of course this is some of thy work." At this Sancho awoke, and feeling this mass almost on top of him fancied he had the nightmare and began to distribute fisticuffs all round, of which a certain share fell upon Maritornes, who, irritated by the pain and flinging modesty aside, paid back so many in return to Sancho that she woke him up in spite of himself. He then, finding himself so handled, by whom he knew not, raising himself up as well as he could, grappled with Maritornes, and he and she between them began the bitterest and drollest scrimmage in the world. The carrier, however, perceiving by the light of the innkeeper's candle how it fared with his lady-love, quitting Don Quixote, ran to bring her the help she needed; and the innkeeper did the same but with a different intention, for his was to chastise the lass, as he believed that beyond a doubt she alone was the cause of all the harmony. And so, as the saying is, cat to rat, rat to rope, rope to stick, the carrier pounded Sancho, Sancho the lass, she him, and the innkeeper her, and all worked away so briskly that they did not give themselves a moment's rest; and the best of it was that the innkeeper's lamp went out, and as they were left in the dark they all laid on one upon the other in a mass so unmercifully that there was not a sound spot left where a hand could light.

It so happened that there was lodging that night in the inn an officer of what they call the Old Holy Brotherhood of Toledo, who, also hearing the extraordinary noise of the conflict, seized his staff and the tin case with his warrants, and made his way in the dark into the room crying, "Hold! in the name of this Jurisdiction! Hold! in the name of the Holy Brotherhood!" The first that he came upon was the pummelled Don Quixote, who lay stretched senseless on his back upon his broken-down bed, and, his hand falling on the beard as he felt about, he continued to cry, "Help for the Jurisdiction!" but perceiving that he whom he had laid hold of did not move or stir, he concluded that he was dead and that those in the room were his murderers, and with this suspicion he raised his voice still higher, calling out, "Shut the inn gate; see that no one goes out; they have killed a man here!" This cry startled them all, and each dropped the contest at the point at which the voice reached him. The innkeeper retreated to his room, the carrier to his pack-saddles, the lass to her crib; the unlucky Don Quixote and Sancho alone were unable to move from where they were. The officer on this let go Don Quixote's beard, and went out to look for a light to search for and apprehend the culprits; but not finding one, as the innkeeper had purposely extinguished the lantern on retreating to his room, he was compelled to have recourse to the hearth, where after much time and trouble he lit another lamp.

CHAPTER XVII

In which are contained the innumerable troubles which the brave Don Quixote and his good squire Sancho Panza endured in the inn, which to his misfortune he took to be a castle

By this time Don Quixote had recovered from his swoon; and in the same tone of voice in which he had called to his squire the day before when he lay stretched "in the vale of the stakes," he began calling to him now, "Sancho, my friend, art thou asleep? sleepest thou, friend Sancho?"

"How can I sleep, curses on it!" returned Sancho discontentedly and bitterly, "when it is plain that all the devils have been at me this night?"

"Thou mayest well believe that," answered Don Quixote, "because, either I know little, or this castle is enchanted, for thou must know — but this that I am now about to tell thee thou must swear to keep secret until after my death."

"I swear it," answered Sancho.

"I say so," continued Don Quixote, "because I hate taking away anyone's good name."

"I say," repeated Sancho, "that I swear to hold my tongue about it till the end of your worship's days, and God grant I may be able to let it out to-morrow."

"Do I do thee such injuries, Sancho," said Don Quixote, "that thou wouldst see me dead so soon?"

"It is not for that," replied Sancho, "but because I hate keeping things long, and I don't want them to grow rotten with me from over-keeping."

"At any rate," said Don Quixote, "I have more confidence in thy affection and good nature; and so I would have thee know that this night there befell me one of the strangest adventures that I could describe, and to relate it to thee briefly thou must know that a little while ago the daughter of the lord of this castle came to me, and that she is the most elegant and beautiful damsel that could be found in the wide world. What I could tell thee of the charms of her person! of her lively wit! of other secret matters which, to preserve the fealty I owe to my lady Dulcinea del Toboso, I shall pass over unnoticed and in silence! I will only tell thee that, either fate being envious of so great a boon placed in my hands by good fortune, or perhaps (and this is more probable) this castle being, as I have already said, enchanted, at the time when I was engaged in the sweetest and most amorous discourse with her, there came, without my seeing or knowing whence it came, a hand attached to some arm of some huge giant, that planted such a cuff on my jaws that I have them all bathed in blood, and then pummelled me in such a way that I am in a worse plight than yesterday when the carriers, on account of Rocinante's misbehaviour, inflicted on us the injury thou knowest of; whence I conjecture that there must be some enchanted

Moor guarding the treasure of this damsel's beauty, and that it is not for me."

"Nor for me either," said Sancho, "for more than four hundred Moors have so thrashed me that the drubbing of the stakes was cakes and fancy-bread to it. But tell me, señor, what do you call this excellent and rare adventure that has left us as we are left now? Though your worship was not so badly off, having in your arms that incomparable beauty you spoke of; but I, what did I have, except the heaviest whacks I think I had in all my life? Unlucky me and the mother that bore me! for I am not a knight-errant and never expect to be one, and of all the mishaps, the greater part falls to my share."

"Then thou hast been thrashed too?" said Don Quixote.

"Didn't I say so? worse luck to my line!" said Sancho.

"Be not distressed, friend," said Don Quixote, "for I will now make the precious balsam with which we shall cure ourselves in the twinkling of an eye."

By this time the officer had succeeded in lighting the lamp, and came in to see the man that he thought had been killed; and as Sancho caught sight of him at the door, seeing him coming in his shirt, with a cloth on his head, and a lamp in his hand, and a very forbidding countenance, he said to his master, "Señor, can it be that this is the enchanted Moor coming back to give us more castigation if there be any thing still left in the ink-bottle?"

"It cannot be the Moor," answered Don Quixote, "for those under enchantment do not let themselves be seen by anyone."

"If they don't let themselves be seen, they let themselves be felt," said Sancho; "if not, let my shoulders speak to the point."

"Mine could speak too," said Don Quixote, "but that is not a sufficient reason for believing that what we see is the enchanted Moor."

The officer came up, and finding them engaged in such a peaceful conversation, stood amazed; though Don Quixote, to be sure, still lay on his back unable to move from pure pummelling and plasters. The officer turned to him and said, "Well, how goes it, good man?"

"I would speak more politely if I were you," replied Don Quixote; "is it the way of this country to address knights-errant in that style, you booby?"

The officer finding himself so disrespectfully treated by such a sorry-looking individual, lost his temper, and raising the lamp full of oil, smote Don Quixote such a blow with it on the head that he gave him a badly broken pate; then, all being in darkness, he went out, and Sancho Panza said, "That is certainly the enchanted Moor, señor, and he keeps the treasure for others, and for us only the cuffs and lamp-whacks."

"That is the truth," answered Don Quixote, "and there is no use in troubling oneself about these matters of enchantment or being angry or vexed at them, for as they are invisible and visionary we shall find no one on whom to avenge ourselves, do what we may; rise, Sancho, if thou canst, and call the alcaide of this fortress, and get him to give me a little oil, wine, salt, and rosemary to make the salutiferous balsam, for indeed I believe I have great need of it now, because I am losing much blood from the wound that phantom gave me."

Sancho got up with pain enough in his bones, and went after the innkeeper in the dark, and meeting the officer, who was looking to see what had become of his enemy, he said to him, "Señor, whoever you are, do us the favour and kindness to give us a little rosemary, oil, salt, and wine, for it is wanted to cure one of the best knights-errant on earth, who lies on yonder bed sorely wounded by the hands of the enchanted Moor that is in this inn."

When the officer heard him talk in this way, he took him for a man out of his senses, and as day was now beginning to break, he opened the inn gate, and calling the host, he told him what this good man wanted. The host furnished him with what he required, and Sancho brought it to Don Quixote, who, with his hand to his head, was bewailing the pain of the blow of the lamp, which had done him no more harm than raising a couple of rather large lumps, and what he fancied blood was only the sweat that flowed from him in his sufferings during the late storm. To be brief, he took the materials, of which he made a compound, mixing them all and boiling them a good while until it seemed to him they had come to perfection. He then asked for some vial to pour it into, and as there was not one in the inn, he decided on putting it into a tin oil-bottle or flask of which the host made him a free gift; and over the flask he repeated more than eighty paternosters and as many more ave-marias, salves, and credos, accompanying each word with a cross by way of benediction, at all which there were present Sancho, the innkeeper, and the officer; for the carrier was now peacefully engaged in attending to the comfort of his mules.

This being accomplished, he felt anxious to make trial himself, on the spot, of the virtue of this precious balsam, as he considered it, and so he drank near a quart of what could not be put into the flask and remained in the pipkin in which it had been boiled; but scarcely had he done drinking when he began to vomit in such a way that nothing was left in his stomach, and with the pangs and spasms of vomiting he broke into a profuse sweat, on account of which he bade them cover him up and leave him alone. They did so, and he lay sleeping more than three hours, at the end of which he awoke and felt very great bodily relief and so much ease from his bruises that he thought himself quite cured, and verily believed he had hit upon the balsam of Fierabras; and that with this remedy he might thenceforward, without any fear, face any kind of destruction, battle, or combat, however perilous it might be.

Sancho Panza, who also regarded the amendment of his master as miraculous, begged him to give him what was left in the pipkin, which was no small quantity. Don Quixote consented, and he, taking it with both hands, in good faith and with a better will, gulped down and drained off very little less than his master. But the fact is, that the stomach of poor Sancho was of necessity not so delicate as that of his master, and so, before vomiting, he was seized with such gripings and retchings, and such sweats and faintness, that verily and truly he believed his last hour had come, and finding himself so racked and tormented he cursed the balsam and the thief that had given it to him.

Don Quixote seeing him in this state said, "It is my belief, Sancho, that this mischief comes of thy not being dubbed a knight, for I am persuaded this liquor cannot be good for those who are not so."

"If your worship knew that," returned Sancho,—"woe betide me and all my kindred!—why did you let me taste it?"

At this moment the draught took effect, and the poor squire began to discharge both ways at such a rate that the rush mat on which he had thrown himself and the canvas blanket he had covering him were fit for nothing afterwards. He sweated and perspired with such paroxysms and convulsions that not only he himself but all present thought his end had come. This tempest and tribulation lasted about two hours, at the end of which he was left, not like his master, but so weak and exhausted that he could not stand. Don Quixote, however, who, as has been said, felt himself relieved and well, was eager to take his departure at once in quest of adventures, as it seemed to him that all the time he loitered there was a fraud upon the world and those in it who stood in need of his help and protection, all the more when he had the security and confidence his balsam afforded him; and so, urged by this impulse, he saddled Rocinante himself and put the pack-saddle on his squire's beast, whom likewise he helped to dress and mount the ass; after which he mounted his horse and turning to a corner of the inn he laid hold of a pike that stood there, to serve him by way of a lance. All that were in the inn, who were more than twenty persons, stood watching him; the inn-keeper's daughter was likewise observing him, and he too never took his eyes off her, and from time to time fetched a sigh that he seemed to pluck up from the depths of his bowels; but they all thought it must be from the pain he felt in his ribs; at any rate they who had seen him plastered the night before thought so.

As soon as they were both mounted, at the gate of the inn, he called to the host and said in a very grave and measured voice, "Many and great are the favours, Señor Alcaide, that I have received in this castle of yours, and I remain under the deepest obligation to be grateful to you for them all the days of my life; if I can repay them in avenging you of any arrogant foe who may have wronged you, know that my calling is no other than to aid the weak, to avenge those who suffer wrong, and to chastise perfidy. Search your memory, and if you find anything of this kind you need only tell me of it, and I promise you by the order of knighthood which I have received to procure you satisfaction and reparation to the utmost of your desire."

The innkeeper replied to him with equal calmness, "Sir Knight, I do not want your worship to avenge me of any wrong, because when any is done me I can take what vengeance seems good to me; the only thing I want is that you pay me the score that you have run up in the inn last night, as well for the straw and barley for your two beasts, as for supper and beds."

"Then this is an inn?" said Don Quixote.

"And a very respectable one," said the innkeeper.

"I have been under a mistake all this time," answered Don Quixote, "for in truth I thought it was a castle, and not a bad one; but since it appears that it is not a castle but an inn, all that can be done now is that you should excuse the payment, for I cannot contravene the rule of knights-errant, of whom I know as a fact (and up to the present I have read nothing to the contrary) that they never paid for lodging or anything else in the inn where they might be; for any hospitality that might be offered them is their due by law and right in return for the insufferable toil they endure in seeking adventures by night and by day, in summer and in winter, on foot and on horseback, in hunger and thirst, cold and heat, exposed to all the inclemencies of heaven and all the hardships of earth."

"I have little to do with that," replied the innkeeper; "pay me what you owe me, and let us have no more talk or chivalry, for all I care about is to get to my money."

"You are a stupid, scurvy innkeeper," said Don Quixote, and putting spurs to Rocinante and bringing his pike to the slope he rode out of the inn before anyone could stop him, and pushed on some distance without looking to see if his squire was following him.

The innkeeper when he saw him go without paying him ran to get payment of Sancho, who said that as his master would not pay neither would he, because, being as he was squire to a knight-errant, the same rule and reason held good for him as for his master with regard to not paying anything in inns and hostelries. At this the innkeeper waxed very wroth, and threatened if he did not pay to compel him in a way that he would not like. To which Sancho made answer that by the law of chivalry his master had received he would not pay a rap, though it cost him his life; for the excellent and ancient usage of knights-errant was not going to be violated by him, nor should the squires of such as were yet to come into the world ever complain of him or reproach him with breaking so just a law.

The ill-luck of the unfortunate Sancho so ordered it that among the company in the inn there were four wool-carders from Segovia, three needle-makers from the Colt of Cordova, and two lodgers from the Fair of Seville, lively fellows, tender-hearted, fond of a joke, and playful, who, almost as if instigated and moved by a common impulse, made up to Sancho and dismounted him from his ass, while one of them went in for the blanket of the host's bed; but on flinging him into it they looked up, and seeing that the ceiling was somewhat lower than what they required for their work, they decided upon going out into the yard, which was bounded by the sky, and there, putting Sancho in the middle of the blanket, they began to make sport with him as they would with a dog at Shrovetide. The cries of the poor blanketed wretch were so loud that they reached the ears of his master, who, halting to listen attentively, was persuaded that some new adventure was coming, until he clearly perceived that it was his squire who uttered them. Wheeling about he came up to the inn with a laborious gallop, and finding it shut went round it to see if he could find some way of getting in; but as soon as he came to the wall of the yard, which was not very high, he discovered the game that was being played with his squire. He saw him rising and falling in the air with such grace and nimbleness that, had his rage allowed him, it is my belief he would have laughed. He tried to climb from his horse on to the top of the wall, but he was so bruised and battered that he could not even dismount; and so from the back of his horse he began to utter such maledictions and objurgations against those who were blanketing Sancho as it would be impossible to write down accurately: they, however, did not stay their laughter or their work for this, nor did the flying Sancho cease his lamentations, mingled now with threats, now with entreaties, but all to little purpose, or none at all, until from pure weariness they left off. They then brought him his ass, and mounting him on top of it they put his jacket round him; and the compassionate Maritornes, seeing him so exhausted, thought fit to refresh him with a jug of water, and that it might be all the cooler she fetched it from the well. Sancho took it, and as he was raising it to his mouth he was stopped by the cries of his master exclaiming, "Sancho, my son, drink not water; drink it not, my son, for it will kill thee; see, here I have the blessed balsam (and he held up the flask of liquor), and with drinking two drops of it thou wilt certainly be restored."

At these words Sancho turned his eyes asquint, and in a still louder voice said, "Can it be your worship has forgotten that I am not a knight, or do you want me to end by vomiting up what bowels I have left after last night? Keep your liquor in the name of all the devils, and leave me to myself!" and at one and the same instant he left off talking and began drinking; but as at the first sup he perceived it was water he did not care to go on with it, and begged Maritornes to fetch him some wine, which she did with right good will, and paid for it with her own money; for indeed they say of her that, though she was in that line of life, there was some faint and distant resemblance to a Christian about her. When Sancho had done drinking he dug his heels into his ass, and the gate of the inn being thrown open he passed out very well pleased at having paid nothing and carried his point, though it had been at the expense of his usual sureties, his shoulders. It is true that the innkeeper detained his alforjas in payment of what was owing to him, but Sancho took his departure in such a flurry that he never missed them. The inkeeper, as soon as he saw him off, wanted to bar the gate close, but the blanketers would not agree to it, for they were fellows who would not have cared two farthings for Don Quixote, even had he been really one of the knights-errant of the Round Table.

CHAPTER XVIII

In which is related the discourse Sancho Panza held with his master, Don Quixote, together with other adventures worth relating

Sancho reached his master so limp and faint that he could not urge on his beast. When Don Quixote saw the state he was in he said, "I have now come to the conclusion, good Sancho, that this castle or inn is beyond a doubt enchanted, because those who have so atrociously diverted themselves with thee, what can they be but phantoms or beings of another world? and I hold this confirmed by having noticed that when I was by the wall of the yard witnessing the acts of thy sad tragedy, it was out of my power to mount upon it, nor could I even dismount from Rocinante, because they no doubt had me enchanted; for I swear to thee by the faith of what I am that if I had been able to climb up or dismount, I would have avenged thee in such a way that those braggart thieves would have remembered their freak for ever, even though in so doing I knew that I contravened the laws of chivalry, which, as I have often told thee, do not permit a knight to lay hands on him who is not one, save in case of urgent and great necessity in defence of his own life and person."

"I would have avenged myself too if I could," said Sancho, "whether I had been dubbed knight or not, but I could not; though for my part I am persuaded those who amused themselves with me were not phantoms or enchanted men, as your worship says, but men of flesh and bone like ourselves; and they all had their names, for I heard them name them when they were tossing me, and one was called Pedro Martinez, and another Tenorio Hernandez, and the innkeeper, I heard, was called Juan Palomeque the Left-handed; so that, señor, your not being able to leap over the wall of the yard or dismount from your horse came of something else besides enchantments; and what I make out clearly from all this is, that these adventures we go seeking will in the end lead us into such misadventures that we shall not know which is our right foot; and that the best and wisest thing, according to my small wits, would be for us to return home, now that it is harvest-time, and attend to our business, and give over wandering from Zeca to Mecca and from pail to bucket, as the saying is."

"How little thou knowest about chivalry, Sancho," replied Don Quixote; "hold thy peace and have patience; the day will come when thou shalt see with thine own eyes what an honourable thing it is to wander in the pursuit of this calling; nay, tell me, what greater pleasure can there be in the world, or what delight can equal that of winning a battle, and triumphing over one's enemy? None, beyond all doubt."

"Very likely," answered Sancho, "though I do not know it; all I know is that since we have been knights-errant, or since your worship has been one (for I have no right to reckon myself one of so honourable a number), we have never won any battle except the one with the Biscayan, and even out of that your worship came with half an ear and half a helmet the less; and from that till now it has been all cudgellings and more cudgellings, cuffs and more cuffs, I getting the blanketing over and above, and falling in with enchanted persons on whom I cannot avenge myself so as to know what the delight, as your worship calls it, of conquering an enemy is like."

"That is what vexes me, and what ought to vex thee, Sancho," replied Don Quixote; "but henceforward I will endeavour to have at hand some sword made by such craft that no kind of enchantments can take effect upon him who carries it, and it is even possible that fortune may procure for me that which belonged to Amadis when he was called 'The Knight of the Burning Sword,' which was one of the best swords that ever knight in the world possessed, for, besides having the said virtue, it cut like a razor, and there was no armour, however strong and enchanted it might be, that could resist it."

"Such is my luck," said Sancho, "that even if that happened and your worship found some such sword, it would, like the balsam, turn out serviceable and good for dubbed knights only, and as for the squires, they might sup sorrow."

"Fear not that, Sancho," said Don Quixote: "Heaven will deal better by thee."

Thus talking, Don Quixote and his squire were going along, when, on the road they were following, Don Quixote perceived approaching them a large and thick cloud of dust, on seeing which he turned to Sancho and said, "This is the day, O Sancho, on which will be seen the boon my fortune is reserving for me; this, I say, is the day on which as much as on any other shall be displayed the might of my arm, and on which I shall do deeds that shall remain written in the book of fame for all ages to come. Seest thou that cloud of dust which rises yonder? Well, then, all that is churned up by a vast army composed of various and countless nations that comes marching there."

"According to that there must be two," said Sancho, "for on this opposite side also there rises just such another cloud of dust."

Don Quixote turned to look and found that it was true, and rejoicing exceedingly, he concluded that they were two armies about to engage and encounter in the midst of that broad plain; for at all times and seasons his fancy was full of the battles, enchantments, adventures, crazy feats, loves, and defiances that are recorded in the books of chivalry, and everything he said, thought, or did had reference to such things. Now the cloud of dust he had seen was raised by two great droves of sheep coming along the same road in opposite directions, which, because of the dust, did not become visible until they drew near, but Don Quixote asserted so positively that they were armies that Sancho was led to believe it and say, "Well, and what are we to do, señor?"

"What?" said Don Quixote: "give aid and assistance to the weak and those who need it; and thou must know, Sancho, that this which comes opposite to us is conducted and led by the mighty emperor

Alifanfaron, lord of the great isle of Trapobana; this other that marches behind me is that of his enemy the king of the Garamantas, Pentapolin of the Bare Arm, for he always goes into battle with his right arm bare."

"But why are these two lords such enemies?" asked Sancho.

"They are at enmity," replied Don Quixote, "because this Alifanfaron is a furious pagan and is in love with the daughter of Pentapolin, who is a very beautiful and moreover gracious lady, and a Christian, and her father is unwilling to bestow her upon the pagan king unless he first abandons the religion of his false prophet Mahomet, and adopts his own."

"By my beard," said Sancho, "but Pentapolin does quite right, and I will help him as much as I can."

"In that thou wilt do what is thy duty, Sancho," said Don Quixote; "for to engage in battles of this sort it is not requisite to be a dubbed knight."

"That I can well understand," answered Sancho; "but where shall we put this ass where we may be sure to find him after the fray is over? for I believe it has not been the custom so far to go into battle on a beast of this kind."

"That is true," said Don Quixote, "and what you had best do with him is to leave him to take his chance whether he be lost or not, for the horses we shall have when we come out victors will be so many that even Rocinante will run a risk of being changed for another. But attend to me and observe, for I wish to give thee some account of the chief knights who accompany these two armies; and that thou mayest the better see and mark, let us withdraw to that hillock which rises yonder, whence both armies may be seen."

They did so, and placed themselves on a rising ground from which the two droves that Don Quixote made armies of might have been plainly seen if the clouds of dust they raised had not obscured them and blinded the sight; nevertheless, seeing in his imagination what he did not see and what did not exist, he began thus in a loud voice: "That knight whom thou seest yonder in yellow armour, who bears upon his shield a lion crowned crouching at the feet of a damsel, is the valiant Laurcalco, lord of the Silver Bridge; that one in armour with flowers of gold, who bears on his shield three crowns argent on an azure field, is the dreaded Micocolembo, grand duke of Quirocia; that other of gigantic frame, on his right hand, is the ever dauntless Brandabarbaran de Boliche, lord of the three Arabias, who for armour wears that serpent skin, and has for shield a gate which, according to tradition, is one of those of the temple that Samson brought to the ground when by his death he revenged himself upon his enemies; but turn thine eyes to the other side, and thou shalt see in front and in the van of this other army the ever victorious and never vanquished Timonel of Carcajona, prince of New Biscay, who comes in armour with arms quartered azure, vert, argent, and or, and bears on his shield a cat or on a field tawny with a motto which says *Miau,* which is the beginning of the name of his lady, who according to report is the peerless Miaulina, daughter of the duke Alfeñiquén of the Algarve; the other, who burdens and presses the loins of that powerful charger and bears arms white as snow and a shield blank and without any device, is a novice knight, a Frenchman by birth, Pierres Papin by name, lord of the baronies of Utrique; that other, who with iron-shod heels strikes the flanks of that nimble party-coloured zebra, and for arms bears azure cups, is the mighty duke of Nervia, Espartafilardo del Bosque, who bears for device on his shield an asparagus plant with a motto in Castilian that says, '*Rastrea mi suerte.*'" And so he went on naming a number of knights of one squadron or the other out of his imagination, and to all he assigned off-hand their arms, colours, devices, and mottoes, carried away by the illusions of his unheard-of craze; and without a pause, he continued, "People of divers nations compose this squadron in front; here are those that drink of the sweet waters of the famous Xanthus, those that scour the woody Massilian plains, those that sift the pure fine gold of Arabia Felix, those that enjoy the famed cool banks of the crystal Thermodon, those that in many and various ways divert the streams of the golden Pactolus, the Numidians, faithless in their promises, the Persians renowned in archery, the Parthians and the Medes that fight as they fly, the Arabs that ever shift their dwellings, the Scythians as cruel as they are fair, the Ethiopians with pierced lips, and an infinity of other nations whose features I recognise and descry, though I cannot recall their names. In this other squadron there come those that drink of the crystal streams of the olive-bearing Betis, those that make smooth their countenances with the water of the ever rich and golden Tagus, those that rejoice in the fertilising flow of the divine Genil, those that roam the Tartesian plains abounding in pasture, those that take their pleasure in the elysian meadows of Jerez, the rich Manchegans crowned with ruddy ears of corn, the wearers of iron, old relics of the Gothic race, those that bathe in the Pisuerga renowned for its gentle current, those that feed their herds along the spreading pastures of the winding Guadiana famed for its hidden course, those that tremble with the cold of the pine-clad Pyrenees or the dazzling snows of the lofty Apennine; in a word, as many as all Europe includes and contains."

Good God! what a number of countries and nations he named! giving to each its proper attributes with marvellous readiness; brimful and saturated with what he had read in his lying books! Sancho Panza hung upon his words without speaking, and from time to time turned to try if he could see the knights and giants his master was describing, and as he could not make out one of them he said to him, "Señor, devil take it if there's a sign of any man you talk of, knight or giant, in the whole thing; maybe it's all enchantment, like the phantoms last night."

"How canst thou say that!" answered Don Quixote; "dost thou not hear the neighing of the steeds, the braying of the trumpets, the roll of the drums?"

"I hear nothing but a great bleating of ewes and sheep," said Sancho; which was true, for by this time the two flocks had come close.

"The fear thou art in, Sancho," said Don Quixote, "prevents thee from seeing or hearing correctly, for one of the effects of fear is to derange the senses and make things appear different from what they are; if thou art in such fear, withdraw to one side and leave me to myself, for alone I suffice to bring victory to that side to which I shall give my aid;" and so saying he gave Rocinante the spur, and putting the lance in rest, shot down the slope like a thunderbolt. Sancho shouted after him, crying, "Come back, Señor Don Quixote; I vow to God they are sheep and ewes you are charging! Come back! Unlucky the father that begot me! what madness is this! Look, there is no giant, nor knight, nor cats, nor arms, nor shields quartered or whole, nor cups azure or bedevilled. What are you about? Sinner that I am before God!" But not for all these entreaties did Don Quixote turn back; on the contrary he went on shouting out, "Ho, knights, ye who follow and fight under the banners of the valiant emperor Pentapolin of the Bare Arm, follow me all; ye shall see how easily I shall give him his revenge over his enemy Alifanfaron of Trapobana."

So saying, he dashed into the midst of the squadron of ewes, and began spearing them with as much spirit and intrepidity as if he were transfixing mortal enemies in earnest. The shepherds and drovers accompanying the flock shouted to him to desist; but seeing it was no use, they ungirt their slings and began to salute his ears with stones as big as one's fist. Don Quixote gave no heed to the stones, but, letting drive right and left, kept saying, "Where art thou, proud Alifanfaron? Come before me; I am a single knight who would fain prove thy prowess hand to hand, and make thee yield thy life a penalty for the wrong thou dost to the valiant Pentapolin Garamanta." Here came a sugar-plum from the brook that struck him on the side and buried a couple of ribs in his body. Feeling himself so smitten, he imagined himself slain or badly wounded for certain, and recollecting his liquor he drew out his flask, and putting it to his mouth began to pour the contents into his stomach; but ere he had succeeded in swallowing what seemed to him enough, there came another almond which struck him on the hand and on the flask so fairly that it smashed it to pieces, knocking three or four teeth and grinders out of his mouth in its course, and sorely crushing two fingers of his hand. Such was the force of the first blow and of the second, that the poor knight in spite of himself came down backwards off his horse. The shepherds came up, and felt sure they had killed him; so in all haste they collected their flock together, took up the dead beasts, of which there were more than seven, and made off without waiting to ascertain anything further.

All this time Sancho stood on the hill watching the crazy feats his master was performing, and tearing his beard and cursing the hour and the occasion when fortune had made him acquainted with him.

Seeing him, then, brought to the ground, and that the shepherds had taken themselves off, he came down the hill and ran to him and found him in very bad case, though not unconscious; and said he, "Did I not tell you to come back, Señor Don Quixote; and that what you were going to attack were not armies but droves of sheep?"

"That's how that thief of a sage, my enemy, can alter and falsify things," answered Don Quixote; "thou must know, Sancho, that it is a very easy matter for those of his sort to make us take what form they choose; and this malignant being who persecutes me, envious of the glory he knew I was to win in this battle, has turned the squadrons of the enemy into droves of sheep. At any rate, do this much, I beg of thee, Sancho, to undeceive thyself, and see that what I say is true; mount thy ass and follow them quietly, and thou shalt see that when they have gone some little distance from this they will return to their original shape and, ceasing to be sheep, become men in all respects as I described them to thee at first. But go not just yet, for I want thy help and assistance; come hither and see how many of my teeth and grinders are missing, for I feel as if there was not one left in my mouth."

Sancho came so close that he almost put his eyes into his mouth; now just at that moment the balsam had acted on the stomach of Don Quixote, so, at the very instant when Sancho came to examine his mouth, he discharged all its contents with more force than a musket, and full into the beard of the compassionate squire.

"Holy Mary!" cried Sancho, "what is this that has happened me? Clearly this sinner is mortally wounded, as he vomits blood from the mouth;" but considering the matter a little more closely he perceived by the colour, taste, and smell, that it was not blood but the balsam from the flask which he had seen him drink; and he was taken with such a loathing that his stomach turned, and he vomited up his inside over his very master, and both were left in a precious state. Sancho ran to his ass to get something wherewith to clean himself, and relieve his master, out of his alforjas; but not finding them, he well-nigh took leave of his senses, and cursed himself anew, and in his heart resolved to quit his master and return home, even though he forfeited the wages of his service and all hopes of the government of the promised island.

Don Quixote now rose, and putting his left hand to his mouth to keep his teeth from falling out altogether, with the other he laid hold of the bridle of Rocinante, who had never stirred from his master's side — so loyal and well-behaved was he — and betook himself to where the squire stood leaning over his ass with his hand to his cheek, like one in deep dejection. Seeing him in this mood, looking so sad, Don Quixote said to him, "Bear in mind, Sancho, that one man is no more than another, unless he does more than another; all these tempests that fall upon us are signs that fair weather is coming shortly, and that things will go well with us, for it is impossible for good or evil to last for ever; and hence it follows that the evil having lasted long, the good must be now nigh at hand; so thou must not distress thyself at the misfortunes which happen to me, since thou hast no share in them."

"How have I not?" replied Sancho; "was he whom they blanketed yesterday perchance any other than my father's son? and the alforjas that are missing to-day with all my treasures, did they belong to any other but myself?"

"What! are the alforjas missing, Sancho?" said Don Quixote.

"Yes, they are missing," answered Sancho.

"In that case we have nothing to eat to-day," replied Don Quixote.

"It would be so," answered Sancho, "if there were none of the herbs your worship says you know in these meadows, those with which knights-errant as unlucky as your worship are wont to supply such-like shortcomings."

"For all that," answered Don Quixote, "I would rather have just now a quarter of bread, or a loaf and a couple of pilchards' heads, than all the herbs described by Dioscorides, even with Doctor Laguna's notes. Nevertheless, Sancho the Good, mount thy beast and come along with me, for God, who provides for all things, will not fail us (more especially when we are so active in his service as we are), since he fails not the midges of the air, nor the grubs of the earth, nor the tadpoles of the water, and is so merciful that he maketh his sun to rise on the evil and on the good, and sendeth rain on the just and on the unjust."

"Your worship would make a better preacher than knight-errant," said Sancho.

"Knights-errant knew and ought to know everything, Sancho," said Don Quixote; "for there were knights-errant in former times as well qualified to deliver a sermon or discourse in the middle of a highway, as if they had graduated in the University of Paris; whereby we may see that the lance has never blunted the pen, nor the pen the lance."

"Well, be it as your worship says," replied Sancho; "let us be off now and find some place of shelter for the night, and God grant it may be somewhere where there are no blankets, nor blanketeers, nor phantoms, nor enchanted Moors; for if there are, may the devil take the whole concern."

"Ask that of God, my son," said Don Quixote; "and do thou lead on where thou wilt, for this time I leave our lodging to thy choice; but reach me here thy hand, and feel with thy finger, and find out how many of my teeth and grinders are missing from this right side of the upper jaw, for it is there I feel the pain."

Sancho put in his fingers, and feeling about asked him, "How many grinders used your worship have on this side?"

"Four," replied Don Quixote, "besides the back-tooth, all whole and quite sound."

"Mind what you are saying, señor," said Sancho.

"I say four, if not five," answered Don Quixote, "for never in my life have I had tooth or grinder drawn, nor has any fallen out or been destroyed by any decay or rheum."

"Well, then," said Sancho, "in this lower side your worship has no more than two grinders and a half, and in the upper neither a half nor any at all, for it is all as smooth as the palm of my hand."

"Luckless that I am!" said Don Quixote, hearing the sad news his squire gave him; "I had rather they had despoiled me of an arm, so it were not the sword-arm; for I tell thee, Sancho, a mouth without teeth is like a mill without a millstone, and a tooth is much more to be prized than a diamond; but we who profess the austere order of chivalry are liable to all this. Mount, friend, and lead the way, and I will follow thee at whatever pace thou wilt."

Sancho did as he bade him, and proceeded in the direction in which he thought he might find refuge without quitting the high road, which was there very much frequented. As they went along, then, at a slow pace — for the pain in Don Quixote's jaws kept him uneasy and ill-disposed for speed — Sancho thought it well to amuse and divert him by talk of some kind, and among the things he said to him was that which will be told in the following chapter.

CHAPTER XIX

Of the shrewd discourse which Sancho held with his master, and of the adventure that befell him with a dead body, together with other notable occurrences

"It seems to me, señor, that all these mishaps that have befallen us of late have been without any doubt a punishment for the offence committed by your worship against the order of chivalry in not keeping the oath you made not to eat bread off a table-cloth or embrace the queen, and all the rest of it that your worship swore to observe until you had taken that helmet of Malandrino's, or whatever the Moor is called, for I do not very well remember."

"Thou art very right, Sancho," said Don Quixote, "but to tell the truth, it had escaped my memory; and likewise thou mayest rely upon it that the affair of the blanket happened to thee because of thy fault in not reminding me of it in time; but I will make amends, for there are ways of compounding for everything in the order of chivalry."

"Why! have I taken an oath of some sort, then?" said Sancho.

"It makes no matter that thou hast not taken an oath," said Don Quixote; "suffice it that I see thou art not quite clear of complicity; and whether or no, it will not be ill done to provide ourselves with a remedy."

"In that case," said Sancho, "mind that your worship does not forget this as you did the oath; perhaps the phantoms may take it into their heads to amuse themselves once more with me; or even with your worship if they see you so obstinate."

While engaged in this and other talk, night overtook them on the road before they had reached or discovered any place of shelter; and what made it still worse was that they were dying of hunger, for with the loss of the alforjas they had lost their entire larder and commissariat; and to complete the misfortune they met with an adventure which without any invention had really the appearance of one. It so happened that the night closed in somewhat darkly, but for all that they pushed on, Sancho feeling sure that as the road was the king's highway they might reasonably expect to find some inn within a league or two. Going along, then, in this way, the night dark, the squire hungry, the master sharp-set, they saw coming towards them on the road they were travelling a great number of lights which looked exactly like stars in motion. Sancho was taken aback at the sight of them, nor did Don Quixote altogether relish them: the one pulled up his ass by the halter, the other his hack by the bridle, and they stood still, watching anxiously to see what all this would turn out to be, and found that the lights were approaching them, and the nearer they came the greater they seemed, at which spectacle Sancho began to shake like a man dosed with mercury, and Don Quixote's hair stood on end; he, however, plucking up spirit a little, said, "This, no doubt, Sancho, will be a most mighty and perilous adventure, in which it will be needful for me to put forth all my valour and resolution."

"Unlucky me!" answered Sancho; "if this adventure happens to be one of phantoms, as I am beginning to think it is, where shall I find the ribs to bear it?"

"Be they phantoms ever so much," said Don Quixote, "I will not permit them to touch a thread of thy garments; for if they played tricks with thee the time before, it was because I was unable to leap the walls of the yard; but now we are on a wide plain, where I shall be able to wield my sword as I please."

"And if they enchant and cripple you as they did the last time," said Sancho, "what difference will it make being on the open plain or not?"

"For all that," replied Don Quixote, "I entreat thee, Sancho, to keep a good heart, for experience will tell thee what mine is."

"I will, please God," answered Sancho, and the two retiring to one side of the road set themselves to observe closely what all these moving lights might be; and very soon afterwards they made out some twenty encamisados, all on horseback, with lighted torches in their hands, the awe-inspiring aspect of whom completely extinguished the courage of Sancho, who began to chatter with his teeth like one in the cold fit of an ague; and his heart sank and his teeth chattered still more when they perceived distinctly that behind them there came a litter covered over with black and followed by six more mounted figures in mourning down to the very feet of their mules — for they could perceive plainly they were not horses by the easy pace at which they went. And as the encamisados came along they muttered to themselves in a low plaintive tone. This strange spectacle at such an hour and in such a solitary place was quite enough to strike terror into Sancho's heart, and even into his master's; and (save in Don Quixote's case) did so, for all Sancho's resolution had now broken down. It was just the opposite with his master, whose imagination immediately conjured up all this to him vividly as one of the adventures of his books. He took it into his head that the litter was a bier on which was borne some sorely wounded or slain knight, to avenge whom was a task reserved for him alone; and without any further reasoning he laid his lance in rest, fixed himself firmly in his saddle, and with gallant spirit and bearing took up his position in the middle of the road where the encamisados must of necessity pass; and as soon as he saw them near at hand he raised his voice and said, "Halt, knights, whosoever ye may be, and render me account of who ye are, whence ye come, what it is ye carry upon that bier, for, to judge by appearances, either ye have done some wrong or some wrong has been done to you, and it is fitting and necessary that I should know, either that I may chastise you for the evil ye have done, or else that I may avenge you for the injury that has been inflicted upon you."

"We are in haste," answered one of the encamisados, "and the inn is far off, and we cannot stop to render you such an account as you demand;" and spurring his mule he moved on.

Don Quixote was mightily provoked by this answer, and seizing the mule by the bridle he said, "Halt, and be more mannerly, and render an account of what I have asked of you; else, take my defiance to combat, all of you."

The mule was shy, and was so frightened at her bridle being seized that rearing up she flung her rider to the ground over her haunches. An attendant who was on foot, seeing the encamisado fall, began to abuse Don Quixote, who now moved to anger, without any more ado, laying his lance in rest charged one of the men in mourning and brought him badly wounded to the ground, and as he wheeled round upon the others the agility with which he attacked and routed them was a sight to see, for it seemed just as if wings had that instant grown upon Rocinante, so lightly and proudly did he bear himself. The encamisados were all timid folk and unarmed, so they speedily made their escape from the fray and set off at a run across the plain with their lighted torches, looking exactly like maskers running on some gala or festival night. The mourners, too, enveloped and swathed in their skirts and gowns, were unable to bestir themselves, and so with entire safety to himself Don Quixote belaboured them all and drove them off against their will, for they all thought it was no man but a devil from hell come to carry away the dead body they had in the litter.

Sancho beheld all this in astonishment at the intrepidity of his lord, and said to himself, "Clearly this master of mine is as bold and valiant as he says he is."

A burning torch lay on the ground near the first man whom the mule had thrown, by the light of which Don Quixote perceived him, and coming up to him he presented the point of the lance to his face, calling on him to yield himself prisoner, or else he would kill him; to which the prostrate man replied, "I am prisoner enough as it is; I cannot stir, for one of my legs is broken: I entreat you, if you be a Christian gentleman, not to kill me, which will be committing grave sacrilege, for I am a licentiate and I hold first orders."

"Then what the devil brought you here, being a churchman?" asked Don Quixote.

"What, señor?" said the other. "My bad luck."

"Then still worse awaits you," said Don Quixote, "if you do not satisfy me as to all I asked you at first."

"You shall be soon satisfied," said the licentiate; "you must know, then, that though just now I said I was a licentiate, I am only a bachelor, and my name is Alonzo Lopez; I am a native of Alcobendas, I come from the city of Baeza with eleven others, priests, the same who fled with the torches, and we are going to the city of Segovia accompanying a dead body which is in that litter, and is that of a gentleman who died in Baeza, where he was interred; and now, as I said, we are taking his bones to their burial-place, which is in Segovia, where he was born."

"And who killed him?" asked Don Quixote.

"God, by means of a malignant fever that took him," answered the bachelor.

"In that case," said Don Quixote, "the Lord has relieved me of the task of avenging his death had any other slain him; but, he who slew him having slain him, there is nothing for it but to be silent, and shrug one's shoulders; I should do the same were he to slay myself: and I would have your reverence know that I am a knight of La Mancha, Don Quixote by name, and it is my business and calling to roam the world righting wrongs and redressing injuries."

"I do not know how that about righting wrongs can be," said the bachelor, "for from straight you have made me crooked, leaving me with a broken leg that will never see itself straight again all the days of its life; and the injury you have redressed in my case has been to leave me injured in such a way that I shall remain injured for ever; and the height of misadventure it was to fall in with you who go in search of adventures."

"Things do not all happen in the same way," answered Don Quixote; "it all came, Sir Bachelor Alonzo Lopez, of your going, as you did, by night, dressed in those surplices, with lighted torches, praying, covered with mourning, so that naturally you looked like something evil and of the other world; and so I could not avoid doing my duty in attacking you, and I should have attacked you even had I known positively that you were the very devils of hell, for such I certainly believed and took you to be."

"As my fate has so willed it," said the bachelor, "I entreat you, sir knight-errant, whose errand has been such an evil one for me, to help me to get from under this mule that holds one of my legs caught between the stirrup and the saddle."

"I would have talked on till to-morrow," said Don Quixote; "how long were you going to wait before telling me of your distress?"

He at once called to Sancho, who, however, had no mind to come, as he was just then engaged in unloading a sumpter mule, well laden with provender, which these worthy gentlemen had brought with them. Sancho made a bag of his coat, and, getting together as much as he could, and as the mule's sack would hold, he loaded his beast, and then hastened to obey his master's call, and helped him to remove the bachelor from under the mule; then putting him on her back he gave him the torch, and Don Quixote bade him follow the track of his companions, and beg pardon of them on his part for the wrong which he could not help doing them.

And said Sancho, "If by chance these gentlemen should want to know who was the hero that served them so, your worship may tell them that he is the famous Don Quixote of La Mancha, otherwise called the Knight of the Rueful Countenance."

The bachelor then took his departure. I forgot to mention that before he did so he said to Don Quixote, "Remember that you stand excommunicated for having laid violent hands on a holy thing, *juxta illud, si quis, suadente diabolo.*"

"I do not understand that Latin," answered Don Quixote, "but I know well I did not lay hands, only this pike; besides, I did not think I was committing an assault upon priests or things of the Church, which, like a Catholic and faithful Christian as I am, I respect and revere, but upon phantoms and spectres of the other world; but even so, I remember how it fared with Cid Ruy Diaz when he broke the chair of the ambassador of that king before his Holiness the Pope, who excommunicated him for the same; and yet the good Roderick of Bivar bore himself that day like a very noble and valiant knight."

On hearing this the bachelor took his departure, as has been said, without making any reply; and Don Quixote asked Sancho what had induced him to call him the "Knight of the Rueful Countenance" more then than at any other time.

"I will tell you," answered Sancho; "it was because I have been looking at you for some time by the light of the torch held by that unfortunate, and verily your worship has got of late the most ill-favoured countenance I ever saw: it must be either owing to the fatigue of this combat, or else to the want of teeth and grinders."

"It is not that," replied Don Quixote, "but because the sage whose duty it will be to write the history of my achievements must have thought it proper that I should take some distinctive name as all knights of yore did; one being 'He of the Burning Sword,' another 'He of the Unicorn,' this one 'He of the Damsels,' that 'He of the Phœnix,' another 'The Knight of the Griffin,' and another 'He of the Death,' and by these names and designations they were known all the world round; and so I say that the sage aforesaid must have put it into your mouth and mind just now to call me 'The Knight of the Rueful Countenance,' as I intend to call myself from this day forward; and that the said name may fit me better, I mean, when the opportunity offers, to have a very rueful countenance painted on my shield."

"There is no occasion, señor, for wasting time or money on making that countenance," said Sancho; "for all that need be done is for your worship to show your own, face to face, to those who look at you, and without anything more, either image or shield, they will call you 'Him of the Rueful Countenance;' and believe me I am telling you the truth, for I assure you, señor (and in good part be it said), hunger and the loss of your grinders have given you such an ill-favoured face that, as I say, the rueful picture may be very well spared."

Don Quixote laughed at Sancho's pleasantry; nevertheless he resolved to call himself by that name, and have his shield or buckler painted as he had devised.

Don Quixote would have looked to see whether the body in the litter were bones or not, but Sancho would not have it, saying, "Señor, you have ended this perilous adventure more safely for yourself than any of those I have seen: perhaps these people, though beaten and routed, may bethink themselves that it is a single man that has beaten them, and feeling sore and ashamed of it may take heart and come in search of us and give us trouble enough. The ass is in proper trim, the mountains are near at hand, hunger presses, we have nothing more to do but make good our retreat, and, as the saying is, let the dead go to the grave and the living to the loaf;" and driving his ass before him he begged his master to follow, who, feeling that Sancho was right, did so without replying; and after proceeding some little distance between two hills they found themselves in a wide and retired valley, where they alighted, and Sancho unloaded his beast, and stretched upon the green grass, with hunger for sauce, they breakfasted, dined, lunched, and supped all at once, satisfying their appetites with more than one store of cold meat which the dead man's clerical gentlemen (who seldom put themselves on short allowance) had brought with them on their sumpter mule. But another piece of ill-luck befell them, which Sancho held the worst of all, and that was that they had no wine to drink, nor even water to moisten their lips; and as thirst tormented them, Sancho, observing that the meadow where they were was full of green and tender grass, said what will be told in the following chapter.

CHAPTER XX

Of the unexampled and unheard-of adventure which was achieved by the valiant Don Quixote of La Mancha with less peril than any ever achieved by any famous knight in the world

"It cannot be, señor, but that this grass is a proof that there must be hard by some spring or brook to give it moisture, so it would be well done to move a little farther on, that we may find some place where we may quench this terrible thirst that plagues us, which beyond a doubt is more distressing than hunger."

The advice seemed good to Don Quixote, and, he leading Rocinante by the bridle and Sancho the ass by the halter, after he had packed away upon him the remains of the supper, they advanced up the meadow feeling their way, for the darkness of the night made it impossible to see anything; but they had not gone two hundred paces when a loud noise of water, as if falling from great high rocks, struck their ears. The sound cheered them greatly; but halting to make out by listening from what quarter it came they heard unseasonably another noise which spoiled the satisfaction the sound of the water gave them, expecially for Sancho, who was by nature timid and faint-hearted; they heard, I say, strokes falling with a measured beat, and a certain rattling of iron and chains that, together with the furious din of the water, would have struck terror into any heart but Don Quixote's. The night was, as has been said, dark, and they had happened to reach a spot in among some tall trees, whose leaves stirred by a gentle breeze made a low ominous sound; so that, what with the solitude, the place, the darkness, the noise of the water, and the rustling of the leaves, everything inspired awe and dread; more especially as they perceived that the strokes did not cease, nor the wind lull, nor morning approach; to all which might be added their ignorance as to where they were. But Don Quixote, supported by his intrepid heart, leaped on Rocinante, and bracing his buckler on his arm, brought his pike to the slope, and said, "Friend Sancho, know that I by Heaven's will have been born in this our iron age to revive in it the age of gold, or the golden as it is called; I am he for whom perils, mighty achievements, and valiant deeds are reserved; I am, I say again, he who is to revive the Knights of the Round Table, the Twelve of France and the Nine Worthies; and he who is to consign to oblivion the Platirs, the Tablantes, the Olivantes and Tirantes, the Phœbuses and Belianises, with the whole herd of famous knights-errant of days gone by, performing in these in which I live such exploits, marvels, and feats of arms as shall obscure their brightest deeds. Thou dost mark well, faithful and trusty squire, the gloom of this night, its strange silence, the dull confused murmur of those trees, the awful sound of that water in quest of which we came, that seems as though it were precipitating and dashing itself down from the lofty mountains of the moon, and that incessant hammering that wounds and pains our ears; which things all together and each of itself are enough to instil fear, dread, and dismay into the breast of Mars himself, much more into one not used to hazards and adventures of the kind. Well, then, all this that I put before thee is but an incentive and stimulant to my spirit, making my heart burst in my bosom through eagerness to engage in this adventure, arduous as it promises to be; therefore tighten Rocinante's girths a little, and God be with thee; wait for me here three days and no more, and if in that time I come not back, thou canst return to our village, and thence, to do me a favour and a service, thou wilt go to El Toboso, where thou shalt say to my incomparable lady Dulcinea that her captive knight hath died in attempting things that might make him worthy of being called hers."

When Sancho heard his master's words he began to weep in the most pathetic way, saying, "Señor, I know not why your worship wants to attempt this so dreadful adventure; it is night now, no one sees us here, we can easily turn about and take ourselves out of danger, even if we don't drink for three days to come; and as there is no one to see us, all the less will there be anyone to set us down as cowards; besides, I have many a time heard the curate of our village, whom your worship knows well, preach that he who seeks danger perishes in it; so it is not right to tempt God by trying so tremendous a feat from which there can be no escape save by a miracle, and Heaven has performed enough of them for your worship in delivering you from being blanketed as I was, and bringing you out victorious and safe and sound from among all those enemies that were with the dead man; and if all this does not move or soften that hard heart, let this thought and reflection move it, that you will have hardly quitted this spot when from pure fear I shall yield my soul up to anyone that will take it. I left home and wife and children to come and serve your worship, trusting to do better and not worse; but, as covetousness bursts the bag, it has rent my hopes asunder, for just as I had them highest about getting that wretched unlucky island your worship has so often promised me, I see that instead and in lieu of it you mean to desert me now in a place so far from human reach: for God's sake, master mine, deal not so unjustly by me, and if your worship will not entirely give up attempting this feat, at least put it off till morning, for by what the lore I learned when I was a shepherd tells me it cannot want three hours of dawn now, because the mouth of the Horn is overhead and makes midnight in the line of the left arm."

"How canst thou see, Sancho," said Don Quixote, "where it makes that line, or where the mouth or head is that thou talkest of, when the night is so dark that there is not a star to be seen in the whole heaven?"

"That's true," said Sancho, "but fear has sharp eyes, and sees things underground, much more above in the heavens; besides, there is good reason to show that it now wants but little of day."

"Let it want what it may," replied Don Quixote, "it shall not be said of me now or at any time that tears or entreaties turned me aside from doing what was in accordance with knightly usage; and so I beg of thee, Sancho, to hold thy peace, for God, who has put it into my heart to undertake now this so unexampled and terrible adventure, will take care to watch over my safety and console thy sorrow; what thou hast to do is to tighten Rocinante's girths well, and wait here, for I shall come back shortly, alive or dead."

Sancho perceiving it his master's final resolve, and how little his tears, counsels, and entreaties prevailed with him, determined to have recourse to his own ingenuity and compel him if he could to wait till daylight; and so, while tightening the girths of the horse, he quietly and without being felt, tied both Rocinante's fore-legs, so that when Don Quixote strove to go he was unable as the horse could only move by jumps. Seeing the success of his trick, Sancho Panza said, "See there, señor! Heaven, moved by my tears and prayers, has so ordered it that Rocinante cannot stir; and if you will be obstinate, and spur and strike him, you will only provoke fortune, and kick, as they say, against the pricks."

Don Quixote at this grew desperate, but the more he drove his heels into the horse, the less he stirred him; and not having any suspicion of the tying, he was fain to resign himself and wait till daybreak or until Rocinante could move, firmly persuaded that all this came of something other than Sancho's ingenuity. So he said to him, "As it is so, Sancho, and as Rocinante cannot move, I am content to wait till dawn smiles upon us, even though I weep while it delays its coming."

"There is no need to weep," answered Sancho, "for I will amuse your worship by telling stories from this till daylight, unless indeed you like to dismount and lie down to sleep a little on the green grass after the fashion of knights-errant, so as to be fresher when day comes and the moment arrives for attempting this extraordinary adventure you are looking forward to."

"What art thou talking about dismounting or sleeping for?" said Don Quixote. "Am I, thinkest thou, one of those knights that take their rest in the presence of danger? Sleep thou who art born to sleep, or do as thou wilt, for I will act as I think most consistent with my character."

"Be not angry, master mine," replied Sancho, "I did not mean to say that;" and coming close to him he laid one hand on the pommel of the saddle and the other on the cantle, so that he held his master's left thigh in his embrace, not daring to separate a finger's length from him; so much afraid was he of the strokes which still resounded with a regular beat. Don Quixote bade him tell some story to amuse him as he had proposed, to which Sancho replied that he would if his dread of what he heard would let him; "Still," said he, "I will strive to tell a story which, if I can manage to relate it, and it escapes me not, is the best of stories, and let your worship give me your attention, for here I begin. What was, was; and may the good that is to come be for all, and the evil for him who goes to look for it — your worship must know that the beginning the old folk used to put to their tales was not just as each one pleased; it was a maxim of Cato Zonzorino the Roman that says 'the evil for him that goes to look for it,' and it comes as pat to the purpose now as ring to finger, to show that your worship should keep quiet and not go looking for evil in any quarter, and that we should go back by some other road, since nobody forces us to follow this in which so many terrors affright us."

"Go on with thy story, Sancho," said Don Quixote, "and leave the choice of our road to my care."

"I say then," continued Sancho, "that in a village of Estremadura there was a goat-shepherd — that is to say, one who tended goats — which shepherd or goatherd, as my story goes, was called Lope Ruiz, and this Lope Ruiz was in love with a shepherdess called Torralva, which shepherdess called Torralva was the daughter of a rich grazier, and this rich grazier" —

"If that is the way thou tellest thy tale, Sancho," said Don Quixote, "repeating twice all thou hast to say, thou wilt not have done these two days; go straight on with it, and tell it like a reasonable man, or else say nothing."

"Tales are always told in my country in the very way I am telling this," answered Sancho, "and I cannot tell it in any other, nor is it right of your worship to ask me to make new customs."

"Tell it as thou wilt," replied Don Quixote; "and as fate will have it that I cannot help listening to thee, go on."

"And so, lord of my soul," continued Sancho, "as I have said, this shepherd was in love with Torralva the shepherdess, who was a wild buxom lass with something of the look of a man about her, for she had little moustaches; I fancy I see her now."

"Then you knew her?" said Don Quixote.

"I did not know her," said Sancho, "but he who told me the story said it was so true and certain that when I told it to another I might safely declare and swear I had seen it all myself. And so in course of time, the devil, who never sleeps and puts everything in confusion, contrived that the love the shepherd bore the shepherdess turned into hatred and ill-will, and the reason, according to evil tongues, was some little jealousy she caused him that crossed the line and trespassed on forbidden ground; and so much did the shepherd hate her from that time forward that, in order to escape from her, he determined to quit the country and go where he should never set eyes on her again. Torralva, when she found herself spurned by Lope, was immediately smitten with love for him, though she had never loved him before."

"That is the natural way of women," said Don Quixote, "to scorn the one that loves them, and love the one that hates them: go on, Sancho."

"It came to pass," said Sancho, "that the shepherd carried out his intention, and driving his goats before him took his way across the plains of Estremadura to pass over into the Kingdom of Portugal, Torralva, who knew of it, went after him, and on foot and barefoot followed him at a distance, with a pilgrim's staff in her hand and a scrip round her neck, in which she carried, it is said, a bit of looking-glass, and a piece of a comb and some little pot or other of paint for her face; but let her carry what she did, I am not going to trouble myself to prove it; all I say is, that the shepherd, they say, came with his flock to cross over the river Guadiana, which was at that time swollen and almost overflowing its banks, and at the spot he came to there was neither ferry nor boat nor anyone to carry him or his flock to the other side, at which he was much vexed, for he perceived that Torralva was approaching and would give him great annoyance with her tears and entreaties; however, he went looking about so closely that he discovered a fisherman who had alongside of him a boat so small that it could only hold one person and one goat; but for all that he spoke to him and agreed with him to carry himself and his three hundred goats across. The fisherman got into the boat and carried one goat over; he came back and carried another over; he came back again, and again brought over another—let your worship keep count of the goats the fisherman is taking across, for if one escapes the memory there will be an end of the story, and it will be impossible to tell another word of it. To proceed, I must tell you the landing place on the other side was miry and slippery, and the fisherman lost a great deal of time in going and coming; still he returned for another goat, and another, and another."

"Take it for granted he brought them all across," said Don Quixote, "and don't keep going and coming in this way, or thou wilt not make an end of bringing them over this twelvemonth."

"How many have gone across so far?" said Sancho.

"How the devil do I know?" replied Don Quixote.

"There it is," said Sancho, "what I told you, that you must keep a good count; well then, by God, there is an end of the story, for there is no going any farther."

"How can that be?" said Don Quixote; "is it so essential to the story to know to a nicety the goats that have crossed over, that if there be a mistake of one in the reckoning, thou canst not go on with it?"

"No, señor, not a bit," replied Sancho; "for when I asked your worship to tell me how many goats had crossed, and you answered you did not know, at that very instant all I had to say passed away out of my memory, and faith, there was much virtue in it, and entertainment."

"So, then," said Don Quixote, "the story has come to an end?"

"As much as my mother has," said Sancho.

"In truth," said Don Quixote, "thou hast told one of the rarest stories, tales, or histories, that anyone in the world could have imagined, and such a way of telling it and ending it was never seen nor will be in a lifetime; though I expected nothing else from thy excellent understanding. But I do not wonder, for perhaps those ceaseless strokes may have confused thy wits."

"All that may be," replied Sancho, "but I know that as to my story, all that can be said is that it ends there where the mistake in the count of the passage of the goats begins."

"Let it end where it will, well and good," said Don Quixote, "and let us see if Rocinante can go;" and again he spurred him, and again Rocinante made jumps and remained where he was, so well tied was he. . . .

With this and other talk of the same sort master and man passed the night, till Sancho, perceiving that daybreak was coming on apace, very cautiously untied Rocinante and tied up his breeches. As soon as Rocinante found himself free, though by nature he was not at all mettlesome, he seemed to feel lively and began pawing—for as to capering, begging his pardon, he knew not what it meant. Don Quixote, then, observing that Rocinante could move, took it as a good sign and a signal that he should attempt the dread adventure. By this time day had fully broken and everything showed distinctly, and

Don Quixote saw that he was among some tall trees, chestnuts, which cast a very deep shade; he perceived likewise that the sound of the strokes did not cease, but could not discover what caused it, and so without any further delay he let Rocinante feel the spur, and once more taking leave of Sancho, he told him to wait for him there three days at most, as he had said before, and if he should not have returned by that time, he might feel sure it had been God's will that he should end his days in that perilous adventure. He again repeated the message and commission with which he was to go on his behalf to his lady Dulcinea, and said he was not to be uneasy as to the payment of his services, for before leaving home he had made his will, in which he would find himself fully recompensed in the matter of wages in due proportion to the time he had served; but if God delivered him safe, sound, and unhurt out of that danger, he might look upon the promised island as much more than certain. Sancho began weeping afresh on again hearing the affecting words of his good master, and resolved to stay with him until the final issue and end of the business. From these tears and this honourable resolve of Sancho Panza's the author of this history infers that he must have been of good birth and at least an old Christian; and the feeling he displayed touched his master somewhat, but not so much as to make him show any weakness; on the contrary, hiding what he felt as well as he could, he began to move towards that quarter whence the sound of the water and of the strokes seemed to come.

Sancho followed him on foot, leading by the halter, as his custom was, his ass, his constant comrade in prosperity or adversity; and advancing some distance through the shady chestnut trees they came upon a little meadow at the foot of some high rocks, down which a mighty rush of water flung itself. At the foot of the rocks were some rudely constructed houses looking more like ruins than houses, from among which came, they perceived, the din and clatter of blows, which still continued without intermission. Rocinante took fright at the noise of the water and of the blows, but quieting him Don Quixote advanced step by step towards the houses, commending himself with all his heart to his lady, imploring her support in that dread pass and enterprise, and on the way commending himself to God, too, not to forget him. Sancho, who never quitted his side, stretched his neck as far as he could and peered between the legs of Rocinante to see if he could now discover what it was that caused him such fear and apprehension. They went it might be a hundred paces farther, when on turning a corner the true cause, beyond the possibility of any mistake, of that dread-sounding and to them awe-inspiring noise that had kept them all the night in such fear and perplexity, appeared plain and obvious; and it was (if, reader, thou art not disgusted and disappointed) six fulling hammers which by their alternate strokes made all the din.

When Don Quixote perceived what it was, he was struck dumb and rigid from head to foot. Sancho glanced at him and saw him with his head bent down upon his breast in manifest mortification; and

Don Quixote glanced at Sancho and saw him with his cheeks puffed out and his mouth full of laughter, and evidently ready to explode with it, and in spite of his vexation he could not help laughing at the sight of him; and when Sancho saw his master begin he let go so heartily that he had to hold his sides with both hands to keep himself from bursting with laughter. Four times he stopped, and as many times did his laughter break out afresh with the same violence as at first, whereat Don Quixote grew furious, above all when he heard him say mockingly, "Thou must know, friend Sancho, that of Heaven's will I was born in this our iron age to revive in it the golden or age of gold; I am he for whom are reserved perils, mighty achievements, valiant deeds;" and here he went on repeating all or most of the words that Don Quixote uttered the first time they heard the awful strokes.

Don Quixote, then, seeing that Sancho was turning him into ridicule, was so mortified and vexed that he lifted up his pike and smote him two such blows that if, instead of catching them on his shoulders, he had caught them on his head, there would have been no wages to pay, unless indeed to his heirs. Sancho seeing that he was getting an awkward return in earnest for his jest, and fearing his master might carry it still further, said to him very humbly, "Calm yourself, sir, for by God I am only joking."

"Well, then, if you are joking I am not," replied Don Quixote. "Look here, my lively gentleman, if these, instead of being fulling hammers, had been some perilous adventure, have I not, think you, shown the courage required for the attempt and achievement? Am I, perchance, being, as I am, a gentleman, bound to know and distinguish sounds and tell whether they come from fulling mills or not; and that, when perhaps, as is the case, I have never in my life seen any as you have, low boor as you are, that have been born and bred among them? But turn me these six hammers into six giants, and bring them to beard me, one by one or all together, and if I do not knock them head over heels, then make what mockery you like of me."

"No more of that, señor," returned Sancho; "I own I went a little too far with the joke. But tell me, your worship, now that peace is made between us (and may God bring you out of all the adventures that may befall you as safe and sound as he has brought you out of this one), was it not a thing to laugh at, and is it not a good story, the great fear we were in?—at least that I was in; for as to your worship I see now that you neither know nor understand what either fear or dismay is."

"I do not deny," said Don Quixote, "that what happened to us may be worth laughing at, but it is not worth making a story about, for it is not everyone that is shrewd enough to hit the right point of a thing."

"At any rate," said Sancho, "your worship knew how to hit the right point with your pike, aiming at my head and hitting me on the shoulders, thanks be to God and my own smartness in dodging it.

But let that pass; all will come out in the scouring; for I have heard say 'he loves thee well that makes thee weep;' and moreover that it is the way with great lords after any hard words they give a servant to give him a pair of breeches; though I do not know what they give after blows, unless it be that knights-errant after blows give islands, or kingdoms on the mainland."

"It may be on the dice," said Don Quixote, "that all thou sayest will come true; overlook the past, for thou art shrewd enough to know that our first movements are not in our own control; and one thing for the future bear in mind, that thou curb and restrain thy loquacity in my company; for in all the books of chivalry that I have read, and they are innumerable, I never met with a squire who talked so much to his lord as thou dost to thine; and in fact I feel it to be a great fault of thine and of mine: of thine, that thou hast so little respect for me; of mine, that I do not make myself more respected. There was Gandalin, the squire of Amadis of Gaul, that was Count of the Insula Firme, and we read of him that he always addressed his lord with his cap in his hand, his head bowed down and his body bent double, *more turquesco*. And then, what shall we say of Gasabal, the squire of Galaor, who was so silent that in order to indicate to us the greatness of his marvellous taciturnity his name is only once mentioned in the whole of that history, as long as it is truthful? From all I have said thou wilt gather, Sancho, that there must be a difference between master and man, between lord and lackey, between knight and squire: so that from this day forward in our intercourse we must observe more respect and take less liberties, for in whatever way I may be provoked with you it will be bad for the pitcher. The favours and benefits that I have promised you will come in due time, and if they do not your wages at least will not be lost, as I have already told you."

"All that your worship says is very well," said Sancho, "but I should like to know (in case the time of favours should not come, and it might be necessary to fall back upon wages) how much did the squire of a knight-errant get in those days, and did they agree by the month, or by the day like bricklayers?"

"I do not believe," replied Don Quixote, "that such squires were ever on wages, but were dependent on favour; and if I have now mentioned thine in the sealed will I have left at home, it was with a view to what may happen; for as yet I know not how chivalry will turn out in these wretched times of ours, and I do not wish my soul to suffer for trifles in the other world; for I would have thee know, Sancho, that in this there is no condition more hazardous than that of adventurers."

"That is true," said Sancho, "since the mere noise of the hammers of a fulling mill can disturb and disquiet the heart of such a valiant errant adventurer as your worship; but you may be sure I will not open my lips henceforward to make light of anything of your worship's, but only to honour you as my master and natural lord."

"By so doing," replied Don Quixote, "shalt thou live long on the face of the earth; for next to parents, masters are to be respected as though they were parents."

CHAPTER XXI

Which treats of the exalted adventure and rich prize of Mambrino's helmet, together with other things that happened to our invincible knight

It now began to rain a little, and Sancho was for going into the fulling mills, but Don Quixote had taken such a disgust to them on account of the late joke that he would not enter them on any account; so turning aside to the right they came upon another road, different from that which they had taken the night before. Shortly afterwards Don Quixote perceived a man on horseback who wore on his head something that shone like gold, and the moment he saw him he turned to Sancho and said, "I think, Sancho, there is no proverb that is not true, all being maxims drawn from experience itself, the mother of all the sciences, especially that one that says, 'Where one door shuts, another opens.' I say so because if last night fortune shut the door of the adventure we were looking for against us, cheating us with the fulling mills, it now opens wide another one for another better and more certain adventure, and if I do not contrive to enter it, it will be my own fault, and I cannot lay it to my ignorance of fulling mills, or the darkness of the night. I say this because, if I mistake not, there comes towards us one who wears on his head the helmet of Mambrino, concerning which I took the oath thou rememberest."

"Mind what you say, your worship, and still more what you do," said Sancho, "for I don't want any more fulling mills to finish off fulling and knocking our senses out."

"The devil take thee, man," said Don Quixote; "what has a helmet to do with fulling mills?"

"I don't know," replied Sancho, "but, faith, if I might speak as I used, perhaps I could give such reasons that your worship would see you were mistaken in what you say."

"How can I be mistaken in what I say, unbelieving traitor?" returned Don Quixote; "tell me, seest thou not yonder knight coming towards us on a dappled grey steed, who has upon his head a helmet of gold?"

"What I see and make out," answered Sancho, "is only a man on a grey ass like my own, who has something that shines on his head."

"Well, that is the helmet of Mambrino," said Don Quixote; "stand to one side and leave me alone with him; thou shalt see how, without saying a word, to save time, I shall bring this adventure to an issue and possess myself of the helmet I have so longed for."

"I will take care to stand aside," said Sancho; "but God grant, I say once more, that it may be marjoram and not fulling mills."

"I have told thee, brother, on no account to mention those fulling mills to me again," said Don Quixote, "or I vow — and I say no more — I'll full the soul out of you."

Sancho held his peace in dread lest his master should carry out the vow he had hurled like a bowl at him.

The fact of the matter as regards the helmet, steed, and knight that Don Quixote saw, was this. In that neighbourhood there were two villages, one of them so small that it had neither apothecary's shop, nor barber, which the other that was close to it had, so the barber of the larger served the smaller, and in it there was a sick man who required to be bled and another man who wanted to be shaved, and on this errand the barber was going, carrying with him a brass basin; but as luck would have it, as he was on the way it began to rain, and not to spoil his hat, which probably was a new one, he put the basin on his head, and being clean it glittered at half a league's distance. He rode upon a grey ass, as Sancho said, and this was what made it seem to Don Quixote to be a dapple-grey steed and a knight and a golden helmet; for everything he saw he made to fall in with his crazy chivalry and ill-errant notions; and when he saw the poor knight draw near, without entering into any parley with him, at Rocinante's top speed he bore down upon him with the pike pointed low, fully determined to run him through and through, and as he reached him, without checking the fury of his charge, he cried to him, "Defend thyself, miserable being, or yield me of thine own accord that which is so reasonably my due."

The barber, who without any expectation or apprehension of it saw this apparition coming down upon him, had no other way of saving himself from the stroke of the lance but to let himself fall off his ass; and no sooner had he touched the ground than he sprang up more nimbly than a deer and sped away across the plain faster than the wind. He left the basin on the ground, with which Don Quixote contented himself, saying that the pagan had shown his discretion and imitated the beaver, which finding itself pressed by the hunters bites and cuts off with its teeth that for which, by its natural instinct, it knows it is pursued.

He told Sancho to pick up the helmet, and he taking it in his hands said, "By God the basin is a good one, and worth a real of eight if it is worth a maravedi," and handed it to his master, who immediately put it on his head, turning it round, now this way, now that, in search of the visor, and not finding it he said, "Clearly the pagan to whose measure this famous head-piece was first forged must have had a very large head; but the worst of it is half of it is wanting."

When Sancho heard him call the basin a head-piece he was unable to restrain his laughter, but remembering his master's wrath he checked himself in the midst of it.

"What art thou laughing at, Sancho?" said Don Quixote.

"I am laughing," said he, "to think of the great head the pagan must have had who owned this helmet, for it looks exactly like a regular barber's basin."

"Dost thou know what I suspect, Sancho?" said Don Quixote; "that this wonderful piece of this enchanted helmet must by some strange accident have come into the hands of some one who was unable to recognise or realise its value, and who, not knowing what he did, and seeing it to be of the purest gold, must have melted down one half for the sake of what it might be worth, and of the other made this which is like a barber's basin as thou sayest; but be it as it may, to me who recognise it, its transformation makes no difference, for I will set it to rights at the first village where there is a blacksmith, and in such style that that helmet the god of smithies forged for the god of battles shall not surpass it or even come up to it; and in the meantime I will wear it as well as I can, for something is better than nothing; all the more as it will be quite enough to protect me from any chance blow of a stone."

"That is," said Sancho, "if it is not shot with a sling as they were in the battle of the two armies, when they signed the cross on your worship's grinders and smashed the flask with that blessed draught that made me vomit my bowels up."

"It does not grieve me much to have lost it," said Don Quixote, "for thou knowest, Sancho, that I have the receipt in my memory."

"So have I," answered Sancho, "but if ever I make it, or try it again as long as I live, may this be my last hour; moreover, I have no intention of putting myself in the way of wanting it, for I mean, with all my five senses, to keep myself from being wounded or from wounding anyone: as to being blanketed again I say nothing, for it is hard to prevent mishaps of that sort, and if they come there is nothing for it but to squeeze our shoulders together, hold our breath, shut our eyes, and let ourselves go where luck and the blanket may send us."

"Thou art a bad Christian, Sancho," said Don Quixote on hearing this, "for once an injury has been done thee thou never forgettest it: but know that it is the part of noble and generous hearts not to attach importance to trifles. What lame leg hast thou got by it, what broken rib, what cracked head, that thou canst not forget that jest? For jest and sport it was, properly regarded, and had I not seen it in that light I would have returned and done more mischief in revenging thee than the Greeks did for the rape of Helen, who, if she were alive now, or if my Dulcinea had lived then, might depend upon it she would not be so famous for her beauty as she is;" and here he heaved a sigh and sent it aloft; and said Sancho, "Let it pass for a jest as it cannot be revenged in earnest, but I know what sort of jest and earnest it was, and I know it will never be rubbed out of my memory any more than off my shoulders. But putting that aside, will your worship tell me what are we to do with this dapple-grey steed that looks like a grey ass, which that Martino that your worship overthrew has left deserted here? for, from the way he took to his heels and bolted, he is not likely ever to come back for it; and by my beard but the grey is a good one."

"I have never been in the habit," said Don Quixote, "of taking spoil of those whom I vanquish, nor is it the practice of chivalry to take away their horses and leave them to go on foot, unless indeed it be that the victor have lost his own in the combat, in which case it is lawful to take that of the vanquished as a thing won in lawful war; therefore, Sancho, leave this horse, or ass, or whatever thou wilt have it to be; for when its owner sees us gone hence he will come back for it."

"God knows I should like to take it," returned Sancho, "or at least to change it for my own, which does not seem to me as good a one: verily the laws of chivalry are strict, since they cannot be stretched to let one ass be changed for another; I should like to know if I might at least change trappings."

"On that head I am not quite certain," answered Don Quioxte, "and the matter being doubtful, pending better information, I say thou mayest change them, if so be thou hast urgent need of them."

"So urgent is it," answered Sancho, "that if they were for my own person I could not want them more;" and forthwith, fortified by this licence, he effected the *mutatio capparum,* and rigged out his beast to the ninety-nines, making quite another thing of it. This done, they broke their fast on the remains of the spoils of war plundered from the sumpter mule, and drank of the brook that flowed from the fulling mills, without casting a look in that direction, in such loathing did they hold them for the alarm they had caused them; and, all anger and gloom removed, they mounted and, without taking any fixed road (not to fix upon any being the proper thing for true knights-errant), they set out, guided by Rocinante's will, which carried along with it that of his master, not to say that of the ass, which always followed him wherever he led, lovingly and sociably; nevertheless they returned to the high road, and pursued it at a venture without any other aim.

As they went along, then, in this way Sancho said to his master, "Señor, would your worship give me leave to speak a little to you? For since you laid that hard injunction of silence on me several things have gone to rot in my stomach, and I have now just one on the tip of my tongue that I don't want to be spoiled."

"Say on, Sancho," said Don Quixote, "and be brief in thy discourse, for there is no pleasure in one that is long."

"Well, then, señor," returned Sancho, "I say that for some days past I have been considering how little is got or gained by going in search of these adventures that your worship seeks in these wilds and cross-roads, where, even if the most perilous are victoriously achieved, there is no one to see or know of them, and so they must be left untold for ever, to the loss of your worship's object and the credit they deserve; therefore it seems to me it would be better (saving your worship's better judgment) if we were to go and serve some emperor or other great prince who may have some war on hand, in whose service your worship may prove the worth of your person, your great might, and greater understanding, on perceiving which the lord in whose service we may be will perforce have to reward us, each according to his merits; and there you will not be at a loss for some one to set down your achievements in writing so as to preserve their memory for ever. Of my own I say nothing, as they will not go beyond squirely limits, though I make bold to say that, if it be the practice in chivalry to write the achievements of squires, I think mine must not be left out."

"Thou speakest not amiss, Sancho," answered Don Quixote, "but before that point is reached it is requisite to roam the world, as it were on probation, seeking adventures, in order that, by achieving some, name and fame may be acquired, such that when he betakes himself to the court of some great monarch the knight may be already known by his deeds, and that the boys, the instant they see him enter the gate of the city, may all follow him and surround him, crying, 'This is the Knight of the Sun'—or the Serpent, or any other title under which he may have achieved great deeds. 'This,' they will say, 'is he who vanquished in single combat the gigantic Brocabruno of mighty strength; he who delivered the great Mameluke of Persia out of the long enchantment under which he had been for almost nine hundred years.' So from one to another they will go proclaiming his achievements; and presently at the tumult of the boys and the others the king of that kingdom will appear at the windows of his royal palace, and as soon as he beholds the knight, recognising him by his arms and the device on his shield, he will as a matter of course say, 'What ho! Forth all ye, the knights of my court, to receive the flower of chivalry who cometh hither!' At which command all will issue forth, and he himself, advancing half-way down the stairs, will embrace him closely, and salute him, kissing him on the cheek, and will then lead him to the queen's chamber, where the knight will find her with the princess her daughter, who will be one of the most beautiful and accomplished damsels that could with the utmost pains be discovered anywhere in the known world. Straightway it will come to pass that she will fix her eyes upon the knight and he his upon her, and each will seem to the other something more divine than human, and, without knowing how or why, they will be taken and entangled in the inextricable toils of love, and sorely distressed in their hearts not to see any way of making their pains and sufferings known by speech. Thence they will lead him, no doubt, to some richly adorned chamber of the palace, where, having removed his armour, they will bring him a rich mantle of scarlet wherewith to robe himself, and if he looked noble in his armour he will look still more so in a doublet. When night comes he will sup with the king, queen, and princess; and all the time he will never take his eyes off her, stealing stealthy glances, unnoticed by those present, and she will do the same, and with equal cautiousness, being, as I have said, a damsel of great discretion. The tables being removed, suddenly through the door of the hall there will enter a hideous and diminutive dwarf followed by a fair dame, between two giants, who comes with a certain adventure, the work of an ancient sage; and he who shall achieve it shall be deemed the best knight in the world. The king will then command all those present to essay it, and none will bring it to an end and conclusion save the stranger knight, to the great enhancement of his fame, whereat the princess will be overjoyed and will esteem herself happy and fortunate in having fixed and placed her thoughts so high. And the best of it is that this king, or prince, or whatever he is, is engaged in a very bitter war with another as powerful as himself, and the stranger knight, after having been some days at his court, requests leave from him to go and serve him in the said war. The king will grant it very readily, and the knight will courteously kiss his hands for the favour done to him; and that night he will take leave of his lady the princess at the grating of the chamber where she sleeps, which looks upon a garden, and at which he has already many times conversed with her, the go-between and confidante in the matter being a damsel much trusted by the princess. He will sigh, she will swoon, the damsel will fetch water, he will be distressed because morning approaches, and for the honour of his lady he would not that they were discovered; at last the princess will come to herself and will present her white hands through the grating to the knight, who will kiss them a thousand and a thousand times, bathing them with his tears. It will be arranged between them how they are to inform each other of their good or evil fortunes, and the princess will entreat him to make his absence as short as possible, which he will promise to do with many oaths; once more he kisses her hands, and takes his leave in such grief that he is well-nigh ready to die. He betakes him thence to his chamber, flings himself on his bed, cannot sleep for sorrow at parting, rises early in the morning, goes to take leave of the king, queen, and princess, and, as he takes his leave of the pair, it is told him that the princess is indisposed and cannot receive a visit; the knight thinks it is from grief at his departure, his heart is pierced, and he is hardly able to keep from showing his pain. The confidante is present, observes all, goes to tell her mistress, who listens with tears and says that one of her greatest distresses is not knowing who this knight is, and whether he is of kingly lineage or not; the damsel assures her that so much courtesy, gentleness, and gallantry of bearing as her knight possesses could not exist in any save one who was royal and illustrious; her anxiety is thus relieved, and she strives to be of good cheer lest she should excite suspicion in her parents, and at the end of two days she appears in public. Meanwhile the knight has taken his departure; he fights in the war, conquers the king's enemy, wins many cities, triumphs in many battles, returns to the court, sees his lady where he was wont to see her, and it is agreed that he shall demand her in marriage of her parents as the reward of his services; the king is unwilling to give her, as he knows not who he is, but nevertheless, whether carried off or in whatever other way it may be, the princess comes to be his bride, and her father comes to regard it as very good fortune; for it so happens that this knight is proved to be the son of a valiant king of some kingdom, I know not what, for I fancy it is not likely to be on the map; the father dies, the princess inherits, and in two words the knight becomes king. And here comes in at once the bestowal of rewards upon his squire and all who have aided him in rising to so exalted a rank. He marries his squire to a damsel of the princess's, who will be, no doubt, the one who was confidante in their amour, and is daughter of a very great duke."

"That's what I want, and no mistake about it!" said Sancho. "That's what I'm waiting for; for all this, word for word, is in store for your worship under the title of The Knight of the Rueful Countenance."

"Thou needst not doubt it, Sancho," replied Don Quixote, "for in the same manner, and by the same steps as I have described here, knights-errant rise and have risen to be kings and emperors; all we want now is to find out what king, Christian or pagan, is at war and has a beautiful daughter; but there will be time enough to think of that, for, as I have told thee, fame must be won in other quarters before repairing to the court. There is another thing, too, that is wanting; for supposing we find a king who is at war and has a beautiful daughter, and that I have won incredible fame throughout the universe, I know not how it can be made out that I am of royal lineage, or even second cousin to an emperor; for the king will not be willing to give me his daughter in marriage unless he is first thoroughly satisfied on this point, however much my famous deeds may deserve it; so that by this deficiency I fear I shall lose what my arm has fairly earned. True it is I am a gentleman of a known house, of estate and property, and entitled to the five hundred sueldos mulct; and it may be that the sage who shall write my history will so clear up my ancestry and pedigree that I may find myself fifth or sixth in descent from a king; for I would have thee know, Sancho, that there are two kinds of lineages in the world; some there be tracing and deriving their descent from kings and princes, whom time has reduced little by little until they end in a point like a pyramid upside down; and others who spring from the common herd and go on rising step by step until they come to be great lords; so that the difference is that the one were what they no longer are, and the others are what they formerly were not. And I may be of such that after investigation my origin may prove great and famous, with which the king, my father-in-law that is to be, ought to be satisfied; and should he not be, the princess will so love me that even though she well knew me to be the son of a water-carrier, she will take me for her lord and husband in spite of her father; if not, then it comes to seizing her and carrying her off where I please; for time or death will put an end to the wrath of her parents."

"It comes to this, too," said Sancho, "what some naughty people say, 'Never ask as a favour what thou canst take by force;' though it would fit better to say, 'A clear escape is better than good men's prayers.' I say so because if my lord the king, your worship's father-in-law, will not condescend to give you my lady the princess, there is nothing for it but, as your worship says, to seize her and transport her. But the mischief is that until peace is made and you come into the peaceful enjoyment of your kingdom, the poor squire is famishing as far as rewards go, unless it be that the confidante damsel that is to be his wife comes with the princess, and that with her he tides over his bad luck until Heaven otherwise orders things; for his master, I suppose, may as well give her to him at once for a lawful wife."

"Nobody can object to that," said Don Quixote.

"Then since that may be," said Sancho, "there is nothing for it but to commend ourselves to God, and let fortune take what course it will."

"God guide it according to my wishes and thy wants," said Don Quixote, "and mean be he who makes himself mean."

"In God's name let him be so," said Sancho; "I am an old Christian, and to fit me for a count that's enough."

"And more than enough for thee," said Don Quixote; "and even wert thou not, it would make no difference, because I being the king can easily give thee nobility without purchase or service rendered by thee, for when I make thee a count, then thou art at once a gentleman; and they may say what they will, but by my faith they will have to call thee 'your lordship,' whether they like it or not."

"Not a doubt of it; and I'll know how to support the tittle," said Sancho.

"Title thou shouldst say, not tittle," said his master.

"So be it," answered Sancho, "I say I will know how to behave, for once in my life I was beadle of a brotherhood, and the beadle's gown sat so well on me that all said I looked as if I was fit to be steward of the same brotherhood. What will it be, then, when I put a duke's robe on my back, or dress myself in gold and pearls like a foreign count? I believe they will come a hundred leagues to see me."

"Thou wilt look well," said Don Quixote, "but thou must shave thy beard often, for thou hast it so thick and rough and unkempt, that if thou dost not shave it every second day at least, they will see what thou art at the distance of a musket shot."

"What more will it be," said Sancho, "than having a barber, and keeping him at wages in the house? and even if it be necessary, I will make him go behind me like a nobleman's equerry."

"Why, how dost thou know that noblemen have equerries behind them?" asked Don Quixote.

"I will tell you," answered Sancho. "Years ago I was for a month at the capital, and there I saw taking the air a very small gentleman who they said was a very great man, and a man following him on horseback in every turn he took, just as if he was his tail. I asked why this man did not join the other man, instead of always going behind him; they answererd me that he was his equerry, and that it was the custom with nobles to have such persons behind them, and ever since then I know it, for I have never forgotten it."

"Thou art right," said Don Quixote, "and in the same way thou mayest carry thy barber with thee, for customs did not come into use all together, nor were they all invented at once, and thou mayest be the first count to have a barber to follow him; and, indeed, shaving one's beard is a greater trust than saddling one's horse."

"Let the barber business be my look-out," said Sancho; "and your worship's be it to strive to become a king, and make me a count."

"So it shall be," answered Don Quixote, and raising his eyes he saw what will be told in the following chapter.

PART TWO

[Don Quixote and Sancho return home at the end of Part One. Part Two deals with the third sally. In Chapter V, Sancho announces their resolve to launch out again to his wife, Teresa.]

CHAPTER V

Of the shrewd and droll conversation that passed between Sancho Panza and his wife Teresa Panza, and other matters worthy of being duly recorded

The translator of this history, when he comes to write this fifth chapter, says that he considers it apocryphal, because in it Sancho Panza speaks in a style unlike that which might have been expected from his limited intelligence, and says things so subtle that he does not think it possible he could have conceived them; however, desirous of doing what his task imposed upon him, he was unwilling to leave it untranslated, and therefore he went on to say:

Sancho came home in such glee and spirits that his wife noticed his happiness a bowshot off, so much so that it made her ask him, "What have you got, Sancho friend, that you are so glad?"

To which he replied, "Wife, if it were God's will, I should be very glad not to be so well pleased as I show myself."

"I don't understand you, husband," said she, "and I don't know what you mean by saying you would be glad, if it were God's will, not to be well pleased; for, fool as I am, I don't know how one can find pleasure in not having it."

"Hark ye, Teresa," replied Sancho, "I am glad because I have made up my mind to go back to the service of my master Don Quixote, who means to go out a third time to seek for adventures; and I am going with him again, for my necessities will have it so, and also the hope that cheers me with the thought that I may find another hundred crowns like those we have spent; though it makes me sad to have to leave thee and the children; and if God would be pleased to let me have my daily bread, dry-shod and at home, without taking me out into the byways and cross-roads — and he could do it at small cost by merely willing it — it is clear my happiness would be more solid and lasting, for the happiness I have is mingled with sorrow at leaving thee; so that I was right in saying I would be glad, if it were God's will, not to be well pleased."

"Look here, Sancho," said Teresa; "ever since you joined on to a knight-errant you talk in such a roundabout way that there is no understanding you."

"It is enough that God understands me, wife," replied Sancho; "for he is the understander of all things; that will do; but mind, sister, you must look to Dapple carefully for the next three days, so that he may be fit to take arms; double his feed, and see to the pack-saddle and other harness, for it is not to a wedding we are bound, but to go round the world, and play at give and take with giants and dragons and monsters, and hear hissings and roarings and bellowings and howlings; and even all this would be lavender, if we had not to reckon with Yanguesans and enchanted Moors."

"I know well enough, husband," said Teresa, "that squires-errant don't eat their bread for nothing, and so I will be always praying to our Lord to deliver you speedily from all that hard fortune."

"I can tell you, wife," said Sancho, "if I did not expect to see myself governor of an island before long, I would drop down dead on the spot."

"Nay, then, husband," said Teresa; "let the hen live, though it be with her pip; live, and let the devil take all the governments in the world; you came out of your mother's womb without a government, you have lived until now without a government, and when it is God's will you will go, or be carried, to your grave without a government. How many there are in the world who live without a government, and continue to live all the same, and are reckoned in the number of the people. The best sauce in the world is hunger, and as the poor are never without that, they always eat with a relish. But mind, Sancho, if by good luck you should find yourself with some government, don't forget me and your children. Remember that Sanchico is now full fifteen, and it is right he should go to school, if his uncle the abbot has a mind to have him trained for the Church. Consider, too, that your daughter Mari-Sancha will not die of grief if we marry her; for I have my suspicions that she is as eager to get a husband as you to get a government; and, after all, a daughter looks better ill married than well kept."

"By my faith," replied Sancho, "if God brings me to get any sort of a government, I intend, wife, to make such a high match for Mari-Sancha that there will be no approaching her without calling her 'my lady.'"

"Nay, Sancho," returned Teresa; "marry her to her equal, that is the safest plan; for if you put her out of wooden clogs into high-heeled shoes, out of her grey flannel petticoat into hoops and silk gowns, out of the plain 'Marica' and 'thou,' into 'Doña So-and-so' and 'my lady,' the girl won't know where she is, and at every turn she will fall into a thousand blunders that will show the thread of her coarse homespun stuff."

"Tut, you fool," said Sancho; "it will be only to practise it for two or three years; and then dignity and decorum will fit her as easily as a glove; and if not, what matter? Let her be 'my lady,' and never mind what happens."

"Keep to your own station, Sancho," replied Teresa; "don't try to raise yourself higher, and bear in mind the proverb that says, 'wipe the nose of your neighbour's son, and take him into your house.' A fine thing it would be, indeed, to marry our Maria to some great count or grand gentleman, who, when the humour took him, would abuse her and call her clownbred and clodhopper's daughter and spinning wench. I have not been bringing up my daughter for that all this time, I can tell you, husband. Do you bring home money, Sancho, and leave marrying her to my care; there is Lope Tocho, Juan Tocho's son, a stout, sturdy young fellow that we know, and I can see he does not look sour at the girl; and with him, one of our own sort, she will be well married, and we shall have her always under our eyes, and be all one family, parents and children, grandchildren and sons-in-law, and the peace and blessing of God will dwell among us; so don't you go marrying her in those courts and grand palaces where they won't know what to make of her, or she what to make of herself."

"Why, you idiot and wife for Barabbas," said Sancho, "what do you mean by trying, without why or wherefore, to keep me from marrying my daughter to one who will give me grandchildren that will be called 'your lordship'? Look ye, Teresa, I have always heard my elders say that he who does not know how to take advantage of luck when it comes to him, has no right to complain if it gives him the go-by; and now that it is knocking at our door, it will not do to shut it out; let us go with the favouring breeze that blows upon us." (It is this sort of talk, and what Sancho says lower down, that made the translator of the history say he considered this chapter apocryphal.) "Don't you see, you animal," continued Sancho, "that it will be well for me to drop into some profitable government that will lift us out of the mire, and marry Mari-Sancha to whom I like; and you yourself will find yourself called 'Doña Teresa Panza,' and sitting in church on a fine carpet and cushions and draperies, in spite and in defiance of all the born ladies of the town? No, stay as you are, growing neither greater nor less, like a tapestry figure — Let us say no more about it, for Sanchica shall be a countess, say what you will."

"Are you sure of all you say, husband?" replied Teresa. "Well, for all that, I am afraid this rank of countess for my daughter will be her ruin. You do as you like, make a duchess or a princess of her, but I can tell you it will not be with my will and consent. I was always a lover of equality, brother, and I can't bear to see people give themselves airs without any right. They called me Teresa at my baptism, a plain, simple name, without any additions or tags or fringes of Dons or Doñas; Cascajo was my father's name, and as I am your wife, I am called Teresa Panza, though by right I ought to be called Teresa Cascajo; but 'kings go where laws like,' and I am content with this name without having the 'Don' put on top of it to make it so heavy that I cannot carry it; and I don't want to make people talk about me when they see me go dressed like a countess or governor's wife; for they will say at once, 'See what airs the slut gives herself! Only yesterday she was always spinning flax, and used to go to mass with the tail of her petticoat over her head instead of a mantle, and there she goes to-day in a hooped gown with her brooches and airs, as if we didn't know her!' If God keeps me in my seven senses, or five, or whatever number I have, I am not going to bring myself to such a pass; go you, brother, and be a government or an island man, and swagger as much as you like; for by the soul of my mother, neither my daughter nor I are going to stir a step from our village; a respectable woman should have a broken leg and keep at home; and to be busy at something is a virtuous damsel's holiday; be off to your adventures along with your Don Quixote, and leave us to our misadventures, for God will mend them for us according as we deserve it. I don't know, I'm sure, who fixed the 'Don' to him, what neither his father nor grandfather ever had."

"I declare thou hast a devil of some sort in thy body!" said Sancho. "God help thee, woman, what a lot of things thou hast strung together, one after the other, without head or tail! What have Cascajo, and the brooches and the proverbs and the airs, to do with what I say? Look here, fool and dolt (for so I may call you, when you don't understand my words, and run away from good fortune), if I had said that my daughter was to throw herself down from a tower, or go roaming the world, as the Infanta Doña Urraca wanted to do, you would be right in not giving way to my will; but if in an instant, in less than the twinkling of an eye, I put the 'Don' and 'my lady' on her back, and take her out of the stubble, and place her under a canopy, on a daïs, and on a couch, with more velvet cushions than all the Almohades of Morocco ever had in their family, why won't you consent and fall in with my wishes?"

"Do you know why, husband?" replied Teresa; "because of the proverb that says 'who covers thee, discovers thee.' At the poor man people only throw a hasty glance; on the rich man they fix their eyes; and if the said rich man was once on a time poor, it is then there is the sneering and the tattle and spite of backbiters; and in the streets here they swarm as thick as bees."

"Look here, Teresa," said Sancho, "and listen to what I am now going to say to you; maybe you never heard it in all your life; and I do not give my own notions, for what I am about to say are the opinions of his reverence the preacher, who preached in this town last Lent, and who said, if I remember rightly, that all things present that our eyes behold, bring themselves before us, and remain and fix themselves on our memory much better and more forcibly than things past." (These observations which Sancho makes here are the other ones on account of which the translator says he regards this chapter as apocryphal, inasmuch as they are beyond Sancho's capacity.) "Whence it arises," he continued, "that when we see any person well dressed and making a figure with rich garments and retinue of servants, it seems to lead and impel us perforce to respect him, though memory may at the same moment recall to us some lowly condition in which we have seen him, but which, whether it may have been poverty or low birth, being now a thing of the past, has no existence; while the only thing that has any existence is what we see before us; and if this person whom fortune has raised from his original lowly state (these were the very words the padre used) to his present height of prosperity, be well bred, generous, courteous to all, without seeking to vie with those whose nobility is of ancient date, depend upon it, Teresa, no one will remember what he was, and every one will respect what he is, except indeed the envious, from whom no fair fortune is safe."

"I do not understand you, husband," replied Teresa; "do as you like, and don't break my head with any more speechifying and rhetoric; and if you have revolved to do what you say"—

"Resolved, you should say, woman," said Sancho, "not revolved."

"Don't set yourself to wrangle with me, husband," said Teresa; "I speak as God pleases, and don't deal in out-of-the-way phrases; and I say if you are bent upon having a government, take your son Sancho with you, and teach him from this time on how to hold a government; for sons ought to inherit and learn the trades of their fathers."

"As soon as I have the government," said Sancho, "I will send for him by post, and I will send thee money, of which I shall have no lack, for there is never any want of people to lend it to governors when they have not got it; and do thou dress him so as to hide what he is and make him look what he is to be."

"You send the money," said Teresa, "and I'll dress him up for you as fine as you please."

"Then we are agreed that our daughter is to be a countess," said Sancho.

"The day that I see her a countess," replied Teresa, "it will be the same to me as if I was burying her; but once more I say do as you please, for we women are born to this burden of being obedient to our husbands, though they be dogs;" and with this she began to weep in downright earnest, as if she already saw Sanchica dead and buried.

Sancho consoled her by saying that though he must make her a countess, he would put it off as long as possible. Here their conversation came to an end, and Sancho went back to see Don Quixote, and make arrangements for their departure.

[Additional selected readings: Chapters 30–33, 35, the episode of the Duke and Duchess; Chapters 45, 47, 50, 53, Sancho and his Island; Chapters 64, 72–74, Don Quixote's return home and death.]

SELECTED GENERAL BIBLIOGRAPHY

Allen, Don C., "Latin Literature," a survey of recent scholarship in the period of the Renaissance, *Mod. Lang. Quar.*, II (1941), 403–20.

Cambridge Modern History, I. *The Renaissance,* Cambridge Univ. Press, 1902.

Epistolae Obscurorum Virorum, ed. and trans. F. G. Stokes, London, Chatto & Windus, 1909.

Ferguson, Wallace K., *The Renaissance in Historical Thought: Five Centuries of Interpretation,* Boston, Houghton Mifflin, 1948.

Gilmore, Myron P., *The World of Humanism: 1453–1517,* New York, Harpers, 1952.

Haydn, Hiram, *The Counter-Renaissance,* New York, Scribners, 1950.

Herford, Charles H., *The Literary Relations of England and Germany in the Sixteenth Century,* Cambridge Univ. Press, 1886.

Highet, Gilbert, *The Classical Tradition: Greek and Roman Influence on Western Literature,* Oxford Univ. Press, 1949.

Lee, Vernon, *Euphorion: Studies of the Antique and the Mediaeval in the Renaissance,* London, Unwin, 1885.

Matthews, G. M., "Sex and the Sonnet," *Essays in Criticism,* II (1952), 119–37.

Matthiessen, F. O., *Translation: An Elizabethan Art,* Harvard Univ. Press, 1931.

Pater, Walter, *The Renaissance. Studies in Art and Poetry,* Macmillan, 1873.

Spingarn, J. E., *A History of Literary Criticism in the Renaissance,* Columbia Univ. Press, first pub. 1899.

Swain, Barbara, *Fools and Folly during the Middle Ages and the Renaissance,* Columbia Univ. Press, 1932.

Taylor, Henry Osborn, *Thought and Expression in the Sixteenth Century,* 2 vols., New York, Macmillan, 1920.

ITALIAN

Bembo, Pietro, *Gli Asolani,* trans. R. B. Gottfried, Indiana Univ. Press, 1954.

Burckhardt, Jacob, *The Civilization of the Renaissance in Italy,* trans. S. G. C. Middlemore, London, Harrap, 1929 (original German edit., 1860).

Cartwright, Julia, *Beatrice d' Este,* New York, Dutton, 1899.

Cartwright, Julia, *Isabella d' Este,* London, Murray, 1903.

Cellini, Benvenuto, *The Life,* trans. R. H. H. Cust, London, Navarre Soc., 1927.

Crane, Thomas F., *Italian Social Customs of the Sixteenth Century,* Yale Univ. Press, 1920.

Durant, Will, *The Renaissance. A History of Civilization in Italy from 1304 to 1576,* New York, Simon and Schuster, 1953.

Einstein, Lewis, *The Italian Renaissance in England,* Columbia Univ. Press, 1902.

Fletcher, Jefferson B., *Literature of the Italian Renaissance,* New York, Macmillan, 1934.

King, R. W., "Italian Influence on English Scholarship and Literature during the Romantic Revival," *Mod. Lang. Rev.*, XX (1925), 48–63 and XXI (1926), 24–33.

Lyric Poetry of the Italian Renaissance, compiled by L. R. Lind, Yale Univ. Press, 1954.

Marshall, Roderick, *Italy in English Literature, 1755–1815,* Columbia Univ. Press, 1934.

Mather, Frank J., *A History of Italian Painting,* New York, Holt, 1923.

Michaelangelo Buonarroti, *The Sonnets,* trans. J. A. Symonds, London, Smith, Elder, 1878.

Pico della Mirandola, *A Platonick Discourse upon Love,* ed. E. G. Gardner, Humanists' Lib., Boston, Updike, 1914.

Robb, Nesca A., *Neoplatonism of the Italian Renaissance,* London, Allen & Unwin, 1935.

Rossi, Vittorio, *Il Quattrocento,* Milan, Vallardi, 1934.

Sanctis, Francesco de, *History of Italian Literature,* trans. Joan Redfern, New York, Harcourt, Brace, 1931 (original Italian edit., 1870–71).

Sapegno, Natalino, *Il Trecento,* Milan, Vallardi, 2nd edit., 1942.

Schevill, Ferdinand, *History of Florence,* New York, Harcourt, Brace, 1936.

Symonds, John A., *Renaissance in Italy,* 7 vols., London, Smith, Elder, 1875, now in Modern Lib. Giant Edit.

Toffanin, Giuseppe, *Il Cinquecento,* Milan, Vallardi, 1929.

Vasari's Lives of the Artists, abridged and ed. Betty Burroughs, New York, Simon & Schuster, 1946.

Vespasiano da Bisticci, *The Vespasiano Memoirs,* trans. W. G. and E. Waters, New York, Dial Press, 1926.

Wilkins, Ernest Hatch, *A History of Italian Literature,* Harvard Univ. Press, 1954.

Young, G. F., *The Medici,* 2 vols., London, Murray, 1909, now in Modern Lib. Giant Edit.

FRENCH

Bédier, Joseph, and Hazard, Paul, editors, *Histoire de la Littérature Française Illustrée,* 2 vols., Paris, Larousse, 1923.

Bellay, Joachim du, *The Defence and Illustration of the French Language,* trans. Gladys M. Turquet, London, Dent, 1939.

Champion, Pierre, *Histoire Poétique du Quinzième Siècle,* Paris, Champion, 1923.

Lee, Sidney, *The French Renaissance in England,* New York, Scribner, 1910.

Marguerite of Navarre, *The Heptameron,* trans. George Saintsbury, London, Aldus Soc., 1903.

Nitze, W. A. and Dargan, F. P., *A History of French Literature,* 3rd edit., New York, Holt, 1938.

Tilley, Arthur, *The Literature of the French Renaissance,* 2 vols., Cambridge Univ. Press, 1904.

Tilley, Arthur, *The Dawn of the French Renaissance,* Cambridge Univ. Press, 1918.

Tilley, Arthur, *Studies in the French Renaissance,* Cambridge Univ. Press, 1922.

Upham, Alfred H., *The French Influence in English Literature,* Columbia Univ. Press, 1908.

Wiley, W. L., *The Gentleman of Renaissance France,* Harvard Univ. Press, 1954.

Will, Samuel F., "French Literature," a survey of recent scholarship in the period of the Renaissance, *Mod. Lang. Quar.,* II (1941), 439–64.

Wright, C. H. C., *French Classicism,* Harvard Univ. Press, 1920.

Wright, C. H. C., *A History of French Literature,* New York, Oxford Univ. Press, 1925.

SPANISH

Fitzmaurice-Kelly, James, *A New History of Spanish Literature,* London, Milford, 1926.

Ford, J. D. M., *Main Currents of Spanish Literature,* New York, Holt, 1919.

Green, Otis H., "A Critical Survey of Scholarship in the Field of Spanish Renaissance Literature, 1914–1944," *Stud. in Philol.,* XLIV (1947), 228–64.

Lynn, Caro, *A College Professor of the Renaissance,* Univ. of Chicago Press, 1937.

Mérimée, Ernest, *A History of Spanish Literature,* trans. and rev. by S. G. Morley, New York, Holt, 1930.

Underhill, John G., *Spanish Literature in the England of the Tudors,* New York, Macmillan, 1899.

APPENDIX

A list of works in English literature that show influence from the writers included in this volume or are analogues of their various writings.

The following list consists of readings in English literature of interest to students of the eleven writers included in this volume. In compiling it, the term "influence" has been construed in its widest meaning. The works here included comprise not only those showing influence in parallel passages, but also those that notably carry on a tradition, or those that are the expression of a mind deeply influenced by the ideas or spirit of the continental writer listed.

In general the works are listed in chronological sequence. Selections from many of those from the sixteenth and seventeenth centuries may be found in *Poetry of the English Renaissance,* ed. J. W. Hebel and H. H. Hudson, New York, Crofts, and *Seventeenth-Century Prose and Poetry,* ed. R. P. T. Coffin and A. M. Witherspoon, New York, Harcourt, Brace and Co.

PETRARCH

(See Sidney Lee, *Elizabethan Sonnets,* London, Constable, 1904, 2 vols.; Lu Emily Pearson, *Elizabethan Love Conventions,* Univ. of California Press, 1933.)

Geoffrey Chaucer, *Troilus and Criseyde,* i, ll. 400–20; the Clerk's Prologue in *The Canterbury Tales.*

Thomas Wyatt, sonnets and other poems.

Henry Howard, Earl of Surrey, sonnets and other poems.

Philip Sidney, *Astrophel and Stella.*

Samuel Daniel, *Delia.*

Michael Drayton, *Idea.*

Edmund Spenser, *Amoretti,* "The Visions of Petrarch."

William Shakespeare, *Sonnets.*

Walter Raleigh, sonnet: "Methought I saw the grave, where Laura lay."

William Drummond of Hawthornden, poems, madrigals.

William Wordsworth, sonnet: "Scorn not the Sonnet; Critic, you have frowned."

Walter Savage Landor, "Boccaccio and Petrarca," "Chaucer Boccaccio and Petrarca," in *Imaginary Conversations; The Pentameron;* "The Dream of Petrarca."

George Gordon, Lord Byron, *Childe Harold,* iv, 30–32.

Percy Bysshe Shelley, "The Triumph of Life."

John Keats, sonnet: "Keen, fitful gusts are whisp'ring here and there."

Elizabeth Barrett Browning, *Sonnets from the Portuguese.*

Dante Gabriel Rossetti, *The House of Life.*

Christina Rossetti, "Monna Innominata"; "By Way of Remembrance"; "Later Life"; "Sonnets Written to Bouts-rimés."

William Ellery Leonard, *Two Lives.*

Edna St. Vincent Millay, *Fatal Interview.*

BOCCACCIO

Geoffrey Chaucer, *Troilus and Criseyde* (also Robert Henryson, *The Testament of Cresseid;* William Shakespeare, *Troilus and Cressida*); in *The Canterbury Tales:* "The Knight's Tale" (also *The Two Noble Kinsmen,* by Shakespeare and Fletcher), "The Clerk's Tale" (*Decameron,* x, 10), "The Merchant's Tale" (*Decameron,* vii, 9), "The Franklin's Tale" (*Decameron,* x, 5), "The Shipman's Tale" (*Decameron,* viii, 1).
Thomas Elyot, *The Boke Named The Governour,* ii, 12.
William Painter, *The Palace of Pleasure.* London, Cresset Press, 1929.
George Turberville, *Tragicall Tales.*
Robert Greene, "Perimedes the Blacksmith."
Richard Tarleton, "Tarleton's News out of Purgatory" (1590).
Thomas Dekker and others, *The Pleasant Comedy of Patient Grissil* (*Decameron,* x, 10).
William Shakespeare, *All's Well That Ends Well* (*Decameron,* iii, 9); *Cymbeline* (Iachimo's wager, *Decameron,* ii, 9).
John Dryden, *Fables Ancient and Modern.*
Samuel Taylor Coleridge, "The Garden of Boccaccio."
George Gordon, Lord Byron, *Don Juan,* iii, 105–6 (*Decameron,* v, 8).
Bryan Waller Procter, "The Falcon, A Sicilian Story."
John Keats, "Isabella, or the Pot of Basil" (*Decameron,* iv, 5).
John Hamilton Reynolds, "The Garden of Florence."
Walter Savage Landor, "Boccaccio and Petrarca," "Chaucer Boccaccio and Petrarca," in *Imaginary Conversations; The Pentameron.*
Alfred, Lord Tennyson, "The Falcon" (*Decameron,* v, 9).
Henry Wadsworth Longfellow, "The Student's Tale — The Falcon of Ser Federigo," in *Tales of a Wayside Inn.*

MACHIAVELLI

(See Mario Praz, *Machiavelli and the Elizabethans,* London, Oxford Univ. Press, 1928.)

Thomas Kyd, *The Spanish Tragedy.*
Christopher Marlowe, *The Jew of Malta.*
Edmund Spenser, *A View of the Present State of Ireland.*
Fulke Greville, "Treatise on Monarchy."
Walter Raleigh, "The Cabinet Council containing the chief Arts of Empire"; "The Prince or Maxims of State."
John Donne, "Ignatius His Conclave."
Thomas Scott, *The Second Part of Vox Populi, or Gondomar appearing in the likeness of Matchiavell in a Spanish Parliament . . .* (1620).
Thomas Middleton, *A Game at Chess.*
Francis Bacon, *Advancement of Learning; Essays* (in 1625 edit.).
Walter Savage Landor, "Machiavelli and Michel-Angelo," "Machiavelli and Guicciardini," in *Imaginary Conversations.*
H. G. Wells, *The New Machiavelli.*
W. Somerset Maugham, *Then and Now.*

CASTIGLIONE

Thomas Elyot, *The Boke Named The Governour.*
Roger Ascham, *The Scholemaster.*

Edmund Spenser, *The Faerie Queene,* Book vi; *Fowre Hymnes.*
John Milton, "Of Education."

ARIOSTO

Philip Sidney, *Arcadia.*
Edmund Spenser, *The Faerie Queene,* especially Books iii, iv, v.
Robert Greene, *The History of Orlando Furioso.*
William Shakespeare, *Much Ado about Nothing,* (O. F., cantos iv–vi).
John Milton, *Paradise Lost,* iii, 440–97 (limbo of vanities); *Paradise Regained,* iii, 337–43.
John Dryden, "Of Heroic Plays," prefatory essay to *The Conquest of Granada.*
Richard Hurd, *Lectures on Chivalry and Romance,* ix, x.
Richard Wharton, *Fables: Consisting of Select Parts from Dante, Berni, Chaucer, Ariosto.*
John Hookham Frere, *Prospectus and Specimen of an Intended National Work* by W. and R. Whistlecraft, later printed as *The Monks and Giants.* Ed. R. D. Waller, Manchester Univ. Press, 1926.
Walter Scott, see J. G. Lockhart's *Life of Sir Walter Scott,* iv.
George Gordon, Lord Byron, "Parisina"; *Childe Harold,* iv, 40–41; The *Morgante Maggiore* of Pulci; "Beppo"; *Don Juan.*
Leigh Hunt, *Stories from the Italian Poets.*
John Keats, "The Cap and Bells."
A. C. Hollway-Calthrop, *Paladin and Saracen. Stories from Ariosto,* London, Macmillan, 1882.
Joseph Shield Nicholson, *Tales from Ariosto,* London, Macmillan, 1913.

ERASMUS

Sebastian Brant, *The Ship of Fools,* trans. Alexander Barclay (1509).
Thomas More, *Utopia.*
Thomas Elyot, *The Boke Named The Governour.*
Mery Tales, Wittie Questions, and Quicke Answeres (1567).
John Lyly, *Euphues; Euphues and His England.*
Ben Jonson, *Volpone* (Erasmus' Colloquy, "Sordid Wealth"); *The Alchemist; Every Man out of His Humor,* iii, 1 (Erasmus' Colloquy, "The Inns").
Laurence Sterne, *Tristram Shandy.*
Walter Scott, *Ann of Geierstein,* xix (Erasmus' Colloquy, "The Inns").
Charles Reade, *The Cloister and the Hearth.*

RABELAIS

(See Huntington Brown, *Rabelais in English Literature,* Harvard Univ. Press, 1933.)

"A Wonderful, strange and miraculous, Astrologicall Prognostication for this year of our Lord God . . ." by Adam Fouleweather (1591).
Gabriel Harvey, "Foure Letters"; "A New Letter of Notable Contents"; "Pierces Supererogation."
Thomas Nash, "Pierce Penilesse his Supplication to the Divell"; "Have with you to Saffron Walden"; "Lenten Stuffe."
John Eliot, *Ortho-Epia Gallica, Eliot's Fruits for the French,* part 2 (1593).

John Harington, *The Metamorphosis of Aiax.*
Ben Jonson, *Volpone; Epicoene or the Silent Woman; The Alchemist; Pleasure Reconciled to Virtue.*
Thomas Brown, "Letters from the Dead to the Living" (1702).
Jonathan Swift, *A Tale of a Tub; Gulliver's Travels.*
John Arbuthnot, *The Memoirs of Martinus Scriblerus.*
Tobias Smollett, *The Adventures of An Atom.*
Laurence Sterne, *The Life and Opinions of Tristram Shandy.*

RONSARD

(See Sidney Lee, *Elizabethan Sonnets,* London, Constable, 1904, 2 vols.)

Thomas Watson, *Hecatompathia or Passionate Centurie of Love.*
Richard Tarleton, "Tarleton's News out of Purgatory" (1590).
Philip Sidney, *Astrophel and Stella.*
Samuel Daniel, *Delia.*
Henry Constable, *Diana.*
Thomas Lodge, *Phillis.*
Michael Drayton, *Idea.*
Edmund Spenser, *Amoretti.*
Robert Herrick, *Hesperides* (Herrick and Ronsard wrote under same influences).
John Keats, letter to John Hamilton Reynolds, 21 or 22 September 1818. Forman Edit., No. 83.
Walter Pater, *Gaston de Latour.*

MONTAIGNE

(See Charles Dédéyan, *Montaigne chez Ses Amis Anglo-Saxons,* Paris, Boivin, 1946, 2 vols.)

William Cornwallis, *Essayes.*
Walter Raleigh, "The Skeptick."
William Shakespeare, *The Tempest* (ii, 1 and Montaigne's "Of Cannibals").
Robert Burton, *The Anatomy of Melancholy.*
William Drummond of Hawthornden, "A Cypress Grove."
Kenelm Digby, *Private Memoirs.*
Ben Jonson, *Timber.*
Thomas Browne, *Religio Medici.*
Abraham Cowley, *Essays.*
William Temple, *Essays.*
Charles Lamb, *Essays of Elia.*
William Hazlitt, essays, especially in *Table Talk* and *The Plain Speaker. Selected Essays,* ed. G. Keynes, New York, Random House, 1930.
Leigh Hunt, *Essays.* Everyman's Lib. No. 829.
Walter Savage Landor, "Joseph Scaliger and Montaigne" in *Imaginary Conversations.*
Ralph Waldo Emerson, *The Heart of Emerson's Journals,* ed. Bliss Perry, Boston, Houghton Mifflin, 1926; *Essays;* "Montaigne" in *Representative Men;* poem, "Etienne de la Boéce." (See Charles L. Young, *Emerson's Montaigne,* New York, Macmillan, 1941.)

Robert Louis Stevenson, *Essays,* ed. W. L. Phelps, New York, Scribner, Mod. Student's Lib.

Walter Pater, *Gaston de Latour.*

TASSO

Edmund Spenser, *The Faerie Queene, passim,* but see especially Book ii, canto 12, and Book vi, canto 9.

William Browne, *Britannia's Pastorals.*

John Milton, *Paradise Lost, passim,* but see especially the infernal council in ii; "Mansus" ("To Manso").

John Dryden, "Of Heroic Plays," prefatory essay to *The Conquest of Granada.*

Richard Hurd, *Letters on Chivalry and Romance,* ix, x.

George Gordon, Lord Byron, *Childe Harold,* iv, 3 and 36 ff.; "The Lament of Tasso."

Leigh Hunt, *Stories from the Italian Poets.*

Walter Savage Landor, "Tasso and Cornelia," in *Imaginary Conversations.*

CERVANTES

Francis Beaumont and John Fletcher, *The Knight of the Burning Pestle.*

James Shirley, *The Triumph of Peace.*

Samuel Butler, *Hudibras.*

Thomas D'Urfey, *The Comical History of Don Quixote.*

Henry Fielding, *Don Quixote in England; Joseph Andrews; Tom Jones.*

Tobias Smollett, *Humphrey Clinker.*

Laurence Sterne, *The Life and Opinions of Tristram Shandy.*

Hugh H. Brackenridge, *Modern Chivalry,* ed. Claude M. Newlin, Am. Fiction Series, 1937.

Washington Irving, *The Knickerbocker History of New York.*

Mark Twain, *Tom Sawyer; Huckleberry Finn; A Connecticut Yankee in King Arthur's Court.*

E. G. Morrison (Elkin Mathews), *Alonzo Quixano, Otherwise Don Quixote* (1895).